Microwave Integrated Circuits

The Artech House Microwave Library

Introduction to Microwaves by Fred E. Gardiol
Receiving Systems Design by Stephen J. Erst
Applications of GaAs MESFETs by R.A. Soares, J. Graffeuil, and J. Obregon
GaAs Processing Techniques by R.E. Williams
GaAs FET Principles and Technology, J.V. DiLorenzo and D. Khandelwal, eds.
Modern Spectrum Analyzer Theory and Applications by Morris Engelson
Microwave Materials and Fabrication Techniques by Thomas S. Laverghetta
Handbook of Microwave Testing by Thomas S. Laverghetta
Microwave Measurements and Techniques by Thomas S. Laverghetta
Principles of Electromagnetic Compatibility by Bernhard E. Keiser
Microwave Filters, Impedance Matching Networks, and Coupling Structures by G.L. Matthaei, Leo Young, and E.M.T. Jones
Microwave Engineer's Handbook, 2 vol., Theodore Saad, ed.
Computer-Aided Design of Microwave Circuits by K.C. Gupta, R. Garg, and R. Chadha
Microstrip Lines and Slotlines by K.C. Gupta, R. Garg, and I.J. Bahl
Microstrip Antennas by I.J. Bahl and P. Bhartia
Microwave Circuit Design Using Programmable Calculators by J. Lamar Allen and Max Medley, Jr.
Stripline Circuit Design by Harlan Howe, Jr.
Microwave Transmission Line Filters by J.A.G. Malherbe
Electrical Characteristics of Transmission Lines by W. Hilberg
Multiconductor Transmission Line Analysis by Sidney Frankel
Microwave Diode Control Devices by Robert V. Garver
A Practical Introduction to Impedance Matching by Robert Thomas
Active Filter Design by A.B. Williams
Adaptive Electronics by Wolfgang Gaertner
Laser Applications by W.V. Smith
Electronic Information Processing by W.V. Smith
Logarithmic Video Amplifiers by Richard S. Hughes
Avalanche Transit-Time Devices, George Haddad, ed.
Gallium Arsenide Bulk and Transit-Time Devices, Lester Eastman, ed.
Ferrite Control Components, 2 vol., Lawrence Whicker, ed.

MICROWAVE INTEGRATED CIRCUITS

Jeffrey Frey, Ph.D.
School of Electrical Engineering
Cornell University
Ithaca, New York

Kul B. Bhasin, Ph.D.
National Aeronautics and Space Administration
Lewis Research Center
Cleveland, Ohio

ARTECH HOUSE, INC.
610 Washington Street
Dedham, MA 02026

International Standard Book Number: 0-89006-160-2
Library of Congress Catalog Card Number: 85-047747

CONTENTS

FOREWORD

Since the first edition of this volume a decade ago, the field of microwave integrated circuits (MICs) has advanced considerably. For example, GaAs monolithic microwave integrated circuits (MMICs), discussed only in the introduction of the first edition, are now in production. There have also been dramatic developments in computer aided design (CAD). These advances have necessitated a revised edition of this work.

This new edition is intended to provide a comprehensive theoretical and technological background for working engineers involved in the design, fabrication, and testing of MICs and MMICs. The emphasis is on the theoretical background of design techniques, design of commonly encountered microwave components and circuit elements, and measurement techniques.

We have included new key developments in the theoretical and technological aspects of GaAs monolithic microwave integrated circuits and examples of their applications. A new section on computer aided design has been added. Wherever possible, aspects of millimeter wave integrated circuits are included.

The revised book should be useful as a text for a one-semester senior or early graduate-level course in microwave integrated circuit technology. It can also serve as a supplemental text to a hybrid microelectronics technology or GaAs IC technology course. The book is, finally, designed to be useful as a reference handbook on MIC and MMIC technology.

The authors are thankful for the assistance provided by Mr. R. Romanofsky, Dr. V. Sokolov, and Ms. C. Bhasin. Mr. G. Anzic, Mr. A. Downey, Dr. D. Connolly, and Mr. G. Ponchak, are appreciated for their helpful discussions.

Portions of this project were completed under NASA-Lewis Research Center Grant NCC3-44, awarded to the Department of Electrical and Computer Engineering, University of Cincinnati, Cincinnati, Ohio.

MICROWAVE INTEGRATED CIRCUITS: AN INTRODUCTION

Microwave circuits can be integrated by hybrid or monolithic techniques on a variety of substrates. Hybrid and monolithic integrated circuits for both low and microwave frequencies will be described here to illustrate their differences. The key elements of microwave integrated circuits, the transmission media, and active devices, such as GaAs MESFETs, are presented. Technology trends are also discussed to provide the reader with a look at what the future may hold.

I. Hybrid and Monolithic Integrated Circuits

A hybrid integrated circuit is one in which the circuit interconnections are formed by metal lines deposited on an insulating substrate. The active devices in the circuit are attached to the substrate and may be made of different materials (e.g., Si, GaAs, InP); hence the term "hybrid." In thin-film hybrid circuits the metalization is deposited by evaporation and the desired pattern is defined by photolithographic techniques; in thick-film hybrid circuits the metalization is usually deposited by silk-screening, in which the desired pattern is incorporated into the screen itself. [1] In hybrid circuits both active and passive components may be separately fabricated and attached to the substrate by soldering, thermocompression bonding, or by using a conductive adhesive; alternatively, capacitors, resistors, and inductors may be fabricated using the substrate metalization itself, along with deposited insulating films. Component values achievable by the latter method are usually somewhat limited.

A monolithic integrated circuit is one in which all components are formed by various processes, such as diffusion or ion implantation, which change the physical properties of the same block of substrate material. Due to the limited values and types of passive components available in monolithic IC technology, the functions of "passive" components, in such circuits may be accomplished using active components, either directly (e.g., by using transistors as active loads to substitute for high-value passive resistors) or indirectly (e.g., by using the junction capacitance of a back-biased *p-n* junction as a circuit component). Inductors are not available at all in low-frequency monolithic ICs, leading to the use of such non-integrable external components, such as piezo-electric crystals, to establish circuit resonances. Circuit interconnections in monolithic ICs are established by metalization in the same fashion as in thin-film hybrid ICs. [2]

II. Hybrid Integrated Circuits at Microwave Frequencies

Microwave hybrid integrated circuits differ from lower-frequency hybrid ICs in that circuit interconnections are usually established by TEM-mode transmission lines. [3] Some types of these lines require ground plane metalization on one side of the insulating substrate. In Table I the characteristics of the various insulating substrates suitable for microwave circuits have been compiled. Substrates, in addition to providing support for the metal transmission lines, influence the wave transmission characteristics. Microwave ICs using lumped-elements are also feasible. [4] To minimize loss, thin-film rather than thick-film techniques are used at microwave frequencies. [1] An example of a hybrid microwave integrated circuit is shown in Figure 1.

Active devices, such as IMPATT, Gunn diodes, or transistors, are now commonly used in hybrid microwave integrated circuits in packaged form. Packaging protects the device against abuse to which it may be subjected during mounting in the circuit. In addition, a subsystems (or microwave IC) manufacturer who purchases a packaged device can place the burden of characterization of that device, at the package terminals, on the device manufacturer. Such a manufacturer hopes that, with terminal parameters that are repeatable due to device selection and uniform packaging, circuit design for these devices can be standardized. However, unpackaged devices, or devices which are mounted on ceramic carriers, exhibit fewer parasitic circuit elements, and can thus be used at higher frequencies than packaged devices. Consequently, in the future one can expect increased use of bare chips, chips with beam leads for circuit interconnection, chips on inverted ceramic carriers, or chips on metal pedestals, in hybrid microwave ICs.

The set-up cost for hybrid IC production, which involves only circuit design and the making of only one or two masks, is generally much less than that for a monolithic IC, which involves circuit design, the making of four to nine masks, and standardization of various processing techniques. Consequently, hybrid ICs are used, where possible, instead of monolithic ICs in relatively low-volume applications. Once the capital investment has been made and all processes stabilized, monolithic ICs can be made easily in very large quantities due to their small size and the parallel nature of their production.

III. Monolithic Integrated Circuits at Microwave Frequencies

The basic concept of a monolithic IC is simple: active devices are fabricated in a single block of semi-conductor material and connected by metal lines. Various practical considerations dictate some necessary differences between low-frequency and high-frequency monolithic ICs. For example, the metal lines in the microwave IC are segments of transmission lines and must be designed as such. A typical microwave monolithic IC on a GaAs substrate is shown in Figure 2.

In general, low-noise and power MESFETs and Schottky barrier diodes are the active devices, while thin-film resistors, spiral inductors, MIM capacitors and transmission lines are the passive components which form MMICs. Air bridges and through-substrate-via-holes provide the device and component interconnections and ground connection, respectively.

For various reasons, gallium arsenide, rather than silicon, has been primarily used for microwave monolithic ICs. Many of the interesting microwave solid-state active devices achieve their optimum performance in GaAs. In addition, the higher dielectric constant of GaAs permits narrower transmission lines.

The two key elements of microwave circuits are transmission lines and active solid-state devices. Both are described below.

IV. Transmission Media

Transmission line structures which are commonly considered for microwave integrated circuits are illustrated in Table 2. These planar transmission lines consist of thin conductor layers on a microwave substrate and, in most cases, a conducting ground plane. In Table 2, the characteristic impedance, range of frequency operation, loss and dispersion, and integrability of solid-state devices to transmission line structures are summarized. Each structure is applicable to various situations.

The most frequently used transmission line structure is microstrip, as its top conductor line is accessible for connecting solid-state devices and various microwave components.

A microstrip line on GaAs may take the form shown in Figure 3. The width of the line for a required characteristic impedance Z can be predicted by various design equations with certain accuracy. However, accurate knowledge of the relative dielectric constant of GaAs is essential. The thickness of the Au-line should not be less than three skin depths to prevent loss due to radiative surface modes generated by the presence of electric fields at the conductor-air interface. This critical skin depth can be calculated using the formula for skin depth δ:

$$\delta = (\rho / \pi \mu f)^{1/2}$$

for gold, with $\rho = 2.4 \times 10^{-6}$ ohm-cm, $\delta = 0.61$ micron at 10 GHz. Thus, the gold microstrip metallization thickness must be on the order of three microns for an integrated 10 GHz circuit. Other aspects of microstrip lines such as loss, dispersion, *et cetera* are covered by various authors in Chapter I.

V. Microwave Solid-State Active Devices

Since the discovery of the Gunn effect in 1963, considerable progress has led to the application of compound semiconductor microwave devices, especially GaAs devices, in many of today's microwave devices. IMPATT, Gunn devices, low noise GaAs MESFETs and GaAs power MESFETs are some of the devices now available. These devices offer advantages in size, reliability, and cost for system applications.

One particular development that has had a great effect on the field of microwave ICs is that of the GaAs field-effect transistor. A GaAs MESFET structure is shown in Figure 4(a) and its cross-section in Figure 4(b). This structure consists of a GaAs substrate, the active layers obtained by ion-implantation or epitaxial techniques, and source, gate, and drain contacts formed by metalization techniques. The structure is fabricated by growing an *n*-type epitaxial film by either liquid phase epitaxy (LPE), vapor phase epitaxy (VPE) [6], or molecular beam epitaxy (MBE) [7] on a semi-insulating GaAs substrate. Ion-implantation [8] is also used in creating an *n*-type region. The next step is the formation of ohmic contacts by sequential evaporation of Au, Ge, and Ni, which lift off, and alloy at 450°C. After contact metalization, sub-micron gates are defined by photolithography or electron-beam lithography [9] and subsequent deposition of TiW or Al to form the gate, followed by lift off.

Active layer formation by epitaxy or ion implantation, sub-micron lithography, and the subsequent packaging of these devices are primary to the development of microwave solid-state devices. The operating frequency of GaAs MESFETs has expanded to 60 GHz and further developments in this technology could extend it beyond this range.

VI. Future Trends

GaAs monolithic microwave integrated circuits (MMICs) are moving from the laboratory into production. Their increased usage will depend on decreased cost, which will lead to an increased emphasis on design and modeling to obtain higher circuit densities on the substrate, and larger yields of these circuits. As requirements develop, another trend to be expected will be increased operating frequency, making monolithic millimeter-wave integrated circuits a possibility. InP is another substrate on the horizon for millimeter-wave operations. [10,11] The performance of optoelectronic devices is being pushed into microwave millimeter-wave frequency ranges. [12,13] Eventual integration of microwave millimeter-wave integrated circuits with opto-electrical functions can be expected to resolve signal distribution problems.

Ingenuity and advances in III-V materials technology (molecular beam epitaxy, organo-metallic epitaxy, the use of vapor-phase epitaxy for growing tertiary and quanternary compounds [7]) have made new devices possible [15,16], possibly with improved properties. These devices may be integrable in monolithic form.

One can also foresee the application of microwave IC technology to digital logic applications, as the speed of logic circuits increase. In effect, Gbit-rate logic circuits, which can be integrated using GaAs FETs, are "microwave" integrated circuits and must use distributed-line techniques for signal transmission. [17] Here at last the need will arise for large arrays of identical devices, large packing densities, low cost, and high reliability, ultimately creating a great need for microwave IC technology.

Finally, with the development of MMICs, the usage of microwave integrated circuits is expected to grow in advanced phase array radar, satellite communications, intersatellite links, and military EW systems. [5]

TABLE 1

PROPERTIES OF MICROWAVE SUBSTRATES

TYPE OF SUBSTRATE	RELATIVE DIELECTRIC CONSTANT (ϵ_r) AT 25 C	TAN δ (X10) MEASURED AT 10 GHz	THERMAL CONDUCTIVITY (W/cm/C)
SEMICONDUCTOR			
Si	11.7-12	40-150	0.9 (high resistivity)
GaAs	12.8-13	16	0.3 (high resistivity)
InP	12.5-14	—	.68
CERAMIC			
Alumina	9.6-9.9	1-2	0.2 to 0.3
Beryllia	6.6-6.8	1-3	2.5
Fused Silica	3.8	1	.013
Sapphire	9.3-11.7	<1	.38-.46
POLYMERIC			
Woven PTFE/glass	2.2	9	.0026
Non-woven PTFE/glass	2.1	.00045	~.003
Ceramic filled PTFE/glass	10.5	15	.004
Polyolefin	2.3	1	0.001
Ferrite/garnite	1316	2	0.03

TABLE 2

TRANSMISSION LINE STRUCTURES	CHARACTERISTIC IMPEDANCE IN Ω	FREQUENCY OF OPERATION IN GHz	LOSS	DISPERSION	DEVICE/COMPONENT COMPATABILITY INTEGRATION LEVEL	
					IN SERIES	IN PARALLEL
MICROSTRIP	25-95	UP TO 100	MEDIUM	LOW	EASY	DIFFICULT
COPLANAR LINE	30-150	UP TO 60	HIGH	HIGH	EASY	EASY
SLOT LINE	60-200	——	HIGH	NON TEM MODE	DIFFICULT	EASY
SUSPENDED STRIPLINE	40-150	>100	LOW	HIGH	EASY	DIFFICULT
FIN LINE	10-400	30-100	LOW	LOW	EASY	EASY

CS-85-0818

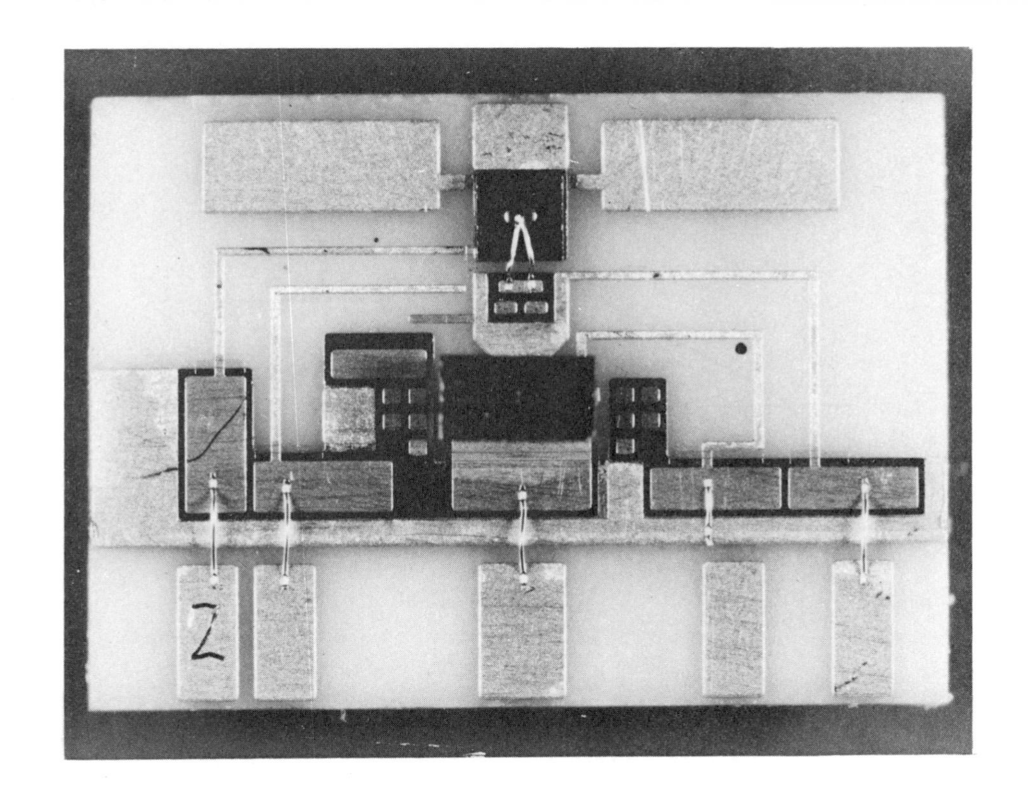

Figure 1 16 GHz, 60 mW, voltage controlled oscillator circuit on BeO substrate (courtesy of RCA Corporation).

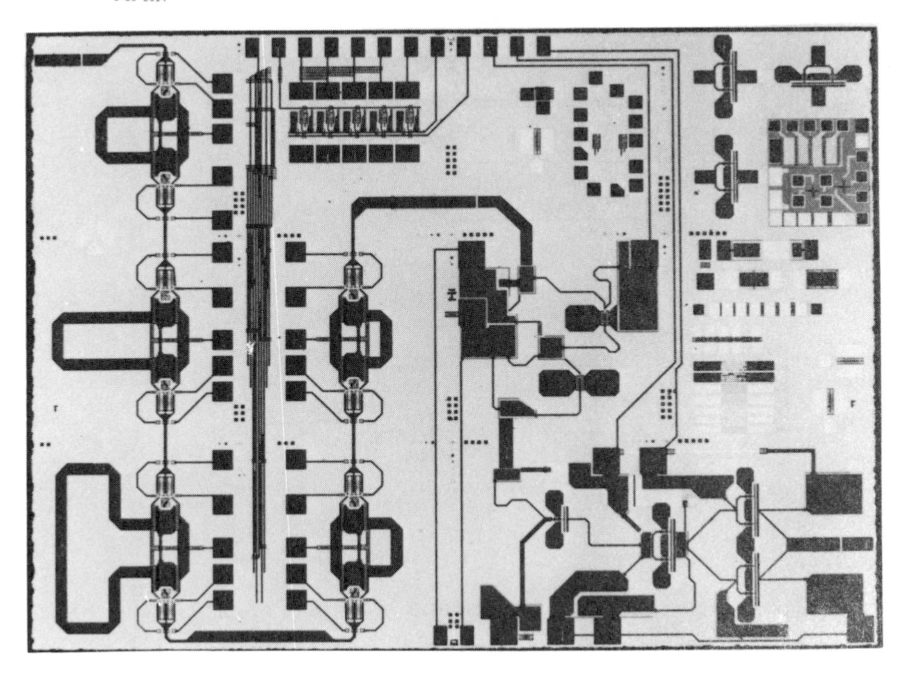

Figure 2 20 GHz GaAs MMIC transmit module (courtesy of NASA-Lewis Research Center/Rockwell).

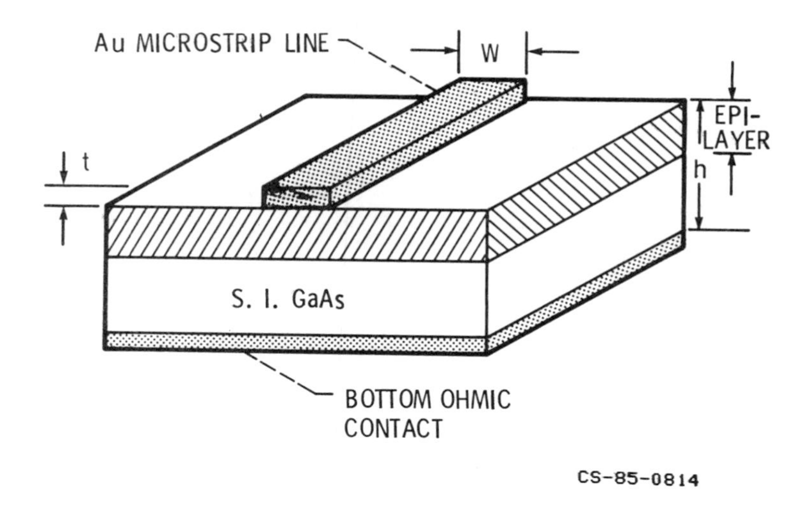

Figure 3 Au Microstrip on GaAs substrate.

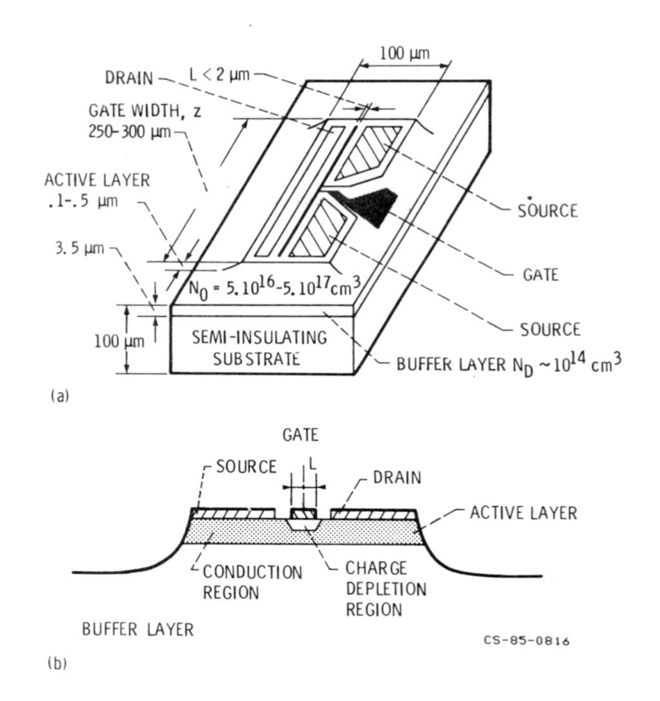

Figure 4 (a) A schematic diagram of a GaAs MESFET. (b) Cross-section of a GaAs MESFET. [5]

REFERENCES

1. Z.H. Meiksin, *Thin and Thick Films for Hybrid Microelectronics*, (D.C. Heath, Lexington, Massachusetts, 1976).
2. R.A. Colclaser, *Microelectronics: Processing and Device Design*, (John Wiley and Sons, New York, 1980).
3. T.C. Edwards, *Foundation for Microstrip Circuit Design*, (John Wiley and Sons, New York, 1981).
4. H. Sobol, "Applications of Integrated Circuit Technology to Microwave Frequencies," *Proc. IEEE* 59, 1200 (1971).
5. R. Soares, J. Graffeuil, and J. Obregon, eds., *Applications of GaAs MESFETs*, (Artech House, Dedham, Massachusetts, 1982).
6. T.Nakanisi, "Growth of High-Purity GaAs Epilayers by MOCVD and Their Application to Microwave MESFETs," *J. Cryst. Growth* 55, 252-262 (1981); see other articles in this special issue on MOCVD process.
7. L.L. Chang and K. Ploog, eds., *Molecular Beam Epitaxy and Heterostructures*, (Martinus Nijhoff, Boston, 1985).
8. J.P. Donnelly, "Ion Implantation in GaAs," *Inst. Phys. Conf. Series* 336, 166-190 (1977).
9. D.A. McGillis, *Lithography in VLSI Technology*, S.M. Sze, ed., (McGraw-Hill, New York, 1983).
10. M. Armand, D.V. Bui, J. Cherrier, and N.T. Linh, "High Power InP MESFETs," *Electron. Lett.*, 19, 433 (1983).
11. K.J. Sleger, B.E. Spielman, R.E. Neidert, H.B. Dietrich, A. Christon, R.L. Henry, S.G. Bishop, and J.F. Weller, "InP Monolithic Integrated Circuits for Millimeter-Wave Applications," *Microwave Journal*, 27, 5, 175-188 (1984).
12. S. Wang, D. Bloom, and D. Collins, "100 GHz Bandwidth Planar GaAs Schottky Photodiode," *Electron. Lett.*, 19, 554-555 (1983).
13. K.Y. Lan, N. Bar-chaim, I. Ury, C. Harder, and A. Yariv, "Divert Amplitude Modulation of Short-Cavity GaAs Lasers up to X-band Frequencies," *Appl. Phys. Lett.*, 43, 1:1 (1983).
14. M. Ito, O. Wada, K. Nakai, and T. Sakurai, "Monolithic Integration of a Metal-Semiconductor-Metal Photodiode and a GaAs Preamplifier," *IEEE Electron Device Lett.*, EDL-5, 531-532 (1984).
15. U.K. Mishra, S.C. Palmateer, P.C. Chao, P.M. Smith, and J.C.M. Hwang, "Microwave Performance of 0.25 μm Gate Length High Electron Mobility Transistors," *IEEE Electron Device Lett.*, EDL-6, 142-145 (1985).
16. H. Morkoc, "Modulation Doped $Al_x Ga_{x-1} As$/GaAs Field Effect Transistors (Mod Fet): Analysis, Application, and Performance," in L.L. Chang and K. Ploog, eds., *Molecular Beam Epitaxy and Heterostructures*, (Martinus Nijhoff, Boston, 1985).
17. S. Seki and H. Hasegawa, "Analysis of Crosstalk in Very High-Speed LSI/VLSI's Using a Coupled Multiconductor MIS Microstrip Line Model," *IEEE Trans. Electron. Devices, ED-31, 1948-1953 (1984).*

CHAPTER I

TRANSMISSION MEDIA

The theoretical and experimental bases for the design of microwave transmission line structures and circuit components are covered in this chapter. Examples of transmission line structures such as microstrip, coplanar waveguides, slot-line, and fin-line are included.

TEM-mode microstrip analysis is included in the article by Wheeler. Analysis including dispersion is covered in the articles by Getsinger; Pramanick and Bhartia; and Kirschning, *et al.* Various types of microstrip discontinuities are also included: edge effects (Kirschning, *et al.*), gaps (Maeda) and bends and other discontinuities (Silvester and Benedek; Wolff, *et al.*). Losses in microstrip are comprehensively covered by Denlinger.

Coplanar waveguide structures are discussed by Wen; Shih and Itoh; and Ghion and Nalde. An introduction to slotline is presented by Cohn. The designs of two waveguide-to-microstrip transitions are also included (Moochalla and Chae; and Lavedan).

Microstrip and coplanar transmission line structures on magnetic substrates (Pucel and Masse) and on GaAs substrates (Hasegawa and Okizaki; Shih and Itoh), are described to develop a basis for microwave integrated circuits. Transmission lines on aluminum oxide and silicon substrates are described by Becker and Jager. Analysis of coupled microstrip lines on ferrite substrates are presented by Janiczak and Kitlinski.

Finally, an analysis of multiconductor transmission lines in multilayered dielectric media applicable to the design of high speed multilayer printed circuit boards (Wei, *et al.*) is presented.

Transmission-Line Properties of a Strip on a Dielectric Sheet on a Plane

HAROLD A. WHEELER, FELLOW, IEEE

Abstract—**The subject is a strip line formed of a strip and a parallel ground plane separated by a dielectric sheet (commonly termed "microstrip"). Building on the author's earlier papers [1], [2], all the significant properties are formulated in explicit form for practical applications. This may mean synthesis and/or analysis. Each formula is a close approximation for all shape ratios, obtained by a gradual transition between theoretical forms for the extremes of narrow and wide strips. The effect of thickness is formulated to a second-order approximation. Then the result is subjected to numerical differentiation for simple evaluation of the magnetic-loss power factor from the skin depth.**

The transition formulas are tested against derived formulas for overlapping narrow and wide ranges of shape. Some of these formulas are restated from the earlier derivations and others are derived herein. The latter include the second-order approximation for a narrow thin strip, and a close approximation for a narrow or wide square cross section in comparison with a circular cross section.

Graphs are given for practical purposes, showing the wave resistance and magnetic loss for a wide range of shape and dielectric. For numerical reading, the formulas are suited for programming on a digital pocket calculator.

I. Introduction

ONE FORM of strip line is naturally suited for the simplest fabrication in a printed circuit. It is the familiar type made of a dielectric sheet with a shield-plane conductor bonded on the bottom side and a pattern of strip lines on the top side.

The purpose of this paper is to present some improved formulas and graphs, including not only the wave resistance but also the losses. The effect of strip thickness is simply formulated to enable the evaluation of magnetic loss.

In the vernacular, this type of line is termed "microstrip," a term which is avoided in this scientific article because it is commonly used without a clear definition and is not self-descriptive. Apparently it was intended to be a short designation for "microwave strip line." The "microwave" description is ambiguous and only partially relevant. Furthermore it does not distinguish from the "sandwich" form of a microwave strip line.

Here also the descriptive term "wave resistance" is used in preference to the nondescriptive term "characteristic impedance."

The subject strip line may be described as half-shielded, by the ground plane on one side, as distinguished from the sandwich type, which is fully shielded, by ground planes on both sides. The half-shielding is adequate for some practical purposes, because the external field is relatively weak and does decay with distance.

Manuscript received October 29, 1976; revised February 23, 1977.
The author is with the Hazeltine Corporation, Greenlawn, NY 11740.

A peculiarity of the half-shielded line is the mixture of two different dielectrics. One is the material of the sheet between the strip and plane. The other is the air above the sheet. The simple rules of conformal mapping are restricted to a uniform dielectric or to some discrete boundaries that are different from the subject configuration. Various other approaches have been directed to this problem.

The first close approximation for this strip line with mixed dielectric was published by the author in 1965 [2]. It is based on some rigorous derivations for a thin strip by conformal mapping. These are supplemented by some logical concepts for interpolation between the extremes of dielectric. The uncertainties of interpolation are small enough to meet design requirements within practical tolerances. The result is a collection of formulas and charts which are complete for the wave resistance of a thin strip.

The loss power factor ($PF = 1/Q$) in a strip line has components of electric loss in the dielectric and magnetic loss in the conductor boundaries. These were not treated in the early paper but have been addressed by some other authors in the meantime.

In the frequency range where a strip line may have a length comparable with the wavelength, the magnetic loss is usually the dominant component. It is largely dependent on the strip thickness, so the formulas for a thin strip do not suffice. This loss PF can be evaluated from knowledge of the inductance of the line, which is independent of the dielectric. This evaluation can be made with the aid of the "incremental-inductance rule," published by the author in 1942 [3]. Other authors have applied this rule to the formulas of the early papers [13], [17] with the first-order thickness effect stated therein.

In the sandwich line, it has been simpler to evaluate its properties, for various reasons. First, the homogeneity of the dielectric avoids the problem of mixed dielectric, which is relevant for wave resistance. Second, the symmetry and two-sided shielding cause much greater decay of a field with distance. The symmetry simplifies the evaluation of the thickness effects, so those have been published, including the magnetic-loss PF [8]. These give an indication of trends in the subject line, but not quantitative values.

As in most of the previous articles, only the lowest mode of wave propagation in the line shall be considered, and, furthermore, only at frequencies so low that there is negligible interaction between the electric and magnetic fields. This is valid if the transverse dimensions are much less than half the wavelength in the dielectric. This mode may be termed the "quasi-TEM" mode, ignoring second-order effects of dispersion and surface-wave phenomena.

After the following list of symbols, the configuration will be defined and the scope of this article will be indicated.

II. Symbols

The units are MKS rationalized (meters, ohms, etc.).

k	=	dielectric constant of the sheet of material separating the strip and the ground plane.
k'	=	$1 + q(k-1)$ = effective dielectric constant of all space around the strip.
q	=	$(k'-1)/(k-1)$ = effective filling fraction of the dielectric material.
R_c	=	$377 = 120\pi$ = wave resistance of a square area of free space or air.
R	=	wave resistance of the transmission line formed by the strip and the ground plane (of perfect conductor) separated by a sheet of dielectric k.
R_1	=	R without dielectric ($k = 1$).
R_δ	=	R_1 subject to skin depth δ in a real conductor.
R/R_1	=	$1/\sqrt{k'} = \lambda_g/\lambda_0$ = speed ratio in mixed dielectric k' relative to free space or air.
w	=	width of the strip conductor.
h	=	height (separation) of the strip from the ground plane.
h	=	thickness of the dielectric sheet.
t	=	thickness of the strip conductor.
w'	=	effective width of a strip with some thickness.
w'	=	width of an equivalent thin strip ($t \to 0$).
Δw	=	$w' - w$ = width adjustment for thickness.
$\Delta w'$	=	width adjustment with mixed dielectric k'.
δ	=	skin depth in the conductor.
p	=	$1/Q$ = magnetic PF of the strip line.
p_k	=	electric PF of the dielectric material k.
p'	=	effective PF of mixed dielectric k'.
P	=	$p \div \delta/h = ph/\delta$ = normalized p.
α	=	rate of attenuation (nepers/meter).
λ_0	=	wavelength in free space or air.
λ_g	=	guide wavelength in mixed dielectric k'.
e	=	2.718 = base of natural logarithms.
$\exp x$	=	e^x = natural exponential function.
$\ln x$	=	$\log_e x$ = natural logarithm.
acosh x	=	anticosh $x = \cosh^{-1} x$.
asinh x	=	antisinh $x = \sinh^{-1} x$.
asin x	=	antisin $x = \sin^{-1} x$.

The following table translates some symbols from the author's earlier papers.

Here	[1] [2]
$w, h, t, \Delta w$	$2a, b, \Delta b, 2\Delta a$
R of 1 strip	R of 2 strips (twice as great)
(A-)(B-)	( )( ) formulas

III. A Strip Line on a Dielectric Sheet on a Plane

Fig. 1(a) shows the cross section of the subject line. It corresponds to the 1965 article [2] except for the translation to "practical" parameters. The latter are the wave resistance R of the asymmetric model (single strip and ground plane) and the descriptive dimensions w,h,t. Here the thickness is featured, and the equivalence between a practical strip and a wider theoretical thin strip (a perfect conductor with a thickness approaching zero). This equivalence is described in terms of the width adjustment Δw.

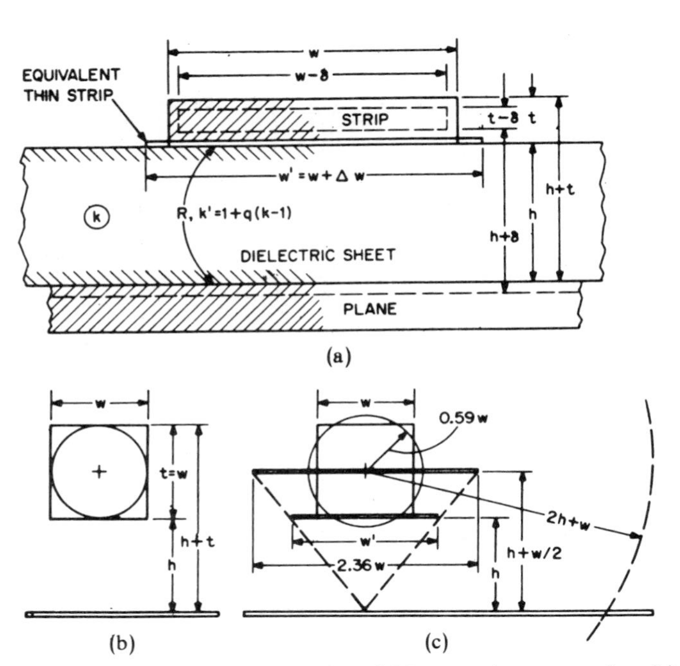

Fig. 1. A strip line parallel to a plane. (a) Rectangular cross section. (b) Cross-section square or inscribed circle. (c) Cross-section small square or equivalent circle.

For evaluation of the magnetic-loss PF, the skin effect is indicated in dashed lines. These boundaries are recessed by one half the skin depth ($\delta/2$) so they indicate the actual center of current. The actual boundary is the theoretical current center in a perfect conductor. The change between one and the other is involved in the computation of the magnetic PF. It is assumed that all conductive boundaries are nonmagnetic and have equal conductivity and skin depth.

As an extreme case of strip thickness, a square cross section is introduced, as shown in Fig. 1(b) and (c). These are related to a circular cross section in either of two ways, the inscribed circle (b) or the equivalent circle (c). Each is found to be helpful in some studies, mainly because the circle yields to simple exact formulation for comparison with an approximation for the square. Both will be used for reference.

IV. Scope

The thrust of this article is to enable explicit synthesis of a line to meet some specifications. This is achieved for various sequences. The wave resistance R is related to the dielectric k and the shape. On the other hand, the magnetic PF can be decreased by increasing the size, while the shape has a lesser effect. The PF is usually a tolerance rather than a requisite. The wave-speed ratio is taken not to be specified, but rather evaluated after synthesis of a design of a cross section.

Some graphs are introduced here, for reference in various sections. They present the relations needed for the purposes

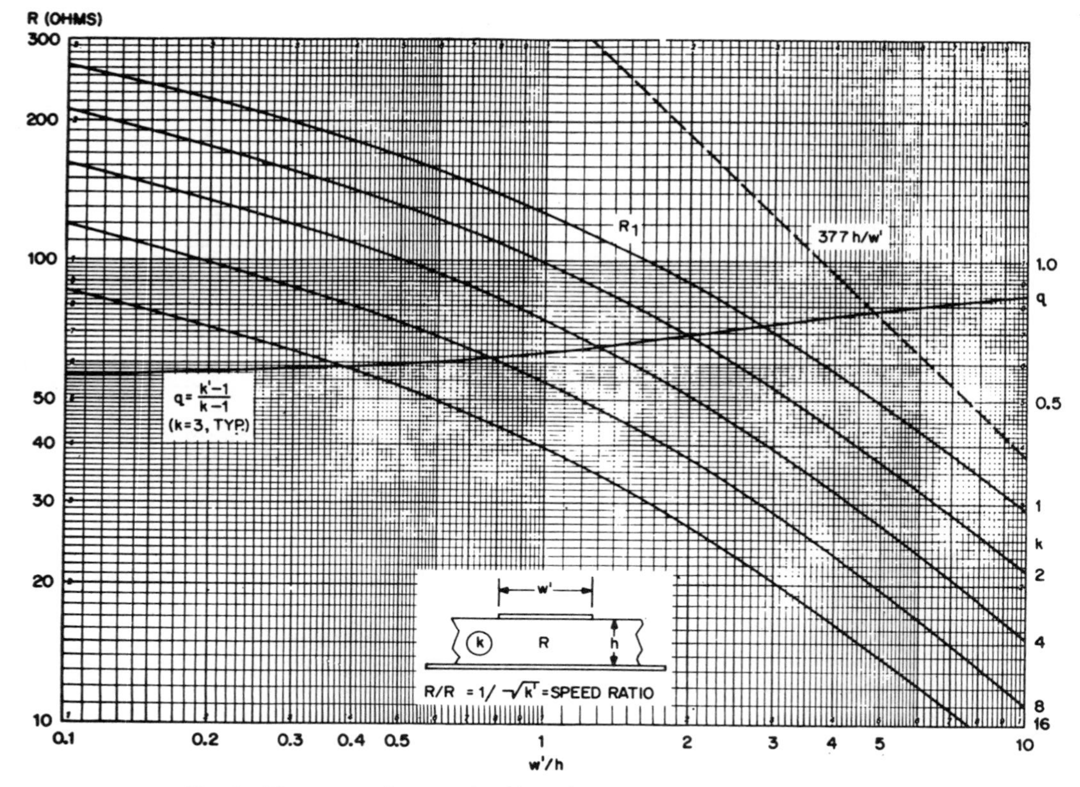

Fig. 2. The wave resistance of a thin strip on a dielectric sheet on a plane.

of practical design, and can be read close enough for ordinary purposes. The formulas to be given are intended as an alternative to the graphs, and also to give further insight into the relations. The formulas are designed for programming in a small digital calculator such as the HP-25 or HP-65.

Fig. 2 is a graph of the wave resistance of a thin strip, the same as previously published [2]. It is made with closest approximation by complete computation for overlapping ranges of narrow and wide strips. An alternative to this graph is the simple empirical formulas to be given for the entire range of width. The wave-speed ratio (relative to air or free space) for any width ratio is equal to the ratio of wave resistance with and without dielectric (R/R_1).

The effective filling fraction q of the dielectric is also graphed on Fig. 2 for a mean value of the dielectric constant ($k = 3$). It enables an alternative computation of the effective dielectric constant k' and the resulting speed ratio ($1/\sqrt{k'}$).

Fig. 3 is a graph of the thickness effect on the wave resistance without dielectric. The relative effect is less with dielectric, so the indicated effect is an upper bound. It is a small effect with respect to wave resistance but has a greater effect on the magnetic PF. This is generally similar to the first-order effect of thickness as previously stated [2] but is refined and extended to include the second-order effect in some degree.

Fig. 4 is a graph of the normalized magnetic PF ($P = p \div \delta/h$) as evaluated from the thickness effect. The magnetic PF is independent of the dielectric and its normalized value is independent of the size. The thickness parameter t/h is chosen as being a property of the laminate, specifically the thickness ratio of the conductive strip and the dielectric sheet.

New formulas are presented here in the main text without derivation. Most of them are empirical formulas providing a gradual transition between narrow and wide extremes. These are tested against the derived close approximations for overlapping narrow and wide ranges, which are reviewed in Appendix VI. Some derivations, not previously available, are given in Appendixes IV and V. Special emphasis is placed on some formulas which are "reversible" in the sense that a formula can be expressed explicitly in a simple form for either analysis or synthesis.

V. A Thin Strip Without Dielectric

The 1964 paper [1] gave the derivation for a wide thin strip without dielectric, and, incidentally, also gave formulas for a narrow thin strip. These together covered any width. Explicit formulas were given for both purposes, analysis and synthesis.

Recent studies yielded the discovery that the "narrow" formula could be put into a form which would also be asymptotic to the "wide" formula. This is accomplished while retaining its principal features for "narrow" approximation. Furthermore, this has been so arranged that the formula is "reversible." By this is meant that an explicit formula for either analysis or synthesis can be converted to an explicit formula for the other. This conversion is permitted no complication beyond the solution of a quadratic equation. The resulting formulas are empirical in the sense that they must be tested against derived formulas in the "wide" range and in the overlap of "wide" and "narrow." For

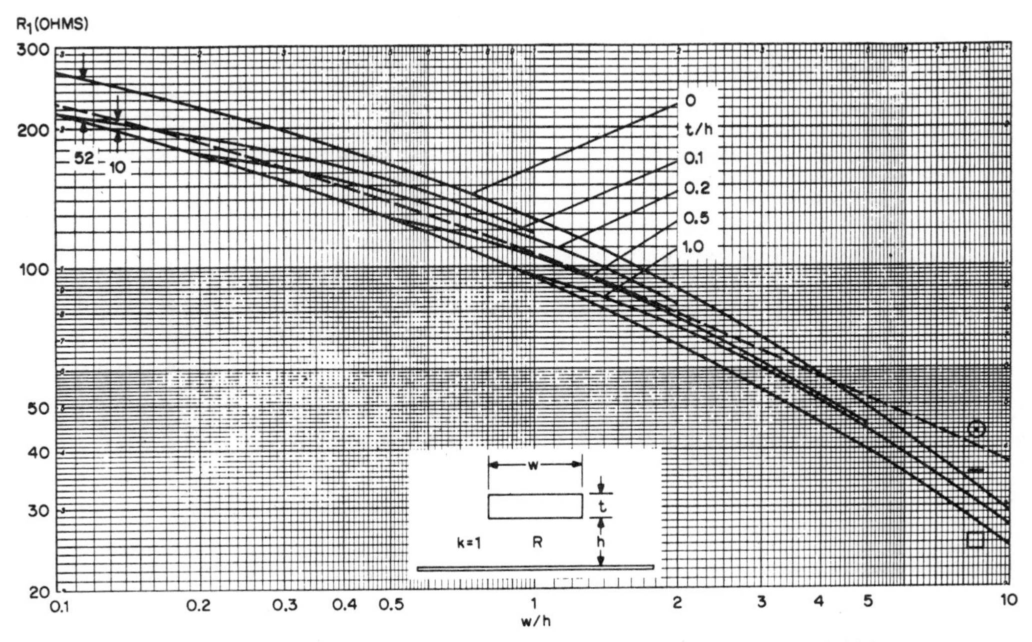

Fig. 3. The wave resistance of a strip without dielectric, showing the effect of thickness.

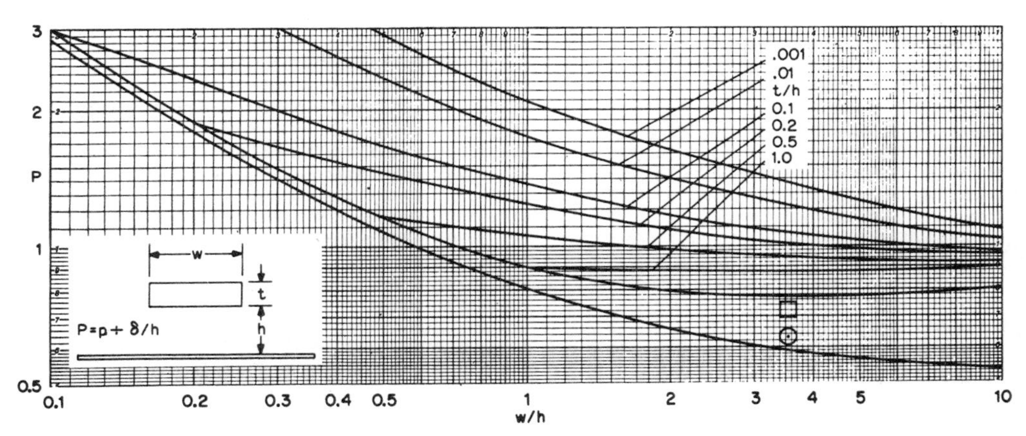

Fig. 4. The magnetic power factor of a strip, showing the effect of thickness.

the thin strip without dielectric, such derived formulas are the subject of the 1964 paper. The resulting formulas herein are based on "narrow" derivations which are relatively simple although the derivation of the second term has not been published before. It is based on a two-wire second-order approximation for a narrow thin strip. The overlap of the "narrow" and "wide" derivations is indicated, by stating the small error of either at the transition.

The new formulas are to be generalized for dielectric, but they are first given here in simplest form to show some features. Reversible formulas are here shown first for synthesis and then for analysis:

$$w'/h = 8\frac{\sqrt{(\exp R_1/30 - 1) + \pi^2/4}}{(\exp R_1/30 - 1)} \tag{1}$$

$$R_1 = 30 \ln \{1 + \tfrac{1}{2}(8h/w')[(8h/w') + \sqrt{(8h/w')^2 + \pi^2}]\} \tag{2}$$

where the error is $<0.01R_1$.

The following are the asymptotic forms for the narrow and wide extremes: narrow:

$$w'/h = 8(\exp - R_1/60)[1 + 1.73(\exp - R_1/60)^2]$$

$$R_1 = 60 \ln (8h/w' + 1.73(w'/8h)) \tag{3}$$

wide:

$$w'/h = 120\pi/R_1;\ R_1 = 120\pi(h/w'). \tag{4}$$

In the "narrow" formula, the second-order term has the proper form but its coëfficient is compromised (1.73 instead of 2) to accomplish asymptotic "wide" behavior.

The asymptotic behavior at both extremes could be accomplished by any of several variants, yielding somewhat different behavior in the transition region. The form chosen was found to give close enough approximation with the minimum number of terms.

The form of these transitional approximate formulas shows some points of similarity to the exact formulas for a round wire near a plane, which are to be given here.

VI. Square or Circular Cross Section

As an extreme departure from the thin strip, a square or circular cross section is considered, still without dielectric. Fig. 1(b) shows a square or an inscribed circle as the cross section, with the description in the same terms as Fig. 1(a) ($t/w = 1$). It is noted that the distance from the plane is described by the separation height h, not by the distance to center (which is $h + t/2$). Hence it is compatible with separation by a dielectric sheet.

For the narrow case, simple formulations for a square wire and the equivalent round wire are known. See Appendix III. Fig. 1(c) shows this relation and the radius $(2h + w)$ of the outer circle equivalent to the plane.

For the wide case, the exact formula is known for the round wire but not for the square one. Therefore a close approximation for the square wire has been derived and is presented in Appendix IV.

For the round wire, the exact formula for any width ratio is known in simple reversible form. By modifying this form, a reversible empirical formula has been derived for the square shape. These formulas are presented here. (R_1 without dielectric is here simplified to R, because here there is no need for this distinction.)

For round wire without dielectric the exact formulas are as follows:

$$w/h = \frac{2}{\cosh R/60 - 1} = \frac{1}{(\sinh R/120)^2} = \left(\frac{2}{\exp R/120 - \exp - R/120}\right)^2 = \frac{4}{\exp R/60 + \exp - R/60 - 2} = \frac{4 \exp - R/60}{(1 - \exp - R/60)^2} = \frac{4 \exp R/60}{(\exp R/60 - 1)^2} \tag{5}$$

$$R = 60 \operatorname{acosh} (2h/w + 1) = 120 \operatorname{asinh} \sqrt{h/w} = 60 \ln \left[(2h/w + 1) + \sqrt{(2h/w + 1)^2 - 1}\right] = 120 \ln \left(\sqrt{h/w} + \sqrt{h/w + 1}\right). \tag{6}$$

For square wire without dielectric the approximate formulas are as follows:

$$w/h = \frac{1/0.59}{\exp R/60 - 0.2} \frac{2 + \exp - R/60}{1 - \exp - R/60} = \frac{1}{0.118\,5 \exp R/60 + \exp - R/60 - 6} \frac{2 + \exp - R/60}{} \tag{7}$$

$$R = 60 \ln \left[\left(\frac{h}{0.59w} + 1.1\right) - 0.5 + \sqrt{\left(\frac{h}{0.59w} + 1.1\right)^2 - 1.05}\right]. \tag{8}$$

The relative error is < 0.025 or $< (0.005R + 0.5\,\Omega)$. If $R \to 0$, $w/h \to 381/R$ (near $377/R$). Each of these formulas is asymptotic in the first- and second-order terms for "narrow" and the first-order term for "wide."

These formulas are intended mainly for the magnetic-loss PF, for which there is no effect of dielectric, and only the "analysis" form (R of w/h) is used. The synthesis form (w/h of R) is shown mainly for academic interest, since it formed the basis for the empirical formulas for the square wire over the entire range of width ratio.

In Fig. 1(c), in addition to the equivalent circular and square cross sections, there are shown some equivalent thin strips. A round wire far from the plane has an equivalent concentric thin strip whose width is double the wire diameter ($2.36w$). If not so far from the plane, there is a thin strip of lesser width (w') which is equivalent by the following two tests:

a) height above the plane equal to that of the lower side of the square;
b) equal wave resistance.

The indicated geometric proportionality of the two strip widths is of interest in kind but not in degree, because their difference becomes substantial for a square so wide that the simple rules of equivalence are failing.

The lesser thin strip, compared with the square, determines the width adjustment here associated with the thickness of the square.

VII. A Thin Strip with Dielectric

The 1965 paper [2] gave the derivation for a thin strip with dielectric. Two sets of formulas covered wide and narrow strips, with close agreement in the transition region. The reversible formulas given above are here adapted to dielectric. Asymptotic behavior is achieved for the following conditions:

a) narrow strip, low-k and high-k extremes, with a logical interpolation therebetween;
b) wide strip, all k.

The resulting empirical formulas are found to track the derived formulas over the entire range of width and dielectric:

$$w'/h = 8 \frac{\sqrt{\left[\exp\left(\frac{R}{42.4}\sqrt{k+1}\right) - 1\right] \frac{7 + 4/k}{11} + \frac{1 + 1/k}{0.81}}}{\left[\exp\left(\frac{R}{42.4}\sqrt{k+1}\right) - 1\right]} \tag{9}$$

$$R = \frac{42.4}{\sqrt{k+1}} \ln \left\{1 + \left(\frac{4h}{w'}\right)\left[\left(\frac{14 + 8/k}{11}\right)\left(\frac{4h}{w'}\right) + \sqrt{\left(\frac{14 + 8/k}{11}\right)^2 \left(\frac{4h}{w'}\right)^2 + \frac{1 + 1/k}{2} \pi^2}\right]\right\}. \tag{10}$$

The error is $< 0.02R$ (or $< 0.01R$ over most of range).

The analytic form gives R (for k) and R_1 (for $k = 1$), from which the speed ratio is

$$R/R_1 = 1/\sqrt{k'} < 1. \tag{11}$$

Therefore no other formula is needed for the speed ratio. The simpler formula (2) for R_1 may be used, but that is no advantage if the more general formula is recorded in a program for numerical computation.

While the effective filling fraction q [2] of the dielectric is not required in the procedures given here for design computations, it is a matter of some interest. Particularly, it is a factor in the electric-loss PF to be formulated. Schneider [14] has given an ingenious simple empirical formula, based on [2], which is close enough for practical purposes:

$$q = \frac{1}{2}\left(1 + \frac{1}{\sqrt{1 + 10h/w}}\right). \tag{12}$$

Compared with the derived formulas for narrow and wide ranges (for a mean value, $k = 3$) the departure is <0.02. It is a simple transition between the bounds $(\frac{1}{2},1)$. It lacks the shape that is peculiar to either extreme, which is contained in the derived formulas.

VIII. Strip Thickness and the Loss Power Factor

The earlier papers did not make any attempt to evaluate conductor loss, because it is not determined in the limit of a thin strip. However, there was given a width adjustment for the edge effect of a small thickness. From this adjustment, some other authors have formulated the losses to be expected, and their reduction by thickness [13], [17].

This subject has been reviewed. The width adjustment has been verified for small thicknesses of a narrow strip, and has been formulated more closely for a wide strip. A single formula is given here for the entire range of width. Also it is adapted to moderately large thicknesses (up to a square cross section for a narrow strip).

The loss PF (PF $= 1/Q$) of the magnetic field (bounded by the conductors) is evaluated by the rule proposed by the author in 1942 [3]. This "incremental-inductance rule" is based on differentiation of the inductance relative to the skin depth δ in the conductor boundaries, as indicated in Fig. 1. In a transmission line with perfect boundaries and no dielectric material, the inductance is proportional to the wave resistance. Only the relative change is significant, so the rule is here applied to the wave resistance R_1. This avoids the nuisance of magnetic units and surface resistivity.

A great simplification is now available by numerical differentiation. This was not available in the slide-rule computations of earlier days so analytical differentiation was necessary, however cumbersome. It was used by the other authors. It is no longer needed. What is needed is an analytic formula giving the wave resistance in terms of all dimensions but without dielectric.

The edge effect related to the strip thickness is here described in terms of the extra width Δw of a thin strip having equal wave resistance R_1 without dielectric. This is indicated in Fig. 1.

The first-order effect of a small thickness is given in the 1965 paper, for the extreme cases of narrow and wide strips. Three advances are here presented:

a) a refinement for the wide strip (Appendixes I and II),
b) a unified formula for the entire range of width,
c) a second approximation for greater thickness, within some restrictions.

The resulting formula is expressed in terms of the actual width w or the equivalent-thin-strip width w'. As mentioned above, these relations are based on free space, without dielectric:

$$\frac{\Delta w}{t} = \frac{1}{\pi} \ln \frac{4e}{\sqrt{\left(\frac{t}{h}\right)^2 + \left(\frac{1/\pi}{w/t + 1.10}\right)^2}} \tag{13}$$

or

$$\frac{1}{\pi} \ln \frac{4e}{\sqrt{\left(\frac{t}{h}\right)^2 + \left(\frac{1/\pi}{w'/t - 0.26}\right)^2}}. \tag{14}$$

This adjustment enables a width conversion either way between equivalent strips with or without thickness.

The development of this formula for the wide and intermediate regions has been enabled by complete computation of a few examples (Appendix II). These were accomplished by the technique of conformal mapping. Specifically, a few shapes (w,h,t) of rather small thickness were evaluated by numerical integration of the space gradient. This process is laborious and required some ingenuity near some bounds of integration.

Three examples so evaluated were sufficient to indicate two features implicit in this formula.

a) For a wide strip, the previous formula (1965) is refined in respect to its second-order effect. The ratio previously included as $2h/t$ is here changed to $4h/t$. The former ratio was based on unlimited width, and the change is an adaption to the limited width.
b) The "narrow" and "wide" formulas appear to be upper bounds, as would be expected. Furthermore, the quadratic sum of the two inverse ratios fits the sample points.

The adaptation of this formula for a greater thickness has been enabled by derivations for a square cross section. The extra numbers ($+1.10$ or -0.26) are chosen to match the square condition ($t = w$) for a narrow strip. The formula is a close approximation for moderate thicknesses ($t < h$) of a wide strip. (Another formula has been derived for a wide strip of square cross section, Appendix IV.)

For loss computation, the actual width and thickness (w,t) are converted to the width of an equivalent thin strip ($w' = w + \Delta w$). Then the thin-strip formula (R_1 of w') can be used for differentiation with respect to the actual dimensions (w,h,t).

As indicated in Fig. 1, each dimension is incremented by $\pm\delta$ and the same formula is used again to obtain R_δ. Then the (small) loss PF is computed by the incremental-inductance rule:

$$p = \frac{R_\delta - R_1}{R_\delta} = 1 - R_1/R_\delta = \ln R_\delta/R_1 \ll 1. \tag{15}$$

A normalized form for loss PF is proposed, which gives the effect of shape, independent of the size, frequency, and conductor material. It is normalized to the height h:

$$P = p \div (\delta/h) = p(h/\delta) \qquad p = P(\delta/h). \tag{16}$$

The reference (δ/h) is the nominal PF of a very wide strip.

In computing the normalized PF P, the value of the skin depth is immaterial if it is sufficiently small to approach the limiting behavior of the skin effect (which is usually of interest). Also it must not approach the sensitivity of the computer. In a computer giving ten decimal places, a fair compromise is $\delta/h = 0.0001$. Then the skin effect is well represented if all dimension ratios exceed 0.001.

For evaluation of a resonator made of a strip line, the loss PF (or dissipation factor or $1/Q$) is usually the most significant factor. The wave R is incidentally relevant in the circuit application of the resonator. The loss PF of the magnetic field is evaluated by the simplest formulas (R_1 and Δw without dielectric). For any shape, the value of P enables a computation of the size of the cross section to realize a value of p:

$$h = P\delta/p = P\delta Q. \tag{17}$$

The graphs in Fig. 4 show the loss PF in terms of P for a wide range of shapes. The common reference is the height h and the thickness ratio t/h because they may be fixed by a dielectric sheet and a conductive sheet bonded thereto.

For small thicknesses, the loss PF exceeds the reference value, as would be expected. Also the amount of excess is greater for lesser thickness, as a result of the current concentration at the edges. For example, reducing the thickness from square to $t/h = 0.02$ may double the PF (in the moderately narrow range).

An unexpected result is the loss PF being less than the reference value for a wide strip of substantial thickness. This happens because part of the magnetic energy is beyond the region bounded by the height. This part has boundaries further apart, and hence a lesser value of loss PF.

In Fig. 4, the two lowest curves give the loss PF for square and circular cross sections of the same width. It is less for the latter, the lower bound for the wide extreme being one half the reference value $(P \to \frac{1}{2})$. In the narrow region, it is less because of the following.

a) The two shapes are known to have equal skin resistance [9].
b) The circular shape has greater reactance. The proportionate wave resistance is greater by $60 \ln 1.18 = 10\,\Omega$; this is denoted, "the rule of 10 Ω."

If the thickness is comparable with the height, the relevant restriction may be the overall height $(h + t)$, perhaps for reasons of clearance space. Also the width may be restricted. Then the thickness ratio has an optimum value. This is found by minimizing a related normalized PF defined as follows:

$$P_{ht} = P\frac{h+t}{h} = P(1 + t/h) = (p/\delta)(h + t) \tag{18}$$

Square: w/h near 0.55, $\min P_{ht} = 1.65$ (19)

Circular: w/h near 0.50, $\min P_{ht} = 1.56.$ (20)

Within specified bounds of the overall height and width (not less than the overall height), the optimum rectangular cross section is one which is bounded by these two dimensions and has a certain thickness $(t/h < 1)$. The extreme optimum is a peculiar rounded shape bounded by these dimensions.

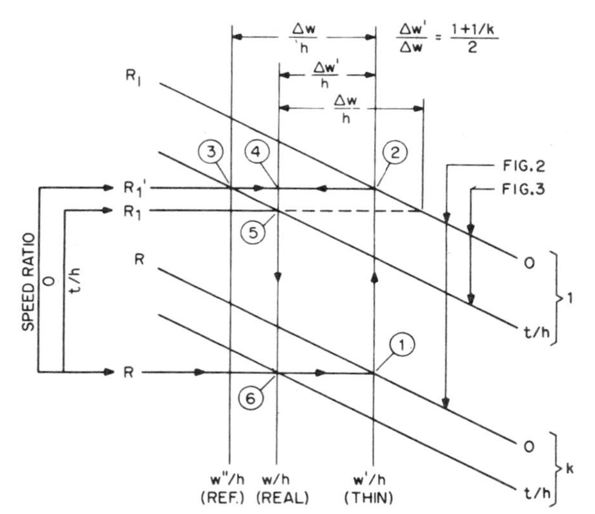

Fig. 5. Relations which determine the speed ratio.

IX. Strip Thickness with Dielectric

The effect of strip thickness is formulated above, but without the effect of dielectric. A width adjustment for thickness may be made in the synthesis for a specified wave resistance with dielectric.

The width of an equivalent thin strip is defined as one which is wider by the amount which yields an equal value of wave resistance. This involves both inductance and capacitance. The width adjustment for the former is independent of dielectric. That for the latter is less for a greater dielectric constant, because the thickness of the edge is somewhat spaced from the dielectric.

To approximate this effect, the width adjustment is divided in two equal parts, and one part is decreased by the factor $1/k$. The modified value becomes:

$$\Delta w' = \frac{1 + 1/k}{2}\Delta w, \qquad w = w' - \Delta w'. \tag{21}$$

The entire width adjustment Δw is effective for wave resistance without dielectric ($k = 1$) or for inductance alone. For capacitance alone, the entire width adjustment would be decreased by the factor $1/k$.

Fig. 5 shows the behavior of the width adjustment without or with dielectric. Especially it shows its graphic determination from Figs. 2 and 3. The full value of Δw is effective without dielectric, decreasing the wave resistance R_1 equally by decreasing inductance and by increasing capacitance. Its amount is represented by the horizontal separation of the upper pair of curves, both shown in Fig. 3. The effect of dielectric with a thin strip is represented by the separation of the upper curves (R_1, R) in the upper and lower pairs, both shown in Fig. 2. The reduced amount of width adjustment with dielectric is constructed and projected downward to give the lesser horizontal separation of the lower pair of curves.

The speed ratio for a thin strip is R/R_1 from Fig. 2. The interpolation for mixed dielectric, taking account of thickness, gives a greater speed ratio from this construction. The latter locates a point on the lower curve of the lower pair, not shown elsewhere.

As will be seen in a procedure and example to be given, the indicated numerical sequence yields all the quantities from the graphs in Figs. 2 and 3. Or they may be computed in this sequence by these formulas:

Sequence	Formulas
1	(9)
2	(2)
3	(14)
4	(21)
5	(13) (2)
6	(—)

In this sequence, 2–3 is the width adjustment downward from the upperbound for a thin strip. A parallel dashed line shows also the width adjustment upward from a strip with thickness. The former will be used in a synthesis procedure, the latter in analysis. The amount of the adjustment is designated alike in both ($\Delta w/h$) although it may differ slightly (too little for any practical significance).

X. Attenuation

The rate of attenuation with distance in a transmission line is simply expressed in terms of the average PF (magnetic p and electric p') and the wavelength λ_g in the line:

$$\alpha = \frac{p + p'}{2} \frac{2\pi}{\lambda_g} = \frac{p + p'}{2} \sqrt{k'} \frac{2\pi}{\lambda_0} = \frac{p + p'}{2} \frac{R_1}{R} \frac{2\pi}{\lambda_0} \text{ (Np/m)}. \tag{22}$$

In words, this is the average PF (nepers) per radian length. The magnetic PF is evaluated by the skin effect, as described above.

The electric PF p' of the effective dielectric in the line (k') can be expressed in terms of the various parameters involved:

speed ratio:

$$\lambda_g/\lambda_0 = 1/\sqrt{k'} = R/R_1 \tag{23}$$

filling fraction:

$$q = \frac{k' - 1}{k - 1} = \frac{1}{k - 1}[(R_1/R)^2 - 1] \tag{24}$$

electric PF:

$$p' = \frac{p_k}{1 + \dfrac{1/q - 1}{k}} \tag{25}$$

bounds:

$$p_k > p' > \left\{ \begin{matrix} qp_k \\ \dfrac{p_k}{1 + 1/k} \end{matrix} \right\} > \tfrac{1}{2}p_k. \tag{26}$$

The electric PF p' is seen to be within $(\frac{3}{4} \pm \frac{1}{4})$ of the dielectric-material PF p_k, and usually it is nearer the upper bound. Therefore the electric PF is only slightly less than that of the material, so the complete formulation is not critical and may be unnecessary. If desired, it can be computed (as above) from R/R_1 and p_k.

Either attenuation or PF may be deduced from the other. However, it is preferable to evaluate the magnetic PF directly, because it is independent of the dielectric and the speed ratio. In a wide range of situations, it represents nearly all of the loss PF.

XI. Procedures for Computation

The formulas are intended for useful applications, which may be theoretical and/or practical. As brought out in the earlier papers, "synthesis" and "analysis" are the alternative objectives, the former for practical design and the latter for evaluation of a configuration (the classical textbook approach). Both are needed here for a practical design to meet some specifications and tests. Therefore a few procedures and examples will be outlined to show the use of these formulas in arriving at a practical design.

The first few procedures start with the synthesis of a line to meet a specification of wave resistance. The subsequent evaluation of speed ratio and skin effect are inherently analysis, but the procedures build on the synthesis.

First Procedure: On a specified printed-circuit board, find the width for a 50-Ω line:

a) specify properties of a dielectric sheet with metal faces: $k = 2.5$, $h = 1$ mm, $t = 0.1$ mm;
b) specify wave resistance: $R = 50\ \Omega$;
c) width of thin strip by (9) or Fig. 2: $w'/h = 2.85$;
d) width adjustment (without dielectric) by (14) or Fig. 3: $\Delta w/h = 0.15$;
e) effect of dielectric by (21): $\Delta w'/h = 0.10$;
f) width by (21): $w/h = w'/h - \Delta w'/h = 2.75$; $w = 2.75$ mm.

Second Procedure: For the same line, evaluate the speed ratio, referring to Fig. 5:

g) no. 1 in sequence, c) above: $w'/h = 2.85$;
h) no. 2, find R'_1 of thin strip by (2) or Fig. 2 or 3: $R'_1 = 71.5$;
i) no. 3, d) above: $\Delta w/h = 0.15$, $w''/h = w'/h - \Delta w/h = 2.70$;
j) no. 4, e) above: $\Delta w'/h = 0.10$, $w/h = w'/h - \Delta w'/h = 2.75$;
k) no. 5, by Fig. 3: $R_1 = 71$, or can be computed by the "fourth procedure";
l) speed ratio $= R/R_1 = 50/71 = 0.70$.

Third Procedure: For the same line, evaluate the magnetic PF and the attenuation from this cause, referring to Fig. 4, Appendixes VII and VIII:

m) find the normalized PF by Fig. 4: $P = 1.10$; or it may be computed by (16) using a nominal small δ and numerical differentiation;
n) specify the frequency (or wavelength λ_0): $f = 1$ GHz, $\lambda_0 = 0.3$ m;

o) specify the conductivity (or material) of the metal boundaries: copper;
p) evaluate the skin depth by (62) or [7]: $\delta = 2.1$ μm;
q) compute the PF by (16): $p = 0.0023 = 2.3$ mil, $Q = 440$;
r) compute the attenuation rate from PF, speed ratio, etc., by (22): $\alpha = 0.034$ Np/m or 0.30 dB/m.

If used for a long line, the attenuation rate may be significant. If used for a resonator, the PF and speed ratio are relevant.

In the third procedure, if one is concerned with only one example (size, shape, materials, frequency) the actual skin depth may be used directly, then the procedure assumes this order: (n,o,p) (m,q,r).

A lesser PF may be required, or it may be desired to explore the compromise between the loss PF and the height and/or thickness. The first-order relation gives the PF inversely proportional to size (h,t,w). A closer evaluation may require complete computation of various examples, then interpolation.

The following example and procedure are modified to develop from analysis only. In particular, the width adjustment corresponds to the dashed line in Fig. 5.

Another Example: Design a resonator to be made of a square wire bonded to a printed-circuit board. Similarly lettered items refer to the foregoing procedures:

a) $k = 2.5$, $h = 1$ mm, $t = w$;
m) from Fig. 4: near-minimum $P = 0.8$ for $w/h = 2$, $w = t = 2$ mm;
p) $\delta = 2.1$ μm;
q) $p = 0.0017 = 1.7$ mil, $Q = 590$.

The speed ratio can be evaluated by the following procedure. It is found to be $50/67 = 0.75$.

Fourth Procedure: For any configuration, find the speed ratio. For a thin strip, see (11) and Fig. 2 for the simple rule. The following gives the effect of thickness:

a) specify configuration: $k = 2.5$, $w = 2.75$ mm, $h = 1$ mm, $t = 0.1$ mm, $w/h = 2.75$, $t/h = 0.1$;
b) width adjustment (without dielectric) by (14) or Fig. 3: $\Delta w/h = 0.15$, $w'/h = 2.90$;
c) wave resistance (without dielectric) by (2) or Fig. 2 or 3: $R_1 = 71$;
d) effect of dielectric by (21): $\Delta w'/h = 0.7$, $\Delta w/h = 0.10$, $w'/h = 2.85$;
e) wave resistance (with dielectric) by (10) or Fig. 2: $R = 50$;
f) speed ratio: $R/R_1 = 0.70$.

The speed ratio is slightly greater than that for a thin strip of the same width.

If resonance (small PF or high Q) is the principal objective (rather than wave resistance) a different procedure may be indicated. The following outline gives some relevant considerations.

a) Choose between a specified printed-circuit material (h,t) and the alternative of an attached thick strip (which may have a square or circular cross section). The latter offers a lesser PF.
b) If a thick strip is to be afforded, specify the bounds of the space (overall height and width, $h + t$ and w).
c) Specify whether the conductor (strip or whatever) is to be supported in contact with a dielectric sheet. If so, specify the height of the latter (h).
d) Subject to these restrictions, choose a cross section giving near-minimum P_{ht} (18).
e) If using a strip of small thickness t, a lesser PF is obtainable by greater width w and greater height h.
f) If using a square cross section in contact with a dielectric sheet ($t/h = w/h$), the least PF is obtainable by a moderately wide shape (say w/h near 3).
g) If using a round wire in contact, a lesser PF is obtainable by greater width (diameter), but little reduction is obtainable beyond a moderate width (say w/h near 3).
h) If using a square or round wire with no need for contact, the least PF is obtainable by a width near one third the overall height.
i) If a rectangular space is specified, with the width not less than the overall height, the least PF obtainable with a rectangular cross section requires some thickness less than one third the overall height.

There is usually not available an explicit formula for the synthesis to realize a specified value of the loss PF. The graphs in Fig. 4 can be applied to this problem. Knowing the skin depth δ and specifying the material (h,t), a value of the loss PF p requires the P computed from (16). In Fig. 4, this value of P determines the shape ratio w/h and hence the width w. If this P is lower than a practical curve, the size (h,t) may be increased to permit a greater value of P.

XII. Conclusion

The transmission-line properties of a strip parallel to a plane, with or without an intervening dielectric sheet, are evaluated in simple formulas, each one adapted for all shape ratios. The formulas relating the width/height ratio with wave resistance are stated explicitly for both analysis and synthesis, with or without dielectric. The wave-speed ratio and the magnetic-loss PF are stated from the viewpoint of analysis, which is usually what is needed.

The advance over previous publications appears mainly in two areas:

a) a relation is expressed explicitly by a single simple formula for the entire range of the shape ratio;
b) the width adjustment for thickness is formulated and used for evaluation of the magnetic loss.

Each formula is an empirical relation obtained by designing a gradual transition between known simple formulas for both extremes of narrow and wide shapes.

All formulas are designed for ease of programming on a pocket calculator such as the HP-25 or HP-65. Particularly, the digital calculator enables the numerical differentiation (for loss evaluation) which is here used to realize a great simplification. While beyond the scope of this article, the writer would welcome inquiries relating to programs for the HP-25, some of which may be available on request.

The subject line, formed by a strip parallel to a plane, has presented problems of evaluation which are much more difficult than those of the strip between two planes (sandwich line). That configuration is symmetrical and the dielectric is homogeneous, so even the thickness effects have yielded to straightforward formulation [8]. The asymmetrical strip line is here formulated in a manner that is competitive, although necessarily involving mixed dielectric.

While there is always room for further progress, the graphs and formulas presented here are complete in that they offer the option of graphical or numerical reading for the all numerical values that may be needed for design purposes. Preliminary estimating is usually aided most by the graphs.

XIII. Acknowledgment

This study has been stimulated by the attempts of other authors, building on the writer's early papers. The stimulation has come partly from a perception of some deficiencies in progress, but more from an appreciation of the constructive efforts and interesting results of a few of the intervening workers. The final impetus was provided by the advent of the HP-25, which offered the computational power best suited for the "close support" essential to such a development.

Appendix I
Behavior of the Width Adjustment for Thickness

Formulas (13) and (14) for the width adjustment are based on some asymptotic relations and a transition therebetween. Asymptotic formulas for narrow and wide extremes were given in the early papers [1], [2]. Here a revision of the wide formula and an integrated formula with a simple form of transition were presented. This appendix is a graphical description of the behavior of this adjustment, for the purpose of visualizing the transition and some associated relations.

Fig. 6(a) shows a graph for a constant ratio of thickness/height (t/h). This may be the practical situation when designing for a printed circuit to be made by etching a conductive sheet bonded to a dielectric sheet. The width adjustment ratio $\pi\Delta w/t$ is plotted on the width ratio w/h. The scales are, respectively, linear and logarithmic, to give straight lines for the sloping graphs.

The normalized form for the width adjustment takes out the principal dependence on thickness, so one can see the variations of the coefficient which is dependent on shape. A higher value indicates a greater coefficient (responsive to thinness) but the amount of the adjustment is still nearly proportional to thickness.

There are two upper bounds (UB's) for this coefficient, based on the narrow and wide asymptotic behavior. The level upper line is based on the wide extreme, the edge-field pattern being influenced mainly by the proximity of the shield plane. The sloping lower line is based on the narrow

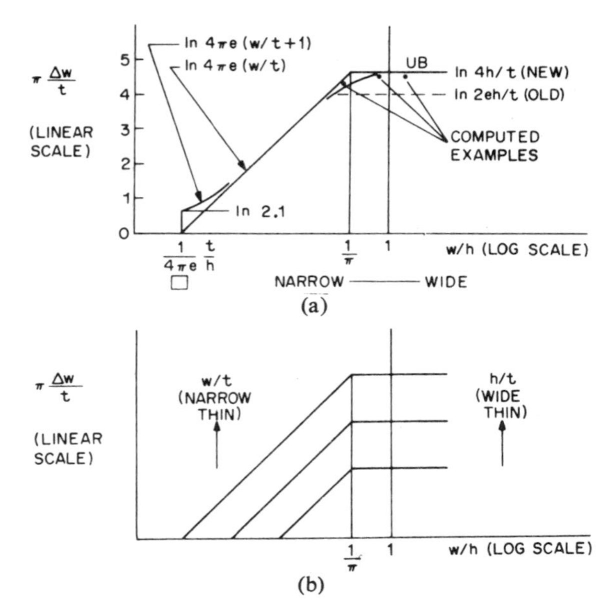

Fig. 6. The behavior of the width adjustment for thickness. (a) Transition between narrow and wide. (b) Family of transitions.

extreme, the edge-field pattern being influenced mainly by the proximity of the two edges.

A smooth transition at the knee is provided by a quadrature combination in formula (13). This is validated by some computations to be described in Appendix II, indicated as three points on the curve. This validation requires a change in the wide formula, from the "old" in [2] to the "new" in (13). The computed points indicated that the level UB should be raised by a factor of two under the logarithm, as seen. (This factor is not exactly determined, but two appears to be the nearest and simplest number that might be indicated, and it may have an exact basis.) This is regarded as a refinement of the previous rule, whose derivation ignored the second-order interaction between the edges far apart. It is noted that the transition occurs in the vicinity of a width ratio somewhat less than unity ($w/h = 1/\pi$).

The asymptotic relations are based on the limiting condition of a thin strip. Formula (13) includes an adaptation ($w/t + 1.1$) which extends the close approximation to the square condition. This introduces another curved transition at the foot of the graph, raising the curve from the "square" point ($t/w = 1$). While beyond the present scope, it is noted that the curve has a minimum near the foot and approaches a higher level (π) in the narrow extreme ($w/t \ll 1$).

Fig. 6(b) is a diagram showing a family of such graphs. For greater thickness, the knee is closer to the foot of the graph, so the two curved transitions would merge as the thickness approaches the square shape. Then their separate descriptions become indefinite, so the validity of formula (13) is further tested on square shapes, as evaluated in Appendixes III and IV.

Appendix II
Small-Thickness Examples by Conformal Mapping

Formula (13) gives the width adjustment for thickness. It is an empirical transition between the narrow and wide

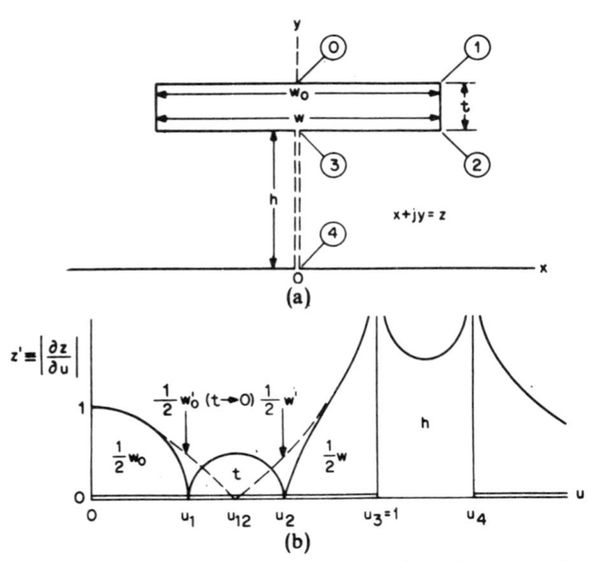

Fig. 7. Conformal mapping of the cross section of the strip line. (a) Contour in space. (b) Space gradient. (Each area equals dimension in space.)

extremes of the asymptotic behavior in the limit of a thin strip. The first-order relations for these extremes have been known [2] but not the behavior in the transition regions. Also there is found a second-order effect requiring a revision for the wide extreme.

The validation of this formula, especially in the transition region, is provided by some complete computations of a few examples by a procedure based on conformal mapping. The contour of the cross section is mapped on a straight line. The space gradient on this line is integrated to evaluate the dimensional ratios on the contour. Rather than implicit elliptic integrals, numerical integration is used. Even that is confronted by difficulties of integration where there is an infinite value and/or slope at either bound ($\infty, \sqrt{\infty}$, or $\sqrt{0}$).

Fig. 7 shows the essentials of the conformal mapping of the cross section of the strip line. The actual contour, Fig. 7(a), is described on the space plane ($x + jy = z$) in terms of the shape dimensions w,h,t whose ratios determine the properties. This contour is mapped on a straight line, Fig. 7(b). On the scale of this line u is graphed the space gradient (or inverse field gradient) on the contour. The area under the space gradient in each interval is equal to the dimension on the contour.

The space gradient is formulated by inspection, as follows:

$$Z' = |\partial z/\partial u| = \left| \frac{[1 - (u/u_1)^2][1 - (u/u_2)^2]}{[1 - (u/u_3)^2][1 - (u/u_4)^2]} \right|^{1/2}. \quad (27)$$

Only the area ratios are significant, so the scale is arbitrarily chosen for simplicity.

The analytic integration would involve elliptic integrals. There is a constraint that precludes an explicit solution. The upper and lower faces of the strip must have equal width ($w_0 = w$), to be realized by proportioning one of the critical values on the straight line.

Numerical integration is simple in concept and has been found useful in computing a few examples. Some special rules have been devised for closer convergence near the singular points which correspond to the angles of the contour. The result is a close approximation in cases where the singular points are not too closely spaced.

TABLE I
COMPUTED EXAMPLES

No.	1	2	3
R_1	188.5	133.7	88.5
u_4	1.414	1.1	1.01
u_{12}	0.7368	0.7774	0.8412
u_2	0.8867	0.8720	0.8988
u_1	0.5267	0.6520	0.7648
w'/h	0.348	0.879	2.020
w/h	0.237	0 .754	1.894
t/h	0.0755	0.0816	0.0838
Δw/h	0.111	0.125	0.126
Δw/t	1.48	1.53	1.51
(14)	1.47	1.55	1.56
dif.	+.01	-.02	-.05

The wave resistance is determined by the gaps in the straight line, both sides of center. For the upper half-plane,

$$R = \tfrac{1}{2}R_c \frac{K'(k)}{K(k)} = \frac{\left(\dfrac{1 + 1.14k^2}{\pi} \ln \dfrac{16}{k^2}\right)^{1-k^2}}{\left(\dfrac{1 + 1.14(1 - k^2)}{\pi} \ln \dfrac{16}{1 - k^2}\right)^{k^2}} \quad (28)$$

in which $k = 1/u_4$.

The latter (empirical) formula has a relative error <0.005. It has the correct center value, skew symmetry, and asymptotic behavior at both extremes. A closer simple formula for a wide strip is

$$R = \frac{60\pi^2}{\ln \dfrac{8}{\ln 1/k}} = \frac{60\pi^2}{\ln \dfrac{8}{\ln u_4}}. \quad (29)$$

If $1/k = u_4 < 1.4$, the relative error is $<0.001R$.

Three examples have been computed. They are summarized in Table I, numbered in order of increasing width. The first is a critical shape ($R_1 = 377/2$) while the others are chosen to give a range of widths in the transition region. These three examples have comparable values of the thickness ratio (t/h near 0.08). This ratio is small enough to be representative of small thicknesses ($t/h \ll 1$ and $w/h \ll 1$). Its value is the basis for the graph in Fig. 6(a), and the three points are plotted in relation to the curve of formula (13). The close agreement is regarded as confirmation of that formula (for small thicknesses), especially in the transition region which does not have a clear theoretical basis. This result was the objective of the complete computation of these few examples.

APPENDIX III
EQUIVALENT SQUARE AND CIRCULAR CROSS SECTIONS

The extreme thickness of a narrow strip line is taken to be a square cross section ($t/w = 1$). Therefore the formula for width adjustment contains a constant which assures a close approximation up to this thickness. Its derivation is based on the relations among three equivalent concentric cross sections, the square, the circle, and the thin strip, shown to scale in Fig. 1(c). Their dimensional ratios are such as to give equal values of capacitance and inductance (assuming a small skin depth) and the resulting wave resistance (all in free space).

Starting with the square (of width = w), the equivalent circle has a diameter which is greater in the ratio:

$$\sqrt{9/2\pi}\frac{\Gamma(5/4)}{\Gamma(7/4)} = 1.1803 = 1/0.8472. \tag{30}$$

The equivalent strip has a width which is double this diameter.

In Fig. 1(c), the large dashed arc is the circular boundary equivalent to the ground plane (radius = $2h + w$).

Based on these equivalents, a narrow strip of square cross section has the following wave resistance:

$$R = 60 \ln \frac{2h + w}{0.59w} = 60 \ln 1.70(2h/w + 1) = 60 \ln 8h/w' \tag{31}$$

in which

$$w' = \frac{2.36w}{1 + w/2h}.$$

In terms of width and thickness, the corresponding adjustment is

$$\Delta w = w' - w = w\left(\frac{2.36}{1 + t/2h} - 1\right) = w'\left(1 - \frac{1 + t/2h}{2.36}\right). \tag{32}$$

In formula (13) or (14) for Δw, the constant $+1.1$ or -0.26 is inserted to give the correct value for a narrow strip of square cross section.

From another viewpoint, Fig. 1(b) shows cross sections of a square and an inscribed circle (having equal width). In the narrow case, these have wave resistances differing by

$$60 \ln 1.18 = 9.93 \text{ (near } 10\ \Omega). \tag{33}$$

This is denoted, the "10-Ω rule" for these two cross sections. They are known to have equal skin resistances [9] so the loss PF of the circular wire is less in the inverse ratio of its greater reactance and wave resistance.

Appendix IV
Wide Square Cross Section

The wide square cross section is here evaluated in simple terms by invoking a variety of techniques in four regions of each of the two active quadrants. These regions are described in Fig. 8(a). Each is to be evaluated first in terms of normalized capacitance C, which is the simplest concept for the boundaries involved. The dimensions are referred to the height ($h = 1$).

The first region, 1, is taken to be filled with uniform field:

$$C_1 = w/2. \tag{34}$$

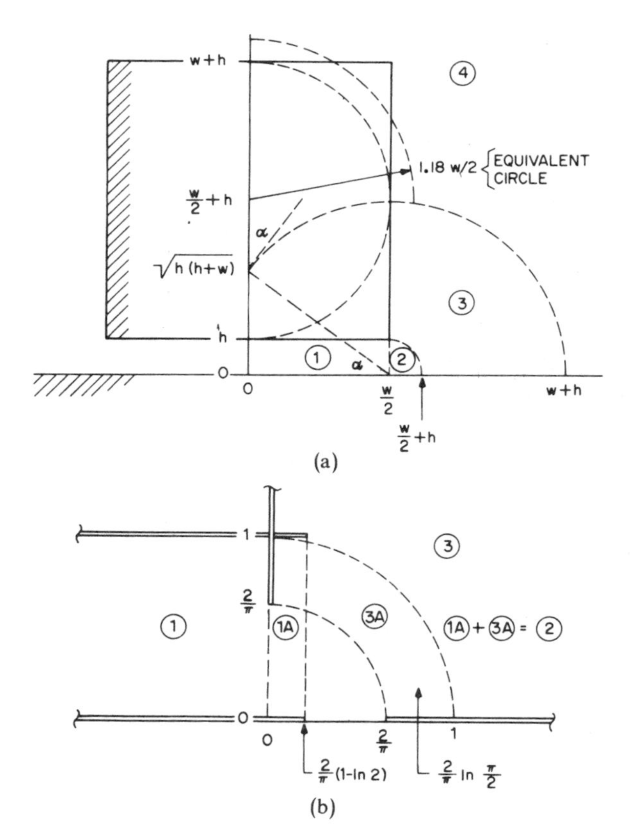

Fig. 8. Derivation for a wide square cross section. (a) The four regions in one quadrant. (b) Analysis of the corner region.

The third region, 3, is taken to be filled with logarithmic field, which is described by radial lines and concentric circles:

$$C_3 = \frac{2}{\pi} \ln (1 + w/2). \tag{35}$$

The second region, 2, is the excess in the transition between 1 and 3, taking into account the nearby distortion in both of those regions. The upper and lower boundaries (corner and straight line) are mapped on parallel straight lines. Then the relative displacement of far points evaluates a "stretch" which represents the excess in the transition. This is divided in two parts for the two directions from the corner. Fig. 8(b) shows this result diagrammatically. Region 2 is represented by 1A and 3A, the respective extensions of the adjacent regions. The validity of this viewpoint resides in the fact that the distortion from the transition decays rapidly in either direction, and also tends to average out. The resulting value of the transition region is

$$C_2 = \frac{2}{\pi}(1 - \ln 2) + \frac{2}{\pi}\ln\frac{\pi}{2} = \frac{2}{\pi}\left(1 - \ln\frac{4}{\pi}\right) = 0.483. \tag{36}$$

The fourth region, 4, is closely related to an inscribed circle, as shown. The region around the inscribed circle would contribute

$$(C_4) = \frac{\alpha}{\pi} \frac{\pi}{\text{acosh}\ (1 + 2/w)} = \frac{\text{asin}\dfrac{1}{\sqrt{w + 1}}}{\text{asinh}\sqrt{1/w}} < 1. \tag{37}$$

For ease of computation, this ratio can be approximated by

$$(C_4) = \left(\frac{1}{1 + 2/w}\right)^{1/3} < 1. \tag{38}$$

Between the inscribed circle and the equivalent circle (of 1.18 times the radius) the nominal capacitance is that of one quadrant:

$$[C_4] = \frac{\pi/2}{\ln 1.18} = 9.49 = 1/0.105. \tag{39}$$

This is used to increase (C_3) to approximate the capacitance of the square in this quadrant:

$$C_4 = \frac{1}{1/(C_4) - 1/[C_4]} < 1.12. \tag{40}$$

The resulting wave resistance of the two quadrants (restoring w to w/h) is

$$R = \frac{377}{2C_1 + 2C_2 + 2C_3 + 2C_4}$$

$$= \frac{377}{w/h + 0.966 + \frac{4}{\pi}\ln(1 + w/2h) + \frac{2}{(1 + 2h/w)^{1/3} - 0.1}}. \tag{41}$$

This formula is best for a wide square cross section. The best for narrow is formula (31) for the equivalent round wire shown in Fig. 1(c). Their effective overlap is indicated by their close values for a transition shape ($w/h = 1$):

1) wide (41) above: 94.91;
2) narrow (31): 95.11 (close lower bound);
3) all (13) (2): 95.32.

The intermediate value is believed to be the closest approximation for this case.

Appendix V
Narrow Thin Strip

For a narrow thin strip (without dielectric) there is here derived the second-order approximation stated without proof in the early papers [1], [2]. It is based on a pair of small wires equivalent to the strip. It forms the basis for the simple formulas (1), (2) for any width.

Fig. 9(a) shows a single round wire of unit radius and its known equivalent thin strip whose width is 4 units. It is described on the z plane. It is to be transformed to another plane, $z' = \sqrt{z}$.

This transformation is here performed about one end of the strip cross section, and the result is seen in Fig. 9(b). An equal strip survives but the wire becomes a pair of smaller wires. This pair provides a second-order approximation to the far field of the strip. (This simple equivalence has not been seen by the author in any of the many published exercises in conformal mapping.) It is noted that the smaller wires are not strictly circular in cross section, but that is irrelevant in the use of the concept herein.

Fig. 9(c) shows the thin strip (or equivalent pair of wires) and its image in a ground plane. From this geometry, the

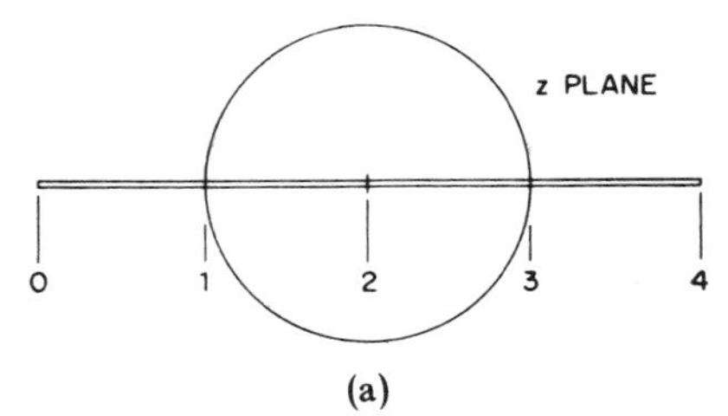

(a)

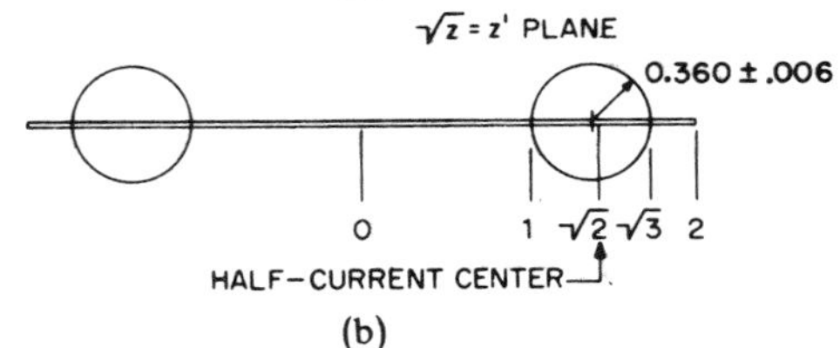

(b)

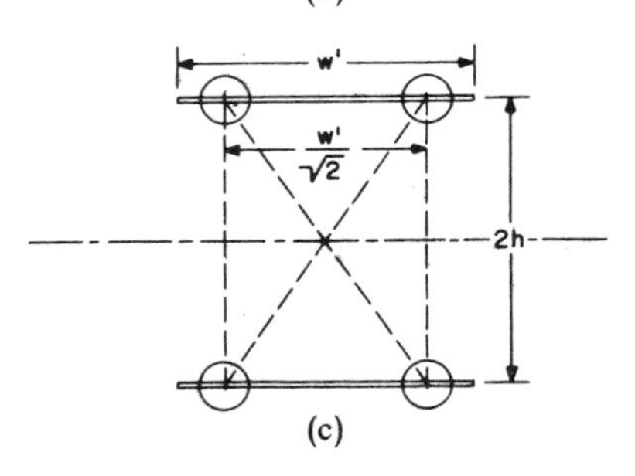

(c)

Fig. 9. The pair of small wires equivalent to a thin strip. (a) Thin strip and equivalent round wire. (b) Thin strip and equivalent pair of round wires. (c) Thin strip and its image in a ground plane.

mean distance between one pair of current centers and the other pair is increased to

$$2h' = \sqrt{2h\sqrt{(2h)^2 + w^2/2}} = 2h[1 + \tfrac{1}{8}(w/h)^2]^{1/4}$$
$$= 2h[1 + \tfrac{1}{32}(w/h)^2 - \cdots]. \tag{42}$$

The narrow-strip formula becomes

$$R = 60 \ln 8h'/w$$
$$= 30 \ln \left[(8h/w)\sqrt{(8h/w)^2 + 8}\right]. \tag{43}$$

This is a reversible formula, giving the following for synthesis:

$$w/h = 8\frac{\sqrt{\sqrt{\exp R/15 + 16} + 4}}{\exp R/30}. \tag{44}$$

For a narrow strip, the 4 term is of the second order (exp $R/30$) and the 16 is of the fourth order (exp $R/15$) relative to the first order (exp $R/60$).

A modification of the above formula gives a simpler form which has a linear slope for $R \to 0$, while retaining the second-order approximation:

$$w/h = 8\frac{\sqrt{\exp R/30 + 2}}{\exp R/30 - 1}. \tag{45}$$

In the limit, $w/h \to (\sqrt{3})240/R = 416/R$.

This is not far from the desired $377/R$. The latter result can be obtained by substituting a slightly lesser value ($\pi^2/4 - 1 = 1.467$) for the constant 2. Asymptotic behavior for a wide strip is then realized at the cost of a slight deficiency in the second-order term. The result is the simple formula (1) giving a close approximation for any width.

The two preceding formulas are extremely close (the relative difference is <0.0002) in the narrow range ($w/h < 2$). The first term of error is proportional to $(w/h)^3$. Their average has a relative error <0.003 if $w/h < 4$. The second formula is closer for greater widths, and therefore probably for all widths. The corresponding formula for analysis is (2) except change π^2 to 12.

This exercise is a striking example of the technique of higher order approximation and its application to obtain a simple and versatile empirical formula with support from various theoretical relations.

Appendix VI
Previously Derived Formulas

Any empirical formula must be validated by comparison with derived formulas. These are typically more complicated and/or restricted as to the range of the width ratio.

Here are some such formulas for a thin strip, selected from the earlier papers, (A-#) referring to the first [1] and (B-#) referring to the second [2]. They are stated in a form that is convenient for computation, to provide a comparison test for the more recent empirical formulas covering the entire range of the width ratio. They are converted to the dimensions used herein (w, h, etc.).

Every one of the derived formulas is essentially the first few terms of a series converging in the extreme of a narrow or wide shape (and small thickness). Therefore a "narrow" or "wide" identity is necessary. The transition between the two occurs for a shape which may be "borderline" for close approximation by either. Hopefully the two kinds will overlap to give a coverage for all shapes. As stated in the early papers and as supported by more recent studies, the transition occurs near $w/h = 1$. The more sophisticated formulas give substantial overlap.

For a narrow thin strip without dielectric, the second-order approximation was not supported by a derivation. One is given here in Appendix VI. Formula (45) and the corresponding modification of (2) are presented as the closest approximation known to date. It provides overlap of the wide range. The relative error is $<0.003R$ if $w/h < 2$.

For a wide thin strip without dielectric, the first paper yields a remarkably close approximation with overlap of the narrow range. The synthesis form is an explicit formulation. Specify

$$R_1 < 60\pi = 188$$

(A-1), (A-45) $$d' = \frac{\pi}{2} R_c/R_1 = 592/R_1 > \pi \quad (46)$$

(A-67) $$d = d' + (2d')^2 \exp - (2d') > \pi \quad (47)$$

(A-10) $$c = \sqrt{(d-1)^2 - 1} = \sqrt{d(2d-1)} \quad (48)$$

(A-68) $$w/h = \frac{2}{\pi}[c - \text{acosh}\,(d-1)]$$

$$= \frac{2}{\pi}[c - \ln\,(c + d - 1)] > 0.3. \quad (49)$$

The relative error is $<0.001R_1$.

The two preceding approximations give a large overlap. They are closest near $R_1 = 126$ or $w/h = 1$, where the relative difference is $0.0005R_1$. For the graphs in Fig. 2, the computation of any one point is made with the formula judged to be the closer of the two; if so, its relative error is less than this amount.

A comparison of these two formulas can be made in explicit form by the following sequence:

1) wide (49): w/h from R_{1w};
2) narrow (2) (modified): R_{1n} from w/h;
3) ratio: $R_{1n}/R_{1w} = 1 +$ relative difference. (50)

The relative difference of R_1 is the significant comparison.

A thin strip with dielectric likewise has different formulations for narrow and wide. The effective dielectric constant k' depends on the shape w/h and on the dielectric k. One sequence can be used for explicit formulations in any case:

1) specify: R_1;
2) compute (45): w/h;
3) specify: k;
4) compute (53), (57), (52): q, k', $R = R_1/\sqrt{k'}$;
5) graph: R for k, w/h. (51)

The "effective filling fraction" [2], defined as follows, depends mainly on the shape and less on the dielectric:

$$q = \frac{k' - 1}{k - 1}, \qquad k' = 1 + q(k-1). \quad (52)$$

Because it has only second-order dependence on the dielectric, a simple formula for a mean value of k is sufficient for practical purposes. A mean value ($k = 3$) is chosen because it places the effective dielectric k' midway between the extremes (for $1 < k < \infty$) and within the midrange of practical values. Some formulas will be stated for this mean value, with a supplemental term which may be ignored, having a factor $(1/k - \frac{1}{3})$. It is graphed in Fig. 2 in terms of w/h directly and R_1 indirectly.

The shape dependence of the filling fraction was derived in terms of the wave resistance without dielectric (R_1) and is most simply expressed in those terms. This R_1 and the actual shape w/h are related by various formulas. The filling fraction is here expressed in very simple form from the previous derivations for narrow and wide.

For a narrow thin strip with dielectric, the effective dielectric constant is formulated as follows. The shape is introduced in terms of the wave resistance without dielectric (R_1):

(B-32), (B-44) $$q = \frac{1}{2} + \frac{30}{R_1}\left(\ln\frac{\pi}{2} + \frac{1}{k}\ln\frac{4}{\pi}\right)$$

$$= \frac{1}{2} + \frac{16}{R_1}\left[1 + 0.453\left(\frac{1}{k} - \frac{1}{3}\right)\right] \quad (53)$$

(B-32), (B-45) $$k' = \frac{k+1}{2} + \frac{60}{R_1}\frac{k-1}{2}\left(\ln\frac{\pi}{2} + \frac{1}{k}\ln\frac{4}{\pi}\right). \quad (54)$$

The relative error is <0.01 of k' if R' is >70; w/h is <3; q is <0.72.

For a wide thin strip with dielectric, the effective dielectric constant is formulated in terms of parameters defined above and here:

(B-8) $$d = \frac{\pi}{2}R_c/R_1 = 592/R_1 > \pi, \qquad R_1 < 188$$

(A-14), (A-16), (B-16)

$$s' = 0.732[\text{acosh}(d-1) - \text{acosh}(0.358d + 0.598)] \quad (55)$$

(B-25) $$s'' = \ln 4 - 1 - 1/(2d-1) = 0.386 - 1/(2d-1) \quad (56)$$

(B-4) $$q = 1 - \frac{1}{d}\left[\text{acosh}(d-1) - s'' + \frac{s''-s'}{k}\right]. \quad (57)$$

The relative error is <0.01 (estimated).

For the mean case ($k = 3$), this result is approximated very closely by the simple formula

$$q = 1 - \frac{R_1}{592}\ln\frac{710}{R_1}. \quad (58)$$

The overlap between the two simple formulas (53) and (58) occurs near $R_1 = 100$ or $w/h = 1.5$.

The narrow and wide simple formulas for the mean case can be integrated and supplemented by an adjustment for any k, as follows:

$$q = \frac{1}{7}\left[1 + \frac{6}{1 + \frac{R_1}{507}\ln\left(\frac{710}{R_1} + 1\right)}\right] - \frac{0.2}{\frac{R_1}{220} + \frac{220}{R_1}} + \left(\frac{1}{k} - \frac{1}{3}\right)\frac{0.05}{\frac{R_1}{90} + \frac{90}{R_1}}. \quad (59)$$

The relative error is <0.01 of k'. The first term is a transition between the narrow and wide extremes. The second term is a very close adjustment for the intermediate range. The last term is negligible in the practical effect on k', so it serves mainly to indicate the weakness of the dependence on k.

One simple example is here reviewed in Table II as a test of various derivations for a thin strip without dielectric. It is a shape ($w/h = 1$) which is in the region of transition between narrow and wide approximations. The wave resistance R_1 is based on free space (120π). The items are listed in order of increasing error from the first. The derivation is described with respect to its development from the extreme of narrow and/or wide strip. The following notes give further comments.

TABLE II
COMPARISON OF FORMULAS FOR ONE EXAMPLE

Identification	Derivation	R_1 (ohms)	Error
(S) [14]	unrestricted	126.553	0
(W.1) (43)	narrow	126.533	-.020
(W.2) (2) (modified)	narrow	126.528	-.025
(W.3) [1] (A-68)	wide	126.473	-.042
(W.4) [1] (A-66)	narrow	126.641	+.088
(W.5) (2)	narrow-wide	126.310	-.243
(K) [16]	wide	127.857	+1.304
(W.6) [1] (A-71)	wide	124.424	-2.129

(S) Schneider's example is derived rigorously from elliptic integrals and is taken to be "exact" for purposes of comparison. Its relation to the other items tends to confirm its validity.

(W.1) This is the derivation based on the pair of wires equivalent to a narrow thin strip. It is the closest approximation (the relative error is <0.0002).

(W.2) This is similar to (W.1) but modified to a form suitable for matching the wide extreme. It is the reverse of formula (45).

(W.3) (W.4) These are the closest approximations given in the 1964 paper. They bracket the correct value within a relative difference of ± 0.0007. Their computation is much easier than (S).

(W.5) This is the only item providing a rather close approximation over the entire range of shape.

(K) Kaden's "wide" formula is an approximation to his derivation from elliptic integrals. The error (about 1 percent) indicates that this shape is "borderline" for his approximation. It is comparable with (W.6) in its explicit form and in simplicity, and gives a closer approximation.

This concludes a summary of the earlier formulas, and some more recent, as required for the above procedure. They are adequate for a set of close computations for a thin strip with any dielectric. These may be used for checking any empirical formula such as those proposed herein. They are used for the graphs in Fig. 2.

APPENDIX VII
COMPUTATION OF LOSS BY NUMERICAL DIFFERENTIATION

In practical applications of a strip line, the PF of conductor loss is usually determined by the skin effect. Some simple rules are applicable if the skin depth δ is much less than the least transverse dimension. One is the "incremental-inductance rule" stated by the author [3]. It relates the skin loss with the inductance, by a formula based on differentiation.

In a transmission line made of perfect conductors, the wave resistance without dielectric (R_1) is uniquely related to the inductance, so that formula may be used instead. Then the loss PF of the skin effect may be expressed as follows:

$$p = \Delta L/L = \frac{R_\delta - R_1}{R_\delta} = 1 - R_1/R_\delta \ll 1. \tag{60}$$

The incremental-inductance rule is here represented by the relative increment of inductance ($\Delta L/L$) that would be caused by removing a thickness ($\delta/2$) from the face of every conductor bounding the field. The wave resistance (R_1) for a perfect conductor would be increased in the same ratio if the boundary were modified in the same manner. Then this change (from R_1 to R_δ) is used to compute the PF.

The elegant application of the incremental-inductance rule was stated in terms of the analytic differentiation of an inductance formula in terms of a simple continuous function. In its more general application, such a formula may not be available. The rule is still useful if the inductance variation is formulated continuously over a range of dimensions. Such a formula can be subjected to analytic differentiation, but the resulting expression may be much more complicated than the inductance formula from which it is derived. This has been the experience of some workers who have taken this approach in evaluating the loss PF in a strip line [13], [17].

In the meantime, the advent of the digital calculator has opened up a new opportunity for the differentiation of a complicated formula. It enables a close approximation of the derivative by computing a small finite difference. The basic formula is used twice, which requires little more effort in a programmable calculator. The versatility of this procedure reaches a peak in the Hewlett-Packard pocket models, HP-25 and HP-65. The convenience and availability of the HP-25 provided the author with the tools and incentive to prepare this paper.

Having stated the objective of numerical differentiation by finite differences, the programming is routine. Fig. 10 shows the flow chart of one such program. It serves to bring out the application of some features available in the HP-25. It includes as the principal subroutine, some formula for R_1 in terms of the transverse dimensions. After incrementing the dimensions in accord with the skin effect, this subroutine is traversed a second time for R_δ. The relative increase is interpreted as the PF in direct or normalized form. The following features of the program are notable.

The skin depth δ may be evaluated and then utilized to give the PF p for any example. The more versatile normalized PF P may be obtained by arbitrarily choosing a small difference (say $\delta = 0.0001$). Then the result approaches the analytic derivative. The value of the difference cancels out in the normalized form. The number of decimal places in the small difference may be somewhat less than one half the number available in the computation. The skin depth or small difference is entered once in one register (R4) where it need not be renewed unless a change is desired.

The dimensions w,h,t are entered in assigned registers R0,R1,R2. For the second computation, each dimension is incremented by $\pm\delta$. Each dimension is between two conductor faces so the removal of $\delta/2$ on each face requires that the dimension be changed by δ, either increased or decreased. The increment is entered by arithmetic in the register.

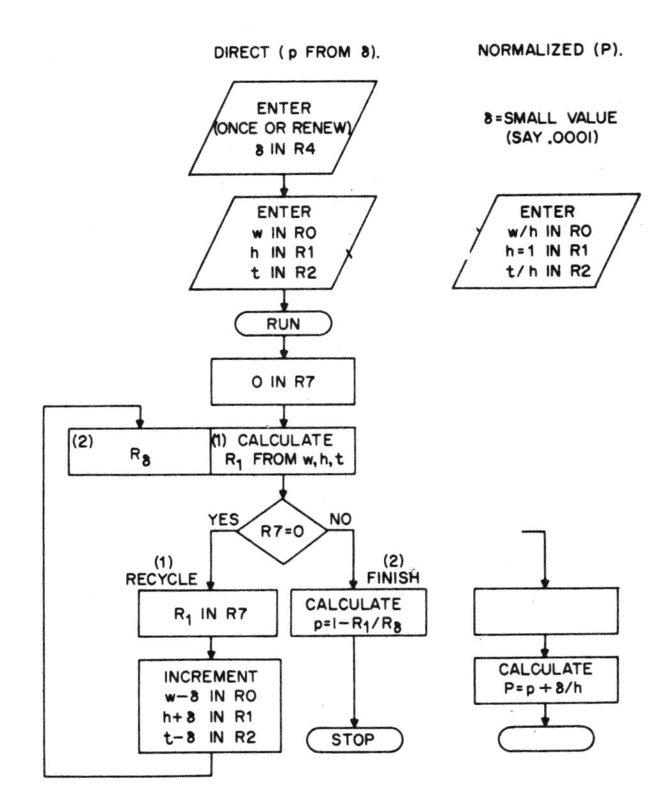

Fig. 10. Flow chart for computing the loss power factor by numerical differentiation.

Conditional branching is required at the end of each execution of the R_1 subroutine. One register (R7) is vacated until the end of the first execution, then occupied by R_1, which signals the end of the second. This serves also to retain R_1 for comparison with R_δ.

If the program storage is inadequate for the principal subroutine and also the transitional subroutines, one or more of the latter is easily performed manually.

In Fig. 10, the right-hand column of notes describe the program changes for the normalized form.

Appendix VIII
Formulas for the Skin Depth

Here are some formulas for the skin depth in nonmagnetic conductors [3], [7]:

$$\delta = \sqrt{\frac{2}{\omega\mu_0\sigma}} = \frac{1}{\sqrt{\pi f \mu_0 \sigma}} = \sqrt{\frac{\lambda G_0}{\pi\sigma}} = \sqrt{\frac{\lambda\rho}{\pi R_0}}$$

$$= \frac{1}{2\pi}\sqrt{\frac{\lambda}{30\sigma}} = \frac{1}{2\pi}\sqrt{\frac{\lambda\rho}{30}}$$

$$= 0.0291\sqrt{\lambda/\sigma} = \frac{1}{34.4}\sqrt{\lambda/\sigma}. \tag{61}$$

In copper ($\sigma = 58$ Mmho/m):

$$\delta_c = 3.81\sqrt{\lambda}\ \mu\text{m} = \sqrt{\frac{4.36\ \text{kHz}}{f}}\ \text{mm}$$

$$= \sqrt{\frac{4.36\ \text{GHz}}{f}}\ \mu\text{m}$$

$$= \frac{66}{\sqrt{f}}\ \text{mm} = \frac{0.066}{\sqrt{f\ (\text{MHz})}}\ \text{mm}. \quad (62)$$

Symbols used in (61) and (62) are defined below.

ω = $2\pi f$ = radian frequency (radians/second).
λ = wavelength in free space (meters).
R_0 = $1/G_0$ = wave resistance of a plane wave in a square area in free space (ohms).
μ_0 = magnetivity (magnetic permeability) in free space (henries/meter).
σ = $1/p$ = conductivity in copper (mhos/meter).
R_0 = $377 = 120\pi\ \Omega$.
μ_0 = $0.4\pi = 1.257\ \mu$H/m.

Appendix IX
Recent Article on Wide Strip with Thickness

Subsequent to the preparation of this paper, the author has seen a recent article related to the subject [19]. W. H. Chang has described an ingenuous and powerful approximation based on conformal mapping. To that extent, it has something in common with the author's 1964 paper [1]. Some thickness is accommodated at the expense of some refinements in other respects. The result is a very useful approximation for wide strips with thickness. To yield this in analytic form is a major achievement. Moreover, it appears that his result may be closely bracketed by further appreciation of his approximation.

Relevant to the present paper, Chang gives a table of examples computed from his formula and also by a numerical approximation from W. J. Weeks [18]. The agreement is very close. Most of those examples fall within the range of validity of the present paper, formulas (1), (2), (13), (14) without dielectric. The agreement is well within $0.01R$. The formulas herein offer a close approximation for any width. They are based on a thin strip with width adjustment for thickness. Chang's formulas for a wide strip are remarkable for including the width and the thickness in one formula.

The small-thickness examples reported in Appendix II are in the range of marginal approximation by Chang, so they have not been compared.

References

[1] H. A. Wheeler, "Transmission-line properties of parallel wide strips by a conformal-mapping approximation," *IEEE Trans. Microwave Theory Tech.*, vol. MTT-12, pp. 280–289, May 1964.
[2] ——, "Transmission-line properties of parallel strips separated by a dielectric sheet," *IEEE Trans. Microwave Theory Tech.*, vol. MTT-13, pp. 172–185, Mar. 1965.
[3] ——, "Formulas for the skin effect," *Proc. IRE*, vol. 30, pp. 412–424, Sept. 1942. (Skin loss by the "incremental-inductance rule.")
[4] F. Oberhettinger and W. Magnus, *Applications of Elliptic Functions in Physics and Technology*. New York: Springer, 1949. (Wave resistance of coplanar strip, p. 63. Tables of K'/K, p. 114.)
[5] E. Weber, *Electromagnetic Fields—Theory and Applications—Mapping of Fields*. New York: Wiley, 1950. (Thickness, p. 347.)
[6] H. A. Wheeler, "Transmission-line impedance curves," *Proc. IRE*, vol. 38, pp. 1400–1403, Dec. 1950.
[7] ——, "Universal skin-effect chart for conducting materials," *Electronics*, vol. 25, no. 11, pp. 152–154, Nov. 1952.
[8] S. Cohn, "Problems in strip transmission lines," *IEEE Trans. Microwave Theory Tech.*, vol. MTT-3, pp. 119–126, Mar. 1955. (Sandwich line, thickness and loss.)
[9] H. A. Wheeler, "Skin resistance of a transmission-line conductor of polygon cross section," *Proc. IRE*, vol. 43, pp. 805–808, July 1955.
[10] D. S. Lerner (Wheeler Labs., Inc.), unpublished notes, Nov. 1963. (Very wide strip, width adjustment for thickness. Half-shielded type compared with sandwich type.)
[11] M. Caulton, J. J. Hughes, and H. Sobol, "Measurements on the properties of microstrip transmission lines for microwave integrated circuits," *RCA Rev.*, vol. 27, pp. 377–391, Sept. 1966.
[12] H. Sobol, "Extending IC technology to microwave equipment," *Electronics*, vol. 40, no. 6, pp. 112–124, Mar. 1967. (A simple empirical formula, remarkably close for a practical range.)
[13] R. A. Pucel, D. J. Masse, and C. P. Hartwig, "Losses in microstrip," *IEEE Trans. Microwave Theory Tech.*, vol. MTT-16, pp. 342–350, June 1968. (By analytic differentiation.)
[14] M. V. Schneider, "Microstrip lines for microwave integrated circuits," *Bell Syst. Tech. J.*, vol. 48, pp. 1421–1444, May 1969.
[15] ——, "Dielectric loss in integrated microwave circuits," *Bell Syst. Tech. J.*, vol. 48, pp. 2325–2332, Sept. 1969.
[16] H. Kaden, "Advances in microstrip theory," *Siemens Forsch. u. Entwickl. Ber.*, vol. 3, pp. 115–124, 1974. (Computation of wave resistance and loss for a wide strip of small thickness.)
[17] R. Mittra and T. Itoh, "Analysis of microstrip transmission lines," in *Advances in Microwaves*, vol. 8. New York: Academic Press, 1974, pp. 67–141. (Latest review, many references.)
[18] W. J. Weeks, "Calculation of coefficients of capacitance for multiconductor transmission lines," *IEEE Trans. Microwave Theory Tech.*, vol. MTT-18, pp. 35–43, Jan. 1970. (Numerical method for a rectangular cross section with a parallel plane.)
[19] W. H. Chang, "Analytical IC metal-line capacitance formulas," *IEEE Trans. Microwave Theory Tech.*, vol. MTT-24, pp. 608–611, Sept. 1976. (Conformal mapping approximation for a wide strip with thickness. Examples compared with numerical method of Weeks [18] using his program.)

Microstrip Dispersion Model

WILLIAM J. GETSINGER

***Abstract*—The assumption that the quasi-TEM mode on microstrip is primarily a single longitudinal-section electric (LSE) mode leads to a transmission line model whose dispersion behavior can be analyzed and related to that of microstrip. Appropriate approximations yield simple, closed-form expressions that allow slide-rule prediction of microstrip dispersion.**

Nomenclature

a, a', b, b', s, w	Mechanical dimensions of conventional microstrip and the LSE mode model (Fig. 2).
c	Speed of light in free space = 11.8 in/ns.
C'	Capacitance per unit length of microstrip line at zero frequency.
D	Width of the zero-frequency parallel-plate microstrip equivalent structure.
f	Frequency.
f_i	Frequency of inflection of the dispersion curve.
f_p	Parameter of the dispersion function.
G	Empirical parameter used to simplify the microstrip dispersion function.
k_o	Free-space wavenumber.
L'	Inductance per unit length of microstrip line at zero frequency.
Z_f	Microstrip characteristic impedance at frequency f.
Z_0	Microstrip characteristic impedance at zero frequency.
γ	Propagation constant along the microstrip line.
γ_a	Transverse propagation constant in the air-filled part of the microstrip model.
γ_s	Transverse propagation constant in the dielectric-filled part of the microstrip model.
ϵ_e	Microstrip effective dielectric constant (a function of frequency).
ϵ_{ei}	Microstrip effective dielectric constant at the inflection point.
ϵ_{e0}	Microstrip effective dielectric constant at zero frequency.
ϵ_o	Permittivity of free space = 8.85×10^{-12} F/m.
ϵ_s	Substrate relative dielectric constant.
η_o	Impedance of free space = 376.7 Ω.
μ_o	Permeability of free space = 31.92 nH/in, or $4\pi\times10^{-7}$ H/m.
ω	Radian frequency.

Manuscript received April 13, 1972; revised July 10, 1972. This paper is based upon work performed at COMSAT Laboratories under Corporate sponsorship.

The author is with COMSAT Laboratories, Clarksburg, Md. 20734.

Introduction

PROPAGATION on microstrip is usually handled as though the line were filled with dielectric and carried a TEM mode. This is an adequate representation except that the effective dielectric constant changes slowly with frequency, making microstrip dispersive [1].

Both analytical [2] and empirical [3], [4] attempts to describe microstrip dispersion have been published. (A good bibliography is given in [4].) The analytical techniques have been nearly exact, but have required numerical solution on large electronic computers. Thus these techniques have been too ponderous for practical engineering application. The empirical techniques, on the other hand, have had limited ranges of applicability and inadequate theoretical foundations for confidence in application.

With the intention of achieving analytical simplicity, this paper considers microstrip propagation as a single longitudinal-section electric (LSE) [5] mode. Physical reasoning indicates that this might be a practical approximation for investigating dispersion on microstrip. However, the structure of microstrip precludes analysis by direct means. Thus a structure (the model) has been conceived that resembles microstrip in all but shape, but whose LSE-mode propagation can be analyzed directly. It is assumed that the propagation characteristics (dispersion) of the model can be applied to microstrip by appropriate adjustment of parameters.

Since it does not follow from theory that the dispersion functions of the two structures must be the same, as it does for differently shaped, homogeneously filled waveguides, the validity of the model must be tested by its agreement with measured dispersion of actual microstrip.

It turns out that the model yields a simple closed-form algebraic expression that closely describes measured dispersion in microstrip. It is found that only one parameter in addition to those available from static analyses of microstrip, such as the MSTRIP program [6], is necessary to describe microstrip dispersion.

For convenience, the results of this paper are illustrated in Fig. 1. The symbols are defined in the Nomenclature list. The dispersion relationships shown in Fig. 1 have been found to agree with a theoretical prediction [2] based on coupled integral equations, with published [1] measurements of a 20-Ω microstrip line on a rutile ($\epsilon_s = 104$) substrate and with measurements on 0.025- and 0.050-in alumina ($\epsilon_s \approx 10$) substrates.

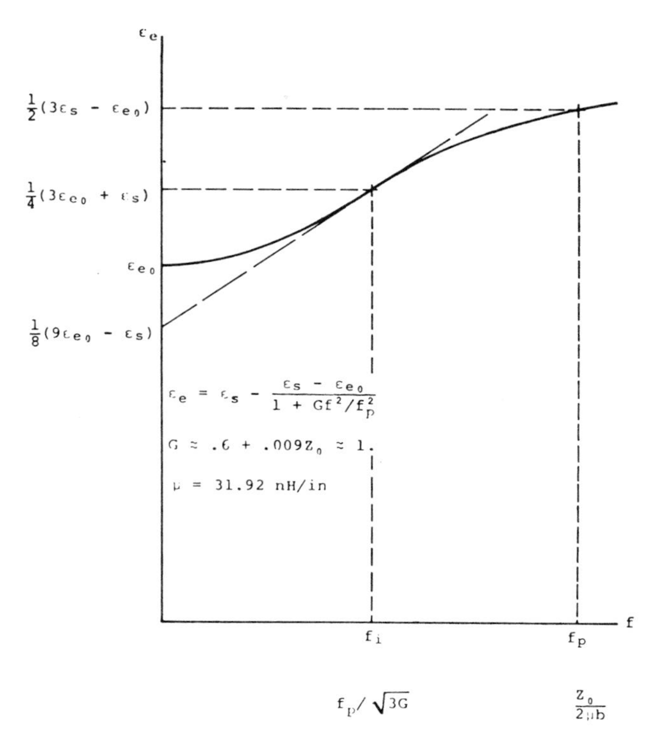

Fig. 1. Microstrip dispersion relationships.

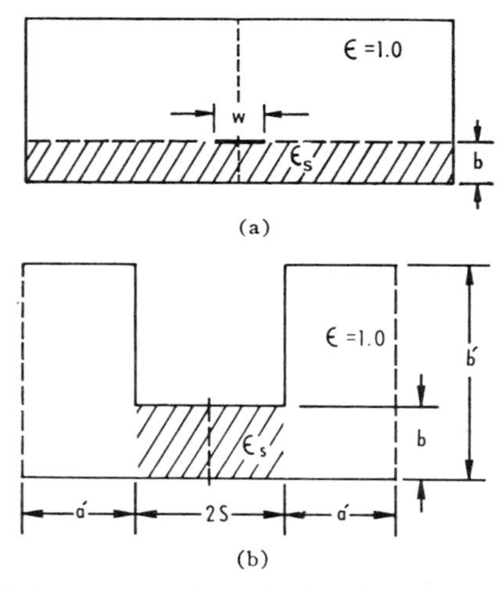

Fig. 2. (a) Conventional microstrip. (b) LSE model for microstrip.

The Analytical Model

A conventional microstrip structure is shown in Fig. 2(a). The fields are concentrated around the edges of the strip and in the dielectric beneath the center strip. Near the strip edges, the magnetic field is predominantly normal to and the electric field predominantly tangential to the air–dielectric interface. This is characteristic of the LSE mode [5], [7]. The structure of Fig. 2(a) is intractable to direct analysis on this basis, but its boundaries can be distorted to result in a model, shown in Fig. 2(b), that can be analyzed.

The electric field lines emanating from the lower surface of the center strip of the microstrip in Fig. 2(a) pass only through the substrate dielectric, as do the electric field lines emanating from the center portion of the model of Fig. 2(b). The electric fields emanating from the upper surface of the center strip of the microstrip occupy a much larger space, which is mostly filled with air. This space is approximated by the large, air-filled end sections of the model. The magnetic wall (indicated by a dashed line) above the center strip of Fig. 2(a) is split and the upper wall of the center strip is unfolded at the edge, stretched out, and bent to form the end-section boundaries of Fig. 2(b). Thus the model consists of one parallel-plate transmission line, which has a dielectric constant ϵ_s, width $2s$, and height b, connected without junction effect to other parallel-plate transmission lines that have a dielectric constant of one, width a', and height b'.

The heuristic assumption made is that because the two regions, air filled and dielectric filled, of the model and the microstrip are grossly similar, the two structures will have the same dispersion behavior for the same mode of propagation. It is clear that junction capacitance could be included at the steps of the model to make it more realistic, or more

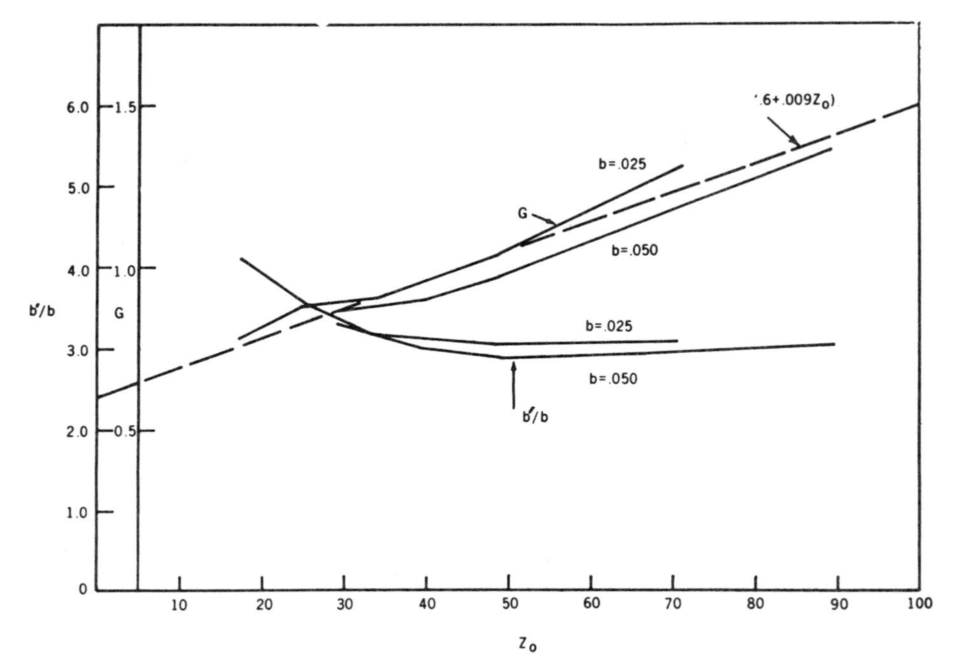

Fig. 3. Microstrip dispersion parameters.

like microstrip, but this would greatly complicate the analysis and has not been found necessary for practical results.

The model is, after all, only an intuitive aid in setting up the simplest mathematics that lead to a useful dispersion relation; it need not be physically realizable.

The analysis proceeds by forcing the model to have the same electrical characteristics at zero frequency as the microstrip. (These characteristics can be found from well-known and widely available computer programs, such as MSTRIP [6].) Next, a transverse resonance analysis of the model relates the propagation constant (or effective dielectric constant) to frequency. A closed-form approximation of this function is then found and compared with measured microstrip dispersion to determine the unknown parameter b'/b [see Fig. 2(b)]. Finally, the results show that b'/b and related parameters are nearly constant or linear with characteristic impedance. Hence, it is possible to derive simple formulas that can be used to predict the dispersion of microstrip transmission lines.

Zero-Frequency Relationships

A static analysis such as the MSTRIP program [6] is employed to yield the effective relative dielectric constant ϵ_{e0} and the characteristic impedance Z_0 for given w/b, ϵ_s, and possibly other dimensional parameters, such as strip thickness or proximity of an upper ground plane. [See Fig. 2(a).]

The inductance L' and capacitance C' per unit length of the microstrip can be written as

$$\frac{L'}{\mu_o} = \frac{Z_0}{\eta_o}\sqrt{\epsilon_{e0}} \tag{1a}$$

$$\frac{C'}{\epsilon_o} = \frac{\eta_o\sqrt{\epsilon_{e0}}}{Z_0} \tag{1b}$$

respectively, where

$$\eta_o = \sqrt{\frac{\mu_o}{\epsilon_o}} = 376.7\,\Omega. \tag{2}$$

The subscript o indicates free-space values of the constitutive parameters, while the subscript 0 indicates zero-frequency values of the characteristic impedance and effective dielectric constant.

Inductance and capacitance per unit length for the LSE model [Fig. 2(b)] at zero frequency can be written as

$$\frac{L'}{\mu_o} = \frac{1}{2[(a'/b') + (s/b)]} \tag{3a}$$

$$\frac{C'}{\epsilon_o} = 2\left(\frac{a'}{b'} + \epsilon_s\frac{s}{b}\right) \tag{3b}$$

respectively. Equating equivalent parameters yields

$$\frac{a'}{b'} = \frac{\eta_o}{2Z_0\sqrt{\epsilon_{e0}}}\cdot\frac{\epsilon_s - \epsilon_{e0}}{\epsilon_s - 1} \tag{4a}$$

$$\frac{s}{b} = \frac{\eta_o}{2Z_0\sqrt{\epsilon_{e0}}}\cdot\frac{\epsilon_{e0} - 1}{\epsilon_s - 1}\,. \tag{4b}$$

Transverse Resonance Solution

The sum of the admittances on the left and right of either air–dielectric interface of Fig. 2(b) must equal to zero according to the transverse resonance [5], [7] technique. The propagation constants are related by

$$\gamma_a^2 + \gamma^2 + k_o^2 = 0 \tag{5}$$

in the air-filled section and by

$$\gamma_s^2 + \gamma^2 + \epsilon_s k_o^2 = 0 \tag{6}$$

in the dielectric-filled section. In (5), (6), γ is the propagation constant along the transmission line and applies to both air-

and dielectric-filled sections, while γ_a is the constant in the transverse direction in the air-filled section and γ_s is the constant in the transverse direction in the dielectric-filled section. Finally,

$$k_o = \omega/c \tag{7}$$

is the free-space wave number.

The vertical dashed lines of Fig. 2(b) indicate magnetic walls or open-circuit boundaries. The characteristic admittances in the two sections are proportional to their propagation constants and inversely proportional to their heights. Thus the sum of the admittances at the interface is

$$\frac{\gamma_a}{b'} \tanh \gamma_a a' + \frac{\gamma_s}{b} \tanh \gamma_s s = 0. \tag{8}$$

The following approximation is used to solve the preceding transcendental equation:

$$\tanh x \approx \frac{1}{(1/x) + (x/3)} \cdot \tag{9}$$

Equation (9) is in error by about 1.5 percent at $x=1$ rad. As an example of the range of applicability, $\gamma_s s = 1.0$ for a 25-Ω line on a 0.05-in alumina substrate at about 10 GHz. The use of higher impedances and thinner substrates raises the frequency at which an error of this magnitude occurs.

Substituting (9) into (8) yields

$$\frac{b'/a'}{\gamma_a^2} + \frac{b/s}{\gamma_s^2} = -\frac{a'b' + sb}{3} \tag{10}$$

after some manipulation.

The longitudinal propagation constant can be expressed in terms of the effective dielectric constant; i.e.,

$$\gamma^2 = -k_o^2 \epsilon_e. \tag{11}$$

Substituting (11) into (5) and (6) results in

$$\gamma_a^2 = k_o^2(\epsilon_e - 1) \tag{12}$$

$$\gamma_s^2 = -k_o^2(\epsilon_s - \epsilon_e). \tag{13}$$

Substituting (12) and (13) into (10) yields

$$\frac{b/s}{\epsilon_s - \epsilon_e} - \frac{b'/a'}{\epsilon_e - 1} = \frac{a'b' + sb}{3} k_o^2 \tag{14}$$

which is the basic dispersion relationship.

The unknown parameters a' and b' can be reduced to a single unknown by assuming that a is the solution of (4a) when b' is given the value of b, which is known. That is,

$$a' = a\left(\frac{b'}{b}\right) \tag{15}$$

where b'/b is the new unknown parameter. When (15) is substituted into (14), the basic dispersion relationship becomes

$$\frac{1/s}{\epsilon_s - \epsilon_e} - \frac{1/a}{\epsilon_e - 1} = \frac{a(b'/b)^2 + s}{3} k_o^2. \tag{16}$$

When (16) is solved for $\epsilon_s - \epsilon_e$ as the dependent variable, a quadratic results. Its solution is

$$\epsilon_s - \epsilon_e = \frac{B}{2}\left\{1 - \sqrt{1 - \frac{4(\epsilon_s - 1)/s}{B^2[\{[a(b'/b)^2+s]/3\} k_o^2]}}\right\} \tag{17}$$

where

$$B = (\epsilon_s - 1) + \frac{(a+s)/as}{\{[a(b'/b)^2+s]/3\} k_o^2} \tag{18}$$

and the negative root has been selected because it is physically meaningful.

Equation (17) can be simplified by observing that the second term under the radical is considerably less than one for practical cases and then by using the usual square-root approximation. (For a 25-Ω line on a 0.05-in alumina substrate at 12.5 GHz, the error is about 5 percent.) After a small amount of algebra, the result is

$$\epsilon_e = \epsilon_s - \frac{[(\epsilon_s - 1)a]/(a+s)}{1 + k_o^2(as/3)(\epsilon_s - 1)\{[a(b'/b)^2+s]/(a+s)\}} \cdot \tag{19}$$

Substituting (4) and (15) into (19) makes it possible to express (19) in terms of known quantities, except for the parameter b'/b; i.e.,

$$\epsilon_e = \epsilon_s - \frac{\epsilon_s - \epsilon_{e0}}{1 + G(f^2/f_p^2)} \tag{20}$$

where

$$f_p = \frac{Z_0}{2\mu_o b} \tag{21}$$

and

$$G = \frac{\pi^2}{12} \frac{[(\epsilon_{e0} - 1) + (b'/b)^2(\epsilon_s - \epsilon_{e0})](\epsilon_{e0} - 1)(\epsilon_s - \epsilon_{e0})}{\epsilon_{e0}(\epsilon_s - 1)^2} \cdot \tag{22}$$

Nonmagnetic substrates are assumed; therefore, $\mu_o = 31.9186$ nH/in. Equation (20) is the final analytical expression for dispersion of microstrip. Investigation of experimental results shows that G approximates unity.

Evaluation of Parameters

Dispersion curves for microstrip lines on alumina substrates 0.025 and 0.050 in thick were measured. The microwave measurements were made on ring resonators [8], and the 1-MHz points were determined from the MSTRIP program by using the value of the substrate dielectric constant ϵ_s found from capacitance measurements of each fully metallized substrate. These data were used to calculate the multiplier of f^2 in (20) that forced a fit at 10 GHz for each microstrip line. Then, values of b'/b were calculated using (21) and (22). The results are shown in Fig. 3, which indicates that $b'/b \simeq 3$ for characteristic impedances above about 35 Ω. The experimentally determined values of G are also plotted in Fig. 3.

Equations (20) and (21) clearly demonstrate the nature of the dependence of the effective dielectric constant on the substrate thickness b and microstrip characteristic impedence Z_0.

In many engineering applications of microstrip, dispersion can be treated as a correction factor to the zero-frequency effective dielectric constant ϵ_{e0}; thus only approximate values are required. In such situations, it is sufficient to assume that $G=1.0$ in (20). For greater accuracy, the curves in Fig. 3, or an equivalent based on other careful measurements, can be used. A linear approximation of curves of Fig. 3 is

$$G = 0.6 + 0.009\,Z_0. \tag{23}$$

The Inflection Point

Study of the dispersion function (20) can provide some general information about typical dispersive behavior. Equation (20) shows that the effective dielectric constant goes from a value of ϵ_{e0} at zero frequency to a value of ϵ_s at infinite frequency, in agreement with theory [2], and that the slope of ϵ_e with respect to frequency is zero at both extremes. The frequency of the maximum slope between these two points is called the inflection point. The requirement that the second derivative of ϵ_e with respect to frequency must equal zero gives the inflection frequency

$$f_i = \frac{f_p}{\sqrt{3G}}\,. \tag{24}$$

Using (24) in (20) yields the value of the effective dielectric constant ϵ_{ei} at the inflection frequency:

$$\epsilon_{ei} = \tfrac{1}{4}(\epsilon_s + 3\epsilon_{e0}) \tag{25}$$

and the slope with respect to frequency at ϵ_{ei}:

$$\left.\frac{d\epsilon_e}{df}\right|_{f=f_i} = \tfrac{3}{8}(\epsilon_s - \epsilon_{e0}). \tag{26}$$

A graphical construction that makes it possible to draw a straight line tangent to the inflection point of the dispersion curve has been shown in Fig. 1.

It can be observed that the dispersion and the inflection relationships agree closely with measured data. Equations (24) and (25) do in fact predict the frequency and effective dielectric constant values at which measured dispersion curves have maximum slope, and that slope is in very good agreement with (26) for an ideal dispersion function. This detailed agreement between theory and experiment supports the validity of the LSE model of microstrip propagation.

Comparison with Measurements

The theory developed in this paper will first be compared with the theoretical prediction of Zysman and Varon [2] for a microstrip line having the following characteristics: $\epsilon_s=9.7$, $\epsilon_{e0}=6.50$, $Z_0=50$, and $b=0.05$ in. The unknown parameter G will be found from the inflection point formulas and the graphical data of [2].

Using (25) to calculate the inflection point gives $\epsilon_{ei}=7.3$; [2, fig. 5] then gives $f_i=9$ GHz. Equation (24) predicts

$$\frac{G}{f_p^2} = \frac{1}{3f_i^2} = 0.00412. \tag{27}$$

Using values given above in (21) yields

$$f_p = \frac{Z_0}{2\mu b} = \frac{50}{2 \times 31.92 \times 0.05} = 15.66\ \text{GHz}. \tag{28}$$

Substituting (28) into (27) yields

$$G = 0.00412 \times 15.66^2 = 1.01. \tag{29}$$

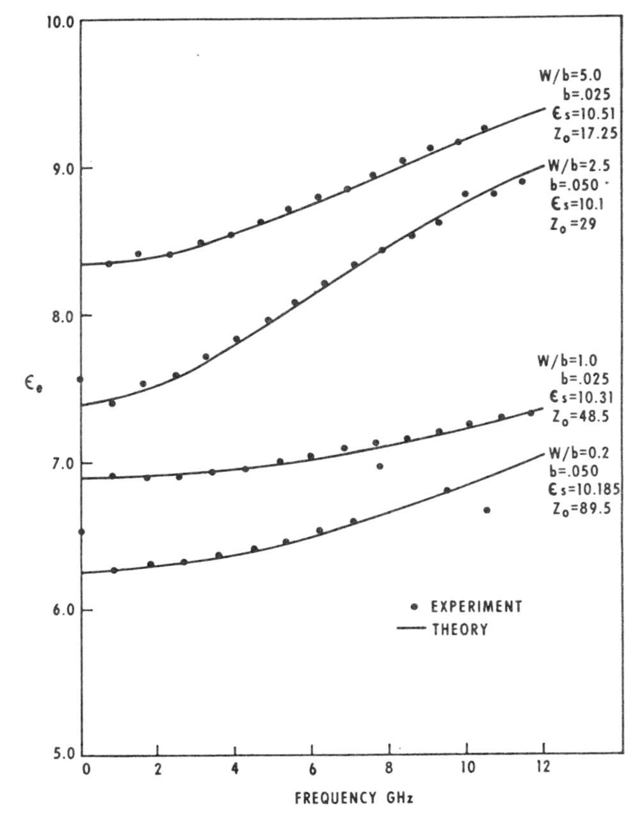

Fig. 4. Comparison of dispersion function and measurements.

This value can be compared with the approximate value $G=1.0$ or the curve-fit formula (23), which gives $G=1.05$.

The next problem is to determine the model parameters of the dispersion measurements on rutile reported by Hartwig *et al.* [1]. The given parameters are $\epsilon_s=104$, $\epsilon_{e0}=62$ (calculated from capacitance measurement), $b=0.05$, and $Z_0=20$ Ω. However, since the dispersion curve must have a zero slope at zero frequency, an extrapolation of the measured points on [1, fig. 3] clearly yields a greater value of ϵ_{e0} than 62. A value of 63.5 will be used in these calculations.

Following the same procedure used in the preceding example gives $\epsilon_{ei}=73.6$ and $f_i \approx 4.4$, so that $G/f_p^2=0.0172$. Equation (21) gives $f_p=6.22$ GHz; thus $G=6.22^2 \times 0.0172 = 0.667$. The approximate formula (23) gives $G=0.78$. Either value of G gives a calculated curve that is within the scatter of the measured points. The first value of G, based on inflection point formulas, seems to average out a little better, however. This is reasonable because it is based in part on the data it characterizes.

The last comparison of theory and experiment is shown in Fig. 4. The solid-line curves were calculated from the dispersion function (20) by using (23) to set the value of G in each case. The round points are values of effective dielectric constant measured at COMSAT Laboratories. The circuits used were ring resonators [8] on commercial 0.025- and 0.05-in alumina substrates. In each case, the value of ϵ_{e0} was found by extrapolating the curve of microwave measurements to zero frequency. Then, curves generated by the MSTRIP program [6] were used to determine a value of ϵ_s for the appropriate width-to-height ratio of the line. The shapes and values of the experimental and theoretical curves are found to be in good agreement.

Limitations and Applications

The basic hypothesis of this paper is that the dispersion function (20) describes the propagation characteristics of any microstrip-like transmission line. So far, measurements on microstrip have supported this point of view.

A more general theoretical investigation than given in this paper would be necessary to explore the fundamental limitations on applying the dispersion function. Some points can be considered, however.

The dispersion relation applies only to the fundamental LSE mode. It probably holds closely only for thin ($b<\lambda/4$ in ϵ_s) substrates and strips that are not very wide ($w<\lambda/3$ in ϵ_s) to insure that the LSE mode is dominant, but these restrictions seldom arise in microstrip applications. Also, the dispersion relation takes on the correct value at infinite frequency, and so there is no clearly defined upper-frequency limit at which it no longer applies. The practical upper-frequency limit of microstrip, where every junction and discontinuity radiate strongly via surface wave modes [1], probably occurs before the dispersion function becomes unreliable.

Since the dispersion function appears to have general applicability to all structures having the same types of boundaries as microstrip and propagating an LSE mode, it would be expected to hold for microstrip with or without an enclosure, for the even and odd modes of the parallel-coupled microstrip, and possibly for other quasi-TEM structures, such as inhomogeneously loaded coaxial line. It would, of course, be necessary to have appropriate values for ϵ_s, ϵ_{e0}, Z_0, and G for each structure.

Acknowledgment

The author wishes to thank Dr. W. J. English for his technical discussions and T. J. Lynch for his careful measurements.

References

[1] C. Hartwig, D. Massé, and R. Pucel, "Frequency dependent behavior of microstrip," in *1968 G-MTT Symp. Dig.*, pp. 110–116.

[2] G. Zysman and D. Varon, "Wave propagation in microstrip transmission lines," in *1969 G-MTT Symp. Dig.*, pp. 3–9.

[3] O. Jain, V. Makios, and W. Chudobiak, "Coupled-mode model of dispersion in microstrip," *Electron. Lett.*, vol. 7, pp. 405–407, July 15, 1971.

[4] M. V. Schneider, "Microstrip dispersion," *Proc. IEEE* (*Special Issue on Computers in Design*) (Lett.), vol. 60, pp. 144–146, Jan. 1972.

[5] R. Collin, *Field Theory of Guided Waves*. New York: McGraw-Hill, 1960, p. 224.

[6] T. G. Bryant and J. A. Weiss, "MSTRIP (parameters of microstrip)," *IEEE Trans. Microwave Theory Tech.*, vol. MTT-19, pp. 418–419, Apr. 1971.

[7] C. Montgomery, R. Dicke, and E. Purcell, *Principles of Microwave Circuits* (M.I.T. Radiation Laboratory Series), vol. 8. New York: McGraw-Hill, 1948.

[8] P. Troughton, "Measurement techniques in microstrip," *Electron. Lett.*, vol. 5, pp. 25–26, Jan. 23, 1969.

ACCURATE MODEL FOR EFFECTIVE DIELECTRIC CONSTANT OF MICROSTRIP WITH VALIDITY UP TO MILLIMETRE-WAVE FREQUENCIES

Indexing terms: Microwave devices and components, Modelling, Microstrip

A closed-form expression is presented for the effective dielectric constant of single microstrip lines which is valid with high accuracy up to mm-wave frequencies. The formula given has been designed for use in MIC and MMIC CAD programs as well as in the indirect measurement of substrate permittivities by resonance techniques.

Introduction: As pointed out in a recent study by Pucel[1] the last three years have witnessed an intensive revival in the field of monolithic microwave integrated circuits (MMICs). For the economic design of MMICs the accurate broadband characterisation of transmission-line characteristics, discontinuities and components is of great importance. Also, qualified circuit modelling provides the possibility for the elimination of cut-and-try methods from hybrid MIC design. For this reason, in the last decade a variety of research groups has started activities in order to characterise planar transmission lines and discontinuities by simple analytical models. On the other hand, meanwhile a number of rigorous methods exists for the frequency-dependent characterisation of thin-film transmission lines and a few approaches have been made to the rigorous description of components too. However, numerical methods for the solution of planar circuit electromagnetic boundary-value problems are too laborious and time-consuming for direct application in CAD programs. Nevertheless, they are very well suited to provide a basis for the generation of analytical approximate circuit models which is the strategy followed by the authors.

Results with a broad range of applicability can be achieved if in addition the correct asymptotic behaviour of the considered structures for very small and very large values of the physical parameters is taken into account. Finally, for tolerance analyses and for statistical CAD concepts to be applied along with future MMIC mass production it is thought to be useful to focus some attention on the modelling of the first derivative of electrical characteristics with respect to the geometrical parameters. The accuracy which has to be achieved in modelling is mainly determined by the fabrication tolerances of thin-film structures and the variation of the parameters of the employed substrates. With highly sophisticated technologies tolerances in the order of a fraction of a percent are feasible. Therefore, approximate analytical models to be developed should exhibit an error which is about 1% or less compared to rigorous numerical solutions. Among these presuppositions the generation of models suited for MMIC CAD has been started by the authors. Analytical results have already been given for the open-end effect of microstrip,[2–4] and for the asymmetric microstrip gap,[5–7] and are presented here for the frequency-dependent effective dielectric constant of microstrip.

Results: The dispersion formula given here has been developed using Jansen's numerical hybrid mode technique[8,9] and the associated computer programs[10] as a source for the generation of a reliable data basis. As Kuester and Chang pointed out in a recent paper[11] this technique appears to be one of the most accurate considered by them. Furthermore, a large number of test measurements with resonating microstrip transmission-line structures on different commercially available substrates has been performed at ATE (see address) and related laboratories in the last few years and has led to agreement with the computer results[10] which generally was of the order of 1% for strip widths in the whole range of technologically meaningful values.

That the analytical formulas available still need improvement can be seen by comparison with rigorous results produced according to Reference 9 and 10. This comparison is performed in Fig. 1 for the expression published by Yamashita *et al.*[12] and the more recent formula provided by Hammerstad and Jensen.[13] The considered substrate thickness is $h = 1$ mm, the strip width is $w = h$ and the range of operating frequencies is $f = 0, \ldots, 28$ GHz. It can be seen from Fig. 1 that only near $f = 0$ is an accuracy of 0·2 percent, as claimed in Reference 13, verified. Otherwise, the maximum discrepancies visible in Fig. 1 are 2·8% (Reference 12, $\varepsilon_r = 12{\cdot}9$, $f = 14$ GHz) and 5·4% (Reference 13, $\varepsilon_r = 12{\cdot}9$, $f = 26$ GHz) and are not tolerable before the background discussed here.

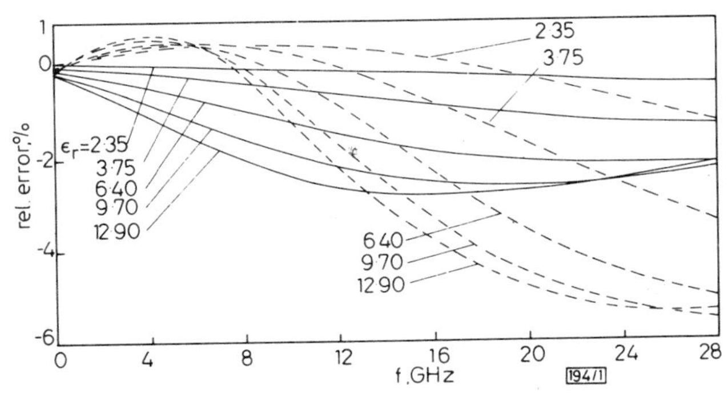

Fig. 1 *Comparison between the approximate models of Yamashita et al.*[12] *and Hammerstad and Jensen*[13] *and the numerical data*[9,10]

$w/h = 1{\cdot}0$, $h = 1$ mm
——— Yamashita *et al.*
– – – – Hammerstad and Jensen

The expression developed in this letter has a mathematical structure which is identical to that of Getsinger's formula describing microstrip dispersion,[14] namely

$$\varepsilon_{eff}(f) = \varepsilon_r - \frac{\varepsilon_r - \varepsilon_{eff}(f=0)}{1 + P(f)} \tag{1}$$

The frequency-dependent term $P(f)$, however, has been modelled here anew, making use of the ideas mentioned in the introduction, incorporating the correct asymptotic behaviour and by computer-matching with the frequency-dependent hybrid mode results supplied by the programs of Reference 10. With $u = w/h$ denoting the microstrip width w normalised with respect to the substrate thickness h, and fh representing the normalised frequency in GHz cm (note: $fh \sim h/\lambda_0$ where λ_0 is the free space wavelength) this results in

$$P(f) = P_1 P_2[(0{\cdot}1844 + P_3 P_4)10fh]^{1{\cdot}5763}$$

with

$$\begin{aligned} P_1 &= 0{\cdot}27488 + [0{\cdot}6315 + 0{\cdot}525/(1 + 0{\cdot}157fh)^{20}]u \\ &\quad - 0{\cdot}065683 \exp(-8{\cdot}7513u) \\ P_2 &= 0{\cdot}33622[1 - \exp(-0{\cdot}03442\varepsilon_r)] \\ P_3 &= 0{\cdot}0363 \exp(-4{\cdot}6u) \\ &\quad \times \{1 - \exp[-(fh/3{\cdot}87)^{4{\cdot}97}]\} \\ P_4 &= 1 + 2{\cdot}751\{1 - \exp[-(\varepsilon_r/15{\cdot}916)^8]\} \end{aligned} \tag{2}$$

Compared to the converged numerical results of the employed computer program,[10] the accuracy of expr. 1 in conjunction with eqns. 2 is better than 0·6% in the range $0{\cdot}1 \le w/h \le 100$, $1 \le \varepsilon_r \le 20$ and $0 \le h/\lambda_0 \le 0{\cdot}13$, i.e. up to about 60 GHz for

25 mm substrates. This covers and even goes beyond useful upper operating frequencies. The range of applicability of eqns. 1 and 2 exceeds that of existing formulas considerably. For two different frequencies, $f = 10$ GHz and $f = 30$ GHz, Figs. 2*a* and *b* show the relative error $(\varepsilon_{eff,num} - \varepsilon_{eff,mod})/\varepsilon_{eff,num}$ as a function of the strip width w/h. The high accuracy of the new expression is further illuminated by Fig. 3 which depicts the first derivative of the effective dielectric constant with respect to the strip width. Thus, the agreement between the analytical model (eqns. 1 and 2) and the rigorous numerical values derived from References 9 and 10 can be seen to be in accordance with the requirements outlined before.

Applications: The new expression has been developed for use in CAD programs which includes analysis and design, tolerance analysis and the statistical design of MICs and

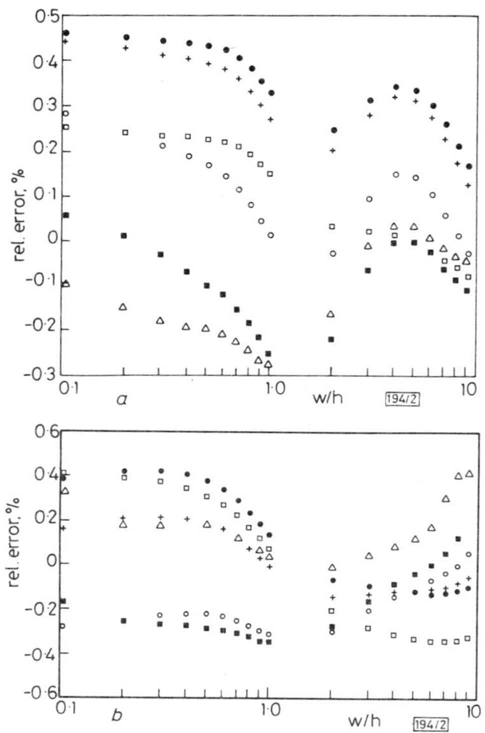

Fig. 2 *Comparison between formula presented here and numerical data*[9,10]

$h = 1$ mm
$f = 10$ GHz
$f = 30$ GHz

□□□ $\varepsilon_r = 2$ ●●● $\varepsilon_r = 4$ +++ $\varepsilon_r = 5$
○○○ $\varepsilon_r = 8$ ■■■ $\varepsilon_r = 12$ △△△ $\varepsilon_r = 20$

MMICs. In addition, it is intended to use this formula together with the open-end effect expression of Reference 2 and the asymmetric gap model of Reference 5 in the measurement of microwave substrate dielectric constants by strip or ring resonator techniques. Using the presented model for the simulation of the results obtained by the mentioned measurement techniques it should be possible to determine substrate dielectric constants ε_r with accuracies in the order of the maximum errors inherent in $\varepsilon_{eff}(f)$ and without time-consuming computer programs.

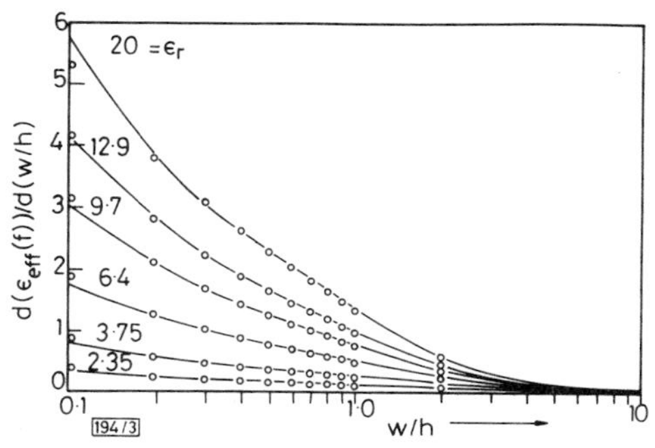

Fig. 3 *Comparison of derivative* $d(\varepsilon_{eff}(f))/d(w/h)$ *as following from the model presented and the rigorous numerical solution*[9,10]

$f = 30$ GHz, $h = 1$ mm
○○○ References 9 and 10
——— analytical model

M. KIRSCHNING
R. H. JANSEN

Duisburg University
Department of Electrical Engineering FB9/ATE
Bismarckstrasse 81, 4100 Duisburg 1, W. Germany

1st February 1982

References

1 PUCEL, R. A.: 'Design considerations for monolithic microwave circuits', *IEEE Trans.*, 1981, **MTT-29**, pp. 513–534

2 KIRSCHNING, M., JANSEN, R. H., and KOSTER, N. H. L.: 'Accurate model for open end effect of microstrip lines', *Electron. Lett.*, 1981, **17**, pp. 123–125

3 JANSEN, R. H.: 'Hybrid mode analysis of the end-effect of planar microwave and millimeter-wave transmission lines', *IEE Proc. H, Microwaves, Opt. & Antennas*, 1981, **128**, (2), pp. 77–86

4 JANSEN, R. H., and KOSTER, N. H. L.: 'Accurate results on the end effect of single and coupled microstrip lines for use in microwave circuit design', *AEÜ*, 1980, **34**, pp. 453–459

5 KIRSCHNING, M., and JANSEN, R. H.: 'Development of accurate transmission line and discontinuity models for the computer-aided design of planar microwave circuits'. Biannual report of ATE, Duisburg University/FB9, 1980/81

6 JANSEN, R. H., and KOSTER, N. H. L.: 'A unified CAD basis for the frequency dependent characterization of strip, slot and coplanar MIC components'. 11th European microwave conference, Amsterdam, 1981, pp. 682–687

7 KOSTER, N. H. L., and JANSEN, R. H.: 'The equivalent circuit of the asymmetrical series gap in microstrip and suspended substrate lines'. Submitted for publication to *IEEE Trans. MTT*, Dec. 1981

8 JANSEN, R. H.: 'High-speed computation of single and coupled microstrip parameters including dispersion, high-order modes, loss and finite strip thickness', *ibid.*, 1978, **MTT-26**, pp. 75–82

9 JANSEN, R. H.: 'Unified user-oriented computation of shielded, covered and open planar microwave and millimeter-wave transmission line characteristics', *IEE J. Microwaves, Opt. & Acoust.*, 1979, **3**, (1), pp. 14–22

10 JANSEN, R. H.: 'Computer programs for the numerical computation of planar microwave and millimeter-wave transmission line characteristics—short descriptions'. Microstrip computer programs 1–4, Verlag H. Wolff, Aachen, West Germany, 1981

11 KUESTER, E. F., and CHANG, D. C.: 'An appraisal of methods for computation of the dispersion characteristics of open microstrip', *IEEE Trans.*, 1979, **MTT-27**, pp. 691–694

12 YAMASHITA, E., ATSUKI, K., and UEDA, T.: 'An approximate dispersion formula of microstrip lines for computer-aided design of microwave integrated circuits', *ibid.*, 1979, **MTT-27**, pp. 1036–1038

13 HAMMERSTAD, E., and JENSEN, O.: 'Accurate models for microstrip computer-aided design'. 1980 IEEE MTT-S international microwave symposium digest, Washington, 1980, pp. 407–409

14 GETSINGER, W. J.: 'Microstrip dispersion model', *IEEE Trans.*, 1973, **MTT-21**, p. 34

An Accurate Description of Dispersion in Microstrip

Protap Pramanick and **Prakash Bhartia**
Department of Electrical Engineering
University of Ottawa
Ottawa, Ontario, Canada

The authors express the dispersion in microstrip by considering that this is the frequency at which the quasi-TEM microstrip mode couples strongly with the lowest order transverse electric wave mode. The dispersion equations developed yield close agreement with experimental results.

Introduction

Microstrip plays a very important and essential role as a fundamental component in modern microwave devices. For low frequency applications of microstrip, the quasi-static analyses do not take into account the non-TEM nature of the microstrip mode.[1] In fact, with the increasing use of microstrip at higher frequencies, a number of researchers have studied the dispersion phenomenon in microstrips both theoretically and experimentally.[2–8] Although the theoretical studies are accurate, they do not provide any closed-form solution useful for computer aided design of microstrip circuits.

On the other hand, the various semi-empirical formulae for microstrip dispersion, based on assumptions of different equivalent models for microstrip and experimental results, provide closed-form solutions to the problem, defining the effective width and the dielectric constant as functions of frequency. Each of these equations has its own range of validity as far as the substrate dielectric constant and usable frequency range are concerned. Moreover, since these assumed models differ widely amongst themselves, the physical phenomenon actually responsible for dispersion in microstrip remains vague.

For instance, Schneider[4] evaluates the frequency-dependent effective dielectric constant using the inflection frequency as a function of the cutoff frequency of the lowest order TE surface wave mode. Getsinger[5] uses an equivalent ridged waveguide model for the microstrip and determines a semiempirical parameter of the model from curve fitting to experimental data. Nobel and Carlin[6] use a coupled TE-TM mode transmission line model and develop a semiempirical equation quite similar to that of Getsinger. Jain et al[7] describe another model, based on coupling between the quasi TEM microstrip mode and TM_0 surface wave mode. Based completely on experimental results, Edwards and Owen[8] developed a purely empirical equation for dispersion in microstrips with alumina type substrates.

In a recent report, Kobayashi[9] has described the role of inflection frequency in the dielectric dispersion curve in microstrip. According to Kobayashi's observation[9] the inflection frequency is a function of the strip width W, the substrate-height h, and the substrate dielectric constant ε_r. Since the cut-off frequency of the lowest order TE surface wave mode is not a function of the strip width W of the microstrip, Kobayashi's observations are not explained by Schneider's equation.[4]

Kobayashi considers the frequency $f_{K,TM}$ at which the coupling between the quasi TEM mode of the microstrip and the TM_0 surface wave mode is a maximum[9]. In order for the resulting equation to explain the experimental observations on the inflection frequency, he divides $f_{K,TM}$ by a factor of (1+W/h). But such a modification is not justified, first because the resulting frequency does not correspond to any physical phenomenon in the microstrip and, second, Kobayashi compares his equation with that of Schneider[4] which has inaccuracies on the order of three percent.

Observations regarding the inflection frequency by Kobayashi can be explained by the models of Getsinger[5] and Carlin[6], because, in either case, the inflection frequency is a function of the static TEM characteristic impedance Z_0 of the microstrip, which in turn is a function of W, h and ε_r. Although it can also be done with the purely empirical equation of Edwards and Owen, the equation[8] does not have any basis on physical phenomenon in microstrip. Moreover, it shows multiple inflection frequencies. Despite these facts, Edwards and Owen's equation does give the closest agreement with experimental results and shows large deviations from results obtained using other methods.[4–7]

As a consequence of dielectric dispersion in microstrip, the effective width W_e (f) of the equivalent planar waveguide model for microstrip shows dispersive nature. There have been a number of reported equations[10,11,12] for predicting such dispersive behavior, but there is some controversy regarding their validity.[11] Moreover, since the dispersion in the W_e (f) is due to dispersion in ε_e (f), it is quite likely that both the dispersions will have the same inflection frequency.

In the present work we have tried to express the dispersion in microstrip by considering that this is the frequency at which the quasi TEM microstrip mode couples strongly with the lowest order transverse electric wave mode. The dispersion equations developed with the help of this frequency yield excellent agreement with experimental results, and explain Kobayashi's observations[9] on the inflection frequency.

Theory

Dispersion of effective dielectric constant.

From a physical point of view, the dielectric dispersion in microstrip obeys the following rules:

(a) ε_e (f) is a monotonically increasing function of frequency f, i.e.

$$\frac{\partial \varepsilon_e (f)}{\partial f} \geq 0 \quad (1)$$

(b)
$$\frac{\partial \varepsilon_e (f)}{\partial f} = 0 \text{, at } f = 0 \quad (2)$$

(c)
$$\underset{f \to \infty}{Lt} \frac{\partial \varepsilon_e (f)}{\partial f} = 0 \quad (3)$$

(d)
$$\varepsilon_e (0) = \varepsilon_{eff} \quad (4)$$

where ε_{eff} is the static TEM effective dielectric constant of the microstrip.

(e)
$$\underset{f \to \infty}{Lt} \varepsilon_e (f) = \varepsilon_r \quad (5)$$

(f)
$$\frac{\partial^2 \varepsilon_e (f)}{\partial_f^2} = 0 \quad (6)$$

at the inflection frequency $f = f_i$.

All the above conditions are satisfied by the following equation for ε_e (f)

$$\varepsilon_e (f) = \varepsilon_r - \frac{\varepsilon_r - \varepsilon_{eff}}{1 + (f/f_T)^2} \quad (7)$$

where f_T, the cutoff frequency of the lowest order TE mode of the microstrip, is defined by

$$f_T = \frac{C}{2 (W + \Delta W) \sqrt{\varepsilon_r}} \quad (8)$$

where C is the velocity of light in free-space and ΔW, which accounts for the fringing field effects at the edges of the strip, is defined by Napoli and Hughes[13] as:

$$\Delta W = \frac{h \sqrt{\varepsilon_{eff}}}{Z_o C \varepsilon_o \varepsilon_r} - W \quad (9)$$

where Z_o is the characteristic impedance of the microstrip and ε_o is the free-space permittivity.

Condition (f) is satisfied at

$$f = \frac{f_T}{\sqrt{3}} \quad (10)$$

which is the inflection frequency f_i.

From equation (7) the value of ε_e (f) at f_i is given by

$$\varepsilon_e (f_i) = \frac{1}{4} (\varepsilon_r + 3\varepsilon_{eff}) \quad (11)$$

as predicted by Getsinger.[5]

The computed results using equation (7) are shown and compared with other existing theories and experimental results in figures 1, 2, 3 and 4.

A qualitative explanation of the behavior of the inflection frequency with respect to the strip width W, substrate height h, and substrate dielectric constant ε_r, can be given by using Hammerstad's[14] expressions for the quasi-static parameters for microstrip. Using the expressions for Z_o and ε_{eff} we have

$$f_i = \frac{\eta_0 C^2 \sqrt{\varepsilon_r} \ln \left(8 \frac{h}{W} + 0.25 \frac{W}{h}\right)}{2\pi \sqrt{3}\, h \left[\varepsilon_r + 1 + (\varepsilon_r - 1) \left(1 + 12 \frac{h}{W}\right)^{-1/2}\right]} \quad (12)$$

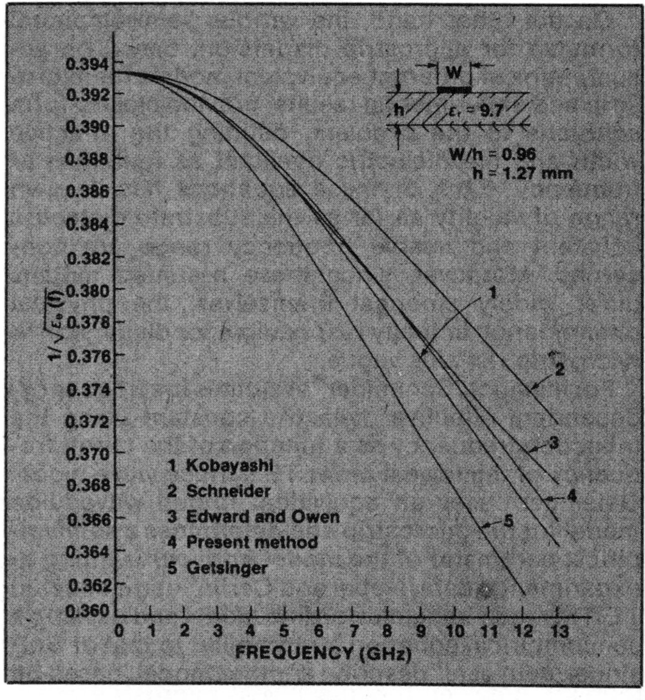

Fig. 1 Normalized phase velocity vs. frequency curve for ε_r = 9.7, w/h = 0.96 and h = 1.27 mm.

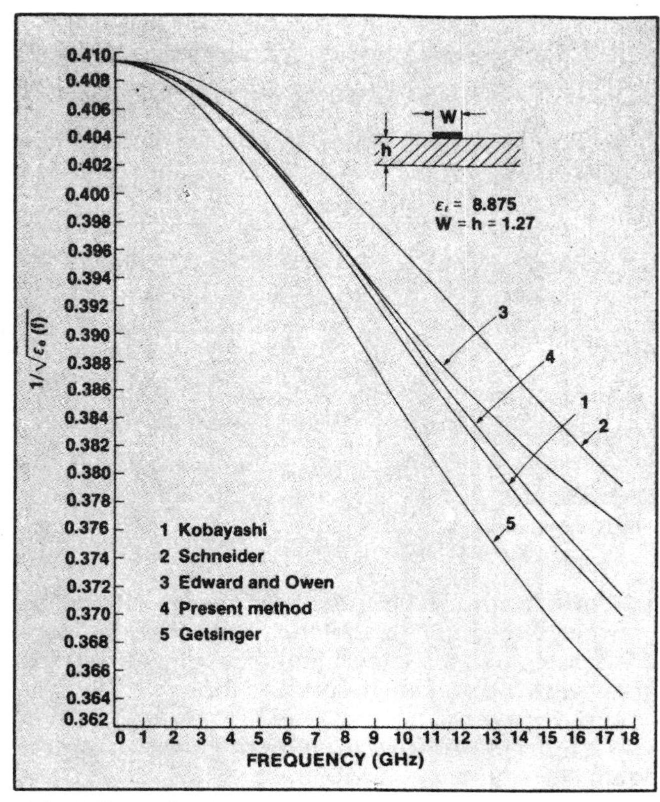

Fig. 2 Normalized phase velocity vs. frequency curve for ε_r = 8.875, w/h = 1.00 and h = 1.27 mm.

where $\eta_o = 120\pi$ ohm, the impedance of free space.

Equation (12) shows that the larger W/h, h or ε_r is, the lower is the inflection frequency f_i as observed by Kobayashi.[9]

Dispersion in effective width, $W_e(f)$

Like $\varepsilon_e(f)$, $W_e(f)$ satisfied the following conditions.

(a) $W_e(f)$ is a monotonically decreasing function of frequency, i.e.

$$\frac{\partial W_e(f)}{\partial f} \leq 0 \tag{13}$$

(b)
$$\frac{\partial W_e(f)}{\partial f} = 0 \text{ at } f = 0 \tag{14}$$

(c)
$$\underset{f\to\infty}{Lt} \frac{\partial W_e(f)}{\partial f} = 0 \tag{15}$$

(d)
$$W_e(0) = W_{eff} \tag{16}$$

where W_{eff} is the effective width of the equivalent planar waveguide model at zero frequency.

(e)
$$\underset{f\to\infty}{Lt} W_e(f) = W \tag{17}$$

and (f)
$$\frac{\partial^2 W_e(f)}{\partial^2 (f)} = 0 \tag{18}$$

at the inflection frequency f_i.

We choose the same inflection frequency (8) -(10) and define $W_e(f)$ as

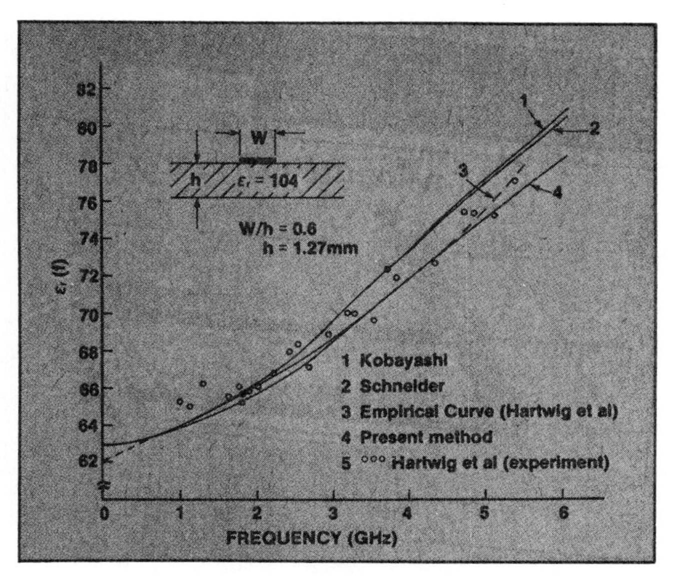

Fig. 3 Comparison with experimental results, ε_r = 104, w/h = 0.6 and h = 1.27 mm.

$$W_e(f) = W + \frac{W_{eff} - W}{1 + (f/f_T)^2} \tag{19}$$

Knowing $\varepsilon_e(f)$ and $W_e(f)$ from (7) and (19) respectively, one can obtain the frequency-dependent characteristic impedance of the microstrip as

$$Z_o(f) = \frac{\eta_o h}{W_e(f)\sqrt{\varepsilon_e(f)}} \tag{20}$$

Results

Figure 1 shows a plot of normalized phase velocity as a function of frequency using different theories, for a commonly used material, alumina of ε_r = 9.7. The microstrip line has the dimensions W/h = 0.96 and h = 1.27 mm. Curve (3), due to Edwards and Owen[8], is the most accurate and is accurate to ±0.8 percent over 0 to 12 GHz. A comparison with other theories shows that the present theory is closest to the curve due to Edwards and Owen. Similar results are shown in Figure 2 for ε_r = 8.875 W/h = 1 and h =

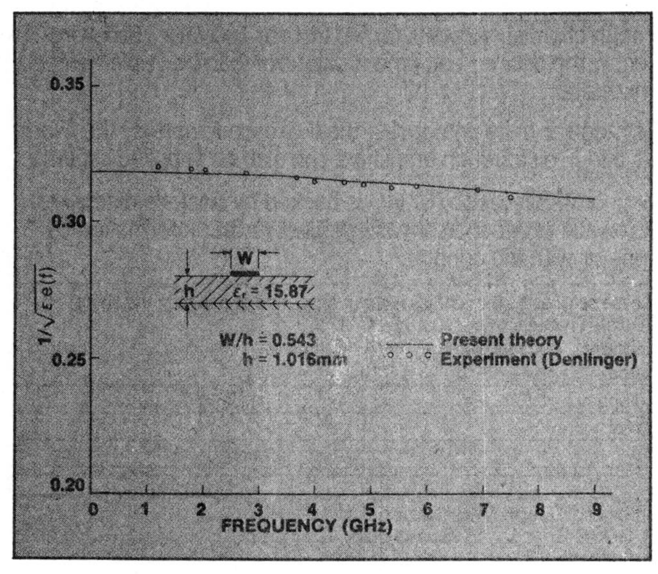

Fig. 4 Comparison with experimental results, ε_r = 15.87, w/h = 0.543 and h = 1.016 mm.

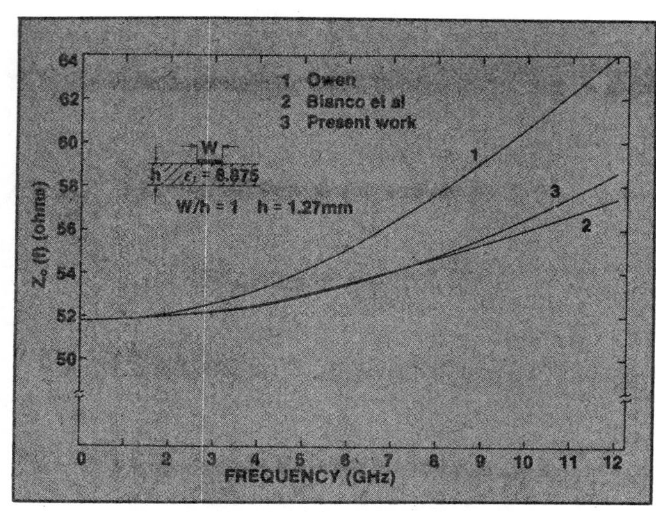

Fig. 5 Variation of characteristic impedance with frequency, for ε_r = 8.875, w/h = 1.00 and h = 1.27 mm.

1.27 mm. Both the figures show a large difference between Getsinger's and Schneider's theories. Figure 3 compares the experimental results of Hartwig et al[15] with the present theory and those of Schneider and Kobayashi.

The figure shows that the experimental results are again more consistent with the present theory than those of the other authors. In addition, the empirical curve due to Hartwig et al is closer to that of the present theory than are those obtained by Kobayashi and Schneider. Figure 4 compares the experimental results of Denlinger[16] for ε_r = 15.87 W/h = 0.543 and h = 1.016 mm. The agreement is found to be excellent.

The computed results using equations (7), (19) and (20) are shown in Figure 5 for ε_r = 8.875, W/h = 1.00 and h = 1.27 mm. The results show excellent agreement with those obtained for Bianco et al.[12]

Conclusion

The present work expresses for the first time the dispersions in effective dielectric constant and the effective width of the equivalent planar waveguide model of the microstrip in terms of a single inflection frequency.

Expressions have been derived for evaluating the frequency dependence of effective dielectric constant and the width of the equivalent planar waveguide model for microstrip, keeping in mind the experimentally observed facts about the inflection frequency as a function of the strip width, substrate height and substrate dielectric constant.

The resulting equations show excellent agreement with experimental results and other existing empirical equations. ■

REFERENCES

1. Wheeler, H.A., "Transmission Line Properties of Parallel Wide Strips Separated by a Dielectric Sheet," IEEE Trans., Vol. MTT-13, 1965, pp. 172-185.
2. Itoh, T. and R. Mitra, "Spectra Domain Approach for Calculating Dispersion Characteristic of Microstrip Lines," IEEE, Vol. MTT-21, 1973, pp. 496-498.
3. Saad, A.K., and K. Schuneman, "Efficient Eigen Mode Analysis for Planar Transmission Lines," IEEE Trans., Vol. MTT-30, No. 12, 1982, pp. 2125-2131.
4. Schneider, M.V., "Microstrip Dispersion," Proc. IEEE, Vol. 60, 1972, pp. 144-146.
5. Getsinger, W.J., "Microstrip Dispersion Model," IEEE Trans., Vol. MTT-21, 1973, pp. 589-591.
6. Nobel, O.F. and H.J. Carlin, "Circuit Properties of Coupled Dispersive Transmission Lines," IEEE Trans. on Circuit Theory, Vol. CT-20, 1973, pp. 56-65.
7. Jain, O.P. et. al., "Coupled Mode Model for Dispersion in Microstrip," Electronic Letters, Vol. 7, 1971, pp. 405-407:
8. Edwards, T.C., and R.P. Owen, "2-18 GHz Dispersion Measurements on 10-100 Ohm Microstrip Line on Sapphire," IEEE Trans., Vol. MTT-24, 1976, pp. 506-513.
9. Kobayashi, M., "Important Role of Inflection Frequency in the Dispersive Properties of Microstrip Lines," IEEE Trans. Vol. MTT-30, No. 11, 1982, pp. 2057-2059.
10. Kompao, G. and R. Mehran, "Planar Waveguide Model for Calculating Microstrip Components," Electronic Letters, Vol. 11, 1975, pp. 459-460.
11. Owen, R.P., "Predicted Frequency Dependence of Microstrip Characteristic Impedance Using Planar Waveguide Model," Electronic Letters, Vol. 12, 1976, pp. 269-270.
12. Bianco, B. et. al., "Frequency Dependence of Microstrip Parameters," Alta Frequenza, Vol. 43, 1974, pp. 413-416.
13. Napoli, S.I. and J.J. Hughes, "Foreshortening of Microstrip Open Circuits on Alumina Substrates" in *Microwave Integrated Circuits* by Jeffrey Frey., Artech House, inc., Dedham, MA, 1975.
14. Hammerstad, E.O., "Equations for Microstrip Circuit Design," Proc. European Microwave Conference, 1975, pp. 268-272.
15. Hartwig, C.P., D. Massé, and R.A. Pucel, "Frequency Dependent Behaviour of Microstrip", in 1968 G.MTT. Int. Microwave Symposium Digest (Detroit, Mich., May-1968). pp. 110-116, (IEEE Conf. 68C38).
16. Denlinger, E.J., "A Frequency-Dependent Solution for Microstrip Transmission Lines", IEEE Trans., Vol. MTT-19, Jan. 1971, pp. 30-39.

ACCURATE MODEL FOR OPEN END EFFECT OF MICROSTRIP LINES

Indexing terms: Microstrip, Transmission lines

A closed form expression for the equivalent line length associated with the single microstrip open end is presented for the use in microwave CAD programs. The maximum relative error involved is less than 2·5% and its effect can be shown to be below physical tolerances.

Introduction: In modern microwave CAD programs, like for example those recently reported by Jansen[1] and Kirchhoff,[2] the geometrical parameters of a microstrip network are computed for a given set of electrical design objectives. Such computer programs always involve an optimisation algorithm and perform a high number of circuit analyses during the course of the automated design process. Therefore, in this class of CAD procedures, it is mandatory that the circuit models used are introduced in closed form expressions. The rigorous numerical methods which presently are available for the computation of microstrip effective dielectric constant, characteristic impedance, loss and discontinuities are not suited for direct use in CAD programs since this would result in excessive computer time consumption. However, they are very useful to serve as a basis of the generation of reliable closed form circuit models, as will be demonstrated here.

The required model accuracies are mainly dictated by the fact that the substrate dielectric constants of today's high quality ceramic substrates, and even more that of semi-insulating GaAs substrates, for monolithic microwave integrated circuit (MMIC) production can be controlled closely, i.e. to a fraction of a percent.

On the other hand, it is obvious that for microwave circuit models it should be a goal to obtain accuracies in accordance with the typical tolerances caused by variations in the substrate parameters or by the manufacturing process. In the CAD of MMICs this is of even greater importance since tuning of the circuits is not provided for in the monolithic concept.

New end effect formula and comparison: Only recently, an improved formula for the microstrip effective dielectric constant ε_{eff} has been developed by Hammerstad and Jensen.[3] Besides its direct applicability to the computation of the microstrip line phase constant, this formula was also meant to serve as a basis for the calculation of discontinuities. Its accuracy is given to be better than 0·2% for the range of normalised widths $0{\cdot}01 \le w/h \le 100$ and $\varepsilon_r \le 128$. This satisfies the requirements associated with high quality substrates and even MMIC design. However, the high accuracy approximation of ε_{eff} as a fundamental microstrip parameter can only pay off in design if the modelling error introduced by discontinuities does not dominate. So the maximum error inherent in the ε_{eff} formula of Reference 3 can be considered as an approximate upper limit for all further microstrip circuit models based on this microstrip parameter. For this sake, a new model for the microstrip open end reference plane extension, i.e. equivalent line length, is presented here. The well-known open end effect formula given by Hammerstad some years ago[4] is useful for design but it is shown to violate the above mentioned accuracy condition considerably.

The closed form end effect expression of this letter has been derived from a rigorous numerical hybrid mode solution of the microstrip open end problem[5,6] by computer matching. With reference to Fig. 1 it described the displacement Δl of the hypothetical electric microstrip open circuit end with respect to the abrupt physical end of the strip. In a form which is normalised to the substrate thickness h this gives

$$\Delta l/h = (\xi_1 \xi_3 \xi_5 / \xi_4) \tag{1}$$

with

$$\begin{aligned}
\xi_1 &= 0{\cdot}434907\,\frac{\varepsilon_{eff}^{0\cdot81} + 0{\cdot}26}{\varepsilon_{eff}^{0\cdot81} - 0{\cdot}189}\cdot\frac{(w/h)^{0\cdot8544} + 0{\cdot}236}{(w/h)^{0\cdot8544} + 0{\cdot}87}\\
\xi_2 &= 1 + \frac{(w/h)^{0\cdot371}}{2{\cdot}358\varepsilon_r + 1}\\
\xi_3 &= 1 + \frac{0{\cdot}5274 \arctan\left[0{\cdot}084(w/h)^{1\cdot9413/\xi_2}\right]}{\varepsilon_{eff}^{0\cdot9236}}\\
\xi_4 &= 1 + 0{\cdot}0377 \arctan\left[0{\cdot}067(w/h)^{1\cdot456}\right]\\
&\quad \times \left\{6 - 5\exp\left(0{\cdot}036(1-\varepsilon_r)\right)\right\}\\
\xi_5 &= 1 - 0{\cdot}218 \exp(-7{\cdot}5 w/h)
\end{aligned} \tag{2}$$

and makes use of the effective dielectric constant ε_{eff} of Reference 3.

Compared to the converged numerical results of the method of References 5 and 6 and evaluated for a frequency of $f = 1$ GHz the accuracy of expr. 1 is better than 2·5% in the range of $0{\cdot}01 \le w/h \le 100$ and for dielectric constants less than $\varepsilon_r = 50$. To put this maximum relative error of $\Delta F = 2{\cdot}5\%$ in relation to the 0·2% accuracy of the effective dielectric constant ε_{eff} used in eqns. 1 and 2, the influence of ΔF and of the error inherent in ε_{eff} on the phase shift associated with a physical length l of microstrip has to be considered. With $\beta l \sim \sqrt{\varepsilon_{eff}}$ the maximum relative error of βl caused by ε_{eff} is less than 0·1%. The maximum relative phase error $F_{\beta l}$ caused by the open end effect is

$$F_{\beta l} = \frac{\Delta F}{1 + (l/\Delta l)} \qquad [\%] \tag{3}$$

Thus, given $F_{\beta l}$ and ΔF, we can calculate $\Delta l/l$. With $F_{\beta l} = 0{\cdot}4\%$, for example, and $\Delta F = 2{\cdot}5\%$, an open stub of microstrip line of physical length $l \simeq 5\,\Delta l$, which is a practical order of magnitude, would be affected by a 0·4% relative phase error due to the end effect model uncertainty. Making use of the end effect formula of Reference 4 the relative error ΔF involved can be shown to become as high as about 15% for high values of the substrate dielectric constant ε_r and up to 80% for low permittivities (see Fig. 2). For a stub of length $l \approx 5\,\Delta l$ this would induce relative phase errors of $F_{\beta l} = 2{\cdot}4\%$–$12{\cdot}8\%$ which is much larger than the error inherent in the basic parameter ε_{eff}.

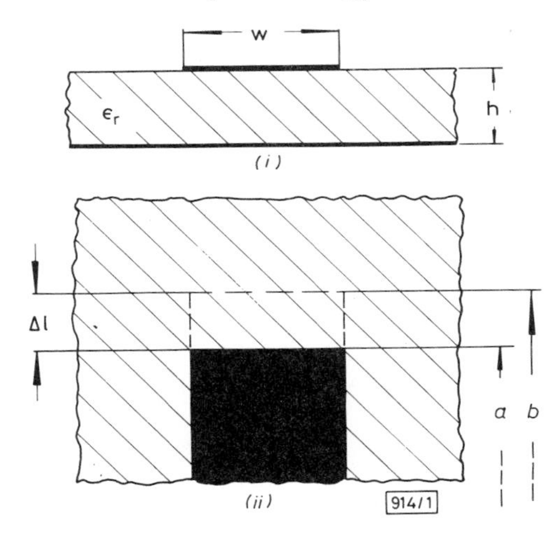

Fig. 1 *Single microstrip line cross-sectional and end effect geometry*

a Physical end *b* Hypothetical end

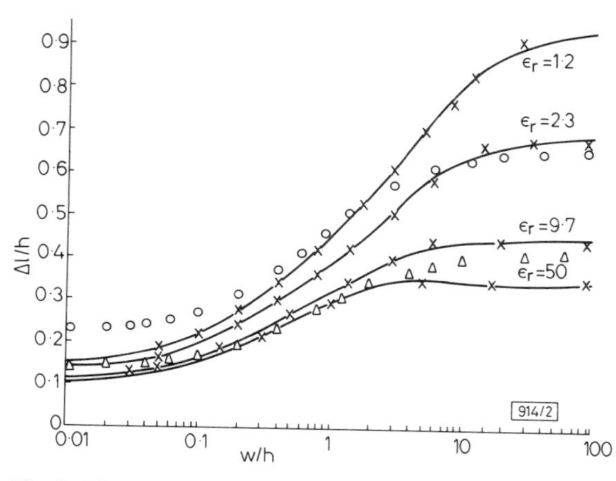

Fig. 2 *Microstrip end effect chart for comparison between this model, the Hammerstad equation*[4] *and the rigorous numerical solution*[5,6]

— Present formula ○ Hammerstad, $\varepsilon_r = 1{\cdot}2$
△ Hammerstad, $\varepsilon_r = 50$ × Jansen & Koster

Conclusion: A new accurate equation for the microstrip open end effect equivalent line length Δl is supplied. Its maximum relative error is in conjunction with the general efforts of CAD groups to improve the quality of microwave and millimetre wave design data. For empirical and start design purposes the well-known Hammerstad formula[4] should possibly be preferred because of its extreme simplicity.

M. KIRSCHNING
R. H. JANSEN
N. H. L. KOSTER

22nd December 1980

Department of Electrical Engineering
University of Duisburg
Bismarckstrasse 81, 4100 Duisburg 1, W. Germany

References

1 JANSEN, R. H.: 'Computer-aided design of transistorised microstrip broadband amplifiers on the base of physical circuit structures', *AEÜ*, 1978, **32**, pp. 145–152
2 KIRCHHOFF, H.: 'Rechnergestützter Entwurf passiver Mikrowellenkomponenten mit Streifenleitungen', *Frequenz*, 1980, **34**, pp. 218–223
3 HAMMERSTAD, E., and JENSEN, O.: 'Accurate models for microstrip computer-aided design'. 1980 IEEE MTT-S International Microwave Symposium Digest, Washington 1980, pp. 407–409
4 HAMMERSTAD, E. O.: 'Equations for microstrip circuit design'. 5th European Microwave Conference, Sept. 1975, Hamburg
5 JANSEN, R. H., and KOSTER, N. H. L.: 'Accurate results on the end effect of single and coupled microstrip lines for use in microwave circuit design', *AEÜ*, 1980, **34**, pp. 453–459
6 JANSEN, R. H.: 'Hybrid mode analysis of the end effects of planar microwave and millimeter-wave transmission lines', *IEE Proc. H (Microwaves, Opt. & Antennas)*, 1981, **128** (to be published)

An Analysis of Gap in Microstrip Transmission Lines

MINORU MAEDA, MEMBER, IEEE

***Abstract*—Although microstrip transmission lines have been widely used in microwave integrated circuits, the discontinuity structures in the microstrip transmission lines such as a gap, an abruptly ended strip conductor, and so on, have hardly been analyzed. An analytical method and numerical results for a gap capacitance in the microstrip transmission line are described. The equivalent circuit parameters are formulated with three-dimensional Green's functions, based on a variational principle. The numerical results are in good agreement with the published experimental data. The fringing effect of an abruptly ended strip conductor is also investigated.**

I. Introduction

WITH THE RECENT development of microwave integrated circuits, microstrip transmission lines have been widely used as fundamental structures. Since the microwave integrated circuits are fabricated through many processes, such as vacuum deposition, sputtering, electroplating, photoetching, and so on, it is primarily important to design the circuit precisely.

Although a great deal of work has been published on the properties of the microstrip transmission lines [1]–[5], the theoretical and/or experimental results obtained thus far have been almost entirely limited to the characteristic impedance and the phase velocity. Practical microwave integrated circuits, however, have been constructed using a variety of discontinuity structures in the strip conductor, such as a gap, an abruptly ended strip conductor, a tee junction, and so on. Since the discontinuity structures have not been investigated yet, there appears to be a need for rigorous theoretical formulas on the discontinuity structures.

This paper describes an analytical method and numerical results for a gap capacitance in the strip conductor of the microstrip transmission line. The gap capacitance of the symmetric-strip transmission line has been investigated theoretically and experimentally by Altschuler and Oliner [6]. For the gap capacitance of the microstrip transmission line, however, only experimental results obtained by Stinehelfer have been published [7]. The analytical method presented here employs a variational principle for formulating the problems based on an electrostatic approximation, and derives the theoretical expressions for the equivalent circuit parameters using three-dimensional potential Green's functions. The numerical results, obtained with the aid of a digital computer, are compared with the published experimental data. The derived formulas can be applied to investigate the fringing effect of the abruptly ended strip conductor when the gap is of in-

Manuscript received July 12, 1971; revised September 7, 1971.
The author is with Central Research Laboratory, Hitachi, Ltd., Kokubunji, Tokyo, Japan.

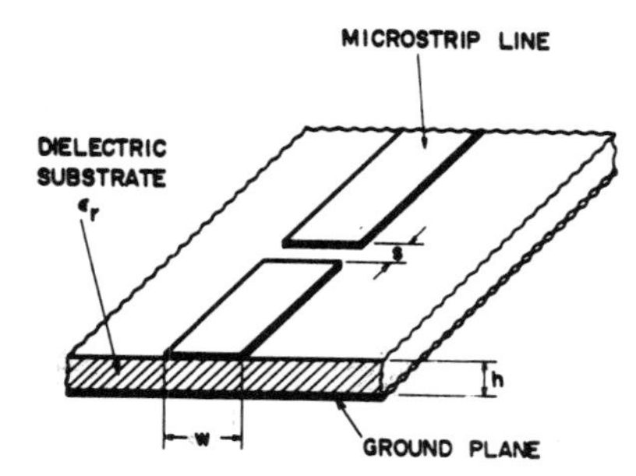

Fig. 1. Physical structure of gap in microstrip transmission line.

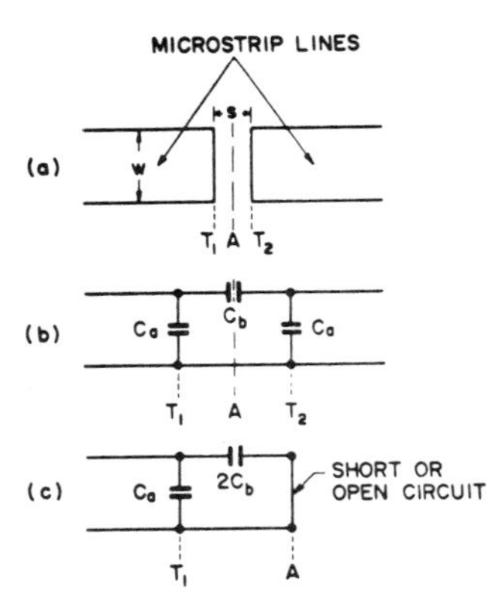

Fig. 2. Gap in microstrip transmission line. (a) Physical structure. (b) Equivalent circuit. (c) Equivalent circuit for analysis.

finite spacing. The fringing capacitances are also calculated [8] and compared with the experimental data of Napoli and Hughes [9].

II. Equivalent Circuit Parameters of Gap Structure

The physical gap structure in the strip conductor of the microstrip transmission line is shown in Fig. 1. The arbitrary discontinuity at a junction of two transmission lines can be generally represented by either the equivalent tee or pi circuit [10]. It is preferable to represent the gap structure with the equivalent pi circuit as shown in Fig. 2, because the parameters of the equivalent pi circuit show the physical meanings well. The shunt-gap capacitance C_a can be inferred from the effect of the disorder of the electrostatic field distribution at the edge of the strip conductor. The series capacitance C_b arises from the coupling effect of the adjacent strip conductors. The terminal plane T of the equivalent circuit in Fig. 2 is chosen at the edge of the strip conductor.

Let the electric wall or the magnetic wall be placed along the center line as shown in Fig. 2(a). This corresponds to the equivalent circuit with a short circuit or an open circuit in the symmetrical plane. Hence, the equivalent-circuit parameters C_e and C_m for the new equivalent circuit shown in Fig. 2(c) are given by

$$C_e = C_a + 2C_b \tag{1}$$

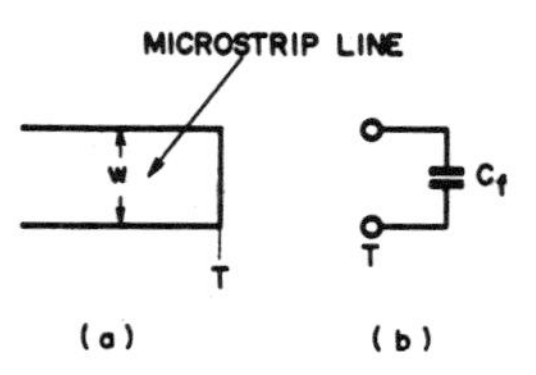

Fig. 3. Abruptly ended strip conductor in microstrip transmission line. (a) Physical structure. (b) Equivalent circuit.

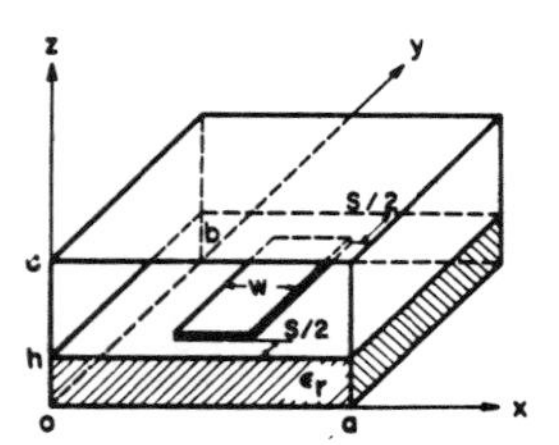

Fig. 4. Analytical configuration of gap in microstrip transmission line.

$$C_m = C_a \tag{2}$$

where the subscripts e and m correspond to the electric and magnetic walls, respectively.

The abruptly ended strip conductor can be represented by the equivalent circuit as shown in Fig. 3. The fringing capacitance C_f, which arises from the disorder of the electrostatic field at the edge of the strip conductor, can be obtained when the gap is of infinite spacing.

The analytical configuration of the gap is illustrated in Fig. 4. If the electric walls or the magnetic walls are placed at $y=0$ and $y=b$, the total capacitance C_{ti} is given by

$$C_{ti} = C_0 + 2C_i, \qquad i = e, m \tag{3}$$

where C_0 is the line capacitance of the uniform microstrip transmission line with its length of b–s. Let the three-dimensional potential Green's function, satisfying the boundary conditions with the electric walls ($i=e$) or the magnetic walls ($i=m$) at $y=0$, and b be $G_i(x, y, z|x', y', z')$, and the charge distribution on the strip conductor be $\rho_i(x, y, z)$. Then the capacitance C_{ti} is given by the variational expression which is stationary with respect to arbitrary first-order variations in the charge distribution $\rho_i(x, y, z)$ [11]:

$$\frac{1}{C_{ti}} = \frac{\displaystyle\iint \rho_i(x, y, z) G_i(x, y, z, |x', y', z') \rho_i(x', y', z')\, dv dv'}{\left[\displaystyle\int \rho_i(x, y, z)\, dv\right]^2} \tag{4}$$

where the integral is to be taken through all the volume in which the charge is distributed. Since this is a "lower bound" type of variational expression, the capacitance can be obtained by maximizing, with a suitable choice of the charge distribution as a trial function.

III. Derivation of Green's Function

The three-dimensional potential Green's function is the solution of the following Poisson's equation:

$$\nabla^2 G_i(x, y, z|x', y', z') = -\frac{1}{\epsilon}\delta(x-x')\delta(y-y')\delta(z-z') \quad (5)$$

where $\delta(x-x')$ is a Dirac's delta function. If it is assumed that the strip conductor is infinitely thin, the Green's functions for the case $z=h$ are adequate for the calculation of the capacitance C_{ti} using the variational expression (4). Of course, the Green's functions should satisfy the required boundary and continuity conditions.

The Green's function $G_e(x, y, z|x', y', h)$ for the electric walls should satisfy the following conditions:

$$G_e(0, y, z|x', y', h) = 0 \quad (6a)$$

$$G_e(a, y, z|x', y', h) = 0 \quad (6b)$$

$$G_e(x, 0, z|x', y', h) = 0 \quad (6c)$$

$$G_e(x, b, z|x', y', h) = 0 \quad (6d)$$

$$G_e(x, y, 0|x', y', h) = 0 \quad (6e)$$

$$G_e(x, y, c|x', y', h) = 0 \quad (6f)$$

$$G_e(x, y, h-0|x', y', h) = G_e(x, y, h+0|x', y', h) \quad (6g)$$

$$\frac{\partial}{\partial x}G_e(x, y, h-0|x', y', h) = \frac{\partial}{\partial x}G_e(x, y, h+0|x', y', h) \quad (6h)$$

$$\frac{\partial}{\partial y}G_e(x, y, h-0|x', y', h) = \frac{\partial}{\partial y}G_e(x, y, h+0|x', y', h). \quad (6i)$$

The Poisson's equation (5) can be readily solved as a linear combination of hyperbolic sinusoidal functions. By applying the above boundary conditions to the solution, $G_e(x, y, z|x', y', h)$ is found to be

$$G_e(x, y, z|x', y', h) = \begin{cases} \displaystyle\sum_{m=1}^{\infty}\sum_{n=1}^{\infty} \frac{4}{ab\gamma_{mn}\Gamma_{mn}} \sin\left(\frac{m\pi x}{a}\right)\sin\left(\frac{m\pi x'}{a}\right) \cdot \sin\left(\frac{n\pi y}{b}\right)\sin\left(\frac{n\pi y'}{b}\right)\sinh(\gamma_{mn}z) \cdot \sinh(\gamma_{mn}(c-h)), & 0 \leqq z \leqq h \\ \displaystyle\sum_{m=1}^{\infty}\sum_{n=1}^{\infty} \frac{4}{ab\gamma_{mn}\Gamma_{mn}} \sin\left(\frac{m\pi x}{a}\right)\sin\left(\frac{m\pi x'}{a}\right) \cdot \sin\left(\frac{n\pi y}{b}\right)\sin\left(\frac{n\pi y'}{b}\right)\sinh(\gamma_{mn}(c-z)) \cdot \sinh(\gamma_{mn}h), & h \leqq z \leqq c \end{cases} \quad (7)$$

where

$$\gamma_{mn} = \sqrt{\left(\frac{m\pi}{a}\right)^2 + \left(\frac{n\pi}{b}\right)^2} \quad (8)$$

$$\Gamma_{mn} = \epsilon_r \cosh(\gamma_{mn}h)\sinh(\gamma_{mn}(c-h)) + \sinh(\gamma_{mn}h)\cosh(\gamma_{mn}(c-h)). \quad (9)$$

On the other hand, the Green's function $G_m(x, y, z|x', y', h)$ for the magnetic walls should satisfy the following boundary conditions at $y=0$ and $y=b$:

$$\frac{\partial}{\partial y}G_m(x, 0, z|x', y', h) = 0 \quad (10a)$$

$$\frac{\partial}{\partial y}G_m(x, b, z|x', y', h) = 0. \quad (10b)$$

The other boundary and continuity conditions are the same as the case of the Green's function $G_e(x, y, z|x', y', h)$. Through similar mathematical manipulations, $G_m(x, y, z|x', y', h)$ can be derived as follows:

$$G_m(x, y, z|x', y', h) = \begin{cases} \displaystyle\sum_{m=1}^{\infty}\sum_{n=0}^{\infty} \frac{4\sigma_n}{ab\gamma_{mn}\Gamma_{mn}} \sin\left(\frac{m\pi x}{a}\right)\sin\left(\frac{m\pi x'}{a}\right) \cdot \cos\left(\frac{n\pi y}{b}\right)\cos\left(\frac{n\pi y'}{b}\right)\sinh(\gamma_{mn}z) \cdot \sinh(\gamma_{mn}(c-h)), & 0 \leqq z \leqq h \\ \displaystyle\sum_{m=1}^{\infty}\sum_{n=0}^{\infty} \frac{4\sigma_n}{ab\gamma_{mn}\Gamma_{mn}} \sin\left(\frac{m\pi x}{a}\right)\sin\left(\frac{m\pi x'}{a}\right) \cdot \cos\left(\frac{n\pi y}{b}\right)\cos\left(\frac{n\pi y'}{b}\right)\sinh(\gamma_{mn}(c-z)) \cdot \sinh(\gamma_{mn}h), & h \leqq z \leqq c \end{cases} \quad (11)$$

where

$$\sigma_n = \begin{cases} \frac{1}{2}, & n = 0 \\ 1, & n \neq 0. \end{cases}$$

The term for $n=0$ in (11) can be written as

$$\begin{cases} \displaystyle\sum_{m=1}^{\infty} \frac{1}{b}\frac{2}{m\pi\Gamma_{m0}} \sin\left(\frac{m\pi x}{a}\right)\sin\left(\frac{m\pi x'}{a}\right)\sinh\left(\frac{m\pi z}{a}\right) \cdot \sinh\left(\frac{m\pi(c-h)}{a}\right), & 0 \leqq z \leqq h \\ \displaystyle\sum_{m=1}^{\infty} \frac{1}{b}\frac{2}{m\pi\Gamma_{m0}} \sin\left(\frac{m\pi x}{a}\right)\sin\left(\frac{m\pi x'}{a}\right)\sinh\left(\frac{m\pi(c-z)}{a}\right) \cdot \sinh\left(\frac{m\pi h}{a}\right), & h \leqq z \leqq c. \end{cases} \quad (12)$$

It should be noted that the term, except for the coefficient $1/b$, corresponds to the two-dimensional Green's function in the rectangular boundary for the cross section of the uniform microstrip transmission line obtained by Yamashita [12]. This fact indicates that the capacitance calculated with (12) is the line capacitance of the uniform microstrip transmission line with its length of b.

IV. Formulation of Equivalent Circuit Parameters

For the infinitely thin strip-conductor case, the charge distribution may take the form

$$\rho_i(x, y, z) = \rho_i'(x, y)\delta(z-h). \quad (13)$$

Then (4) becomes

$$\frac{1}{C_{ti}}=\frac{\iint \rho_i'(x, y)G_i(x, y, h|x', y', h)\rho_i'(x', y')\, ds ds'}{\left[\int \rho_i(x, y)\, ds\right]^2}. \tag{14}$$

As a charge distribution on an infinitely thin strip conductor of the uniform microstrip transmission line, the following expression has been used by Yamashita [13] and found to give sufficiently accurate results on the characteristic impedance and the phase velocity:

$$f(x) = 1 + \left|\frac{2}{w}\left(x - \frac{a}{2}\right)\right|^3, \qquad \left|x - \frac{a}{2}\right| \leqq \frac{w}{2}. \tag{15}$$

It is reasonable to consider that the charge density in the longitudinal direction also increases near the edge of the strip conductor. Hence the following form of the charge distribution is assumed in this paper:

$$\rho_i'(x, y) = f(x)g(y) \tag{16}$$

and

$$g(y) = \begin{cases} 0, & \dfrac{b}{2} - \dfrac{s}{2} \leqq \left|y - \dfrac{b}{2}\right| \leqq \dfrac{b}{2} \\ 1 + \dfrac{K}{h}\left(\left|y - \dfrac{b}{2}\right| - \dfrac{b}{2} + \dfrac{s}{2} + h\right), & \dfrac{b}{2} - \dfrac{s}{2} - h \leqq \left|y - \dfrac{b}{2}\right| \leqq \dfrac{b}{2} - \dfrac{s}{2} \\ 1, & \left|y - \dfrac{b}{2}\right| \leqq \dfrac{b}{2} - \dfrac{s}{2} - h \end{cases} \tag{17}$$

where the shield walls are assumed to be sufficiently apart from the strip conductor. The coefficient K is to be determined so as to maximize the capacitance C_{ti}.

The capacitances C_{te}, C_{tm}, and C_0 can be obtained by substituting (7), (11), (12), (15), and (17) into (14) as follows:

$$C_{te} = \frac{\dfrac{25}{16} b\left(1 - \dfrac{s}{b} + K\dfrac{h}{b}\right)^2}{\displaystyle\sum_{m=1,3,\cdots}^{\infty}\sum_{n=1,3,\cdots}^{\infty} \frac{4P_m^2R_n^2}{a\gamma_{mn}\Gamma_{mn}}\left(\frac{s}{b}\right)^2 \sinh(\gamma_{mn}h)\sinh(\gamma_{mn}(c-h))} \tag{18}$$

$$C_{tm} = \frac{\dfrac{25}{16} b\left(1 - \dfrac{s}{b} + K\dfrac{h}{b}\right)^2}{\displaystyle\sum_{m=1,3,\cdots}^{\infty} \frac{2P_m^2}{m\pi\Gamma_{m0}}\left(1 - \frac{s}{b} + K\frac{h}{b}\right)^2 \sinh\left(\frac{m\pi h}{a}\right)\sinh\left(\frac{m\pi(c-h)}{a}\right) + \sum_{m=1,3,\cdots}^{\infty}\sum_{n=2,4,\cdots}^{\infty}\frac{4P_m^2Q_n^2}{a\gamma_{mn}\Gamma_{mn}}\left(\frac{s}{b}\right)^2 \sinh(\gamma_{mn}h)\sinh(\gamma_{mn}(c-h))} \tag{19}$$

$$C_0 = \frac{\dfrac{25}{16}(b-s)}{\displaystyle\sum_{n=1,3,\cdots}^{\infty} \frac{2P_m^2}{m\pi\Gamma_{m0}} \sinh\left(\frac{m\pi h}{a}\right)\sinh\left(\frac{m\pi(c-h)}{a}\right)} \tag{20}$$

where

$$P_m = 2\left(\frac{2a}{m\pi w}\right)\sin\left(\frac{m\pi w}{2a}\right) + 3\left(\frac{2a}{m\pi w}\right)^2\cos\left(\frac{m\pi w}{2a}\right) - 6\left(\frac{2a}{m\pi w}\right)^3\sin\left(\frac{m\pi w}{2a}\right) - 6\left(\frac{2a}{m\pi w}\right)^4 \cdot\cos\left(\frac{m\pi w}{2a}\right) - 6\left(\frac{2a}{m\pi w}\right)^4 \tag{21}$$

$$Q_n = \left(\frac{2b}{n\pi s}\right)\cos\left(\frac{n\pi s}{2b}\right) + K\left[\left(\frac{2b}{n\pi s}\right)\sin\left(\frac{n\pi s}{2b}\right) - \left(\frac{2b}{n\pi s}\right)\left(\frac{2b}{n\pi h}\right)\sin\left(\frac{n\pi s}{2b} + \frac{n\pi h}{2b}\right) \cdot\sin\left(\frac{n\pi h}{2b}\right)\right] \tag{22}$$

$$R_n = \left(\frac{2b}{n\pi s}\right)\cos\left(\frac{n\pi s}{2b}\right) + K\left[\left(\frac{2b}{n\pi s}\right)\cos\left(\frac{n\pi s}{2b}\right) - \left(\frac{2b}{n\pi s}\right)\left(\frac{2b}{n\pi h}\right)\cos\left(\frac{n\pi s}{2b} + \frac{n\pi h}{2b}\right) \cdot\sin\left(\frac{n\pi h}{2b}\right)\right]. \tag{23}$$

Numerical data for the equivalent circuit parameters of the gap can be readily obtained by computing the above formulas with the aid of a digital computer and using (1)-(3).

V. Numerical Results

The formulas derived above are for the gap in the shielded microstrip transmission line in the strict sense. However, when the shield walls in Fig. 4 are sufficiently removed from the strip conductor, the structure approaches the microstrip case. The numerical computations were carried out in this paper for the case where the effects of the shield walls are negligible.

The values of the gap capacitances C_a and C_b for 50-Ω microstrip transmission lines with the dielectric thickness of 0.5 mm are plotted as a function of s/h in Fig. 5. The series capacitance C_b decreases as the gap spacing increases. This tendency has been expected because the

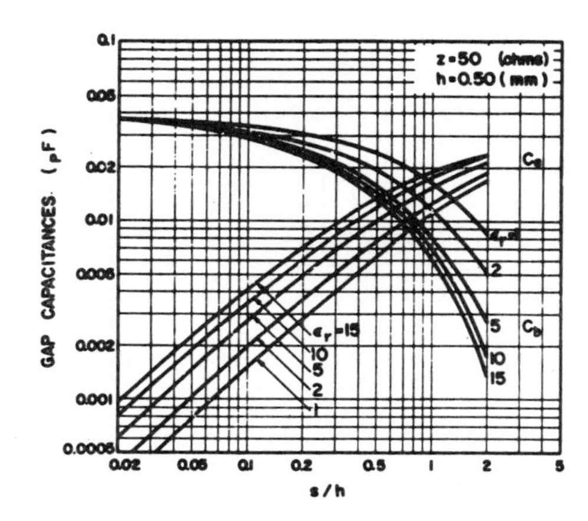

Fig. 5. Gap capacitances for 50-Ω microstrip transmission line as a function of s/h ($h=0.50$ mm).

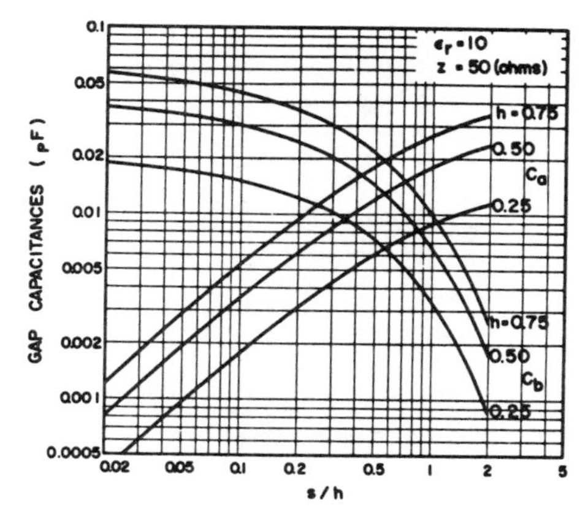

Fig. 6. Gap capacitances for 50-Ω microstrip transmission line as a function of s/h ($\epsilon_r=10$).

TABLE I

OPTIMUM COEFFICIENT OF CHARGE DISTRIBUTION

	K_e							K_m							
s/h \ ϵ_r	1	2	3	5	7	10	15	1	2	3	4	5	7	10	15
0.02	2	2	2	2	2	2	2	0	0	0	0	0	0	0	0
0.04	2	2	2	2	2	2	2	0	0	0	0	0	0	0	0
0.06	2	2	2	2	2	2	2	0	0	0	0	0	0	0	0
0.1	2	2	2	2	2	2	1	0	0	0	0	0	0	0	0
0.2	2	2	2	2	2	1	1	0	0	0	0	0	0	0	0
0.4	2	2	2	1	1	1	1	0	0	0	0	0	0	0	0
0.6	2	2	1	1	1	1	1	1	0	0	0	0	0	0	0
1.0	2	1	1	1	1	1	1	1	1	1	1	1	1	1	1
2.0	2	1	1	1	1	1	1	1	1	1	1	1	1	1	1

Note: $Z=50$ Ω; $h=0.50$ mm.

electrostatic coupling between two conductors becomes loose when the conductors keep apart from each other. When the ratio s/h is sufficiently large, C_b becomes negligible and the structure approaches the simple abruptly ended strip conductor.

The numerical calculations were carried out by the digital computer HITAC 5020 F. The summation of the infinite series was truncated when the last term added was less than one 10^8th of the first term. The calculation time of C_a and C_b was about 200 s/structure, although it depended on the dimensions of a gap structure. Of course, the coefficient K of the charge distribution $g(y)$ was chosen so as to maximize the variational expression. In order to reduce the computation time, integers were employed for K. Optimum coefficients for the electric and magnetic walls are tabulated in Table I. It can be seen from Table I that the charge distributions for the electric and magnetic walls take the same shape

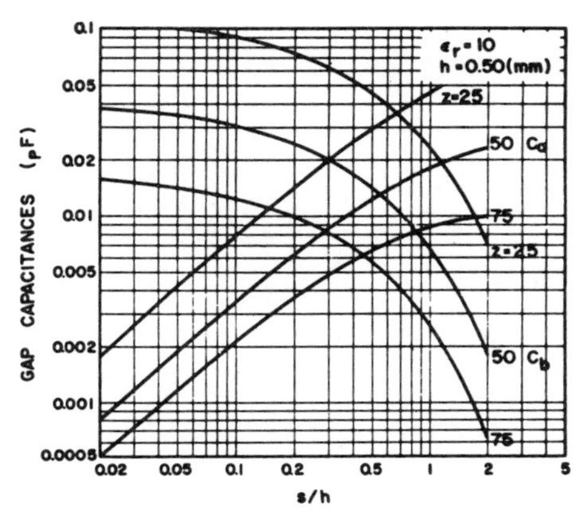

Fig. 7. Gap capacitances for microstrip transmission line as a function of s/h ($\epsilon_r=10$, $h=0.50$ mm).

when the gap spacing becomes large, and that we may set K equal to unity for calculating the fringing capacitance of the abruptly ended strip conductor.

The calculated gap capacitances for various structures are shown in Figs. 6 and 7. Fig. 8 shows the normalized strip width w/h as a function of relative dielectric constant ϵ_r for typical values of characteristic impedance.

Since the numerical data for the fringing capacitance of the abruptly ended strip conductor are useful for the designs of filters, open stubs, and so on, the calculated results for various parameters are shown in Fig. 9. The computation time C_f was about 40 s/structure, because the coefficient K was set equal to unity beforehand.

The present theory was compared with the experimental data of Stinehelfer for the series gap capacitance C_b, with $\epsilon_r=8.875$, $h=0.508$ mm, and $w=0.508$ mm. The calculated gap capacitances for the parameters are shown along with the experimental ones in Fig. 10. It is seen in the figure that the calculated values are in fairly good agreement with the measured values. The fringing capacitance of the abruptly ended strip con-

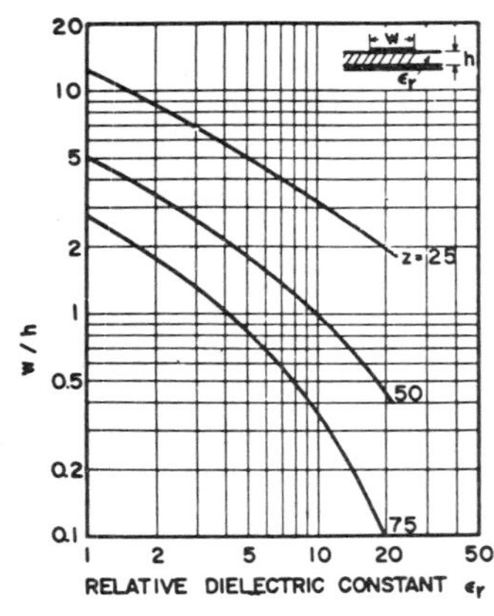

Fig. 8. Normalized strip width as a function of relative dielectric constant ϵ_r.

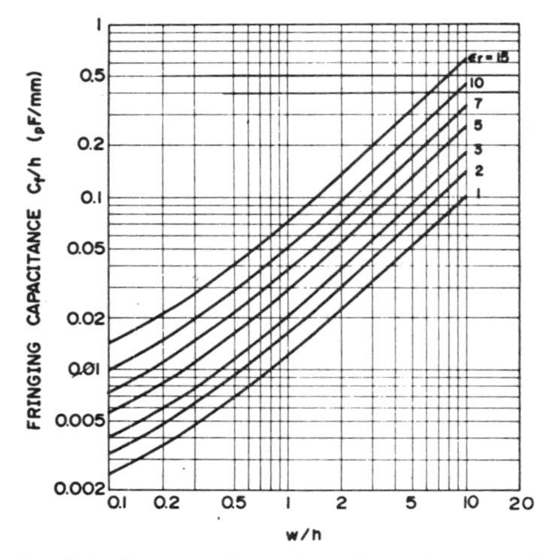

Fig. 9. Fringing capacitance for microstrip transmission line as a function of w/h.

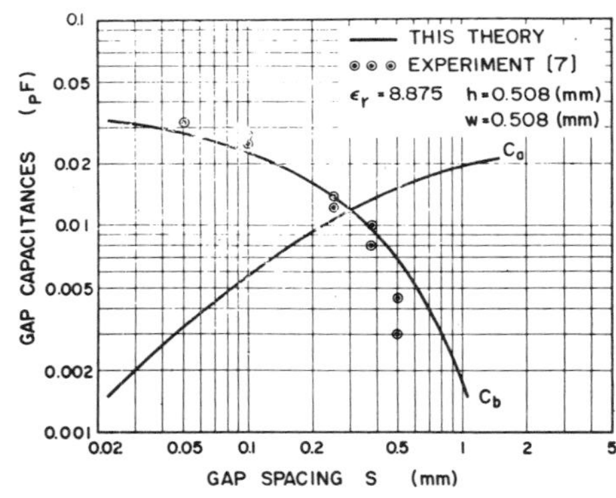

Fig. 10. Theoretical and experimental gap capacitances for microstrip transmission line.

ductor calculated by this theory was compared with the one experimentally obtained by Napoli and Hughes. Since the experimental data have been obtained in terms of an effective increase in line length, the calcu-

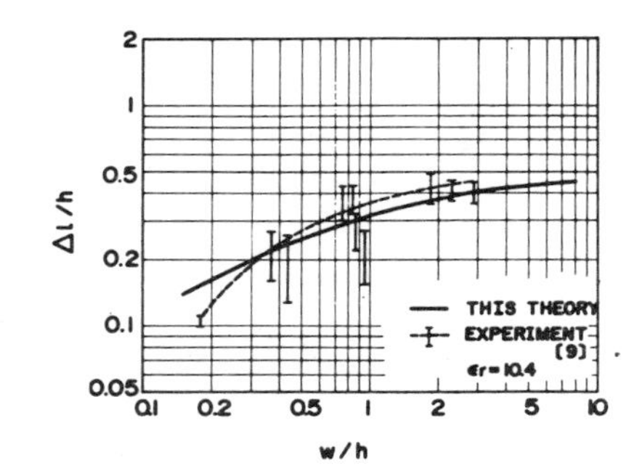

Fig. 11. Comparison of this theory with measured fringing effect of abruptly ended strip conductor.

lated fringing capacitance was transformed into the same expression, based on the following equation:

$$\frac{\Delta l}{h} = C_f \frac{Z_0 v}{h} \tag{24}$$

where Z_0 is a characteristic impedance and v a phase velocity. Fig. 11 compares the calculated and measured fringing effect, and shows a good fit.

VI. Conclusion

In this paper the gap in the strip conductor of the microstrip transmission line is analyzed by the application of a variational principle. The equivalent circuit parameters of the gap are formulated using potential Green's functions and approximate charge distributions. The theoretical formulas can be applied to the fringing effect of the abruptly ended strip conductor when the gap is of infinite spacing. Numerical calculations are carried out with the aid of a digital computer. The theoretical results are compared with the published experimental data, and are shown to give accurate results.

Acknowledgment

The author wishes to thank his colleagues for many helpful discussions.

References

[1] H. A. Wheeler, "Transmission-line properties of parallel strips separated by a dielectric sheet," *IEEE Trans. Microwave Theory Tech.*, vol. MTT-13, pp. 172–175, Mar. 1965.

[2] H. E. Stinehelfer, Sr., "An accurate calculation of uniform microstrip transmission lines," *IEEE Trans. Microwave Theory Tech.*, vol. MTT-16, pp. 439–444, July 1968.

[3] E. Yamashita and R. Mittra, "Variational method for the analysis of microstrip lines," *IEEE Trans. Microwave Theory Tech.*, vol. MTT-16, pp. 251–256, Apr. 1968.

[4] T. G. Bryant and J. A. Weiss, "Parameters of microstrip transmission lines and of coupled pairs of microstrip lines," *IEEE Trans. Microwave Theory Tech.*, vol. MTT-16, pp. 1021–1027, Dec. 1968.

[5] P. Silvester, "TEM wave properties of microstrip transmission lines," *Proc. Inst. Elec. Eng. (London)*, vol. 115, pp. 43–48, Jan. 1968.

[6] H. M. Altschuler and A. A. Oliner, "Discontinuity in the center conductor of symmetric strip transmission line," *IRE Trans. Microwave Theory Tech.*, vol. MTT-8, pp. 328–339, May 1960.

[7] The Microwave Engineers' Handbook and Buyers' Guide. New York: Horizon House, Feb. 1969, p. 72.

[8] A. Farrar and A. T. Adams, "Computation of lumped microstrip capacities by matrix methods—Rectangular sections and end effect," *IEEE Trans. Microwave Theory Tech.* (Corresp.), vol. MTT-19, pp. 495–497, May 1971.

[9] L. S. Napoli and J. J. Hughes, "Foreshortening of microstrip open circuits on alumina substrates," *IEEE Trans. Microwave Theory Tech.* (Corresp.), vol. MTT-19, pp. 559–561, June 1971.

[10] N. Marcuvitz, *Waveguide Handbook*. New York: McGraw-Hill, 1951, p. 108.

[11] R. E. Collin, *Field Theory of Guided Waves*. New York: McGraw-Hill, 1960, p. 148.

[12] E. Yamashita and K. Atsuki, "Strip line with rectangular outer conductor and three dielectric layers," *IEEE Trans. Microwave Theory Tech.*, vol. MTT-18, pp. 238–244, May 1970.

[13] E. Yamashita, "Variational method for the analysis of microstrip-like transmission lines," *IEEE Trans. Microwave Theory Tech.*, vol. MTT-16, pp. 529–535, Aug. 1968.

Microstrip Discontinuity Capacitances for Right-Angle Bends, T Junctions, and Crossings

PETER SILVESTER AND PETER BENEDEK

***Abstract*—The integral equations governing the electrostatics of the excess charge distribution near microstrip right-angle bends, T junctions, and crossings are formulated and subsequently solved by a projective method. Extensive discontinuity capacitances are presented in graphical form. Where possible, the data are compared to the available experimental results.**

Introduction

NUMEROUS papers have been published, mostly during the past year, treating various microstrip discontinuities such as open circuits [1]–[7], gaps [1], [8]–[10], and steps [9]–[12]. In earlier papers by the authors, a new method capable of determining the microstrip discontinuity capacitances for open circuits [7], gaps, and steps [10] has been presented. This method determines the excess discontinuity capacitance directly, so that the overall accuracy realized does not suffer degradation from subtraction of nearly equal numbers. This approach can be readily extended to other structures, such as microstrip right-angle bends, T junctions, and crossings, for which the available data are very scarce.

Definitions and Methodology

The best way to introduce the methodology utilized is by actually obtaining the governing integral equations for the excess charges, and hence excess capacitances, at various discontinuities. First, symbols are defined and a key artifice is described. Let $\phi_\infty^{(1)}(P_x)$ denote the potential, at a point P_x in the plane of the microstrip resulting from an infinite microstrip-like charge distribution $\sigma_\infty^{(1)}(P_x')$, i.e., a charge distribution of exactly the form that results when an infinitely long microstrip line is electrostatically charged. The subscript x on the charge and potential coordinates P_x' and P_x indicates that the axis of the microstrip is parallel to the x axis, while the superscript 1 indicates a microstrip of width-to-height ratio $(w/h)_1$. When the meaning is obvious both of these will be omitted. Therefore

$$\phi_\infty^{(1)}(P_x) = \int \sigma_\infty^{(1)}(P_x')G_\infty(P_x; P_x')\, dP_x'. \tag{1}$$

$G_\infty(P_x; P_x')\, dP_x'$ is the Green's function appropriate to the dielectric substrate employed (see (3) following).

Now let $\phi_\xi^{(1)}(P_x)$ represent the potential, in the plane of the microstrip, associated with a microstrip-like charge-density distribution with a sudden polarity reversal in the charge at $x=\xi$. It can be shown that

$$\phi_\xi^{(1)}(P_x) = \int \sigma_\infty^{(1)}(P_x')G_\xi(P_x; P_x')\, dP_x'. \tag{2}$$

Manuscript received August 8, 1972; revised December 15, 1972.
The authors are with the Department of Electrical Engineering, McGill University, Montreal, Quebec, Canada.

The Green's function required in (1) is given by

$$G_\infty(y, y') = \frac{1}{2\pi(\epsilon_0+\epsilon_1)} \sum_{n=1}^{\infty} K^{n-1} \log \frac{4n^2 + \left(\dfrac{y-y'}{h}\right)^2}{4(n-1)^2 + \left(\dfrac{y-y'}{h}\right)^2} \tag{3}$$

where y, y' are potential and charge coordinates in the cross-sectional plane of the microstrip parallel to the microstrip, while that required in (2) is

$$G_\xi(x, y; y') = \frac{1-K}{4\pi\epsilon_0}\left[f(0) - (1-K)\sum_{n=1}^{\infty} K^{n-1} f(n)\right] \tag{4}$$

where

$$f(n) = \log \frac{\sqrt{(x-\xi)^2 + (y-y')^2 + 4n^2h^2} + (x-\xi)}{\sqrt{(x-\xi)^2 + (y-y')^2 + 4n^2h^2} - (x-\xi)}. \tag{5}$$

The Green's function $G_\xi(x, y; y')$ represents the potential value at any point (x, y) of the top of the substrate, when a unit line charge with sudden polarity reversal at $x=\xi$ is placed at y'.

The charge distribution that causes $\phi_\xi^{(1)}$ is exactly the same as $\sigma_\infty^{(1)}(P_x')$ over the interval (ξ, ∞) and equal to $-\sigma_\infty^{(1)}(P_x')$ over the interval $(-\infty, \xi)$. While this situation may be physically difficult to realize, there is no mathematical objection to it. This simple artifice holds the key to the useful formulation of the excess charge problem, as will be shown in the following.

To evaluate the integral in (2), note that the charge distribution resulting from (1) is of the form given by

$$\sigma_\infty(y') = \frac{1}{\sqrt{1-y'^2}} \sum_{i=1}^{k} a_i f_i(y') \tag{6}$$

where

$$f_j(y') = \begin{cases} \prod_{i=1}^{j-1}\left[\left(\dfrac{i}{j-1}\right) - y'^2\right], & j > 1 \\ 1, & j = 1. \end{cases} \tag{7}$$

Note that the Green's function in (4) has a singularity at $y=y'$, while the ratio

$$r_\xi(y; y') = \frac{G_\xi(x, y; y')}{\log \dfrac{|y-y'|}{|y-y'|+1}} \tag{8}$$

is no longer singular. Substituting into the integration to be

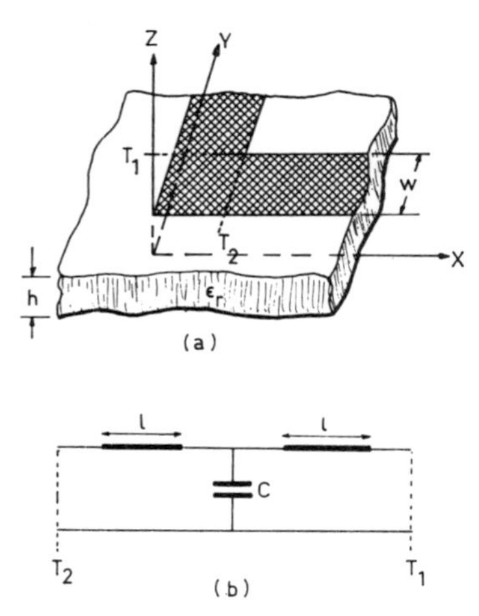

Fig. 1. Microstrip right-angle bend together with equivalent circuit proposed by Stephenson and Easter [13].

performed in (2)

$$\phi_\xi^{(1)}(x, y) = \sum_{i=1}^{k} a_i \int_{-1}^{1} \frac{\log \dfrac{|y-y'|}{|y-y'|+1}}{\sqrt{1-y'^2}} f_i(y') r_\xi(y; y')\, dy'. \quad (9)$$

In this integrand $f_i(y')r_\xi(y; y')$ is nonsingular over the interval $y' \in [-1, 1]$; all the singularities are incorporated in the weight function $\log [|y-y'|/(|y-y'|+1)]/\sqrt{1-y'^2}$. Gaussian quadrature formulas with this weight can be developed for each y. This work is confined to microstrips assumed to be of zero thickness.

Microstrip Right-Angle Bends

For the case of a microstrip right-angle bend, the only data available appear to be the experimental results of Stephenson and Easter [13]. Their equivalent circuit includes a shunt capacitance to account for charge accumulation at the corner, and series lengths of transmission lines on either side to account for the increase in current path length around the corner. This circuit, together with the reference planes used, is shown in Fig. 1. Stephenson and Easter devised two types of resonant measurements: 1) two 90° corners incorporated into a closed-ring resonator; 2) a right-angle bend in a symmetrical open-ended resonator. At various frequencies, voltage maxima or minima occur at the corners, and the two unknowns in the model can be evaluated.

The excess charges which constitute C_{bend} are due to the potential residual, when two microstrip-type charge distributions that exist on the arms of a right-angle bend up to terminal planes T_1 and T_2, as shown in Fig. 1.

Let $\frac{1}{2}\phi_\infty(P_x)$ be the potential corresponding to an infinite microstrip-like charge distribution of $\frac{1}{2}\sigma_\infty(P_x')$ parallel to the x axis. Also let $\frac{1}{2}\phi_{1.0}(P_x)$ represent the potential corresponding to a microstrip-like charge distribution with a polarity reversal at $x=1.0$. Therefore, the potential corresponding to a microstrip-like charge on the interval $x \in (1, \infty)$ is, by superposition, $\frac{1}{2}[\phi_\infty(P_x)+\phi_{1.0}(P_x)]$. Similarly, in the y direction, the potential corresponding to a microstrip-like charge on the interval $y \in (1, \infty)$ is $\frac{1}{2}[\phi_\infty(P_y)+\phi_{1.0}(P_y)]$. By superposition one can generate microstrip-like distributions parallel to the positive x and y axes up to terminal planes T_1 and T_2. Therefore, the potential residual required is

$$\phi_x^{\text{bend}}(P) = \phi_\infty - \tfrac{1}{2}[\phi_\infty(P_x) + \phi_{1.0}(P_x) + \phi_\infty(P_y) + \phi_{1.0}(P_y)] \quad (10)$$

while the governing integral equation for the excess charge is

$$\phi_x^{\text{bend}}(P) = \int \sigma_x^{\text{bend}}(P') G^{\text{bend}}(P; P')\, dP'. \quad (11)$$

Although the indicated integration is over the entire bend including the semi-infinite arms, both potential residual and excess charge fall to zero on moving away from the discontinuity region.

The Green's function can be shown, in a manner analogous to that used for the rectangular plates separated by a dielectric sheet [14], to be

$$G^{\text{bend}}(x, y; x', y') = \frac{1}{2\pi(\epsilon_0+\epsilon_1)}\left[f(0) - (1-K)\sum_{n=1}^{\infty} K^{n-1} f(n)\right] \quad (12)$$

where

$$f^{\text{bend}}(n) = \left[(2n)^2 + \left(\frac{x-x'}{h}\right)^2 + \left(\frac{y-y'}{h}\right)^2\right]^{-1/2} \quad (13)$$

and the bend capacitance is calculated from

$$C_{\text{bend}} = \int \sigma_x^{\text{bend}}(P')\, dP'. \quad (14)$$

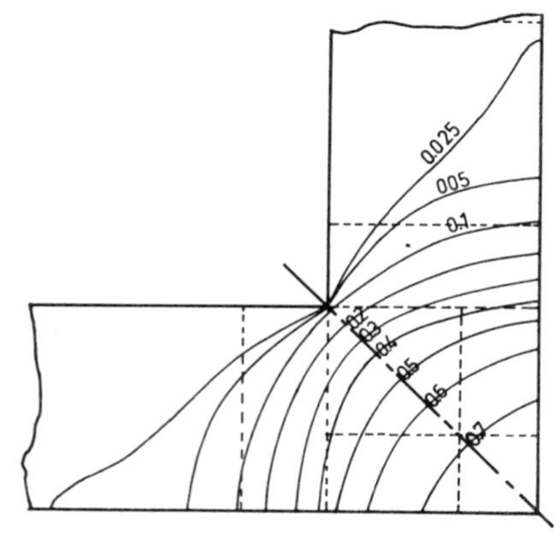

Fig. 2. Potential residual near a microstrip right-angle bend ($w_1/h=1.0$ and $\epsilon_r=1.0$).

A typical residual voltage for dielectric substrate of $\epsilon_r=1.0$ and microstrip width-to-height ratio $w/h=1$ is shown in Fig. 2. Not shown in this figure is that by moving further away from the discontinuity, some small amount of negative potential residual appears and then it dies down to zero. This is due to the interaction between the two normal microstrip-like distributions and is most noticeable for small ϵ_r and w/h. Numerical experiments indicate that the most significant part of the excess charge is located near the outer edge of the corner region. Thus, the typical discretization used is also shown in Fig. 2. Although the symmetry about the 45° angle is not accounted for in (13), the discretization of the region is done so

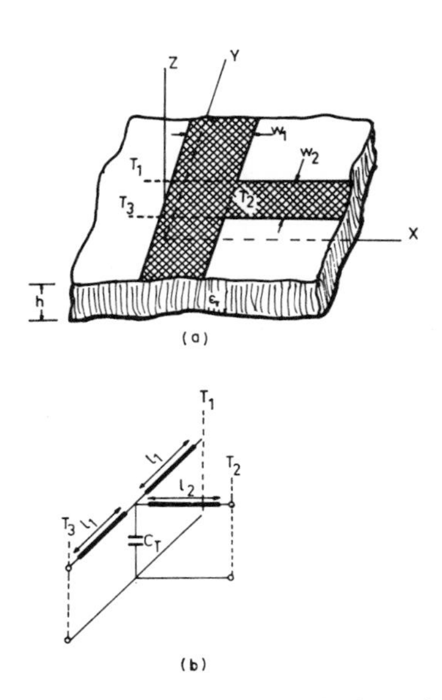

Fig. 3. Microstrip T junction together with its equivalent circuit.

that full advantage may be taken of this symmetry during computation.

Microstrip T Junctions

In the case of microstrip T junctions, five sources of data were located. Stinehelfer [1] and Troughton [2] presented experimental results. They both performed transmission loss measurements on microstrip T structures to determine the electrical length of a stub; comparing this with the physical length, the "electrical defining plane" [2] for the stub can be determined. Stinehelfer presented results obtained using quarter-wavelength-long short-circuited stubs, while Troughton used quarter- and three-quarter-wavelength-long open-circuited stubs. Both investigators indicated that a correction to the separation between two stubs is also required.

On the theoretical side, Leighton and Milnes [15], as well as Wolff, Kompa, and Mehran [11], [12], used a parallel-plate waveguide approximation valid over a restricted range of parameters, with magnetic walls on the sides. Leighton and Milnes then used a Babinet equivalent of this model to obtain a new model with a T junction equivalent circuit previously determined by Marcuvitz [16]. Wolff, Kompa, and Mehran, on the other hand, matched wave components at the discontinuity planes and were able to obtain scattering coefficients for the T junction.

The simplest equivalent circuit for the T junction is an outcropping of the work of experimentalists. The microstrip T junction, together with this model, is shown in Fig. 3. The lengths of transmission lines are used to correct for the electrical defining planes of the stub and main lines, while the shunt capacitor accounts for the charge surplus or deficiency at the junction.

The potential residual, causing a charge surplus or deficiency at the T junction, is that due to three microstrip-like charge distributions on the arms of the T structure, up to the terminal planes T_1, T_2, and T_3, shown in Fig. 3(a). To evaluate this potential residual, take a microstrip-like charge distribution $\frac{1}{2}\sigma_\infty^{(2)}(P_x')$, of width-to-height ratio (w_2/h), parallel to the x axis, with corresponding potential $\frac{1}{2}\phi_\infty^{(2)}(P_x)$, given by (1). Take another microstrip-like charge distribution $\frac{1}{2}\sigma_\infty^{(2)}(P_x')$, having a polarity reversal at $x=w_1$, with the corresponding potential $\frac{1}{2}\phi w_1^{(2)}(P_x)$, given by (2). The superposition of these two distributions yields a microstrip-like charge of width-to-height ratio (w_2/h) on the interval $x\in[w_1, \infty]$ and a corresponding potential of $\frac{1}{2}[\phi_\infty^{(2)}(P_x)+\phi_{w_1}^{(2)}(P_x)]$. Similarly, in the y direction, an infinite microstrip-like charge distribution $\sigma_\infty^{(1)}(P_x')$ together with charge distributions $\frac{1}{2}\sigma_\infty^{(1)}(P_y')$ with polarity reversals at $y=1.0$ and -1.0 are required. The respective potentials, by (1) and (2), are $\phi_\infty^{(1)}(P_y)$, $\frac{1}{2}\phi_{1.0}^{(1)}(P_y)$, and $\frac{1}{2}\phi_{-1.0}^{(1)}(P_y)$. The superposition of these three yields a microstrip-like distribution on the two intervals $|y|>1.0$, with corresponding potential $\{\phi_\infty^{(1)}(P_y)+\frac{1}{2}[\phi_{1.0}^{(1)}(P_y)-\phi_{-1.0}^{(1)}(P_y)]\}$.

Now, superposing the two resulting distributions, microstrip-like charges are generated on the arms of the T structure up to the terminal planes T_1, T_2, and T_3. Therefore, the potential residual, in this case, is

$$\phi_x^T(P) = \phi_\infty - \{\tfrac{1}{2}[\phi_\infty^{(2)}(P_x) + \phi_{w_1}^{(2)}(P_x)] + \phi_\infty^{(1)}(P_y) + \tfrac{1}{2}[\phi_{1.0}^{(1)}(P_y) - \phi_{-1.0}^{(1)}(P_y)]\} \quad (15)$$

while the integral equation governing the excess charge is

$$\phi_x^T(P) = \int \sigma_x^T(P')G^T(P; P')\,dP'. \quad (16)$$

In (16) both the potential residual and the excess charge fall to zero moving away from the discontinuity, so that integration over finite regions suffices.

The Green's function $G^T(P; P')$ is the same as $G^{\text{bend}}(P; P')$ given by (12); however

$$f^T(n) = \left[(2n)^2 + \left(\frac{x-x'}{h}\right)^2 + \left(\frac{y-y'}{h}\right)^2\right]^{-1/2} + \left[(2n)^2 + \left(\frac{x-x'}{h}\right)^2 + \left(\frac{y+y'}{h}\right)^2\right]^{-1/2} \quad (17)$$

and the T junction capacitance is given by

$$C_T = \int \sigma_x^T(P')\,dP'. \quad (18)$$

The potential residual on a dielectric substrate of $\epsilon_r=9.9$, with main line $(w_1/h)=1.0$ and stub line $(w_2/h)=1.0$ is shown in Fig. 4. In this case regions of negative residuals are much more pronounced than for the right-angle bend. A typical discretization of the region is also shown in Fig. 4.

Microstrip Crossings

For microstrip crossings, it appears that the only published source of data is that obtained experimentally by Stinehelfer [1]. He performed transmission loss measurements, as in the case of T junctions, on a pair of quarter-wavelength short-circuited stubs placed back to back, so as to determine the electrical lengths of the stubs. Similarly, a correction to the physical distance between a pair of crossings was noted.

The circuit model shown in Fig. 5(b) for the crossing shown in Fig. 5(a) was arrived at as a consequence of the results obtained in the above experiments The lengths of transmission lines correct for the electrical lengths of the stubs and their electrical spacing from various other discontinuities. The shunt capacitor C_+ takes care of the charge surplus or deficiency near the crossing.

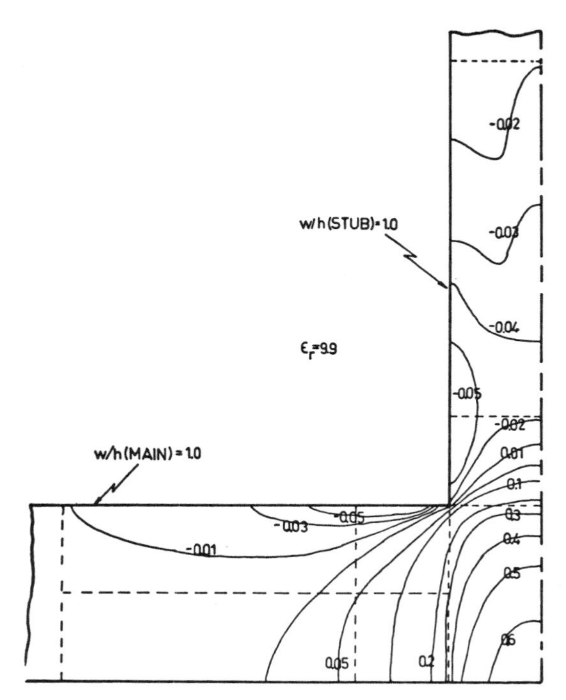

Fig. 4. Potential residual near a microstrip T junction ($w_1/h=1.0$, $w_2/h=1.0$, and $\epsilon_r=9.9$).

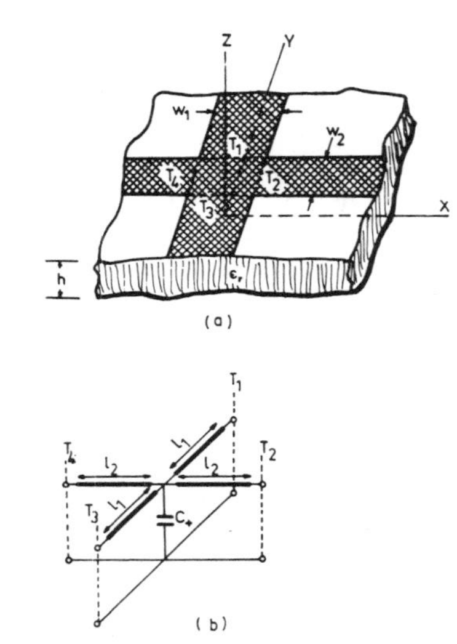

Fig. 5. Microstrip crossing together with its equivalent circuit.

As in earlier discontinuities, the potential residual sought is obtained from the potential due to microstrip-like charge distributions of the four arms of the crossing, up to the reference planes T_1, T_2, T_3, and T_4.

To obtain such a distribution, an infinite microstrip-like charge $\sigma_\infty^{(2)}(P_x')$ of width-to-height ratio (w_2/h) is required. Also needed are two charge distributions $\frac{1}{2}\sigma_\infty^{(2)}(P_x')$ with polarity reversals at $x=w_1/2$ and $-w_1/2$. The corresponding potential distributions, given by (1) and (2) are $\phi_\infty^{(2)}(P_x)$, $\phi_{w_1/2}^{(2)}(P_x)$, and $\phi_{-w_1/2}^{(2)}(P_x)$, respectively. By superposition, microstrip-like charge densities of (w_2/h) are obtained on the two intervals $|x|>w_1/2$, and the resulting potential is

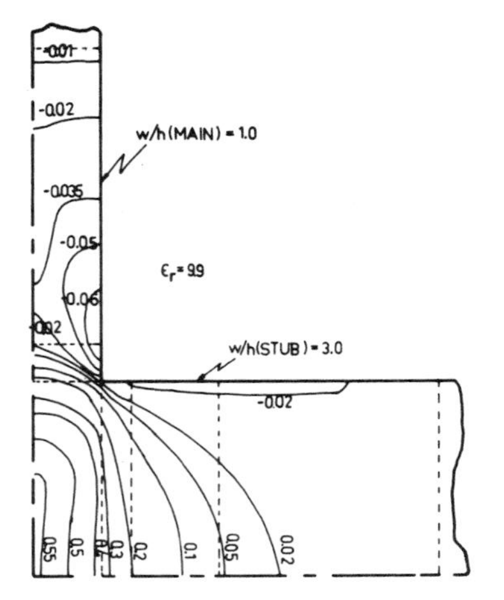

Fig. 6. Potential residual near a microstrip crossing ($w_1/h=3$, $w_2/h=1$, and $\epsilon_r=9.9$).

$\{\phi_\infty^{(2)}(P_x)+\frac{1}{2}[\phi_{w_1/2}^{(2)}(P_x)-\phi_{-w_1/2}^{(2)}(P_x)]\}$. Similarly, the potential corresponding to microstrip-like charge distribution $\sigma_\infty^{(1)}(P_y')$ of width-to-height ratio (w_1/h) on the intervals $|y|>1.0$ is $\{\phi_\infty^{(1)}(P_y)+\frac{1}{2}[\phi_{1.0}^{(1)}(P_y)-\phi_{-1.0}^{(1)}(P_y)]\}$.

By superposition of these two resultant distributions, microstrip-like charge densities of appropriate width-to-height ratios are generated, on the arms of the crossing, up to the four terminal planes. Therefore, the potential residual sought is

$$\phi_x^+(P)=\phi_\infty-\{\phi_\infty^{(1)}(P_y)+\tfrac{1}{2}[\phi_{1.0}^{(1)}(P_y)-\phi_{-1.0}^{(1)}(P_y)] +\phi_\infty^{(2)}(P_x)+\tfrac{1}{2}[\phi_{w_1/2}^{(2)}(P_x)-\phi_{-w_1/2}^{(2)}(P_x)]\} \quad (19)$$

and the integral equation governing the excess charge is

$$\phi_x^+(P) = \int \sigma_x^+(P')G^+(P;P')\,dP'. \quad (20)$$

As in earlier instances, integration over a finite region is sufficient, since both potential residual and charge-density distribution go to zero on moving away from the discontinuity.

The Green's function given by (12) is also valid for $G^+(P;P')$ with

$$f^+(n) = \left[(2n)^2+\left(\frac{x-x'}{h}\right)^2+\left(\frac{y-y'}{h}\right)^2\right]^{-1/2} +\left[(2n)^2+\left(\frac{x-x'}{h}\right)^2+\left(\frac{y+y'}{h}\right)^2\right]^{-1/2} +\left[(2n)^2+\left(\frac{x+x'}{h}\right)^2+\left(\frac{y-y'}{h}\right)^2\right]^{-1/2} +\left[(2n)^2+\left(\frac{x+x'}{h}\right)^2+\left(\frac{y+y'}{h}\right)^2\right]^{-1/2} \quad (21)$$

while the crossing capacitance is given by

$$C_+ = \int \sigma_x^+(P')\,dP'. \quad (22)$$

In Fig. 6 the potential residual for a stub of $(w_1/h)=3$ and main line of $(w_2/h)=1$, on a substrate of relative dielectric

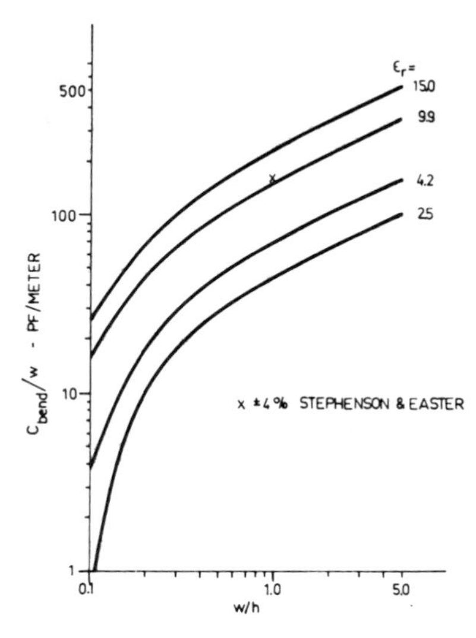

Fig. 7. Microstrip bend capacitances normalized to strip width as a function of width-to-height ratio and substrate permittivity.

constant $\epsilon_r = 9.9$, is shown. Also shown in the figure is a typical discretization of the region.

Results and Comparison with Existing Data

The bend capacitances obtained by Stephenson and Easter [13] by means of their two resonant measurements agree with each other in order of magnitude only. However, the two types of measurements, both 90° bends and chamfered corners for a 50-Ω microstrip line on alumina substrate, indicate that the lengths of transmission line in the model of Fig. 1 are negligible.

For various sound reasons, Stephenson and Easter conclude that the result obtained via the right-angle bend in a symmetrical open-ended resonator is the better of the two. Error limits are also indicated. Their measurement, at 10 GHz on 0.5-mm Lucalox with a strip width corresponding to approximately 50-Ω characteristic impedance, is shown in Fig. 7 together with their indicated error limits.

Also shown in Fig. 7 are bend capacitances, calculated by this method, normalized with respect to strip width for various commonly used substrates. As expected, the calculated values are lower than those obtained experimentally. Nevertheless, the close agreement between the results is an indication of the accuracy of the method. Typical computation time on an IBM S360/75 is 50 s for $\epsilon_r = 1.0$ and 110 s for $\epsilon_r = 9.9$.

Stinehelfer's [1] measurements, on quarter-wavelength-long short-circuited stubs, indicate that the electrical length of the stubs is shorter than the physical length, while Troughton's measurements, on quarter- and three-quarter-wavelength open-circuited stubs, indicate that the electrical length of the stub is longer than the physical length. Troughton also indicates that "if the stub is $\lambda/4$ and $3\,\lambda/4$, Δl (the correction to the physical length) is consistent, but differs from the value found from a half-wavelength stub." In addition to the specific problems in each measurement (such as accurate end-effect correction in Troughton's case, difficulty of determining the exact frequency at which total transmission occurs in Stinehelfer's case, and accurate phase velocity in both cases), part of the discrepancy is resolved considering the model given in

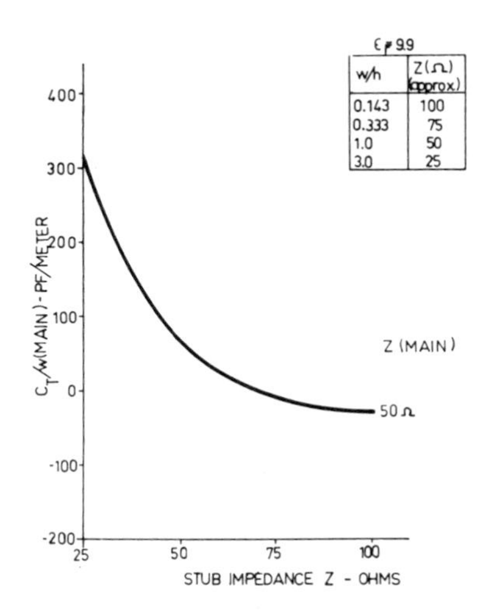

Fig. 8. Microstrip T junction capacitances, normalized to main-line width, as a function of stub-line impedance.

Fig. 3(b). If L denotes the physical length of the stub, in Troughton's case already corrected for the end effect, then Troughton measured the frequency at which $(l_2+L)=\lambda/4$, while Stinehelfer measured the conditions under which cot $[2\pi(l_2+L)/\lambda]=\omega C_T Z$. As a matter of fact, in principle, performing measurements on open- and short-circuited quarter-wavelength stubs, it would be possible to determine both l_2 and C_T. This, however, may be frustrated by the difficulties already enumerated.

The theoretical results of Leighton and Milnes [15] on the approximate model of the microstrip line, are valid over a restricted range of parameters. Since both the model and the reference planes used here are totally different, no comparison was made with their data.

The approximate theoretical results of Wolff, Kompa, and Mehran [11], [12] are in terms of magnitudes of scattering coefficients of the T junction. The data given are for polyguide substrate, relative dielectric constant of $\epsilon_r = 2.33$, and they show very pronounced frequency dependence, especially above 5 GHz. This, at first sight, cannot be explained in terms of the capacitor C_T obtained here. A quick calculation, however, will indicate that at 5 GHz for $\epsilon_r = 2.33$ the wavelength is about 40 mm, while the typical dimensions required for the characteristic impedances utilized range from 4.5 to about 10 mm. For such structures the excess charges occupy a significant fraction of the wavelength, so that the electrostatic approximation is not valid. This argument is further substantiated by their note to the effect that the frequency dependence is small for alumina substrate ($\epsilon_r = 9.9$), where realistic impedances are obtained for smaller width-to-height ratios and the commonly available substrate thicknesses are 0.020 and 0.025 in.

Fig. 8 shows the capacitance C_T normalized to main-line width plotted against stub-line impedance. The behavior of C_T, in that it varies from positive to negative depending whether there is charge deficiency or charge surplus, is similar to that observed experimentally by Matthaei, Young, and Jones [17] in stripline. Due to the variation of the sign of the potential residual, generally speaking, the capacitances thus obtained are expected to have somewhat larger errors than, for example, in the open-circuit case, where the potential

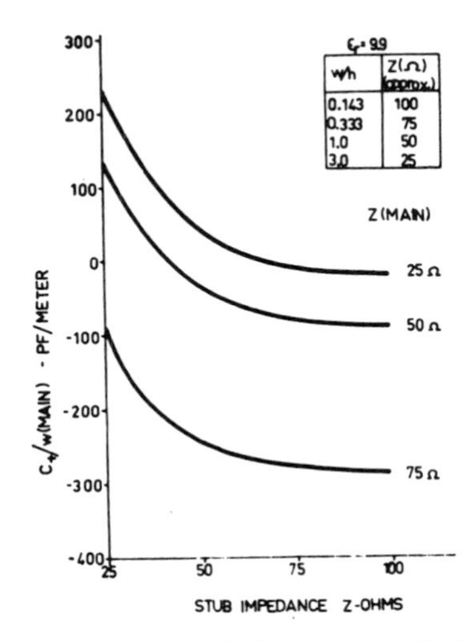

Fig. 9. Microstrip crossing capacitances, normalized to main-line width, as a function of stub-line impedance.

residual is of uniform sign. The central processing unit (CPU) time required on an IBM S360/75 to evaluate C_T on a dielectric substrate of $\epsilon_r = 9.9$ is 3.6 min.

The results given by Stinehelfer [1], done on two short-circuited quarter-wavelength-long stubs back to back, indicate that the electrical length of the stubs is shorter than the physical length. However, arguing as for the T junction, the model given in Fig. 5(b) would indicate that such a measurement in effect determines the frequency at which 2 cot $[2\pi(l_2+L)]/\lambda = \omega C_+ Z$. L is the physical length of the stub. Another transmission loss measurement, on quarter-wavelength-long open-circuited stubs, would give the frequency at which $(l_2+L) = \lambda/4$. In principle, l_2 and C_+ may be determined from two such measurements. The difficulties with such an experimental approach were outlined in [1, sec. 5.7.4]. Using the results given by Stinehelfer, no estimate of C_+ can be made. There appear to be no other data available for comparison.

In the computer program the computational details for the stub and main line are somewhat different. Therefore, interchanging the width-to-height ratios of the stub and main line left C_+ unchanged. This, in a small measure, provided a check on the program details.

Fig. 9 shows crossing capacitance values C_+ normalized to main-line width for various main-line impedances, plotted against stub-line impedance. The stub characteristic impedances range from 25 to 100 Ω. The substrate dielectric constant used is $\epsilon_r = 9.9$. As in the case of T junctions, due to the variation in the sign of the potential residual, generally speaking the errors in capacitance values can be expected to be larger than in those cases where the potential residual is of uniform sign. The computation time required on an IBM S360/75, for C_+ on a relative dielectric constant $\epsilon_r = 9.9$ is about 3.7 min.

Conclusions

Extensive microstrip discontinuity capacitance values are presented. In the case of microstrip right-angle bends the only available experimental result is in close agreement with the calculations. It is hoped that more experimental results will become available in the future.

The methodology utilized can be extended to analyze the electrostatic capacitive effect of virtually any microstrip discontinuity.

References

[1] H. E. Stinehelfer, Sr., "Microstrip circuit design," Tech. Rep. AFAL-TR-69-10, AD 848 947, Feb. 1969.

[2] P. Troughton, "Design of complex microstrip circuits by measurements and computer modeling," *Proc. Inst. Elec. Eng.*, vol. 118, no. 3/4, pp. 469–474, Mar./Apr. 1971.

[3] L. S. Napoli and J. J. Hughes, "Foreshortening of microstrip open circuits on alumina substrates," *IEEE Trans. Microwave Theory Tech.* (Corresp.), vol. MTT-19, pp. 559–561, June 1971.

[4] A. Farrar and A. T. Adams, "Computation of lumped microstrip capacities by matrix methods—Rectangular sections and end effect," *IEEE Trans. Microwave Theory Tech.* (Corresp.), vol. MTT-19, pp. 495–497, May 1971.

[5] ——, "Correction to 'Computation of lumped microstrip capacities by matrix method—Rectangular sections and end effect,' " *IEEE Trans. Microwave Theory Tech.* (Lett.), vol. MTT-20, p. 294, Apr. 1972.

[6] D. S. James and S. H. Tse, "Microstrip end effects," *Electron. Lett.*, pp. 46–47, Jan. 22, 1972.

[7] P. Silvester and P. Benedek, "Equivalent capacitances for microstrip open circuits," *IEEE Trans. Microwave Theory Tech.*, vol. MTT-20, pp. 511–516, Aug. 1972.

[8] M. Maeda, "An analysis of gap in microstrip transmission lines," *IEEE Trans. Microwave Theory Tech.*, vol. MTT-20, pp. 390–396, June 1972.

[9] A. Farrar and A. T. Adams, "Matrix methods for microstrip three-dimensional problems," *IEEE Trans. Microwave Theory Tech.*, vol. MTT-20, pp. 497–504, Aug. 1972.

[10] P. Benedek and P. Silvester, "Equivalent capacitances for microstrip gaps and steps," *IEEE Trans. Microwave Theory Tech.*, vol. MTT-20, pp. 729–733, Nov. 1972.

[11] I. Wolff, G. Kompa, and R. Mehran, "Calculation method for microstrip discontinuities and T-junctions," *Electron. Lett.*, vol. 8, no. 7, pp. 177–179, Apr. 6, 1972.

[12] ——, "Sreifenleitungsdiskontinuitaten und-Verzweigungen," *Nachrichtentech. Z.*, vol. 25, no. 5, pp. 217–264, May 1972.

[13] I. M. Stephenson and B. Easter, "Resonant techniques for establishing the equivalent circuits of small discontinuities in microstrip," *Electron. Lett.*, vol. 7, no. 19, pp. 582–584, Sept. 23, 1971.

[14] P. Benedek and P. Silvester, "Capacitance of parallel rectangular plates separated by a dielectric sheet," *IEEE Trans. Microwave Theory Tech.*, vol. MTT-20, pp. 504–510, Aug. 1972.

[15] W. H. Leighton, Jr., and A. G. Milnes, "Junction reactance and dimensional tolerance effects on *X*-band 3-dB directional couplers," *IEEE Trans. Microwave Theory Tech.*, vol. MTT-19, pp. 818–824, Oct. 1971.

[16] N. Marcuvitz, Ed., *Waveguide Handbook*. New York: Dover, 1965.

[17] G. L. Matthaei, L. Young, and E. M. T. Jones, *Microwave Filters Impedance—Matching Networks and Coupling Structures.* New York: McGraw-Hill, 1964

CALCULATION METHOD FOR MICROSTRIP DISCONTINUITIES AND T JUNCTIONS

Indexing terms: Stripline components, Waveguide junctions, Modelling

A method for calculating microstrip discontinuities and T junctions is described, and a waveguide model for the microstrip line is defined. With the help of this model and the use of an orthogonal series expansion, a solution of the above problems is found. Numerical results for the scattering matrices of both the discontinuities and the junctions are given.

Calculation methods for stripline discontinuities and junctions have been described by Oliner,[1] Altschuler and Oliner,[2] Franco and Oliner[3] and Campell,[4] using Babinet's principle and the well known solutions for equivalent problems given by Marcuvitz.[5] Leighton and Milnes[6] published a method for calculating T junctions in microstrip techniques, expanding the theory given by Altschuler and Oliner[2] to the case of the microstrip problem.

As is known, there are well tested methods for calculating discontinuities and junctions in the waveguide techniques. These methods use orthogonal-series expansions of the fields in the waveguide (e.g. see References 7–11). A necessary condition for applying orthogonal-series-expansion methods is that a complete set of field solutions for the problem considered must be known. A further condition should be that

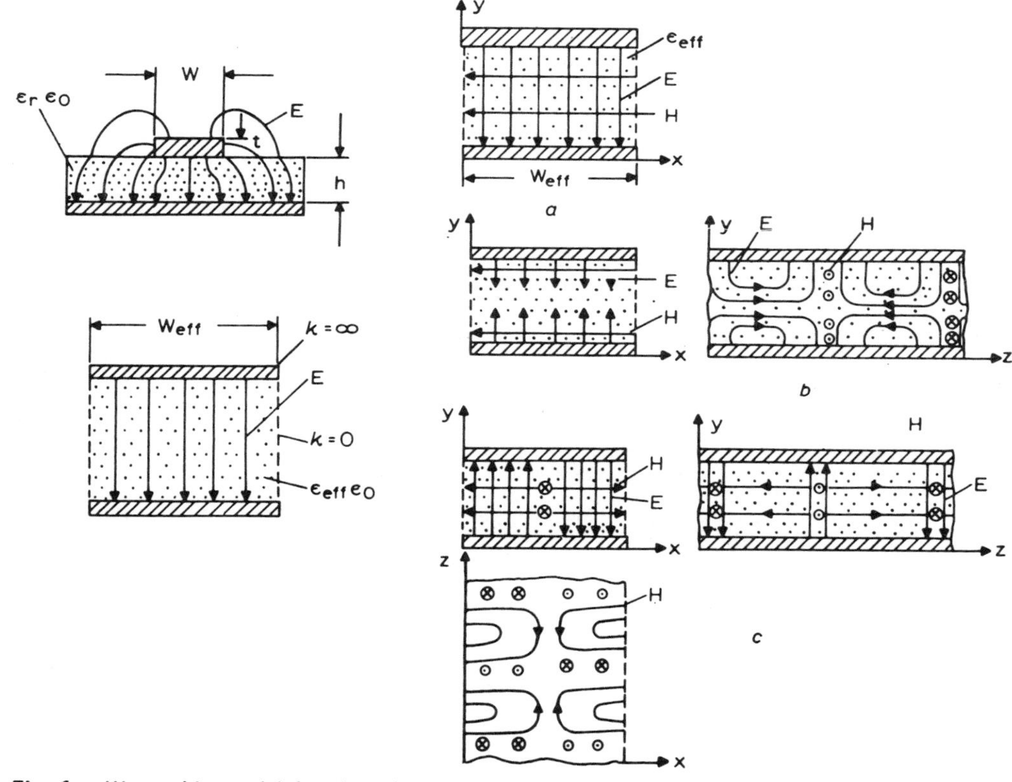

Fig. 1 *Waveguide model for the microstrip line and field distribution of the lowest-order modes of the model*

$W_{eff} = f(w, h, t)$
$\epsilon_{eff} = g(w, h, t, \epsilon_r)$
a TEM mode
b E_{10} mode
c H_{10} mode

the solutions are orthogonal. As is well known, no complete set of solutions for the field problem of the microstrip line has yet been published.

For this reason, we took the waveguide model given by Wheeler[12, 13] for the lowest-order mode, which, to a first approximation, is a TEM mode. Wheeler showed that the behaviour of the TEM mode on the microstrip line can be described by a parallel-plate waveguide of width W_{eff} and relative permittivity ε_{eff}:

$$\left.\begin{aligned} w_{eff} &= \frac{h}{Z_w}\sqrt{\left(\frac{\mu_0}{\varepsilon_{eff}\,\varepsilon_0}\right)} \\ \varepsilon_{eff} &= \left(\frac{\lambda_0}{\lambda_g}\right)^2 \end{aligned}\right\} \quad \ldots\ldots (1)$$

where Z_w is the characteristic impedance defined by Wheeler[12] and λ_g is the wavelength on the microstrip line. Leighton and

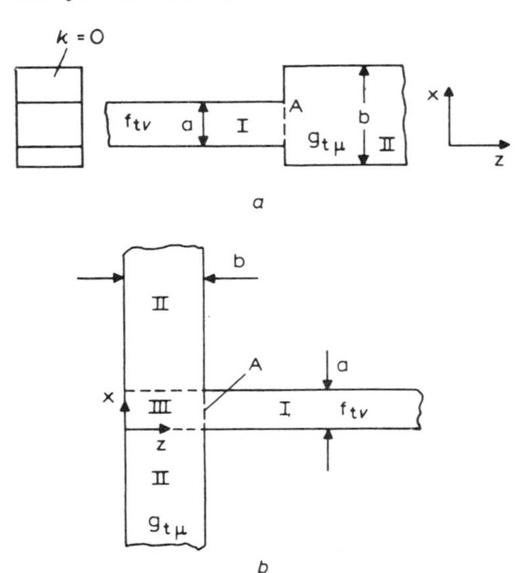

Fig. 2 *Discontinuity and T junction in microstrip technique*
a Discontinuity
b *T* junction

Milnes[6] also use this waveguide model, but they apply Babinet's principle to make use of a solved problem for an equivalent T junction.[5] In contrast to all solutions of the above problem that have been published, we make direct use of the waveguide model of the microstrip line described above to compute the energy stored in the discontinuities and T junctions. This is done by making the assumption that the higher-order modes of the above waveguide model describe, to a first approximation, the physical fields on the microstrip line. This assumption may, at first sight, look very arbitrary, but for solving an eigenvalue problem, an arbitrary, infinite and complete set of solutions, which satisfy the boundary conditions, can be taken. Then, if we take the waveguide model for the microstrip line which is exact only for the TEM mode, and take into account the higher-order modes of this model, we shall obtain better results than those obtained by methods which do not consider any higher-order modes on the microstrip line. Fig. 1 shows the waveguide model and the lowest-order modes on this waveguide.

Fig. 2 shows the discontinuity and the T junction which has been calculated. Using the waveguide model described, we can find an orthogonal and complete set of field solutions f_{tv} in the left-hand guide with effective width a (Fig. 2a) and a complete set $g_{t\mu}$ in the waveguide with effective width b. To compute the scattering matrix of the discontinuity, the transversal magnetic-field strength of the left-hand part of the structure is developed into a series expansion of the

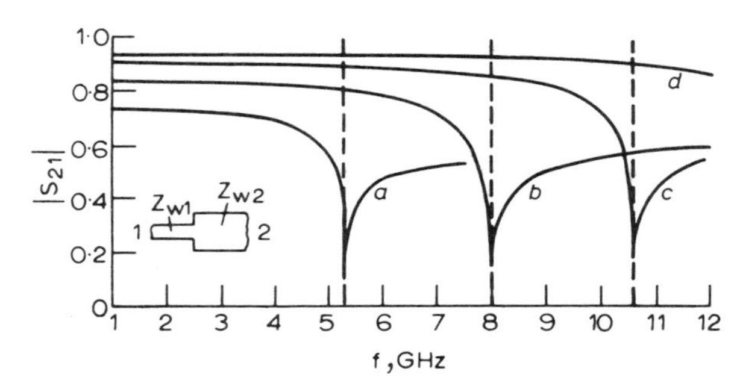

Fig. 3 *Numerical results for the transmission coefficients of a symmetric microstrip discontinuity on a polyguide substrate material ($\varepsilon_r = 2{\cdot}33$, $h = 1{\cdot}5$ mm)*
Change of the characteristic impedance from $Z_{w1} = 50\,\Omega$ to (*a*) $Z_{w2} = 10\,\Omega$, (*b*) $Z_{w2} = 15\,\Omega$, (*c*) $Z_{w2} = 20\,\Omega$ and (*d*) $Z_{w2} = 25\,\Omega$

functions $g_{t\mu}$, and the transversal electric-field strength of the right-hand part is developed into a series expansion of the functions f_{tv}, as follows:

$$\left.\begin{aligned} H_{tI} &= \sum_{\mu=1}^{\infty} \frac{B_\mu}{Z_\mu}(e_z \times g_{t\mu}) \\ E_{tII} &= \sum_{v=1}^{\infty} A_v f_{tv} \end{aligned}\right\} \quad \ldots\ldots\ldots (2)$$

The coefficients A_v and B_μ can be computed so that the boundary conditions in the discontinuity are met. From the amplitudes of the lowest-order TEM mode, the scattering matrix of the discontinuity can be derived. Fig. 3 shows the calculated transmission coefficients for a symmetric discontinuity with the characteristic impedances $Z_{w1} = 50\,\Omega$ and (*a*) $Z_{w2} = 10\,\Omega$, (*b*) $Z_{w2} = 15\Omega$, (*c*) $Z_{w2} = 20\,\Omega$ and (*d*) $Z_{w2} = 25\,\Omega$. The curves are computed for microstrip lines on a polyguide substrate material with a relative permittivity $\varepsilon_r = 2{\cdot}33$ and a height $h = 0{\cdot}625$ mm. As can

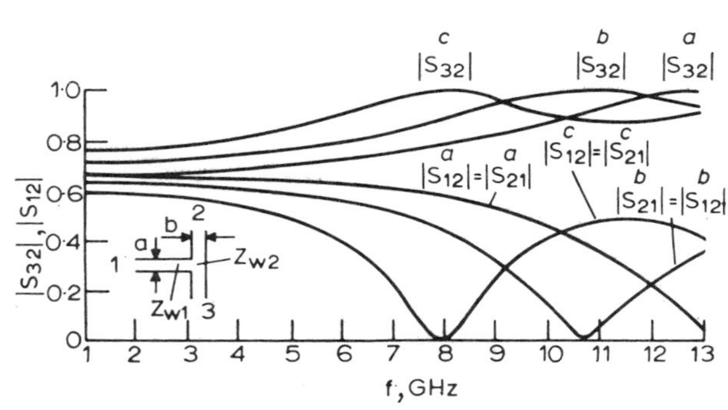

Fig. 4 *Numerical results for transmission coefficients of a microstrip T junction on polyguide substrate material ($\varepsilon_r = 2{\cdot}33$, $h = 1{\cdot}5$ mm)*
$Z_{w1} = 50\,\Omega$
a $Z_{w2} = 50\,\Omega$
b $Z_{w2} = 40\,\Omega$
c $Z_{w2} = 30\,\Omega$

be seen from Fig. 3, the scattering matrix depends strongly on the frequency for those substrate materials, especially if the characteristic impedance Z_{w2} is small. As calculations for aluminium substrate material show, the frequency dependence is negligible at frequencies up to 20 GHz.

If the T junction (Fig. 2*b*) is calculated in the same way, it must be noticed that the field solutions $g_{t\mu}$ of region II do not satisfy the boundary conditions in region III, as has been shown by Lewin[10] for a waveguide problem. Therefore the series expansion which has been used to calculate the discontinuity must be substituted by an integral representation, as shown in References 10 and 11. This means that, for the H_x component of the magnetic-field strength in regions II and III, a relationship

$$H_x = \int_{-\infty}^{+\infty} f(\alpha z) \frac{B}{\beta z_w} \sqrt{\left(\frac{2}{bh}\right)} \sin(\alpha z) dz \quad . \quad . \quad (3)$$

must be used. The function $f(\alpha z)$ can be chosen so that the boundary conditions between region I and region III are satisfied and the tangential magnetic-field strength vanishes on the magnetic walls of region II ($z = 0$, $z = b$). From the amplitudes of the TEM mode in both microstrip lines, the scattering matrix of the T junction can be evaluated. Fig. 4 shows the calculated transmission coefficients of the T junction as functions of the frequency. For the T junction also, the frequency dependence is great if substrate material with a small relative permittivity is used (Fig. 4, $\varepsilon_r = 2{\cdot}33$). The frequency dependence once more is small for aluminium substrate material.

Measurements show that the agreement between our theory and experiments is good. For polyguide substrate material, a large influence of radiation losses on the scattering matrix can be measured. For aluminium substrate material, this influence is small.[6] The radiation loss can be calculated by a first approximation (e.g. see Reference 15), and taken into account in our theory. More detailed results of the theory and the experimental work will be published shortly.[14]

ELECTRONICS LETTERS 6th April 1972 Vol. 8 No. 7

I. WOLFF
G. KOMPA
R. MEHRAN

10th March 1972

Institut für Hochfrequenztechnik
Technische Hochschule Aachen
W. Germany

References

1 OLINER, A. A.: 'Equivalent circuits for discontinuities in balanced strip transmission line', *IRE Trans.*, 1955, **MTT-3,** pp. 134–143
2 ALTSCHULER, H. M., and OLINER, A. A.: 'Discontinuities in the center conductor of symmetric strip transmission line', *ibid.*, 1960, **MTT-8,** pp. 328–338
3 FRANCO, A. G., and OLINER, A. A.: 'Symmetric strip transmission line tee junction', *ibid.*, 1962, **MTT-10,** pp. 118–124
4 CAMPBELL, J. J.: 'Application of the solution of certain boundary value problems to the symmetrical four-port junction and specially truncated bends in parallel-plate waveguides and balanced strip-transmission lines', *IEEE Trans.*, 1968, **MTT-16,** pp. 165–176
5 MARCUVITZ, N.: 'Waveguide handbook' (MIT Radiation Laboratory Series, 1950)
6 LEIGHTON, W. M., and MILNES, G.: 'Junction reactance and dimensional tolerance effects on X-Band 3 dB directional couplers', *IEEE Trans.*, 1971, **MTT-19,** pp. 818–824
7 MASTERMAN, P. H., and CLARRICOATS, P. J. B.: 'Computer field-matching solution of waveguide transverse discontinuities', *Proc. IEE*, 1971, **118,** (1), pp. 51–63
8 KNETSCH, H. D.: 'Beitrag zur Theorie spunghafter Querschnitts-veränderungen von Hohlleitern', *Arch. Elek. Übertrag.*, 1968, **22,** pp. 591–600
9 SHARP, E. D.: 'An exact calculation for a T-junction of rectangular waveguide having arbitrary cross-section', *IEEE Trans.*, 1967, **MTT-15,** pp. 109–116
10 LEWIN, L.: 'On the inadequacy of discrete mode-matching techniques in some waveguide discontintuity problems', *ibid.*, 1970, **MTT-18,** pp. 364–369
11 BRÄCKELMANN, W.: 'Hohlleiterverbindungen für Rechteckhohlleiter', *Nachrichtentech. Z.*, 1970, **23,** pp. 2–7
12 WHEELER, H. A.: 'Transmission-line properties of parallel wide strips by a conformal mapping approximation', *IEEE Trans.*, 1964, **MTT-12,** pp. 280–289
13 WHEELER, H. A.: 'Transmission-line properties of parallel wide strips separated by a dielectric sheet', *ibid.*, 1965, **MTT-13,** pp. 172–185
14 WOLFF, I., KOMPA, G., and MEHRAN, R.: 'Streifenleitungsdiskontinuitäten und-Verzweigungen', *Nachrichtentech. Z.* (to be published)
15 LEWIN, L.: 'Radiation from discontinuities in strip-line', *Proc. IEE*, 1960, **107C,** pp. 163–170

Losses of Microstrip Lines

EDGAR J. DENLINGER, MEMBER, IEEE

Invited Paper

Abstract—**This article summarizes state-of-the-art information on losses of single and coupled microstrip lines. Conductor loss, substrate loss (for pure dielectric or magnetic materials), and radiation loss are considered along with the effect of dispersion. Finally, a rough comparison is made between the losses of microstrip and that of several other types of lines used in microwave integrated circuits.**

NOMENCLATURE

a	Height of ground plane above substrate surface in shielded microstrip.
$\bar{E}_0$	Unperturbed electric field.
$F(\epsilon_{eff})$	Radiation form factor.
f	Frequency.
f_m	Natural resonant frequency of magnetic substrate $= \gamma 4\pi M_s$.
f_c	Cutoff frequency of TE_1 surface wave.
g_r	Radiation conductance.
h	Substrate thickness.
H_{IM}	Separation between substrate surface and ground plane for inverted microstrip line.
H_{TIM}	Separation between strip and bottom of channel for trapped inverted microstrip.
$\bar{H}_0$	Unperturbed magnetic field.
$\lvert H_t \rvert$	Amplitude of magnetic field at conducting surfaces for the lossless case.
$J_z(X)$	Current density distribution on strip.
k_0	Free-space wavenumber.
L	Inductance.
m	Mutual resistive factor.
$4\pi M$	Magnetization.
$4\pi M_s$	Saturation magnetization.
p	Magnetic power factor.
P_r	Radiated power from microstrip discontinuity.
P_t	Total power incident on microstrip discontinuity.
$\underline{P}_d$	Time-averaged power dissipated per-unit-length.
P_F	Time-averaged power flow along line.
q	Filling factor for the dielectric constant.
Q_0	Circuit Q including conductor and substrate losses.
Q_r	Radiation Q.
Q_t	Total Q of resonator.
R	Series skin resistance of transmission line.
R_s	Surface skin resistivity of conductor (ohms/square).
R_{sj}	Surface skin resistivity of wall j.
R_a	Surface roughness.
s	Separation between edges of coupled pair of microstrip lines.
s_{cp}	Separation between edges of strip and coplanar ground plane of coplanar waveguide.
s_{TIM}	Separation between edge of strip and side of channel for trapped inverted microstrip.
t	Strip thickness.
V_0	Velocity of light in free space.
w	Strip width.
Z_0	Characteristic impedance.
α_c	Conductor attenuation constant.
α_d	Dielectric attenuation constant.
α_{ST}	Total substrate attenuation constant.
α_t	Total attenuation constant of line.
α_d^e	Dielectric attenuation constant for even mode.
α_d^o	Dielectric attenuation constant for odd mode.
γ	Gyromagnetic ratio $= 2.8$ MHz/G.
δ	Skin depth of conductor.
$\tan\delta_d$	Loss tangent of dielectric.
$\tan\delta_m$	Magnetic loss tangent.
ϵ	Permittivity $= \epsilon_R \epsilon_0$.
ϵ_R	Relative dielectric constant of substrate.
ϵ_{eff}	Effective dielectric constant of line.
ϵ_0	Permittivity of free space.
ϵ_{eff}^e	Effective dielectric constant of even mode.
ϵ_{eff}^o	Effective dielectric constant for odd mode.
κ	Off-diagonal term of permeability tensor.
λ_0	Free-space wavelength.
λ_g	Guide wavelength along line.
μ_0	Permeability of free space.
μ_R	Relative permeability of substrate.
μ	Diagonal term of permeability tensor.
μ_{eff}	Effective relative permeability of line.
ρ	Spacing between dipoles.
σ	Conductivity.
ω	Angular frequency.
ω_m/ω	Normalized saturation magnetization.

Manuscript received October 30, 1979; revised January 9, 1980.

The author is with the RCA Laboratories, David Sarnoff Research Center, Princeton, NJ 08540.

I. INTRODUCTION

MICROSTRIP transmission lines have had widespread use in microwave integrated circuits. The forms of single and coupled lines, shown in Fig. 1, are used for a great variety of functions. For performing accurate circuit design, it is necessary to have adequate knowledge of the phase velocity, impedance, and losses of the line. A great deal has been written on the first two

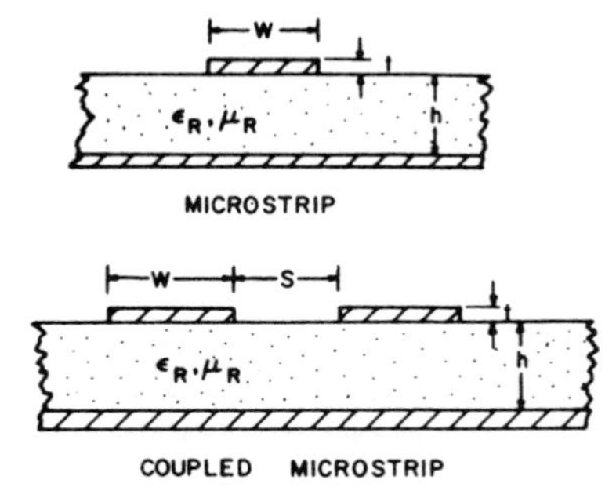

Fig. 1. Single and coupled microstrip lines.

subjects, both of which are usually covered together because they are closely interrelated. However, microstrip losses have usually been treated separately in terms of either conductor and dielectric loss, magnetic loss, or radiation loss. The purpose of this paper is to bring together all that is available on this important subject and thus provide the circuit designer with an improved overall picture of the various losses that should be considered. For completeness, there is also a need to consider the dispersive behavior of microstrip in order to avoid coupling of energy to surface waves and higher order modes, and to accurately calculate losses (especially when using magnetic substrates as well as thick, high dielectric constant substrates which are highly dispersive). Finally, a rough comparison of losses in microstrip to those in other commonly used transmission lines such as coplanar line, slotline, inverted and trapped inverted microstrip, suspended substrate, and stripline-like microstrip will be made.

II. Conductor and Substrate Losses of Single Microstrip

The loss components of a single microstrip line (neglecting radiation) include dielectric loss, conductor loss, and for the case of a magnetic substrate, magnetic loss. For dielectric losses in a nonmagnetized mixed dielectric system, Welch and Pratt [1] followed the approach of Wheeler [2] in determining the filling factor q for the dielectric constant. They derived a corresponding filling factor for the loss tangent $\tan\delta_d$ and obtained the following results for the case when the upper dielectric is air (assumed lossless):

$$\alpha_d = 27.3 \frac{q\epsilon_R}{\epsilon_{\text{eff}}} \frac{\tan\delta_d}{\lambda_g} \text{dB/unit length} \tag{1}$$

where ϵ_R is the substrate dielectric constant and

$$\epsilon_{\text{eff}} = 1 + q(\epsilon_R - 1)$$
$$= \text{microstrip's effective dielectric constant.}$$

The filling factor for the loss tangent $q\epsilon_R/\sqrt{\epsilon_{\text{eff}}}$ is a function of ϵ_R and w/h and is an approximation based on the assumption that the air–dielectric interface is parallel to an electric field line. The correct equation for the filling factor derived by Schneider, Glance, and Bodtmann [3] is equal to the ratio r of stored electric field energy to the total field energy in microstrip

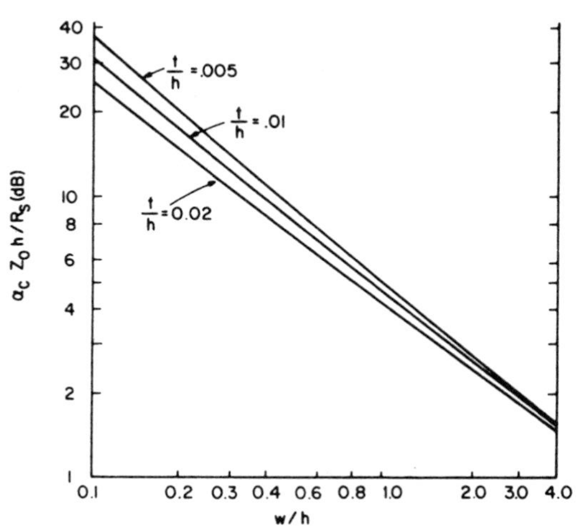

Fig. 2. Theoretical conductor attenuation factor of microstrip as a function of w/h (Pucel *et al.* [4]).

$$r = \frac{\epsilon_R}{\epsilon_{\text{eff}}} \frac{\partial \epsilon_{\text{eff}}}{\partial \epsilon_R}. \tag{2}$$

However, (1) is reasonably accurate since the dielectric –air interface is parallel to the electric field at both corners of the strip conductor where field intensities reach their maximum value.

Conductor loss was first analyzed by Pucel *et al.* [4] and more recently by Wheeler [5]. Both papers derived expressions for the series skin resistance in terms of the incremental inductance associated with the penetration of magnetic flux into the conducting surfaces. From Wheeler's incremental inductance rule [6], the series skin resistance is

$$R = \frac{1}{\mu_0} \sum_j R_{sj} \frac{\partial L}{\partial n_j} \tag{3}$$

where $\partial L/\partial n_j$ is the derivative of the inductance L with respect to the incremental recession of wall j; R_{sj} is the surface skin resistivity of wall j;

$$L = \mu_0 \epsilon_0 Z_0 \left(\frac{w + \Delta w(w,t)}{h}, \frac{t}{h}, \epsilon_R \right)$$

as derived by Wheeler [2]. The conductor attenuation constant is given by

$$\alpha_c = \frac{R}{2Z_0}. \tag{4}$$

Fig. 2 shows a plot from Pucel *et al.* of the conductor attenuation factor $\alpha_c Z_0 h/R_s$ as a function of w/h and t/h. Wheeler's recent theory [5] uses a more accurate correction for strip thickness than used in Pucel's calculations and also treated the case of square and circular conductor cross sections. Fig. 3 shows a plot of the magnetic power factor p normalized to the value δ/h (the value for a very wide strip) as a function of w/h and t/h. The two lower curves are for square and circular cross-sections. δ is the skin depth of the conductor. The conductor attenuation constant is obtained from the power factor

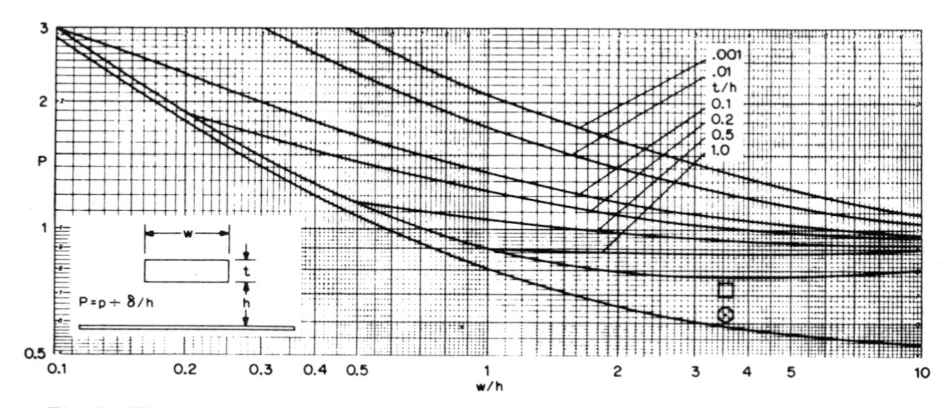

Fig. 3. The magnetic power factor of a strip, showing the effect of thickness (Wheeler [5]).

by

$$\alpha_c = \frac{27.3p}{\lambda_g} \text{ dB/unit length.} \quad (5)$$

For the case of magnetic substrates such as ferrites or garnets, the substrate's magnetic loss must also be included as well as the effect of the magnetic material on the conductor loss, since the characteristic impedance and thus the loss is a function of both ϵ_{eff} and the effective permeability μ_{eff}. Pucel and Massé [7] derived expressions for losses on magnetic substrates by first determining the functional dependence of μ_{eff} on w/h and the substrate's relative permeability μ_R. This was done by using the following duality relationship between dielectric and magnetic substrates and the known functional dependence of ϵ_{eff} on w/h and ϵ_R:

$$\mu_{\text{eff}}(w/h, \mu_R) = \frac{1}{\epsilon_{\text{eff}}(w/h, 1/\mu_R)}. \quad (6)$$

In short, the duality allows the conversions of $\epsilon_R \to 1/\mu_R$ and $\epsilon_{\text{eff}} \to 1/\mu_{\text{eff}}$ in the formulas for the pure dielectric case, which were already derived by Wheeler [2]. From Welch and Pratt's formula for the dielectric loss [1], an effective dielectric loss tangent can be defined by

$$\tan\delta_{d\,\text{eff}} = \left[\frac{1-\epsilon_{\text{eff}}^{-1}}{1-\epsilon_R^{-1}}\right]\tan\delta_d. \quad (7)$$

By the duality rule, an effective magnetic loss tangent can be written as

$$\tan\delta_{m\,\text{eff}} = \left[\frac{1-\mu_{\text{eff}}}{1-\mu_R}\right]\tan\delta_m. \quad (8)$$

Finally, the total magnetic substrate loss is the sum of dielectric and magnetic losses and is given by

$$\alpha_{ST} = \frac{27.3}{\lambda_g}(\tan\delta_{d\,\text{eff}} + \tan\delta_{m\,\text{eff}}) \text{ dB/unit length.} \quad (9)$$

What remains undetermined are the substrate's magnetic loss tangent and relative permeability. The former has been determined from experimental data for a number of commonly used magnetic substrate materials by Green *et al.* [8]. This parameter is a strong function of the material's normalized saturation magnetization $(\omega m/\omega)$. The relative permeability can be determined from a theoretical expression derived by Schloemann [9] for a demagnetized substrate and from an empirical expression based on experimental data by Green and Sandy [10] for a partially magnetized substrate. For the demagnetized case, Schloemann used a cylindrical model to obtain the following equation for μ_R:

$$\mu_{R\,\text{dem}} = \frac{1}{3}\left\{1 + 2\sqrt{1-\left(\frac{\omega_m}{\omega}\right)^2}\right\}. \quad (10)$$

For the partially magnetized case (usually when the substrate is latched in its remanent state), the empirical formulas derived by Green and Sandy for the diagonal and off-diagonal terms of the substrate's permeability tensor are given by

$$\mu = \mu_{R\,\text{dem}} + (1-\mu_{R\,\text{dem}})\left[\frac{4\pi M}{4\pi M_s}\right]^{3/2} \quad (11)$$

$$\kappa = \gamma\frac{4\pi M}{\omega} \quad (12)$$

where $4\pi M$ is the material's magnetization, and $4\pi M_s$ is the material's saturation magnetization.

The analytical approximation for $\mu_{R\,\text{mag}}$ of the magnetized substrate in terms of w/h, μ, and κ was derived by Sandy [11] from a formula for the inductance per unit length. It is given by

$$\mu_R = \frac{\mu^2-\kappa^2}{\mu}\,\frac{1}{1-\frac{1}{7}\sqrt{h/w}\,(\kappa/\mu)^2\ln[1+\mu/(\mu^2-\kappa^2)]}. \quad (13)$$

Now we have everything needed for calculating μ_{eff} from which we can determine $Z_0(\mu_{\text{eff}}, \epsilon_{\text{eff}})$ and, finally, the conductor and substrate losses. An example of the computed and measured loss data for microstrip on a garnet substrate is shown in Fig. 4. The large increase in loss near the material's natural resonant frequency f_m is due to the rapid increase in the magnetic loss tangent and the rapid decrease of Z_0 near this frequency. The latter phenomena causes the conductor loss to increase since $\alpha_c \propto 1/Z_0$.

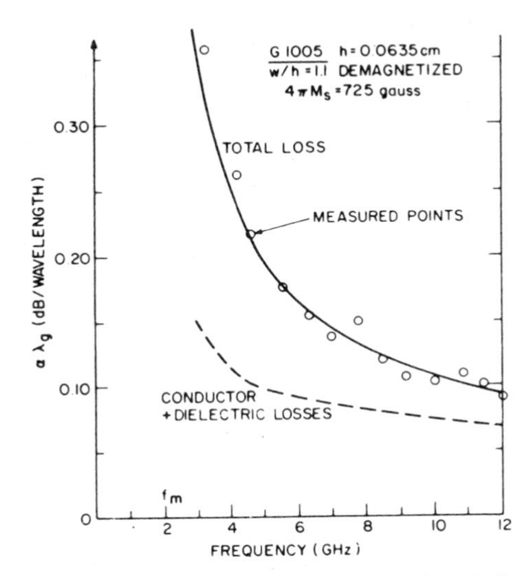

Fig. 4. Theoretical and measured loss per wavelength for microstrip on a demagnetized garnet substrate (Massé and Pucel [7]).

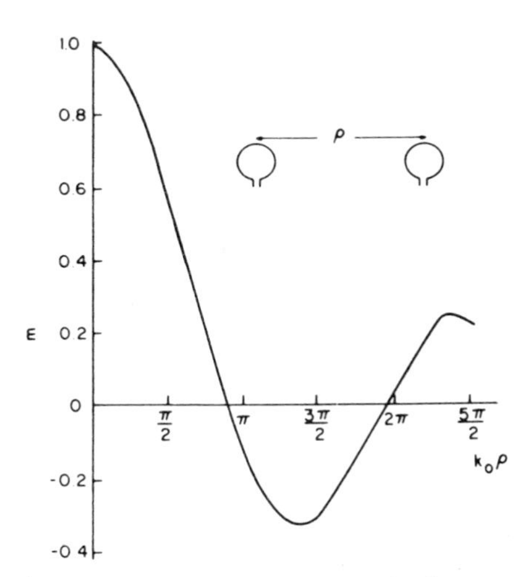

Fig. 5. Mutual coupling (resistive component) of two equatorially displaced magnetic dipoles, normalized to zero displacement (Lewin [13]).

III. Radiation Losses from Microstrip Discontinuities

Radiation loss from a number of different microstrip discontinuities such as open circuits, short circuits, and corners was first theoretically treated by Lewin [12] in 1960 with corrections and additions to this work recently published [13]. In his theory, the strip and polarization currents flowing from strip-to-ground plane are integrated with suitable phase and distance factors to evaluate the Hertz potential from which the fields may be found and the radiated power obtained. The radiated power from the discontinuities is expressed by $P_r = 60(k_0h)^2F(\epsilon_{eff})$, where k_0 is free-space wavenumber, and h is substrate thickness, and the form factor $F(\epsilon_{eff})$ is different for each of the discontinuities and can be found in references [12] and [13].

Table I shows the values of F for $\epsilon_{eff}=2.25$ and for large ϵ_{eff} [13]. Note that the two largest contributors to radiation among the various circuit discontinuities are the open circuit and the right-angle bend.

For many circuit applications there may be two discontinuities, such as open circuits spaced considerably less than a free-space wavelength apart. As shown in [13] and [14], the resultant radiation pattern is similar to that of a magnetic dipole. Fig. 5 shows a plot of the mutual resistive factor m as a function of the spacing ρ between two such dipoles. The form factor F for each of the open circuit discontinuities must then be multiplied by the term $(1+m)$ to obtain the radiated power. For an $n\lambda_g/2$ open-ended microstrip resonator, the value $k_0\rho$ is equal to $n\pi/\epsilon_{eff}$. Thus, for high dielectric constant substrates and low mode number, the mutual resistive factor can be close to one, which causes the radiated power to be nearly doubled when $n=1$.

A different theory on radiation by Van der Pauw [15] uses the fact that the power radiated by the microstrip discontinuity should be equal to the power necessary to maintain the current density on the strip at a stationary value. His results for an open-ended microstrip resonator agree to within 10 percent of Lewin's theoretical results. Other types of commonly used resonators analyzed by him were the circular resonator and the "hairpin" resonator. The former gives a radiation Q nearly equal to that of a stretched open-ended resonator, while the hairpin resonator exhibits particularly low radiation losses. The overall gain in quality factor Q_T may be small due to ohmic losses.

The influence of radiation losses based on Lewin's derivation on the overall Q of microstrip open-ended resonators for a variety of frequencies, characteristic impedances, substrate materials, and thicknesses, was treated by Belohoubek and Denlinger [16]. As shown in Fig. 6, radiation becomes a dominant factor for low impedance

TABLE I
Radiation Form Factors for Various Microstrip Discontinuities (Lewin [13])

VALUES OF F:

DISCONTINUITY	LARGE ϵ_{eff}	ϵ_{eff} = 2.25
Open Circuit	$8/(3\epsilon_{eff})$	1.073
Short Circuit	$16/(15\epsilon_{eff}^2)$	0.246
Match	$2/(3\epsilon_{eff})$	0.330
90° Corner	$4/(3\epsilon_{eff})$	0.610
Impedance Change	$\frac{8}{3\epsilon_{eff}}\left(\frac{Z_2-Z_1}{Z_2+Z_1}\right)^2$	0.268 (3 to 1 change)
Side-Arm Divider	$\frac{4}{3\epsilon_{eff}}\left(\frac{Z_3}{Z_2+Z_3}\right)^2$	0.152 (3 dB case)
T-Junction	$2/(3\epsilon_{eff})$	0.349
Series Impedance	$\frac{8}{3\epsilon_{eff}}\left\lvert\frac{Z}{Z+2Z_s}\right\rvert^2$	0.119 $(Z=Z_s)$

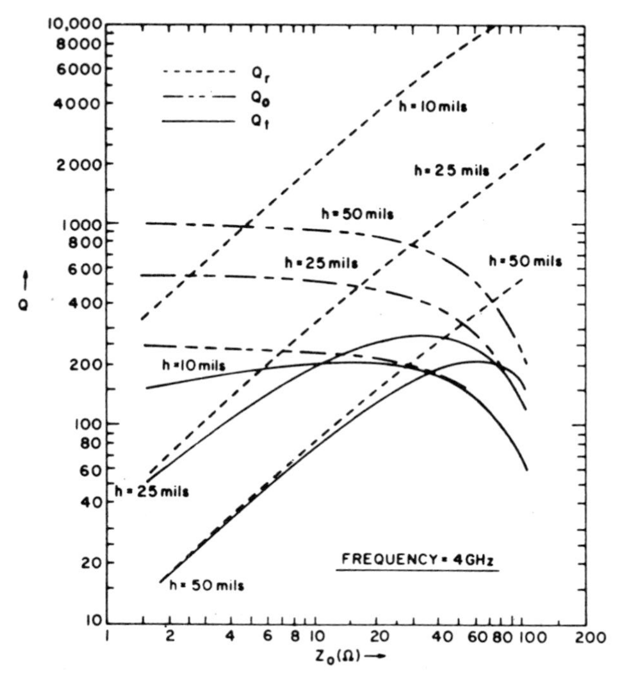

Fig. 6. Q factors for $\lambda_g/4$ microstrip resonator on alumina substrate for $f = 4$ GHz (Belohoubek and Denlinger [16]).

lines and thick substrates. The graph in this figure is for a $\lambda_g/4$ resonator defined on alumina and shows the circuit quality factor Q_0, which includes the combined conductor and substrate losses, the radiation Q_r, and the overall Q_t of the resonator, which is given by

$$\frac{1}{Q_t} = \frac{1}{Q_0} + \frac{1}{Q_r}. \tag{14}$$

Similar graphs for alumina and teflon fiberglass substrates calculated for various frequencies (up to 8 GHz) illustrate that radiation becomes even more dominant for lower dielectric constant substrates and at higher frequencies. Although the energy may not truly be lost in fully enclosed circuits, the high radiation level will cause cross coupling between circuit elements. The radiation losses based on Lewin's derivation were compared with experimental results for $n\lambda_g/2$ open-ended resonators [16], [17]. The theoretical expressions for radiation Q_r and the fractional radiated power are given by [16]

$$Q_r = \frac{nZ_0}{480\pi(h/\lambda_0)^2(1+m)F(\epsilon_{eff})} \tag{15}$$

$$\frac{P_r}{P_t} = \frac{Q_0}{Q_0 + Q_r} \tag{16}$$

where the factor $(1+m)$ has been added to account for the mutual resistive effect between the two ends of the resonator [13]. In terms of measured results, P_r/P_t is given by

$$\frac{P_r}{P_t} = \frac{Q_0' - Q_t'}{Q_0'} \tag{17}$$

where Q_0' is the measured Q of the resonator when located in a waveguide below cutoff, and Q_t' is the value obtained

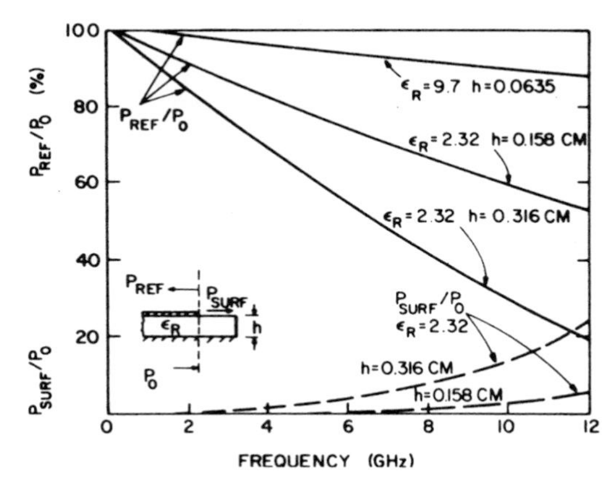

Fig. 7. Percentage of power reflected and transmitted at open end of wide microstrip lines against frequency for $w/h > 3$ (Kompa [18]).

TABLE II
FRACTIONAL RADIATED POWER VERSUS NORMALIZED SUBSTRATE THICKNESS ($Z_0 = 50\Omega, \epsilon_{eff} = 2.25$)

$1+m$	n	h/λ_o	Q_o	Q_t	P_r/P_t (%) Exper.	Theor.
0.66	2	.00537	340	300	12	9.5
0.66	2	.00609	345	298	13.6	12.0
1.038	3	.00807	360	291	19.0	20.7
1.038	3	.00931	370	286	22.7	26.4
0.66	2	.01069	540	366	32.0	39.6
1.038	3	.01603	605	194	68.0	63.5

TABLE III
FRACTIONAL RADIATED POWER VERSUS SUBSTRATE DIELECTRIC CONSTANT ($Z_0 = 50\,\Omega, h/\lambda_0 \simeq 0.009$)

$k_o\ell$	$1+m$	n	ϵ_R	ϵ_{eff}	$F(\epsilon_{eff})$	Q_o	Q_t	P_r/P_t (%) Exper.	Theor.
6.283	1.038	3	2.47	2.25	1.07	370	286	22.7	26.4
3.030	0.8868	2	6.0	4.3	0.5903	213	183	14.0	12.0
3.848	0.687	3	9.0	6.0	0.4293	273	263	4.0	5.7
1.987	1.362	2	16.0	10.0	0.2613	152	148	3.0	2.6

without shielding. A comparison between experimental and theoretical values of fractional radiated power is given in Tables II and III. Table II is for resonators with a fixed dielectric constant and varying h/λ_0 while Table III is for resonators having approximately the same h/λ_0 but varying ϵ_r.

Some other different theories on radiation from open-ended microstrip were reported by Kompa [18], Sobol [19], and Wood [20]. Kompa [18] has used the analysis due to Angulo and Chang [21] for open-ended dielectrically loaded parallel-plate waveguide to approximate the reflection coefficient of the end of a wide microstrip line. This theory is not applicable for narrow stripwidths but does allow one to separate the amount of power concentrated in the radiating field from that existing in the TM_0 surface mode. As shown in Fig. 7, both excitations increase with the substrate thickness and with lower dielectric constant; however, the surface wave power is considerably smaller than the radiation power.

Sobol [19] and Wood [20] have considered radiation

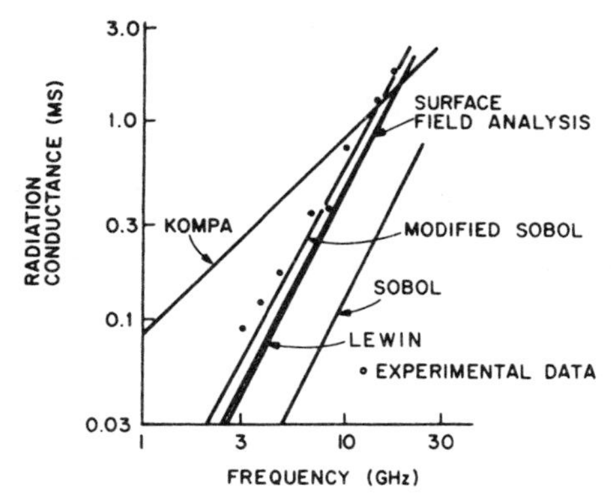

Fig. 8. Radiation conductance of open circuited 2.82-mm-wide microstrip line as function of frequency ($h = 1.58$ mm, $\epsilon_R = 2.32$; Wood *et al.* [20]).

from an open-circuited line as coming out of the aperture at the end. The radiating source used by Sobol [19] was a uniform electric field distribution confined to the physical strip width. Wood [20] tried to make allowance for the spreading of the source due to fringing fields at the strip edges by proposing to use an equivalent width rather than the physical strip width. This equivalent width is defined as the width of a parallel-plate line of separation h, filled with a medium of dielectric constant ϵ_{eff}, and having an impedance equal to that of the line

$$w_{eq} = \frac{120\pi h}{Z_0 \sqrt{\epsilon_{eff}}}. \tag{18}$$

The resulting radiation conductance is given by

$$g_r = \frac{\sqrt{\epsilon_{eff}}}{240\pi^2} F\left(\sqrt{\epsilon_{eff}} \frac{2\pi}{\lambda_0} w_{eq}\right) \tag{19}$$

where

$$F(X) = X\,\mathrm{Si}(X) - 2\sin^2(X/2) - 1 + \sin(X)/X.$$

Wood also derived a conductance formula based on radiation from the electric-field distribution at the substrate surface

$$g_r = \frac{1}{120\pi^2} F\left(\frac{2\pi}{\lambda_0} w_{eq}\right) \tag{20}$$

where $F(X)$ is the same as shown above. Shown in Fig. 8 is Wood's comparison of various theoretical curves of radiation conductance versus frequency by Kompa, Lewin, Sobol, modified Sobol (using w_{eq}), and Wood's surface field analysis. Experimental data by Wood indicates best agreement with the modified Sobol analysis. Recently, James and Henderson [43] calculated that surface-wave generation becomes appreciable when $h/\lambda_0 > 0.09$ for $\epsilon_R \simeq 2.3$ and $h/\lambda_0 > 0.03$ for $\epsilon_R \simeq 10$.

IV. Other Microstrip Loss Considerations

The remaining contributors to microstrip losses are surface roughness, the thin films of high resistivity metal used for adhesion and metallurgical stability in a deposited metal system, and the thickness of the metal system. The effect of surface roughness on microwave losses was studied more than thirty years ago by Morgan [22], who calculated eddy current losses for triangular and

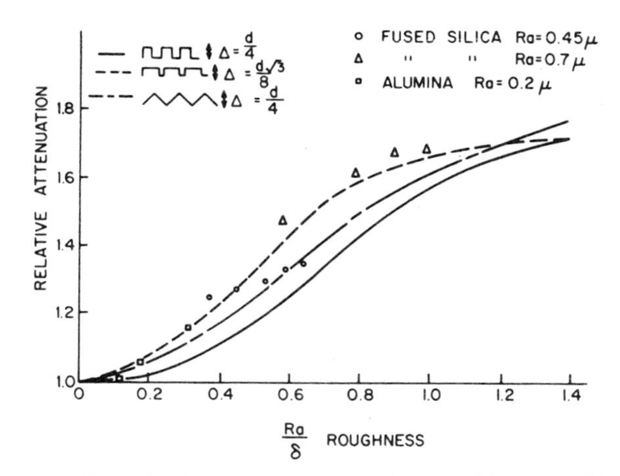

Fig. 9. Relationship between surface roughness and increase of loss in shielded open-ended line resonators on fused quartz (Van Heuven [23]).

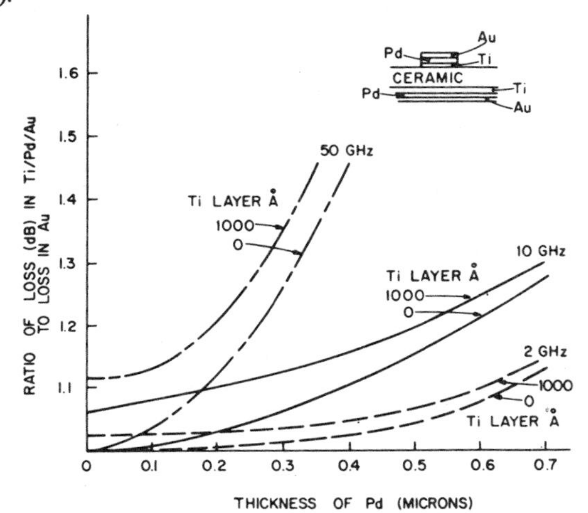

Fig. 10. Loss in Ti–Pd–Au microstrip conductor as a function of Ti and Pd Thickness (Sobol and Caulton [25]).

rectangular grooves perpendicular to the current flow. Data shown in Fig. 9 by Van Heuven [23] for both fuzed silica and alumina substrates show good agreement with Morgan's results. Here the increase in attenuation is plotted against the surface roughness R_a which is normalized to the skin depth δ. These measurements were made with shielded open-ended line resonators.

The losses due to the high resistivity metal films were calculated by Sobol ([24], [25]) for two-layered and three-layered metal systems. A typical adhesion metal, e.g., Cr, in a two-layered system produces only a negligible loss at frequencies well into the millimeter-wave region. However, the losses of the three-layered system should be seriously considered. For example, the Ti–Pd–Au system, which is attractive because of its metallurgical stability and compatibility with beam leads, has losses relative to that of a pure gold system as shown in Fig. 10. Typically, the thickness of the adhesion film Ti is a few hundred angstroms, and that of the buffer layer Pd is 2000–4000 Å. Thus, at X-band frequencies the losses may be 10 percent higher than those of the pure gold systems, and for millimeter waves the increase may be as high as 30–50 percent.

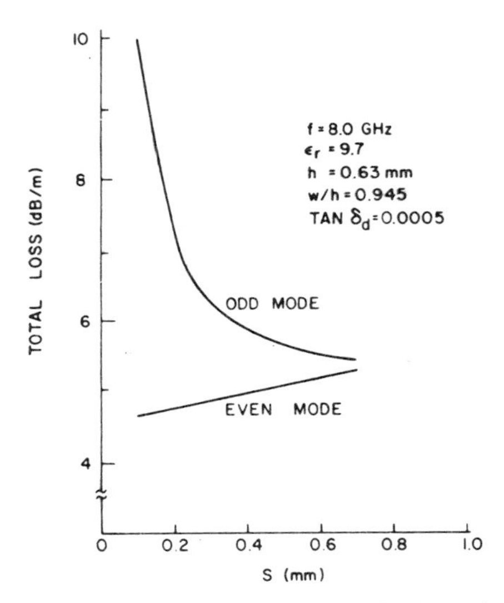

Fig. 11. Even- and odd-mode losses in coupled microstrip lines (Garg and Bahl [27]).

Conductor losses are also significantly affected by the ratio of metal thickness to the skin depth at the frequency of interest. It was shown in references [1] and [44] that the conductor loss reaches a minimum if the strip thickness is about three skin depths.

V. Losses for Coupled Microstrip

Conductor losses in coupled microstrip lines have been analyzed by Rao [26] and more recently by Garg and Bahl [27] using the incremental inductance rule of Wheeler [5]. The two solutions are similar and agree within 1 dB for the even- and odd-mode attenuation constants. Typical curves showing dependence of even- and odd-mode losses on the strip spacing s are presented in Fig. 11. Included in these losses are those due to dielectric loss which are given by [26]

$$\alpha_d^e = 27.3 \frac{\epsilon_R}{\sqrt{\epsilon_{\text{eff}}^e}} \frac{\epsilon_{\text{eff}}^e - 1}{\epsilon_R - 1} \frac{\tan\delta_d}{\lambda_0} \text{dB/unit length} \quad (21)$$

$$\alpha_d^o = 27.3 \frac{\epsilon_R}{\sqrt{\epsilon_{\text{eff}}^o}} \frac{\epsilon_{\text{eff}}^o - 1}{\epsilon_R - 1} \frac{\tan\delta_d}{\lambda_0} \text{dB/unit length.} \quad (22)$$

A second method of solution using the quasi-TEM propagation assumption was employed by Horton [28] and Spielman [29]. It involved finding the charge distributions on the conductors along with the even- and odd-mode effective dielectric constants and impedances; then, via a numerical integration, the even- and odd-mode attenuation constants could be calculated from a general formula given by

$$\alpha = \bar{P}_d / (2\bar{P}_F) \quad (23)$$

where $\bar{P}_d$ is time-averaged power dissipated per-unit-length; and $\bar{P}_F$ is time-averaged power flow along line. By relating the losses to the charge density distributions, the transmission-line geometry may contain any number of lossy conductors and inhomogenous dielectrics.

The final two methods by Jansen [30] and Mirshekar-Syahkal and Davies [31] use hybrid mode solutions for the fields and propagation constants to determine the losses for both single and coupled microstrip lines. Jansen [30] used the transmission-line formula

$$\alpha_t = \alpha_c + \alpha_d = 4.34 \frac{R'}{Z_0} + \frac{27.3}{\lambda_g} \tan\delta_d \text{ dB/unit length} \quad (24)$$

with the line resistance per-unit-length R' given by

$$R' = \left[\frac{R_s}{w_{\text{eff}}} + \frac{F_j R_s}{w_t} \right] F_{sR} \quad (25)$$

$$F_j = \frac{\int_0^1 |\bar{J}_Z(X)|^2 dx}{\left(\int_0^1 \bar{J}_Z(X) dX \right)^2}. \quad (26)$$

The factor F_j is the increase of strip loss due to the nonuniform current distribution compared with a uniform one. W_t is the correct strip width which takes into account the finite value of strip thickness while w_{eff} is the width of an equivalent parallel-plate waveguide of height h and with the frequency-dependent microstrip values of impedance and effective dielectric constant

$$w_{\text{eff}} = \frac{120\pi h}{\left(Z_0(f) \cdot \sqrt{\epsilon_{\text{eff}}(f)} \right)}. \quad (27)$$

Finally, R_s is the surface skin resistivity and F_{sR} is a factor which describes the additional loss due to substrate surface roughness.

In the solutions of microstrip losses by Mirshekar-Syahkal and Davies [31], perturbation theory is used to express the losses in terms of the unperturbed fields which were derived by the spectral domain method

$$\alpha_{\text{cond}} = \frac{R_s \int_c |H_t|^2 dl}{2 R_e \int_s E_0 \times H_0^* \cdot \bar{a}_Z dS} \quad (28)$$

$$\alpha_{\text{diel}} = \frac{\omega\epsilon \tan\delta_d \int_{S_{\text{diel}}} |E_0|^2 dS}{2 R_e \int_s E_0 \times H_0^* \cdot \bar{a}_Z dS} \quad (29)$$

The results of the two hybrid mode methods described above show similar characteristics for the even and odd modes as those indicated in Fig. 11.

VI. Considerations of Dispersion and Higher Order Mode Propagation

Dispersion of microstrip becomes increasingly more important as the substrate's dielectric constant and thickness are made greater. In addition, when the substrate is magnetic, e.g., for a ferrite or garnet material, the microstrip line becomes highly dispersive near the material's natural resonant frequency $f_m = \gamma 4\pi M_s$. Hartwig *et al.* [32] described dispersion of microstrip as coupling of a fundamental TEM mode to TM_0 and TE_1 surface-wave modes. The TM_0 mode has a zero frequency cutoff while the TE_1 surface-wave mode starts propagating above the cutoff

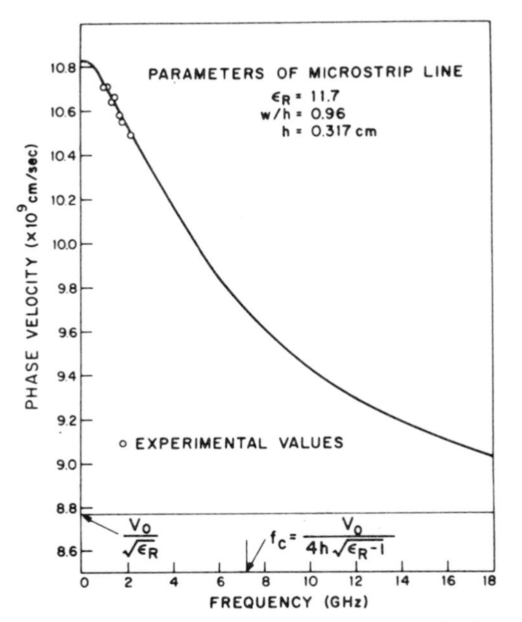

Fig. 12. Microstrip phase velocity versus frequency (Denlinger [33]).

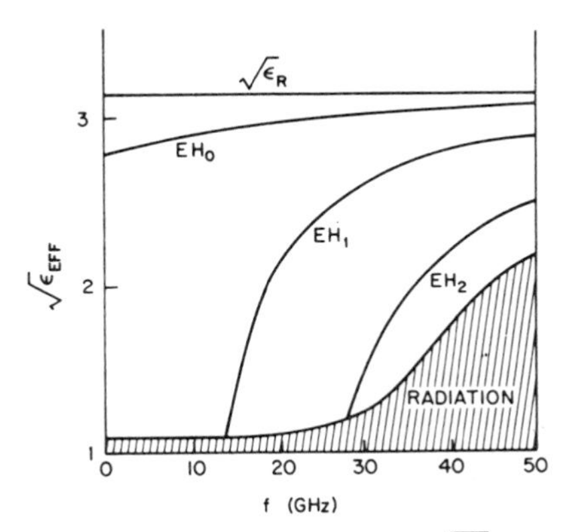

Fig. 13. Normalized phase constant ($\beta/k_0=\sqrt{\epsilon_{eff}}$) versus frequency for some guided modes and region of radiation ($\epsilon_R=9.8, w/h=4.74, h=0.635$ mm, $a/h=5$; Ermert [35]).

frequency

$$f_c=\frac{V_0}{4h\sqrt{\epsilon_R-1}}. \tag{30}$$

The resulting microstrip mode has a dispersive behavior that is illustrated in Fig. 12 and taken from Denlinger's hybrid mode solution [33]. There have been many other frequency-dependent solutions (e.g., [30], [31], [34], and [35]) involving spectral domain analysis, transverse mode-matching techniques, etc., which not only show the dispersion of the fundamental mode but also the existence of higher order modes such as illustrated in Fig. 13.

Dispersion of coupled microstrip lines has also been described by several authors [30], [31], [36], [37]. As shown in Fig. 14, the even mode is considerably more dispersive than the odd mode for typical strip spacings and widths. Work by Jansen [30] and Krage and Haddad [37] show that the characteristic impedance increases very slowly with frequency for both the even and odd modes and also

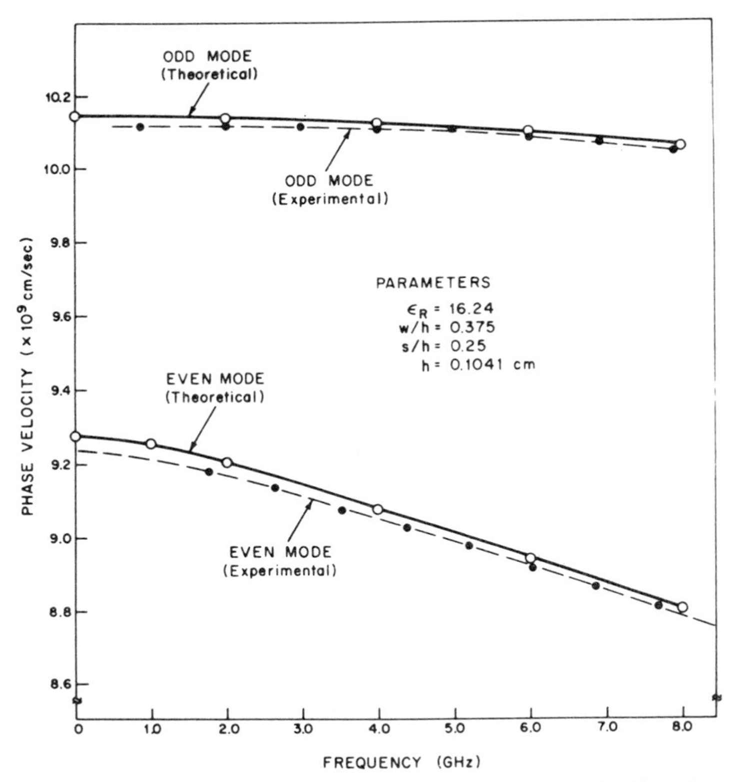

Fig. 14. Theoretical and experimental curves of even- and odd-mode phase velocity versus frequency for coupled microstrip lines (Denlinger [36]).

for single microstrip lines. Some other theories [33], [38], [39] claim that Z_0 decreases with frequency. The effect is so small that it is very hard to accurately measure and confirm the theoretical values.

VII. Comparison of Microstrip Losses to Other Commonly Used Quasi-TEM Lines

A comparison of losses in microstrip with those for other types of MIC lines is difficult since the variation of loss with impedance is different for the various lines and also the optimum substrate thicknesses may be different. In addition, the substrate's electrical characteristics (loss tangent, dielectric constant, etc.) has a significant impact on the relative losses of the various lines. Spielman's [29] computer-aided analysis of quasi-TEM lines, which was discussed previously, was used to compare losses of four types of 50-Ω transmission lines: microstrip, coplanar waveguide, trapped inverted microstrip and inverted microstrip. As shown in Fig. 15, the coplanar waveguide is considerably more lossy than microstrip whereas both the trapped inverted and inverted microstrip are considerably less lossy. The losses of suspended stripline is expected to be similar to the trapped inverted and inverted microstrip since all three types have strip widths two to three times greater than that for microstrip. By concentrating more of the field energies in air, a prescribed impedance level requires wider strips than for microstrip or coplanar lines, which results in lower conductor and dielectric losses. Another line, called stripline-like microstrip, where a top

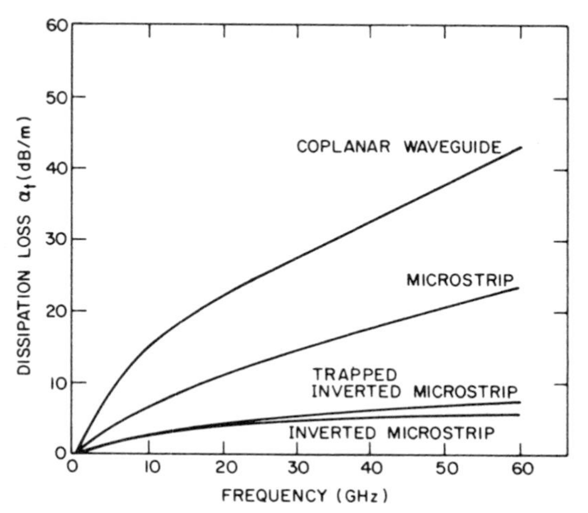

Fig. 15. Comparison of total dissipative losses for four 50-Ω transmission lines (Spielman [29]) (line parameters: (1) microstrip $-\epsilon_R = 10, w = 0.61$ mm, $h = 0.635$ mm, $t = 6.35$ μm; (2) coplanar waveguide $-\epsilon_R = 10.4, w = h = 0.635$ mm, $s_{cp} = 0.27$ mm, $t = 6.35$ μm; (3) trapped inverted microstrip $-\epsilon_R = 10, w = 1.25$ mm, $H_{TIM} = h = 0.508$ mm, $s_{TIM} = 1.27$ mm, $t = 6.35$ μm; (4) inverted microstrip $-\epsilon_R = 3.78, w = 1.524$ mm, $H_{IM} = 0.381$ mm, $h = 0.508$ mm, $t = 6.35$ μm).

ground plane is placed one substrate thickness above the strip, has also been shown to have slightly lower losses than microstrip, and about half the loss of stripline [40]. Due to having low radiation losses, stripline-like microstrip may be employed for circuits requiring high Q. Finally, losses for a non-TEM line called slotline has not been theoretically treated. Measurement of loss for substrates with $\epsilon_R = 16$ by Robinson and Allen [41] show about the same loss as for microstrip. However, these results do not agree with another experiment that showed unloaded-Q factors of slotline resonators to be about half that of microstrip resonators [42]. Radiation loss from slotline is expected to be quite high.

VIII. Conclusions

There is good understanding of conductor and substrate losses for dielectric and demagnetized ferrite-loaded microstrip. Losses for magnetized ferrite microstrip is less understood since it is still based on empirical formulas derived from experimental data. Dispersion of microstrip lines can have a significant effect on the calculation of losses. This is especially true for thick, high dielectric constant ceramic substrates as well as ferrite substrates. Theoretical radiation losses of open-ended microstrip agree fairly well with a limited amount of experimental data. However, no experimental data have been reported to confirm the theory for radiation from other types of microstrip discontinuities.

References

[1] J. D. Welch and H. J. Pratt, "Losses in microstrip transmission systems for integrated microwave circuits," *NEREM Rec.*, vol. 8, pp. 100–101, 1966.

[2] H. A. Wheeler, "Transmission-line properties of parallel strips separated by a dielectric sheet," *IEEE Trans. Microwave Theory Tech.*, vol. MTT-13, pp. 172–185, Mar. 1965.

[3] M. V. Schneider, B. Glance, and W. F. Bodtmann, "Microwave and millimeter wave hybrid integrated circuits for radio systems," *Bell Syst. Tech. J.*, vol. 48, no. 6, pp. 1703–1727, July/Aug. 1969.

[4] R. A. Pucel, D. J. Massé, and C. P. Hartwig, "Losses in microstrip," *IEEE Trans. Microwave Theory Tech.*, vol. MTT-16, pp. 342–350, June 1968.

[5] H. A. Wheeler, "Transmission-line properties of a strip on a dielectric sheet on a plane," *IEEE Trans. Microwave Theory Tech.*, vol. MTT-25, pp. 631–641, Aug. 1977.

[6] ——, "Formulas for the skin effect," *Proc. IRE*, vol. 30, pp. 412–424, Sept. 1942.

[7] R. A. Pucel and D. J. Massé, "Microstrip propagation on magnetic substrates—Part I: Design theory and Part II: Experiment," *IEEE Trans. Microwave Theory Tech.*, vol. MTT-20, pp. 304–313, May 1972.

[8] J. J. Green and F. Sandy, "A catalog of low power loss parameters and high power thresholds for partially magnetized ferrites," *IEEE Trans. Microwave Theory Tech.*, vol. MTT-22, pp. 645–651, June 1974.

[9] E. Schloemann, "Microwave behavior of partially magnetized ferrites," *J. Appl. Phys.*, vol. 41, p. 204, 1970.

[10] J. J. Green and F. Sandy, "Microwave characterizations of partially magnetized ferrites," *IEEE Trans. Microwave Theory Tech.*, vol. MTT-22, pp. 641–645, June 1974.

[11] F. Sandy, private communication to D. Massé and R. Pucel, Jan. 1971.

[12] L. Lewin, "Radiation from discontinuities in strip-line," *Proc. Inst. Elec. Eng.*, vol. 107C, pp. 163–170, 1960.

[13] ——, "Spurious radiation from microstrip," *Proc. Inst. Elec. Eng.*, vol. 125, pp. 633–642, July 1978.

[14] J. Watkins, "Radiation loss from open circuited dielectric resonators," *IEEE Trans. Microwave Theory Tech.*, vol. MTT-21, pp. 636–639, Oct. 1973.

[15] L. J. Van der Pauw, "The radiation of electromagnetic power by microstrip configurations," *IEEE Trans. Microwave Theory Tech.*, vol. MTT-25, pp. 719–725, Sept. 1977.

[16] E. Belohoubek and E. Denlinger, "Loss considerations for microstrip resonators," *IEEE Trans. Microwave Theory Tech.*, vol. MTT-23, pp. 522–526, June 1975.

[17] E. Denlinger, "Radiation from microstrip resonators," *IEEE Trans. Microwave Theory Tech.*, vol. MTT-17, pp. 235–236, Apr. 1969.

[18] G. Kompa, "Approximate calculation of radiation from open-ended wide microstrip lines," *Electron. Lett.*, vol. 12, pp. 222–224, Apr. 29, 1976.

[19] H. Sobol, "Radiation conductance of open-circuit microstrip," *IEEE Trans. Microwave Theory Tech.*, vol. MTT-19, pp. 885–887, Nov. 1971.

[20] C. Wood, P. S. Hall and J. R. James, "Radiation conductance of open-circuit low dielectric constant microstrip," *Electron. Lett.*, vol. 14, pp. 121–123, Feb. 16, 1978.

[21] C. M. Angulo and W. S. C. Chang, "The launching of surface waves by a parallel plate waveguide," *IRE Trans. Antennas Propagat.*, vol. AP-7, pp. 359–368, Oct. 1959.

[22] S. P. Morgan, "Effect of surface roughness on eddy current losses at microwave frequencies," *J. Appl. Phys.*, vol. 20, pp. 352–362, Apr. 1949.

[23] J. H. C. Van Heuven, "Conduction and radiation losses in microstrip," *IEEE Trans. Microwave Theory Tech.*, vol. MTT-22, pp. 841–844, Sept. 1974.

[24] H. Sobol, "Technology and design of hybrid microwave integrated circuits," *Solid State Technol.*, pp. 49–57, Feb. 1970.

[25] H. Sobol and M. Caulton, "Technology of microwave integrated circuits," in *Advances in Microwaves*. New York: Academic Press, 1974, vol. 8, pp. 12–64.

[26] B. R. Rao, "Effect of loss and frequency dispersion on the performance of microstrip directional couplers and coupled line filters," *IEEE Trans. Microwave Theory Tech.*, vol. MTT-22, pp. 747–750, July 1974.

[27] R. Garg and I. J. Bahl, "Characteristics of coupled microstriplines," *IEEE Trans. Microwave Theory Tech.*, vol. MTT-27, pp. 700–705, July 1979.

[28] R. Horton, "Loss calculations of coupled microstrip lines," *IEEE Trans. Microwave Theory Tech.*, vol. MTT-21, pp. 359–360, May 1973.

[29] B. E. Spielman, "Dissipation loss effects in isolated and coupled transmission lines," *IEEE Trans. Microwave Theory Tech.*, vol. MTT-25, pp. 648–655, Aug. 1977.

[30] R. H. Jansen, "High-speed computation of single and coupled microstrip parameters including dispersion, high-order modes, loss and finite strip thickness," *IEEE Trans. Microwave Theory Tech.*, vol. MTT-26, pp. 75–82, Feb. 1978.

[31] D. Mirshekar-Syahkal and J. B. Davies, "Accurate solution of microstrip and coplanar structures for dispersion and for dielectric and conductor losses," *IEEE Trans. Microwave Theory Tech.*, vol. MTT-27, pp. 694–699, July 1979.

[32] C. P. Hartwig, D. Massé and R. A. Pucel, "Frequency dependent behavior of microstrip," 1968 *Int. Symp. Dig.*, pp. 110–116.

[33] E. J. Denlinger, "A frequency dependent solution for microstrip transmission lines," *IEEE Trans. Microwave Theory Tech.*, vol. MTT-19, pp. 30-39, Jan. 1971.

[34] T. Itoh and R. Mittra, "Spectral-domain approach for calculating dispersion characteristics of microstrip lines," *IEEE Trans. Microwave Theory Tech.*, vol. MTT-21, pp. 496–498, July 1973.

[35] H. Ermert, "Guided modes and radiation characteristics of covered microstrip lines," *Arch. Electron. Übertragung.*, vol. 30, pp. 65–70, 1976.

[36] E. Denlinger, "Frequency dependence of a coupled pair of microstrip lines," *IEEE Trans. Microwave Theory Tech.*, vol. MTT-18, pp. 731–733, Oct. 1970.

[37] M. K. Krage and G. I. Haddad, "Frequency-dependent characteristics of microstrip transmission lines," *IEEE Trans. Microwave Theory Tech.*, vol. MTT-20, pp. 678–688, Oct. 1972.

[38] W. J. Getsinger, "Microstrip characteristic impedance," *IEEE Trans. Microwave Theory Tech.*, vol. MTT-27, p. 293, Apr. 1979.

[39] F. Arndt and G. U. Paul, "The reflection definition of the characteristic impedance of microstrips," *IEEE Trans. Microwave Theory Tech.*, vol. MTT-27, pp. 724–731, Aug. 1979.

[40] R. Garg, "Stripline-like microstrip configuration," *Microwave J.*, pp. 103–116, Apr. 1979.

[41] G. H. Robinson and J. L. Allen, "Slotline application to miniature ferrite devices," *IEEE Trans. Microwave Theory Tech.*, vol. MTT-17, pp. 1097–1101, Dec. 1969.

[42] G. P. Kurpis, "Coplanar and slotlines—Are they here to stay?" in *Proc. Int. Microelectric Symposium*, (Washington, DC), pp. 3B.6.1–3B.6.5, 1972.

[43] J. James and A. Henderson, "High-frequency behavior of microstrip open-circuit terminations," *IEEE J. Microwave, Optics, and Acoustics*, vol. 3, pp. 205–218, Sept. 1979.

[44] R. Horton, B. Easter, and A. Gopinath, "Variation of microstrip losses with thickness of strip," *Electron. Lett.*, vol. 17, no. 17, pp. 490–491, Aug. 26, 1971.

Coplanar Waveguide: A Surface Strip Transmission Line Suitable for Nonreciprocal Gyromagnetic Device Applications

CHENG P. WEN, MEMBER, IEEE

Abstract—**A coplanar waveguide consists of a strip of thin metallic film on the surface of a dielectric slab with two ground electrodes running adjacent and parallel to the strip. This novel transmission line readily lends itself to nonreciprocal magnetic device applications because of the built-in circularly polarized magnetic vector at the air–dielectric boundary between the conductors. Practical applications of the coplanar waveguide have been experimentally demonstrated by measurements on resonant isolators and differential phase shifters fabricated on low-loss dielectric substrates with high dielectric constants. Calculations have been made for the characteristic impedance, phase velocity, and upper bound of attenuation of a transmission line whose electrodes are all on one side of a dielectric substrate. These calculations are in good agreement with preliminary experimental results. The coplanar configuration of the transmission system not only permits easy shunt connection of external elements in hybrid integrated circuits, but also adapts well to the fabrication of monolithic integrated systems. Low-loss dielectric substrates with high dielectric constants may be employed to reduce the longitudinal dimension of the integrated circuits because the characteristic impedance of the coplanar waveguide is relatively independent of the substrate thickness; this may be of vital importance for low-frequency integrated microwave systems.**

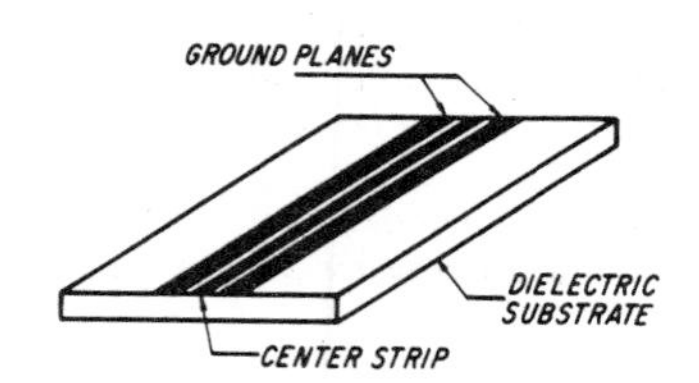

Fig. 1. Coplanar waveguide (CPW), a surface strip transmission line.

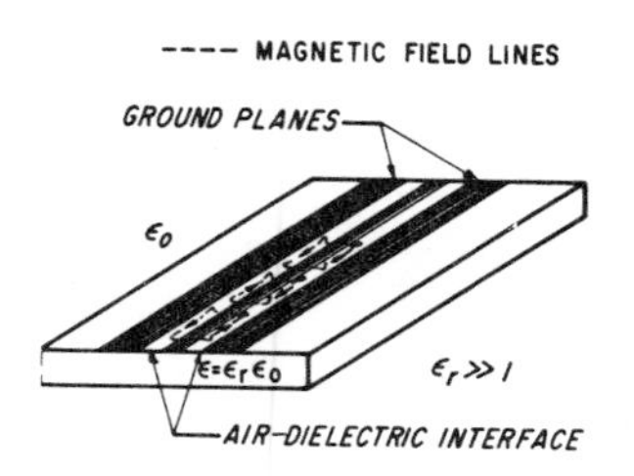

Fig. 2. RF magnetic field configuration in a CPW.

MICROWAVE integrated circuits offer system engineers prospects of small, batch processed modules for radar and communication systems. In the past, radar and communication systems included a variety of nonreciprocal magnetic devices. These devices require circularly polarized RF magnetic fields for their operation, and present microstrip and strip lines do not provide such fields. In addition, the ground plane of these lines, which is located on the opposite side of a dielectric substrate, is not easily accessible for shunt connections necessary for many active microwave devices. Direct dependence of the characteristic impedance on the thickness of the substrate makes it difficult to use a low-loss, high-dielectric-constant material, such as a temperature-compensated ceramic. This is a definite drawback for low-frequency operation where size consideration dominates. All these disadvantages may either be overcome or alleviated by a novel integrated-circuit transmission-line configuration in which all conducting elements, including the ground planes, are on the same side of a dielectric substrate. This is called the coplanar waveguide, a surface-strip transmission line.

A coplanar waveguide (CPW) consists of a strip of thin metallic film deposited on the surface of a dielectric slab with two ground electrodes running adjacent and parallel to the strip on the same surface, as shown in Fig. 1. There is no low-frequency cutoff because of the quasi-TEM mode of propagation. However, the RF electric field between the center conducting strip and the ground electrodes tangential to the air–dielectric boundary produces a discontinuity in displacement current density at the interface, giving rise to an axial, as well as transverse, component of RF magnetic field. These components provide the elliptical polarization needed for nonreciprocal gyromagnetic microwave device applications [1]. If the relative dielectric constant ϵ_r of the substrate is very large compared to unity, the magnetic field at the interface is nearly circularly polarized with the plane of polarization perpendicular to the surface of the substrate, as shown in Fig. 2. Such a transmission line readily lends itself to integrated-circuit fabrication techniques and nonreciprocal gyromagnetic device applications because of the built-in circularly polarized magnetic vector which is easily accessible at the surface of the substrate. The coplanar configuration of all conducting elements permits easy connection of external shunt elements such as active devices as well as the fabrication of series and shunt capacitances. It is also ideal for connecting various elements in monolithic microwave integrated circuits built on semiconducting substrates or ferromagnetic semiconductors. All ground planes may be connected together through a metallic capsule as shown in

Manuscript received March 28, 1969; revised July 9, 1969. This paper was presented at the International Microwave Symposium, Dallas, Tex., May 5–7, 1969.

The author is with RCA Laboratories, David Sarnoff Research Center, Princeton, N. J. 08540.

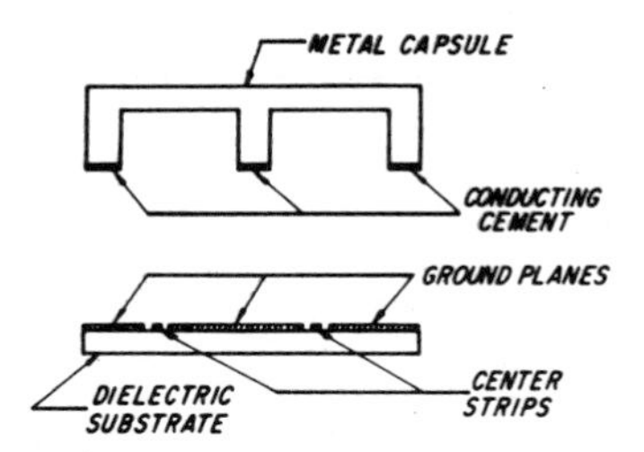

Fig. 3. Metallic capsule for CPW ground connections.

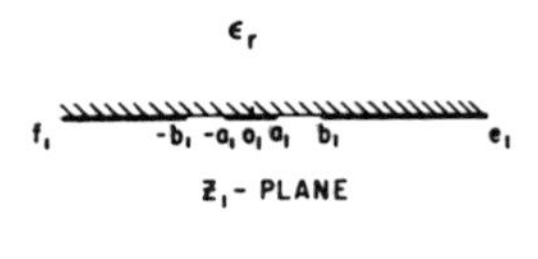

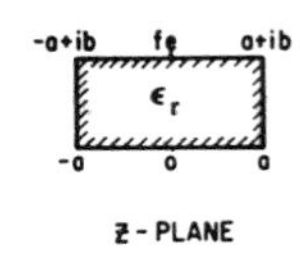

Fig. 4. Conformal mapping transformation of the upper half-plane of a CPW into the interior of a rectangle.

Fig. 3, serving both as a common ground and a protective cover. Because of the high dielectric constant of the substrate, most of the RF energy is stored in the dielectric and the loading effect of the grounded cover is negligible if it is more than two slot widths away from the surface.

Characteristic impedances Z_0 of CPWs fabricated on dielectric half-planes with relative dielectric constants ϵ_r have been calculated as a function of the ratio a_1/b_1, where $2a_1$ is the width of the center strip and $2b_1$ is the distance between two ground electrodes. A zeroth-order quasi-static approximation is employed. The dielectric half-plane Z_1 in Fig. 4 may be transformed to the interior of a rectangle in the Z-plane by conformal mapping [2]:

$$\frac{dZ}{dZ_1} = \frac{A}{(Z_1^2 - a_1^2)^{1/2}(Z_1^2 - b_1^2)^{1/2}} \tag{1}$$

where A is a constant. The ratio a/b of the rectangle in the Z plane may be evaluated by multiplying both sides of (1) by dZ_1 and carrying out the integration

$$a + jb = \int_0^{b_1} \frac{A\,dZ_1}{(Z_1^2 - a_1^2)^{1/2}(Z_1^2 - b_1^2)^{1/2}} \cdot \tag{2}$$

As a result

$$\frac{a}{b} = \frac{K(k)}{K'(k)} \tag{3}$$

where

$k = a_1/b_1$,

$K(k)$ = complete elliptical integral of the first kind [3],

$K'(k) = K(k')$,

$k' = (1-k^2)^{1/2}$.

If the relative dielectric constant of the material filling the rectangle in the Z plane of Fig. 4 is ϵ_r, a uniform electric field E is set up in the capacitor with the top and bottom plates charged up to opposite polarities and the capacitance per unit length of the line, including the empty space half-plane, is

$$C = (\epsilon_r + 1)\epsilon_0 \frac{2a}{b} \cdot \tag{4}$$

A zeroth-order quasi-static approximation has been employed to estimate the phase velocities and the characteristic impedances of CPWs. The approximation simply treats the CPW as a transmission line totally immersed in a dielectric with effective dielectric constant $(\epsilon_r+1)/2$. The resulting phase velocity is

$$v_{ph} = \left(\frac{2}{\epsilon_r + 1}\right)^{1/2} c \tag{5}$$

where c is the velocity of light in free space and the characteristic impedance is

$$Z_0 \doteq \frac{1}{Cv_{ph}} \cdot \tag{6}$$

The ratio v_{ph}/c is shown in Fig. 5 as a function of ϵ_r. In Fig. 6 the characteristic impedance Z_0 is shown as a function of a_1/b_1 with the relative dielectric constant ϵ_r as a parameter ranging from unity to 250. Experimental confirmation has been obtained at three points shown on the same figure with transmission lines fabricated on substrates of relative dielectric constant $\epsilon_r = 9.5$, 16, and 130, respectively. The calculated characteristic impedance of a parallel-strip coplanar line, the dual of the CPW, is shown in Fig. 7 as a function of a_1/b_1 with the relative dielectric constant ϵ_r of the substrate as a parameter [4]. The configuration of this line can be found on the same figure.

The thickness of the dielectric substrate becomes less critical with higher relative dielectric constants. In the CPW configuration the characteristic impedance increases by less than 10 percent when the thickness of the substrate is reduced from infinity to $b_1 - a_1$, the width of the slots, for infinitely large ϵ_r. In practice, the thickness t of the substrate should be one or two times the width of the slots. It is obvious that the finite thickness of the substrate will influence the dispersion characteristics of the transmission line but no estimate has been made on the extent of the effect. The experimentally measured dispersion characteristic of a coplanar waveguide fabricated on a single-crystal rutile substrate is shown on the frequency versus βL plot of Fig. 8. It is not known what portion of the dispersion is caused by the crystal anisotropy of the substrate and what portion is attributed to the inherent characteristics of the CPW mode of propagation on a dielectric half-space.

At microwave frequencies up to X band the attenuation of a CPW is due mainly to the copper loss of the conductors if the loss tangent of the dielectric is 0.001 or smaller. Measurements made on a 16.6-ohm CPW fabricated on a rutile substrate ($\epsilon_r \cong 130$, $k = \frac{1}{3}$, center conductor width is 0.025

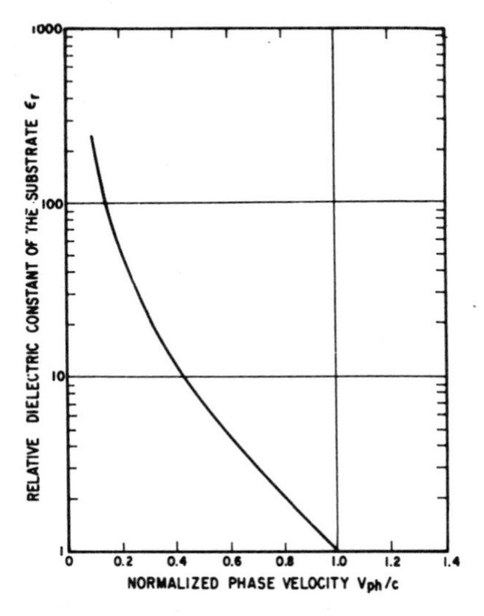

Fig. 5. Relationship between the relative dielectric constant ϵ_r of the substrate and the normalized phase velocity v_{ph}/c in a CPW.

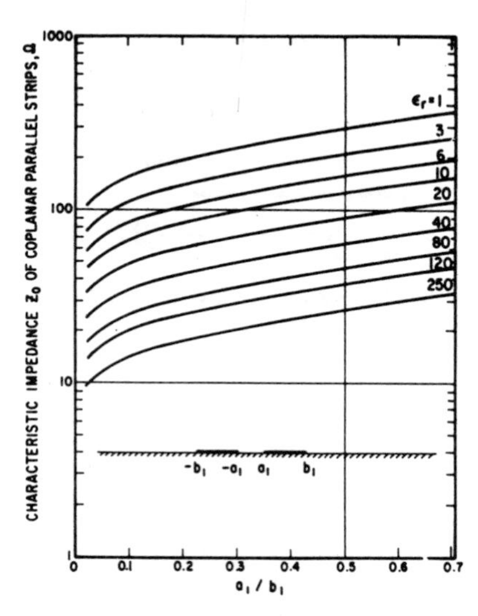

Fig. 7. Characteristic impedance Z_0 of coplanar parallel strips as a function of the ratio a_1/b_1 with the relative dielectric constant ϵ_r as a parameter.

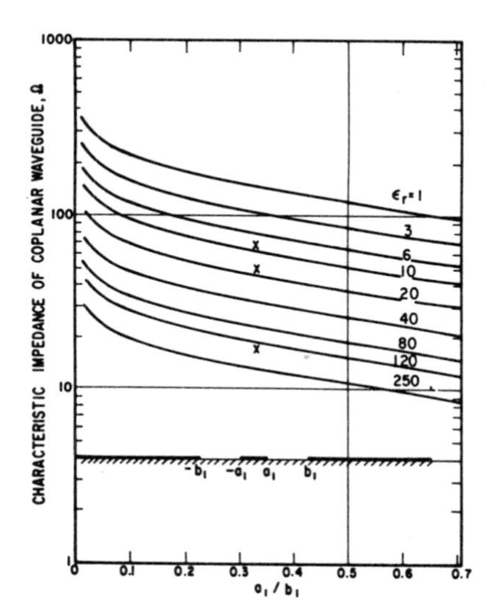

Fig. 6. Characteristic impedance Z_0 of CPW as a function of the ratio a_1/b_1 with the relative dielectric constant ϵ_r as a parameter

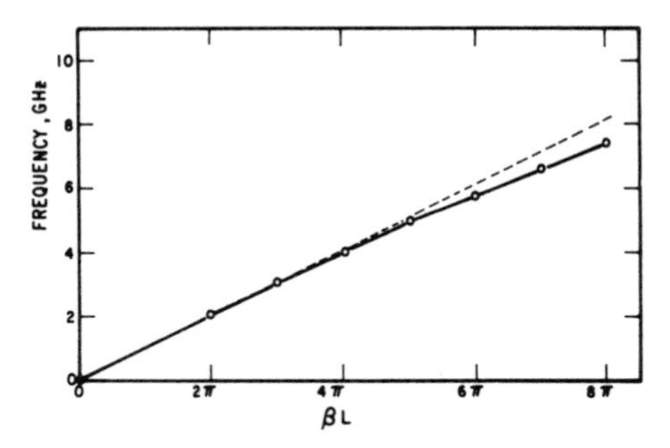

Fig. 8. Dispersion characteristics of a CPW on a TiO_2 substrate.

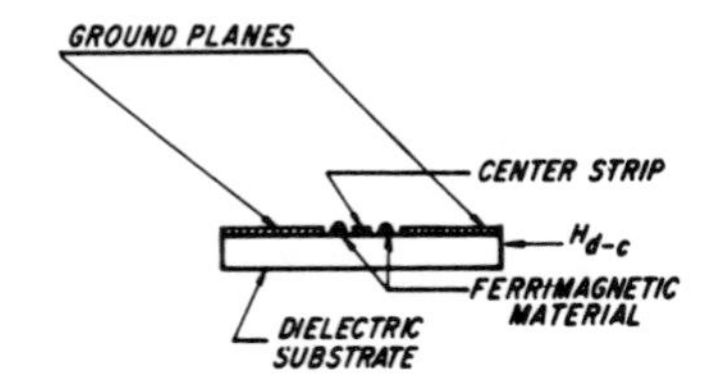

Fig. 9. Resonant isolator or differential phase shifter in CPW configurations.

inch, thickness of gold film is 2 microns, thickness of the dielectric substrate is 0.025 inch), yielded a Q of 173 at 4 GHz, corresponding to an attenuation of only 0.158 dB per wavelength.

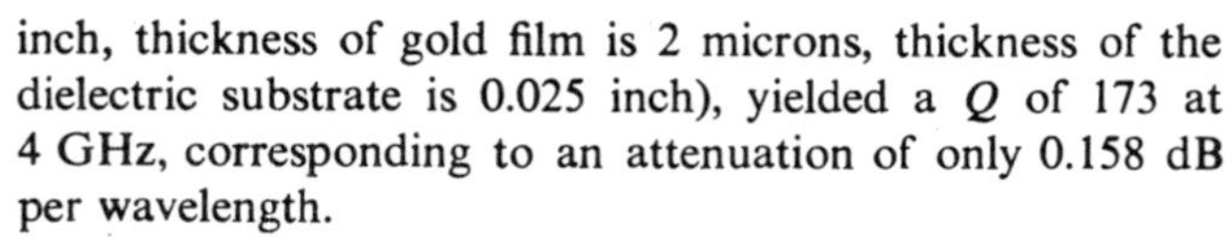

Other design considerations include radiation problems when the total distance from one ground plane to another approaches $\lambda/2$. This will pose a limit on the dielectric constant of the substrate employed at a given frequency and the transverse dimension of the transmission line. CPWs can be easily adapted to coaxial systems using OSM connectors. Broad-band (2–12 GHz) matching has been achieved with a 50-ohm CPW deposited on a magnesium oxide substrate with $\epsilon_r = 16$.

Nonreciprocal gyromagnetic devices such as resonant isolators and differential phase shifters have been fabricated by attaching ferrimagnetic slabs at the air–dielectric interface between the conductors, as shown in Fig. 9. A differential phase shifter fabricated on an all-magnetic garnet substrate has also been built. A transverse dc magnetic field parallel to the surface of the substrate is required to provide appropriate bias conditions As shown in Fig. 10, a CPW ferrimagnetic-resonance isolator built on the surface perpendicular to the c axis of a single rutile crystal provides 37-dB isolation at the center frequency of 6 GHz while the forward attenuation is below 2 dB. Overall length of the line is 0.8 inch including a quarter-wave transformer at each end. The center conductor width is 0.030 inch, $k = 0.33$, and the substrate is 0.025 inch thick. Strips of Trans-Tech G-1000 YIG

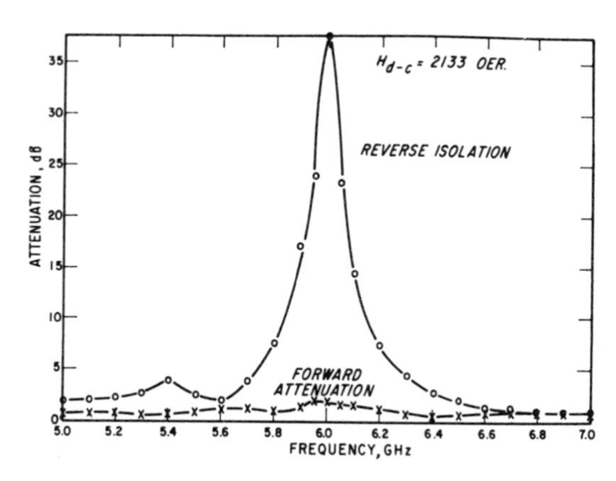

Fig. 10. Performance of a CPW ferrimagnetic-resonant isolator on a single-crystal rutile substrate.

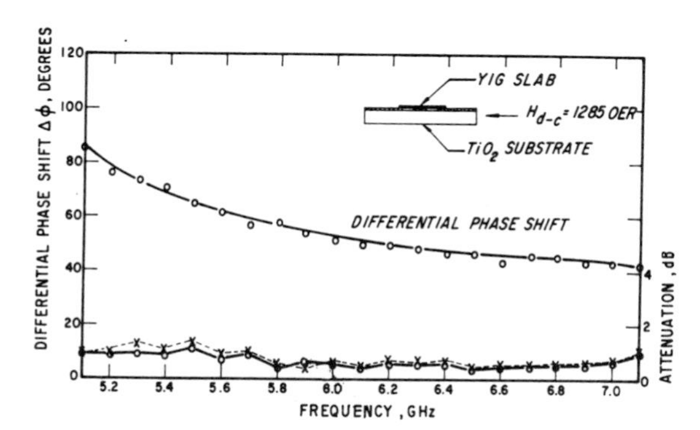

Fig. 11. Performance of a CPW ferrimagnetic differential phase shifter on a single-crystal rutile substrate.

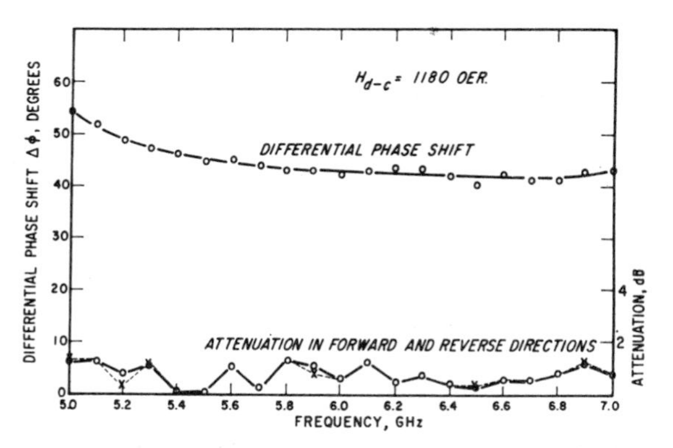

Fig. 12. Performance of a CPW ferrimagnetic differential phase shifter on a YIG substrate.

(0.010 inch×0.005 inch×0.60 inch) are attached by low-loss cement to the rutile surface with the center line of the YIG 0.010 inch from the ground planes. The performance of a phase shifter whose configurations are similar to the previously discussed isolator, are shown in Fig. 11. No attempt has been made to equalize the amount of differential phase shift across the band of frequencies. Average differential phase shift is over 45° while the insertion loss in either direction is less than 1 dB between 5.6 GHz and 7.1 GHz. Higher loss is observed at the lower frequencies which are near the ferrimagnetic resonance. Differential phase shift and loss data for a CPW fabricated on a YIG substrate is shown in Fig. 12. A tapered ceramic piece (0.800 inch long, 10° tapering on both ends, $\epsilon_r = 83$) is placed on top to provide the circularly polarized magnetic vector in the ferrite. The amount of differential phase shift varies little with frequency beyond 5.5 GHz. Insertion loss of 1.3 dB or less has been measured from 5.0 GHz to 7.0 GHz without special effort to match the device to the 50-ohm test system. These preliminary results demonstrate the gyromagnetic nonreciprocal device capabilities of coplanar waveguides.

In summary, the practicality of a novel microwave integrated circuit transmission line suitable for nonreciprocal gyromagnetic device applications has been demonstrated. Some preliminary calculations for characteristic impedance, phase velocity, and attenuation characteristics are presented and compared with experimental results. The coplanar configuration of the transmission system not only permits easy shunt connections of external elements, it also adapts well to the fabrication of monolithic integrated circuits.

Acknowledgment

The author wishes to thank H. Davis for his able assistance in preparation and during experimentation and R. Goodrich for the deposition of thin film circuits. Constant encouragement and valuable suggestions from B. Hershenov and L. S. Napoli are gratefully acknowledged.

References

[1] B. J. Duncan, L. Swern, K. Tomiyasu, and J. Hannwacker, "Design considerations for broad-band ferrite coaxial line isolators," *Proc. IRE*, vol. 45, pp. 483–490, April 1957.

[2] W. R. Smythe, *Static and Dynamic Electricity*. New York: McGraw-Hill, 1950.

[3] E. Jahnke and F. Emde, *Tables of Functions with Formulae and Curves*, 4th ed. New York: Dover, 1945.

[4] R. F. Frazita, "Transmission line properties of coplanar parallel strips on a dielectric sheet," M.S. thesis, Polytechnic Institute of Brooklyn, Brooklyn, N. Y., 1965.

ANALYSIS OF CONDUCTOR-BACKED COPLANAR WAVEGUIDE

Indexing terms: Waveguides, Spectral analysis

The transmission properties of a coplanar waveguide printed on conductor-backed substrates are analysed using the spectral-domain technique. For a fixed substrate thickness, the characteristic impedance and the phase constant may be varied independently by simply adjusting the widths of the centre strip and the slots in the transmission line.

Introduction: Recently, remarkable progress has been achieved in GaAs monolithic microwave integrated circuits (MMIC). It is, therefore, necessary to acquire the knowledge of propagation properties in various structures appearing in GaAs MMICs.

The structure in Fig. 1 is a modification of the coplanar waveguide in that it has an additional ground plane. The latter is useful to increase mechanical strength of the circuit as the GaAs substrate is typically thin and fragile. To date, no analytical results have been reported on the propagation characteristics for such a structure. In this letter, the analysis based on the spectral-domain technique is described and the resulting propagation constants and characteristic impedances are reported.

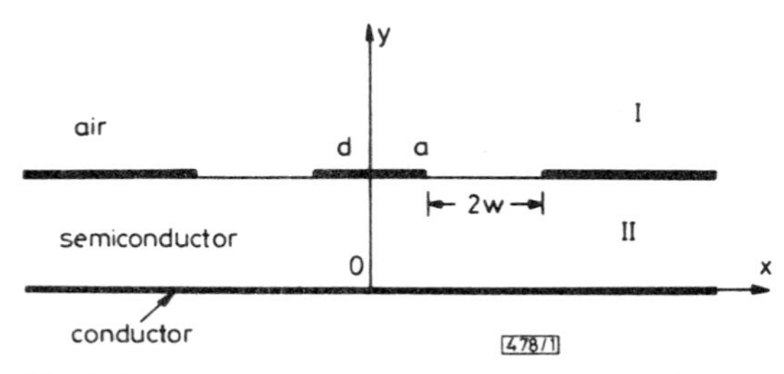

Fig. 1 *Cross-sectional view of conductor-backed coplanar waveguide*

Method: The spectral-domain technique has been successfully applied to analyse a number of planar transmission lines.[1–3] A simple method for formulating the dyadic Green's functions in the spectral domain has been proposed by Itoh,[4] which is based on the transverse equivalent transmission lines for a spectral wave and on a simple co-ordinate transformation. By following this method, a set of coupled equations result:

$$\begin{bmatrix} \tilde{Y}_{xx}(\alpha, \beta) & \tilde{Y}_{xz}(\alpha, \beta) \\ \tilde{Y}_{zx}(\alpha, \beta) & \tilde{Y}_{zz}(\alpha, \beta) \end{bmatrix} \begin{bmatrix} \tilde{E}_x(\alpha) \\ \tilde{E}_z(\alpha) \end{bmatrix} = \begin{bmatrix} \tilde{J}_x(\alpha) \\ \tilde{J}_z(\alpha) \end{bmatrix} \tag{1}$$

where $\tilde{Y}_{xx}$, $\tilde{Y}_{xz}$, $\tilde{Y}_{zx}$ and $\tilde{Y}_{zz}$ are dyadic Green's functions similar to those derived in Reference 4, and $\tilde{E}_x$, $\tilde{E}_z$, $\tilde{J}_x$ and $\tilde{J}_z$ are the Fourier transforms of x- and z-components of the electric fields (E_x and E_z) and current densities (J_x and J_z), respectively. Alpha (α) is the Fourier transform variable and β is the phase constant that we seek. The solution is then found by means of Galerkin's method in the spectral domain, in which the slot field components $E_x(x)$ and $E_z(x)$ are expanded in terms of complete sets of known basis functions:

$$E_x(x) = \sum_{n=1}^{\infty} c_n E_{xn}$$

$$E_z(x) = \sum_{n=1}^{\infty} d_n E_{zn}$$

where c_n and d_n are unknown coefficients.

After taking Fourier transforms of these expressions, they are substituted into eqn. 1. Then the inner products of the resultant equations with each of the basis functions are performed and result in homogeneous linear simultaneous equations as the right-hand side becomes identically zero by the inner product process.[1,2] By equating the determinant to zero, the eigenvalue β is obtained. The relative magnitudes of c_n and d_n are then obtained, and provide information necessary to calculate the modal field and the characteristic impedance.

In the study, the following sets of basis functions are chosen for the fields in each slot:

$$E_{xn} = \frac{\cos\left(\frac{n\pi}{2w}x\right)}{\sqrt{(w^2 - x^2)}}, \quad n = 0, 2, 4, \ldots$$

$$\frac{\sin\left(\frac{n\pi}{2w}x\right)}{\sqrt{(w^2 - x^2)}}, \quad n = 1, 3, 5, \ldots$$

$$E_{zn} = \frac{\cos\left(\frac{n\pi}{2w}x\right)}{\sqrt{(w^2 - x^2)}}, \quad n = 1, 3, 5, \ldots$$

$$\frac{\sin\left(\frac{n\pi}{2w}x\right)}{\sqrt{(w^2 - x^2)}}, \quad n = 2, 4, 6, \ldots$$

These sets of basis functions satisfy the edge conditions at the edge and their Fourier sine and cosine transformations are simple zero-order Bessel functions of the first kind.

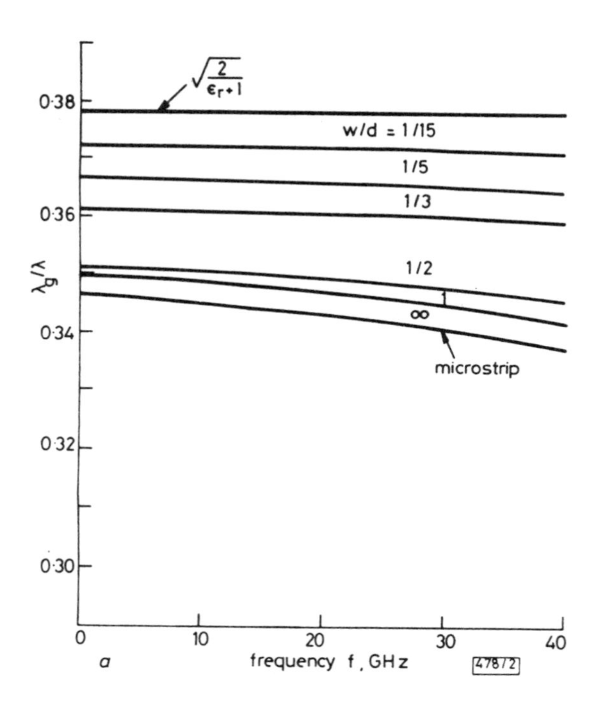

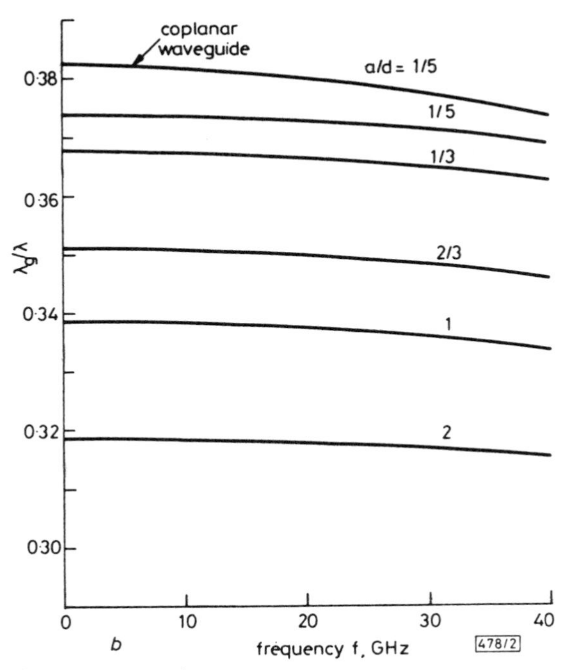

Fig. 2 *Dispersion characteristics*

a $\varepsilon_r = 13$ $d = 150\ \mu m$ $a/d = 1/3$

b $\varepsilon_r = 13$ $a = 100\ \mu m$ $w/a = 1/2$

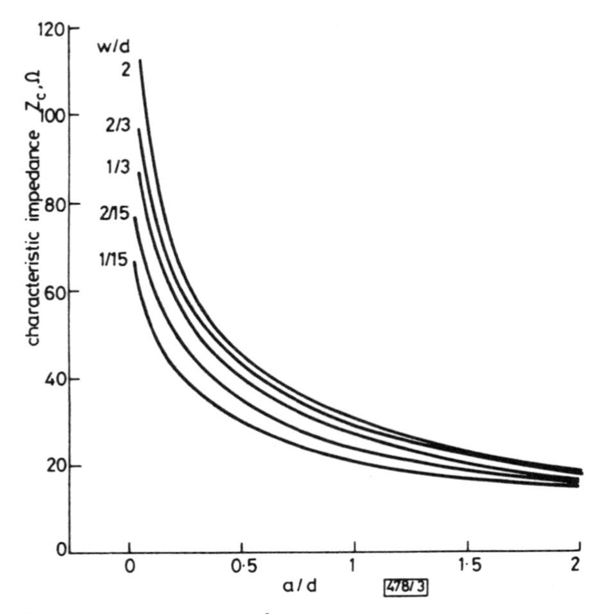

Fig. 3 *Characteristic impedance*

$\varepsilon_r = 13$ $d = 150\ \mu m$

Numerical results: The conductor-backed coplanar waveguide has been studied for a wide range of geometric parameters. Fig. 2 shows typical results of the dispersion property, assuming GaAs as the substrate ($\varepsilon_r = 13{\cdot}0$). Aspect ratios a/d and w/d are varied as parameters. Since the present structure is a mixture of a microstrip line and a coplanar waveguide, properties of either become predominant depending on the structural parameters. As the slot width increases for a fixed substrate thickness, the characteristics approach that of microstrip line. This behaviour is shown in Fig. 2*a*. On the other hand, when the slot width is fixed and the thickness increases, the behaviour approaches the coplanar waveguide case, as depicted in Fig. 2*b*.

For a moderate aspect ratio (e.g. $a/d = 1/3$, $w/d = 1/3$), the transmission line becomes less dispersive than the corresponding microstrip line with the same aspect ratio ($a/d = 1/3$). This suggests that we may define the characteristic impedance of the transmission line as $Z_c = Z_0/\sqrt{\varepsilon_{eff}}$, where ε_{eff} is the effective dielectric constant defined as $(\beta/k)^2$ and Z_0 is the characteristic impedance when $\varepsilon_r = 1$. The impedance Z_c computed in this manner is plotted in Fig. 3. It is observed that the characteristic impedance decreases as the slot widths decrease, while the phase constant is relatively unaffected. Therefore, by adjusting both centre strip width and slot widths, independent control of the phase constant and the characteristic impedance may be obtained.

The number of basis functions required for accuracy is largely dependent on the aspect ratios. For small w/a and w/d, only E_{x0} is required since both the slot coupling effect and the effect of the ground-backing are small. For larger w/a, E_{x1} is needed to represent the stronger coupling effect between the slots. Finally, when the thickness becomes comparable to the slot width, more basis functions are required for accurate results. In this study, up to seven basis functions have been used for some extreme cases. The computation time for such a solution is about 5 s on a CDC Dual Cyber 170/750.

Acknowledgment: This work was supported by the Office of Naval Research N00014-79-0053, Joint Services Electronics Program F49620-79-C-0101 and US Army Research Office contract DAAG29-81-K-0053.

Y. C. SHIH
T. ITOH

Department of Electrical Engineering
The University of Texas at Austin
Austin, TX 78712, USA

30th April 1982

References

1 ITOH, T., and MITTRA, R.: 'Spectral-domain approach for calculating the dispersion characteristics of microstrip lines', *IEEE Trans.*, 1973, **MTT-21**, pp. 496–499

2 ITOH, T., and MITTRA, R.: 'Dispersion characteristics of slot lines', *Electron. Lett.*, 1971, **7**, pp. 364–365

3 KNORR, J., and KUCHLER, K.-D.: 'Analysis of coupled slots and coplanar strips on dielectric substrate', *IEEE Trans.*, 1975, **MTT-23**, pp. 541–548

4 ITOH, T.: 'Spectral domain immittance approach for dispersion characteristics of generalized printed transmission lines', *ibid.*, 1980, **MTT-28**, pp. 733–736

0013-5194/82/120538-03$1.50/0

ANALYTICAL FORMULAS FOR COPLANAR LINES IN HYBRID AND MONOLITHIC MICs

Indexing terms: Integrated circuits, Microwave circuits and systems

Some analytical formulas for the parameters of coplanar lines are discussed and validated; a chart is given for the design of coplanar waveguides on GaAs. The formulas discussed here, together with those presented previously by us (1983) represent a suitable set for the design of coplanar lines for hybrid and monolithic MICs (microwave integrated circuits).

Owing to the increasing popularity of coplanar waveguides (CPW, Fig. 1) and coplanar striplines (CPS, Fig. 3) for the design of hybrid and monolithic microwave integrated circuits, it is important to have a set of reliable analytical formulas for their quasi-TEM electrical parameters (characteristic impedance Z_ϕ and effective dielectric constant ε_{eff}). While exact formulas are available for lines having infinitely thick substrates, the analytical expressions published so far for lines having finite substrates are approximate in principle and should be validated by a more rigorous (numerical) analysis. The purpose of the present letter is to assess the validity of some formulas published in the literature, also suggesting possible improvements where results of questionable correctness are found. Finally, an example of design chart is presented for integrated coplanar waveguides on GaAs substrate.

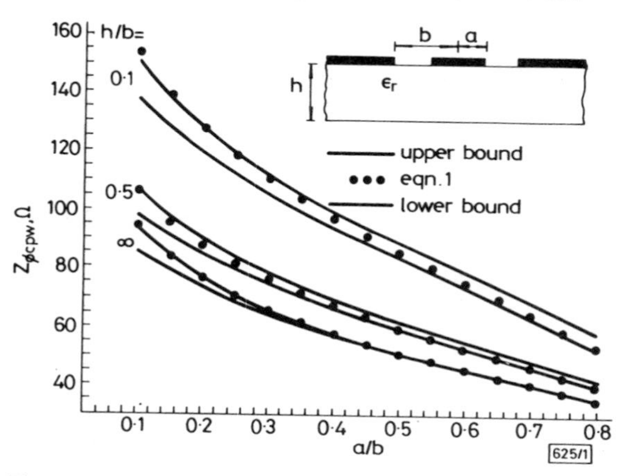

Fig. 1 *Characteristic impedance of coplanar waveguides (CPW) as a function of the shape ratio $k = a/b$, taking the normalised substrate thickness h/b as a parameter*
$\varepsilon_r = 10$

Analytical expressions for coplanar waveguides are found in References 1 and 2. Gupta's formulas are obtained by fitting the data published in Reference 3, and only hold for moderately thick substrates ($h > b - a$), while Fouad-Hanna's formulas are based on an approximated theory whose general validity is questionable. However, they can deal with lines having arbitrarily thin substrates and yield the correct limit for $h \to 0$. A comparison has been carried out between the results obtained through a spectral-domain variational analysis (Figs. 1 and 2) and Fouad-Hanna's expressions:

$$Z_{\phi(CPW)} = \frac{30\pi}{\sqrt{\varepsilon_{eff}}} \frac{K(k')}{K(k)} \tag{1}$$

$$\varepsilon_{eff} = 1 + \frac{\varepsilon_r - 1}{2} \frac{K(k')K(k_1)}{K(k)K(k_1')} \tag{2}$$

where

$$k = a/b \tag{3a}$$

$$k_1 = \sinh(\pi a/2h)/\sinh(\pi b/2h) \tag{3b}$$

K is the complete elliptic integral of the first kind, and $k' = \sqrt{(1 - k^2)}$. As a result, it has been found that eqns. 1 and 2 are satisfactorily accurate in a wide range of substrate thicknesses and approach the variational upper limit for small

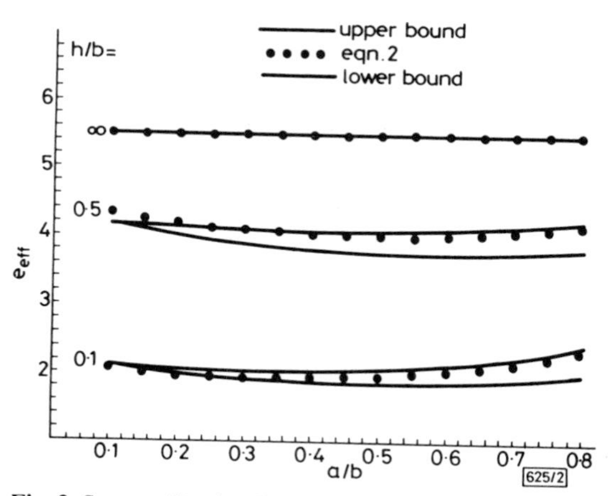

Fig. 2 *Same as Fig. 1: effective dielectric permittivity*

shape ratios ($k = a/b$) and the lower limit for large shape ratios, as could be expected from the variational trial functions used in the analysis; besides, Fouad-Hanna's formulas yield practically the same results as Gupta's for $h > b - a$, though Gupta's expressions tend to slightly underestimate the characteristic impedance, with respect to the variational lower limit, for rather thin substrates. Good agreement with published experimental values is found to exist for noncritical cases (i.e. for h large), as it happens for Gupta's formulas,[2] whereas for very thin substrates the available experimental data are of uncertain interpretation. It ought to be noticed that the formulas for CPW with lower ground plane, also published in Reference 1, are of dubious validity. This has been pointed out in a previous letter,[4] where a different set of formulas for this structure is proposed.

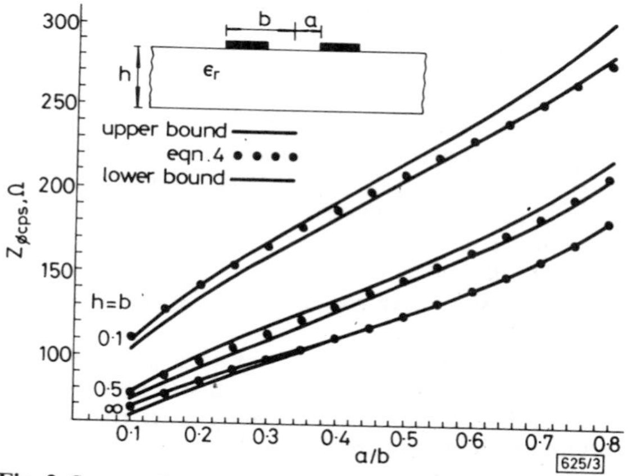

Fig. 3 *Same as Fig. 1 for coplanar striplines (CPS)*

An application of Fouad-Hanna's method to the CPS has been tried in Reference 5, while Gupta's formulas for the same structure are reported in Reference 2. Unfortunately, the analysis published in Reference 5 seems to lead to uncorrect results; in particular, the conclusion according to which the impedance of the line increases when the substrate thickness decreases is unacceptable, and leads to absurd consequences in the limit $h \to 0$. However, reliable formulas for the CPS can be obtained through the assumption that the phase velocities of complementary lines (as CPW and CPS) are equal. Although this is strictly valid only for lines in homogeneous or semi-infinite media, the aforementioned assumption approximately holds for TEM lines on finite substrates as well, and is also used in Gupta's formulas. The proposed set for the parameters of CPS with finite substrate is therefore

$$Z_{\phi(CPS)} = \frac{120\pi}{\sqrt{\varepsilon_{eff}}} \frac{K(k)}{K(k')} \tag{4}$$

while ε_{eff} is always given by eqn. 2. A comparison with the variational upper and lower bounds for the impedance is

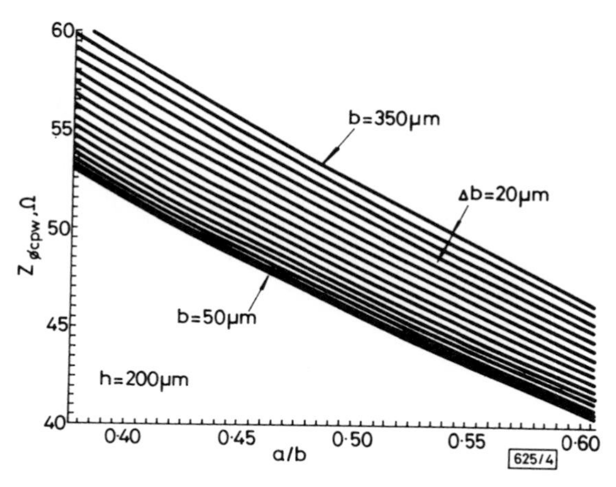

Fig. 4 *Design chart for coplanar waveguides on GaAs substrate ($\varepsilon_r = 13$)*

Characteristic impedance is given as a function of shape ratio $k = a/b$, taking half of the ground-plane spacing (b) as a parameter. The substrate thickness is $h = 200\ \mu m$

shown in Fig. 3; for the effective permittivity, the results coincide with those reported in Fig. 2.

As a possible application for the analytical formulas discussed before, a design chart (Fig. 4) is presented for the design of CPW on GaAs substrate ($\varepsilon_r = 13$). The thickness of the substrate is typical of MIC applications ($h = 200\ \mu m$); the range of impedances considered covers the interval 40–60 Ω. One clearly sees that, in order to realise lines having constant impedance (e.g. 50 Ω) with different ground-plane spacings ($2b$) also the ratio $a/b = k$ has to be changed, whereas for semi-infinite substrates keeping k constant is enough to this purpose.

G. GHIONE
C. NALDI

Department of Electronics
Politecnico di Torino
Corso Duca degli Abruzzi 24, Torino, Italy

17th January 1984

References

1 VEYRES, C., and FOUAD-HANNA, V.: 'Extension of the application of conformal mapping techniques to coplanar lines with finite dimensions', *Int. J. Electron.*, 1980, **48**, pp. 47–56

2 GUPTA, K. G., GARG, R., and BAHL, I. J.: 'Microstrip lines and slotlines' (Artech House, 1979), Par. 7.3.1

3 DAVIS, M. E., WILLIAMS, E. W., and CELESTINI, C.: 'Finite-boundary corrections to the coplanar waveguide analysis', *IEEE Trans.*, 1973, **MTT-21**, pp. 594–596

4 GHIONE, G., and NALDI, C.: 'Parameters of coplanar waveguides with lower ground plane', *Electron. Lett.*, 1983, **19**, pp. 734–735

5 FOUAD-HANNA, V.: 'Finite boundary corrections to coplanar stripline analysis', *ibid.*, 1980, **16**, pp. 604–606

Slot Line on a Dielectric Substrate

SEYMOUR B. COHN, FELLOW, IEEE

***Abstract*—Slot line consists of a narrow gap in a conductive coating on one side of a dielectric substrate, the other side of the substrate being bare. If the substrate's permittivity is sufficiently high, such as $\epsilon_r \doteq 10$ to 30, the slot-mode wavelength will be much smaller than free-space wavelength, and the fields will be closely confined near the slot. Possible applications of slot line to filters, couplers, ferrite devices, and circuits containing semiconductor elements are discussed. Slot line can be used either alone or with microstrip line on the opposite side of the substrate. A "second-order" analysis yields formulas for slot-line wavelength, phase velocity, group velocity, characteristic impedance, and effect of adjacent electric and magnetic walls.**

Manuscript received February 17, 1969; revised May 15, 1969. This work was performed for Stanford Research Institute as a part of their study program for U. S. Army Electronics Command, Contract DAAB07-68-c-0088. This paper covers material presented at the 1968 G-MTT Symposium, Detroit, Mich., May 20–22, 1968.

The author is a consultant to Stanford Research Institute, Menlo Park, Calif.

I. Introduction

SLOT LINE consists of a slot or gap in a conductive coating on a dielectric substrate, as shown in Fig. 1. Both resonant and propagating slots in metal sheets have been used as radiating antenna elements (see [1], [2], and [3], and their bibliographies). For slot line to be practical as a transmission line, radiation must be minimized. This is accomplished through the use of a high permittivity substrate, which causes the slot-mode wavelength λ' to be small compared to free-space wavelength λ, and thereby results in the fields being closely confined to the slot with negligible radiation loss. For example, if $\epsilon_r = 20$, then $\lambda'/\lambda \approx \frac{1}{3}$, and analysis shows the slot-mode fields to be sharply attenuated at a distance $r/\lambda = \frac{1}{8}$, or $r = 0.5$ inch at 3 GHz.

Fig. 2(a) shows the slot-mode fields in a cross-sectional view. A voltage difference exists between the slot edges. The

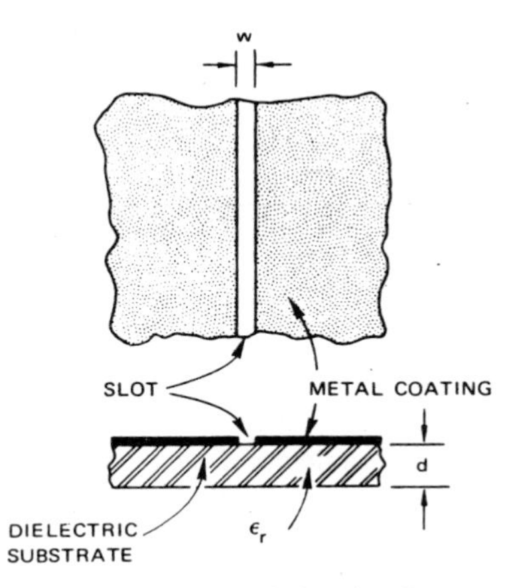

Fig. 1. Slot line on a dielectric substrate.

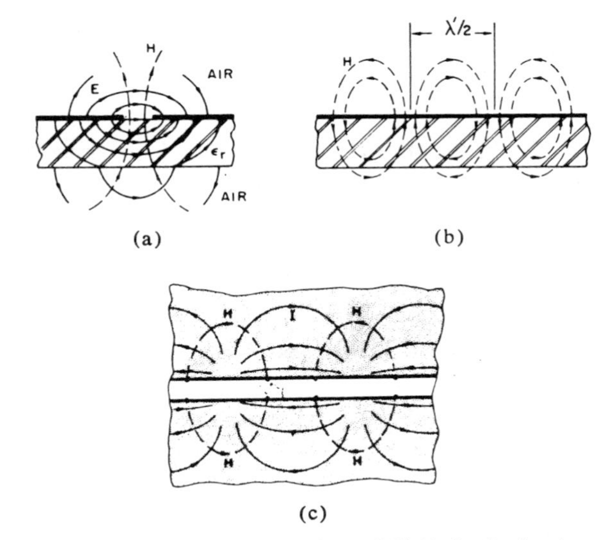

Fig. 2. Field and current distribution. (a) Field distribution in cross section. (b) H field in longitudinal section. (c) Current distribution on metal surface.

electric field extends across the slot; the magnetic field is perpendicular to the slot. Because the voltage occurs across the slot, the configuration is especially convenient for connecting shunt elements such as diodes, resistors, and capacitors. The longitudinal view in Fig. 2(b) shows that in the air regions the magnetic field lines curve and return to the slot at half-wavelength intervals. Consequently, a propagating wave has elliptically polarized regions that can be usefully applied in creating certain ferrite components. The current paths on the conducting surface are shown in Fig. 2(c). The surface–current density is greatest at the edges of the slot and decreases rapidly with distance from the slot. A propagating wave has regions of elliptically polarized current and magnetic field in this view, also.

An interesting possibility for microwave integrated circuits is the use of slot lines on one side of a substrate and microstrip lines on the other. When close to each other, coupling between the two types of lines will exist, and when sufficiently far apart they will be independent. Coupling between a slot

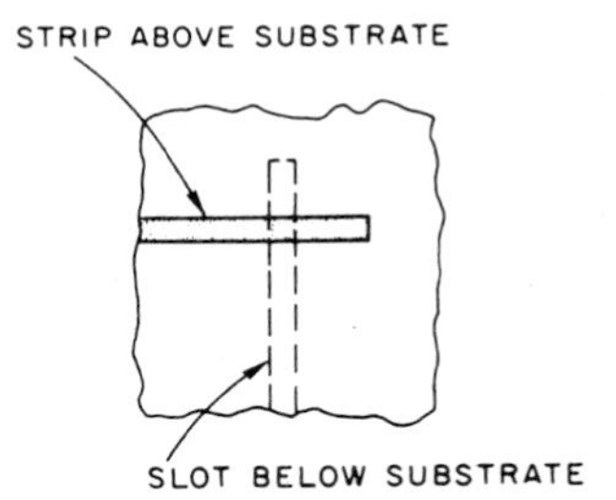

Fig. 3. Simple transition between slot line and microstrip.

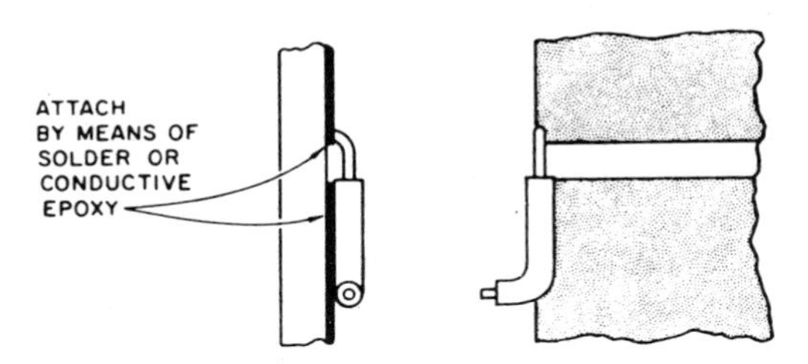

Fig. 4. Broad-band transition between slot line and miniature semirigid coaxial line.

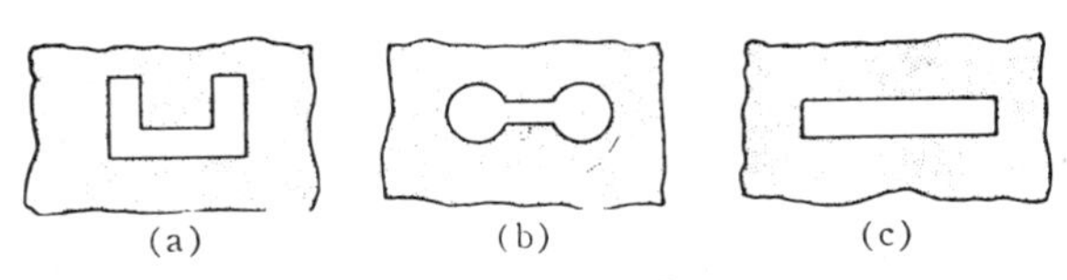

Fig. 5. Resonant slots.

and a strip can be used intentionally in certain components. For example, parallel lengths of slot and strip can be made to act as a directional coupler. If a slot and strip cross each other at right angles, as in Fig. 3, coupling will be especially tight, and a transition covering approximately 30-percent bandwidth can be achieved when the strip and slot widths are optimally related, and when the strip and slot are extended approximately one-quarter wavelength beyond the point of crossing. With matching techniques, a bandwidth of an octave or so should be feasible.

Fig. 4 shows one way that a wide-band transition between miniature-cross-section coaxial line and slot line can be made. Additional structural details may be needed to obtain optimum matching and to prevent radiation loss.

A half-wavelength slot, as shown in Fig. 5(a), can be used as a resonator. If desired, the resonant slot may be made more compact by capacitively loading its center, as in Fig. 5(b), or by bending it, as in Fig. 5(c). Applications to bandstop and bandpass filters are shown in Fig. 6. In the bandstop example, the terminating lines are microstrip, and in the bandpass example they are slot lines. Many other filter configurations are feasible, using slots alone or slots with strips on the opposite side of the substrate.

The basic electrical parameters of slot line are the characteristic impedance Z_0 and the phase velocity v. Because of the non-TEM nature of the slot-line mode these parameters are not constant, but vary with frequency at a rather slow rate per octave. This behavior contrasts with quasi-TEM

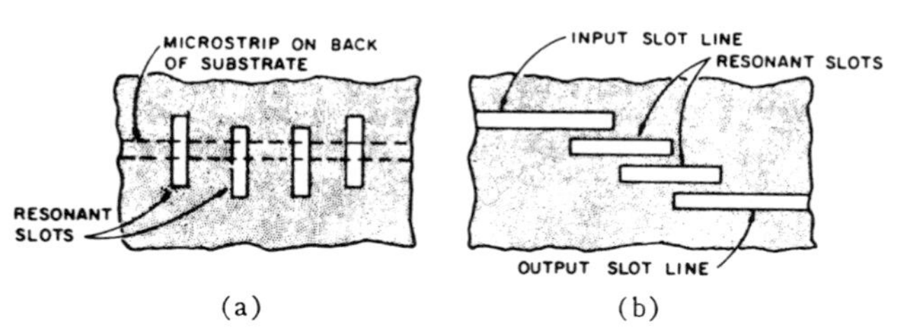

Fig. 6. Filter applications. (a) Bandstop filter. (b) Bandpass filter.

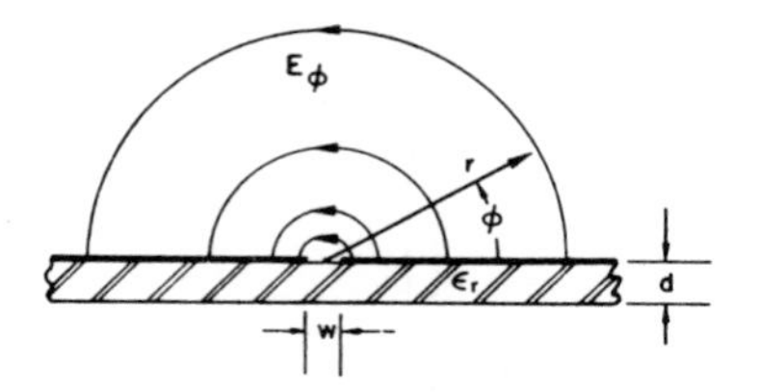

Fig. 7. Cylindrical coordinates with axis on center line of slot.

microstrip line, whose Z_0 and v are first-order independent of frequency. On the other hand, slot line differs from waveguide in that it has no cutoff frequency. Propagation along the slot occurs at all frequencies down to $f=0$, where, if the metal-coated substrate is assumed infinite in length and width, v/c approaches unity and Z_0 approaches zero. Other parameters treated in this paper are the ratio of phase and group velocities v/v_g and the effect of adjacent walls. Attenuation has not yet been treated, but data thus far indicates it to be about the same as for microstrip on the same substrate [20].

II. Approximations for Slot Line

Several references on slot antennas were found in which the presence of a substantial amount of dielectric material in or near the slot was taken into account. Strumwasser, Short, Stegen, and Miller [4] have studied experimentally the effects of filling a slot in a thick metal plate with dielectric material. They give data on resonant-length reduction and radiation resistance coupled into an air-dielectric TEM line, Bailey [5] has measured resonant length and radiation conductance of a slot in a waveguide wall covered by a protective layer of dielectric material. Galejs [6] has analyzed theoretically a slot in a zero-thickness, perfectly conducting sheet separating free space from a lossy dielectric medium of infinite extent. For example, a slot radiator in a wire mesh on the surface of the ground would be simulated by this model.

Galejs utilizes an integral-equation method to obtain complex expressions for radiation efficiency and other parameters of the slot antenna. His *zero-order* solution for the propagation constant along the slot can be easily modified into the following simple formula for relative wavelength:

$$\frac{\lambda'}{\lambda} = \sqrt{\frac{2}{\epsilon_r + 1}}\,. \tag{1}$$

Since wavelength is inversely proportional to the square root of permittivity, an effective permittivity of a uniform medium replacing the two different dielectric half spaces may be defined as

$$\epsilon_r' = \frac{\epsilon_r + 1}{2}\,. \tag{2}$$

The *second-order* solution for slot line derived in this paper shows that (1) is a fair approximation for slot line, yielding values within about 10 percent in typical slot-line cases. The second-order solution shows quantitatively how λ'/λ varies with the parameters d, w, ϵ_r, and λ.

The field components on the air side of the slot can be computed quite easily as a function of λ, λ', and distance r from the slot (Fig. 7). If we assume $w/\lambda \ll 1$, then the electric voltage across the slot may be replaced by an equivalent line source of magnetic current. At a distance r at least several times larger than w the longitudinal component of magnetic field is given by [7]

$$H_z = A H_0^{(1)}(k_c r) \tag{3}$$

where $H_n^{(1)}(x)$ is the Hankel function of first kind, order n, and argument x. The coefficient k_c is

$$k_c = \sqrt{\gamma_z^2 + k^2} = j\frac{2\pi}{\lambda}\sqrt{\left(\frac{\lambda}{\lambda'}\right)^2 - 1} \tag{4}$$

since $\gamma_z = j2\pi/\lambda_z = j2\pi/\lambda'$ and $k = 2\pi/\lambda$.

By (1), a zero-order value of k_c is

$$k_c = j\frac{2\pi}{\lambda}\sqrt{\frac{\epsilon_r - 1}{2}}\,. \tag{5}$$

The other field components are H_r and E_ϕ. They are related to H_z by [7]

$$H_r = -\frac{\gamma_z}{k_c^2}\frac{\partial H_z}{\partial r} = \frac{A}{\sqrt{1 - \left(\frac{\lambda'}{\lambda}\right)^2}} H_1^{(1)}(k_c r) \tag{6}$$

$$E_\phi = \frac{j\omega\mu}{k_c^2}\frac{\partial H_z}{\partial r} = \frac{-\eta(\lambda'/\lambda)A}{\sqrt{1 - \left(\frac{\lambda'}{\lambda}\right)^2}} H_1^{(1)}(k_c r) \tag{7}$$

where the identity $d[H_0^{(1)}(x)]/dx = -H_1^{(1)}(x)$ was used.

The Hankel function of imaginary argument, $H_n^{(1)}(j|x|)$, approaches zero proportional to $e^{-|x|}/\sqrt{|x|}$ for $|x|$ large. Equation (4) shows that the argument $k_c r$ is imaginary for $\lambda'/\lambda < 1$. Hence a relative wavelength ratio less than unity is a sufficient condition to ensure decay of the slot-mode field with radial distance. As λ'/λ is decreased, the decay becomes sharper and the fields become more tightly bound to the slot.

A radius r_{cp} of circular polarization of the magnetic field requires $|H_z/H_r| = 1$. By means of (3) and (6), r_{cp} must satisfy

$$\left|\frac{H_1^{(1)}(k_c r_{cp})}{H_0^{(1)}(k_c r_{cp})}\right| = \sqrt{1 - \left(\frac{\lambda'}{\lambda}\right)^2}\,. \tag{8}$$

However, tables show that $|H_1^{(1)}(j|x|)|>|H_0^{(1)}(j|x|)|$ for all $|x|$ [8]. Since the right-hand side of (8) is less than one, a solution for r_{cp} does not exist. Nevertheless, elliptical polarization occurs for all r, and low axial ratios occur for r sufficiently large.

Also of interest is the ratio of voltage along a semicircular path at constant radius divided by the voltage directly across the slot. This ratio is

$$\frac{V(r)}{V}=\frac{k_c r H_1^{(1)}(k_c r)}{\lim\limits_{|x|\to 0}\left[|x|\,H_1^{(1)}(j\,|x|)\right]} = \frac{\pi}{2}\,k_c r\,|H_1^{(1)}(k_c r)|\,. \tag{9}$$

As an example of field decay, let $\epsilon_r=16$, $f=3$ GHz, and $\lambda=4$ inches. The zero-order value of λ'/λ is 0.343, and of $k_c r$ is 4.30 r, where r is in inches. At $r=0$, 0.7, 1.0, and 1.3 inches, $V(r)/V=1$, 0.120, 0.0382, and 0.0118, respectively. If a plane metal wall is positioned perpendicular to the radius vector at distance $r/2$ from the slot, an image of the slot will appear at distance $r/2$ behind the wall. The effect will be that of two equally excited parallel slots spaced by r. Thus if the metal wall is at distance 0.5 inch in the above example, $r=1$ inch and $V(r)/V$ of one slot is 0.0382, or -28.36 dB, at the other slot. Coupling between slots is even weaker than this, since only part of the total voltage $V(r)$ of one slot affects the other slot. Therefore, a wall or other perturbing object can be as close as $r=0.5$ inch with little effect on λ' or Z_0, and the fields and stored energy of the slot mode are mainly confined within this same radial distance. These conclusions have been verified both by experiment and by computations using the second-order solution.

III. Basis of Second-Order Solution

An analytical approach for slot line offering high accuracy is described in this section. The solution obtained by this approach will be referred to as *second-order.* A first-order solution offering intermediate complexity and accuracy between zero-order (1) and second-order equations would also be useful, but has not yet been completed.

The key feature of the approach used in the second-order solution is the introduction of boundary walls permitting the slot-line configuration to be treated as a rectangular-waveguide problem rather than as a problem in cylindrical coordinates. Thus the infinite orthogonal sets of relatively simple rectangular-waveguide modes apply rather than sets of cylindrical modes embodying all orders of Hankel functions.

Parameters evaluated in this paper are: relative-wavelength ratio λ'/λ, characteristic impedance Z_0, ratio of phase velocity to group velocity v/v_g, and the effect of nearby electric and magnetic walls.

Future plans are to adapt the second-order solution to yield the even- and odd-mode characteristic impedances and velocities of parallel slots, the effect of metal-coating thickness greater than zero, attenuation per unit length, unloaded

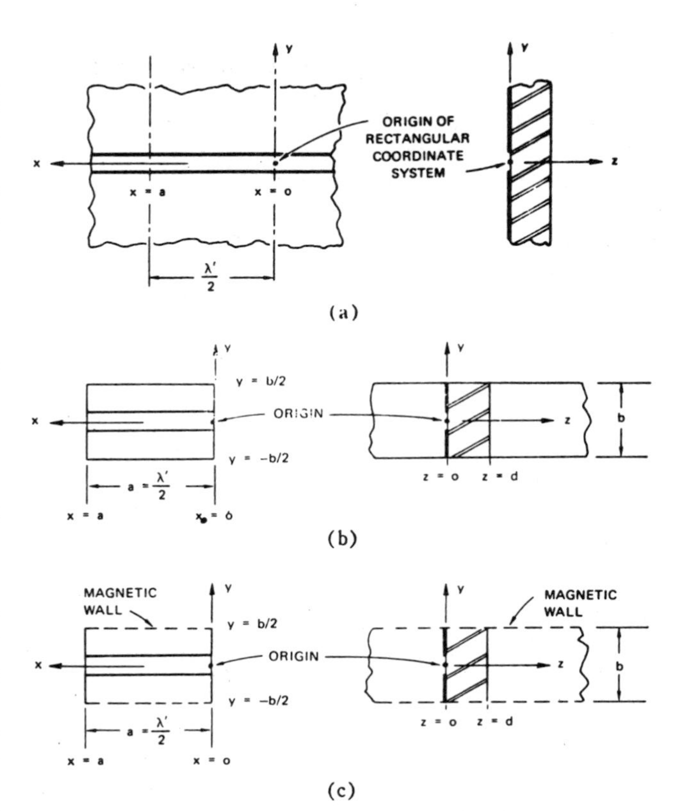

Fig. 8. Development of waveguide models for slot-line solution. (a) Insertion of transverse conducting planes at $x=0$ and a. (b) Insertion of conducting planes at $y=\pm b/2$. (c) Insertion of magnetic walls at $y=\pm b/2$.

Q of a resonant slot, and presence of more than one dielectric substrate on one or both sides of the slotted conductive sheet.

Conversion of the slot-line configuration into a rectangular-waveguide problem is illustrated in Fig. 8. First assume that slot waves of equal amplitude are traveling in the $+x$ and $-x$ directions. Then transverse planes spaced by $\lambda'/2$ exist where the transverse E field and normal H field cancel to zero. Let two such planes occur at $x=0$ and $x=\lambda'/2=a$ in Fig. 8(a). Conducting (or electric) walls of infinite extent may be inserted in these planes without disturbing the field components between the planes, and the semi-infinite regions at $x<0$ and $x>a$ may be eliminated. The section of slot line between the transverse planes supports a resonant slot-wave mode with no loss of energy, if the dielectric substrate and the conducting walls are assumed dissipationless.

Next, conducting walls are inserted in planes parallel to the slot and perpendicular to the substrate at $y=\pm b/2$. The region separated out of the original infinite space has the rectangular-waveguide boundary shown in Fig. 8(b). Since the fields are tightly bound to the vicinity of the slot, the walls at $y=\pm b/2$ will have negligible effect for b sufficiently large (typically one inch at 3 GHz), yet they serve the important function of enabling the use of rectangular-waveguide mode sets, thereby greatly simplifying the analysis.

Magnetic walls may be placed at $y\doteq\pm b/2$ instead of electric walls. The result is the boundary shown in Fig. 8(c), where two magnetic walls spaced by b and two electric walls spaced by a are used.

Images of the slot in the electric or magnetic walls at $y=\pm b/2$ result in an infinite array of parallel slots in the $z=0$ plane having center-to-center spacing of b. Therefore, the effect of adjacent slots may be computed for both electric- and magnetic-wall imaging, allowing the even- and odd-mode characteristic impedances and wavelengths to be evaluated for a slot in an infinite array. For one pair of slots rather than an array, these even- and odd-mode quantities are given approximately by the $b \to \infty$ values modified by one half the change computed for the infinite array.

Thus, the introduction of walls in Fig. 8 has created the configuration of a capacitive iris in a rectangular waveguide, with air and dielectric regions as indicated. Consider the metal-walled case in Fig. 8(b). All waveguide modes must have the $\lambda'/2$ variation of the slot wave in the x direction. Also, because of the symmetry of the structure, all modes must have an E-field maximum at the center of the slot. Therefore, the full set of modes satisfying the boundary conditions are TE_{10}, TE_{12}, TE_{14}, $\cdots$, and TM_{12}, TM_{14}, $\cdots$; that is, $TE_{1,2n}$ for n an integer ≥ 0 and $TM_{1,2n}$ for $n \geq 1$.

For the slot wave, $\lambda' < \lambda$ and hence $a < \lambda/2$. Therefore, the TE_{10} and all higher modes are cut off, or nonpropagating, in the air regions. In the dielectric region the TE_{10} mode is propagating, and the first few higher modes may propagate or all higher modes may be cut off, depending on the size of b. Since all modes are cut off in the two air regions, the energy of the resonant slot-wave mode is trapped near the slot. The amplitude of each mode in each region must be such that when the full set of modes are superimposed, the boundary conditions in the iris plane at $z=0$ will be met, and all field components on either side of the dielectric-to-air interface at $z=d$ will be matched. An alternative but equivalent condition is that transverse resonance occur; that is, the sum of the susceptances at the iris plane must equal zero. This sum includes the susceptances of the TE_{10} mode looking in the $-z$ and $+z$ directions, and the capacitive-iris susceptance representing higher modes on the $-z$ and $+z$ sides of the iris.

A formula for characteristic impedance is derived in Appendix II by a method utilizing the total-susceptance formula. Because of the non-TEM nature of the slot wave, definition of characteristic impedance is somewhat arbitrary. The reasonable and useful definition chosen here is $Z_0 = V^2/2P$, where $V = -\int E_y dy$ is peak voltage amplitude across the slot and P is average power flow of the wave. As in waveguide, this definition does not necessarily yield the best match in a transition to coaxial or microstrip line. In fact, experimental results indicate that a 50 ohm coaxial or microstrip line requires about 75 ohm slot impedance computed by the voltage power definition [19], [20]. Reactive discontinuity effects may also play a part in this discrepancy.

IV. Parameter Formulas—Second-Order Solution

Define as an independent variable $p=\lambda/2a$. At the transverse-resonance frequency, $a=\lambda'/2$ and hence $p=\lambda/\lambda'$ for $B_t=0$ where B_t is the total susceptance at the plane of the slot. Once $p=\lambda/\lambda'$ has been determined as the solution of $B_t=0$ for a given set of parameters ϵ_r, w, d, b, and a, the wavelength and frequency for this solution are simply $\lambda=2a(\lambda/\lambda')$ and $f=c/\lambda$.

The formula for B_t is as follows for the case of electric walls at $y=\pm b/2$:

$$\eta B_t = \frac{a}{2b}\left[-v + u\tan\left(\frac{\pi du}{ap} - \tan^{-1}\frac{v}{u}\right)\right] + \frac{1}{p}\left\{\left(\frac{\epsilon_r+1}{2} - p^2\right)\ln\frac{2}{\pi\delta} + \frac{1}{2}\sum_{n=1,2,3,\cdots}\left[v^2\left(1-\frac{1}{F_n}\right) + M_n\right]\frac{\sin^2(\pi n\delta)}{n(\pi n\delta)^2}\right\}, \tag{10}$$

and as follows for magnetic walls at $y=\pm b/2$:

$$\eta B_t = \frac{1}{p}\left\{\left(\frac{\epsilon_r+1}{2} - p^2\right)\ln\frac{8}{\pi\delta} + \frac{1}{2}\sum_{n=\frac{1}{2},\frac{3}{2},\frac{5}{2},\cdots}\left[v^2\left(1-\frac{1}{F_n}\right) + M_n\right]\frac{\sin^2(\pi n\delta)}{n(\pi n\delta)^2}\right\} \tag{11}$$

where $\eta=\sqrt{\mu_0/\epsilon_0}=376.7$ ohms, $\delta=w/b$, and

$$u=\sqrt{\epsilon_r-p^2}, \qquad v=\sqrt{p^2-1} \tag{12}$$

$$F_n = \sqrt{1+\left(\frac{b}{2an}\cdot\frac{v}{p}\right)^2}, \qquad F_{n1} = \sqrt{1-\left(\frac{b}{2an}\cdot\frac{u}{p}\right)^2}. \tag{13}$$

For F_{n1} real, M_n is

$$M_n = \frac{\epsilon_r\tanh r_n - p^2F_{n1}^2\coth q_n}{\left[1+\left(\frac{b}{2an}\right)^2\right]F_{n1}} - u^2 \tag{14}$$

where

$$r_n = \frac{2\pi ndF_{n1}}{b} + \tanh^{-1}\left(\frac{F_{n1}}{\epsilon_rF_n}\right) \tag{15}$$

$$q_n = \frac{2\pi ndF_{n1}}{b} + \coth^{-1}\left(\frac{F_n}{F_{n1}}\right). \tag{16}$$

For F_{n1} imaginary, M_n is

$$M_n = \frac{\epsilon_r\tan r_n' - p^2|F_{n1}|^2\cot q_n'}{\left[1+\left(\frac{b}{2an}\right)^2\right]|F_{n1}|} - u^2 \tag{17}$$

where

$$r_n' = \frac{2\pi nd|F_{n1}|}{b} + \tan^{-1}\left(\frac{|F_{n1}|}{\epsilon_rF_n}\right) \tag{18}$$

$$q_n' = \frac{2\pi nd|F_{n1}|}{b} + \cot^{-1}\left(\frac{F_n}{|F_{n1}|}\right). \tag{19}$$

Equations (10) and (11) for B_t are valid for $\delta = w/b \leq 0.15$, $w < \lambda/(4\sqrt{\epsilon_r})$, and $w \leq d$. These ranges are more than adequate for usual slot-line dimensions.

The procedure in using the above equations is to substitute a set of values ϵ_r, w, d, b, and $a = \lambda'/2$, and then to solve (10) or (11) for the value of p at which $\eta B_t = 0$. This p is equal to λ/λ'. Wavelength and frequency are then given by $\lambda = 2a(\lambda/\lambda')$ and $f = c/\lambda$. Solution of the above equations is most conveniently accomplished with an electronic computer, arriving at $B_t = 0$ by an iterative process.

The group velocity is $v_g = d\omega/d\beta$, where $\omega = 2\pi f$ and β is the slot-wave phase constant in radians per unit length. From this definition of v_g, one may obtain the following relations for the ratio of phase velocity to group velocity:

$$\frac{v}{v_g} = 1 + \frac{f}{\lambda'/\lambda} \cdot \frac{-\Delta(\lambda'/\lambda)}{\Delta f} = 1 + \frac{f}{\lambda/\lambda'} \cdot \frac{\Delta(\lambda/\lambda')}{\Delta f} \tag{20}$$

where $\Delta(\lambda'/\lambda)$, $\Delta(\lambda/\lambda')$, and Δf are computed from two separate solutions of $\eta B_t = 0$ for fixed values of ϵ_r, w, d, and b, and for two slightly different values of $a = \lambda'/2$ incremented plus and minus from the desired a. The frequency f may be assumed to lie midway in the Δf interval.

The slot-wave characteristic impedance is obtained as follows from the ηB_t formulas:

$$Z_0 = 376.7 \frac{v}{v_g} \frac{\pi}{p} \cdot \frac{\Delta p}{-\Delta \eta B_t} \text{ ohms.} \tag{21}$$

In this equation $\Delta \eta B_t$ is computed from (10) or (11) with ϵ_r, w, d, b, and a held constant, and with p incremented slightly plus and minus from the value $p = \lambda/\lambda'$ at $\eta B_t = 0$; v/v_g is obtained from (20) for the same parameters. Equations (20) and (21) may be used with (10) to yield values for electric walls at $y = \pm b/2$, or with (11) for magnetic walls.

V. Computed Data

The second-order solution equations in Section IV were programmed on an electronic computer and the parameters λ'/λ, v/v_g, and Z_0 were computed for various slot-line cases.[1]

Fig. 9 shows the effect of wall spacing b on the parameters for both electric and magnetic walls. In this computation, $\epsilon_r = 20$, $d = 0.137$ inch, $w = 0.025$ inch, and λ' is constant at 1.360 inches. The corresponding curves for electric and magnetic walls merge together for $b > 1.5$ inches and are only slightly separated for $b = 1$ inch. As b decreases below 1 inch, the λ'/λ curves diverge more and more rapidly. Since λ' is held constant, λ varies inversely and f proportionally with λ'/λ. The ratio v/v_g decreases with b for magnetic walls and increases for electric walls. The behavior of the characteristic impedance is more complex, the electric-wall curve rising and then falling sharply as b decreases, and the magnetic-wall curve falling and then rising sharply. This reversal of direction is caused by the v/v_g factor in (21). The quantity $Z_0/(v/v_g)$ is virtually constant for the two types of walls for

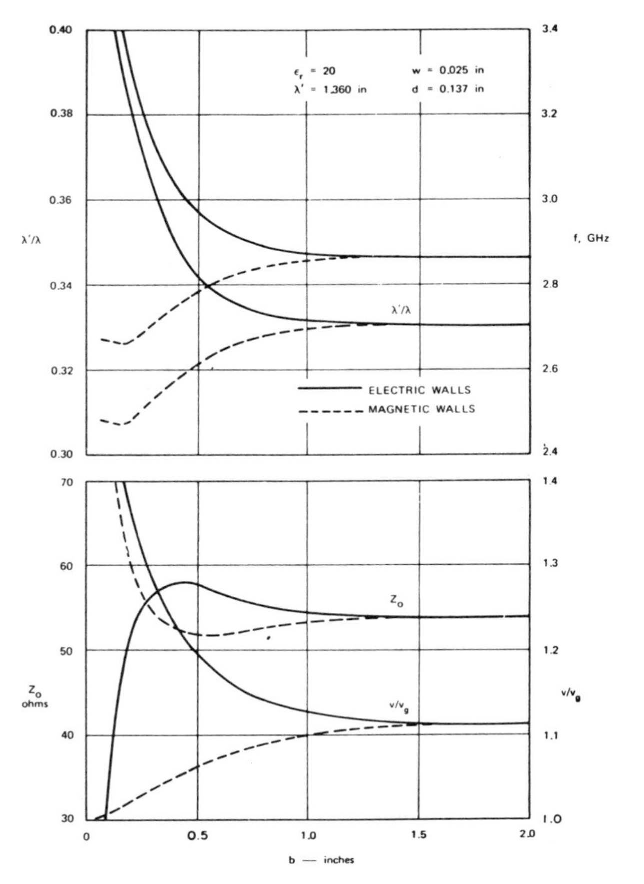

Fig. 9. Slot-line parameters versus b with ϵ_r, w, d and $a = \lambda'/2$ fixed.

b as low as 0.6 inch, while for b smaller, this quantity diverges without changing direction.

The variation of Z_0 and λ'/λ with frequency is shown in Fig. 10 for $\epsilon_r = 20$, $d = 0.137$ inch, $w = 0.025$ inch, and for $\lambda' = 2a$ stepped from 0.5 to 150 inches in the computation. Curves are plotted for $b = 3$ inches and $b \to \infty$ (that is, b sufficiently large at each λ' value such that Z_0 and λ'/λ are essentially independent of b). The ratio λ'/λ decreases monotonically in the plotted range. For increasing f, λ'/λ falls toward $1/\sqrt{\epsilon_r} = 0.224$, while for f approaching zero λ'/λ rises to 0.390 for magnetic walls at $b = 3$ inches and to 1.0 for the two other curves. The zero-order value of λ'/λ calculated from (1) is indicated for comparison.

The characteristic impedance plotted in Fig. 10 has a broad maximum, varying by only ± 7 percent between 1 and 6 GHz. As f approaches zero, Z_0 approaches 40.3 ohms for magnetic walls at $b = 3$ inches, and approaches 0 ohms for the other two cases.

A few experimental λ'/λ points are shown in Fig. 10. The substrate used in the test piece had a specified ϵ_r of 20. Length, width, and thickness were approximately 5 by 1.75 by 0.137 inches. For the circled points one side was covered with Scotch Brand No. 51 aluminum tape, about 0.0007 inch thick, including 0.0001 inch of adhesive. A slot 0.025 inch wide and 3 inches long was left bare. A probe terminating a

[1] Normalized graphs of λ'/λ and Z_0 versus d/λ for $w/d = 0.02$, 0.1, 0.2, 0.4, and 0.6, and for $\epsilon_r = 13$, 16, and 20 have been prepared and are included in another paper [19].

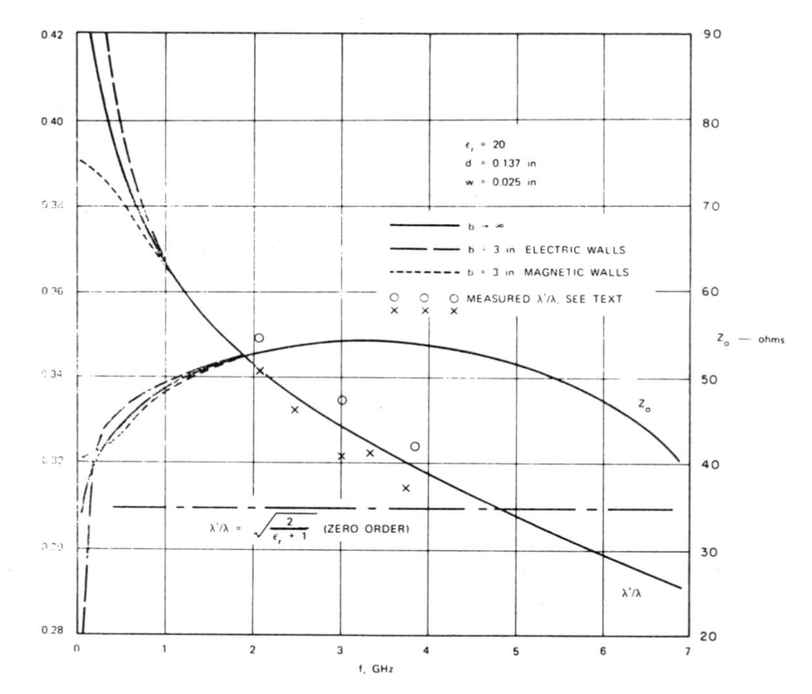

Fig. 10. Graph of λ'/λ and Z_0 versus frequency.

reflectometer coupler was coupled to the slot near one end. Resonance was indicated by a dip in the reflected wave. The slot length was varied by sliding a thin steel scale over the slot from the end opposite the probe. At each of the test frequencies the overlapping length of steel scale was varied until resonance was found. Several lengths for resonance were obtained differing in $\lambda'/2$ steps, thus yielding λ' and λ'/λ. The circled points lie parallel to the theoretical λ'/λ curve, but about 2.3 percent above it. For the crossed points, the same substrate sample was tested with copper plating directly applied. The thickness was about 0.0008 inch and slot width was 0.0235 inch. These points lie about 1.1 percent below the theoretical curve. The difference between the two sets of points may be attributed to the thin layer of adhesive on the aluminum tape. Additional tests with other permittivities and other w, d, and λ yield similar agreement with λ'/λ computations [19].

The effect of varying slot width w on λ'/λ and Z_0 is shown in Fig. 11 for two different cases of ϵ_r and d. In each case λ' is held constant. The ratio λ'/λ increases with w, but only slightly. The characteristic impedance Z_0 increases substantially, although far less than in proportion to w.

Measurements of Z_0 have not yet been made.[2] However, the computed Z_0 values for the magnetic-wall case can be checked when $b/\lambda' \ll 1$, since in the static limit this slot-line cross section becomes equivalent to a TEM-mode transmission line containing an equivalent dielectric medium $\epsilon_r' = (\lambda/\lambda')^2$. The Z_0 formula for this TEM line may be obtained by a straightforward modification of a case treated in [18]:

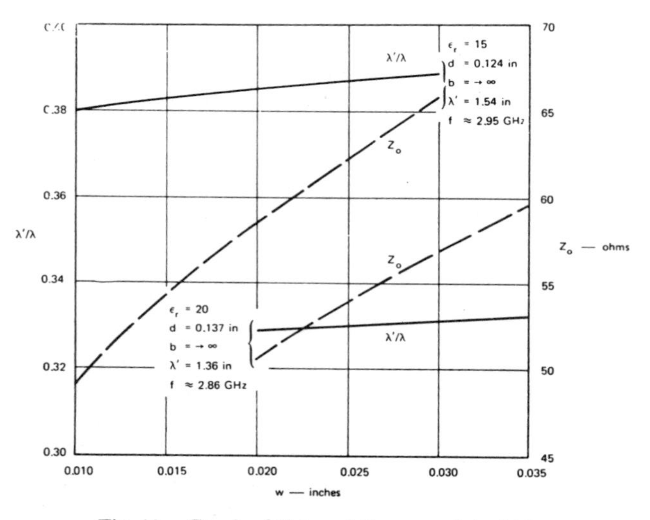

Fig. 11. Graph of λ'/λ and Z_0 versus slot width.

$$Z_0 = \frac{591.7}{\sqrt{\epsilon_r'}\ \ln\left(\dfrac{8b}{\pi w}\right)} = \frac{591.7(\lambda'/\lambda)}{\ln\left(\dfrac{8b}{\pi w}\right)}\ \text{ohms} \qquad \begin{array}{l} b/w > 3 \\ b/\lambda' \to 0. \end{array} \tag{22}$$

[2] Good transitions have been achieved at C and X bands between slot line and 50 ohm coaxial and microstrip lines with $\epsilon_r = 16$, $d = 0.055$ inch, and $w = 0.021$ inch [20]. Another good transition at S band had $\epsilon_r = 16$, $w = 0.031$ inch, and $d = 0.062$ inch [19]. See the discussion at the end of Section III on the arbitrary nature of slot-line Z_0 definition.

TABLE I

COMPARISON OF SECOND-ORDER AND STATIC SOLUTIONS FOR Z_0

Second-Order Solution			Eq. (22)
b (inches)	λ'/λ	Z_0 (Ω)	Z_0 (Ω)
0.10	0.30752	78.38	78.40
0.14	0.30707	68.35	68.37
0.20	0.30763	60.45	60.39
0.30	0.31230	54.60	54.04
0.40	0.31640	52.42	50.50
0.60	0.32384	51.77	46.59

In Table I, (22) is tested against data computed for the curves of Fig. 9 ($\epsilon_r=20$, $d=0.137$ inch, $w=0.025$ inch, $\lambda'=1.360$ inches, $f\approx 2.670$ GHz). Agreement is excellent for $b\leq 0.20$ inch or $b/\lambda'\leq 0.15$. A second test is afforded by a computed point used in plotting the graph in Fig. 10. For $\epsilon_r=20$, $d=0.137$ inch, $w=0.025$ inch, $b=3.00$ inches, and $\lambda'=150.0$ inches, the second-order solution gives $\lambda'/\lambda=0.38987$, $f=30.67$ MHz, and $Z_0=40.33$ ohms. Equation (22) yields 40.32 ohms.

APPENDIX I

DERIVATION OF B_t FORMULAS

Fig. 12 shows a longitudinal yz-plane view through the waveguide model for the slot-line analysis. The waveguide boundaries in this case are conducting, or electric, walls. The TE_{10}-mode susceptance at the iris plane ($z=0$) is B_d looking to the right into the dielectric slab and B_a looking to the left into the air region. The total susceptance in the iris plane is $B_t=B_d+B_a$.

A formula for B_d will be derived first and then modified to yield B_a. The approach is based on a previously published analysis of a waveguide filter consisting of an alternating series of steps between two cross-section heights [9], [10], and on earlier analyses applied to other discontinuities [11], [12]. Fig. 13 shows the basic structure treated in [9] and [10], with notation modified for slot line. A waveguide of height b is driven by a waveguide of height w, with an abrupt step at $z=0$. A reactive plane is placed transverse to the waveguide at $z=l$. This terminating plane can be either an electric or magnetic wall.

Since all walls and the dielectric material are assumed lossless, the admittance looking to the right at $z=0$ is a pure susceptance, B_d. Because of symmetry, only $TE_{1,2n}$ (with $n\geq 0$) and $TM_{1,2n}$ (with $n\geq 1$) modes are present. In a transverse plane the E_y and H_x components of each mode are proportional to $\sin \pi x/a \cos 2\pi n y/b$. Thus the total E_y and H_x fields at the $z=0$ plane and $x=a/2$ are functions of y as follows:

$$E_y = R_0 + \sum_{n>0} R_n \cos \frac{2\pi n y}{b} \tag{23}$$

$$H_x = -y_{i0}R_0 - \sum_{n>0} y_{in}R_n \cos \frac{2\pi n y}{b} \tag{24}$$

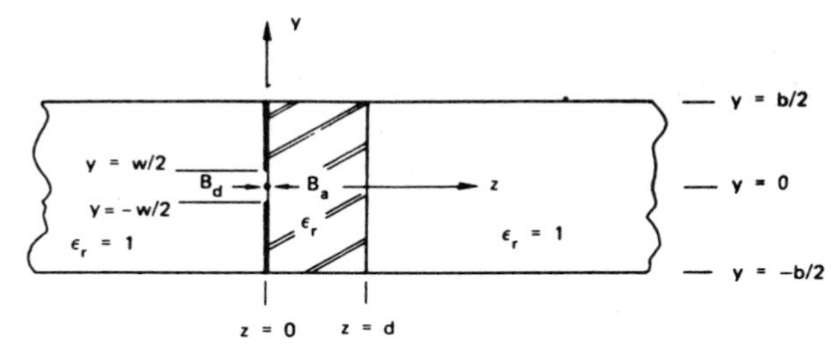

Fig. 12. Waveguide model containing capacitive iris and dielectric slab.

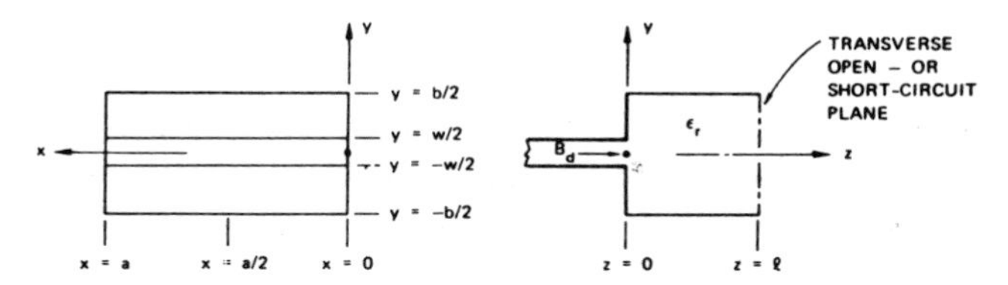

Fig. 13. Waveguide of height b driven by waveguide of height w.

where $n=1, 2, 3, \cdots$, R_0 and R_n are constants, and input wave admittances y_{i0} and y_{in} are defined by

$$y_{i0} = -\left(\frac{H_x}{E_y}\right)_{TE_{10}} \tag{25}$$

$$y_{in} = -\left(\frac{(H_x)_{TE_{1,2n}} + (H_x)_{TM_{1,2n}}}{(E_y)_{TE_{1,2n}} + (E_y)_{TM_{1,2n}}}\right). \tag{26}$$

The analysis will be simplified by assuming that only the TE_{10} mode is present in the waveguide of height w at $z=0$. Therefore, E_y and H_x are constants as follows:

$$E_y = \begin{cases} C_0 & \text{for } |y| \leq w/2 \\ 0 & \text{for } w/2 < |y| \leq b/2 \end{cases} \tag{27}$$

$$H_x = -C_0 y_i' \quad \text{for } |y| \leq w/2 \tag{28}$$

where y_i' is input wave admittance in the waveguide of height w at the plane $z=0$. The error in the analysis due to neglecting higher modes in the region $z<0$ is very small for $\delta=w/b$ small, as would be usual for slot line.

Equation (23) has the form of a Fourier series. Let this series equal E_y as defined by (27). Then R_0 and R_n are determined as follows:

$$R_0 = C_0\delta, \qquad R_n = 2C_0\delta \frac{\sin \pi n\delta}{\pi n\delta}\,. \tag{29}$$

Next, set the right-hand sides of (24) and (28) equal, and integrate with respect to y over the opening of height w to obtain

$$C_0 y_i' = y_{i0}R_0 + \sum_{n>0} y_{in}R_n \frac{\sin \pi n\delta}{\pi n\delta} \tag{30}$$

and, by (29),

$$(b/w)y_i' = y_{i0} + 2\sum_{n>0} y_{in}\left(\frac{\sin \pi n\delta}{\pi n\delta}\right)^2. \tag{31}$$

At this point replace the wave admittances by guide admittances defined on the TE_{10}-mode voltage power basis in the complete waveguide cross section [13]; that is, replace y_{in} by $Y_{in}=(a/2b)y_{in}$ and y_i' by $Y_i=(a/2w)y_i'$. Then

$$Y_i = jB_d = Y_{i0} + 2\sum_{n>0} Y_{in}\left(\frac{\sin \pi n\delta}{\pi n\delta}\right)^2. \tag{32}$$

With reference to Fig. 12, Y_{i0} is the admittance seen by a TE_{10} wave directed into a dielectric-filled waveguide region of length d terminated by an infinite air-filled region:

$$Y_{i0} = jY_{o1}\tan\left(\beta_1 d + \tan^{-1}\frac{Y_0}{jY_{o1}}\right). \tag{33}$$

In the notation used in (33), symbols with the subscript 1 apply to the dielectric-filled region between $z=0$ and $z=d$; without this subscript they apply to the air regions. Y_{o1} and Y_o are TE_{10}-mode characteristic admittances and $\beta_1=\gamma_1/j=2\pi/\lambda_{g1}$ is the TE_{10}-mode phase constant.

$$Y_0 = \frac{a\gamma}{j2b\eta k}, \quad Y_{o1} = -j\frac{a\gamma_1}{2b\eta_1 k_1} = \frac{a}{2b\eta}\cdot\frac{\lambda}{\lambda_{g1}} \tag{34}$$

where $\eta=\sqrt{\mu_0/\epsilon_0}=376.7$ ohms and $\eta_1=\eta/\sqrt{\epsilon_r}$; γ and γ_1 are the TE_{10}-mode z-directed propagation constants; $k=2\pi/\lambda$ and $k_1=2\pi\sqrt{\epsilon_r}/\lambda$ are the plane-wave constants; and λ_{g1} is the TE_{10}-mode guide wavelength in the ϵ_r region.

For $n>0$, both $TE_{1,2n}$ and $TM_{1,2n}$ modes are present. For each n, the corresponding TE and TM amplitudes must be chosen so that E_x exactly cancels at $z=0$. In this way the total E_x field will be zero at $z=0$, as is required by the boundary conditions in that transverse plane. From (26) we obtain for the nth mode

$$Y_{in} = \frac{Y_{iTMn} + Y_{iTEn}D_n}{1+D_n} \tag{35}$$

where

$$D_n = \frac{(E_y)_{TE1,2n}}{(E_y)_{TM1,2n}} \text{ when } (E_x)_{TE1,2n} + (E_x)_{TM1,2n} = 0. \tag{36}$$

From the field-component formulas for the TE and TM modes [7], [9] we obtain

$$D_n = \left(\frac{b}{2an}\right)^2. \tag{37}$$

The input admittances Y_{iTMn} and Y_{iTEn} for each n are[3]

$$Y_{iTMn} = Y_{o1TMn}\tanh\left(\gamma_{n1}d + \tanh^{-1}\frac{Y_{oTMn}}{Y_{o1TMn}}\right) \tag{38}$$

$$Y_{iTEn} = Y_{o1TEn}\coth\left(\gamma_{n1}d + \coth^{-1}\frac{Y_{oTEn}}{Y_{o1TEn}}\right) \tag{39}$$

where the characteristic admittances and propagation constants are

[3] In (38) and (39), the pair of functions tanh and $\tanh^{-1}$ is interchangeable with coth and $\coth^{-1}$. The selection here is appropriate since $Y_{oTMn}/Y_{o1TMn}<1$ and $Y_{oTEn}/Y_{o1TEn}\geq 1$.

$$Y_{o1TMn} = \frac{jak_1}{2b\eta_1\gamma_{n1}}, \quad Y_{oTMn} = \frac{jak}{2b\eta\gamma_n} \tag{40}$$

$$Y_{o1TEn} = \frac{a\gamma_{n1}}{j2b\eta_1 k_1}, \quad Y_{oTEn} = \frac{a\gamma_n}{j2b\eta k} \tag{41}$$

$$\gamma_{n1} = \sqrt{\left(\frac{2\pi n}{b}\right)^2 + \left(\frac{\pi}{a}\right)^2 - \left(\frac{2\pi}{\lambda}\right)^2\epsilon_r} = \frac{2\pi n}{b}\sqrt{1-\left(\frac{b}{n\lambda_{g1}}\right)^2} \tag{42}$$

$$\gamma_n = \frac{2\pi n}{b}\sqrt{1+\left(\frac{b\gamma}{2\pi n}\right)^2}. \tag{43}$$

Then (35) and (37) through (41) yield

$$\eta Y_{in} = j\frac{ak}{2b\gamma_{n1}}\cdot\frac{\epsilon_r\tanh r_n - \left(\frac{b\gamma_{n1}}{2ank}\right)^2\coth q_n}{1+\left(\frac{b}{2an}\right)^2} \tag{44}$$

$$r_n = \gamma_{n1}d + \tanh^{-1}\left(\frac{\gamma_{n1}}{\epsilon_r\gamma_n}\right) \tag{45}$$

$$q_n = \gamma_{n1}d + \coth^{-1}\left(\frac{\gamma_n}{\gamma_{n1}}\right). \tag{46}$$

Now let $p=\lambda/2a$ and

$$u = \frac{\lambda}{\lambda_{g1}} = \frac{\gamma_1}{jk} = \sqrt{\epsilon_r - p^2} \tag{47}$$

$$v = \frac{\gamma}{k} = \sqrt{p^2-1} \tag{48}$$

$$F_{n1} = \frac{b\gamma_{n1}}{2\pi n} = \sqrt{1-\left(\frac{b}{n\lambda_{g1}}\right)^2} = \sqrt{1-\left(\frac{bu}{2anp}\right)^2} \tag{49}$$

$$F_n = \frac{b\gamma_n}{2\pi n} = \sqrt{1+\left(\frac{bv}{2anp}\right)^2} \tag{50}$$

Equations (32) through (34) and (44) through (50) yield

$$\eta B_d = \frac{au}{2b}\tan\left(\frac{\pi ud}{ap} - \tan^{-1}\frac{v}{u}\right) + \frac{1}{2p}\sum_{n=1,2,\cdots}\left[\frac{\epsilon_r\tanh r_n - p^2F_{n1}^2\coth q_n}{\left[1+\left(\frac{b}{2an}\right)^2\right]F_{n1}}\right]\cdot\frac{\sin^2\pi n\delta}{n(\pi n\delta)^2} \tag{51}$$

The first term is the TE_{10}-mode susceptance; the second term is the discontinuity susceptance representing the effect of higher modes. The rate of convergence of the series is very slow but will be improved by the following procedure. If we let $d\to\infty$ and $f\to 0$, then $\lambda'=2a\to\infty$ and each term S_n of the series becomes

$$S_n' = \frac{u^2\sin^2\pi n\delta}{n(\pi n\delta)^2}. \tag{52}$$

The original series may be replaced by

$$\sum_{n=1,2,\cdots} S_n = \sum_{n=1,2,\cdots} (S_n - S_n') + \sum_{n=1,2,\cdots} S_n'. \quad (53)$$

The first series on the right of the equal sign converges rapidly compared to the series in (51), while the second may be summed in closed form by the following identity [11], [15]:

$$\lim_{\delta\to 0} \sum_{n=1,2,3,\cdots} \frac{\sin^2 \pi n\delta}{n(\pi n\delta)^2} = \ln \frac{1}{2\pi\delta} + \frac{3}{2} = \ln \frac{1}{\delta} - 0.3379. \quad (54)$$

The accuracy of this is excellent for $\delta \leq 0.15$. At $\delta = 0.15$ the error is only 0.4 percent. Therefore, the susceptance of both sides of a capacitive iris is approximately

$$\eta B_C \approx \frac{u^2}{p}\left(\ln \frac{1}{\delta} - 0.3379\right). \quad (55)$$

However, the exact formula in the limit $\lambda_{g1} \to \infty$ is [14]

$$\begin{aligned} B_C &= \frac{4bY_{o1}}{\lambda_{g1}} \ln \csc \frac{\pi\delta}{2} = \frac{u^2}{p} \ln \csc \frac{\pi\delta}{2}, \quad \delta \leq 1 \\ &\approx \frac{u^2}{p} \ln \frac{2}{\pi\delta} = \frac{u^2}{p}\left(\ln \frac{1}{\delta} - 0.452\right), \quad \delta \ll 1. \end{aligned} \quad (56)$$

The small difference between the constants in (55) and (56) is the result of assuming in the analysis that E_y and H_x are constant across the slot instead of being the correct functions of y. At this point (53) may be written

$$\sum_{n=1,2,\cdots} S_n = \sum_{n=1,2,\cdots} (S_n - S_n') + u^2 \ln \frac{2}{\pi\delta} \quad (57)$$

where (56) is used instead of (55) for better accuracy. Equation (51) for the susceptance looking into the dielectric section is now

$$\eta B_d = \frac{au}{2b} \tan\left(\frac{\pi ud}{ap} - \tan^{-1}\frac{v}{u}\right) + \frac{u^2}{2p} \ln \frac{2}{\pi\delta} + \frac{1}{2p} \quad (58)$$

$$\sum_{n=1,2,\cdots} \left[\frac{\epsilon_r \tanh r_n - p^2 F_{n1}^2 \coth q_n}{\left[1 + \left(\frac{b}{2an}\right)^2\right] F_{n1}} - u^2\right] \cdot \frac{\sin^2 \pi n\delta}{n(\pi n\delta)^2}.$$

The susceptance B_a looking toward the left from the iris in Fig. 12 may be obtained from (58) by letting $\epsilon_r = 1$ or $d = 0$. With either substitution, the following equation results:

$$\eta B_a = -\frac{av}{2b} - \frac{v^2}{2p} \ln \frac{2}{\pi\delta} + \frac{1}{2p} \sum_{n=1,2,\cdots} v^2\left(1 - \frac{1}{F_n}\right) \frac{\sin^2 \pi n\delta}{n(\pi n\delta)^2}. \quad (59)$$

When (58) and (59) are added, the total susceptance B_t given by (10) is obtained for electric walls at $y = \pm b/2$.

The susceptance B_t for the case of magnetic walls at $y = \pm b/2$ may be obtained easily from the electric-wall solution. Let the cross section be as shown in Fig. 8(c). Modes excited in the waveguide are TE_{11}, TE_{13}, TE_{15}, $\cdots$ and TM_{11}, TM_{13}, TM_{15}, $\cdots$; that is, $TE_{1,2n}$ and $TM_{1,2n}$ where $n = \frac{1}{2}, \frac{3}{2}, \frac{5}{2}$, etc. The TE_{10} mode cannot exist within this boundary. Careful examination of each step of the above analysis for electric walls shows that (51) applies when the first term representing the TE_{10} contribution is dropped, and when the summation is performed for $n = \frac{1}{2}, \frac{3}{2}, \frac{5}{2}, \cdots$ rather than $n = 1, 2, 3, \cdots$. Evaluation of (54) with $n = \frac{1}{2}, \frac{3}{2}, \frac{5}{2}, \cdots$, yields [15]

$$\lim_{\delta\to 0} \sum_{n=\frac{1}{2},\frac{3}{2},\cdots} \frac{\sin^2 \pi n\delta}{n(\pi n\delta)^2} = \ln \frac{4}{\delta} - 0.3379. \quad (60)$$

Therefore, in (58) for ηB_d and (59) for ηB_a drop the first term, replace $\ln 2/\pi\delta$ by $\ln 8/\pi\delta$, and change the summation index from $n = 1, 2, 3, \cdots$ to $n = \frac{1}{2}, \frac{3}{2}, \frac{5}{2}, \cdots$. The resulting expression giving ηB_t for magnetic walls at $y = \pm b/2$ is (11).

Appendix II

Derivation of Formulas for Z_0 and v/v_g

Define the slot-line characteristic impedance Z_0 by

$$Z_0 = \frac{V_+^2}{2P_+} \quad (61)$$

where P_+ is the average power flow of a slot wave traveling in the $+x$ direction (Fig. 8) and V_+ is the peak amplitude of the voltage across the slot. Now assume a resonant length $\lambda'/2$ of slot line having waves of equal power P^+ and P^- traveling in the $+x$ and $-x$ directions. The total stored energy in this length is $W_t = (P^+ + P^-)(\lambda'/2v_g) = P^+\lambda'/v_g = (2\pi P^+/\omega')(v/v_g)$, where v_g is group velocity, or velocity of energy transport along the slot line [16]. Let V_0 be the maximum voltage at the center of the resonant length of slot. Since the waves in the $+x$ and $-x$ directions have equal voltages $V_+ = V_-$, the maximum voltage is $V_0 = 2V_+$, and $Z_0 = (V_0/2)^2/2P^+ = \pi V_0^2 v/4\omega W_t v_g$.

The following general relation holds at a port of a cavity at resonance [16]: $W_t = (V^2/4)(dB/d\omega)$. In the case of the $\lambda'/2$ resonant slot, we shall assume the port to be at the iris plane $z = 0$ in Fig. 8. We shall set B equal to the total waveguide susceptance B_t at that plane and V equal to the slot voltage V_0 at $x = \lambda'/4$. These choices of B and V are consistent with the waveguide impedance and slot impedance definitions, both of which are on a voltage power basis. Therefore,

$$Z_0 = \frac{\pi}{\omega(dB_t/d\omega)} \cdot \frac{v}{v_g} \quad (62)$$

where $dB_t/d\omega$ is evaluated at the resonant frequency; that is, at $B_t = 0$. Let $\omega = 2\pi c/\lambda$ and $p = \lambda/2a$. Then $\omega = \pi c/ap$ and $d\omega = -(\pi c/ap^2)dp = -\omega(dp/p)$. Substitution of these relations in (62) yields (21).

The ratio v/v_g will now be evaluated. Phase and group velocity are given by $v = \omega/\beta_x = f\lambda'$ and $v_g = d\omega/d\beta_x$ [16], [17] where β_x is the slot-wave phase constant. Since $\beta_x = 2\pi/\lambda'$, we obtain $v_g = -\lambda'^2/(d\lambda'/df)$. Differentiate λ'/λ as follows:

$$\frac{d(\lambda'/\lambda)}{df} = \frac{1}{\lambda}\frac{d\lambda'}{df} - \frac{\lambda'}{\lambda^2}\frac{d\lambda}{df}.$$

Solve this for $d\lambda'/df$ and substitute $d\lambda/df = d(c/f)/df = -\lambda/f$. The resulting relations yield the first part of (20). The second part is obtained in a similar manner.

Acknowledgment

The author wishes to thank E. G. Cristal of Stanford Research Institute for preparing the computer program of the second-order solution, and J. P. Agrios, C. Heinzman and E. A. Mariani of U. S. Army Electronics Command for their experimental studies of slot line. The above people, and also L. A. Robinson and L. Young of Stanford Research Institute, participated in numerous discussions with the author.

References

[1] H. Jasik, Ed., *Antenna Engineering Handbook*. New York: McGraw-Hill, 1961, chs. 8, 9.

[2] A. F. Harvey, *Microwave Engineering*. New York: Academic Press, 1963, pp. 633–638.

[3] W. H. Watson, *Waveguide Transmission and Antenna Systems*. New York: Oxford University Press, 1947.

[4] E. Strumwasser, J. A. Short, R. J. Stegen, and J. R. Miller, "Slot study in rectangular TEM transmission line," Hughes Aircraft Company, Tech. Memo 265, Air Force Contract AF 19(122)-454, January 1952.

[5] M. C. Bailey, "Design of dielectric-covered resonant slots in a rectangular waveguide," *IEEE Trans. Antennas and Propagation*, vol. AP-15, pp. 594–598, September 1967.

[6] J. Galejs, "Excitation of slots in a conducting screen above a lossy dielectric half space," *IRE Trans. Antennas and Propagation*, vol. AP-10, pp. 436–443, July 1962.

[7] S. Ramo and J. R. Whinnery, *Fields and Waves in Modern Radio*, 2nd ed. New York: Wiley, 1953, pp. 357–358.

[8] E. Jahnke and F. Emde, *Tables of Functions with Formulae and Curves*. New York: Dover, 1943, pp. 236–243.

[9] S. B. Cohn, "A theoretical and experimental study of a waveguide filter structure," Cruft Lab., Harvard University, Cambridge, Mass., Tech. Rept. 39, Contract N5 ORI-76, Task Order 1, April 25, 1948.

[10] ——, "Analysis of a wide-band waveguide filter," *Proc. IRE*, vol. 37, pp. 651–656, June 1949.

[11] W. C. Hahn, "A new method for the calculation of cavity resonators," *J. Appl. Phys.*, vol. 12, p. 62, 1941.

[12] J. R. Whinnery and H. W. Jamieson, "Equivalent circuits for discontinuities in transmission lines," *Proc. IRE*, vol. 32, pp. 98–115, February 1944.

[13] S. A. Schelkunoff, *Electromagnetic Waves*. Princeton, N. J.: Van Nostrand, 1943.

[14] N. Marcuvitz, *Waveguide Handbook*, M.I.T. Rad. Lab. Ser., vol. 10. New York: McGraw-Hill, 1951, pp. 218–219.

[15] R. E. Collin, *Field Theory of Guided Waves*. New York: McGraw-Hill, 1960. Use $\Sigma_{1,2,3,\ldots} e^{inx}/n^3$ on p. 579 and $\Sigma_{1,3,5,\ldots} e^{inx}/n^3$ on p. 580.

[16] C. G. Montgomery, R. H. Dicke, and E. M. Purcell, *Principles o, Microwave Circuits*, M.I.T. Rad. Lab. Ser., vol. 8. New York: McGraw-Hill, 1948. See p. 230, eq. (40) for relation between W_t, V, and $dB_t/d\omega$; see p. 53, eqs. (103) and (104) for v and v_g.

[17] L. Brillouin, *Wave Propagation in Periodic Structures*. New York: Dover, 1953, pp. 72–76.

[18] F. Oberhettinger and W. Magnus, *Anwendung der Elliptischen Funktionen in Physik und Technik*. Berlin: Springer, 1949, pp. 63, 114–116.

[19] E. Mariani, C. Heinzman, J. Agrios, and S. B. Cohn, "Measurement of slot-line characteristics," presented at the 1969 IEEE G-MTT Internatl. Symp., Dallas, Tex., May 5–7, 1969, to be published in *IEEE Trans. Microwave Theory and Techniques*.

[20] G. H. Robinson and J. L. Allen, "Applications of slot line to miniature ferrite devices," presented at the 1969 IEEE G-MTT Internatl. Symp., Dallas, Tex., May 5–7, 1969.

Ridge waveguide used in microstrip transition

Ridge waveguide can be employed in a microstrip-to-waveguide transition that is easy to fabricate and exhibits excellent loss characteristics.

Sabbir S. Moochalla, Senior Member, Technical Staff, RCA Astro Electronics, Princeton, NJ 08540; and **Chae An,** Co-op Student, Massachusetts Institute of Technology, Cambridge, MA 02139

At 20 GHz, waveguide's low-loss characteristics make it the most common transmission medium. However, microstrip is the most convenient medium for the input and output sections of GaAs FET amplifers, so a low-loss waveguide-to-microstrip transition is needed. Several transitions exist, each with its own advantages and disadvantages.

One technique in particular is for a transition from WR-42 waveguide to 15-mil (0.381-mm) microstrip on a quartz substrate. This technique was established for use in 30/20-GHz advanced communication satellites. The transition, which uses ridge waveguide, emphasizes ease of fabrication and repeatability, and its low-loss characteristics have been proven.[1] The quartz substrate was used because it is less lossy than the commonly used alumina substrate.

The design of the transition is essentially a design of an impedance transformer. A four-step Chebyshev quarter-wave transformer was used.[2] After the desired impedance for each step was found, an in-house computer program was used to determine the ridge-waveguide dimensions (Fig. 1). The impedance of the last section, Z_4, is 50 ohms, and the gap in the ridge, G, is 15 mils, the thickness of the substrate. These two parameters determine the width of the ridge, W, which was the same, 65 mils (1.65 mm), for all four sections.

Theoretically, the first three sections should each be a quarter-wavelength long. However, the discontinuities in the ridge at each step create junction capacitances (Fig. 2) that introduce phase angles to the reflection coefficients.[3] These capaci-

(continued on next page)

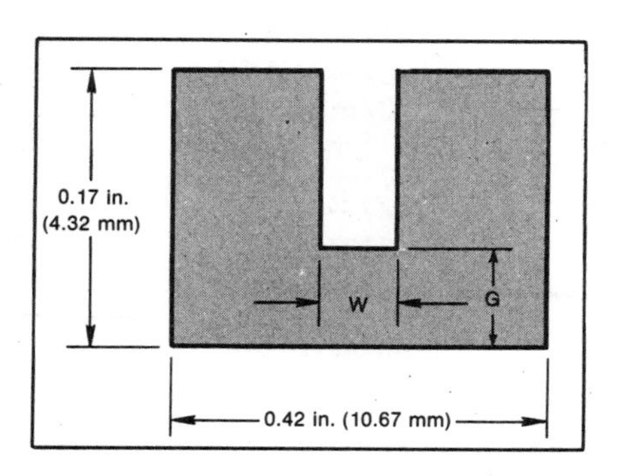

*1. **The ridge gap, G,** is determined by the height of the quartz substrate used. Other waveguide dimensions are determined with the aid of an in-house computer program.*

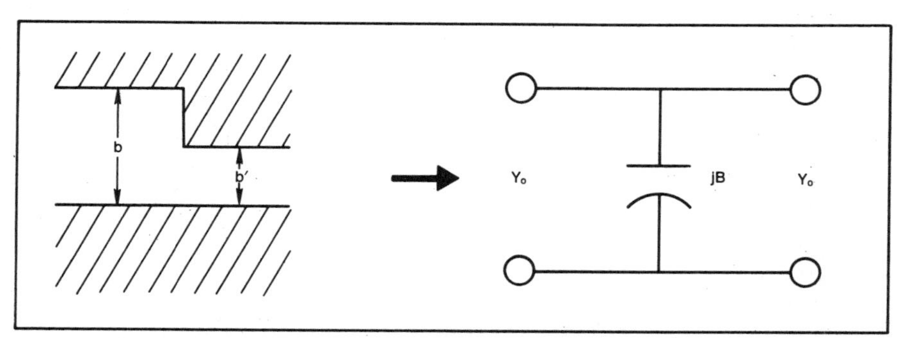

*2. **The discontinuities in the ridge waveguide** at each impedance step represent junction capacitances that must be compensated for by changes in the section lengths.*

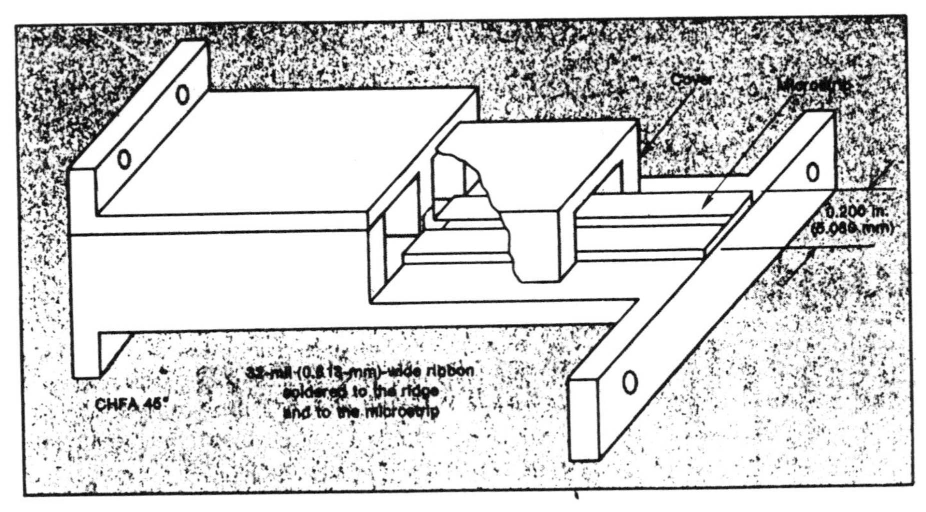

3. A rectangular cover with cutoff waveguide dimensions was used to prevent higher-order modes from being transmitted, which would increase losses.

tances must be calculated so the length of each section can be corrected. Since capacitance calculations for ridge waveguides are not readily available, approximations based on rectangular waveguide were used.

Fabrication considerations

Each section of the ridge waveguide has different loss characteristics; since the last, 50-ohm section has the greatest loss, its length was kept short (50 mils [1.27 mm]). Also, the ridge of the last section was chamferred to provide a smoother transition, reducing insertion loss and improving return loss.

Deembedded S-parameters

Output network

Freq. (GHz)	S_{11}	S_{21}	S_{12}	S_{22}
17000.0	−18.202/−175.76	−.149/−86.44	−.149/−66.44	−18.988/−133.95
17200.0	−17.266/171.89	−.184/−81.46	−.184/−81.46	−17.589/−156.56
17400.0	−16.898/162.58	−.211/83.28	−.211/83.28	−17.077/−179.76
17600.0	−16.954/159.62	−.184/69.04	−.184/69.04	−16.833/156.53
17800.0	−17.077/155.09	−.202/54.05	−.202/54.05	−17.329/132.28
18000.0	−17.589/149.43	−.256/39.85	−.256/39.85	−17.721/105.76
18200.0	−18.862/144.20	−.149/25.25	−.149/25.25	−18.489/82.95
18400.0	−19.914/142.14	−.167/11.19	−.167/11.19	−19.828/61.79
18600.0	−20.915/141.08	−.202/−3.49	−.202/−3.49	−21.310/35.76
18800.0	−23.479/139.58	−.158/−17.97	−.158/−17.97	−23.876/6.94
19000.0	−26.196/139.48	−.220/−31.93	−.220/−31.98	−26.936/−21.49
19200.0	−29.119/155.48	−.193/−45.91	−.193/−45.91	−31.373/−63.42
19400.0	−33.556/156.36	−.291/−59.64	−.291/−59.64	−33.979/−127.79
19600.0	−44.437/−112.19	−.167/−73.39	−.167/−73.39	−39.172/152.80
19800.0	−32.041/−42.50	−.274/−86.90	−.274/−86.90	−32.765/73.45
20000.0	−27.959/−38.94	−.220/79.74	−.220/79.74	−29.119/8.07

Input Network

Freq. (GHz)	S_{11}	S_{21}	S_{12}	S_{22}
17000.0	−25.352/142.58	−.327/−68.49	−.327/−68.49	−26.558/−96.65
17200.0	−30.752/124.62	−.220/−88.73	−.220/−83.73	−33.556/−113.35
17400.0	−36.478/155.81	−.265/81.99	−.295/81.99	−39.172/147.58
17600.0	−33.152/−165.46	−.265/67.31	−.265/67.31	−32.041/103.13
17800.0	−28.404/−174.07	−.274/54.35	−.274/54.35	−27.744/90.35
18000.0	−25.036/168.05	−.211/39.81	−.211/39.81	−24.013/80.89
18200.0	−23.876/140.23	−.300/26.38	−.300/26.38	−22.384/85.65
18400.0	−22.975/117.47	−.282/12.60	−.282/12.60	−21.830/84.70
18600.0	−22.047/88.59	−.229/−.45	−.229/−.45	−20.915/80.24
18800.0	−21.618/62.54	−.247/−13.29	−.247/−13.29	−21.210/87.60
19000.0	−23.223/31.92	−.198/−27.55	−.198/−27.55	−22.615/94.49
19200.0	−24.293/−1.97	−.184/−41.16	−.184/−41.16	−23.876/97.98
19400.0	−26.021/−39.14	−0.79/−54.79	−.079/−54.79	−24.152/109.35
19600.0	−28.874/−73.60	−.238/−67.51	−.238/−67.51	−27.131/123.80
19800.0	−31.057/−112.23	−.131/−81.71	−.131/−81.71	−27.744/146.20
20000.0	−29.370/−166.55	−.167/84.33	−.167/84.33	−29.119/152.45

4. A through-short-delay technique *and an automatic network analyzer were used to determine the S-parameters for the transition.*

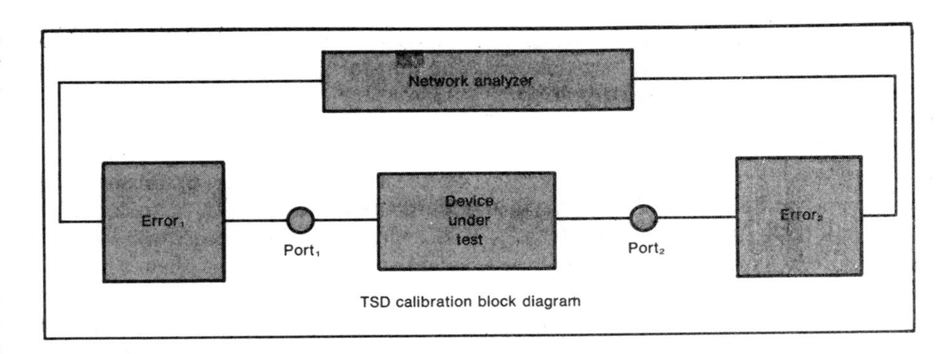

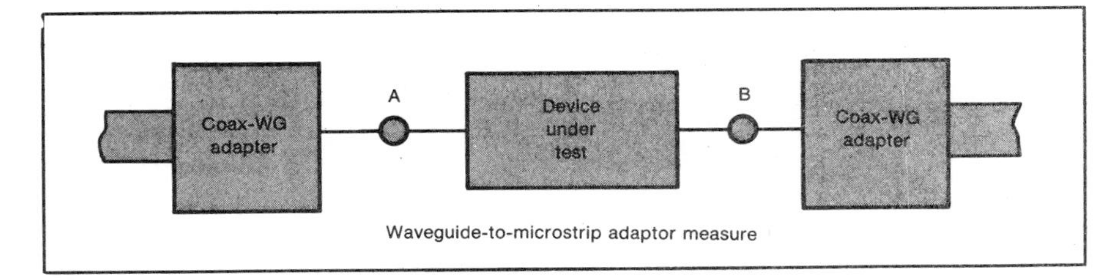

5. Since waveguide-to-coax adapters *were needed, the network analyzer is first calibrated at Points A and B.*

A 32-mil (0.813-mm) gold ribbon was soldered between the ridge and microstrip to provide good electrical contact. Experiments showed that the ribbon width should be about the same as that of the 50-ohm trace on the microstrip. The performance of the transition depends greatly on the quality of this electrical contact, with the best and most repeatable performance attained when there was no space between the ribbon and the ridge or microstrip.

Some higher-order modes may be generated at the waveguide-to-microstrip junction. To prevent them from being transmitted—which would increase the loss—a small rectangular cover with waveguide dimensions was placed over the junction (Fig. 3). The cover is long enough so that the evanescent higher-order modes die out.

When the ridge waveguide section was attached to the microstrip section with screws or dow pins, repeatability suffered greatly. Thus, amplifiers fabricated separately and having substrates at both the input and output should not be attached directly to the ridge waveguide.

Test results

The transition was first tested with a scalar analyzer for insertion loss and return loss. The test setup included two transitions with a 0.880-in.-(2.235-cm)-long microstrip line in between. The typical insertion loss from 17 to 22 GHz was 0.5 dB for both transitions, or 0.25 dB per transition. The typical return loss was about 20 dB.

A full set of S-parameters was determined for a single transition on an automatic network analyzer (ANA). This measurement used deembedding procedures and a calibration

(concluded on next page)

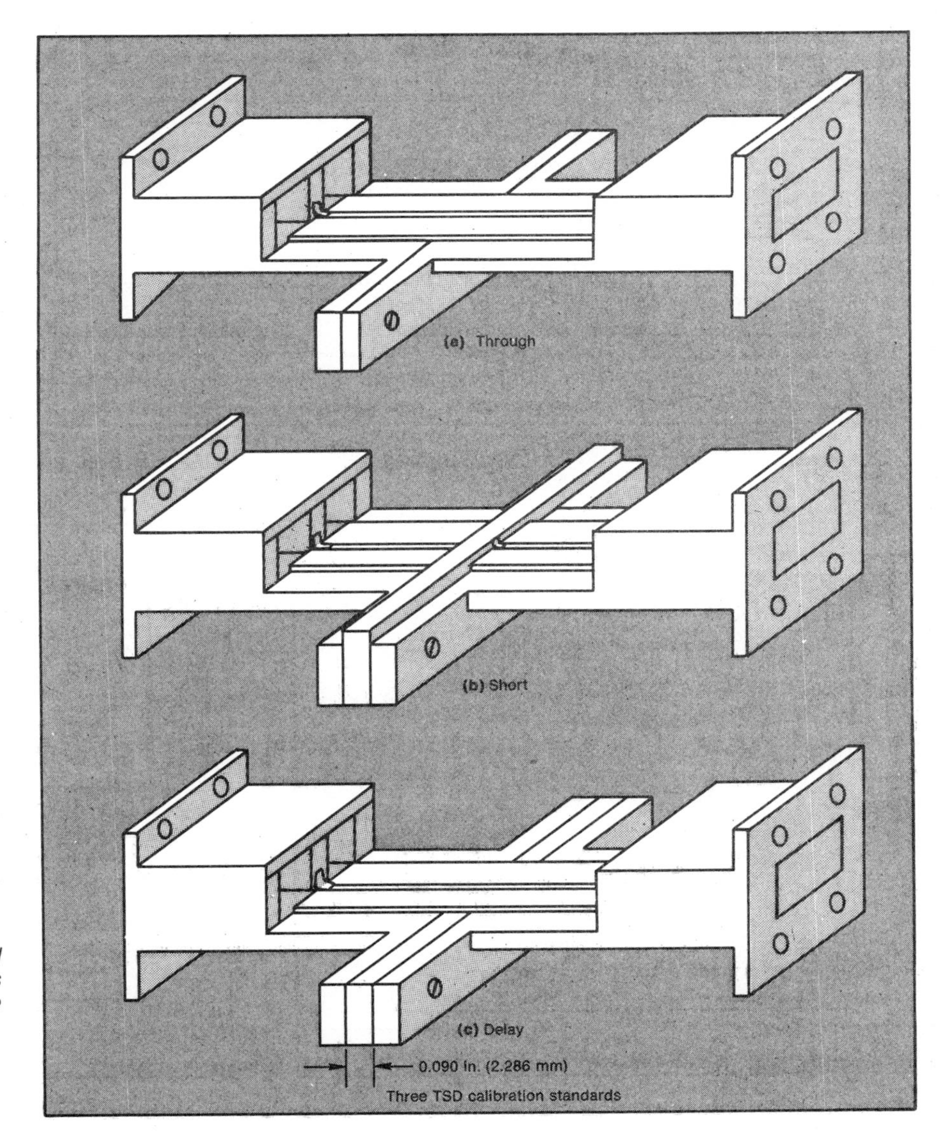

6. The S-parameters *were measured for each of the three configurations shown, and then calculated for a single transition.*

technique called through-short-delay (TSD)[4] (Fig. 4). The measurements were restricted to a maximum of 20 GHz by the available ANA.

First, the error matrixes were determined at Port 1 and Port 2 using a through line, a short line at the desired reference plane, and a delay line (longer than a through line) as calibration standards. These measurements were then deembedded from the normal measurements, which include Error 1, Error 2, and the device under test.

The ANA uses coaxial connectors, so the system must be calibrated at points A and B in Fig. 5, using the TSD method, for the necessary waveguide-to-coax adapters. Then the S-parameters are measured for each of the three waveguide-to-microstrip standards in Fig. 6. Using these three measurements, the S-parameters of a single transition are calculated employing the same technique as used for the error matrixes in the TSD calibration. That is, each transition is treated as an error matrix after the waveguide-to-coax adapters. The calculations were performed using a computer program called "DMBED," which was developed at RCA's Labs-Microwave Technical Center, as was the TSD algorithm used with the ANA.

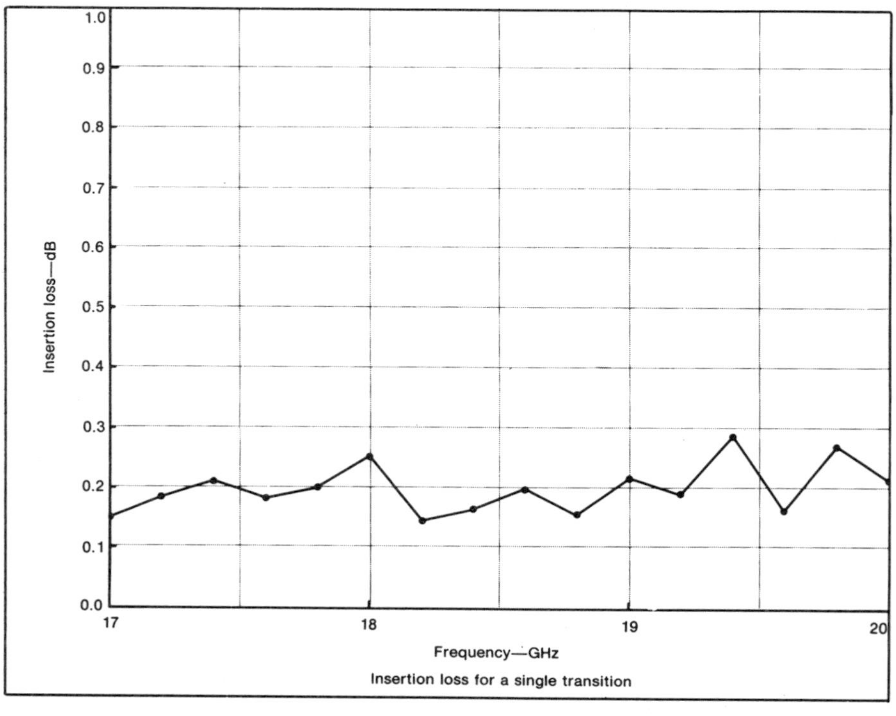

*7. **The insertion loss** for a single transition was approximately 0.2 dB over a 17-to-20-GHz bandwidth.*

The S-parameters for the input and output error networks (the two waveguide-to-microstrip transitions) are listed in the table. Theoretically, these two sets of parameters should be identical. The disagreements arise mainly from the physical differences in the dimensions of the transitions. The large differences in the phases of S_{11} and S_{22} are of little importance because their magnitudes are very small. The measured insertion loss and return losses for a single transition are shown in Figs. 7 and 8.

References

1. E.A. Schneider, "Microwave and MM-Wave Hybrid Integrated Circuits for Radio Systems," *Bell System Technical Journal*, Vol. 48, (Jul.-Aug. 1969), pp. 1703-1725.
2. S.B. Cohen, "Optimum Design of Stepped Transmission Line Transformers," *IRE MTT*, (Jan. 1957), pp. 12-17.
3. G.L. Matthaei, Leo Young, and E.M.T. Jones, *Microwave Filters, Impedance Matching Networks, and Coupling Structures* (Dedham, MA: Artech House, Inc., 1964), pp. 300-304.
4. N.R. Franzen and R.A. Speciale, "A New Procedure for System Calibration and Error Removal in Automated S-Parameter Measurements," *Proc., Fifth European Microwave Conf.*, Hamburg, W. Germany, Sept. 1-4, 1975, pp. 69-73.

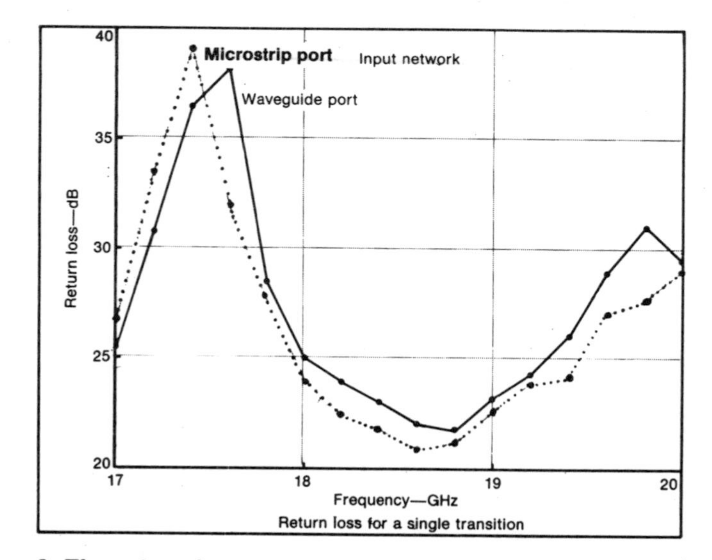

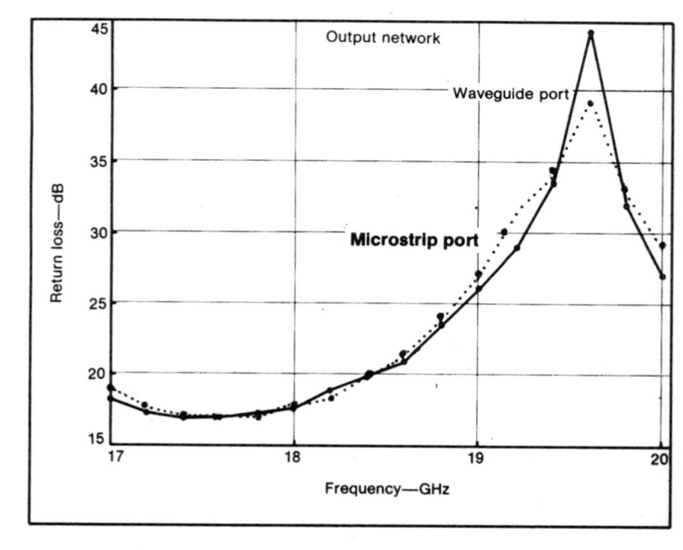

*8. **The return losses** were at least 18 dB for both input and output networks over the measured bandwidth.*

DESIGN OF WAVEGUIDE-TO-MICROSTRIP TRANSITIONS SPECIALLY SUITED TO MILLIMETRE-WAVE APPLICATIONS

Indexing terms: Stripline components, Waveguide couplers

A design procedure for millimetre waveguide-to-microstrip transitions is presented. The analysis is such that existing design information, readily available in practical curve format, can be directly applied. In addition, the procedure can be adapted to all physically realisable microstrip impedances, as well as substrate materials and thicknesses.

A simple waveguide-to-microstrip adaptor for millimetre-wave applications was first demonstrated by van Hewven[1] for a specific substrate material and frequency band. This work has been expanded by a general analysis that permits rapid and successful design throughout the various millimetre frequency bands, with variations in substrate material and thickness.

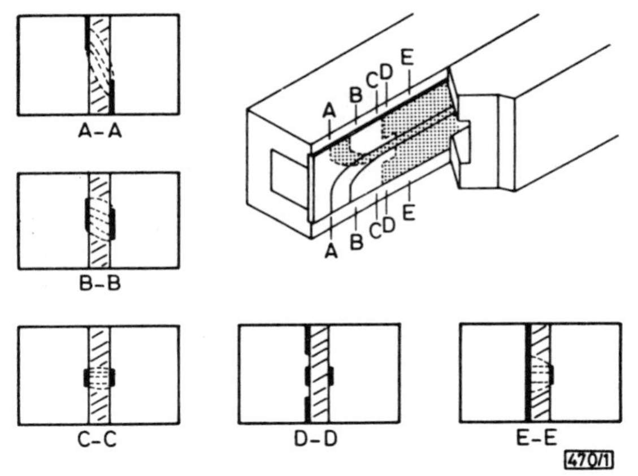

Fig. 1 *Waveguide-to-microstrip transition with cross-section views*

The basic transition is shown in Fig. 1. It consists of a substrate which has been metallised to the proper configuration on two sides located in the centre of a waveguide parallel to the narrow walls. Fig. 1 also includes a series of cross-sections of the device along the direction of propagation.

The device has been divided into these various regions, each representing a specific form of transmission medium, to permit the use of available design information for the various media. As seen in Fig. 1, region A–A can be considered to be a double-ridged waveguide. The ridges can be considered extremely thin and are not on the centre line of the waveguide, but are offset by one-half the substrate thickness. Although this offset coupled with the nonhomogeneous dielectric loading introduces perturbations to most design curves, this region can simply be considered as a transition region from air-filled waveguide to another form of transmission line. The end configurations are defined by other limitations in the design and the only variables for this region are length and shape. It has been found that the use of techniques satisfactory for most ridged-waveguide tapers yields excellent results. Lengths of less than one wavelength have been realised with the use of a modified cosine taper.

As the ridges approach one another, there is a concentration of fields in the region separating the ridges. Because of the offset in the ridges, it is possible to continue them beyond a height equal to one-half the waveguide height, which results in a rotation in the field pattern in region B–B, which culminates in a full $\pi/2$ E-field rotation, at region C–C, relative to the originating waveguide mode.

Since the fields are now rotated and concentrated in the region between the ridges, it is no longer necessary to maintain contact with the waveguide wall in region B–B, resulting in the balanced transmission line of C–C. The impedance of this region can be designed to the characteristic impedance chosen for the final microstrip (usually 50 Ω). An accurate analysis using existing data[2] can be formed by assuming that a virtual ground plane exists one-half the distance between the parallel conductors, and by continuing the analysis based on microstrip information with a substrate thickness one-half the actual thickness (Fig. 2*a*).

Region D–D accomplishes the task of converting the balanced region of C–C into the unbalanced microstrip line of region E–E, and beyond. Since both regions C–C and E–E have been designed for the same characteristic impedance, region D–D should result in a similar impedance, while also performing the function of a balun. A simple balun is not possible in such a structure, however, since any added quarter-wave strucfure results in a direct modification of the primary transmission line.

The cross-section of Fig. 2*b* does produce the necessary transition, but requires further analysis for optimisation. If some liberty is taken with precise location of the various conductors, the structure can be interpreted as two coplanar waveguides in parallel, sharing a common ground plane. The parallel combination of the individual impedances is the design impedance, i.e. 50 Ω, and, since section C–C was not only balanced, but symmetrical, electrically and mechanically, it would be desirable to design each coplanar waveguide to have

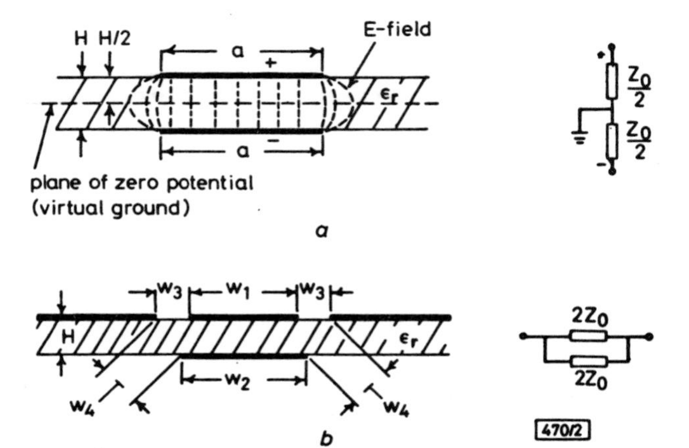

Fig. 2 *Details of (a) region C–C and (b) region D–D*

an impedance twice the design characteristic impedance.

Some of the dimensions of Fig. 2*b* will be dictated by neighbouring regions. The remainder can be derived from the literature.[3] All arbitrary choices should be made in favour of minimum discontinuity capacitances.

The length of this balun region D–D, although theoretically $\pi/4$, is modified by such factors as junction and fringing capacitance that cannot be clearly defined. This length therefore must be found experimentally. It should be noted, however, that positioning of the substrate is not extremely critical, and, once this dimension is found experimentally, no further unit-to-unit fine adjustment is required.

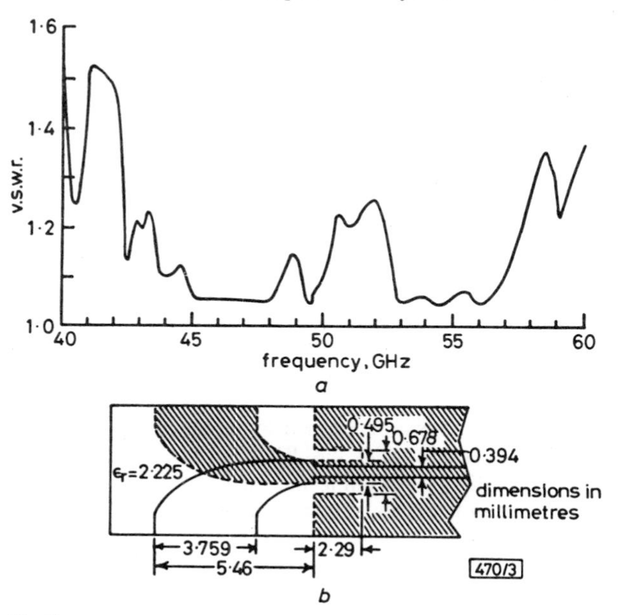

Fig. 3

a Measured v.s.w.r. for two transitions separated by 5 cm of 50 Ω microstrip
b Substrate dimensions for 40–60 GHz transition

Based on design procedures as outlined in this letter, a transition assembly consisting of two waveguide-to-microstrip transitions separated by 5 cm of 50 Ω microstrip was constructed and tested. The balun region D–D was not optimised to include two coplanar waveguides of equal impedance, although the total impedance was designed to 50 Ω. The various dimensions, along with a plot of the v.s.w.r. of this assembly, are given in Fig. 3. The substrate material was Duroid 5880 ($\epsilon_r = 2{\cdot}225$) by Rogers Corporation, Chandler, Arizona, USA, with a substrate thickness of 0·127 mm. The waveguide chosen was WR19/WG24 for operation over the 40–60 GHz frequency band.

Deriving the various dimensions of the transition as outlined above from the available data yields a broadband waveguide-to-microstrip transition, especially suited to millimetre-wave applications, that can quickly be reduced to practice.

L. J. LAVEDAN

Microwave Techniques Branch
Electronics Technology Division
Naval Research Laboratory
Washington, DC 20375, USA

19th August 1977

References

1 VAN HEWVEN, J. H. C.: 'A new integrated waveguide-microstrip transition', *IEEE Trans.*, 1976, **MTT-24**, pp. 144–147
2 Microwave Engineers Handbook–Vol. 1 (Horizon House Microwave Inc., Dedham, Mass., USA), pp. 136–137
3 DAVIS, M. E.: 'Coplanar waveguide fabrication and characteristics'. Technical Report AFAL-TR-73-189, Air Force Avionics Laboratory, Air Force Systems Command, Wright-Patterson Air Force Base, Ohio, USA, Sept. 1973

Microstrip Propagation on Magnetic Substrates—Part I: Design Theory

ROBERT A. PUCEL, SENIOR MEMBER, IEEE, AND DANIEL J. MASSÉ, MEMBER, IEEE

Abstract—**Formulas and graphs are presented for the effective relative permeability and the filling factors of magnetic substrates in microstrip. Both the propagation and the magnetic loss filling factors are included. In the calculation of these quantities, use was made of the filling factors for dielectric substrates obtained from Wheeler's analysis and a duality relationship between magnetic and dielectric substrates derived in this paper.**

I. Introduction

A LARGE BODY of design information for microstrip on dielectric substrates has been accumulated over the last few years [1]–[3]. Equivalent design data for magnetic substrates are incomplete. It is our purpose to present the missing data in a form most useful to the design engineer. Before proceeding, we shall review briefly some basic formulas for dielectric substrates.

A cross section of microstrip on a dielectric–magnetic substrate is shown in Fig. 1. Provided the frequency is not too high, this structure will propagate a wave which for all practical purposes is a transverse electromagnetic wave. If the dielectric constant k of the substrate is much greater than unity, most of the electric energy is confined to the dielectric region in the vicinity of the strip conductor and ground plane. However, because some of the electric field also fringes out into the air space above the strip conductor, the value of the effective dielectric constant k_{eff} entering into the calculation of the characteristic impedance and phase velocity is less than k, that is $1 < k_{eff} < k$. In other words, the propagation "filling factor" for the dielectric, here denoted as q_d, and defined by Wheeler [1] as

$$q_d = \frac{k_{eff} - 1}{k - 1} \tag{1}$$

is less than unity. Both k_{eff} and q_d are functions of the dielectric constant k and the geometrical factor w/h, the ratio of the conductor strip width to substrate height. This functional dependence can be derived from Wheeler's paper.

If dielectric losses are present, the effective value of the dielectric loss tangent $\tan \delta_{eff}$ is also less than the loss tangent of the substrate $\tan \delta_d$ and can be expressed in the form [4], [5]

Manuscript received May 27, 1971; revised August 12, 1971.
The authors are with the Research Division, Raytheon Company, Waltham, Mass. 02154.

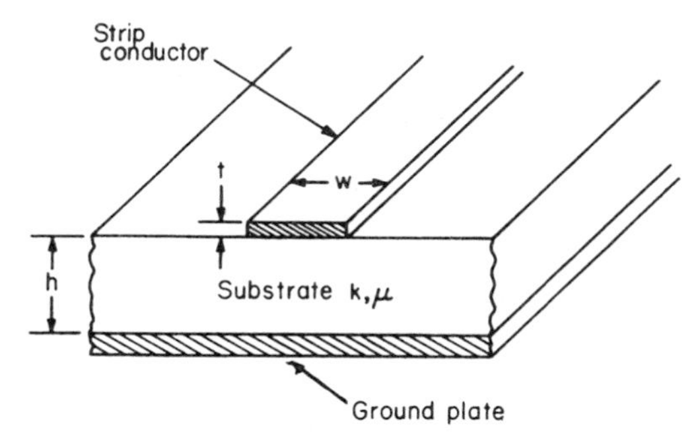

Fig. 1. Microstrip.

$$\tan \delta_{deff} = q_{d,l} \tan \delta_d \tag{2}$$

where $q_{d,l}$ is a filling factor for losses given by [5]

$$q_{d,l} = q_d \frac{k}{k_{eff}} = \frac{1 - k_{eff}^{-1}}{1 - k^{-1}}. \tag{3}$$

II. Magnetic Substrates

It would be convenient to have equivalent design formulas for substrates with magnetic properties. Fortunately, this information can be obtained from the above expressions by using a duality relationship for dielectric and magnetic substrates developed in the Appendix. This duality, based on an observation of Kaneki [6], allows one to calculate the functional dependence of the effective relative permeability μ_{eff} on w/h and the relative permeability μ of the substrate, once the functional dependence of k_{eff} on w/h and k is known. Thus the solution for the magnetic field distribution can be bypassed.

The duality relationship (which derives from the duality of k and $1/\mu$ in Maxwell's equations) is based on a TEM-mode approximation for the magnetic case, the same assumption as used for the dielectric case [1]–[3]. This relationship takes the form

$$\mu_{eff}(w/h, \mu) = \frac{1}{k_{eff}(w/h, \mu^{-1})}. \tag{4}$$

Note that the duality amounts to the conversions $k \rightarrow 1/\mu$ and $k_{eff} \rightarrow 1/\mu_{eff}$ in the formulas for the dielectric case. Equation (4) implies that one need not make a separate determination of the effective relative permeability if one has at hand tables or graphs of the effective dielectric constant.

It follows from (4) and (3) that a magnetic filling factor for propagation can be defined as

$$q_m = \frac{\mu_{eff}^{-1} - 1}{\mu^{-1} - 1}. \tag{5}$$

Note that $q_m(w/h, \mu) = q_d(w/h, \mu^{-1})$.

In like manner the expressions for the filling factor of the magnetic loss tangent $\tan \delta_m$ and the effective value of this loss tangent take the form

$$q_{m,l} = q_m \frac{\mu_{eff}}{\mu} = \frac{1 - \mu_{eff}}{1 - \mu} \tag{6}$$

or

$$\tan \delta_{m_{eff}} = q_{m,l} \tan \delta_m. \tag{7}$$

Our TEM assumption allows us to write simple formulas for the characteristic impedance Z_0, guide wavelength λ_g, and total substrate loss per wavelength $\alpha\lambda_g$ for microstrip on a substrate exhibiting both dielectric and magnetic properties. Thus we have

$$Z_0 = Z_0' \sqrt{\frac{\mu_{eff}}{k_{eff}}} \quad (\Omega) \tag{8}$$

$$\lambda_g = \lambda_0 / \sqrt{k_{eff}\mu_{eff}} \quad (\text{cm}) \tag{9}$$

$$\alpha\lambda_g = 27.3(\tan \delta_{d_{eff}} + \tan \delta_{m_{eff}}) \quad (\text{dB}). \tag{10}$$

The wavelength λ_0 corresponds to free space. Here Z_0' is the characteristic impedance when $\mu = k = 1$, which can be calculated exactly from the capacitance per unit length [7] for an air dielectric or from Wheeler's expressions letting $k = 1$ [1]. The attenuation (10) of course only represents the substrate losses, to which must be added the contribution from conductor losses [5].

In Section III we shall present explicit formulas for μ_{eff} and, by way of review, for k_{eff} based on Wheeler's formulas.

III. Derivation of Formulas

Wheeler's analytic expressions [1] for the characteristic impedance of microstrip as a function of dielectric constant and the ratio w/h are given in piecewise form, one solution valid for $w/h \leq 2$, the other for $w/h \geq 2$. The two solutions do not join exactly at $w/h = 2$ (about a 5–10-percent error). His results may be graphically smoothed in this vicinity to join properly.

If we take Wheeler's expressions for Z_0, and set $k = 1$ to give Z_0', the value for an air dielectric, then the effective value of dielectric constant may be obtained from

$$k_{eff} = \left[\frac{Z_0(w/h, 1)}{Z_0(w/h, k)}\right]^2. \tag{11}$$

For $w/h \leq 2$

$$k_{eff} = \frac{1 + k}{2}\left(\frac{A}{A - B}\right)^2 \tag{12a}$$

and for $w/h \geq 2$

$$k_{eff} = k\left(\frac{C - D}{C}\right)^2 \tag{12b}$$

where

$$A = \ln \frac{8h}{w} + \frac{1}{32}\left(\frac{w}{h}\right)^2 \tag{13a}$$

$$B = \frac{1}{2}\left(\frac{k - 1}{k + 1}\right)\left[\ln \frac{\pi}{2} + \frac{1}{k} \ln \frac{4}{\pi}\right] \tag{13b}$$

$$C = \frac{w}{2h} + \frac{1}{\pi}\left[\ln 2\pi\epsilon\left(\frac{w}{2h} + 0.94\right)\right] \tag{13c}$$

$$D = \frac{k - 1}{2\pi k}\left\{\ln\left[\frac{\pi\epsilon}{2}\left(\frac{w}{2h} + 0.94\right)\right] - \frac{1}{k} \ln\left(\frac{\epsilon\pi^2}{16}\right)\right\} \tag{13d}$$

from which the dielectric filling factors q_d and $q_{d,l}$, (1) and (3), respectively, may be computed.

The expressions for the effective relative permeability may be derived from the above by employing the duality relationship (4). Thus for $w/h \leq 2$

$$\mu_{eff} = \frac{2\mu}{1 + \mu}\left(\frac{A - B'}{A}\right)^2 \tag{14a}$$

and for $w/h \geq 2$

$$\mu_{eff} = \mu\left(\frac{C}{C - D'}\right)^2 \tag{14b}$$

where A and C are given by (13) and B' and D' are derived from B and D by letting $k \rightarrow \mu^{-1}$, that is,

$$B' = \frac{1}{2}\left(\frac{1 - \mu}{1 + \mu}\right)\left[\ln \frac{\pi}{2} + \mu \ln \frac{4}{\pi}\right] \tag{15a}$$

$$D' = \frac{1 - \mu}{2}\left\{\ln\left[\frac{\pi\epsilon}{2}\left(\frac{w}{2h} + 0.94\right)\right] - \mu \ln\left(\frac{\epsilon\pi^2}{16}\right)\right\}. \tag{15b}$$

The two filling factors q_m and $q_{m,l}$, (5) and (6), respectively, may be calculated by use of the expressions for μ_{eff} above.

Equations (14) and (15) together with (5)–(7) provide all the information necessary to design microstrip on magnetic substrates.

IV. Graphical Results

Since the purpose of this paper is to present design graphs for microstrip on ferrite and garnet substrates, our computations for μ_{eff}, q_m, and $q_{m,l}$ were made for values of magnetic constant less than unity, and indeed only for the practical range $0.4 < \mu < 1$. Because μ is less

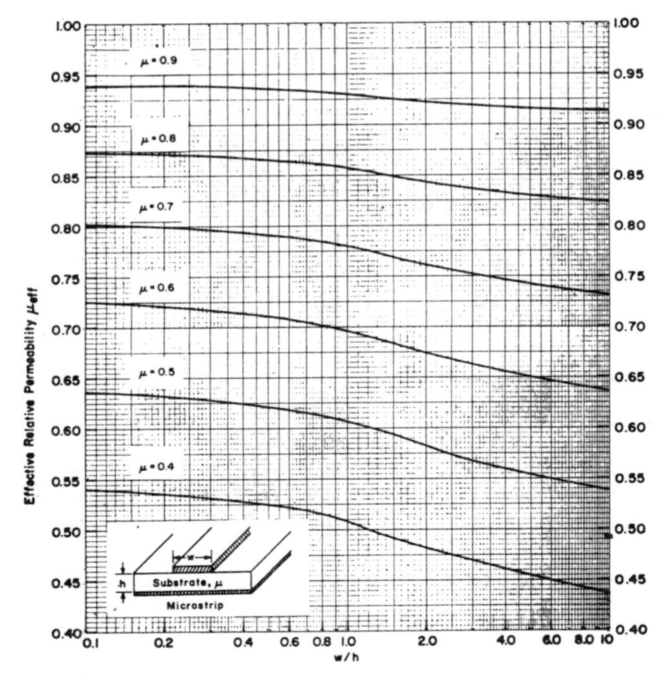

Fig. 2. Effective relative permeability of microstrip as a function of the relative permeability of the substrate and the geometrical parameter w/h.

than unity, the value for the air space above the microstrip, one should expect the effective value μ_{eff} to fall between μ and unity, that is $\mu < \mu_{eff} < 1$. One can show that for $w/h \rightarrow 0$, $\mu_{eff}^{-1} \rightarrow \frac{1}{2}(1+\mu^{-1})$, and for $w/h \rightarrow \infty$, $\mu_{eff} \rightarrow \mu$.[1] In other words, μ_{eff} is bracketed in the range

$$\mu < \mu_{eff} < \frac{2\mu}{1+\mu} \cdot \tag{16}$$

The curves of μ_{eff} in Fig. 2 illustrate this expected behavior.

The filling factors q_m and $q_{m,l}$ derived from μ are shown in Figs. 3 and 4. Because of the mild dependence of q_m on μ, only three curves were plotted to avoid crowding.

Observe in Fig. 4 that the loss filling factor becomes larger with increasing w/h, a reflection of the growing importance of the substrate. Using the limits on μ_{eff} derived above, one may show that $q_{m,l}$ falls in the range

$$\frac{1}{1+\mu} < q_{m,l} < 1. \tag{17}$$

Experimental verification of our design formulas are given in Part II of this paper [8], where we apply them to ferrite and garnet substrates, which, operated in certain biasing states, can be treated to a good approximation as reciprocal media.

[1] Wheeler shows that $\frac{1}{2}(k+1) < k_{eff} < k$, the lower limit applying to $w/h \rightarrow 0$, the upper to $w/h \rightarrow \infty$. Our results for the magnetic case are derived with the help of (4).

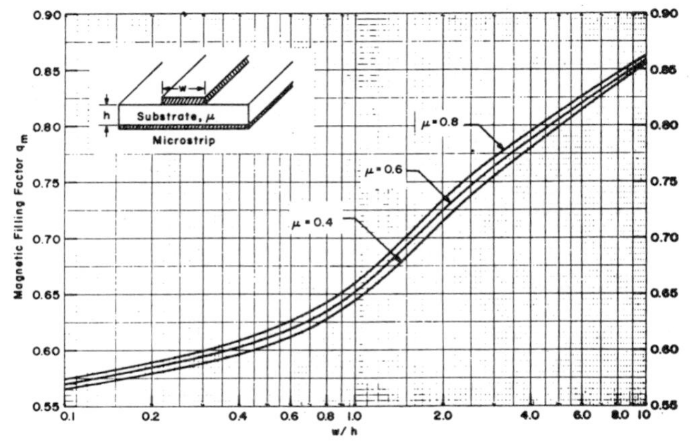

Fig. 3. Propagation magnetic filling factor of microstrip as a function of the relative permeability of the substrate and the geometrical parameter w/h.

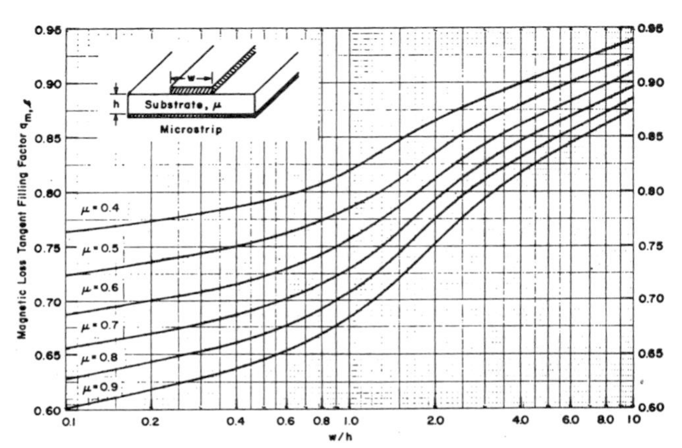

Fig. 4. Filling factor for magnetic loss tangent of microstrip as a function of the relative permeability of the substrate and the geometrical parameter w/h.

V. Summary

Design formulas and graphs were presented for the effective relative permeability and the propagation and attenuation filling factors of microstrip on magnetic substrates. The formulas were obtained by application of a duality relationship which exists between magnetic and dielectric substrates which circumvents the need for solution of the magnetic field distribution in microstrip.

Appendix

We wish to justify the duality relationship between the effective values of the dielectric constant and the relative permeability cited in (4), and establish the conditions under which it is valid.

Our point of departure is an enumeration of the assumptions for our analysis, namely, 1) TEM mode of propagation, 2) perfect conductors (infinite conductivity), and 3) isotropic, homogeneous, nongyromagnetic

TABLE I

RELATIONS PERTAINING TO SOLUTION FOR ELECTRIC AND MAGNETIC FIELDS

Condition	Electric Potential	Magnetic Potential
Potential function	$\psi_e(x, y, k)$	$\boldsymbol{k}\psi_m(x, y, \mu)$
Field vectors	$\boldsymbol{E} = -\nabla\psi_e$	$\boldsymbol{B} = \nabla \times (\boldsymbol{k}\psi_m) = -\boldsymbol{k} \times \nabla\psi_m$
	$\boldsymbol{D} = \epsilon_0 k(x, y)\boldsymbol{E}$	$\boldsymbol{H} = \mu_0^{-1}\mu^{-1}(x, y)\boldsymbol{B}$
Laplace's equation	$\nabla^2\psi_e = 0$	$\nabla^2\psi_m = 0$
Boundary conditions		
on conductor surfaces S_i, S_0	$k(x, y)\nabla\psi_e \cdot \boldsymbol{n} = -\sigma(s)/\epsilon_0$	$(\boldsymbol{k} \times \boldsymbol{n}) \cdot \nabla\psi_m = 0$
	$(\boldsymbol{k} \times \boldsymbol{n}) \cdot \nabla\psi_e = 0$	$\mu^{-1}(x, y)\nabla\psi_m \cdot \boldsymbol{n} = -\mu_0 j(s)$
on interface S_{ai}	$k\nabla\psi_{e,1} \cdot \boldsymbol{n} = \nabla\psi_{e,2} \cdot \boldsymbol{n}$	$(\boldsymbol{k} \times \boldsymbol{n}) \cdot \nabla\psi_{m,1} = (\boldsymbol{k} \times \boldsymbol{n}) \cdot \nabla\psi_{m,2}$
	$(\boldsymbol{k} \times \boldsymbol{n}) \cdot \nabla\psi_{e,1} = (\boldsymbol{k} \times \boldsymbol{n}) \cdot \nabla\psi_{e,2}$	$\mu^{-1}\nabla\psi_{m,1} \cdot \boldsymbol{n} = \nabla\psi_{m,2} \cdot \boldsymbol{n}$

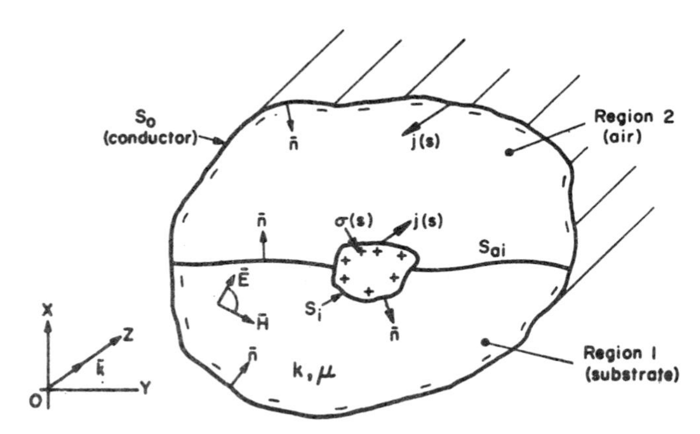

Fig. 5. Cross section of TEM structure relevant to derivation of duality relationship.

substrate. These assumptions are the ones used in all microstrip analyses; hence they are not restrictive for our purposes [1]–[3].

We assume for generality a cylindrical system of arbitrary cross section whose axis is along the Z direction, the assumed direction of propagation as illustrated in Fig. 5. Although a closed system is shown for convenience, our analysis also applies to open systems as well. The assumption of a closed outer conductor is not restrictive, since practical microstrip structures usually have an enclosure for shielding purposes.

With perfect conductors, the currents and charges, denoted by the surface densities $j(s)$ and $\sigma(s)$, reside on the conductor surfaces as shown in Fig. 5. Here s is a transverse surface coordinate on the conductors. For a TEM mode, the electric field $\boldsymbol{E}$ and the magnetic field $\boldsymbol{B} = \mu\boldsymbol{H}$ are in the x–y (transverse) plane. Their spatial distributions in this plane are solutions of a two-dimensional Laplace equation.

It is convenient to express $\boldsymbol{E}$ as the gradient of a scalar potential function ψ_e and $\boldsymbol{B}$ as the curl of a *vector* potential function $\boldsymbol{A}$ which is directed along the Z axis, the direction of the current; that is, $\boldsymbol{A}(x, y) = \boldsymbol{k}\psi_m$, where $\boldsymbol{k}$ is a unit vector along the Z axis. Thus

$$\boldsymbol{E} = -\nabla\psi_e(x, y, k) \tag{18}$$

$$\boldsymbol{B} = \nabla \times \boldsymbol{A} = -\boldsymbol{k} \times \nabla\psi_m(x, y, \mu). \tag{19}$$

Note that like $\boldsymbol{E}$, $\boldsymbol{B}$ is also proportional to the gradient of a scalar function (not to be confused with a scalar magnetic potential). Observe that ψ_e depends on the dielectric constant of the substrate k, but not on the relative permeability μ of the substrate. The converse is true for ψ_m. This is characteristic of a TEM solution. Since Laplace's equation is satisfied by the vector and magnetic potentials, then $\nabla^2\psi_e = 0$ and $\nabla^2\boldsymbol{A} = \boldsymbol{k}\nabla^2\psi_m = 0$ or $\nabla^2\psi_m = 0$. The solutions of these equations are determined by the geometry and the usual boundary conditions imposed on $\boldsymbol{E}$ and $\boldsymbol{B}$ at the conductor surfaces and at the substrate–air interface. These are summarized in Table I.

Perusal of Table I shows that ψ_e and ψ_m satisfy identical *sets* of boundary conditions provided the normal and tangential boundary conditions for $\boldsymbol{E}$ and $\boldsymbol{B}$ are interchanged (which is of no consequence to the solutions for ψ_e and ψ_m). Thus the *form* of the solution for ψ_m is identical to the *form* of the solution for ψ_e, if k is replaced by μ^{-1} and provided the surface densities $\sigma(s)$ and $j(s)$ are proportional. Assuming for a moment the latter to be true, then because of the linearity of the system, we may express ψ_e and ψ_m in the form

$$\psi_e(x, y, k) = \epsilon_0^{-1}QF(x, y, k) \tag{20}$$

$$\psi_m(x, y, \mu) = \mu_0 IF(x, y, \mu^{-1}) \tag{21}$$

where F is a scalar function satisfying Laplace's equation and $Q = \oint_{S_i} \sigma(s)\, ds$, $I = \int_{S_i} j(s)\, ds$ are the total charge/length and current on the conductors. Note that (20) and (21) imply that the magnetic field distribution can be obtained from a solution of an electrostatic problem. It is clear that (20) and (21) in conjunction with (18) and (19) establish the spatial orthogonality of the electric and magnetic fields.

In terms of (20) and (21) the effective dielectric constant k_{eff}, defined as the ratio of the stored electric energy per unit length with and without the substrate present ($k = 1$) at a specified charge Q, is expressible in the form

$$k_{eff} = K(g, k). \tag{22}$$

In a similar fashion, the magnitude of the effective relative permeability μ_{eff} equal to the ratio of the stored magnetic energy per unit length, with and without the substrate present ($\mu = 1$) for a specified current is of the form

$$\frac{1}{\mu_{eff}} = K(g, \mu^{-1}) \tag{23}$$

where the energy density function K is given by

$$K(g, k) = \frac{\int_{\mathcal{A}} |\nabla F(x, y, 1)|^2 \, dx \, dy}{\int_{\mathcal{A}} k(x, y) \, |\nabla F(x, y, k)|^2 \, dx \, dy}. \tag{24}$$

Here $\mathcal{A}$ denotes the cross section of the propagating structure, excluding the conductors. The function $k(x, y)$ equals k in the substrate cross section, and unity in the air space above it. The parameter g is a geometrical factor, which equals w/h for the simple microstrip configuration of Fig. 1.

From (22) and (23) we obtain the interesting and useful duality relation

$$\mu_{eff}(g, \mu) = \frac{1}{k_{eff}(g, \mu^{-1})} \tag{25}$$

which was to be proven.

How realistic is the assumption of proportionality between $j(s)$ and $\sigma(s)$? For a system with a homogeneous cross section propagating a pure TEM mode, it is strictly correct. For a *non*homogeneous system, as we are considering here, $\sigma(s)$ and $j(s)$ *cannot* have identical distributions and this, *because* we postulate a TEM mode. Our reasoning is as follows. Suppose we have a TEM mode, and we assume $\sigma(s)$ and $j(s)$ to be proportional. Now consider a change in the dielectric constant of the substrate. Surely this will alter the charge distribution. By our assumption, the current distribution must also change, and so must the magnetic field distribution. But this cannot happen for a TEM mode, because the dielectric cannot affect the magnetic field.

Experience has shown that the magnetic field distribution, or more precisely, the inductance per unit length of microstrip, is *not* affected noticeably by the presence of a dielectric substrate. We can only conclude then that the charge and current distributions apparently do not deviate appreciably from proportionality and that the capacitance and inductance per unit length are not sensitive so much to the precise distribution of charge and current on the conductors, as they are to the geometrical configuration of the conductors and the substrate.

References

[1] H. A. Wheeler, "Transmission-line properties of parallel strips separated by a dielectric sheet," *IEEE Trans. Microwave Theory Tech.*, vol. MTT-13, pp. 172–186, Mar. 1965.

[2] H. E. Stinehelfer, Sr., "An accurate calculation of uniform microstrip transmission lines," *IEEE Trans. Microwave Theory Tech.*, vol. MTT-16, pp. 439–444, July 1968.

[3] E. Yamashita and R. Mittra, "Variational method for the analysis of microstrip lines," *IEEE Trans. Microwave Theory Tech.*, vol. MTT-16, pp. 251–256, Apr. 1968.

[4] J. D. Welch and J. J. Pratt, "Losses in microstrip transmission systems for integrated microwave circuits," *NEREM Rec. 8*, pp. 100–101, 1966.

[5] R. A. Pucel, D. Massé, and C. P. Hartwig, "Losses in microstrip," *IEEE Trans. Microwave Theory Tech.*, vol. MTT-16, pp. 342–350, June 1968; also "Correction to 'Losses in microstrip'," *IEEE Trans. Microwave Theory Tech.* (Corresp.), vol. MTT-16, p. 1064, Dec. 1968.

[6] T. Kaneki, "Analysis of linear microstrip using an arbitrary ferromagnetic substance as the substrate," *Electron. Lett.*, vol. 5, pp. 465–466, Sept. 18, 1969.

[7] H. B. Palmer, "The capacitance of a parallel-plate capacitor by the Schwarz-Christoffel transformation," *Elec. Eng.*, pp. 363–366, Mar. 1939.

[8] D. J. Massé and R. A. Pucel, "Microstrip propagation on magnetic substrates—Part II: Experiment," *IEEE Trans. Microwave Theory Tech.*, this issue, pp. 309–313.

M.I.S. AND SCHOTTKY SLOW-WAVE COPLANAR STRIPLINES ON GaAs SUBSTRATES

Indexing terms: Microwave integrated circuits, Monolithic integrated circuits, Striplines

Novel slow-wave coplanar striplines on GaAs substrates with m.i.s. or Schottky junctions are described. With these lines, significant reductions in wavelength and bias-dependent behaviours can be achieved at microwave frequencies. The new lines seem potentially very useful for monolithic integration of microwave circuits involving GaAs m.e.s.f.e.t.s.

Introduction: With the remarkable progress in GaAs m.e.s.f.e.t.s in recent years, monolithic integration of the circuits containing these devices now seems to be an interesting and important technological possibility, which should be explored. The availability of high-quality semi-insulating materials in GaAs makes it particularly attractive from the viewpoint of device isolation. The resistivity of these materials appears to be high enough for their use as the dielectric media for strip transmission lines in the microwave and millimetre-wave ranges. The obvious difficulty arises from the wavelength of electromagnetic waves at these frequencies. When distributed-parameter matching networks, filters, couplers etc. are constructed on semi-insulating GaAs substrates, their size would become too large. Apart from the technological complexity caused by the increased range of dimensions involved for integration, the expense spent on the single-crystal substrates will be too large to be economically justified; Torrero describes it as the 'king's ransom'.[1]

The purpose of the present letter is to describe a new class of coplanar strip waveguides on GaAs substrates which support propagation of low-loss slow electromagnetic waves. Substantial reduction of wavelength and bias-dependent behaviour can be achieved with the new striplines, and they may therefore be useful for monolithic integration of GaAs microwave devices, as well as for other applications.

Line structures and transmission properties: The basic line structures are illustrated in Figs. 1*a–d*. These are transverse cross-sections, and the waves are to propagate in the direction perpendicular to them. In Figs. 1*c* and *d*, m.i.s. and Schottky junctions between the ground planes and the epitaxial layers can be replaced by ohmic contacts. The present coplanar lines can also be constructed with silicon s.o.s. technology.

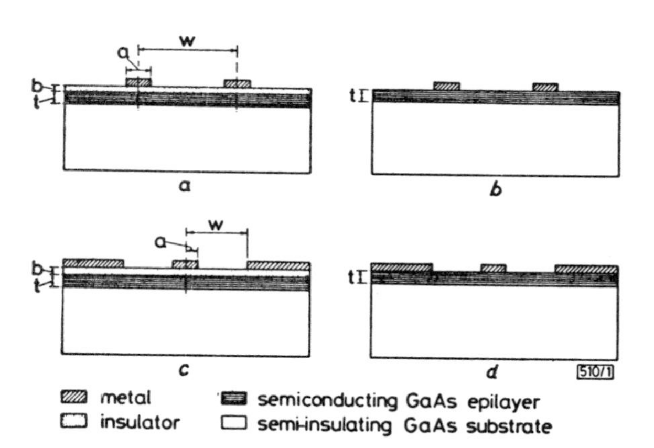

Fig. 1 *Basic line structures*

a Balanced m.i.s. slow-wave coplanar line
b Balanced Schottky slow-wave coplanar line
c Unbalanced m.i.s. slow-wave coplanar line
d Unbalanced Schottky slow-wave coplanar line

The physical principle of slow-wave propagation is based on the semiconducting nature of the thin epitaxial layer, which gives rise to a kind of 'filtering' action against the field lines. This is to say, under certain conditions, the epitaxial layer does not allow the electric-field lines to pass through it, but it does allow the magnetic field lines to pass. Consequently, the electric energy is stored for the most part within the m.i.s. or Schottky capacitance, while the magnetic energy is stored in the whole region near the metal strips. Owing to the separate energy storage, the propagation velocity, which is basically determined by the line inductance L and the capacitance C per unit length, is reduced to a value which is much smaller than that expected from the permittivity and permeability of the media.

Obviously, such a consideration applies only in the quasi-static approximation, and the wave propagation will actually suffer dispersion and attenuation, caused by the relaxation behaviour of line capacitance (or relaxation of interfacial polarisation) and by that of line inductance (owing to the skin effect). It should be emphasised, however, that the relaxation frequencies can at least be made higher than several tens of gigahertz in the present line structures with proper design.

Another unique feature of the new coplanar lines is that the transmission characteristics can be varied electronically by the bias-dependent nonlinear behaviour of the m.i.s. and Schottky capacitances. Useful tunabilities and parametric interactions are expected as applications of this feature.

Slow-wave propagation based on a similar principle has been previously studied by various authors, including one of the present authors, on microstrip lines on Si-SiO_2 substrates and on Si substrates with Schottky contacts.[2-8] Compared with these, the present structures are expected to possess the advantages of (*a*) being more suitable for planar integration, (*b*) providing larger reductions of wavelength, owing to higher inductances, and (*c*) having lower attenuation and smaller dispersion, owing to the small thickness of the epilayer, which can be made much smaller than the skin depth, thereby enhancing the relaxation frequency of the line inductance.

The exact analysis of wave propagation along the present lines is obviously extremely complicated and difficult. A quasistatic approach based on the above physical considerations seems to be much more practical, as in the case of microstrip lines.[4] As an example, calculated values of the characteristic impedance and the slow-wave factor λ_0/λ_g, where λ_0 is the free-space wavelength and λ_g is guide wavelength, using such an approach, are plotted in Fig. 2 for the m.i.s.-type unbalanced coplanar stripline shown in Fig. 1*c*. In the calculation, the ground planes were assumed to be semi-infinite and the semiconductor depletion-layer capacitance was ignored for simplicity. The latter can be easily included with the use of the standard m.o.s.-capacitance theory.

Experimental results: To confirm the propagation of the slow-wave mode along the present coplanar lines, a preliminary experiment was performed on experimental m.o.s. coplanar lines of the type shown in Fig. 1*c*. A tin-doped *n*-type epitaxial GaAs layer was grown from liquid phase on a Cr-doped semi-insulating GaAs substrate, and the top of the epilayer was subsequently oxidised anodically with the a.g.w. process.[9] Metal strips were formed by vacuum deposition of gold. The important line parameters were $a = 50\,\mu m$, $w = 500\,\mu m$, $b = 4000\,Å$, $t = 3\,\mu m$, $\epsilon_i = 8{\cdot}5$, resistivity of epilayer = $5{\cdot}5 \times 10^{-3}\,\Omega\,cm$ and the line lengths = 3 and 8·8 mm. The

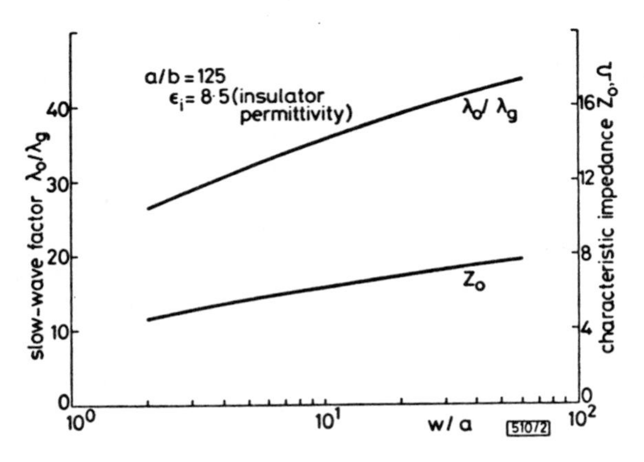

Fig. 2 *Calculated characteristic impedance and slow-wave factor*

measurements of the characteristic impedance and propagation constant were performed by a technique described in Reference 4, using a 50 Ω microstrip standing-wave detector. The measured values of the characteristic impedance and the slow-wave factor are plotted against frequency in Fig. 3 for a line with a length of 8·8 mm. Nearly the same result was obtained for the line with a length of 3 mm, showing the

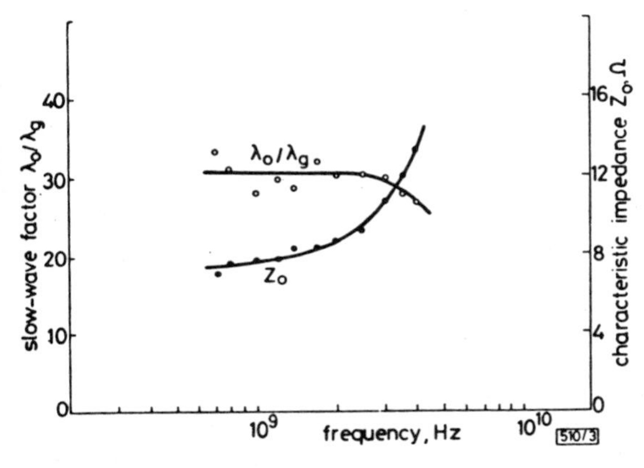

Fig. 3 *Measured characteristic impedance and slow-wave factor against frequency*

consistency of the measurement. These results clearly indicate the propagation of the slow-wave mode. The experimentally observed values of impedance and slowing factor are close to the theoretical ones. A somewhat large attenuation of 0·08 to 0·2 Np/mm was observed, but this is consistent with the low relaxation frequency of line capacitance (2 to 3 GHz) seen in Fig. 3 and should be improved by the miniaturisation and optimisation of the line design. Extensive efforts are being made towards that direction.

Acknowledgments: The authors would like to express their thanks to Prof. Tagashira, of this Department, for his valuable discussions.

H. HASEGAWA
H. OKIZAKI

Department of Electrical Engineering
Faculty of Engineering
Hokkaido University
Sapporo, 060 Japan

7th September 1977

References

1 TORRERO, E. A.: 'High-frequency components play catch-up', *IEEE Spectrum*, 1976, **13**, pp. 30–35
2 GUCKEL, H., BRENNAN, P. A., and PALOCZ, I.: 'A parallel-plate waveguide approach to microminiaturized, planar transmission lines for integrated circuits', *IEEE Trans.*, 1968, **MTT-15**, pp. 468–476
3 HASEGAWA, H., FURUKAWA, M., and YANAI, H.: 'Slow wave propagation along a microstrip line on Si-SiO_2 system', *Proc. IEEE*, 1971, **59**, pp. 297–299
4 HASEGAWA, H., FURUKAWA, M., and YANAI, H.: 'Properties of microstrip line on Si-SiO_2 system', *IEEE Trans.*, 1971, **MTT-19**, pp. 869–881
5 HUGHES, G. W., and WHITE, R. M.: 'MIS and Schottky barrier microstrip devices', *Proc. IEEE*, 1972, **60**, pp. 1460–1461
6 JAFFE, J. M.: 'A high-frequency variable delay line', *IEEE Trans.*, 1972, **ED-19**, pp. 1292–1294
7 HUGHES, G. W., and WHITE, R. M.: 'Microwave properties of nonlinear MIS and Schottky-barrier microstrip', *ibid.*, 1975, **ED-22**,
8 JÄGER, D.: 'Slow-wave propagation along variable Schottky-contact microstrip line', *ibid.*, 1976, **MTT-24**, pp. 566–573
9 HASEGAWA, H., and HARTNAGEL, H.: 'Anodic oxidation of GaAs in mixed solutions of glycol and water', *J. Electrochem. Soc.*, 1976, **123**, pp. 713–723

ANALYSIS OF PRINTED TRANSMISSION LINES FOR MONOLITHIC INTEGRATED CIRCUITS

Indexing terms: Integrated circuits, Transmission lines, Microstrip

Planar transmission lines formed with MIS and Schottky barrier contacts are analysed based on the spectral domain technique. Depending on the frequency and the resistivity of the substrates, three different types of fundamental modes are predicted. The calculated slow-wave factors and attenuation constants agree well with experimental results.

Introduction: Recent developments in monolithic microwave integrated circuits (MMIC) require better understanding of the transmission properties of various transmission lines on semiconductor substrates. The existence of the slow-wave mode has been experimentally observed on metal-insulator-semiconductor (MIS) and Schottky-barrier microstrip lines[1,2] as well as coplanar striplines.[3] Because of the reduction in dimensions of distributed passive components, these slow-wave transmission lines could be preferable in the design of MMICs.

To date, only shielded MIS microstrip line has been analysed rigorously.[4] No theoretical results based on the full-wave analysis have been reported on Schottky-barrier microstrip line and coplanar waveguides. In this letter, the open planar structures as shown in Fig. 1 are studied using a full-wave analysis in the spectral domain. The complex propagation constants directly obtained are in good agreement with the experimental data. An extensive study of the MIS coplanar waveguide shows the existence of the three fundamental mode types (skin-effect, lossy-dielectric and slow-wave) similar to the ones reported in Reference 1. The optimum resistivity for low-loss propagation can also be predicted by the present method.

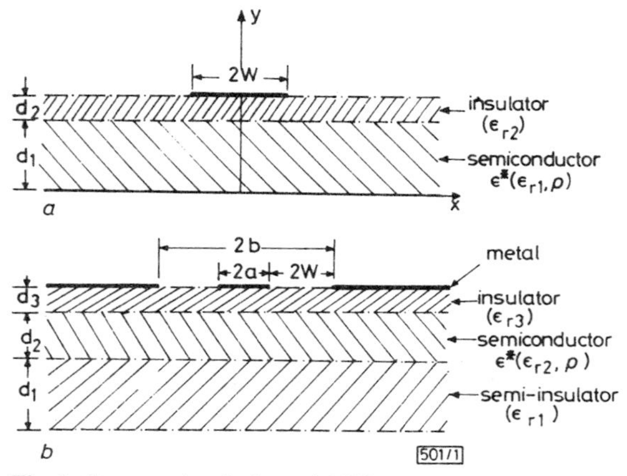

Fig. 1 *Cross-sectional view of MIS microstrip line (a) and coplanar waveguide (b)*

The spectral-domain method has been successfully used to analyse lossless planar and quasiplanar transmission lines such as microstrip line, coplanar waveguide and fin-line.[5,6] By introducing lossy dielectrics, the same procedure as in Reference 5 is followed to obtain the complex propagation constants which predict accurately the wave propagation properties in these structures. The set of basis functions used in Reference 6 is employed in this study. The complex root searching computer program used is based on Muller's method.

Numerical results: For the MIS microstrip lines tested by Hasegawa *et al.*,[1] the slow-wave factor and the attenuation constant experimentally obtained are in good agreement with the results of the present analysis. As mentioned in Reference 4, only one basis function is required to obtain good results for a narrow strip. However, more basis functions are found to be required for a wide strip. Further, the Schottky contact microstrip line tested by Jäger and Rabus[2] was also analysed. In such structures, the depletion layer is usually localised near the strip. Nevertheless, we can apply the present method based on the model in Fig. 1*a*. This is because most of the field lines pass through the depletion layer and the field at large distances from the depletion layer has little effect on the propagation characteristics. It should be noted that the high-frequency characteristics are correctly incorporated in the present method. Such is not the case in the parallel-plate approximation used by References 1 and 2 in which some correction factor must be used. Since all the field contributions are included in the present case, no correction factor is necessary.

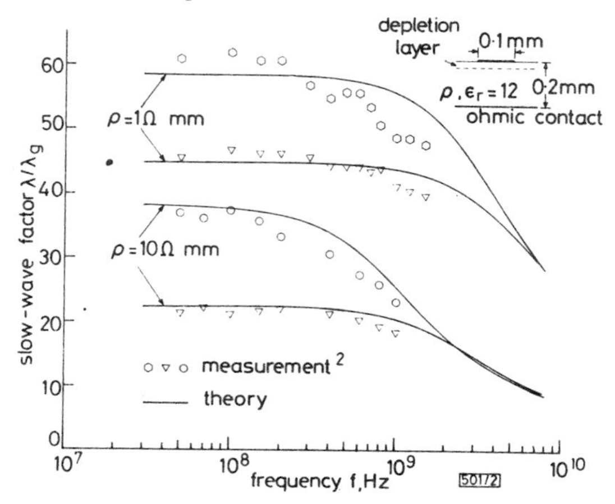

Fig. 2 *Slow-wave characteristics of Schottky-barrier microstrip line*

Fig. 2 shows that the present analysis can accurately describe the propagation properties experimentally obtained.

The MIS coplanar structure in Fig. 1*b* is also studied with this method and the results are compared with measurements reported[3,7] in Fig. 3, in which good agreement is shown in both the slow-wave factors and attenuation constants. Their coplanar line was built on a GaAs substrate with a narrow centre strip and wide slots. Since the coupling between slots is strong, a large number of basis functions are required for

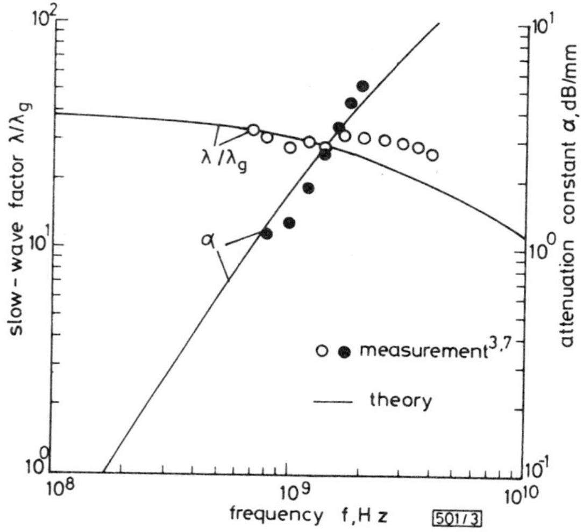

Fig. 3 *Dispersion and attenuation characteristics of MIS coplanar waveguide*

$a = 50\ \mu m$, $b = 500\ \mu m$
$d_3 = 0{\cdot}4\ \mu m$, $\varepsilon_{r3} = 8{\cdot}5$
$d_2 = 3{\cdot}0\ \mu m$, $\varepsilon_{r2} = 13{\cdot}1$
$\varepsilon_{r1} = 13{\cdot}1$, $\rho = 0{\cdot}055\ \Omega$mm

accurate results. Several examples have been studied by increasing the number of basis functions. It was found that good results can be obtained by using seven basis functions which represent axial and transverse electric fields in the slot. More basis functions improve the results somewhat but with much higher computing expense. The general properties of the coplanar waveguide are thus studied by choosing these seven basis functions.

A family of curves was generated relating the propagation constant of the MIS coplanar waveguide to the substrate resistivity. Frequency was varied as a parameter. A mode diagram made from these curves is shown in Fig. 4*a*. It is clear that, depending on the frequency and the resistivity, three types of fundamental modes could exist in this structure. A typical example demonstrating the behaviour of the slow-wave factor and attenuation constant with respect to resistivity is given in Figs. 4*b* and *c*. The structural parameters are given in Fig. 3. In this case, the optimum resistivity for low-loss propagation is about $1 \cdot 5 \times 10^{-2}$ Ωmm.

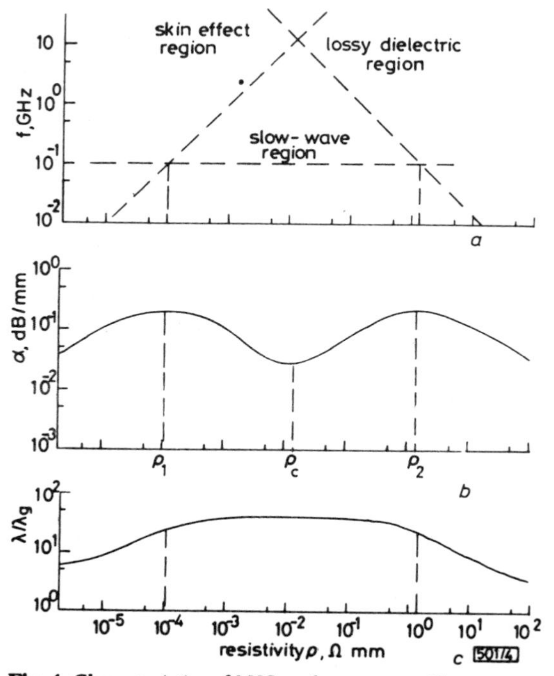

Fig. 4 *Characteristics of MIS coplanar waveguide*
a Mode chart
b Attenuation against resistivity
c Slow-wave factor against resistivity

A GaAs coplanar structure with Schottky contacted centre strip was tested at Hughes Aircraft. The measured slow-wave factors agree reasonably well with the theoretical prediction by the present analysis.

Acknowledgment: This work was supported by the Office of Naval Research N00014-79-C-0553, Joint Services Electronics Program F49620-79-C-0101 and US Army Research Office contract DAAG29-81-K-0053.

Y. C. SHIH
T. ITOH

6th May 1982

Department of Electrical Engineering
University of Texas at Austin
Austin, Texas 78712, USA

References

1 HASEGAWA, H., FURUKAWA, M., and YARAI, H.: 'Properties of microstrip line on Si-SiO_2 system', *IEEE Trans.*, 1971, **MTT-19**, pp. 869–881

2 JÄGER, D., and RABUS, W.: 'Bias dependent phase delay of Schottky contact microstrip line', *Electron. Lett.*, 1973, **9**, pp. 201–203

3 HASEGAWA, H., and OKIZAKI, H.: 'MIS and Schottky slow-wave coplanar strip-lines on GaAs substrates', *ibid.*, 1977, **13**, pp. 663–664

4 KENNIS, P., and FAUCON, L.: 'Rigorous analysis of planar MIS transmission lines', *ibid.*, 1981, **17**, pp. 454–456

5 ITOH, T.: 'Spectral domain immittance approach for dispersion characteristics of generalized printed transmission lines', *IEEE Trans.*, 1980, **MTT-28**, pp. 981–985

6 SCHMIDT, L.-P.: 'A comprehensive analysis of quasiplanar waveguides for millimeter-wave application'. 11th European microwave conference, Amsterdam, The Netherlands, Sept. 1981, pp. 315–320

7 SEKI, S., and HASEGAWA, H.: 'Cross-tie slow-wave coplanar waveguide on semi-insulating GaAs substrate', *Electron. Lett.*, 1981, **17**, pp. 940–951

ELECTRICAL PROPERTIES OF COPLANAR TRANSMISSION LINES ON LOSSLESS AND LOSSY SUBSTRATES

Indexing terms: Electric impedance, Strip lines, Substrates

The characteristic impedance and the propagation constant of coplanar transmission lines on lossless and lossy substrates are given and compared with computed values within the frequency region 0–8 GHz. Al_2O_3 and *n*-Si substrates are used.

Recently, coplanar lines (c.p.l.) have been the subject of growing interest owing to many technological advantages compared with microstrip lines. Although some theoretical works[1,2] were published several years ago, there are only a few experimental results on c.p.l.s. Dupuis and Campbell[3] reported measurements of characteristic impedance and Mueller[4] measured the effective relative permittivity of c.p.l.s on Al_2O_3. Measurements with c.p.l.s on semiconducting substrates, however, have not yet been published, although these materials should be useful for an integration of active structures.

The results presented here have been achieved by *S*-parameter measurements with c.p.l.s on Al_2O_3 and *n*-Si fabricated by standard photoresist technology; their configuration is shown in Fig. 1*a*. The distance between the outer conductors is kept constant ($2b_1 = 1$ mm) for all the samples. Thus the same mounting containing o.s.m. launchers turned out to be very useful for all of them. The width of the outer conductors is constant as well, and large enough compared with the slot width ($c_1 - b_1 = 3{\cdot}5$ mm), for the simplified theory for c.p.l.s with infinitely wide outer conductors to be valid. The thickness of the gold conductors has been galvanically enhanced. The influence of the launchers has been eliminated by varying the line length l of the c.p.l.s.

Fig. 1 shows the experimental and theoretical results of c.p.l.s on Al_2O_3 substrate; the data are listed in the subcaption. Fig. 1*a* presents the measured real part R of characteristic impedance $Z = R + jX$ for five c.p.l.s of various ratios a_1/b_1. The straight lines are the theoretical values achieved by Wens theory,[1] with which the measured values agree well—except for small a_1/b_1 ratios—within the whole frequency region. For small ratios, the measured values are up to 10% smaller than the theoretically predicted ones. It should be noted that the imaginary parts X are almost zero within the measurement accuracy and are not shown here. Fig. 1*b* shows the inverse slowing factor λ/λ_0 of a c.p.l. with $a_1/b_1 = 0{\cdot}56$. The straight line is the theoretical result[1] using $\varepsilon_r = 9{\cdot}7$ and assuming an infinitely thick substrate. The latter condition, however, is not fulfilled; the difference between the theoretical and measured values of λ/λ_0 is the result of finite substrate thickness, as other authors have also reported. The experimental values of the attenuation constant α of c.p.l.s. on Al_2O_3 presented here are less than 0·15 dB/mm in the whole frequency region.

Fig. 1*b*, in addition, summarises the results of the measured real part R of the characteristic impedance, comparing them with theory for various a_1/b_1 ratios. As can be seen—contrary to the measurements of Dupuis and Campbell[3]—the measured values of R are again lower than the theoretical predictions for small a_1/b_1 ratios. However, this may be traced back to the influence of the internal inductance of thick metal conductors[5] exceeding the effect due to finite substrate thickness.

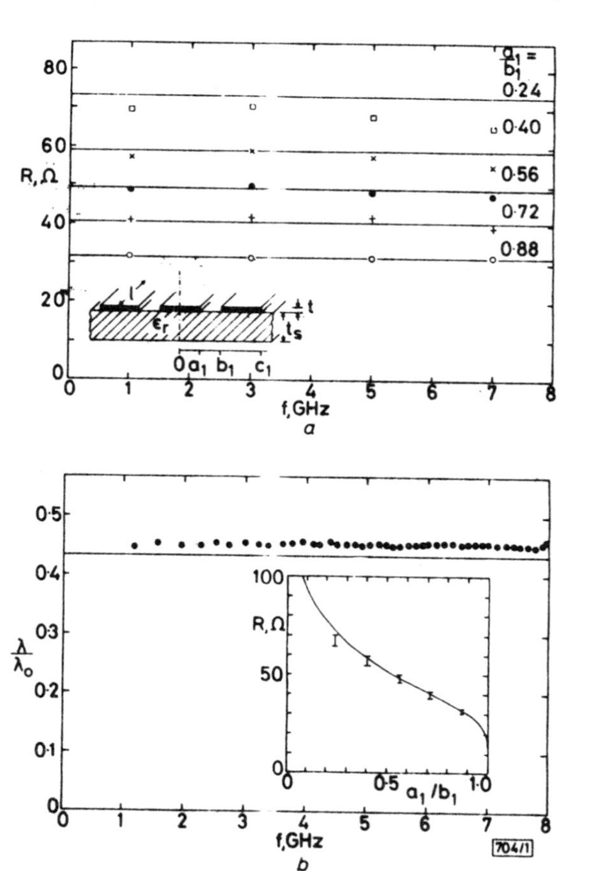

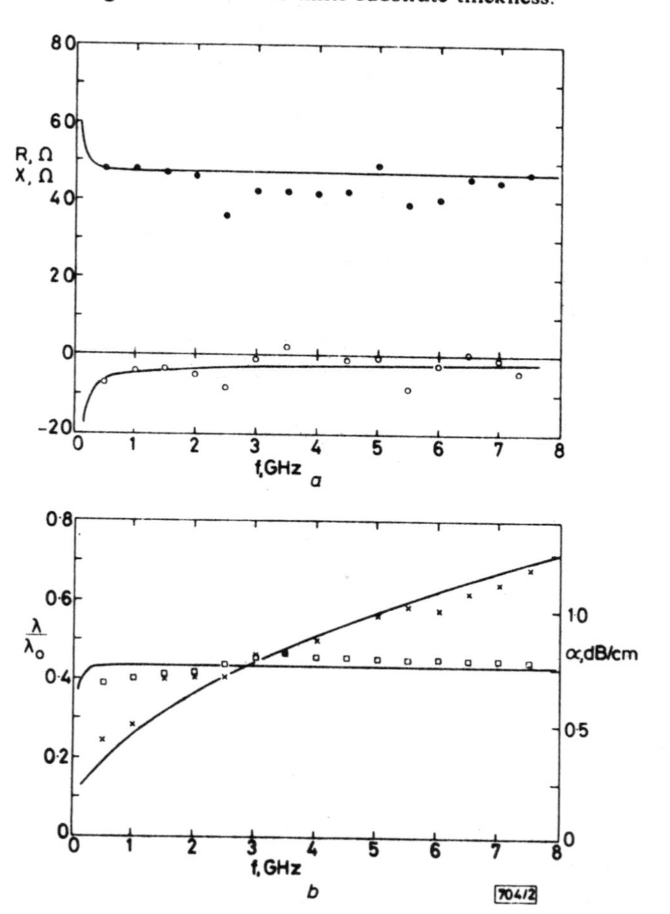

Fig. 1 *Theoretical[1] and experimental results of c.p.l.s on Al_2O_3*

a Real part R of characteristic impedance as function of frequency f sketch of sample is shown in inset

$\varepsilon_r = 9{\cdot}7$, $t = 15$ μm, $t_s = 0{\cdot}64$ mm, $2b_1 = 1{\cdot}0$ mm, $c_1 - b_1 = 3{\cdot}5$ mm, $l = 33{\cdot}8$ mm

b Inverse slowing factor λ/λ_0 as function of frequency f, $a_1/b_1 = 0{\cdot}56$; real part R of characteristic impedance as function of ratio a_1/b_1 is shown in inset

Fig. 2 *Theoretical and experimental results of c.p.l. on n-Si*

a Real part R(●) and imaginary part X(○) of characteristic impedance as function of frequency f

b Inverse slowing factor λ/λ_0(□) and losses (×) as function of frequency f

$\rho = 12$ kΩcm, $\varepsilon_r = 11{\cdot}7$, $t = 0{\cdot}2$ μm, $t_s = 220$ μm, $2b = 1{\cdot}0$ mm, $c_1 - b_1 = 3{\cdot}5$ mm, $a_1/b_1 = 0{\cdot}65$, $l = 22{\cdot}7$ mm

Fig. 2 shows the result of theory and measurement of a c.p.l. on an n-Si substrate with a resistivity of $\rho = 12$ kΩcm. The data of the sample are listed in the subcaption of Fig. 2*b*. The theoretical predictions are obtained by a conforming mapping method, where the losses of the metallic conductors and the substrate are taken into account in a manner similar to that of Reference 5. They were obtained by d.c. measurements and had to be corrected for the skin effect. Because of the small substrate thickness of 220 μm, the influence of lowering the effective dielectric constant has also been taken into account. The straight lines in Fig. 2 are the result of such a calculation. The measured values of the real and imaginary parts of the complex impedance in Fig. 2*a* are in good agreement with theory, and so are the inverse slowing factor λ/λ_0 and the losses α in Fig. 2*b*. It has to be remarked that the losses are of the same order as those of similar microstrip on Si.[5]

In conclusion, theory yields a good prediction of c.p.l. parameters even for lossy substrates. With losses comparable to those of microstrip lines on Si, c.p.l.s are to be preferred because of their technological advantages.

Acknowledgments: The authors wish to thank W. Driemeier and J. Kerntopf for their assistance and Prof. W. Hampe for kindly supporting this work.

J.-P. BECKER
D. JÄGER

Institut für Angewandte Physik
Universität Münster
Roxeler Strasse 70-72, 44 Münster, W. Germany

6th December 1978

References

1 WEN, C. P.: 'Coplanar waveguide: a surface strip transmission line suitable for nonreciprocal gyromagnetic device applications', *IEEE Trans.*, 1969, **MTT-17**, pp. 1087–1090

2 HILBERG, W.: 'Charakteristische Größen elektrischer Leitungen' (Verlag Berliner Union, Stuttgart, 1972)

3 DUPUIS, P. A. J., and CAMPBELL, C. K.: 'Characteristic impedance of surface-strip coplanar waveguides', *Electron. Lett.*, 1973, **9**, pp. 354–355

4 MUELLER, E.: 'Measurement of the effective relative permittivity of unshielded coplanar waveguides', *ibid.*, 1977, **13**, pp. 729–730

5 JÄGER, D., RABUS, W., and EICKHOFF, W.: 'Bias dependent small signal parameters of Shottky-contact microstrip lines', *Solid-State Electron.*, 1974, **17**, pp. 777–783

ANALYSIS OF COUPLED ASYMMETRIC MICROSTRIP LINES ON A FERRITE SUBSTRATE

Indexing terms: Microwave devices and components, Microstrip lines

The dispersion properties of asymmetric coupled microstrip lines filled with ferrite medium magnetised perpendicularly to the substrate surface are analysed by the spectral-domain technique. The dispersion characteristics of the fundamental C- and π-modes are found as a function of various structural parameters and of biasing magnetic field. New interesting properties of guided modes have been observed.

Introduction: The behaviour of guided modes in a ferrite-filled microstrip magnetised transversely to the plane of the substrate has been studied in earlier papers by several investigators who have employed various analytical techniques.[1-4] To date, however, the knowledge of the transmission properties of a ferrite-filled coupled microstrip line is generally not yet known. In this letter a structure of two coupled asymmetric microstrips, shown in Fig. 1, is analysed by the spectral-domain technique first proposed by Itoh and Mittra.[5] This structure is believed to be potentially useful in many reciprocal and nonreciprocal MIC gyromagnetic devices like isolators, couplers, phase shifters, switches etc. It may be expected that the exact analytical results concerning dispersion properties of this line should facilitate the design of these devices.

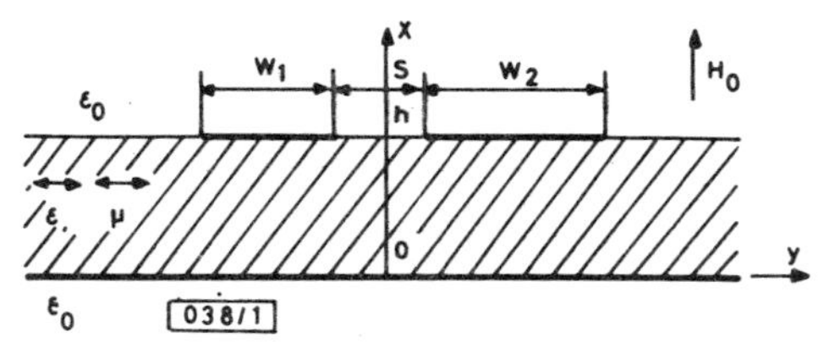

Fig. 1 *Asymmetric coupled microstrip lines on bigyrotropic substrate with perpendicular magnetisation*

Analysis: For generality of the developed analytical formulation a bigyrotropic medium has been assumed as the substrate material with a special anisotropy given by the permittivity $\overleftrightarrow{\varepsilon}$ and permeability $\overleftrightarrow{\mu}$ tensors:

$$\overleftrightarrow{\varepsilon} = \varepsilon_0 \begin{bmatrix} \varepsilon_3 & 0 & 0 \\ 0 & \varepsilon_1 & -j\varepsilon_2 \\ 0 & j\varepsilon_2 & \varepsilon_1 \end{bmatrix}$$

$$\overleftrightarrow{\mu} = \mu_0 \begin{bmatrix} \mu_3 & 0 & 0 \\ 0 & \mu_1 & -j\mu_2 \\ 0 & j\mu_2 & \mu_1 \end{bmatrix} \tag{1}$$

In the spectral-domain procedure the knowledge of the EM field components is required at the stage of the analysis of the boundary conditions at the cross-section interfaces. In the air region the fields can be simply found from the Helmholtz equation; however, in the substrate region the formulation is relatively more involved. It can be shown that in the bigyrotropic medium the Fourier transforms of the fields required in the analysis and resulting from the form of the tensors (eqn. 1) are as follows:

$$\tilde{E}_z = \sum_{i=1}^{4} A_i \exp(s_i x)$$

$$\eta \tilde{H}_z = \sum_{i=1}^{4} A_i B_i \exp(s_i x)$$

$$\tilde{E}_y = \sum_{i=1}^{4} A_i L_i \exp(s_i x)$$

$$\eta \tilde{H}_y = \sum_{i=1}^{4} A_i M_i \exp(s_i x) \tag{2}$$

where $\eta = j\eta_0$ with η_0 being the intrinsic impedance of free space and s_i are the roots of the 4th-order characteristic equation of the set of coupled-wave equations for longitudinal field components. The coefficients B_i, L_i and M_i are given by:

$$B_i = \frac{\varepsilon_1(\varepsilon_3\mu_1 - \beta_n^2)(p^2 - k_0^2 k_{eff}^2) - s_i^2 \varepsilon_3(\varepsilon_1\mu_3 - \beta_n^2)}{s_i(p\beta_n(\varepsilon_3\mu_1 - \varepsilon_1\mu_3) - jk_0(\varepsilon_3\mu_3 \times (\varepsilon_1\mu_2 + \varepsilon_2\mu_1) - \beta_n^2(\varepsilon_2\mu_2 + \varepsilon_2\mu_3)))}$$

$$L_i = \frac{(p\beta_n + jk_0\mu_3\varepsilon_2 - \mu_3 s_i B_i)}{k_0(\mu_3\varepsilon_1 - \beta_n^2)}$$

$$M_i = \frac{-\varepsilon_3 s_i + B_i(p\beta_n + jk_0\varepsilon_3\mu_2)}{k_0(\varepsilon_3\mu_1 - \beta_n^2)} \tag{3}$$

with

$$k_{eff} = \frac{\varepsilon_1^2 - \varepsilon_2^2}{\varepsilon_1} - \beta_n^2$$

$$\beta_n = \beta/k_0 \qquad k_0 = \omega\sqrt{(\mu_0\varepsilon_0)}$$

p denoting the Fourier transform variable and β the unknown phase constant that we seek.

The matching of the boundary conditions at the cross-section interfaces leads to the classical set of coupled algebraic equations.[5,6] The next steps of solutions are similar to those described in Reference 6.

Numerical results: On the basis of the developed formulation some numerical computations have been performed for the asymmetric coupled microstrips on a ferrite substrate with perpendicular magnetisation direction. In the computations we assume $\varepsilon_2 = 0$ and $\varepsilon_1 = \varepsilon_3 = \varepsilon_r$. It was also found that four terms of the basis functions series give accurate results for the phase constants in the case of the assumed line dimensions.

At first, the dispersion properties of the C- and π-modes have been analysed for both possible magnetisation directions. As predicted the structure is practically reciprocal and therefore all results presented below are given only for the positive $(+z)$ propagation direction. Fig. 2 presents the dispersion characteristics against asymmetry ratio w_2/w_1 for a fixed value of the spacing slot width s. It is evident that with increasing w_2/w_1 the phase constants of both fundamental modes increase, apart from the field displacement region of the negative values of $\mu_{eff} = (\mu_1^2 - \mu_2^2)/\mu_1$. In this region the equalisation of the C- and π-mode phase velocities can be exactly accomplished, as can seen from the presented dispersion curves. It is noticeable that the phase constants of these modes exhibit different sensitivities on the asymmetry ratio below and above the resonant frequency that can be explained by the mode field distributions with respect to the different properties of the ferrite material in these regions. It could also be pointed out that this structure is free of the surface waves occurring in ferrite-filled transmission lines propagating at the ferrite-metal (FM) and ferrite-air (FA) boundaries. Therefore, the practical usability of asymmetric coupled microstrips is generally limited by the excitation of the higher-order modes.

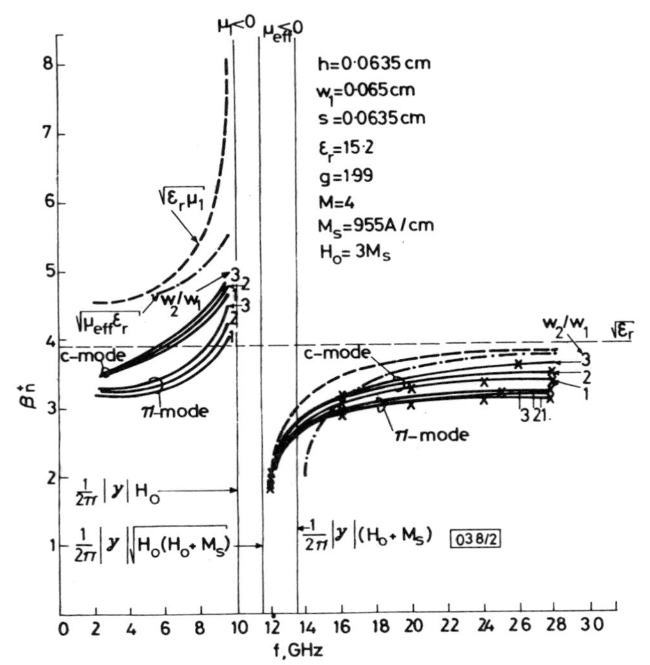

Fig. 2 *Dispersion characteristics of asymmetric coupled microstrip lines on a ferrite substrate against asymmetry ratio*

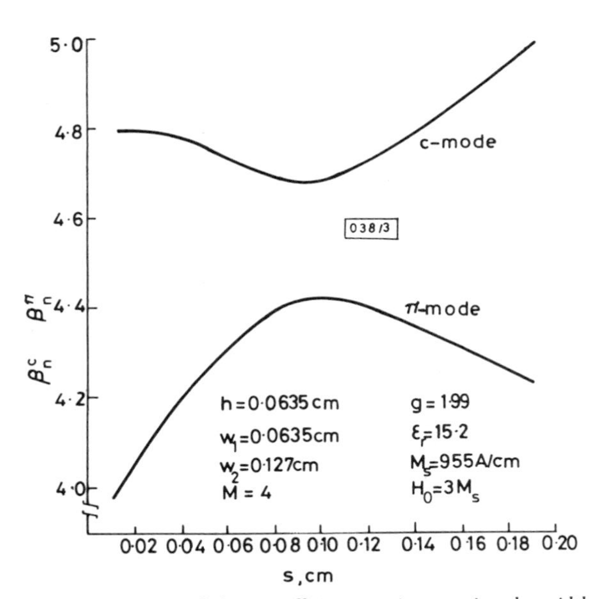

Fig. 3 *Behaviour of phase coefficients against spacing slot width*

Another interesting effect is shown in Fig. 3. The variation of the phase velocities for both modes with spacing slot width s exhibits that by changes of line dimensions these two phase velocities can be made nearly equal. This conclusion seems important due to the possibilities of the construction of electronically tunable directional couplers.

Fig. 4 presents the behaviour of guided modes against the biasing magnetic field. The convergence to the isotropic case in the strong magnetic field is easily deduced. In the resonance region characteristics are very sensitive to magnetic-field changes.

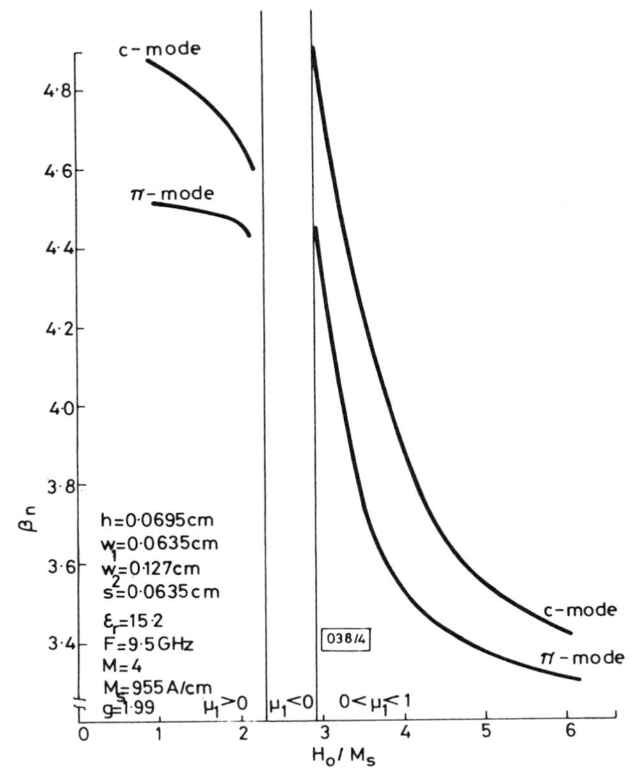

Fig. 4 *Effect of biasing magnetic field on the phase constant characteristics*

Conclusions: A rigorous hybrid-mode analysis of asymmetric coupled microstrips on a ferrite magnetised perpendicularly to the substrate surface has been presented. It is found that this structure can be interesting in the design of several gyromagnetic device applications owing to its transmission properties.

B. JANICZAK
M. KITLIŃSKI

Technical University of Gdańsk
Telecommunication Institute
Majakowskiego 11/12, 80-952 Gdańsk, Poland

29th July 1983

References

1 MAZUR, J.: 'Propagation in the ferrite-microstrip magnetized perpendicularly to the ground-plane'. Proc. 6th European Microwave Conference, Roma, 1976, pp. 555–559

2 HOFMANN, H.: 'Zur Dispersion der Phasenkoeffizienten von Streifenleitungen auf Ferritsubstrat'. Thesis, Aachen, 1975

3 BORBURGH, J.: 'Theoretische Untersuchung der Dispersion und Feldverteilung von Wellentypen einer Mikrostreifenleitung mit gyrotropen Substrat'. Thesis, Erlangen, 1976

4 KRAUZE, N.: 'Ein Verfahren zur Berechnung der Dispersion einer Mikrostreifenleitung auf gyrotropen Substrat', *AEÜ*, 1977, **31**, pp. 205–211

5 ITOH, T., and MITTRA, R.: 'Dispersion characteristics of slot lines', *Electron. Lett.*, 1971, **7**, pp. 364–365

6 KITLIŃSKI, M., and JANICZAK, B.: 'Dispersion characteristics of asymmetric coupled slot lines on dielectric substrates', *ibid.*, 1983, **19**, pp. 91–92

Multiconductor Transmission Lines in Multilayered Dielectric Media

CAO WEI, ROGER F. HARRINGTON, FELLOW, IEEE, JOSEPH R. MAUTZ, SENIOR MEMBER, IEEE, AND TAPAN K. SARKAR, SENIOR MEMBER, IEEE

Abstract — **A method for computing the capacitance matrix and inductance matrix for a multiconductor transmission line in a multilayered dielectric region is presented. The number of conductors and the number of dielectric layers are arbitrary. Some of the conductors may be of finite cross section and others may be infinitesimally thin. The conductors are either above a single ground plane or between two parallel ground planes. The formulation is obtained by using a free-space Green's function in conjunction with total charge on the conductor-to-dielectric interfaces and polarization charge on the dielectric-to-dielectric interfaces. The solution is effected by the method of moments using pulses for expansion and point matching for testing. Computed results are given for some cases where all conducting lines are of finite cross section and other cases where they are infinitesimally thin.**

Manuscript received September 26, 1983; revised November 7, 1983. This work was supported in part by the Digital Equipment Corporation, Marlboro, MA.

C. Wei is a Visiting Scientist at Syracuse University, on leave from the Nanjing Institute of Posts and Telecommunications, China.

R. F. Harrington and J. R. Mautz are with the Department of Electrical and Computer Engineering, Syracuse University, Syracuse, NY 13210.

T. K. Sarkar is with the Department of Electrical Engineering, Rochester Institute of Technology, Rochester, NY 14623.

I. Introduction

THE OBJECTIVE of this analysis is to determine the capacitance matrix and the inductance matrix of a multiconductor transmission-line system. Some of the conductors may be of finite cross section. Others may be infinitesimally thin. All of them are embedded in a multilayered dielectric material that is either above a single ground plane or contained between two ground planes. Each dielectric-to-dielectric interface is parallel to the ground plane(s).

Multiconductor transmission lines in multilayered media have been investigated by means of Green's function techniques [1]–[11], conformal mapping [12], [13], a variational method [14], a Fourier transform method [15], a Fourier integral method [16], and a generalized spectral domain analysis [17], [18]. In [3] and [11], the problem of multiconductor transmission lines in two dielectric layers is approached by using a Green's function obtained from image theory. For a two-layered dielectric, this Green's function consists of four expressions, each containing an infinite series of images. The extension of this type of Green's function to three dielectric layers consists of nine expressions, each containing a doubly infinite series of images [8]. The extension of this type of Green's function to more than three dielectric layers is impractical because, for N dielectric layers, it would consist of N^2 expressions, each containing $N-1$ infinite series.

Taking an alternative approach, the present paper uses a free-space Green's function in conjunction with total charge on the conductor-to-dielectric interfaces and polarization charge on the dielectric-to-dielectric interfaces. This approach is similar to the one in [10]. The free-space Green's function approach results in a simpler formulation of the problem, but requires the solution of a larger matrix equation. This formulation has the advantage that there is no theoretical limit to the number of dielectric layers that can be treated, but a practical limit is imposed by the speed and storage of the computer. For computational reasons, the transverse width of the dielectric layers is taken to be finite instead of infinite. If the upper ground plane is present, its width is also taken to be finite.

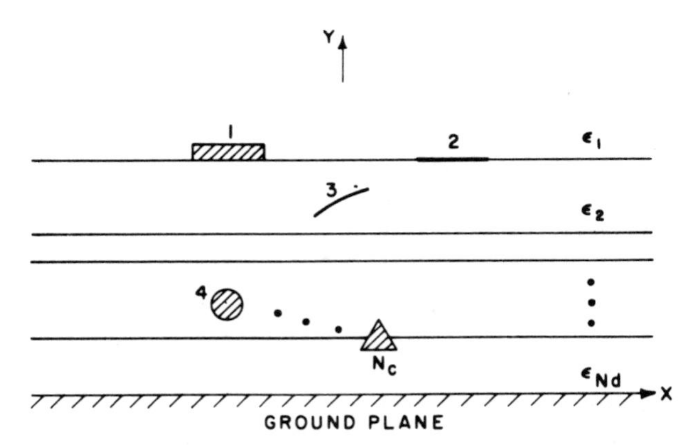

Fig. 1. A multiconductor transmission line in a multilayered dielectric region above a ground plane.

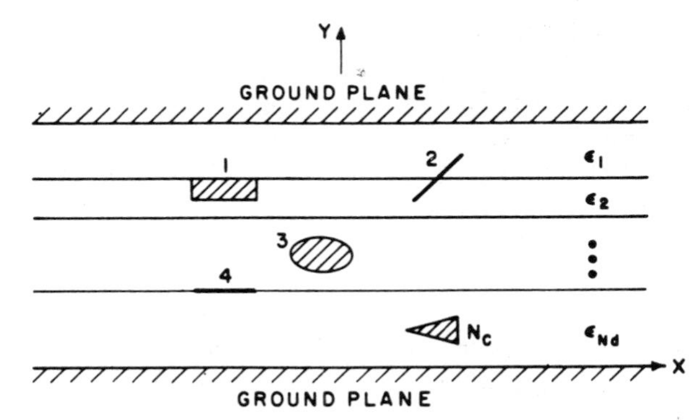

Fig. 2. A multiconductor transmission line in a multilayered dielectric region between two ground planes.

II. Statement of the Problem

Consider a system of multiconductor transmission lines in a multilayered dielectric region above a ground plane as shown in either Fig. 1 or Fig. 2. The system is uniform in the direction perpendicular to the xy plane. An arbitrary number N_c of perfect conductors are embedded in an arbitrary number N_d of dielectric layers. Some of the conductors may be of finite cross section. Others may be infinitesimally thin strips that appear as curves in the xy plane. The permittivity of the jth dielectric layer is ϵ_j. In Fig. 1, the uppermost dielectric extends to $y=\infty$. In Fig. 2, there is an upper ground plane.

A lower ground plane is present in both Figs. 1 and 2. This lower ground plane extends from $x=-\infty$ to $x=\infty$. Nominally, the upper ground plane and the dielectric layers also extend from $x=-\infty$ to $x=\infty$. However, the numerical solution of Section IV is obtained by truncating the upper ground plane and the dielectric layers at a finite negative value of x and a finite positive value of x.

The objective is to determine the capacitance matrix and the inductance matrix of the multiconductor transmission-line system. The ijth element of the capacitance matrix is the free charge per unit length of surface on the ith conductor when the potential of the jth conductor is one volt and the other conductors are grounded. In [3], the elements of the capacitance matrix are called coefficients of capacitance. In [19, p. 97], the diagonal elements of the capacitance matrix are called coefficients of capacitance, but the off-diagonal elements are called coefficients of induction. The inductance matrix is the product of $(\mu_0\epsilon_0)$ with the inverse of the capacitance matrix that would exist if the multilayered dielectric material were replaced by free space [20, eq. (2.24)]. Here, μ_0 is the permeability of free space, and ϵ_0 is the permittivity of free space.

Once the capacitance and inductance matrices of the multiconductor transmission-line system are known, the complete behavior of the system can be determined, to the transmission-line approximation, by multiconductor transmission-line theory [20].

III. Analysis

Consider the capacitance matrix for the problem stated in the previous section. The ijth element of this matrix is the free charge per unit length of surface on the ith conductor when all conductors except the jth conductor are grounded and the jth conductor is charged to a potential of one volt. Hence, the elements of the capacitance matrix can be determined by relating the free charge per unit length of surface on the conductors to the potentials of the conductors. The free charge per unit length of surface on one of the N_c conductors is the integral of the free charge per unit area over the intersection of the surface of the conductor with the xy plane. Thus, the elements of the capacitance matrix can easily be determined once a relationship has been established between the free charge per unit area on the surfaces of the conductors and the potentials of the conductors.

A total charge σ_T per unit area is assumed on the conductor-to-dielectric interfaces and the $N_d - 1$ dielectric-to-dielectric interfaces. The conductor-to-dielectric interfaces consist of the surfaces of the N_c conductors and the upper ground plane, if present. The jth dielectric-to-dielectric interface is the plane of constant y where the dielectric layers ϵ_j and ϵ_{j+1} meet, provided that no conductors lie on this plane. If conductors lie on this plane, then the jth dielectric-to-dielectric interface is the portion of this plane not occupied by conductors. On each conductor-to-dielectric interface, total charge is the sum of free charge and polarization charge. On each dielectric-to-dielectric interface, total charge is polarization charge. In Section IV, the total charge on the upper ground plane, if present, and the dielectric-to-dielectric interfaces is truncated at a finite negative value of x and a finite positive value of x.

At any point $\underline{\rho}$ in the xy plane and above the lower ground plane, the potential ϕ is due to the combination of σ_T and the image of σ_T about the lower ground plane. Hence

$$\phi(\underline{\rho}) = \frac{1}{2\pi\epsilon_0} \sum_{j=1}^{J} \int_{l_j} \sigma_T(\underline{\rho}') \ln\left(\frac{|\underline{\rho} - \underline{\hat{\rho}}'|}{|\underline{\rho} - \underline{\rho}'|}\right) dl' \qquad (1)$$

where l_j is the contour of the jth interface in the xy plane. The first N_c interfaces are the surfaces of the N_c conductors. If there is no upper ground plane, the next $N_d - 1$ interfaces are the dielectric-to-dielectric interfaces. If there is an upper ground plane, the $(N_c + 1)$th interface is the surface of this ground plane, and the next $N_d - 1$ interfaces are the dielectric-to-dielectric interfaces. Accordingly

$$J = J_1 + J_2 \qquad (2)$$

where, in the absence of the upper ground plane

$$J_1 = N_c$$
$$J_2 = N_d - 1 \qquad (3)$$

and, in the presence of the upper ground plane

$$J_1 = N_c + 1$$
$$J_2 = N_d - 1. \qquad (4)$$

It is evident that J_1 is the number of conductor-to-dielectric interfaces and that J_2 is the number of dielectric-to-dielectric interfaces. In (1), dl' is the differential element of length at $\underline{\rho}'$ on l_j, and $\underline{\hat{\rho}}'$ is the image of $\underline{\rho}'$ about the lower ground plane.

The electric field $\underline{E}$ is given by

$$\underline{E}(\underline{\rho}) = -\underline{\nabla}\phi(\underline{\rho}). \qquad (5)$$

Substituting (1) for ϕ in (5), and assuming that $\underline{\rho}$ is not on any of the interfaces $\{l_j\}$ so that the $\underline{\nabla}$ operator may be taken under the integral sign, we obtain

$$\underline{E}(\underline{\rho}) = \frac{1}{2\pi\epsilon_0} \sum_{j=1}^{J} \int_{l_j} \sigma_T(\underline{\rho}') \left(\frac{\underline{\rho} - \underline{\rho}'}{|\underline{\rho} - \underline{\rho}'|^2} - \frac{\underline{\rho} - \underline{\hat{\rho}}'}{|\underline{\rho} - \underline{\hat{\rho}}'|^2} \right) dl' \qquad (6)$$

Taking the limit of (6) as $\underline{\rho}$ approaches the interface l_i, we obtain the following formula for $\underline{E}$ valid on l_i:

$$\left[\underline{E}^{\pm}(\underline{\rho}) = \frac{1}{2\pi\epsilon_0} \sum_{j=1}^{J} \fint_{l_j} \sigma_T(\underline{\rho}') \left(\frac{\underline{\rho} - \underline{\rho}'}{|\underline{\rho} - \underline{\rho}'|^2} - \frac{\underline{\rho} - \underline{\hat{\rho}}'}{|\underline{\rho} - \underline{\hat{\rho}}'|^2} \right) dl' \pm \underline{n}\frac{\sigma_T(\underline{\rho})}{2\epsilon_0}, \quad \begin{cases} \underline{\rho} \text{ on } l_i \\ i = 1, 2, \cdots J \end{cases} \right] \qquad (7)$$

Here, $\underline{n}$ is the unit vector normal to l_i at $\underline{\rho}$. The side of l_i toward which $\underline{n}$ points is called the positive side of l_i. The side of l_i away from which $\underline{n}$ points is called the negative side of l_i. In (7), $\underline{E}^+(\underline{\rho})$ is the electric field on the positive side of l_i, and $\underline{E}^-(\underline{\rho})$ is the electric field on the negative side of l_i. In (7), $\fint_{l_j}$ denotes the principal value of the integral over l_j.

On each conductor-to-dielectric interface, the potential is constant. Denoting the potential on the ith conductor-to-dielectric interface by V_i, we obtain

$$\phi(\underline{\rho}) = V_i, \qquad \begin{cases} \underline{\rho} \text{ on } l_i \\ i = 1, 2, \cdots J_1 \end{cases}. \qquad (8)$$

If the upper ground plane is present, then V_i is zero for $i = J_1$. Substitution of (1) for $\phi(\underline{\rho})$ in (8) yields

$$\frac{1}{2\pi\epsilon_0} \sum_{j=1}^{J} \int_{l_j} \sigma_T(\underline{\rho}') \ln\left(\frac{|\underline{\rho} - \underline{\hat{\rho}}'|}{|\underline{\rho} - \underline{\rho}'|}\right) dl' = V_i, \qquad \begin{cases} \underline{\rho} \text{ on } l_i \\ i = 1, 2 \cdots J_1 \end{cases}. \qquad (9)$$

The displacement vector is called $\underline{D}(\underline{\rho})$. The y component of $\underline{D}(\underline{\rho})$ is continuous across each dielectric-to-dielectric interface. Since $\underline{D}(\underline{\rho})$ is the product of permittivity with electric field, it follows that

$$\epsilon_{i-J_1}\underline{E}^+(\underline{\rho})\cdot\underline{u}_y = \epsilon_{i+1-J_1}\underline{E}^-(\underline{\rho})\cdot\underline{u}_y, \qquad \begin{cases} \underline{\rho} \text{ on } l_i \\ i = J_1 + 1, J_1 + 2, \cdots J \end{cases} \qquad (10)$$

where $\underline{u}_y$ is the unit vector in the y direction. In Figs. 1 and 2, the y direction is upward. In (10), ϵ_{i-J_1} and $\underline{E}^+(\underline{\rho})$ are, respectively, the permittivity and electric field on the upper side of l_i. Moreover, ϵ_{i+1-J_1} and $\underline{E}^-(\underline{\rho})$ are, respectively, the permittivity and electric field on the lower side of l_i. Substitution of (7) for $\underline{E}^{\pm}(\underline{\rho})$ in (10) yields, after division by $(\epsilon_{i-J_1} - \epsilon_{i+1-J_1})$

$$\frac{(\epsilon_{i-J_1} + \epsilon_{i+1-J_1})}{2\epsilon_0(\epsilon_{i-J_1} - \epsilon_{i+1-J_1})}\sigma_T(\underline{\rho}) + \frac{1}{2\pi\epsilon_0} \sum_{j=1}^{J} \fint_{l_j} \sigma_T(\underline{\rho}') \left(\frac{\underline{\rho} - \underline{\rho}'}{|\underline{\rho} - \underline{\rho}'|^2} - \frac{\underline{\rho} - \underline{\hat{\rho}}'}{|\underline{\rho} - \underline{\hat{\rho}}'|^2} \right) \cdot \underline{u}_y \, dl' = 0, \qquad \begin{cases} \underline{\rho} \text{ on } l_i \\ i = J_1 + 1, J_1 + 2, \cdots J \end{cases}. \qquad (11)$$

Equations (9) and (11) are a set of J integral equations in the unknown total charge σ_T per unit area on the interfaces whose contours are $\{l_j, j=1,2,\cdots J\}$. In Section IV, the method of moments will be used to obtain an approximate numerical solution for σ_T in terms of $\{V_i, i=1,2,\cdots N_c\}$. Since (9) and (11) are linear, this solution is of the form

$$\sigma_T = \sum_{i=1}^{N_c} \sigma_T^{(i)} V_i \tag{12}$$

where $\sigma_T^{(i)}$ is the solution which would result if the potential V_i was unity and all other potentials were zero.

As stated earlier, some of the conductors may be of finite cross section, and others may be infinitesimally thin strips. If the ith conductor is of finite cross section, then l_i is a closed curve. On this ith conductor

$$\sigma_T = \epsilon_0 \underline{E} \cdot \underline{n} \tag{13}$$

$$\sigma_F = \epsilon \underline{E} \cdot \underline{n} \tag{14}$$

where $\underline{E}$ is the electric field just outside the conductor, $\underline{n}$ is the unit normal vector which points outward from the surface of the conductor, ϵ is the permittivity just outside the conductor, and σ_F is the free charge per unit area on the conductor. Equations (13) and (14) imply that

$$\sigma_F(\underline{\rho}) = \frac{\epsilon(\underline{\rho})}{\epsilon_0} \sigma_T(\underline{\rho}) \tag{15}$$

on the surface of the ith conductor provided that this conductor is of finite cross section.

If the ith conductor is an infinitesimally thin strip, then l_i runs from one edge of the strip to the other. The free charge σ_F per unit area on the surface of the ith conductor is then given by

$$\sigma_F = (\epsilon^+ \underline{E}^+ - \epsilon^- \underline{E}^-) \cdot \underline{n} \tag{16}$$

where $\underline{n}$ is a unit vector normal to the strip. The side of the strip toward which $\underline{n}$ points is called the positive side. The side of the strip away from which n points is called the negative side. In (16), ϵ^+ and $\underline{E}^+$ are, respectively, the permittivity and electric field on the positive side of the strip. Moreover, ϵ^- and $\underline{E}^-$ are, respectively, the permittivity and electric field on the negative side of the strip. Substitution of (7) for $\underline{E}^{\pm}$ in (16) leads to

$$\sigma_F(\underline{\rho}) = \frac{\epsilon^+(\underline{\rho}) + \epsilon^-(\underline{\rho})}{2\epsilon_0} \sigma_T(\underline{\rho}) + \frac{\epsilon^+(\underline{\rho}) - \epsilon^-(\underline{\rho})}{2\pi\epsilon_0} \sum_{j=1}^{J} \int_{l_j} \sigma_T(\underline{\rho}') \left(\frac{\underline{\rho} - \underline{\rho}'}{|\underline{\rho} - \underline{\rho}'|^2} - \frac{\underline{\rho} - \hat{\underline{\rho}}'}{|\underline{\rho} - \hat{\underline{\rho}}'|^2} \right) \cdot \underline{n}\, dl' \tag{17}$$

on the surface of the ith conductor, provided that this conductor is an infinitesimally thin strip.

Regardless of whether the ith conductor has finite cross section or is an infinitesimally thin strip, the free charge Q_i per unit length on it is given by

$$Q_i = \int_{l_i} \sigma_F(\underline{\rho})\, dl, \qquad i=1,2,\cdots N_c \tag{18}$$

where dl is the differential element of length at $\underline{\rho}$ on l_i. In view of (12) with the index i replaced by j, substitution of (15) or (17) for σ_F in (18) gives

$$Q_i = \sum_{j=1}^{N_c} C_{ij} V_j, \qquad i=1,2,\cdots N_c \tag{19}$$

where, if the ith conductor is of finite cross section

$$C_{ij} = \int_{l_i} \frac{\epsilon(\underline{\rho})}{\epsilon_0} \sigma_T^{(j)}(\underline{\rho})\, dl. \tag{20}$$

If the ith conductor is an infinitesimally thin strip, then

$$C_{ij} = \int_{l_i} \left\{ \frac{\epsilon^+(\underline{\rho}) + \epsilon^-(\underline{\rho})}{2\epsilon_0} \sigma_T^{(j)}(\underline{\rho}) + \frac{\epsilon^+(\underline{\rho}) - \epsilon^-(\underline{\rho})}{2\pi\epsilon_0} \cdot \sum_{k=1}^{J} \int_{l_k} \sigma_T^{(j)}(\underline{\rho}') \left(\frac{\underline{\rho} - \underline{\rho}'}{|\underline{\rho} - \underline{\rho}'|^2} - \frac{\underline{\rho} - \hat{\underline{\rho}}'}{|\underline{\rho} - \hat{\underline{\rho}}'|^2} \right) \cdot \underline{n}\, dl' \right\} dl. \tag{21}$$

In obtaining (21), the index j in (17) was replaced by k in order to avoid confusion with the index j which appears in C_{ij}. The coefficient C_{ij} is the ijth element of the capacitance matrix.

The inductance matrix is called L. The ijth element of L is the magnetic flux passing between a unit length of the ith conductor and the lower ground plane when one ampere of net z-directed electric current flows on the jth conductor and there is no net z-directed electric current on any of the other conductors. Here, z is the coordinate perpendicular to the xy plane. It is shown in the Appendix that

$$L = \mu_0 \epsilon_0 [C_0]^{-1} \tag{22}$$

where C_0 is the capacitance matrix which would result if all dielectric layers were replaced by free space.

IV. Development of the Moment Solution

In this section, the integral equations (9) and (11) are solved numerically for σ_T by means of the method of moments [21].

A solution σ_T to (9) and (11) is sought in the form

$$\sigma_T(\underline{\rho}) = \sum_{n=1}^{N} \sigma_{Tn} P_n(\underline{\rho}) \tag{23}$$

where $\{P_n(\underline{\rho}), n=1,2,\cdots N\}$ are unit pulse functions which cover $\{l_j, j=1,2,\cdots J\}$. Moreover, $\{\sigma_{Tn}, n = 1,2,\cdots N\}$ are constants to be determined. The upper ground plane and dielectric layers are now truncated at a finite negative value of x and a finite positive value of x so that only pulse functions of finite domain are needed.

Given an arbitrary point on the truncated $\{l_j, j=1,2,\cdots J\}$, there is an integer m such that, at this point

$$P_m = 1$$
$$P_n = 0, \qquad n=1,2,\cdots m-1, m+1,\cdots N. \tag{24}$$

It follows from (23) and (24) that

$$\sigma_T = \sigma_{Tm} \tag{25}$$

at this point.

Let $\{P_n(\underline{\rho}), n=1,2,\cdots N_1\}$ be the pulses on $\{l_j, j=1,2,\cdots J_1\}$, and let $\{P_n(\underline{\rho}), n=N_1+1, N_1+2,\cdots N\}$ be the pulses on $\{l_j, j=J_1+1, J_1+2,\cdots,J\}$. Moreover, let $\underline{\rho}_m$ be the midpoint of the domain of $P_m(\underline{\rho})$ for $m=1,2,\cdots N$.

Substituting (23) for σ_T in (9) and then enforcing (9) at $\underline{\rho}=\underline{\rho}_m$ for $m=1,2,\cdots N_1$, we obtain

$$\sum_{n=1}^{N} S_{mn}\sigma_{Tn} = V_i, \qquad m=1,2,\cdots N_1 \tag{26}$$

where i is such that $\underline{\rho}_m$ is on l_i, and

$$S_{mn} = \frac{1}{2\pi\epsilon_0}\int_{\Delta l_n} \ln\left(\frac{|\underline{\rho}_m - \hat{\underline{\rho}}'|}{|\underline{\rho}_m - \underline{\rho}'|}\right) dl', \qquad \begin{cases} m=1,2,\cdots N_1 \\ n=1,2,\cdots N \end{cases} \tag{27}$$

where Δl_n is the domain of $P_n(\underline{\rho})$.

Substituting (23) for σ_T in (11) and then enforcing (11) at $\underline{\rho}=\underline{\rho}_m$ for $m=N_1+1, N_1+2,\cdots N$, we obtain

$$\sum_{n=1}^{N} S_{mn}\sigma_{Tn} = 0, \qquad m=N_1+1, N_1+2,\cdots N \tag{28}$$

where, for $m \neq n$

$$S_{mn} = \frac{1}{2\pi\epsilon_0}\int_{\Delta l_n}\left(\frac{\underline{\rho}_m - \underline{\rho}'}{|\underline{\rho}_m - \underline{\rho}'|^2} - \frac{\underline{\rho}_m - \hat{\underline{\rho}}'}{|\underline{\rho}_m - \hat{\underline{\rho}}'|^2}\right)\cdot \underline{u}_y\, dl', \qquad \begin{cases} m=N_1+1, N_1+2,\cdots N \\ n=1,2,\cdots N \end{cases} \tag{29}$$

In (28), S_{mm} is given by

$$S_{mm} = \frac{\epsilon_{i-J_1}+\epsilon_{i+1-J_1}}{2\epsilon_0(\epsilon_{i-J_1}-\epsilon_{i+1-J_1})} + \frac{1}{2\pi\epsilon_0}\int_{\Delta l_m}\left(\frac{\underline{\rho}_m - \underline{\rho}'}{|\underline{\rho}_m - \underline{\rho}'|^2}\right)\cdot \underline{u}_y\, dl' - \frac{1}{2\pi\epsilon_0}\int_{\Delta l_m}\left(\frac{\underline{\rho}_m - \hat{\underline{\rho}}'}{|\underline{\rho}_m - \hat{\underline{\rho}}'|^2}\right)\cdot \underline{u}_y\, dl',$$

$$m=N_1+1, N_1+2,\cdots N. \tag{30}$$

In (30), i is such that $\underline{\rho}_m$ is on Δl_i. If $m \neq n$, but if $\underline{\rho}_m$ and P_n are on the same dielectric-to-dielectric interface, then (29) reduces to

$$S_{mn} = -\frac{1}{2\pi\epsilon_0}\int_{\Delta l_n}\left(\frac{\underline{\rho}_m - \hat{\underline{\rho}}'}{|\underline{\rho}_m - \hat{\underline{\rho}}'|^2}\right)\cdot \underline{u}_y\, dl'. \tag{31}$$

Formulas for calculating S_{mn} are given later in this section. After S_{mn} has been calculated for $m=1,2,\cdots N$ and $n=1,2,\cdots N$, (26) and (28) combine to form N simultaneous equations in the N unknowns $\{\sigma_{Tn}, n=1,2,\cdots N\}$. These simultaneous equations can then be solved for $\{\sigma_{Tn}, n=1,2,\cdots N\}$ in terms of $\{V_i, i=1,2,\cdots N_c\}$. The solution is of the form

$$\sigma_{Tn} = \sum_{i=1}^{N_c} \sigma_{Tn}^{(i)} V_i \tag{32}$$

where $\{\sigma_{Tn}^{(i)}, n=1,2,\cdots N\}$ is the solution which would result if V_i were unity and all other V's were zero. Substituting (32) into (23) and comparing the result with (12), we obtain

$$\sigma_T^{(i)}(\underline{\rho}) = \sum_{n=1}^{N} \sigma_{Tn}^{(i)} P_n(\underline{\rho}). \tag{33}$$

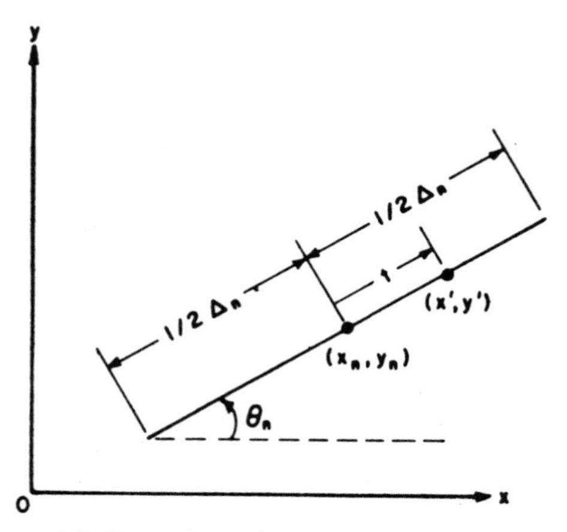

Fig. 3. The straight line segment Δl_n with length Δ_n, midpoint (x_n, y_n), and orientation θ_n.

The elements of the capacitance matrix can be calculated by replacing i by j in (33) and then substituting the resulting expression for $\sigma_T^{(j)}(\underline{\rho})$ in (20) and (21). The integral with respect to l in (21) is approximated by sampling the integrand at $\underline{\rho}=\underline{\rho}_m$ for all values of m for which $\underline{\rho}_m$ is on l_i. At $\underline{\rho}=\underline{\rho}_m$, the integrals with respect to l' in (21) are similar to the integrals appearing in expressions (29) and (30) for S_{mn}.

To facilitate calculation of S_{mn}, Δl_n is approximated by the straight line segment shown in Fig. 3. This segment is of length Δ_n and makes an angle θ_n with the x axis. The midpoint of this segment is $\underline{\rho}_n$. Now

$$\underline{\rho}_n = \underline{u}_x x_n + \underline{u}_y y_n \tag{34}$$

where $\underline{u}_x$ is the unit vector in the x direction, and x_n and y_n are, respectively, the x and y coordinates of $\underline{\rho}_n$. Similarly, the vectors $\underline{\rho}'$ and $\hat{\underline{\rho}}'$ in expression (27) for S_{mn} are written in terms of their rectangular coordinates as

$$\underline{\rho}' = \underline{u}_x x' + \underline{u}_y y' \tag{35}$$

$$\hat{\underline{\rho}}' = \underline{u}_x x' - \underline{u}_y y'. \tag{36}$$

As can be seen from Fig. 3

$$x' = x_n + t\cos\theta_n \tag{37}$$

$$y' = y_n + t\sin\theta_n. \tag{38}$$

Due to the equations of the previous paragraph, (27) becomes

$$S_{mn} = \frac{1}{4\pi\epsilon_0} \int_{-(1/2)\Delta_n}^{(1/2)\Delta_n} \ln\left(\frac{(x_m - x')^2 + (y_m + y')^2}{(x_m - x')^2 + (y_m - y')^2} \right) dt,$$

$$\begin{cases} m = 1, 2, \cdots N_1 \\ n = 1, 2, \cdots N \end{cases} \quad (39)$$

where x' and y' are given by (37) and (38), respectively. After substitution of (37) and (38) for x' and y', (39) reduces to

$$S_{mn} = F_1(a_1, b_1) - F_1(a_2, b_2), \qquad \begin{cases} m = 1, 2, \cdots N_1 \\ n = 1, 2, \cdots N \end{cases} \quad (40)$$

where

$$a_1 = (x_m - x_n)\sin\theta_n + (y_m + y_n)\cos\theta_n \quad (41)$$

$$b_1 = (x_m - x_n)\cos\theta_n - (y_m + y_n)\sin\theta_n \quad (42)$$

$$a_2 = (x_m - x_n)\sin\theta_n - (y_m - y_n)\cos\theta_n \quad (43)$$

$$b_2 = (x_m - x_n)\cos\theta_n + (y_m - y_n)\sin\theta_n \quad (44)$$

and

$$F_1(a, b) = \frac{1}{4\pi\epsilon_0} \int_{-(1/2)\Delta_n - b}^{(1/2)\Delta_n - b} \ln(t^2 + a^2)\, dt. \quad (45)$$

Application of [22, formula 623.] to (45) gives

$$F_1(a, b) = \frac{1}{4\pi\epsilon_0} \left[t\ln(t^2 + a^2) - 2t + 2a\tan^{-1}\left(\frac{t}{a}\right) \right]_{t = -1/2\Delta_n - b}^{t = 1/2\Delta_n - b}. \quad (46)$$

If a is zero, then the $\tan^{-1}$ term should be omitted from (46).

Expressions (29) and (30) become

$$S_{mn} = \frac{1}{2\pi\epsilon_0}(I_{mn} - \hat{I}_{mn}), \qquad m \neq n,$$

$$\begin{cases} m = N_1 + 1, N_1 + 2, \cdots N \\ n = 1, 2, \cdots N \end{cases} \quad (47)$$

$$S_{mm} = \frac{\epsilon_{i-J_1} + \epsilon_{i+1-J_1}}{2\epsilon_0(\epsilon_{i-J_1} - \epsilon_{i+1-J_1})} - \frac{1}{2\pi\epsilon_0}\hat{I}_{mm},$$

$$m = N_1 + 1, N_1 + 2, \cdots N. \quad (48)$$

The first integral in (30) has vanished because Δl_m is a straight line segment. In (48), i is such that $\underline{\rho}_m$ is on l_i. In (47) and (48)

$$I_{mn} = \int_{\Delta l_n} \left(\frac{\underline{\rho}_m - \underline{\rho}'}{|\underline{\rho}_m - \underline{\rho}'|^2} \right) \cdot \underline{u}_y\, dl' \quad (49)$$

and

$$\hat{I}_{mn} = \int_{\Delta l_n} \left(\frac{\underline{\rho}_m - \hat{\underline{\rho}}'}{|\underline{\rho}_m - \hat{\underline{\rho}}'|^2} \right) \cdot \underline{u}_y\, dl'. \quad (50)$$

In the domain of integration of (49), $\underline{\rho}'$ is never equal to $\underline{\rho}_m$, and in (50), $\hat{\underline{\rho}}'$ is never equal to $\underline{\rho}_m$. Hence, the integrands in (49) and (50) are always finite.

Equations (34)–(36) reduce (49) and (50) to

$$I_{mn} = \int_{-1/2\Delta_n}^{1/2\Delta_n} \frac{y_m - y'}{(x_m - x')^2 + (y_m - y')^2} dt \quad (51)$$

$$\hat{I}_{mn} = \int_{-1/2\Delta_n}^{1/2\Delta_n} \frac{y_m + y'}{(x_m - x')^2 + (y_m + y')^2} dt. \quad (52)$$

Substitution of (37) and (38) for x' and y' in (51) and (52) produces

$$I_{mn} = (y_m - y_n - b_2\sin\theta_n)F_2(a_2, b_2) - (\sin\theta_n)F_3(a_2, b_2) \quad (53)$$

$$\hat{I}_{mn} = (y_m + y_n + b_1\sin\theta_n)F_2(a_1, b_1) + (\sin\theta_n)F_3(a_1, b_1) \quad (54)$$

where a_1, b_1, a_2, and b_2 are given by (41)–(44). Moreover

$$F_2(a, b) = \int_{-1/2\Delta_n - b}^{1/2\Delta_n - b} \frac{dt}{t^2 + a^2} \quad (55)$$

and

$$F_3(a, b) = \int_{-(1/2)\Delta_n - b}^{(1/2)\Delta_n - b} \frac{t\,dt}{t^2 + a^2}. \quad (56)$$

If $a = 0$, then, as is evident from the statement just after (50), t is never zero during the integration in (55). Hence, it is easy to obtain

$$F_2(a, b) = -\left[\frac{1}{t}\right]_{-1/2\Delta_n - b}^{1/2\Delta_n - b}, \qquad a = 0 \quad (57)$$

which reduces to

$$F_2(a, b) = \frac{\Delta_n}{b^2 - \frac{1}{4}\Delta_n^2}, \qquad a = 0. \quad (58)$$

If $a \neq 0$, application of [22, formula 120.1.] to (55) gives

$$F_2(a, b) = \left[\frac{1}{a}\tan^{-1}\left(\frac{t}{a}\right)\right]_{-1/2\Delta_n - b}^{1/2\Delta_n - b}, \qquad a \neq 0. \quad (59)$$

It is evident from the statement just after (50) that $(t^2 + a^2)$ is never zero during the integration in (56). Hence, we easily obtain

$$F_3(a, b) = \frac{1}{2}[\ln(t^2 + a^2)]_{-1/2\Delta_n - b}^{1/2\Delta_n - b} \quad (60)$$

which is valid regardless of the value of a.

V. Numerical Examples

A computer program has been written for the special case where all conductors are of finite cross section and for the case where all conductors are infinitesimally thin [23]. This program was used to obtain the results given in this section. These results agree well with those of various references.

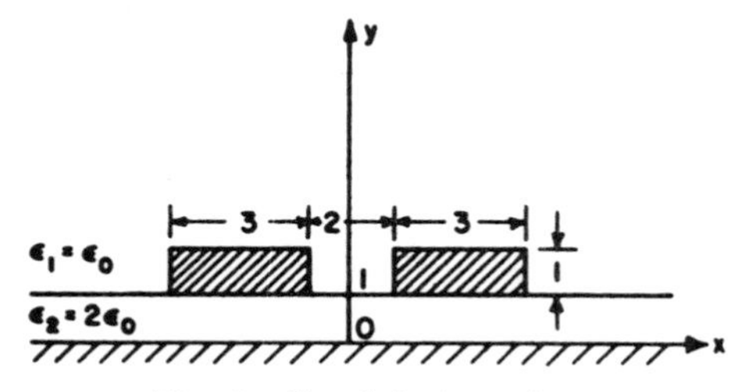

Fig. 4. Coupled microstrips.

TABLE I
COMPARISON OF RESULTS FOR THE COUPLED MICROSTRIP IN FIG. 4. UNITS ARE F/m

	Our Results	Reference [11]	Reference [3]
C_{11}	0.9165×10^{-10}	0.9017×10^{-10}	0.9224×10^{-10}
C_{12}	-0.8220×10^{-11}	-0.8059×10^{-11}	-0.8504×10^{-11}
C_{21}	-0.8220×10^{-11}	-0.8059×10^{-11}	-0.8504×10^{-11}
C_{22}	0.9165×10^{-10}	0.9017×10^{-10}	0.9224×10^{-10}

Example 1

Consider the pair of coupled microstrips touching a dielectric slab over a conducting plane as shown in Fig. 4. The left-hand conductor is conductor 1. The right-hand conductor is conductor 2. Table I compares our computed results with those of [3] and [11]. For comparison, the results of [3] have been changed to farads per meter. For our results, we used 16 subsections on each conductor, and on the dielectric interface we used 10 subsections from -9 to -4, 4 subsections from -1 to $+1$, and 10 subsections from 4 to 9. The difference between our results and those of [3] is less than 4 percent. The difference between our results and those of [11] is less than 2 percent. The difference should become smaller as we increase the number of our subsections.

Example 2

Consider two conductors in two different dielectric layers above a ground plane as shown in Fig. 5. The left-hand conductor is conductor 1. The right-hand conductor is conductor 2. The number of subsections used on conductor 1 is 6, the number on conductor 2 is 6, and the number on the dielectric interface is 16 extending from $x = -0.8$ to $x = +0.8$. In Table II, our results are compared with those obtained by using the computer program of [11]. The agreement is excellent in all cases. In the table, C_{ij} is the ijth element of the capacitance matrix, C_{0ij} is the ijth element of the free-space capacitance matrix, and L_{ij} is the ijth element of the inductance matrix.

Example 3

Here, the two conductors of the transmission line are located in the same dielectric layer, as shown in Fig. 6. The left-hand conductor is conductor 1. The right-hand conductor is conductor 2. The number of subsections used on conductor 1 is 6, the number on conductor 2 is 6, and the number used on the dielectric interface is 16 extending

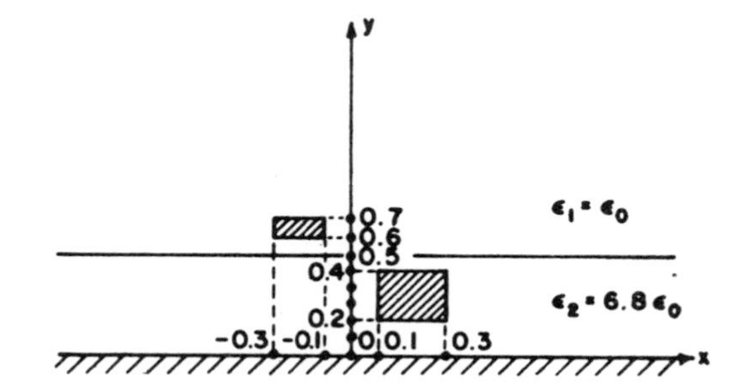

Fig. 5. Two conductors in two different dielectric layers.

TABLE II
COMPARISON OF RESULTS FOR EXAMPLE 2, FIG. 5. CAPACITANCE IS IN F/m. INDUCTANCE IS IN H/m

	Our Results	Reference [11]
C_{11}	0.3651×10^{-10}	0.3701×10^{-10}
C_{12}	-0.1562×10^{-10}	-0.1520×10^{-10}
C_{21}	-0.1562×10^{-10}	-0.1523×10^{-10}
C_{22}	0.2099×10^{-9}	0.2108×10^{-9}
C_{011}	0.2296×10^{-10}	0.2296×10^{-10}
C_{012}	-0.8808×10^{-11}	-0.8805×10^{-11}
C_{021}	-0.8808×10^{-11}	-0.8810×10^{-11}
C_{022}	0.3772×10^{-10}	0.3772×10^{-10}
L_{11}	0.5315×10^{-6}	0.5403×10^{-6}
L_{12}	0.1241×10^{-6}	0.1229×10^{-6}
L_{21}	0.1241×10^{-6}	0.1265×10^{-6}
L_{22}	0.3235×10^{-6}	0.3204×10^{-6}

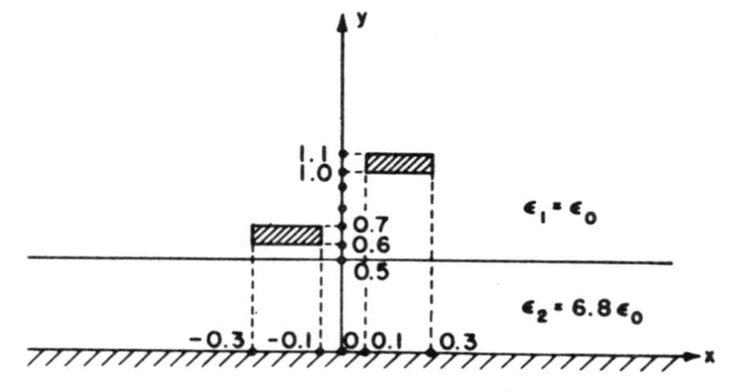

Fig. 6. Two conductors in the same dielectric layer.

TABLE III
COMPARISON OF RESULTS FOR EXAMPLE 3, FIG. 6. CAPACITANCE IS IN F/m. INDUCTANCE IS IN H/m

	Our Results	Reference [11]
C_{11}	0.3720×10^{-10}	0.3757×10^{-10}
C_{12}	-0.6889×10^{-11}	-0.6657×10^{-11}
C_{21}	-0.6889×10^{-11}	-0.6597×10^{-11}
C_{22}	0.2169×10^{-10}	0.2217×10^{-10}
C_{011}	0.2391×10^{-10}	0.2391×10^{-10}
C_{012}	-0.8427×10^{-11}	-0.8427×10^{-11}
C_{021}	-0.8427×10^{-11}	-0.8427×10^{-11}
C_{022}	0.2042×10^{-10}	0.2042×10^{-10}
L_{11}	0.5437×10^{-6}	0.5501×10^{-6}
L_{12}	0.2244×10^{-6}	0.2235×10^{-6}
L_{21}	0.2244×10^{-6}	0.2292×10^{-6}
L_{22}	0.6368×10^{-6}	0.6407×10^{-6}

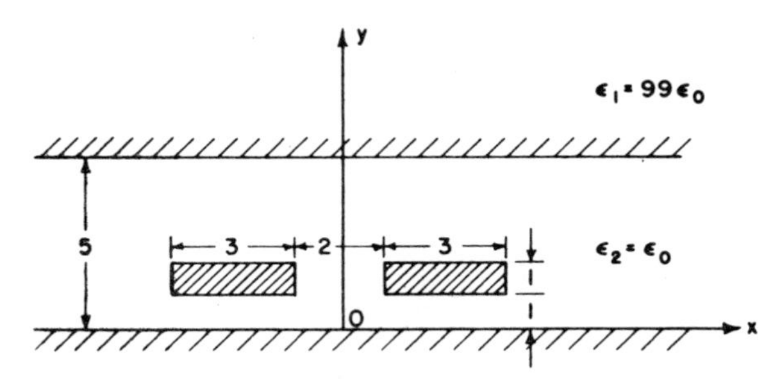

Fig. 7. Coupled microstrips between parallel conducting planes.

TABLE IV
COMPARISON OF RESULTS FOR EXAMPLE 4, FIG. 7. UNITS ARE F/m

	Results obtained by using $\varepsilon_1 = 99\varepsilon_0$	Results obtained by truncating the upper ground plane	Reference [3]
C_{11}	0.6233×10^{-10}	0.6264×10^{-10}	0.6307×10^{-10}
C_{12}	-0.5931×10^{-11}	-0.5724×10^{-11}	-0.5866×10^{-11}
C_{21}	-0.5931×10^{-11}	-0.5724×10^{-11}	-0.5866×10^{-11}
C_{22}	0.6233×10^{-10}	0.6264×10^{-10}	0.6307×10^{-10}

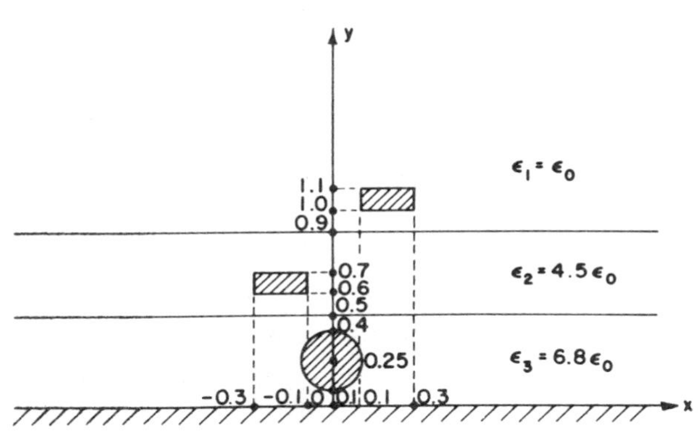

Fig. 8. Three conductors in three different dielectric layers.

TABLE V
RESULTS FOR EXAMPLE 5, FIG. 8. CAPACITANCE IS IN F/m. INDUCTANCE IS IN H/m

i	j	C_{ij}	C_{0ij}	L_{ij}
1	1	0.1244×10^{-9}	0.2828×10^{-10}	0.4965×10^{-6}
1	2	-0.1300×10^{-10}	-0.7678×10^{-11}	0.1996×10^{-6}
1	3	-0.6825×10^{-10}	-0.1181×10^{-10}	0.1183×10^{-6}
2	1	-0.1300×10^{-10}	-0.7678×10^{-11}	0.1996×10^{-6}
2	2	0.3340×10^{-10}	0.2090×10^{-10}	0.6163×10^{-6}
2	3	-0.7196×10^{-11}	-0.3030×10^{-11}	0.7728×10^{-6}
3	1	-0.6825×10^{-10}	-0.1181×10^{-10}	0.1183×10^{-6}
3	2	-0.7196×10^{-11}	-0.3030×10^{-11}	0.7728×10^{-6}
3	3	0.3523×10^{-9}	0.5468×10^{-10}	0.2331×10^{-6}

from $x = -0.8$ to $x = +0.8$. In Table III, our results are compared with those obtained by using the computer program of [11]. The agreement is excellent.

Example 4

Fig. 7 shows an example with two ground planes. The left-hand conductor is conductor 1. The right-hand conductor is conductor 2. The approach taken in this paper is to truncate the upper ground plane at a finite width. Another approach is to replace the upper ground plane with a dielectric layer of permittivity $\epsilon_1 \gg \epsilon_2$ as discussed in [11]. Results are compared in Table IV.

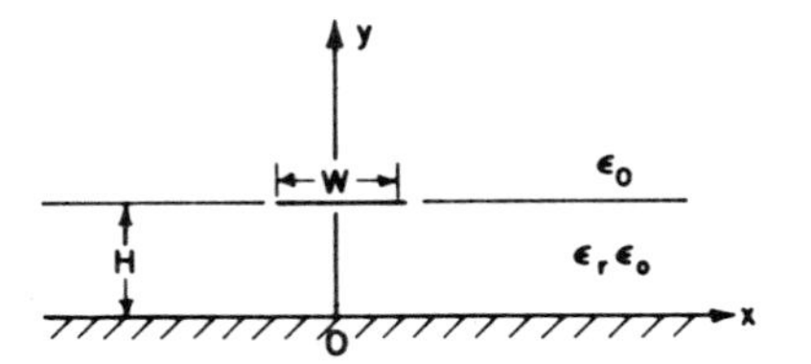

Fig. 9. A microstrip line.

TABLE VI
CHARACTERISTIC IMPEDANCES Z_0 IN OHMS FOR EXAMPLE 6, FIG. 9

	$\varepsilon_r = 6.0$			$\varepsilon_r = 9.5$		
W/H	Our results	Reference [4]	Reference [13]	Our results	Reference [4]	Reference [13]
0.4	92.2785	91.172	89.909	74.8970	73.702	73.290
0.7	73.9626	73.613	71.995	59.9105	59.379	58.502
1.0	62.8109	62.713	60.970	50.8097	50.501	49.431
2.0	42.9980	43.149	41.510	34.6743	34.592	33.493
4.0	26.9709	27.301	26.027	21.6679	21.763	20.906
10.0	12.9961	13.341	12.485	10.3940	10.568	9.981

Example 5

This example consists of three conducting lines in three dielectric layers as shown in Fig. 8. The left-hand conductor is conductor 1, the right-hand conductor is conductor 2, and the cylinder is conductor 3. We used 12 subsections on conductors 1 and 2, 8 subsections on conductor 3, and 20 subsections on each dielectric interface. Our computed results are listed in Table V. No other results are available for comparison.

Example 6

Consider a single microstrip with zero thickness on a dielectric substrate above a conducting plane as shown in Fig. 9. The characteristic impedance Z_0 of the microstrip is [2]

$$Z_0 = \frac{1}{v_0\sqrt{CC_0}} \tag{61}$$

where v_0 is the velocity of light in free space, C is the capacitance of the microstrip, and C_0 is the free-space capacitance of the microstrip. For various ratios W/H, Table VI compares our results for Z_0 with those of [4] and [13]. The results attributed to [13] appear in [4] and were calculated from [13, eq. (1)], which is based on curves obtained from Wheeler's conformal mapping analysis [12]. Our results were obtained by using 12 subsections on the strip, 15 on the part of the dielectric interface from $-2W$

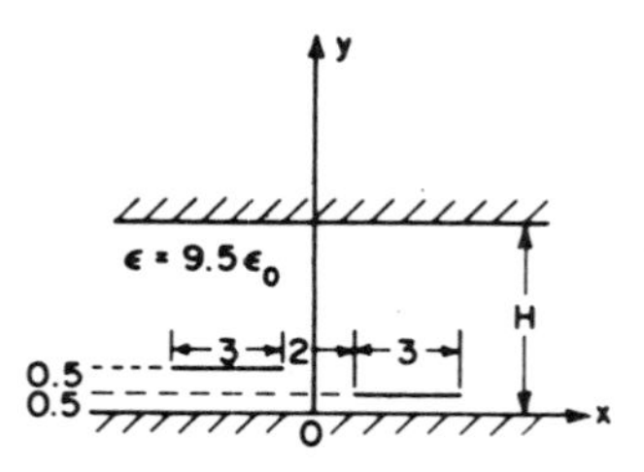

Fig. 10. Two coupled microstrip lines between two ground planes.

TABLE VII
COMPARISON OF RESULTS FOR EXAMPLE 7, FIG. 10. CAPACITANCE IS IN F/m. INDUCTANCE IS IN H/m. ZERO-THICKNESS RESULTS ARE DENOTED BY *. NONZERO-THICKNESS RESULTS ARE DENOTED BY Δ

H	3		5	
	*	Δ	*	Δ
C_{11}	0.5356×10^{-9}	0.5394×10^{-9}	0.4852×10^{-9}	0.4884×10^{-9}
C_{12}	-0.9250×10^{-11}	-0.9547×10^{-11}	-0.1798×10^{-10}	-0.1841×10^{-10}
C_{21}	-0.9250×10^{-11}	-0.9547×10^{-11}	-0.1798×10^{-10}	-0.1841×10^{-10}
C_{22}	0.7834×10^{-9}	0.7895×10^{-9}	0.7557×10^{-9}	0.7615×10^{-9}
C_{011}	0.5466×10^{-10}	0.5504×10^{-10}	0.4951×10^{-10}	0.4984×10^{-10}
C_{012}	-0.9439×10^{-12}	-0.9742×10^{-12}	-0.1835×10^{-11}	-0.1879×10^{-11}
C_{021}	-0.9439×10^{-12}	-0.9742×10^{-12}	-0.1835×10^{-11}	-0.1879×10^{-11}
C_{022}	0.7994×10^{-10}	0.8056×10^{-10}	0.7712×10^{-10}	0.7770×10^{-10}
L_{11}	0.2033×10^{-6}	0.2019×10^{-6}	0.2246×10^{-6}	0.2231×10^{-6}
L_{12}	0.2401×10^{-8}	0.2442×10^{-8}	0.5345×10^{-8}	0.5396×10^{-8}
L_{21}	0.2401×10^{-8}	0.2442×10^{-8}	0.5345×10^{-8}	0.5396×10^{-8}
L_{22}	0.1390×10^{-6}	0.1380×10^{-6}	0.1442×10^{-6}	0.1431×10^{-6}

to $-W/2$, and 15 on the part of the dielectric interface from $W/2$ to $2W$.

Example 7

Consider the two coupled microstrips between two ground planes shown in Fig. 10. The left-hand strip is conductor 1. The right-hand strip is conductor 2. Both strips are infinitesimally thin. Parameters can be calculated directly for the zero-thickness strips. Alternatively, the zero-thickness strips can be approximated by strips having a small but nonzero thickness. Table VII compares the zero-thickness results with the nonzero-thickness results for $H = 3$ and $H = 5$. These results were obtained by using 10 subsections on each zero-thickness strip, 22 subsections on each nonzero-thickness strip, and 36 subsections on the upper ground plane from -9 to $+9$. The nonzero-thickness strips are 0.001 thick.

Example 8

Consider three infinitesimally thin strips embedded in a three-layered dielectric between two ground planes as shown in Fig. 11. The left-hand strip is conductor 1, the right-hand strip is conductor 2, and the center strip is conductor 3. Our computed results are listed in Table VIII. No other results are available for comparison. Our results were obtained by using 6 subsections on each strip, 38 subsections on each dielectric interface, and 38 subsections on the upper ground plane.

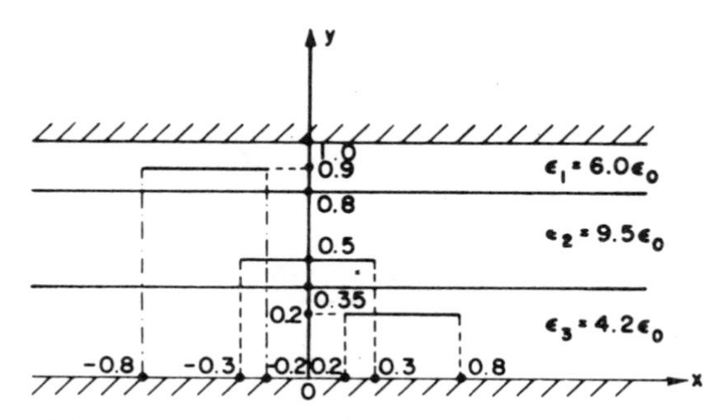

Fig. 11. Three striplines in a three-layered dielectric between two ground planes.

TABLE VIII
RESULTS FOR EXAMPLE 8, FIG. 11. CAPACITANCE IS IN F/m. INDUCTANCE IS IN H/m

i	j	C_{ij}	C_{oij}	L_{ij}
1	1	0.4900×10^{-9}	0.7773×10^{-10}	0.1456×10^{-6}
1	2	-0.5737×10^{-12}	-0.1036×10^{-12}	0.5630×10^{-8}
1	3	-0.6457×10^{-10}	-0.7193×10^{-11}	0.2844×10^{-7}
2	1	-0.5737×10^{-12}	-0.1036×10^{-12}	0.5630×10^{-8}
2	2	0.2459×10^{-9}	0.5212×10^{-10}	0.2240×10^{-6}
2	3	-0.6138×10^{-10}	-0.9788×10^{-11}	0.5762×10^{-7}
3	1	-0.6457×10^{-10}	-0.7193×10^{-11}	0.2844×10^{-7}
3	2	-0.6137×10^{-10}	-0.9788×10^{-11}	0.5762×10^{-7}
3	3	0.2865×10^{-9}	0.3876×10^{-10}	0.3065×10^{-6}

VI. DISCUSSION AND CONCLUSION

The integral equations (9) and (11) for the total charge at the surfaces of the conducting transmission lines, at the upper ground plane, and on the dielectric-to-dielectric interfaces are simple in concept. Their solution by the method of moments using pulse functions for expansion and point matching for testing is also simple. Experience has shown that this type of solution is both versatile and accurate. Improvement in the rate of convergence might be obtained by using better behaved functions for expansion and testing, but at the cost of considerable complication.

The solution is valid for an arbitrary number of conductors and an arbitrary number of dielectric layers. It is valid if a conductor touches a dielectric interface, straddles a dielectric interface, or is totally within one dielectric region. Theoretically, the solution is valid if some conductors are infinitesimally thin and others are of finite cross section. However, the computer program of [23] was not written to include the case where both infinitesimally thin conductors and finite cross-section conductors are present.

Theoretically, the upper ground plane and the dielectric interfaces are infinitely wide. However, the numerical solution is obtained by truncating them at a finite width. From computational experience, it appears that the numerical solution will be sufficiently accurate if they are truncated at a width equal to two or three times the transverse extent of the conducting transmission lines.

The solution can be easily extended to multilayered magnetic media by the concept of duality [24, sec. 3-2].

However, this extension is seldom of practical interest and is not considered here.

It should be remembered that the basic formulation is exact only in the limit as the frequency approaches zero. At high frequencies, the true solution is not a transverse electromagnetic wave, but is a hybrid one. In other words, the true solution is not obtained by solving Laplace's equation, but rather by solving a coupled wave equation. This solution is extremely complicated, and experience indicates that the transverse electromagnetic wave approximation is sufficiently accurate for most purposes.

APPENDIX

Relationship (22) exists between the inductance matrix and the free-space capacitance matrix of a multiconductor transmission line. Since we could not find a general proof of (22) in the literature, we give one here.

Consider the magnetostatic problem in which a specified amperage of steady z-directed electric current is forced to flow on each of the N_c conductors of either Fig. 1 or Fig. 2 where the permeability of each dielectric layer is μ_0. It is assumed that the electric current flows only in the z direction. The specified electric current will distribute itself over the surface of each of the N_c conductors, and surface densities of z-directed electric current will be induced on the ground plane(s) so that the normal component of magnetic field is zero on each of the N_c conductors and the ground plane(s). The surfaces of the N_c conductors are called the first N_c interfaces. If there is an upper ground plane, its surface is called the (N_c+1)th interface.

Let S_i be the surface bounded by a z-directed line from $z=0$ to $z=1$ on the ith interface, a z-directed line from $z=0$ to $z=1$ on the lower ground plane, and connections in the $z=0$ and $z=1$ planes. The magnetic flux ψ_i passing through S_i is given by

$$\psi_i = \iint_{S_i} \underline{B}\cdot d\underline{s} = \iint_{C_i} \underline{A}\cdot d\underline{l} = A_z. \tag{A1}$$

In (A1), C_i is the contour that bounds S_i, $\underline{B}$ is the magnetic field, $\underline{A}$ is the magnetic vector potential, and A_z is the z component of the magnetic vector potential on the line where S_i meets the ith interface. It has been assumed that the z component of the magnetic vector potential vanishes on the lower ground plane. Since the normal component of magnetic field is zero on the ith interface, ψ_i does not depend on the placement of the line where S_i meets the ith interface. It is now evident from (A1) that

$$A_z(\underline{\rho}) = \psi_i \tag{A2}$$

where $A_z(\underline{\rho})$ is the z component of magnetic vector potential at an arbitrary point $\underline{\rho}$ on the ith interface, and ψ_i is a constant flux. Equation (A2) annihilates the normal component of magnetic field on the surface of the ith interface.

Using image currents to annihilate the normal component of magnetic field on the lower ground plane, we write $A_z(\underline{\rho})$ as

$$A_z(\underline{\rho}) = \frac{\mu_0}{2\pi}\sum_{k=1}^{J_1}\int_{l_k} J_z(\underline{\rho}')\ln\left(\frac{|\underline{\rho}-\hat{\underline{\rho}}'|}{|\underline{\rho}-\underline{\rho}'|}\right)dl' \tag{A3}$$

where J_1 is given by either (3) or (4). Furthermore, $J_z(\underline{\rho}')$ is the z component of electric current per unit length on the J_1 interfaces, $\underline{\rho}'$ is the point at which the differential element of length dl' is located, and $\hat{\underline{\rho}}'$ is the image of $\underline{\rho}'$ about the lower ground plane. Substitution of (A3) into (A2) yields the magnetostatic equation

$$\frac{\mu_0}{2\pi}\sum_{k=1}^{J_1}\int_{l_k} J_z(\underline{\rho}')\ln\left(\frac{|\underline{\rho}-\hat{\underline{\rho}}'|}{|\underline{\rho}-\underline{\rho}'|}\right)dl' = \psi_i, \qquad \begin{cases}\underline{\rho} \text{ on } l_i\\ i=1,2,\cdots J_1\end{cases}. \tag{A4}$$

Consider the electrostatic equations (9) and (11). If all dielectric layers are replaced by free space, the total charge density σ_T reduces to the free charge density σ_F. Consequently, the electrostatic equation (9) becomes

$$\frac{1}{2\pi\epsilon_0}\sum_{j=1}^{J_1}\int_{l_j} \sigma_F(\underline{\rho}')\ln\left(\frac{|\underline{\rho}-\hat{\underline{\rho}}'|}{|\underline{\rho}-\underline{\rho}'|}\right)dl' = V_i, \qquad \begin{cases}\underline{\rho} \text{ on } l_i\\ i=1,2,\cdots J_1\end{cases}. \tag{A5}$$

Furthermore, the electrostatic equation (11) disappears.

The solution $J_z(\underline{\rho}')$ to (A4) is of the form

$$J_z(\underline{\rho}') = \sum_{i=1}^{N_c} J_z^{(i)}(\underline{\rho}')\psi_i \tag{A6}$$

where $J_z^{(i)}(\underline{\rho}')$ is the solution that would result if $\psi_i=1$ and all other ψ's were zero. In (A6), the index i terminates at N_c because, if there is an upper ground plane, then it has been assumed that the z component of the magnetic vector potential vanishes on it so that ψ_{N_c+1} is zero. The solution $\sigma_F(\underline{\rho}')$ to (A5) is of the form

$$\sigma_F(\underline{\rho}') = \sum_{i=1}^{N_c} \sigma_F^{(i)}(\underline{\rho}')V_i \tag{A7}$$

where $\sigma_F^{(i)}(\underline{\rho}')$ is the solution which would result if $V_i=1$ and all other V's were zero. In (A7), the index i terminates at N_c because the upper ground plane, if present, is at zero potential. It is evident from (A4) and (A5) that

$$J_z^{(i)}(\underline{\rho}') = \frac{1}{\mu_0\epsilon_0}\sigma_F^{(i)}(\underline{\rho}'). \tag{A8}$$

Substitution of (A8) into (A6) gives

$$J_z(\underline{\rho}') = \frac{1}{\mu_0\epsilon_0}\sum_{i=1}^{N_c}\sigma_F^{(i)}(\underline{\rho}')\psi_i. \tag{A9}$$

The integral over l_j of (A7) is

$$Q_j = \sum_{i=1}^{N_c} C_{0ji}V_i, \qquad j=1,2,\cdots N_c \tag{A10}$$

where Q_j is the free charge per unit length on the jth conductor and C_{0ji} is the jith element of the free-space capacitance matrix.

$$C_{0ji} = \int_{l_j}\sigma_F^{(i)}(\underline{\rho}')\,dl', \qquad \begin{cases} i=1,2,\cdots N_c\\ j=1,2,\cdots N_c\end{cases}. \tag{A11}$$

The integral over l_j of (A9) is

$$I_j = \frac{1}{\mu_0\epsilon_0}\sum_{i=1}^{N_c} C_{0ji}\psi_i, \qquad j=1,2,\cdots N_c \tag{A12}$$

where I_j is the net z-directed electric current on the jth conductor and C_{0ji} is given by (A11).

Solving (A12) for the ψ's in terms of the I's, we obtain

$$\psi_i = \mu_0 \epsilon_0 \sum_{j=1}^{N_c} [C_0]_{ij}^{-1} I_j \tag{A13}$$

where $[C_0]_{ij}^{-1}$ is the ijth element of the inverse of the free-space capacitance matrix. This inverse exists because the free-space capacitance matrix C_0 is positive definite. In view of the definition of the inductance matrix L, the desired relationship (22) between L and C_0 is evident from (A13).

References

[1] P. Silvester, "TEM wave properties of microstrip transmission lines," *Proc. Inst. Elec. Eng.*, vol. 115, pp. 43–48, Jan. 1968.

[2] T. G. Bryant and J. A. Weiss, "Parameters of microstrip transmission lines and of coupled pairs of microstrip lines," *IEEE Trans. Microwave Theory Tech.*, vol. MTT-16, pp. 1021–1027, Dec. 1968.

[3] W. T. Weeks, "Calculation of coefficients of capacitance of multiconductor transmission lines in the presence of a dielectric interface," *IEEE Trans. Microwave Theory Tech.*, vol. MTT-18, pp. 35–43, Jan. 1970.

[4] A. Farrar and A. T. Adams, "Characteristic impedance of microstrip by the method of moments," *IEEE Trans. Microwave Theory Tech.*, vol. MTT-18, pp. 65–66, Jan. 1970.

[5] E. Yamashita and K. Atsuki, "Strip line with rectangular outer conductor and three dielectric layers," *IEEE Trans. Microwave Theory Tech.*, vol. MTT-18, pp. 238–244, May 1970.

[6] J. L. Allen and M. F. Estes, "Broadside-coupled strips in a layered dielectric medium," *IEEE Trans. Microwave Theory Tech.*, vol. MTT-20, pp. 662–669, Oct. 1972.

[7] J. L. Allen, "Odd and even mode capacitances for coupled strips in a layered medium," *Int. J. Electron.*, vol. 35, pp. 1–13, July 1973.

[8] A. Farrar and A. T. Adams, "Multilayer microstrip transmission lines," *IEEE Trans. Microwave Theory Tech.*, vol. MTT-22, pp. 889–891, Oct. 1974.

[9] R. Crampagne, M. Ahmadpanah, and J. Guiraud, "A simple method for determining the Green's function for a large class of MIC lines having multilayered dielectric structures," *IEEE Trans. Microwave Theory Tech.*, vol. MTT-26, pp. 82–87, Feb. 1978.

[10] C. E. Smith and R. S. Chang, "Microstrip transmission line with finite-width dielectric," *IEEE Trans. Microwave Theory Tech.*, vol. MTT-28, pp. 90–94, Feb. 1980.

[11] C. Wei and R. F. Harrington, "Computation of the parameters of multiconductor transmission lines in two dielectric layers above a ground plane," Depart. Electrical Computer Eng., Syracuse Univer., Rep. TR-82-12, Nov. 1982.

[12] H. A. Wheeler, "Transmission-line properties of parallel strips separated by a dielectric sheet," *IEEE Trans. Microwave Theory Tech.*, vol. MTT-13, pp. 172–185, Mar. 1965.

[13] H. Sobol, "Extending IC technology to microwave equipment," *Electronics*, vol. 40, pp. 112–124, Mar. 20, 1967.

[14] E. Yamashita, "Variational method for the analysis of microstrip-like transmission lines," *IEEE Trans. Microwave Theory Tech.*, vol. MTT-16, pp. 529–535, Aug. 1968.

[15] R. Mittra and T. Itoh, "Charge and potential distributions in shielded striplines," *IEEE Trans. Microwave Theory Tech.*, vol. MTT-18, pp. 149–156, Mar. 1970.

[16] A. Farrar and A. T. Adams, "Computation of propagation constants for the fundamental and higher order modes in microstrip," *IEEE Trans. Microwave Theory Tech.*, vol. MTT-24, pp. 456–460, July 1976.

[17] T. Itoh and A. S. Hebert, "A generalized spectral domain analysis for coupled suspended microstriplines with tuning septums," *IEEE Trans. Microwave Theory Tech.*, vol. MTT-26, pp. 820–826, Oct. 1978.

[18] T. Itoh, "Generalized spectral domain method for multiconductor printed lines and its application to turnable suspended microstrips," *IEEE Trans. Microwave Theory Tech.*, vol. MTT-26, pp. 983–987, Dec. 1978.

[19] R. Plonsey and R. E. Collin, *Principles and Applications of Electromagnetic Fields.* New York: McGraw-Hill, 1961.

[20] D. Kajfez, "Multiconductor transmission lines," Depart. Electrical Eng., Univ. Mississippi, June 1972. Also published as Interaction Note 151 by Dr. Carl Baum, Air Force Weapons Laboratory (EL), Kirtland AFB, NM 87117.

[21] R. F. Harrington, *Field Computation by Moment Methods.* New York: Macmillan Co., 1968. Reprinted by Krieger Publishing Co., Melbourne, FL, 1982.

[22] H. B. Dwight, *Tables of Integrals and Other Mathematical Data*, Fourth Ed. New York: Macmillan Co., 1961.

[23] C. Wei and R. F. Harrington, "Extension of the multiconductor transmission line solution to zero-thickness conductors and to conductors between parallel ground planes," Depart. Electrical Computer Eng., Syracuse Univer., Rep. TR-83-5, Mar. 1983.

[24] R. F. Harrington, *Time-Harmonic Electromagnetic Fields.* New York: McGraw-Hill, 1961.

CHAPTER II

MICROWAVE INTEGRATED CIRCUIT COMPONENTS

Articles in this chapter cover important microwave circuit components as they are realized in lumped-element and microstrip form. The use of lumped-elements is described in the articles of Daly, *et al.*, and of Pengelly and Richard.

Filters are discussed by Matthaei; D'Inzeo, *et al.*; and by Williams and Schwarz. Couplers are presented by Leighton and Milnes; Presser; Bastida and Fanelli; and Cuhaci and Lo. Resonators are described by Wolff; Iveland; and Bonetti and Atia. Phase shifters are covered by Opp and Hoffman.

The remaining papers discuss the special components that can be integrated on ferrite substrates. These are presented in the work of Roome and Hair; and of Hansson, *et al.*

Lumped Elements in Microwave Integrated Circuits

DANIEL A. DALY, STANLEY P. KNIGHT, MARTIN CAULTON, SENIOR MEMBER, IEEE, AND ROALD EKHOLDT, MEMBER, IEEE

Abstract—**The use of lumped rather than distributed elements affords a considerable size reduction (typically a factor of 10 in area) in *L*- and *S*-band microwave integrated circuits. The electrical performance of such lumped elements is shown to be good enough to warrant their use in many applications where the size advantage or the resultant cost advantage is important. Miniature elements have been constructed which behave as true lumped reactive components up to at least 2.5 GHz. These elements have been evaluated using an impedance measurement method. Both inductors and capacitors have exhibited *Q*s greater than 50 at lower *S* band. Single-stage transistor power amplifiers at 2 GHz have been breadboarded using a simple arrangement of the lumped elements to match the measured impedances of the transistor pellet. These amplifiers have had gains as high as 4.7 dB at 2 GHz. The transistor used typically exhibits about 5 dB of gain in conventional coaxial circuitry. The loss in the lumped element matching networks has been about 0.5 dB greater than the loss in the distributed matching networks used in a microstrip amplifier built with the same type transistor. It is expected that the lumped circuit loss can be reduced as improved components are developed.**

Manuscript received June 12, 1967; revised August 30, 1967.

D. A. Daly and M. Caulton are with the RCA Laboratories, David Sarnoff Research Center, Princeton, N. J. 08540.

S. P. Knight was on temporary assignment to RCA Laboratories, David Sarnoff Research Center from RCA Astro-Electronics Division, Hightstown, N. J.

R. Ekholdt was on leave of absence to RCA Laboratories, David Sarnoff Research Center. He is with the Norwegian Defense Research Establishment, Kjeller, Norway.

I. Introduction

IT HAS BEEN well established that microwave integrated circuits will play an important role in future systems. Integrated switches,[1] amplifiers,[2] mixers,[2] and oscillators[4] that operate at microwave frequencies have been described. These circuits have all used transmission lines as resonant elements. This paper will describe the use of minute lumped elements for microwave integrated circuits operating in S band.[1] It is important to note that true lumped microwave elements could not have been made without incorporating the advanced technology used for the fabrication of transistors and lower frequency integrated circuits. The lumped elements, because of performance limitations, cannot replace transmission lines in all S-band applications but they do have important uses for certain areas, and indeed an operating power amplifier is described in this paper.

The cost of an integrated circuit is roughly inversely proportional to the number of circuits processed simultaneously on a single starting wafer (ceramic or semiconductor). A fairly large number of X-band circuits using $\lambda/4$ transmission lines ($\lambda/4 \approx 0.125$ inch on Al_2O_3 substrate) can fit on a standard 1 by 1 inch wafer. Few S-band circuits, however, can fit on such a wafer. Thus, if many low-cost S-band circuits are to be made simultaneously, it is necessary to resort to lumped elements.[2]

Section II of this paper will briefly consider the quality characteristic Q of lumped elements. In Section III, the measurement techniques used to determine the impedance and Qs of lumped inductors and capacitors will be described. The results of these measurements on individual elements are described in Sections IV and V. In Section VI the feasibility of constructing amplifiers using elements wire bounded together is demonstrated. This is not an integrated circuit; however, some preliminary work on hybrid integrated amplifiers is reported. Finally applications of these elements in integrated circuits are suggested.

II. Considerations of Reactive Elements

The use of lumped elements in microwave integrated circuits has been considered by several workers,[5]–[8] but to our knowledge operating high-Q tuned circuits composed entirely of thin-film truly lumped components have not been reported at frequencies as high as S band. Fig. 1(a) schematically depicts a simple planar spiral inductor. The current in the inductor, to a first approximation, flows within a skin depth on the top and bottom surfaces and the inner vertical face of the inside turn and the outer vertical face of the outside turn. Fig. 1(a) ignores current crowding that occurs at the higher frequencies, and also leakage flux. The Q is the reactance X divided by the resistance R

$$Q = \frac{\omega L}{R} \tag{1}$$

where ω is the angular frequency and L is the inductance. A simple expression for Q can be derived by relating the resistance to the length and width of the spiral.

[1] The octave frequency band designation is used in this paper, i.e., L band = 1.0 to 2.0 GHz, S band = 2.0 to 4.0 GHz, C band = 4.0 to 8.0 GHz, and X band = 8.0 to 12.0 GHz.

[2] Another method of reducing size is to use transmission lines on high-dielectric constant substrates. These are in the early stages of development. There are problems that are yet to be solved.

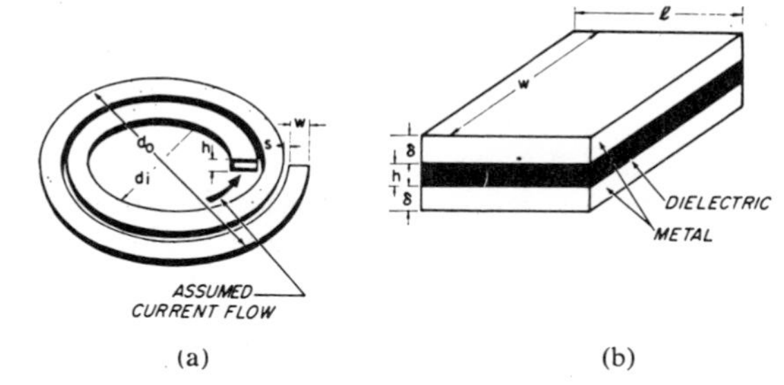

Fig. 1. Sketch of reactive elements.

The ac resistance, ignoring the side walls and losses in the supporting substrate, is

$$R = \frac{an\pi R_s}{W} \tag{2}$$

where

$a = (d_0 + d_i)/4$ [average radius Fig. 1(a)]
n is the number of turns
R_s = surface resistivity in ohms per square $= \sqrt{\pi f \mu / \sigma}$
f is the frequency
μ is the permeability
σ is the conductivity.

Thus,

$$Q = \frac{2fLW}{R_s na} = \frac{2LW}{na}\sqrt{\frac{f\sigma}{\pi\mu}}. \tag{3}$$

According to (3), Q increases with the square root of the frequency. It is apparent that Q benefits by increasing W; keeping the inductance and average radius nearly constant. The maximum width W is limited by self resonance of the inductor resulting from parasitic interturn capacitance. Increasing W, however, would increase the coil size, defeating the purpose of using lumped elements. Inductors with Qs greater than 50 at 2 GHz with a diameter less than 0.050 inch will be reported in Section IV. Based on the assumed current flow, one needs coil heights h of the order of several skin depths; about 6 microns for copper or 8 microns for aluminum at 2 GHz. As the Q is proportional to the volume to surface ratio, circular spirals will have higher Qs than square ones.

Capacitors are now considered. Fig. 1(b) illustrates a simple metal-oxide sandwich capacitor. The metal thickness is 1 to 2 skin depths, about 2 to 4 microns at 2 GHz. A dielectric thickness of 0.5 to 1.0 micron for silicon dioxide appears practical. The loss behavior of a capacitor can be calculated using standard transmission line theory[9] and considering the capacitor to be a short length of open circuited transmission line. The capacitor Q_{cap} is found to be,

$$\frac{1}{Q_{cap}} = \frac{1}{Q_c} + \frac{1}{Q_d} \tag{4}$$

where the conductor Q_c (for a capacitance C of square area) is

$$Q_c \approx \frac{3}{2\omega R_s C} \propto f^{-3/2} \tag{5}$$

and the dielectric Q_d is

$$Q_d \approx \frac{1}{\tan\delta} \tag{6}$$

where $\tan\delta$ is the loss tangent of the dielectric. At 2 GHz, the Q_c for most metals is greater than 500, and for fused quartz (SiO_2) $Q_d = 10\,000$. Unfortunately the values achieved in practice are orders of magnitude below the calculated value, as described in Section V.

III. Measurement Technique

The small size of lumped elements at microwave frequencies complicates their electrical evaluation. The properties of the elements can, however, be completely determined by slotted line impedance measurements, and this was the method used. The measurement system is illustrated in Figs. 2 and 3. The test component, an inductor in Fig. 3, terminates a 50 ohm microstrip line which is clipped onto an OSM connector. This fixture is connected through an adapter to a General Radio-900 precision slotted line. Measurements of VSWR and position of minimum are made and subsequently repeated with the test component replaced by a known termination; a short or an open circuit. The reactance and quality factor Q of the test component are determined by a comparison of the data for the three cases. Although the accuracy of the Q measurement is somewhat limited at the upper edge of the frequency band, this method has been selected for use because it yields both the reactance and Q of the test component over a range of frequencies in a direct manner.

In order to evaluate high-Q reactive components by this method, the transmission line between the slotted line and the test component should meet three requirements:

1) It should be well matched.
2) Its loss should be small compared to the loss in the test component.
3) The reactive end effect at the terminal point on the transmission line where the test component is attached should be negligible.

The system used in Fig. 2 exhibits the following behavior across the frequency band 0.5 to 2.5 GHz. The microstrip transmission line and adaptors terminated in a matched load have a VSWR of less than 1.05 over the frequency range. The VSWR measured on the system of Fig. 2 with open and short terminations is generally high, frequently greater than 200. The measured positions of minimum with open and short terminations are separated by one-quarter wavelength. Thus, all three requirements are fairly well satisfied. The fact that conditions 1) and 2) are not completely met leads to inaccuracies in the Q measurement which are discussed in the Appendix.

Microstrip transmission line is used in the test fixture because connecting joints between the test piece and the line are accessible with the test piece mounted at the end of the line. Mounting the test piece at the end of the 50 ohm line simplifies interpretation of the data. The 50 ohm microstrip line used has physical dimensions which are compatible both with the test pieces and with the OSM connector. The

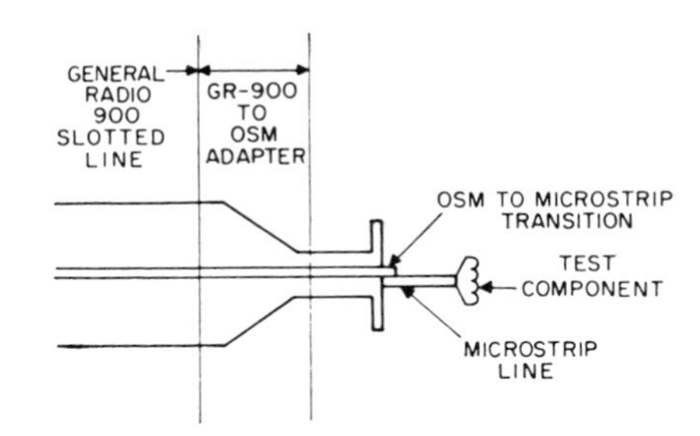

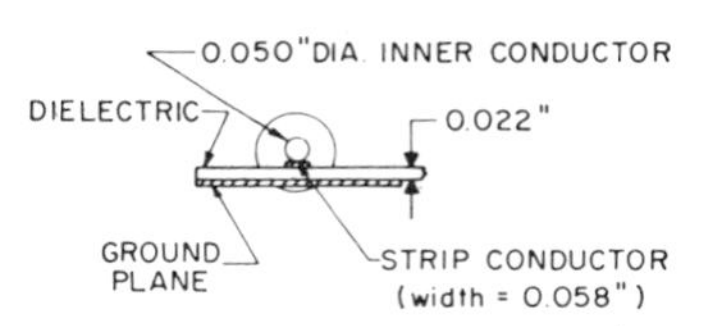

Fig. 2. Sketch of measurement system.

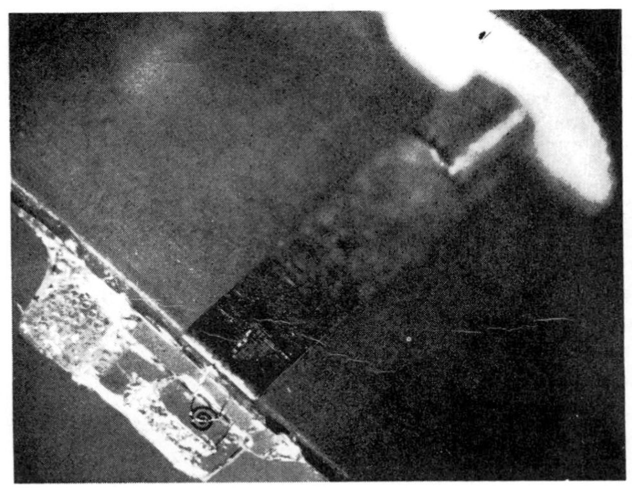

Fig. 3. Photograph of test fixture.

distance between the strip conductor and the ground plane is sufficiently small (0.022 inch) to make the end effect negligible.

The reactance of the test component is determined from the shift in the position of the minimum. Data are taken with the line terminated in several ways:

1) Terminated in a shorted component (shorted by a short wire connecting the ends of the element as shown in Fig. 3).
2) Terminated in the component (shorting wire removed).
3) Terminated in an open circuit (component removed).
4) Terminated in a short (tab of metal).

The lead reactance is determined from measurements 1) and 3) or 4). The total reactance of the leads plus the test component is found from measurements 2) and 3) or 4). Thus, the net reactance of the test component is determined. The accuracy of the reactance measurements has been very good. As an example, the lead inductance of a particular capacitor was determined from sets 1 and 3 to be 1.30 nH and from sets 2 and 3 to be 1.31 nH. Both determinations were made over the frequency range 0.5 to 2.5 GHz.

Component Q is evaluated from the VSWR data once the normalized reactance x is known. When a transmission line is terminated in a reactance and the VSWR is high (above 5 is sufficient), the VSWR is approximately

$$\text{VSWR} \approx |x| Q + \frac{Q}{|x|} + \frac{|x|}{Q}.$$

This expression is derived by combining the following transmission-line relationships, expressed here in functional form: reflection coefficient $\rho = f$(normalized impedance) $= f(|x|, Q)$ and $|\rho| = f$ (VSWR). For the components under consideration the last term $|x|/Q$ on the right-hand side is negligible. Since very high VSWRs are measured, the double minimum[10] or width of minimum method is used. In this method

$$\text{VSWR} = \frac{\lambda}{\pi \Delta}$$

where Δ is the position width of minimum at the points where the probe pickup is twice the minimum value. Then

$$Q \approx \frac{\lambda}{\pi\left(|x| + \frac{1}{|x|}\right)\Delta_{\text{test}}}.$$

In practice, the measurement system losses are significant compared to the test component loss, particularly at the higher frequencies, and must be corrected for. The loss correction is determined from the open and short VSWR data. Because the loss is low it can be shown that

$$Q \approx \frac{\lambda}{\pi\left(|x| + \frac{1}{|x|}\right)(\Delta_{\text{test}} - \Delta_{\text{correction}})}. \tag{7}$$

Both Δs must be corrected to the same point on the slotted line. The output reference plane of the line is used.

Several sources of error in the Q measurement are discussed in the Appendix. More will be said about the effects of these inaccuracies when specific results are given. However, an examination of (7) reveals the general behavior of the errors. Since λ is inversely proportional to frequency, the Δ difference in the denominator decreases sharply with frequency. The uncertainties in the measurement of Δ (see Appendix) thus contribute increasing percentage error with increasing frequency. Consequently, the determinations are accurate at 0.5 GHz but deteriorate with increasing frequency.

IV. Inductor Results

A variety of inductors has been built and tested. Circular spirals have been used in preference to square spirals as tuning elements in an effort to achieve improved Q. These coils were designed using low-frequency inductor formulas.[11],[12] Equation (8) has been found to be in fairly good agreement with experimental results. Errors of about 20 percent have been measured. The formula is[11]

Fig. 4. Photograph of 25 nH inductor.

$$L = \frac{a^2 n^2}{8a + 11c} \tag{8}$$

where

$a = (r_o + r_i)/2$
$c = r_o - r_i$
r_i is the inner radius of the spiral in mils
r_o is the outer radius of the spiral in mils
L is the inductance of the spiral in nanohenries
n is the number of turns.

Square spirals have been designed[13] and fabricated as chokes as described in Section VI.

The fabrication of thick spiral inductors with a cross section similar to that shown in Fig. 1(a) has been difficult in the past[14],[15] principally because of problems connected with making a satisfactory photoresist plating form. We have achieved such coils by plating copper into a thick Shipley-photoresist form.[3] Coils up to 1 mil thick have been made in this way. The dc resistance of these coils has been about $1\frac{3}{4}$ times the value expected for pure copper. The substrate material has been either glass or Al_2O_3. Silicon dioxide is used to insulate the crossovers in integrated circuit applications of these inductors.

A photograph of a 25 nH copper coil is shown in Fig. 4. The coil conductor is 2.5 mils wide and 0.5 mil thick with a 1.5 mil spacing between turns. This coil was tested by the methods described previously. A plot of Q^2 versus f for this coil is shown in Fig. 5. The Q increases as the square root of frequency, as expected from the considerations described earlier. Assuming bulk resistivity, the measured Q is approximately one half of that to be expected if the current

[3] For processing instructions see Shipley Company, Inc. bulletins.

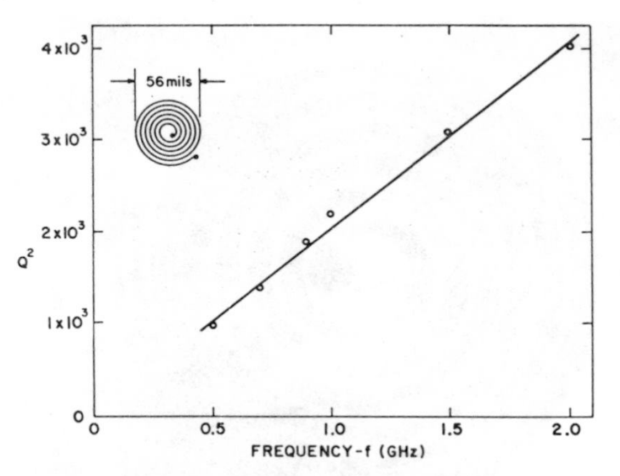

Fig. 5. Measured frequency variation of inductor Q for the Fig. 4 coil.

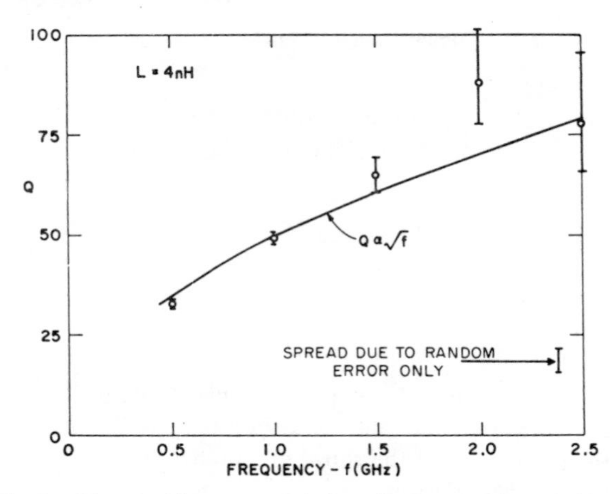

Fig. 6. Measured frequency variation of inductor Q for a 4 nH coil.

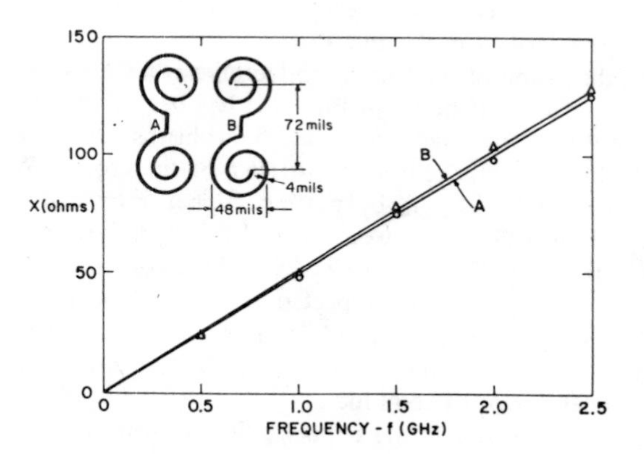

Fig. 7. Evaluation of mutual coupling between coils.

divided itself equally between the upper and lower surfaces of the coil. The accuracy of this Q measurement is enhanced by the fact that the 25 nH coil yields a relatively large reactance over the entire frequency band of the measurement.

Four nanohenry copper coils, a size more suitable for matching circuits at 2 GHz, were tested. The coil conductor is 4 mils wide and 10 microns thick. The coil has $1\frac{3}{4}$ turns with an outside diameter of 48 mils. Fig. 6 shows the measured frequency variation of inductor Q for this coil. The curve shows a Q is proportional to $\sqrt{f}$ variation. The open correction for line loss was used in the measurement of this coil. Although this leads to a conservative result relative to the use of the short correction, the Q values given in Fig. 6 may be somewhat optimistic at the upper edge of the frequency band, as explained in the Appendix. There is no correction for lead loss or connecting joint loss in the results given. The possible uncertainty in the Q values due to random error in the measurement of the Δ s is shown in Fig. 6.

The accuracy of the Q measurements, though limited, is good enough to permit the following two conclusions:

1) The inductor Q increases with frequency; the rate of increase approximates the expected square root of frequency dependency.
2) Qs greater than 50 are at present attainable for such coils in the lower S-band region. With improved conductivity and optimized coil design, Qs of 100 at these frequencies are a distinct possibility.

The dependency of Q on thickness was determined for a multiturn coil similar to the 25 nH coil of Fig. 4. Varying the thickness from 10 microns to 4 mils produced essentially no change in the Q. It is concluded then that two or three skin depths is the upper useful thickness for such a coil. The dependency of Q on conductor width has not yet been evaluated.

Fig. 7 is a plot of reactance versus frequency for a series connection of two of the Fig. 6 coils. Series connection A is electrically identical to series connection B except for the effect of mutual coupling between the coils. The plot shows that the mutual effect is negligible in this case. The smooth variation of X with frequency demonstrates the reliability of the reactance measurements, the coil behaves as a simple lumped element inductor.

V. Capacitor Results

The thin-film capacitor is the most desirable type for microwave integrated circuits. Thin-film capacitors have been constructed using deposited SiO_2 as a dielectric. The deposition technique is the controlled oxidation of silane.[16] Capacitors ranging from 1.5 to 50 pF have been built on glass or Al_2O_3 substrates. These capacitors have a dielectric layer 1 micron thick and range in size from 7 to 44 mils on a side. Measured Q values have clustered around the 40 to 60 level and were essentially constant across the band 0.5 to 2.5 GHz. It has been shown in an earlier section that capacitor Qs of several hundred should be possible if dielectric films having properties close to pure SiO_2 can be produced. The quality of the dielectric obtained from the present deposition technique can be improved, and indeed Texas Instruments Incorporated has reported[17] Qs of 100 at 2 GHz for thin-film capacitors containing reactively sputtered SiO_2.

VI. Lumped Element Power Amplifiers

Thin-film inductors and capacitors have been utilized in several single-stage 2 GHz transistor power amplifiers. Lumped element circuits were designed to match to 50 ohms the measured dynamic input and output impedances of an experimental RCA transistor pellet operated in a common-base class C mode.

The design of these transistor power amplifiers involves two steps: a) the determination of the transistor's input and output dynamic impedances, and b) the design of matching networks which can be realized with thin-film lumped elements.

The first step is accomplished by mounting the transistor chip on a calibrated microstrip test fixture which is attached to a coaxial measurement system.[18] The transistor is tuned for maximum power gain. The external tuning circuits are removed and their impedances measured using a slotted line to determine the optimum source and load impedances transferred to the connection plane of the transistor. It is important to keep the lengths of microstrip and coaxial lines to the tuners short, in order to reduce the effect of their attenuation on the accuracy of the measurements. This empirical method of transistor characterization was used rather than the linear approach found in small signal transistor circuit design[8] because no practical model for the nonlinear behavior of transistors operating in high-power class C amplifier circuits exists at present.

The input and output matching networks should have low loss and provide the optimum dynamic load and source impedances as measured at some specific operating condition. There should be a minimum number of elements in the matching networks in order to minimize losses. To achieve circuits of small size the area occupied by the matching networks should be comparable, within an order of magnitude, with the area of the transistor pellet. During the early work, bandwidth was not a constraint. In fact, designing for a narrow bandwidth would have caused intolerable losses since the particular transistors used have low-loaded Q s.

The requirements listed above can be met by using two-element L networks. This type of network can be easily designed using an impedance admittance chart.[19] A circuit so designed is shown in Fig. 8. Both the input and output impedances can be matched to 50 ohms by any of four different L networks. The choice of which network to use depends on losses, ease of bias connection, and whether the circuit is to be "breadboarded" or "integrated."[4] Assuming that each of the matching elements has a Q of 50 the total loss in the amplifier matching circuits varies from 0.5 to 1.0 dB depending on the configuration chosen. The loss of the circuit of Fig. 8 is 0.7 dB.

[4] As used here, the term breadboard refers to circuits constructed of separately mounted capacitors and inductors interconnected by ultrasonically bonded wires. The term integrated refers to a circuit with no bonds other than those necessary for the transistor connections.

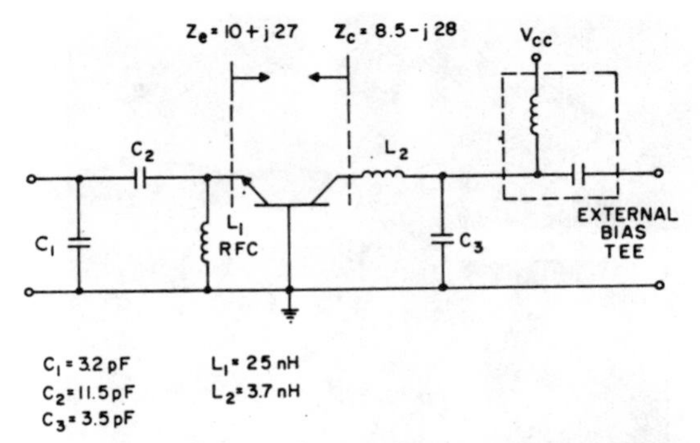

Fig. 8. Circuit diagram for lumped component power amplifier.

A. Breadboard Amplifier

Fig. 9 is a photograph of a breadboard form of the circuit depicted schematically in Fig. 8. Capacitor C_2 has little effect on the input match and is eliminated. OSSM flange mounts are used; they are beveled to facilitate connecting components. The proper values for C_1 and C_3 are achieved by connecting two capacitors in parallel. The circuit ground was brought out to the substrate edge and then silver painted over the edge to the grounded heat sink. The dark areas under the inductors are holes in the heat sink to minimize field distortion.

All interconnections were made by ultrasonically bonding with 1 mil diameter gold wire, which has an inductance of approximately $\frac{1}{4}$ nH per 10 mils of length. Since 1 nH at 2 GHz is 12.5 ohms, the lead lengths are important and must be carefully accounted for during layout. For this reason, several leads are paralleled where inductance is to be minimized.

Tests were made by externally tuning the amplifier for optimum performance, and then determining the impedances at the circuit connection points. In this manner, information was obtained from which the circuit components could be varied to achieve the desired performance.

After adjusting the output circuit elements, this amplifier had input–output matches of 1.5 to 1 and 1.9 to 1, respectively, at 2 GHz for a drive level of 19 dBm.

Fig. 10 is the gain frequency response of this amplifier with a constant drive level. At an input power level of 19 dBm, the 1 dB bandwidth was 9 percent, with a center frequency close to 2 GHz. The response characteristic varied considerably with drive level. This behavior is caused by the device's impedance variations with frequency and drive level. Fig. 11 shows the dynamic characteristics of the amplifier at 2 GHz. A maximum gain of 4.7 dB, with a collector efficiency of 9 percent, was obtained at an input drive of 50 mW. This gain did not occur (see Fig. 10) at the design drive level of 80 mW. However, the same chip when optimally tuned in a microstrip test fixture at the same drive and supply conditions exhibited a gain of 5.4 dB, 15 percent collector efficiency, and an output power of 350 mW. Obviously, the

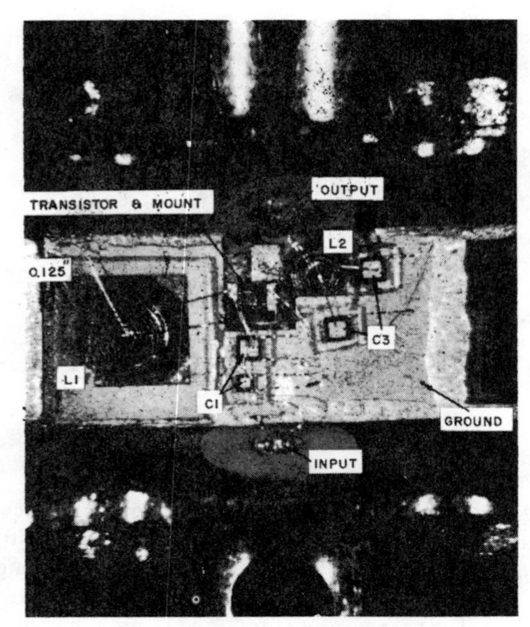

Fig. 9. Photograph of breadboarded lumped component power amplifier.

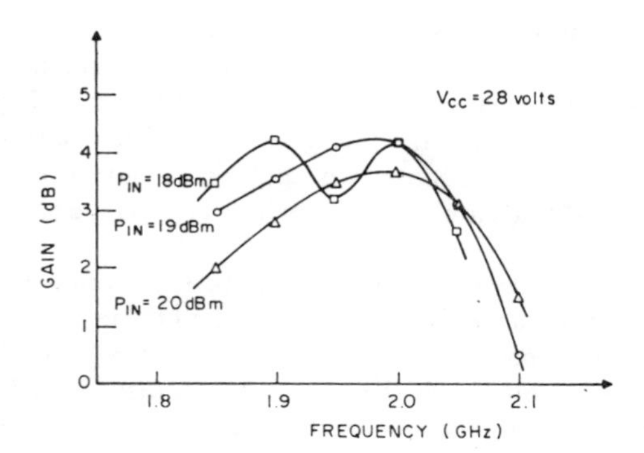

Fig. 10. Frequency response of Fig. 9 amplifier.

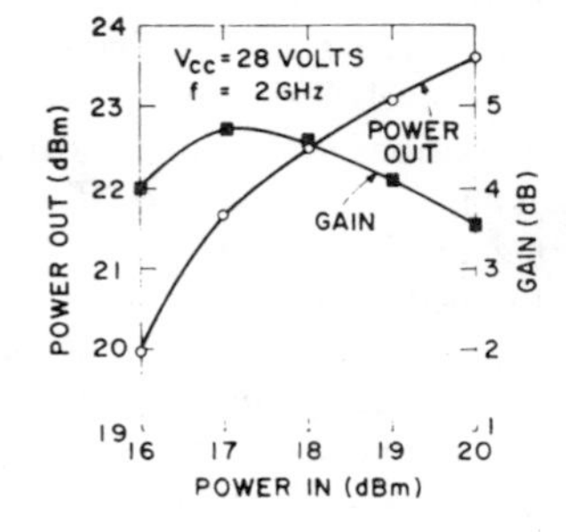

Fig. 11. Dynamic response of Fig. 9 amplifier.

amplifier was not optimally tuned and considerable degradation occurred due to the mismatches.

This particular batch of transistor chips exhibited an increase in collector efficiency and a decrease in gain when tuned at the higher drive level. Therefore, to improve the overall performance, an attempt was made to retune the amplifier. With a matched input and a 3 to 1 VSWR on the output, a gain of 3.6 dB, 17 percent collector efficiency, and 420 mW output power were achieved. The output was matched to 50 ohms by using an external stub tuner. These results are to be compared with the microstrip test fixture data of 3.7 dB gain, 23 percent collector efficiency, and 470 mW output.

Six breadboards have been built and tested to date. None has oscillated; all have performed in a similar fashion, i.e., optimum input and output matches have not been simultaneously achieved at a given drive level. Chips from another experimental run of transistors have yielded higher collector efficiencies, up to 27 percent, and higher output powers, even though their circuits were not optimized.

B. Integrated Amplifier

The breadboarding technique previously described has been useful in demonstrating the feasibility of lumped element microwave integrated circuits. However, the circuits described are a far cry from an integrated amplifier. This section describes briefly a preliminary integrated amplifier similar to that previously breadboarded. The circuit was changed to minimize area and the component interconnection lengths.

Fig. 12 is a photograph showing a portion of a 1 by $\frac{3}{4}$ inch sapphire substrate on which 45 thin-film 2 GHz power amplifier circuits were processed simultaneously. Each circuit contains all necessary elements required for biasing, stage isolation, and tuning. All components are thin-film lumped elements except for the transistor.

Fig. 13 is a detailed view of an individual amplifier and its circuit. In contrast to microstrip amplifiers, the transistor size is about equal to the other circuit elements. A 2 GHz microstrip amplifier using the same transistor and designed for minimum size is about ten times larger.

A desirable feature to design into integrated circuits is the ability to vary component values over a range sufficient to tune the device's expected impedances. This feature was incorporated to some extent in this layout; the top plate area of capacitors C_1, C_2 and C_4 can be increased by silver painting. However, the range available here is not sufficient and future designs must allow more area for this feature plus an additional variable capacitor in series with the inductors so that their values may also be changed.

The top ground area was centralized and is connected through the substrate to the lower ground plane by two "plated-through" holes. Results on the breadboard amplifiers have shown that silver painting the ground over the substrate edge is sufficient and is at present a more econom-

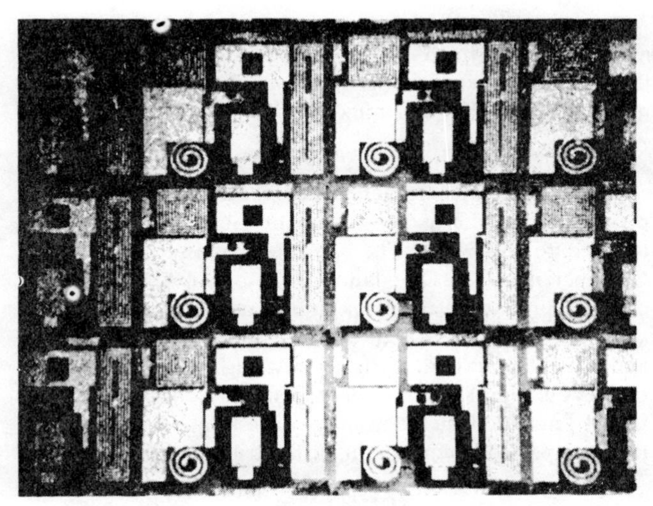

Fig. 12. Photograph of batch fabrication of amplifier circuits.

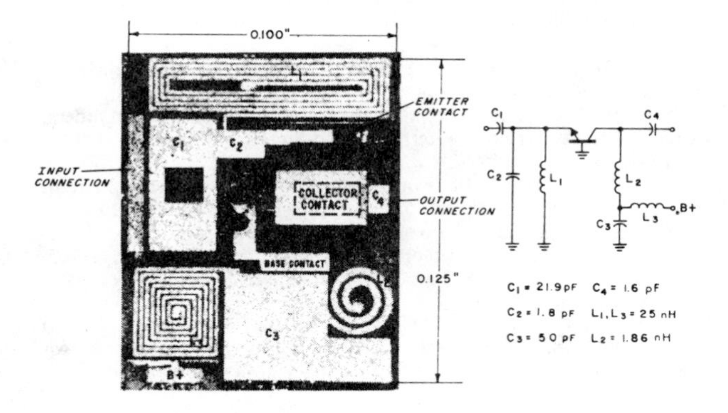

Fig. 13. Individual integrated amplifier and its circuit diagram.

ical technique. This latter technique will be used in future versions to increase yields.

The amplifier shown has not been tested at the time of this writing and is included only to show how lumped elements may be used in integrated amplifiers.

VII. Applications

The construction of microwave integrated circuits can be monolithic (active and passive devices grown into or on a semiconducting or active substrate), hybrid (passive elements deposited on a passive substrate and the active devices bonded and wired into place in a final step), or a quasi-monolithic combination of the two. The monolithic approach offers the possibility of processing more circuits with a minimum of handling, but the most suitable substrate, silicon, is lossy at microwave frequencies. If silicon is used as any part of a field carrying region, such as a support for inductors or an insulating dielectric for distributed elements, the Q will be severely degraded.

Lumped element circuits, with their small size, are very suitable for a quasi-monolithic approach similar to that described by the Decal Circuit Process.[20] Here the active elements can be grown into silicon, the lumped passive elements metalized around the active device, and the substrate then covered and fastened with glass. Finally, the lossy silicon can now be removed from the field carrying regions, and the circuit, which was quasi-monolithically grown, is now dielectrically isolated. The use of lumped elements makes this approach compete with distributed element hybrid circuits.

Lumped elements, mainly because of their small size (low Q), will not find application in critical narrowband high-efficiency amplifier stages, but they can be used in wideband, low- or medium-power stages. Here the amount of power lost in the elements will not be excessive. We envisage high-gain low-power cascaded S-band amplifiers which are quasi-monolithically constructed of lumped element circuits within a small area of perhaps 0.25 inch square. This small package can be fastened to the input of a final high-power higher Q microstrip hybrid amplifier.

Lumped elements can also be used as adjuncts to distributed circuits. One example is lumped element RF chokes which can save much space. Another example is lumped capacitors in series with microstrip lines. Since distributed tuning elements are mainly of a shunt nature, a lumped series high-Q capacitor could simplify networks of microstrip distributed elements.

VIII. Conclusion

Lumped elements suitable for use up to 2.5 GHz have been constructed. The elements have been evaluated using a simple impedance method which gives reasonable accuracies for the frequency range from 0.5 to 2.5 GHz. Both inductors and capacitors have exhibited Qs greater than 50 at lower S band. Simple transistor amplifier circuits have been wired together using lumped elements. Gains up to 4.7 dB were achieved at 2 GHz. The lumped element matching networks had a loss of about 0.5 dB greater than the loss in the distributed matching networks used in a microstrip amplifier built with the same type transistor. It is expected that the lumped circuit loss can be diminished as improved components are developed. Thus, the feasibility of lumped element microwave integrated circuits is demonstrated.

We conclude that because of their size and cost advantage lumped microwave integrated circuits will compete with distributed circuits in many applications at the lower microwave frequencies.

Appendix

Q Error

There are several sources of error in the Q measurement: mismatch error, correction error due to phase differences between the test and correction cases, and random error in the measurement of Δ.

The impedance measurement method assumes that the transmission line is perfectly matched between the slotted

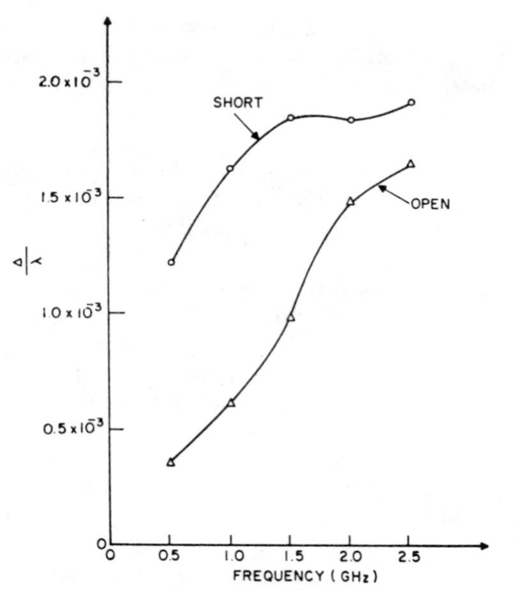

Fig. 14. Comparison of measurement system loss corrections.

line probe and the component mounting terminal. Actually, the transition from coaxial to microstrip lines introduces a small mismatch; in the frequency range of interest this mismatch causes a VSWR up to 1.05. Assuming that the mismatch impedance is reactive, this mismatch will cause an error of about ± 5 percent in the Q value. Since the discontinuity impedance is likely to be a parallel capacitance, the measured Q of an inductor is likely to be lower than the real Q.

The measurement system losses are conductor losses. Because the transverse dimension of the transmission line is much smaller in the test fixture than in the slotted line, the resistance per unit length is much larger in the test fixture. Consequently the measurement system losses depend on the phase of the current standing wave along the line. Fig. 14 is a comparison of measurement system loss with the fixture terminated in a short and in an open. Assuming low loss, it can be shown that the measurement system power loss divided by the incident power is proportional to Δ/λ. The short losses are greater because of the higher current concentration in the fixture in this case. The proper loss correction depends on the reactance of the test component. That is, the open correction is best applied to test components which have large reactances, and the short correction to those having small reactances. At 0.5 GHz, the short and open corrections are upper and lower bounds on the proper correction. However at 2.5 GHz, because the high-loss region covers an important percentage of the $\lambda/4$ phase variation, the proper correction can fall outside of this range. The uncertainty in the correction at the higher frequencies can result in optimistic inductor Qs. A more accurate correction can be determined by experimentally evaluating the measurement system loss as a function of phase for each frequency.

Finally there is a random error of about ± 0.015 mm in the measurement of the Δs. We take as a conservative estimate that the possible error in the difference of two such measurements is therefore ± 0.03 mm.

Acknowledgment

The authors wish to acknowledge the aid of the many people in the Microwave Research Laboratory who contributed to this work. The competent assistance of R. E. Chamberlain, R. D. DiStefano, N. Klein, and A. F. Young in constructing these elements is appreciated. The advice, criticism, and discussions with Drs. H. Sobol, L. S. Nergaard, and L. S. Napoli is gratefully acknowledged. Dr. H. Johnson of RCA Laboratories has been a strong proponent of the use of lumped elements at microwave frequencies, and the results reported herein are, in part, a tribute to his foresight.

References

[1] A. Ertel, "A 9 GHz silicon monolithic integrated TR switching circuit," Internat'l Electron Devices Meeting, October 1966.

[2] T. E. Saunders and P. D. Stark, "An integrated 4 GHz balanced transistor amplifier," Internat'l Solid-State Circuits Conf., February 1966.

[3] C. Genzabella and C. Howell, "Integrated *S*-band mixers," *IEEE Internat'l Conv. Rec.*, pt. 5, p. 113–118, March 1966.

[4] R. R. Webster, "Integrated microwave oscillators, amplifiers, switches, and converters," Internat'l Solid-State Circuits Conf., February 1967.

[5] A. Uhlir, Jr., "Microwave applications of integrated-circuit techniques," *Proc. IEEE*, vol. 52, pp. 1617–1623, December 1964.

[6] B. T. Vincent, Jr., "Microwave transistor amplifier design," presented at the Microwave Theory and Techniques Symp., May 1965.

[7] H. Johnson, RCA Lab., Princeton, N. J., November 1965 (private communication).

[8] R. W. Wyndrum, Jr., "The design of thin-film lumped element UHF amplifiers," Proc. Nat'l Security Industrial Association/Air Force Systems Command Microelectronics Conf., Washington, D. C., December 1965.

[9] S. Ramo, J. R. Whinnery, and T. Van Duzer, *Fields and Waves in Communication Electronics.* New York: Wiley, 1965, pp. 39–43 and pp. 330–334.

[10] E. L. Ginzton, *Microwave Measurements.* New York: McGraw-Hill, 1957, p. 266.

[11] F. E. Terman, *Radio Engineers Handbook.* New York: McGraw-Hill, 1943, p. 47.

[12] F. W. Grover, *Inductance Calculations.* Princeton, N. J.: Van Nostrand, 1946.

[13] H. G. Dill, "Designing inductors for thin-film applications," *Electronic Design*, pp. 52–59, February 17, 1964.

[14] F. R. Gleason, "Final development report for miniature thin-film inductors," Integrated Electronics Research Dept., Motorola, Inc., Scottsdale, Ariz., in contract with Navy Dept. Bureau of Ships, Contract NObsr 85397, Index SR-00803, Task 9636, June 30, 1964.

[15] A. E. Mason, Jr., "Study of solid-state integrated microwave circuits," Sci. Rept. 1, U4-811500-4, Texas Instruments Inc., in contract with NASA, Cambridge, Mass., Contract NAS 12-75, Control ERC/R&D 65-45, December 31, 1965.

[16] N. Goldsmith and W. Kern, "The deposition of vitreous silicon dioxide films from silane," *RCA Rev.*, vol. 28, pp. 153–165, March 1967.

[17] "Molecular electronics for radar applications," 3rd Interim Rept., Phase 2, Texas Instruments Inc., Rept. TI-03-66-80, Contract AF 33(615)-2525, DDC Rept. AD-484 739, June 1966 (unclassified).

[18] H. C. Lee, "Microwave power generation using overlay transistors," *RCA Rev.*, pp. 199–215, June 1966.

[19] J. G. Linvill and J. F. Gibbons, *Transistors and Active Circuits.* New York: McGraw-Hill, 1961.

[20] A. I. Stoller, J. A. Amick, and N. E. Wolff, "Getting the most out of circuits with dielectric isolation," *Electronics*, pp. 97–105, March 20, 1967.

DESIGN, MEASUREMENT AND APPLICATION OF LUMPED ELEMENTS UP TO J-BAND

R.S. Pengelly* and D.C. Rickard*

ABSTRACT

Lumped-element design, fabrication and characterization has been extended for MIC requirements up to 18GHz. Spiral or loop inductors and overlay or interdigital capacitors have been measured at appropriate frequencies leading to satisfactory equivalent circuits. Variations in parasitic reactances and Q-factor with frequency, substrate dielectric constant and component geometry are presented.

Particular applications include filter networks and FET amplifier matching circuits, the latter enabling octave coverage amplifier modules over X and J-band frequencies to be realised.

1. INTRODUCTION

Recent developments in microwave integrated circuits have extended the use of lumped elements, particularly for broadband circuits with minimal size requirements. This paper describes the design and realisation of satisfactory printed inductors and capacitors, using general design techniques over L to J band frequencies. Accurate fabrication and element characterization to closely control parasitic reactances is essential to the higher microwave frequencies.

2. ELEMENT GEOMETRIES AND MEASUREMENT TECHNIQUES

Fig.1 shows the configurations used for spiral, single loop inductors, interdigitated and overlay capacitors. The inductors have been modelled on an equivalent circuit effective to J-band which includes shunt capacitance due to the effects of ground. Also shown in Fig.1 are the self-capacitance and series resistive elements accounting for loss. The interdigitated and overlay capacitors have assumed equivalent circuits of the forms shown in Fig.1. The lumped elements have been fabricated on polished alumina, quartz, sapphire and gallium arsenide. It has been possible to produce elements with metal thicknesses ranging from less than 0.5 microns on GaAs to greater than 15 microns on sapphire.

By connecting the lumped elements on GaAs via wire bonds into a 50Ω test jig, or those on sapphire, alumina or quartz within microstrip or coplanar waveguide, the two port or one port scattering parameters were measured. These measurements used computer correction and extraction routines to separate out the small parasitic reactances. A fitting routine was used to match closely equivalent circuit values to measured and corrected s-parameters over the full frequency range of interest. Using single-port measurements the Q-factors of the components were found by calculating the difference between the measured and the theoretical return losses (based on infinite Q). Parasitic capacitances can also be measured by the use of both self-resonance and resonance conditions induced by using additional long-wire bonds.

Parallel-resonance conditions at X-band have been studied by fabricating suitable LC structures on both polished alumina and sapphire.

*R.S. Pengelly, M.Sc., M.I.E.E., C.Eng./*D.C. Rickard, B.Sc.,(Eng.)
The Plessey Co. Ltd., Roke Manor, Romsey, Hampshire, England.

Following Aitcheson et al [1] the susceptance of the circuit has been measured close to the resonant frequency. This enables measurement of capacitance, C, inductance, L, loss resistance, R and Q.

In order to obtain more accurate Q values for loop inductors and interdigitated capacitors, X and J-band cavity techniques have been used in microstrip and coplanar waveguide. The X-band cavity was fabricated on 0.635mm thick sapphire whilst the J-band cavity used polished alumina. Dielectric constants of these materials were measured over the 1 to 18GHz frequency range using the well known ring resonator principle. Unloaded cavity Q's of greater than 150 were obtained for centre frequencies up to 15GHz. The above measurement methods have produced a series of results only a few examples of which are quoted.

3. INDUCTORS

Spiral inductors have been measured up to 6GHz and indicate that a maximum diamter of $\lambda/30$ is needed to avoid distributed effects. Typically, a 4 to 50nH range is achieved for spiral outer diameters of 1.5 to 3mm with gaps of 0.05 to 0.15mm to suit alternative thin or thick film realisation.

Measurements on spiral designs have shown inductance values to be within 10% of standard formula calculation [2]. The s-parameter method was used to derive practical equivalent circuit parasitics. Typical sets of results for circular spirals printed on alumina are shown in Table 1. Self-capacitance, C_o, and shunt fringing capacitance values C_{f1} and C_{f2} are derived from the effective s-parameter resonances for a π-type equivalent circuit, corresponding to frequencies where S_{21}, Im S_{11} and Im $S_{22} = 0$. Single port measurements of spirals, shunt mounted at the end of a precision coaxial line are included, substantially confirming values of self-capacitance. An approximate empirical law suitable for design purposes in the spiral diameter range 1 to 5mm is $C_o = 0.035d_o + 0.06$pF where d_o is in millimetres.

Measured inductance and self-capacitance values for thick film spirals were within 5% of thin-film versions, confirming the general insensitivity of spiral geometry to printing errors. Typical measured Q values are included in Table 1.

Single loop inductors are most suitable for inductance values of less than 2nH at frequencies above 6GHz. Loop inductors have given Q values of over 60 at 10GHz. Fig.2 shows the variation in Q with metallization thickness and trackwidth for a 0.5nH inductor at 10GHz. Q reduces rapidly below 1 micron due to the skin depth effect. Fig.2 also shows the results obtained using the measurement techniques described in Section 2.

Practical Q values have been found to be of the order of 70% of theoretical values. Component values are within 10% of predicted values taking into account methods of mounting etc.

4. CAPACITORS

Thin film, overlay capacitors (mainly silicon dioxide) have previously been employed at microwave frequencies. Thick film capacitors, extensively used at lower frequencies were investigated up to 6GHz, following recent developments in dielectric compositions. Test samples (Fig.1) were fabricated on alumina using commercial dielectrics ($\varepsilon_R = 9$ to 15) giving capacitance densities in the range 2 to 6pF/mm^2.

Fig.3 presents s-parameter results for a 1pF capacitor, indicating satisfactory lumped performance well into C-band. Series inductance is typically 0.5nH for nominal 1 by 0.5mm dimensions (0.25mm overlap). Typical Q value for a 1.15pF capacitor is 50 at 3GHz. For practical tuning capacitors above S-band, shorter structures are essential, extending normal thick film fabrication limits.

Where a three layer system is not convenient interdigital capacitors can produce acceptable Q's up to J-band. Recent theoretical work [3] has shown that the Q values of interdigitated capacitors are highly dependent on width to gap ratio of the fingers, overall structure geometry, metallization thickness etc. Measurements have confirmed these results for frequencies in X and J-band.

Fig.4(a) shows the frequency at which the apparent capacitance increases by 10% for a series capacitance of 0.2pF at 10GHz. It is seen that for any one value of finger width (W_f) there is an optimum number of fingers to obtain maximum working frequency. To produce interdigitated capacitors which remain lumped up to 18GHz the structures need to have:-

1. Small gap width (i.e. < 5 microns);
2. A large number of fingers consistent with keeping transverse structure self-resonance frequencies high;
3. Short overall length; and
4. Wide fingers to maximize Q.

Fig.5 shows the Q factor of a 0.25pF capacitor versus metallization thickness and finger width to gap ratio. Shunt interdigitated capacitors show a consistently higher Q than series capacitors. Fig.4(b) shows the 10% capacitance increase frequency for various geometries for a 0.2pF capacitor.

When interdigitated capacitors are connected in the shunt mode their transverse inductance must also be taken into account when designing the overall microwave circuit. However shunt parasitic capacitances can be used to advantage in the shunt case where an effective decrease in the number of fingers takes place (when a ground plane is present).

5. APPLICATIONS

The use of lumped elements for low and high pass filters is well known but their use in bandpass filters, particularly at higher frequencies, has been limited due to inaccurate component modelling and non-optimum Q. Bandpass filter designs have been achieved with direct-coupled resonator structures using capacitive coupling. Only shunt resonators and small capacitor values are required, appropriate to lumped element realisation. Initial results for 15-20% bandwidth examples are encouraging up to X-band (Fig.6).

Use of interdigitated capacitors and single loop inductors have enabled the realisation of broadband GaAs FET amplifiers capable of covering 6 to 12.4GHz or 7.2 to 14.5GHz [4]. The lumped elements form a modified Tchebyschev bandpass input match to the FET device which may be self-biased to its minimum noise-measure point. The amplifier is contained on a 1.8 by 1.2mm chip and is mounted in a broadband microwave package (Fig.7). The gain and noise figure of a typical amplifier are shown in Fig.8. Lumped element techniques in J-band are, at present, being investigated to realise a 12-18GHz low-noise GaAs FET amplifier.

CONCLUSIONS

Extensive investigations of lumped elements have extended their useful frequency range to J-band with superior knowledge of their circuit representation. This has led to design guides to optimise component geometry, layout, choice of substrate etc. thus giving improved MIC performance.

ACKNOWLEDGEMENTS

The authors are grateful for useful discussion with Chelsea College, London. The authors thank the Directors of the Plessey Company Limited for permission to publish this paper. The work described was carried out under contracts supported by the Procurement Executive, Ministry of Defence, sponsored by DCVD.

REFERENCES

1. Aitcheson C.S. et al "Lumped Circuit Elements at Microwave Frequencies I.E.E.E. Trans. on Microwave Theory and Techniques, Vol.MTT-19, No.12 pp.928-937, December, 1971.

2. M. Caulton et al "Hybrid Integrated Lumped-Element Microwave Amplifiers" I.E.E.E. Trans. on Electron Devices, Vol.ED-15, No.7, July 1968 pp.459-466.

3. J. Hobdell and C.S. Aitcheson - Private Communication.

4. R.S. Pengelly and J.A. Turner "Monolithic Broadband GaAs FET Amplifiers" Electronics Letters. 13th May 1976, Vol.12. No.10 pp.251-252.

w (mm)	s (mm)	n	d_o (mm)	L(theor) (nH)	L(meas) (nH)	C_o (pF)	C_{f1} (pF)	C_{f2} (pF)	Q @4GHz
0.10	0.10	1.5	1.30	3.7	4.0	0.13	0.10	0.07	87
0.05	0.05	2.5	1.50	14.1	14.3	0.11	0.09	0.05	84
0.10	0.10	2.5	1.80	9.2	9.0	0.14	0.18	0.08	81
0.10	0.10	3.5	2.00	18.7	19.0	0.15	0.17	0.09	91

TABLE 1. SPIRAL INDUCTOR PARAMETERS

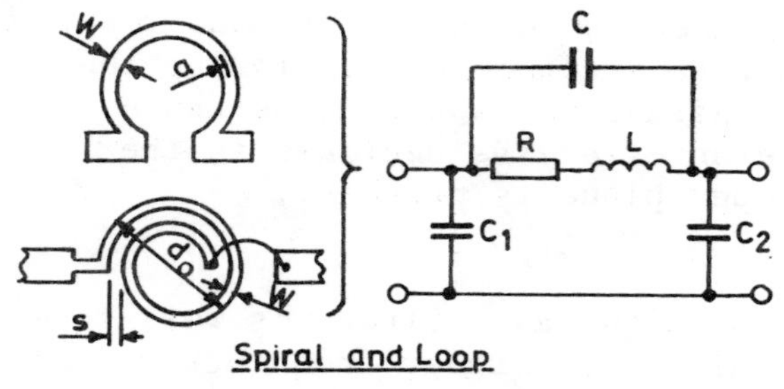

Spiral and Loop

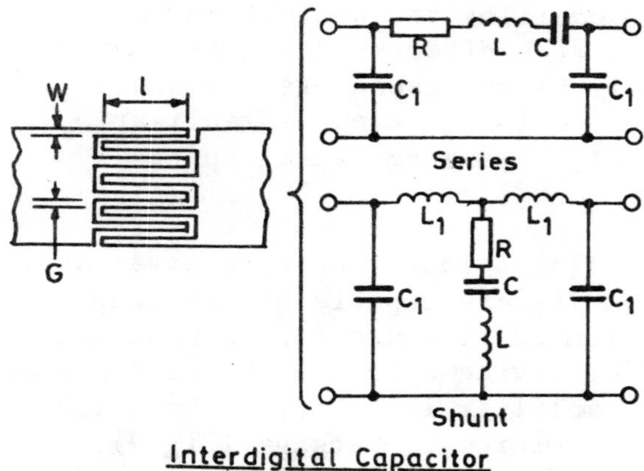

Interdigital Capacitor

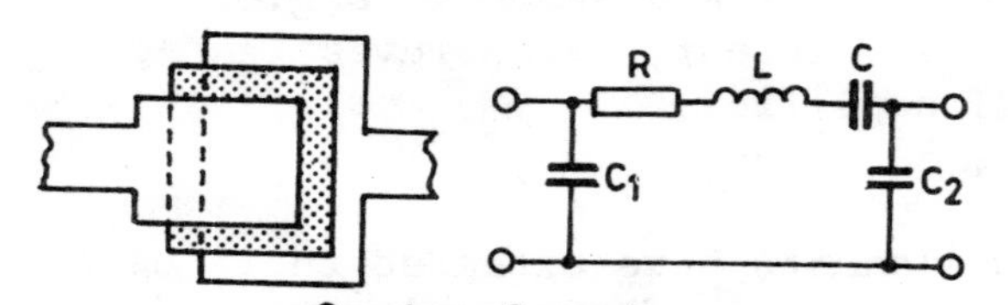

Overlay Capacitor

Fig.1 Printed Element Geometries

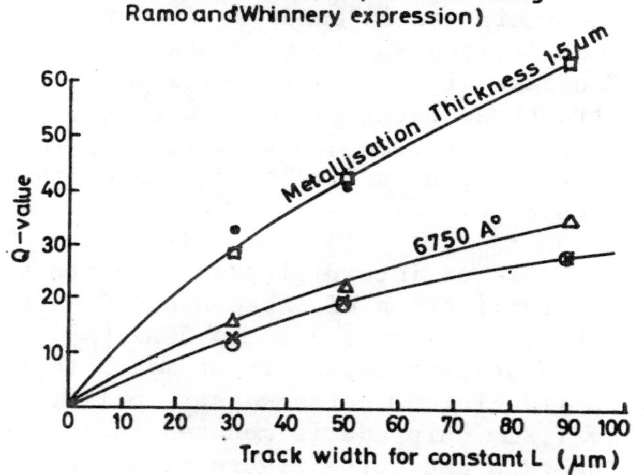

Fig.2 Variation in Q-factor of 1nH Loop Inductor with Track Width and Metallisation Thickness

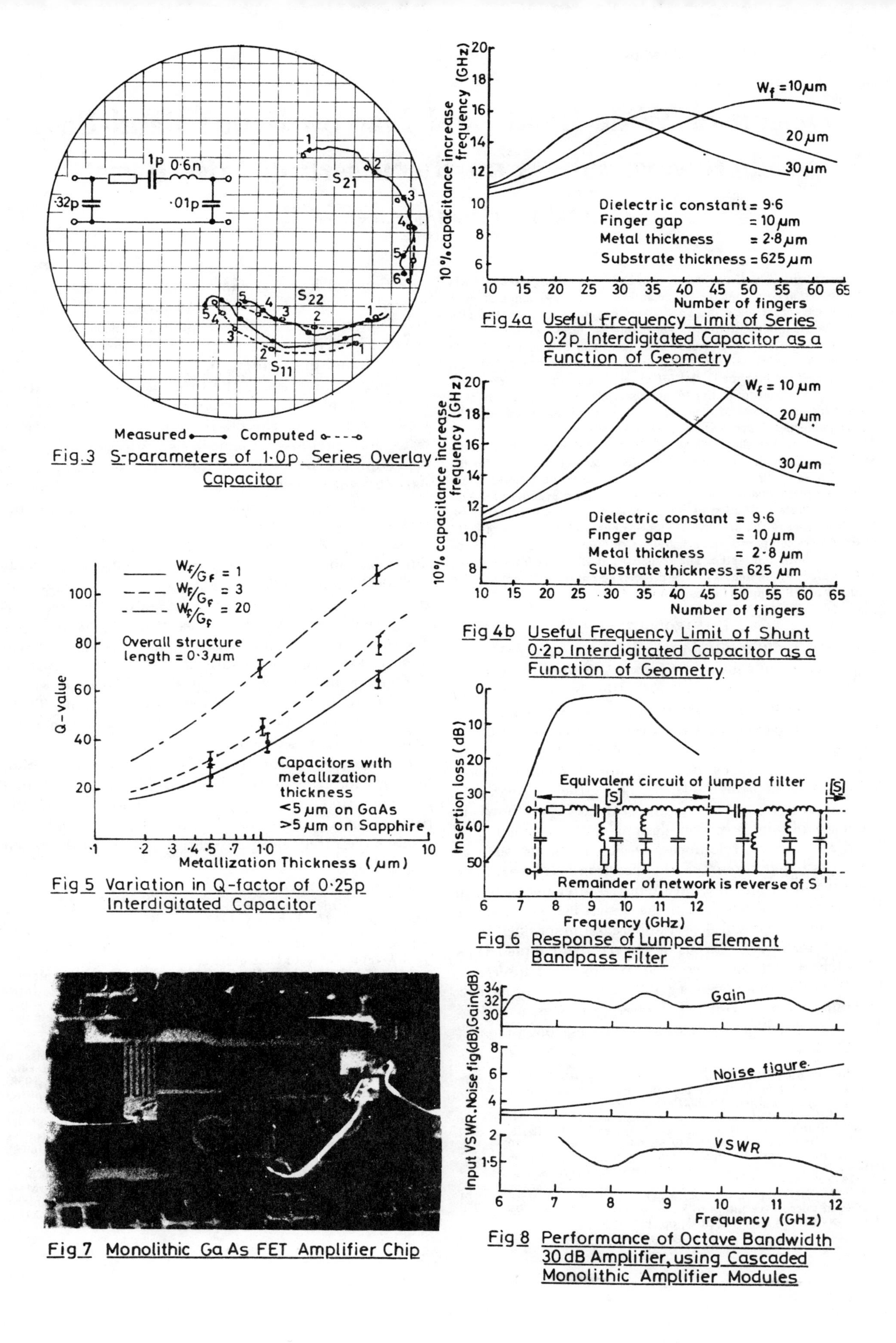

Fig 3 S-parameters of 1·0p Series Overlay Capacitor

Fig 4a Useful Frequency Limit of Series 0·2p Interdigitated Capacitor as a Function of Geometry

Fig 4b Useful Frequency Limit of Shunt 0·2p Interdigitated Capacitor as a Function of Geometry

Fig 5 Variation in Q-factor of 0·25p Interdigitated Capacitor

Fig 6 Response of Lumped Element Bandpass Filter

Fig 7 Monolithic Ga As FET Amplifier Chip

Fig 8 Performance of Octave Bandwidth 30 dB Amplifier, using Cascaded Monolithic Amplifier Modules

Design of Wide-Band (and Narrow-Band) Band-Pass Microwave Filters on the Insertion Loss Basis*

GEORGE L. MATTHAEI†, MEMBER, IRE

Summary—**A method for design of band-pass microwave filters is described that combines the image and insertion-loss points of view to give an approximate design method having simplicity, but also high precision. This method is applicable for filter designs ranging from narrow to very wide bandwidths (2 to 1 or more). The desired insertion loss characteristic is obtained by use of a lumped-element, Tchebycheff, or maximally flat (or other) low-pass prototype. With the aid of the concept of impedance inverters, the prototype is converted into a cascade of symmetrical (but differing) sections. The image properties of symmetrical sections of the band-pass microwave filter structure are then related to those of corresponding sections of the prototype. Straightforward design equations are given for filters using short-circuited or open-circuited stubs, and also for filters using parallel-coupled lines. Mapping functions are derived that permit accurate prediction of the microwave filter cutoff characteristic from that of the prototype. The responses of a number of filter designs were computed, and a Tchebycheff filter with a 2.2 to 1 bandwidth was built and tested. The responses of all of the filter designs were in close agreement with the prescribed characteristics, and the accuracy of the mapping functions was verified.**

I. Introduction

THE TYPES of band-pass filters to be treated in this paper are shown in Figs. 1–3. Filters using some of these structures have often been designed in the past using image design methods. Although these methods are conceptually simple, the over-all filter response to be expected is known only approximately, as a result of reflections at the terminating end sections. Thus, using such methods, it takes either a great deal of trial and error or a great deal of "know how" in order to obtain precision designs with specified pass band attenuation tolerances. Design methods, such as those discussed herein, on the insertion loss basis, have the advantage that the nature of the filter response can be specified at the outset of the design process, and the final filter design will closely adhere to the specifications.

The filter in Fig. 1(a) is of the parallel-coupled type for which Cohn[1] has presented approximate insertion-loss-basis design equations accurate for filters of narrow or moderate bandwidth; the filter form shown in Fig. 1(d) was previously treated by Jones[2] on an exact insertion-loss basis. It can be shown that exact design procedures using Richards' transformation[3] can be derived for all of these filters for either narrow or wide bandwidths. Examples of the use of these procedures will be found in the literature.[2,4–7] However, the paper by Jones,[2] which treats the form of filter in Fig. 1(d), is the only one of these references which deals specifically with any of the filters in Figs. 1(a) to 3 on an exact insertion-loss design basis. A serious practical disadvantage of exact methods for designing these particular filter structures is that the synthesis of special transfer functions is required[8] at the outset of the design process,[2] and, all in all, a great deal of computational labor is needed. Even though the design procedures described herein are computationally very simple and only approximate, the results, as the examples show, are satisfactory for most practical precision-design problems. Another advantage of the methods described herein is that they are quite flexible. As will be seen, the design procedure can be adapted to include changes in impedance level or special forms of structures, as required by special practical situations. These methods can also be used for other types of structures than those discussed herein.[9]

Easy-to-use approximate insertion-loss-basis design methods for band-pass microwave filters have existed for some time. However, these methods have in the past involved narrow-band approximations and as a result have rarely been accurate for bandwidths much

* Received by the PGMTT, May 8, 1960. This research was supported by the Signal Corps under Contract DA 36-039 SC-74862.

† Stanford Res. Inst., Menlo Park, Calif.

[1] S. B. Cohn, *et al.*, "Research on Design Criteria for Microwave Filters," Stanford Res. Inst., Menlo Park, Calif., Final Rept., SRI Project 1331, Contract DA 36-039 SC-64625, ch. 4; June, 1957. Also S. B. Cohn, "Parallel-coupled transmission line-resonator filters," IRE Trans. on Microwave Theory and Techniques, vol. MTT-6 pp. 223–231; April, 1958.

[2] *Ibid.* (SRI Rept.), ch. 3. Also, E. M. T. Jones, "Synthesis of wide-band microwave filters to have prescribed insertion loss," 1956 IRE Convention Record, pt. 5, pp. 119–128.

[3] P. I. Richards, "Resistor-transmission-line circuits," Proc. IRE, vol. 36, pp. 217–220; February, 1948.

[4] H. Ozaki and J. Ishii, "Synthesis of transmission-line networks and the design of UHF filters," IRE Trans. on Circuit Theory, vol. CT-2, pp. 325–336; December, 1955.

[5] H. Ozaki and J. Ishii, "Synthesis of a class of strip-line filters," IRE Trans. on Circuit Theory, vol. CT-5, pp. 104–109; June, 1958.

[6] A. I. Grayzel, "A synthesis procedure for transmission line networks," IRE Trans. on Circuit Theory, vol. CT-5, pp. 172–181; September, 1958.

[7] N. R. Welsh and E. S. Kuh, "Synthesis of Resistor-Transmission Line Networks," Electronics Res. Lab., University of California, Berkeley, Rept. No. 74, ONR Contract N7-onr-29529; July 15, 1958.

[8] In general, whether or not special transfer functions are required depends on the location of the frequencies of infinite attenuation inherent in the desired filter structure. By choosing certain filter structures, the more common transfer functions can be used (see footnotes 5 and 6). Such structures, however, may not always be the most convenient to fabricate.

[9] For example, the case of filters consisting of transmission lines coupled by series capacitors was treated in the report: G. L. Matthaei, "Research on Design Criteria for Microwave Filters," Stanford Res. Inst., Menlo Park, Calif., Tech. Rept. 6, SRI Project 2326, Contract DA 36-039 SC-74862; May, 1959.

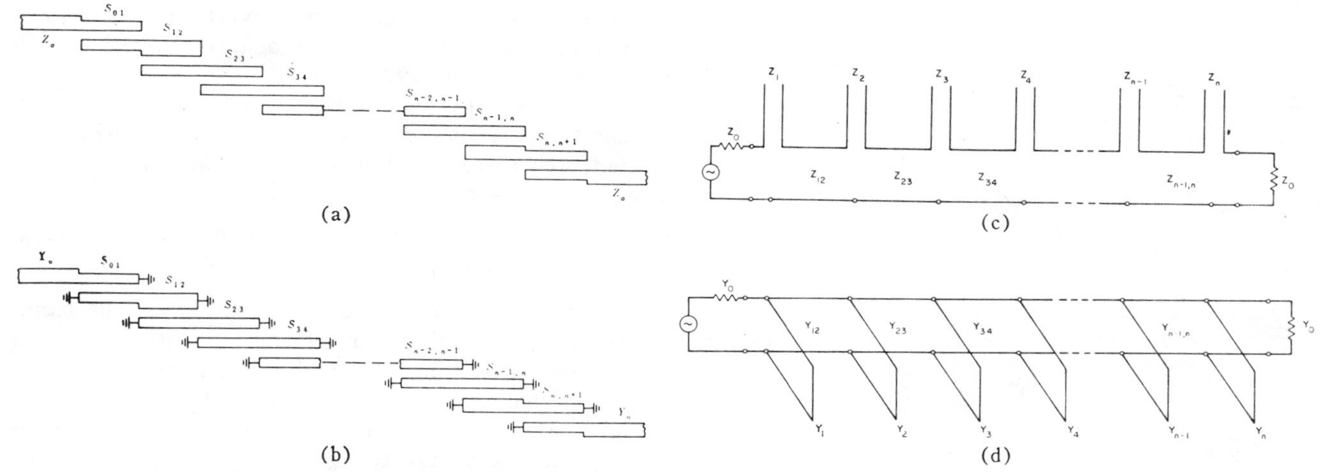

Fig. 1—(a) Parallel-coupled, strip-transmission-line filter with open-circuited sections. Each section is one-quarter wavelength long where the reference wavelength is that at the midband frequency, ω_0. Each section $S_{k,k+1}$ is characterized by even and odd mode impedances $(Z_{oe})_{k,k+1}$ and $(Z_{oo})_{k,k+1}$, respectively.[1,11,16] (b) Parallel-coupled, strip-transmission-line filter with short-circuited sections. This filter is the dual of that in (a). Each section $S_{k,k+1}$ is one-quarter wavelength long where the reference wavelength is the propagation wavelength at the midband frequency, ω_0. Each section $S_{k,k+1}$ is characterized by even and odd mode admittances $(Y_{oe})_{k,k+1}$ and $(Y_{oo})_{k,k+1}$, respectively.[11,16] (c) Band-pass filter using quarter-wavelength series stubs and quarter-wavelength connecting lines. Filters of the form in (a) can always be converted to this form. (d) Band-pass filter using quarter-wavelength shunt stubs and quarter-wavelength connecting lines. This filter is the dual of that in (c). The reference wavelength is the propagation wavelength at the midband frequency, ω_0.

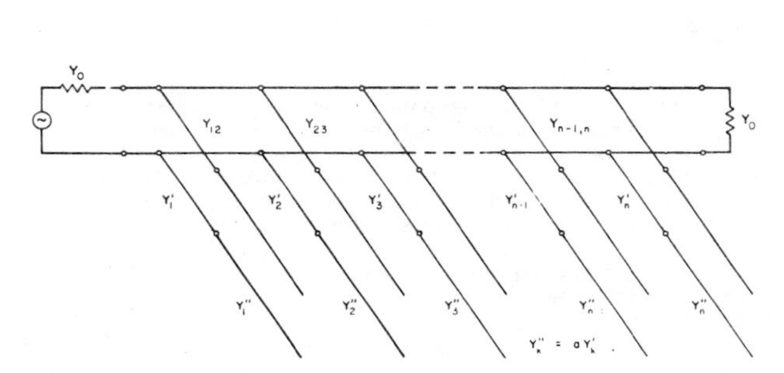

Fig. 2—Band-pass filter with half-wavelength shunt stubs and quarter-wavelength connecting lines. The reference wavelength is the propagation wavelength at the midband frequency, ω_0.

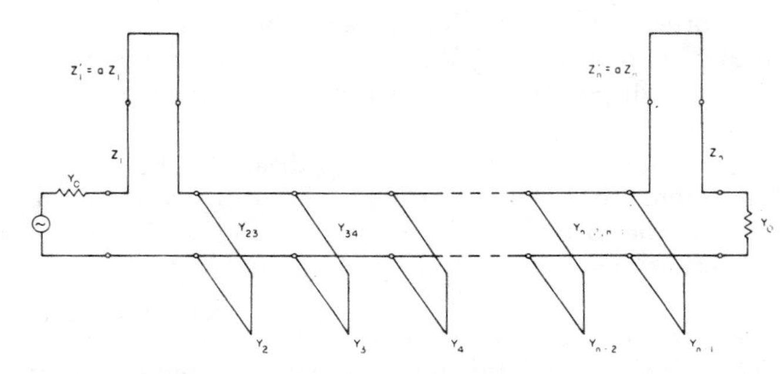

Fig. 3—Band-pass filter with quarter-wavelength shunt stubs, quarter-wavelength connecting lines, and half-wavelength series stubs at the ends. The reference wavelength is that at the midband frequency, ω_0.

over 20 per cent. The design approach used herein has the advantage that it does not involve approximations of a narrow-band sort; hence, it gives good accuracy for narrow bandwidths on out to bandwidths of 2 to 1 or more.

In Section II, the use of the design equations and the results of design examples will be discussed. To make routine use of the design equations more convenient, their derivation will be treated separately in Section III.

II. Practical Application of the Design Equations

A. Equivalence of the Networks in Figs. 1(a)–(d)

The filter in Fig. 1(b) is simply the dual of that in Fig. 1(a). It can be obtained directly from the circuit in Fig. 1(a) by replacing the open circuits by short circuits and by replacing each even- or odd-mode impedance, $(Z_{oe})_{k,k+1}$ and $(Z_{oo})_{k,k+1}$, respectively, by corresponding *odd-* and *even-mode* admittances.

$$(Y_{oo})_{k,k+1} = Y_0^2 (Z_{oe})_{k,k+1},$$
$$(Y_{oe})_{k,k+1} = Y_0^2 (Z_{oo})_{k,k+1}, \tag{1}$$

where $Y_0 = 1/Z_0$ is the characteristic admittance of the input and output lines. By use of the equivalences shown in Fig. 4,[10,11] it is seen that the circuit in Fig. 1(c) is

[10] The correctness of these equivalences can be verified with the aid of the impedance and admittance matrices for parallel-coupled strips given by Jones and Bolljahn (see footnote 11) or by using Richards' viewpoint to map the elements in Equivalent Circuits (5) and (6) of Table II of Ozaki and Ishii's work (see footnote 5) into the corresponding transmission line form.

[11] Cohn, *et al.*, *op. cit.*, (SRI Rept.), ch. 4. Also, E. M. T. Jones and J. T. Bolljahn, "Coupled-strip-transmission-line filters and directional couplers," IRE Trans. on Microwave Theory and Techniques, vol. MTT-4, pp. 75–81; April, 1956.

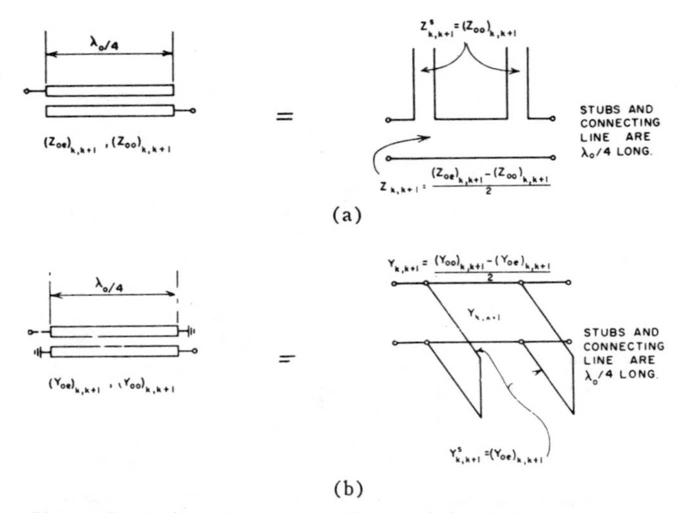

Fig. 4—Equivalence between parallel-coupled strip-line sections and sections consisting of stubs with connecting lines.

exactly equivalent to that in Fig. 1(a), while the circuit in Fig. 1(d) is exactly equivalent to that in Fig. 1(b). Thus, any of these four circuits can be derived from any other, by use of duality and the equivalences in Fig. 4; and when derived from one another in this manner, all will yield exactly the same transmission characteristic.

For simplicity, the design equations applicable for these four filter structures (Fig. 1) will be expressed in the specific form for the structure in Fig. 1(a). Any of the other forms may then be obtained by duality and Fig. 4. In converting from the form in Fig. 1(a) to the form in Fig. 1(d), for example, it should be noted that the characteristic admittance of the shunt stub at each end is determined solely by the end sections of the filter in Fig. 1(a); however, the characteristic admittance of each of the shunt stubs in the interior of the filter in Fig. 1(d) is determined by the corresponding two adjacent sections in Fig. 1(a) so that

$$\begin{aligned} Y_k &= Y^s_{k-1,k} + Y^s_{k,k+1} \\ &= Y_0^2[Z^s_{k-1,k} + Z^s_{k,k+1}] \\ &= Y_0^2[(Z_{oo})_{k-1,k} + (Z_{oo})_{k,k+1}], \end{aligned} \tag{2}$$

where $Y_0 = 1/Z_0$ is again the characteristic admittance of the input and output lines, and the $Y_{k,k+1}{}^s$ and $Z_{k,k+1}{}^s$ are defined in Fig. 4. It is helpful to note that in the case of Fig. 1(d), the characteristic admittances of the connecting lines are given by

$$Y_{k,k+1} = Y_0^2\left[\frac{(Z_{oe})_{k,k+1} - (Z_{oo})_{k,k+1}}{2}\right] = Y_0^2 K_{k,k+1}, \tag{3}$$

where the $K_{k,k+1}$ are impedance inverter parameters to be discussed later. (They are defined numerically in Tables I and II, p. 592.)

The filter structures in Figs. 2 and 3 are not equivalent to those in Fig. 1; however, they are closely related structures which can readily be treated using many of the same concepts and equations.

B. Use of Mapping Functions, and Selection of Appropriate Lumped-Element Prototypes

In the design procedure described herein, the band-pass microwave filter derives characteristic properties of its response from a lumped-element prototype filter having analogous low-pass filter response properties. Fig. 5 shows a typical low-pass prototype and defines the prototype parameters $g_0, g_1 \cdots, g_n, g_{n+1}$. The design equations in Tables I–III (p. 592) assume that the prototype filter is either symmetric or antimetric[12]—a condition satisfied by the common maximally flat or Tchebycheff lossless filter designs (which have one or more frequencies at which zero reflection occurs).

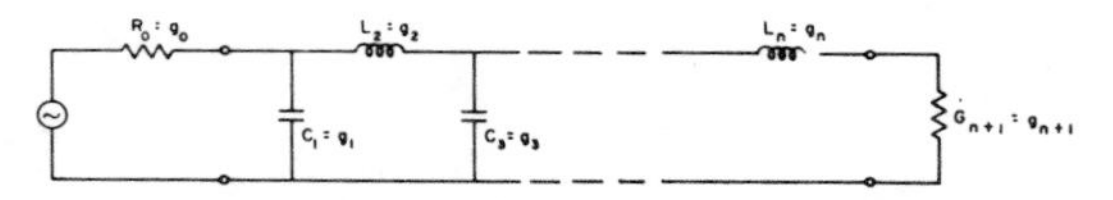

Fig. 5—Definition of the low-pass prototype parameters $g_0, g_1, \cdots, g_n, g_{n+1}$. The symmetry about the middle of the filter indicated in the equations of Tables I–III results from the use of symmetric or antimetric prototypes. The common maximally flat or Tchebycheff prototypes, which have one or more frequencies where zero reflection occurs, always satisfy this symmetry or antimetry condition.

A typical low-pass prototype is shown. The dual of this circuit would also be satisfactory.

$g_k|_{k=1 \text{ to } n}$ = The inductance of a series coil, or the capacitance of a shunt capacitor.

g_0 = The generator resistance R_0 if $g_1 = C_1$, but is defined as the generator conductance G_0 if $g_1 = L_1$.

g_{n+1} = The load resistance R_{n+1} if $g_n = C_n$, but is defined as the load conductance G_{n+1} if $g_n = L_n$.

Note: An additional prototype parameter ω_1' is defined in Figs. 6 and 7.

Weinberg[13] and Technical Report 4 of this project[14] give tables of element values for such filters. (Weinberg[13] also includes tables for filters which are not symmetric or antimetric.) The use of symmetric or antimetric prototypes along with equal terminations in the final microwave filter (as depicted in Figs. 1–3) is usually desirable, and so has been made implicit in the equations in Tables I–III. However, these conditions are not

[12] E. A. Guillemin, "Synthesis of Passive Networks," John Wiley and Sons, Inc., New York, N. Y., p. 371; 1957.

[13] L. Weinberg, "Network Design by Use of Modern Synthesis Techniques and Tables," Res. Labs., Hughes Aircraft Co., Culver City, Calif., Tech. Memo. 427; April, 1956. Also, in *Proc. NEC*, vol. 12; 1956.

[14] W. J. Getsinger, *et al.*, "Research on Design Criteria for Microwave Filters," Stanford Res. Inst., Menlo Park, Calif., Tech. Rept. 4, SRI Project 2326, Contract DA 36–039 SC-74862; December, 1958.

necessary, and equations for other cases may be derived by the theory in Section III.

Fig. 6 shows a typical lossless low-pass-filter maximally flat response along with the equation for this response. The frequency ω_1' establishes the pass-band edge, while A_m is the db attenuation which is permissible within the pass band. The frequency ω_a' is a frequency at which a stated attenuation, A_a db, is required. An analogous maximally flat band-pass response, such as might be obtained by the filters in Fig. 1, is also shown. Note that this response has arithmetic symmetry about ω_0, so that the essential parameters of the respone may be specified simply as ω_1/ω_0, A_m, A_a, and ω_a/ω_0. The response of the band-pass filter may be predicted directly from that of the low-pass filter by mapping the ω' frequency scale of the low-pass filter to the ω frequency scale of the band-pass filter, as indicated in the figure. For the circuits in Fig. 1, and the design equations in Tables I and II, the proper function $F_n(\omega/\omega_0)$ to use is

$$F_n\left(\frac{\omega}{\omega_0}\right) = \frac{-\cos\left(\frac{\pi}{2}\ \frac{\omega}{\omega_0}\right)}{\sqrt[n]{\left|\sin\left(\frac{\pi\omega}{2\omega_0}\right)\right|}}. \tag{4a}$$

For narrow or moderate bandwidths, the simpler function

$$F_n\left(\frac{\omega}{\omega_0}\right) = \left(\frac{\omega}{\omega_0} - 1\right) \tag{4b}$$

will also give good accuracy.[1] As will be shown, the accuracy of (4b) is fair even for wide bandwidths. For the circuit in Fig. 3 and the equations in Table III, the proper function to use is

$$F_n\left(\frac{\omega}{\omega_0}\right) = \frac{-\cos\left(\frac{\pi\omega}{2\omega_0}\right)}{\sqrt[n]{\left|\sin\left(\frac{\pi\omega}{2\omega_0}\right)\right|\left[\sin\left(\frac{\pi}{2}\ \frac{(\omega-\omega_\infty)}{(\omega_0)}\right)\right]^2\left[\sin\ \frac{\pi}{2}\left(\frac{(\omega-2\omega_0+\omega_\infty)}{(\omega_0)}\right)\right]^2}}, \tag{5}$$

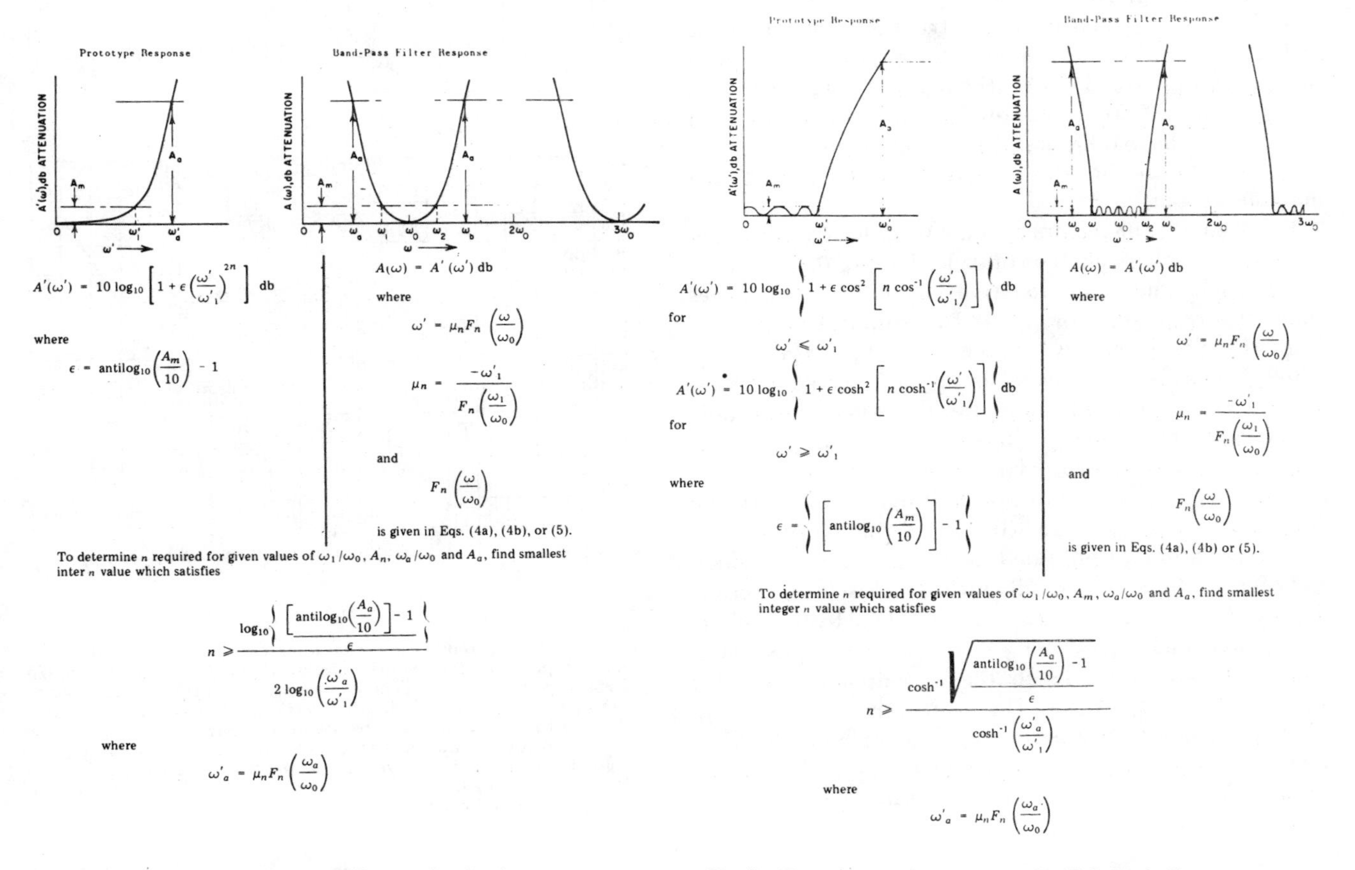

Fig. 6—Equations and parameters for maximally flat response.

Fig. 7—Equations and parameters for Tchebycheff response.

where ω_∞ is a frequency of infinite attenuation, to be specified. An accurate general mapping for the circuit in Fig. 2 has not been determined.

Fig. 7 shows corresponding curves and equations for the case of filters having Tchebycheff responses. Since the choice of mappings is determined by the type of filter structure, rather than by the type of response, the functions in (4) and (5) apply as before. For both the maximally flat and Tchebycheff cases, the number of reactive elements n required in the low-pass prototype is fixed by the parameters ω_1/ω_0, A_m, ω_a/ω_0, and A_a. In Figs. 6 and 7, equations are given for solving for n in terms of these parameters. Since the $F_n(\omega_a/\omega_0)$ in (4a) and (5) are also functions of n, one must estimate a value of n to use in these functions, solve for n to get an improved value, and then repeat the process. However, since the $F_n(\omega_a/\omega_0)$ are only weak functions of n, the process will converge very quickly. In the case of (4a) and (4b), the latter equation may be easily used to obtain n accurately for narrow-band cases, and this equation will also give a fairly accurate value of n in wide-band cases. In wide-band cases, the value of n obtained using (4b) can be inserted in (4a), and the equation for n can then be used again to obtain a more accurate verification of the n value.

C. A Design Procedure Especially Suited to Filters Realized in the Forms in Fig. 1(a) and (b)

Table I summarizes a design procedure which gives good impedance levels for filter structures such as those in Fig. 1(a) and (b). After an appropriate prototype is selected, as described above, the parameters g_0, g_1, $\cdots$, g_n, g_{n+1}, and ω_1' from the low-pass prototype are used along with the band-pass-filter lower-band-edge ratio, ω_1/ω_0, to obtain the filter design in a straightforward manner as outlined.

Fig. 8 shows the results of some trial designs obtained by using a Tchebycheff prototype having 0.10-db pass band ripple and $n=6$ reactive elements. The curves show the response, computed by a digital computer, from the circuit element values. For Fig. 8(a), $\omega_1/\omega_0 = 0.975$ was used, which calls for a 5 per cent bandwidth. As is seen from the figure, there is no noticeable deviation from the design objective, and points mapped from the low-pass prototype response by use of (4a) and also by (4b) are all in excellent agreement with the computed response. Fig. 8(b) shows the computed response for a design obtained using $\omega_1/\omega_0=0.850$, which calls for a 30 per cent bandwidth. In this case, there is a very slight deviation from perfect Tchebycheff character, inasmuch as two of the peaks of the pass band ripples do not quite reach the 0.10-db level. In this case, points mapped from the prototype response using (4a) are in practically perfect agreement with the filter response, while points mapped using (4b) show some noticeable error at the higher attenuation levels.

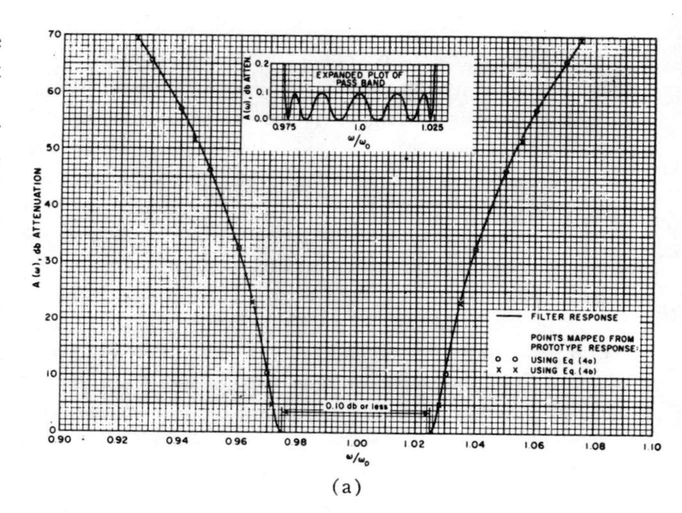

(a)

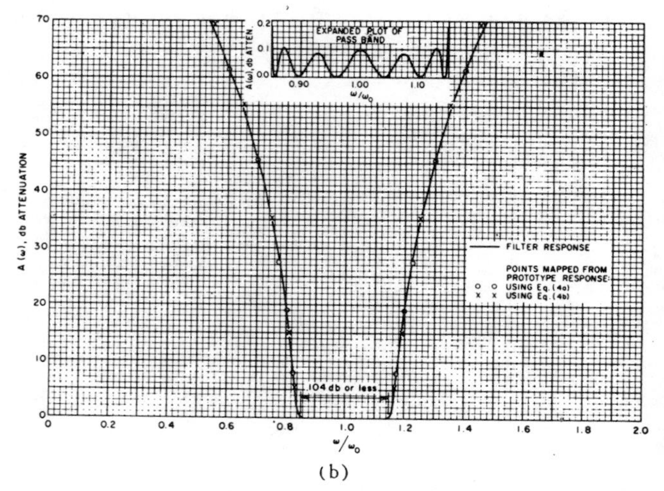

(b)

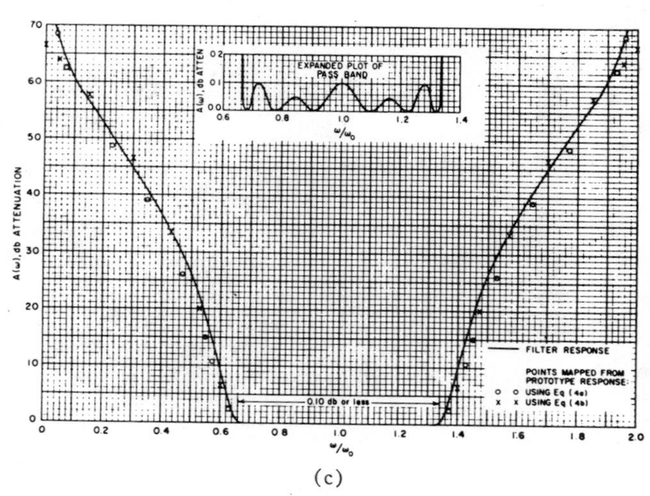

(c)

Fig. 8—(a) Computed response of filter designed as in Table I to have 5 per cent bandwidth. Design value for ω_1/ω_0 was 0.975. Prototype had 0.10-db Tchebycheff pass band ripple with $n=6$ reactive elements). (b) Computed response of filter designed as in Table I to have 30 per cent bandwidth. Design value of ω_1/ω_0 was 0.850. Prototype same as (a). (c) Computed response of filter designed as in Table 1 to have approximately 2 to 1 bandwidth. Design value for ω_1/ω_0 was 0.650, which calls for $\omega_2/\omega_1=2.077$. Prototype same as for (a).

Fig. 8(c) shows the computed response for a design obtained using $\omega_1/\omega_0 = 0.650$, which calls for a band-edge ratio of $\omega_2/\omega_1 = 2.077$. In this case, the deviation from a perfect response is more noticeable, the most important deviation being that the frequency ratio of the 0.10-db band-edge points is about $\omega_2/\omega_1 = 1.96$, instead of 2.077. All of the expected pass band ripples are present, although in this case two of the ripple peaks are reduced to half size. Points mapped from the prototype response by use of (4a) appear to fall almost exactly where the response curve would have been if the slight shrinkage in the pass band width had not occurred. Points mapped by use of (4b) weave across the computed response somewhat, but follow it surprisingly closely.

Table IV (p. 593) gives the odd- and even-mode impedances[11] for these filters realized in the form in Fig. 1(a). Using construction methods to be outlined later, all three of these designs should be quite practical. Filters designed by use of Table I and realized in the form in Fig. 1(a) or (b), are of special practical interest for applications where bandwidths of perhaps 50 per cent or less are desired. Although the forms in Fig. 1(a) and (b) are also practical for larger bandwidths, filters designed by Table II and realized in the form in Fig. 1(d) will have reasonable element values for large bandwidth designs and become attractive because they require two less sections to achieve a given response.

A corresponding filter designed by Cohn's equations[1] was compared with the 5 per cent bandwidth filter described herein, in order to compare the two design methods. The designs were found to be basically similar, except that Cohn's equations yielded slightly different end sections and a 7 per cent higher impedance level in the interior sections of the filter. For filters of about 10 per cent bandwidth or less, either method should give good designs, but Cohn's design method has an advantage of being computationally even simpler than that described herein. For bandwidths greater than about 10 or 15 per cent, the accuracy of Cohn's equations begins to deteriorate noticeably and the design equations described herein are preferable.

D. A Design Procedure Especially Suited to Filters Realized in the Forms in Figs. 1(c) and (d)

In the design procedure of Table I, the end sections S_{01} and $S_{n,n+1}$ are, in a sense, primarily impedance-transforming sections. Using that design procedure, moderate impedance levels are maintained in the interior sections of filters realized in the forms in Figs. 1(a) or (b), regardless of the bandwidth of the filter, but this is achieved by not making full use of all of the natural modes of oscillation of which the circuit is capable. Using the design procedure in Table II, the end sections S_{01} and $S_{n,n+1}$ are eliminated, and the remaining network makes full use of all possible natural modes. Table II is thus seen to call for $n-1$ band-pass filter sections to realize a response mapped from an n-reactive-element prototype, while the design method in Table I calls for $n+1$ band-pass filter sections to achieve the same response. Designs obtained by Table II will usually yield impractical impedance levels for filters of the forms in Fig. 1(a) and (b), but the impedance levels are moderate for wide-band filters of the forms in Fig. 1(c) and (d). The form in Fig. 1(d), which is quite practical for wide-band designs, becomes less practical for narrow-band designs since the characteristic admittances of the shunt stubs then become quite large.

Fig. 9 shows the response of a filter designed using Table II from a 0.10-db ripple, $n=8$, Tchebycheff prototype with $\omega_1/\omega_0 = 0.650$. Table V (p. 593) shows the element values for a realization as in Fig. 1(d). In this case, the pass band ripples are more uneven than in the previous examples; however, the bandwidth suffered less shrinkage than in the previous 2 to 1 bandwidth design, whose response was shown in Fig. 8(c). In both the case of Fig. 8(c) and the case of Fig. 9, the filter has seven sections; however, it should be noted that the latter response has a steeper cutoff, since it was designed from an $n=8$ instead of an $n=6$ prototype. It is thus seen that points mapped from the prototype response by use of (4a) are again quite accurate, but those using (4b) show appreciable error at high attenuation levels.

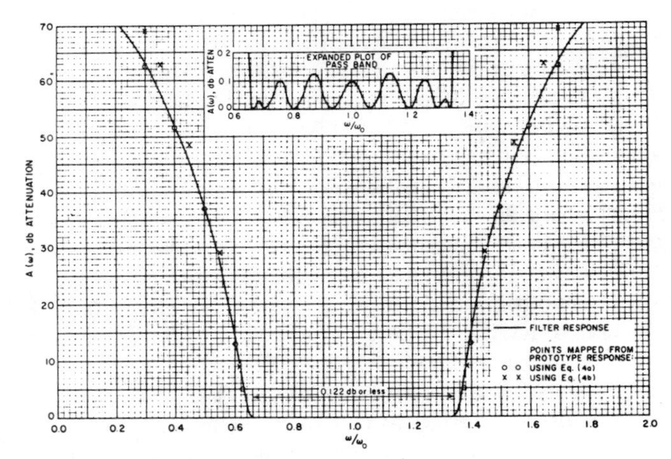

Fig. 9—Computed response of a filter designed as in Table II to have approximately 2 to 1 bandwidth. Design value for ω_1/ω_0 was 0.650. Prototype had 0.10-db Tchebycheff pass band ripple with $n=8$ reactive elements.

If filters in the form of Fig. 1(c) or 1(d) are desired, but with a somewhat different impedance level for their interior sections, they can be achieved by using a modified form of the calculation procedure in Table III, as is described in Section III-D.

E. Design of Filters in the Form in Fig. 2

Filters of the form shown in Fig. 2 can be readily designed by a modified use of Table II. The design is carried out to first give a filter in the form in Fig. 1(d), with the desired pass band characteristic and bandwidth. Then each shunt, quarter-wavelength,[15] short-circuited stub of characteristic admittance Y_k is replaced, as shown in Fig. 2, by a shunt, half-wavelength, open-circuited stub having an inner quarter-wavelength portion with a characteristic admittance,

$$Y_k' = \frac{Y_k(a \tan^2 \theta_1 - 1)}{(a + 1) \tan^2 \theta_1}, \tag{6}$$

and an outer quarter-wavelength portion with a characteristic admittance,

$$Y_k'' = aY_k'. \tag{7}$$

The parameter a is fixed by

$$a = \cot^2 \left(\frac{\pi \omega_\infty}{2\omega_0} \right) \Bigg|_{(\omega_\infty/\omega_0)<(\omega_1/\omega_0)}, \tag{8}$$

where $\theta_1 = \pi\omega_1/2\omega_0$, and ω_∞ is a frequency at which the shunt lines present short circuits to the main line and cause infinite attenuation. The principle upon which the above substitution is made is that (6) to (8) are constrained to yield half-wavelength open-circuited stubs, which have exactly the same susceptance at the band-edge frequency ω_1, as did the quarter-wavelength short-circuited stubs that they replace, while both kinds of stubs have zero admittance at ω_0.

To test out this procedure, a filter was designed as in Table II to give 30 per cent bandwidth ($\omega_1/\omega_0 = 0.850$) using a 0.10-db Tchebycheff prototype with $n = 8$. Then, choosing $\omega_\infty/\omega_0 = 0.500$, which gives $a = 1$, the quarter-wavelength stubs were replaced by half-wavelength stubs as described above, and the resulting computed response is shown in Fig. 10. Note that the pass band is almost exactly as prescribed, and that there are low attenuation regions in the vicinity of $\omega = 0$ and $\omega = 2\omega_0$, which are to be expected. The element values for this filter are shown in Table VI (p. 593).

The 2 to 1 bandwidth filter design (Fig. 9 and Table V) was also converted to this form using $\omega_\infty/\omega_0 = 0.500$, and its response was computed. The features of the pass band looked much the same as those in the expanded plot in Fig. 9, while the stop bands consisted of very sharp attenuation spikes surrounding $\omega/\omega_0 = 0.500$, in a manner similar to that in Fig. 10, except that the attenuation bands were much narrower.

Filters of the form in Fig. 2 should be particularly useful where the pass bands around $\omega = 0$ and $\omega = 2\omega_0$ are not objectionable, and where there is a relatively narrow band of signals to be rejected. By the proper choice of ω_∞, the infinite attenuation point can be placed so as to give maximum effectiveness against the

[15] The reference wavelength is that at the mid-band frequency ω_0

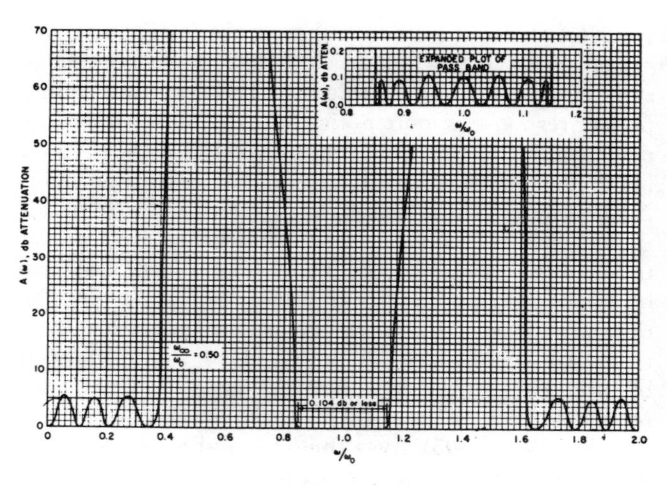

Fig. 10—Computed response of a 30 per cent band-pass filter designed in the form in Fig. 2. Design value for $\omega_1/\omega_0 = 0.850$. Prototype had 0.10-db Tchebycheff ripple with $n = 8$ reactive elements.

unwanted signals. Filters of the form in Fig. 2 are more practical for narrower bandwidths than are those in the form in Fig. 1(d), because of the larger susceptance slope of half-wavelength stubs for a given characteristic admittance. For example, in the case of Fig. 10, the shunt stubs for this filter as shown in Fig. 2 have characteristic admittances $Y_k' = Y_k''$, which are 0.471 times the characteristic admittances of the shunt stubs of the analogous filter in the form in Fig. 1(d), from which it was designed. Thus narrower bandwidths can be achieved without having the characteristic admittances of the shunt stubs become excessive.

F. Design of Filters in the Form in Fig. 3

For filters of the form in Fig. 3, the mapping function in (5) should be used along with the equations in Table III. In this case ω_∞ is the frequency of infinite attenuation created by the half-wavelength series stubs at the ends. The parameter d may be chosen to adjust the impedances of the interior of the filter to a convenient level.

This type of filter gives a cross between the type of response obtained using a filter as in Fig. 1(d), and that obtained by a filter as in Fig. 2. At first, a design of the form in Fig. 1(d) was tried, but with the end stubs (only) replaced with shunt half-wavelength open-circuited stubs. This gave infinite attenuation at $\omega = 0$ and ω_∞ as expected, but yielded a point of very low attenuation (around 10 db) between these two frequencies (and between other corresponding frequencies). It was then found that by using an altered design procedure which yields series half-wavelength short-circuited stubs at the ends, the desired type of response could be obtained without excessive drop in attenuation between $\omega = 0$ and ω_∞.

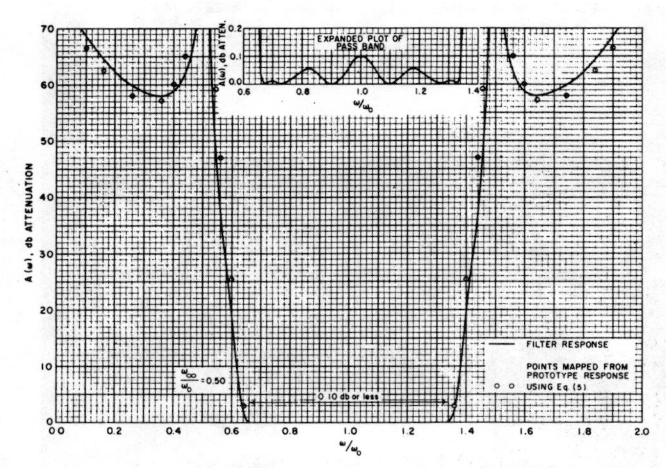

Fig. 11—Computed response of a filter as in Fig. 3, with approximately 2 to 1 bandwidth. Design value for ω_1/ω_0 was 0.650. Prototype had 0.10-db Tchebycheff ripple with $n=8$ reactive elements. Parameters d and ω_∞/ω_0 were both chosen as 0.500.

Fig. 11 shows the computed response of a filter designed using Table III to give approximately 2 to 1 bandwidth. The prototype, again, had 0.10-db Tchebycheff ripple, and $n=8$. The remaining design parameters were $\omega_1/\omega_0=0.650$, $\omega_\infty/\omega_0=0.500$, and $d=0.500$. In this case the pass band ripples are not as well developed as in the previous examples. It has been found that the design theory used herein works best if all of the sections are of the same basic form; since the end sections are different from the other sections in this case, the larger deviation from a 0.10-db equal-ripple response is not surprising. (From a practical standpoint, this deviation may be good, since the ripples are small at the band edges, where incidental dissipation will tend to increase the pass band loss most.) Points mapped from the prototype response using (5) are seen to come fairly close to the computed response, although not as close as (4a) did where it was applicable. Both (4a) and (5) were derived on the same basis and should probably yield similar accuracy. The larger deviations in this case are probably due at least in part to the fact that the pass band response itself deviates more from the design objective. The element values for this filter design are given in Table VII (p. 593).

G. Suggested Ways for Fabricating the Filters Under Consideration

For bandwidths of perhaps around 20 per cent or less, filters of the form in Fig. 1(a) are readily realized in printed-circuit form by use of Cohn's data for zero-thickness parallel-coupled strips.[1,16] Larger bandwidths are difficult using this construction, because the gaps between the conductors must become extremely small. A suggested way for getting around this problem while still using printed circuit construction is shown in Fig. 12. Instead of just two slabs of dielectric, four slabs are used, two of which are relatively thin. Then alternate conductors are printed to form a double layer, as shown in the cross-sectional view, so that the adjacent conductors can be interleaved. This gives a relatively large odd-mode capacitance without the need for extremely close spacings. The cross section of the conductors is no longer balanced geometrically; however, by proper design, the even- and odd-mode impedances for both the single- and double-layer conductors can be made the same.

Fig. 13 shows a suggested way for realizing filters of the type in Fig. 1(b). In this case, the conductors are rectangular bars supported mechanically by the short circuits at their ends. This construction can be used for either narrow- or wide-band filters and has the advantages of not requiring dielectric material (hence having no dielectric loss), and, with rounded corners on the conductors, of having relatively high power-handling capability.

Fig. 14(a) shows a possible way for building filters of the type in Fig. 1(d). This filter uses mostly double stubs instead of single stubs, so that the cross-sectional dimensions of the stubs (and the junction discontinuities) can be made smaller. It was designed in thick bar strip-line construction, in order to reduce the junction discontinuity effects and to make these effects less frequency-sensitive.[17] This filter was designed for a 2.2 to 1 bandwidth from a 0.10-db Tchebycheff ripple ten-reactive-element prototype. Three additional sections identical with the middle sections of the $n=10$ design were added in order to increase the rate of cutoff. This gave a resulting design which is not quite the same as a true $n=13$, 0.10-db-ripple Tchebycheff design, but the difference is small. As can be seen from the measured results in Fig. 14(b), the response is close to the theoretical.

It has been observed that any of the types of filters in Figs. 1, 2, or 3 may have narrow spurious pass bands, at frequencies in the vicinity of $f=2f_0$, if there is deviation from perfect tuning in one part of a filter with respect to the rest of the filter. Since small deviations from perfect tuning are difficult to avoid, some measures should be taken to suppress these spurious pass bands if they are objectionable for the application

[16] S. B. Cohn, *et al.*, "Strip Transmission Lines and Components," Stanford Res. Inst., Menlo Park, Calif., Final Rept., SRI Project 1114, Contract DA-36-039 SC-63232, ch. 3; February, 1957. Also, S. B. Cohn, "Shielded coupled-strip transmission line," IRE Trans. on Microwave Theory and Techniques, vol. MTT-3, pp. 29–38; October, 1955.

[17] P. S. Carter, Jr., G. L. Matthaei, and W. J. Getsinger, "Design Criteria for Microwave Filters and Coupling Structures," Stanford Res. Inst., Menlo Park, Calif., Tech. Rept. 8, pt. 3, SRI Project 2326, Contract DA 36-039 SC-7462. This reference discusses reasons why this bar construction is expected to have less junction discontinuity effect than either thin strip transmission line or coaxial line construction of equivalent size. It also discusses other practical matters with respect to the design of this type of filter.

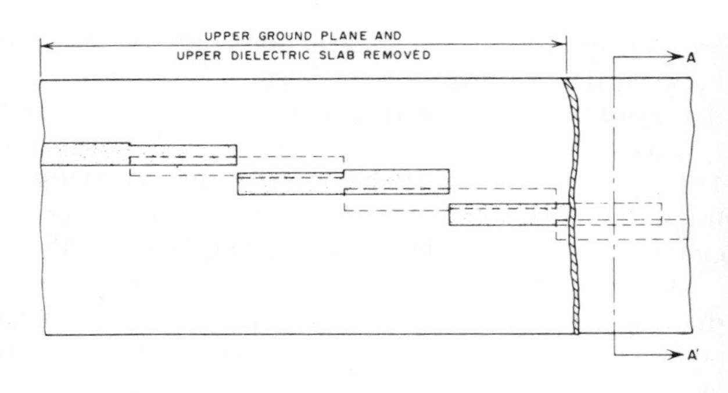

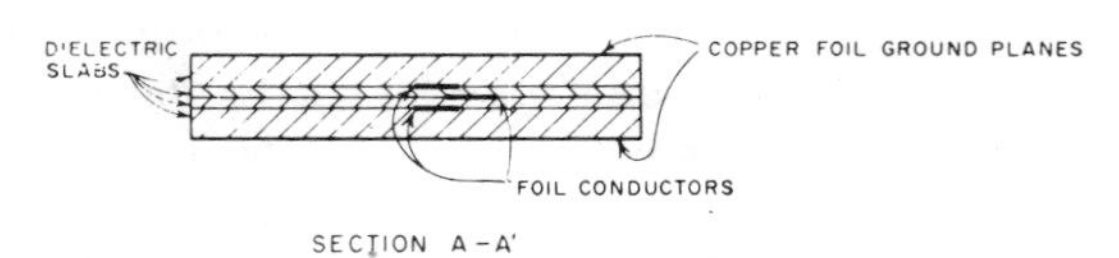

Fig. 12—Possible means for fabricating wide-band filters of the type in Fig. 1(a), using printed circuit techniques. (In order to achieve tight coupling with reasonably large conductor spacings, alternate conductor strips are made to be double so that conductor strips can be interleaved. This construction is electrically balanced with respect to the ground planes and will not excite ground plane modes, as would overlapped strips which did not interleave.)

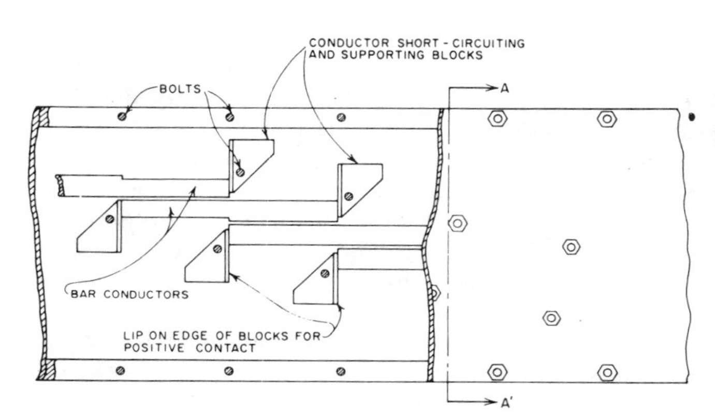

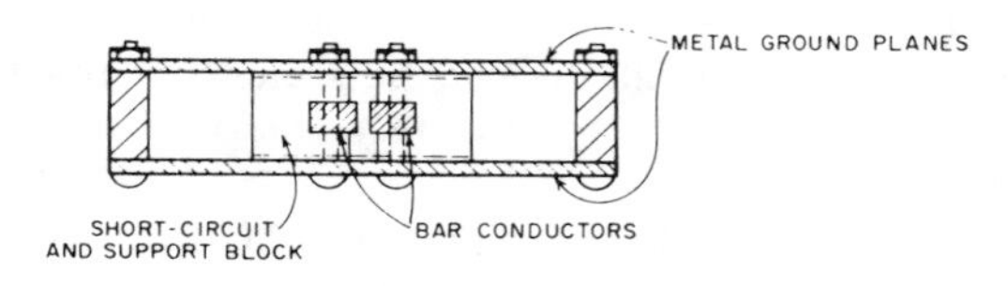

Fig. 13—Possible means for fabricating wide-band filters of the type in Fig. 1(b), in bar-transmission-line construction. (The short-circuiting blocks support the bar conductors so that no dielectric material is required.)

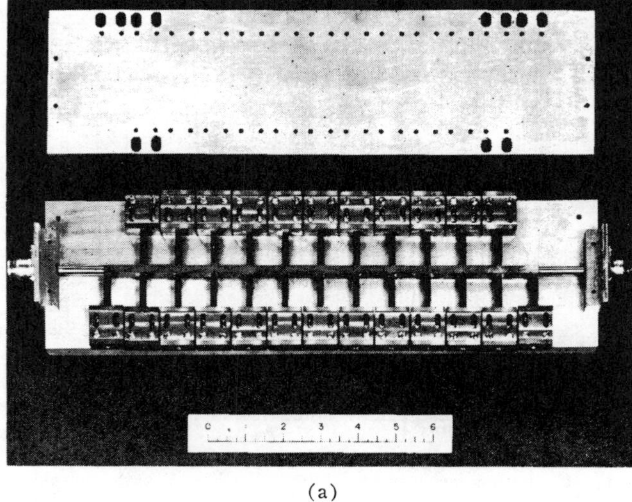

(a)

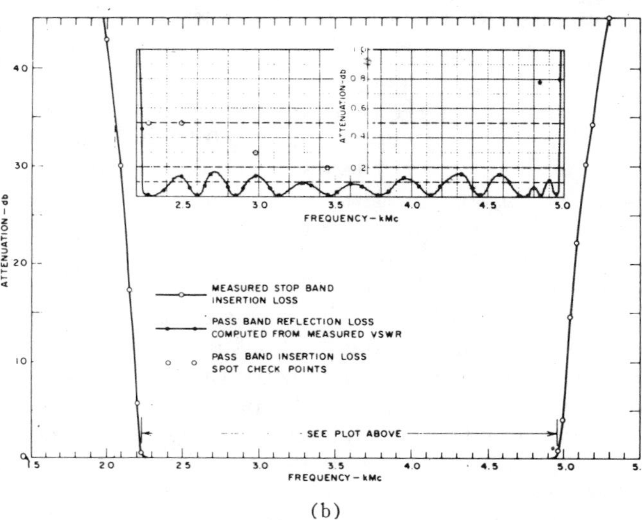

(b)

Fig. 14—(a) Filter of the type in Fig. 1(d) with cover plate removed. Rectangular bar strip transmission line construction is used. The blocks along the sides of the filter short circuit the stubs and support the center-conductor structure. (b) Measured response of the filter in Fig. 14(a). The dissipation loss can be reduced by silver plating since the filter as tested used a brass inner structure with aluminum cover plates.

at hand. A possible way of suppressing such responses is to use a filter of the form in Fig. 3, with $a=\infty$, so that the series stubs become open-circuited stubs one-quarter-wavelength long at f_0. Although this has not been tested as yet, it appears reasonable that series stubs of this sort can be used to maintain high attenuation in the vicinity of $2f_0$, since they present large series reactances at frequencies in the vicinity of $2f_0$, while the spurious responses in the shunt-stub portion of the filter are due to large shunt susceptances of opposite signs cancelling each other. Quarter-wavelength or half-wavelength series stubs, such as those in Fig. 3, can be realized as coaxial structures within the center conductor of the filter.[6]

III. Theoretical Basis for the Filter Equations and Mapping Functions

A. *Modified Prototypes as a Basis for Design*

The first step in deriving the design equations used herein is to convert the low-pass prototype (Fig. 5) to a modified form that involves impedance inverters or admittance inverters. The concept of impedance inverters has previously been discussed in detail by

Cohn;[18] admittance inverters are simply the dual representations of impedance inverters, and are introduced only for convenience. Fig. 15 summarizes the basic properties of these two types of inverters.

Using methods similar to those of Cohn,[18] any circuit like that in Fig. 5 may be converted into either of the dual forms in Fig. 16. In Fig. 16(a), which uses impedance inverters, all of the elements R_g, L_{a1}, L_{a2}, $\cdots$, L_{an}, R_L may be chosen arbitrarily; the inverter parameters $K_{k,k+1}$ are then computed as indicated.

Analogous conditions hold for the dual circuit at (b) in Fig. 16. In the discussion to follow, the impedance (or admittance) inverters will be assumed to be idealized so that their electrical behavior is exactly as indicated in Fig. 15. They will be used merely as an aid to mathematical reasoning, and no direct attempt will be made to find a circuit which approximates their idealized performance. Instead, as indicated below, the approximations will be based upon the impedance inverters plus part of each adjacent element.

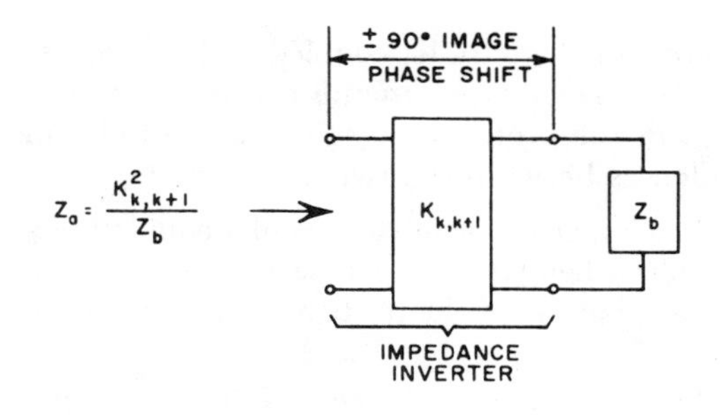

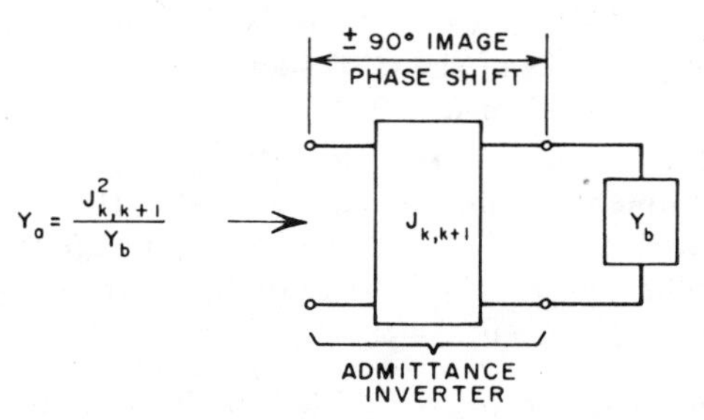

Fig. 15—Definition of impedance inverters and admittance inverters.

B. Procedure for Deriving the Equations in Table I

The design equations in Table I are based on the modified prototype shown at (a) in Fig. 16, while Fig. 17 shows the manner in which the element values are specified, and the manner in which the prototype is broken into sections. The image impedance, $Z^i_{k,k+1}(\omega')$, and phase, $\beta_{k,k+1}$ (in the pass band) for each of the prototype interior sections (S_{12}' to $S_{n-1,n}'$) are readily shown to be

$$Z^i_{k,k+1}(\omega') = K_{k,k+1}\sqrt{1 - \left(\frac{\omega'(L_a/2)}{K_{k,k+1}}\right)^2} \tag{9}$$

and

$$\beta_{k,k+1} = \Big|_{\omega' \leq (K_{k,k+1})/(L_a/2)} = \sin^{-1}\left[\frac{\omega'(L_a/2)}{K_{k,k+1}}\right] \pm \frac{\pi}{2}, \tag{10}$$

where, as before, ω_1' is the cutoff frequency for the low-pass prototype. The choice of $\pm\pi/2$ in (10) depends on whether the inverter is taken to have ± 90 degrees phase shift. The work of Jones and Bolljhan shows[11] that the image impedance and pass band image phase for a parallel-coupled section as shown in Fig. 4(a) are given by

$$Z_I = \frac{\sqrt{(Z_{oe} - Z_{oo})^2 + (Z_{oe} + Z_{oo})^2 \cos^2\theta}}{2 \sin\theta} \tag{11}$$

and

$$\beta = \cos^{-1}\left[\left(\frac{Z_{oe} + Z_{oo}}{Z_{oe} - Z_{oo}}\right)\cos\theta\right], \tag{12}$$

where $\theta = \pi\omega/2\omega_0$, and where Z_{oe} and Z_{oo} are the even- and odd-mode line impedances, respectively. The

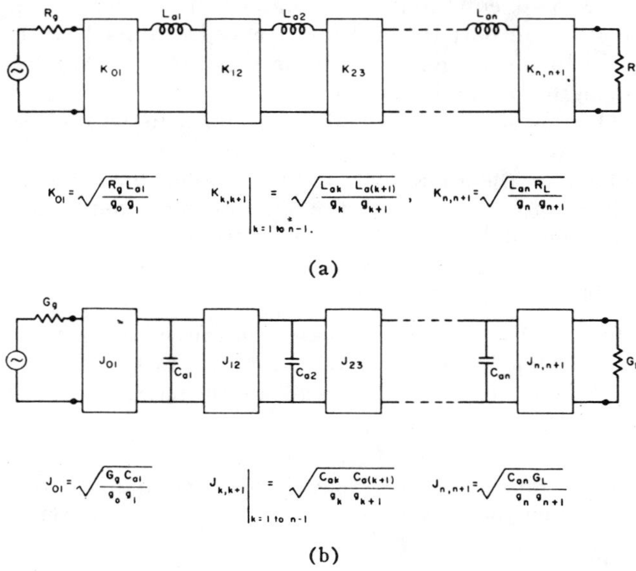

Fig. 16—Low-pass prototypes modified to include impedance inverters or admittance inverters. (The g_0, g_1, $\cdots$, g_n, g_{n+1} are obtained from the original prototype as in Fig. 5, while the R_g, L_{a1}, $\cdots$, L_{an}, and R_L or the G_g, C_{a1}, $\cdots$, C_{an}, and G_L may be chosen as desired.) (a) modified prototype using impedance inverters. (b) Modified prototype using admittance inverters.

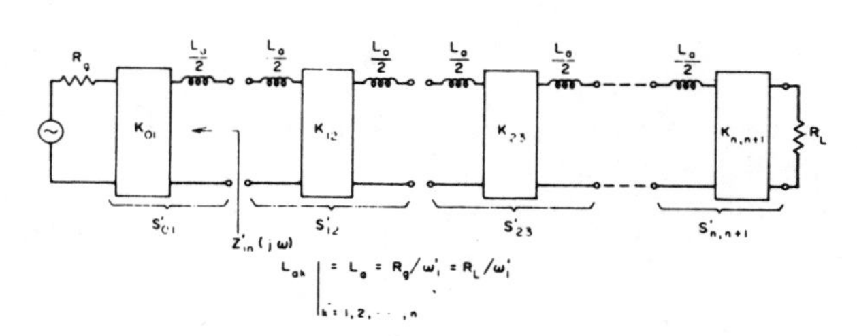

Fig. 17—Modified prototype for deriving the design equations in Table I.

[18] Cohn, *et al.*, *op. cit.*, footnote 1 (SRI Rept.), ch. 2. Also, S. B. Cohn, "Direct-coupled-resonator filters," PROC. IRE, vol. 45, pp. 187–196; February, 1957.

parameters of the parallel-coupled sections S_{12} to $S_{n-1,n}$ in Fig. 1(a) are related to the prototype sections S_{12}' to $S_{n-1,n}$ of the prototype by forcing the following correspondences between the two structures:

(*a*) The image phase of the parallel-coupled sections when $\omega=\omega_0$ must be the same as the image phase of the prototype sections when $\omega'=0$.

(*b*) The image impedances of the parallel-coupled sections when $\omega=\omega_0$ must be the same (within a scale factor s)[19] as the image impedances of the corresponding prototype sections when $\omega'=0$.

(*c*) The image impedance of the parallel-coupled sections when $\omega=\omega_1$ must be the same (within a scale factor s)[19] as the image impedances of the corresponding prototype sections when $\omega'=\omega_1'$. (13)

Correspondence (*a*) is fulfilled in this case by choosing the + sign in (10). Equating (9) and (11) and evaluating each side at the appropriate frequencies indicated above, two equations are obtained from which the equations in part (b) of Table I may be derived (with the help of the information in Figs. 16 and 17) by solving for Z_{oe} and Z_{oo}.

The end sections, S_{01} and $S_{n,n+1}$, must be treated as a special case. Defining $Z_{\text{in}}(j\omega)$ as the impedance seen looking in the right end of the parallel-coupled section S_{01} in Fig. 1(a), with the left end connected to the input line of impedance Z_0, the following correspondences are forced with respect to $Z_{\text{in}}'(j\omega)$ indicated in Fig. 17:

(*a*) $\text{Re } Z_{\text{in}}(j\omega_0)=\text{Re } Z_{\text{in}}(j\omega_1)$ for the parallel-coupled terminating circuit, just as $\text{Re } Z_{\text{in}}'(j0)=\text{Re } Z_{\text{in}}'(-\omega_1')$ for the terminating circuit of the prototype.

(*b*) $\text{Im } Z_{\text{in}}(j\omega_1)/\text{Re } Z_{\text{in}}(j\omega_1)$ must equal $X'/R' = \text{Im } Z_{\text{in}}'(-j\omega_1')/\text{Re } Z_{\text{in}}'(-j\omega_1')$ computed from the prototype. (14)

Defining

$$P = \frac{(Z_{oe})_{01} - (Z_{oo})_{01}}{R_g 2 \sin \theta_1}, \tag{15}$$

and

$$Q = \frac{(Z_{oe})_{01} + (Z_{oo})_{01}}{R_g 2 \tan \theta_1}, \tag{16}$$

it can be shown that correspondence (*a*) in (14) will be obtained if

$$Q = \cot \theta_1 \tag{17}$$

is satisfied, where $\theta=\pi\omega_1/2\omega_0$. Further, correspondence (*b*) requires that

$$Q^3 + Q(1 - P^2) + \frac{X'}{R'} P^2 = 0 \tag{18}$$

be satisfied. Substituting (17) in (18), and solving for $(Z_{oe})_{01}$ and $(Z_{oo})_{01}$ yields the results in part (a) of Table I. Even if $R_g=Z_0$, the above conditions will generally result in an impedance level for $Z_{\text{in}}(j\omega)$ of the band-pass filter, which is different than that of $Z_{\text{in}}'(j\omega')$ for the prototype. The impedances of the interior sections must therefore be corrected by multiplying by the scale factor s indicated in Table I.

[19] Taking $R_g=R_L=Z_0$.

C. *Procedure for Deriving the Equations in Table II*

Fig. 18 shows the manner in which the modified prototype at (a) in Fig. 16 is broken into sections and the elements specified for deriving the equations in Table II. Note that in this case the end impedance inverters, K_{01} and $K_{n,n+1}$, are both made equal to the terminating resistances $R_g=R_L$. For the end inductances, $L_{a1}=L_{an}=R_g g_0 g_1$; however, $L_{a2}=L_{a3}= \cdots =L_{a,n-1}$ are made equal to $2L_{a1}$ so that the structure can be broken into symmetrical sections without the need for end sections. Using the indicated values for the L_{ak}, the $K_{k,k+1}$ are obtained by use of Fig. 16. Then all of the sections are designed by use of (9)–(12) and the correspondences given in (13).

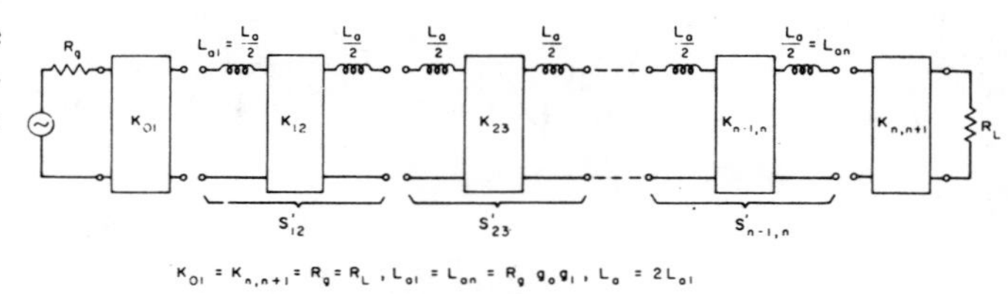

Fig. 18—Modified prototype for deriving the equations in Table II.

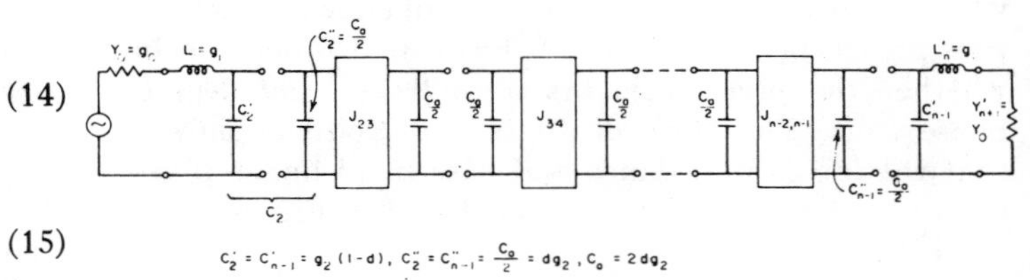

Fig. 19—Modified prototype for deriving the equations in Table III. Parameter d may be used to adjust the impedance level in the center part of the filter. In the example of Fig. 11, d was chosen as one-half, to split $C_2=C_2'+C_2''$ in half.

D. *Procedure for Deriving the Equations in Table III*

Fig. 19 shows the modified prototype used for deriving the equations in Table III. In this case, most of the structure is in the form shown in Fig. 16(b). However, inverters J_{01}, J_{12}, $J_{n-1,n}$, and $J_{n,n+1}$ have been omitted. Here, L_1 and C_2 have the same values that they had in their original prototype form in Fig. 5. Capacitor C_2 is split into two parts, C_2' and C_2'', and the parameter d is used to establish what fraction of C_2 becomes C_2''. Then the capacitance values $C_{a3}=C_{a4}= \cdots =C_{a,n-2}$ are established, so that all of the interior sections can be broken into symmetrical sections. The interior sections are then related to parallel-coupled sections, as in Fig. 4(b) by dual procedures to those used for the interior sections for Tables I and II. The parallel-coupled sections are then converted to stub form by the equivalence in Fig. 4(b). The end sections are designed by forcing the stubs to have reactances at $\omega=\omega_0$ and $\omega=\omega_1$ (on a normalized basis) which are the same as those of the corresponding prototype elements L_1 and C_2', at $\omega'=0$ and $\omega'=-\omega_1'$, respectively.

This same general viewpoint should be useful for designing filters in the form in Fig. 1(c) and (d) to give some desired impedance level in the interior part of the filter. To accomplish this, the prototype in Fig. 18 should be converted to its dual form analogous to that shown in Fig. 16(a). Then, the capacitor C_1 is split, just as C_2 is split in Fig. 19. The resulting design equations are

$$C_a = 2dg_1, \qquad \frac{J_{12}}{Y_0} = \frac{J_{n-1,n}}{Y_0} = \frac{g_0\sqrt{g_1C_a}}{\sqrt{g_1g_2}},$$

$$\left.\frac{J_{k,k+1}}{Y_0}\right|_{k=2 \text{ to } n-2} = \frac{g_0C_a}{\sqrt{g_kg_{k-1}}},$$

$$M_{k,k+1} = \sqrt{\left(\frac{J_{k,k+1}}{Y_0}\right)^2 + \left(\frac{g_0\omega_1'C_a\tan\theta_1}{2}\right)^2},$$

$$\overset{s}{Y}_{k,k+1}\Big|_{k=1 \text{ to } n-1} = Y_0\left(M_{k,k+1} - \frac{J_{k,k+1}}{Y_0}\right),$$

$$Y_1 = Y_n = g_0Y_0\omega_1'(1-d)g_1\tan\theta_1 + \overset{s}{Y}_{12},$$

$$Y_k\Big|_{k=2 \text{ to } n-1} = Y_{n-k+1} = \overset{s}{Y}_{k-1,k} + \overset{s}{Y}_{k,k+1},$$

$$Y_{k,k+1}\Big|_{k=1 \text{ to } n-1} = Y_{n-k,n-k+1} = J_{k,k+1}.$$

Although this technique has been used successfully for achieving small adjustments in impedance level within a filter, the filter-response accuracy resulting when this technique is used to achieve large changes in impedance level has not been tested.

E. Selection of Mapping Functions

Previous work of Cohn,[1] and also the plots presented herein, show that when the function in (4b) is used as indicated in Fig. 6 or 7 to map the response of a low-pass prototype, it will predict quite accurately the response of band-pass filters of the form in Fig. 1(a) having narrow or moderate bandwidth. Although the function in (4b) is very useful, it should not be expected to give high accuracy for wide-band cases because it is not periodic (which the filter response is), nor does it go to infinity for $\omega=0$, $2\omega_0$, $4\omega_0$, etc., which is necessary in order to predict the infinite attenuation frequencies in the response of the band-pass filter structure. It might at first seem that

$$F_n\left(\frac{\omega}{\omega_0}\right) = -\cot\left(\frac{\pi\omega}{2\omega_0}\right) \tag{19}$$

would solve this problem nicely, since it is periodic as desired, it varies similarly to (4b) in the vicinity of ω_0, and it has poles at the desired frequencies $\omega=0$, $2\omega_0$, $4\omega_0$, etc. However, if the structures in Fig. 1 are analyzed, it will be seen that no matter what value of n is used, the poles of attenuation at $\omega=0$, $2\omega_0$, $4\omega_0$, etc., *are always first-order poles*.[20] Meanwhile, an n-reactive-element prototype as in Fig. 5 (which will have an nth-order pole at $\omega'=\infty$) will map so as to give nth order poles at $\omega=0$, $2\omega_0$, etc., if the function in (19) is used. This important source of error is corrected in the case of (4a) by replacing $\cot(\pi\omega/2\omega_0)$ by $\cos(\pi\omega/2\omega_0)/|\sin(\pi\omega/2\omega_0)|$, and then taking the nth root of the denominator. In this manner, the poles generated by the zeros of $|\sin(\pi\omega/2\omega_0)|$ become of $1/n$ order, which causes the nth-order pole at $\omega'=\infty$ for the prototype response to map into first-order poles of the band-pass filter response at the desired frequencies.

In the case of the circuit in Fig. 3, the poles of attenuation at $\omega=0$, $2\omega_0$, $4\omega_0$, etc., will again always be of first order regardless of the value of n used. However, the series stubs at each end produce second-order poles at the frequency ω_∞ and at other corresponding points in the periodic response.[21] Thus, the

$$\sqrt[n]{|\sin(\pi\omega/2\omega_0)|}$$

factor in the denominator of (5) assures that the nth-order poles at $\omega'=\infty$ in the prototype response will always map to first-order poles at $\omega=0$, $2\omega_0$, etc., for the band-pass filter response. In addition, the factor

$$\sqrt[n]{\left[\sin\left(\frac{\pi}{2}\frac{(\omega-\omega_\infty)}{\omega_0}\right)\right]^2\left[\sin\left(\frac{\pi}{2}\frac{(\omega-2\omega_0+\omega_\infty)}{\omega_0}\right)\right]^2}$$

is introduced to cause the nth-order pole at infinity in the prototype response to map to second-order poles at ω_∞ (and other periodic points) for the band-pass filter

[20] For example, for the filter form in Fig. 1(d), as $\omega\rightarrow0$ the effect of all of the shunt stubs can be reduced to that of a single shunt zero-impedance branch which would produce a first-order pole of attenuation $\omega=0$. (One way in which higher-order poles can be generated is to produce shunt zero-impedance branches alternating with series branches having infinite impedance.)

[21] This can be seen as follows: For $\omega=\omega_\infty$, each of the series stubs represents an infinite-impedance series branch. For this single frequency, the interior part of the filter can be replaced by an equivalent T-section with a finite shunt impedance. Thus, the structure can be reduced (for the frequency ω_∞) to two series infinite-impedance branches separated by a finite shunt-impedance branch. This can be seen to result in a second-order pole of attenuation. (If the impedance of the equivalent shunt branch had been zero, the pole of attenuation would have been raised to third order.)

response. In this manner, all of the proper poles of attenuation are introduced with their proper order.

These principles can also be applied to the structure in Fig. 2, but this structure presents some new difficulties. It can be seen that this structure will develop nth-order poles of attenuation at ω_∞ and corresponding periodic points, but the half-wavelength stubs also introduce additional natural modes of oscillation which create, in addition to the desired pass band, a low-pass pass band (and corresponding periodic pass bands) as shown in the response in Fig. 10. This additional low-pass pass band approaches ω_∞ quite closely, with the result that, although the pole at ω_∞ is of relatively high order, its effectiveness is weakened by the close proximity of this low-pass pass band. The function

$$F_n\left(\frac{\omega}{\omega_0}\right) = \tan\left(\frac{\pi\omega}{\omega_0}\right) \quad (20)$$

for the case of $\omega_\infty/\omega_\infty = 0.50$ would map the prototype response to give a low-pass pass band, an nth-order pole at ω_∞, and the desired pass band centered at ω_0. However, it would not properly predict how close the low-pass pass band comes to ω_∞, nor could it account for the oversize attenuation ripples which occur in this band (Fig. 10). As a result, the function in (20) predicts an overly optimistic rate of cutoff at the edges of the pass band centered at ω_0. It is probable that a useful approximation could be obtained by using a mapping function, such as that in (20), with additional factors added which create zeros in $F_n(\omega/\omega_0)$, close to, but somewhat off, the $j\omega$ axis (regarded from the complex-frequency point of view). Proper location of these zeros could then be used to extend the low-pass pass band upwards toward ω_∞, which should give the proper effect.

TABLE I

Design Equations Especially Suited for Filters of the Form in Fig. 1(a) and (b)

Use mapping (4a) or (4b) and Fig. 6 or 7 to select prototype having required value of n. Equations below are for filters in the form of Fig. 1(a). There are $n+1$ parallel-coupled sections for an n-reactive-element prototype when using the design procedure below.

(a) Sections S_{01} and $S_{n,n+1}$

$$\frac{K_{01}}{Z_0} = \frac{1}{\sqrt{g_0 g_1 \omega_1'}} = \frac{K_{n,n+1}}{Z_0}, \qquad \theta_1 = \frac{\pi\omega_1}{2\omega_0}$$

$$Q = \cot\theta_1, \qquad P = \sqrt{\frac{Q(Q^2+1)}{Q + \dfrac{1}{2(K_{01}/Z_0)^2}}}$$

$$s = Z_0\left(\frac{P\sin\theta_1}{K_{01}/Z_0}\right)^2$$

$$(Z_{oe})_{01} = (Z_{oe})_{n,n+1} = Z_0(1 + P\sin\theta_1)$$

$$(Z_{oo})_{01} = (Z_{oo})_{n,n+1} = Z_0(1 - P\sin\theta_1)$$

(b) Sections S_{12} to $S_{n-1,n}$

$$\frac{K_{k,k+1}}{Z_0} = \frac{1}{\omega_1'\sqrt{g_k g_{k+1}}}, \qquad N_{k,k+1} = \sqrt{\left(\frac{K_{k,k+1}}{Z_0}\right)^2 + \frac{\tan^2\theta_1}{4}}$$

$$(Z_{oe})_{k,k+1} = (Z_{oe})_{n-k,n-k+1} = s\left(N_{k,k+1} + \frac{K_{k,k+1}}{Z_0}\right)$$

$$(Z_{oo})_{k,k+1} = (Z_{oo})_{n-k,n-k+1} = s\left(N_{k,k+1} - \frac{K_{k,k+1}}{Z_0}\right)$$

where θ_1 and s are defined as in (a) above and $k = 1, 2, \cdots, n-1$.

TABLE II

Design Equations for Filters Especially Suited for Realization in the Form in Fig. 1(c) and (d)

Use mapping (4a) or (4b) and Figs. 6 or 7 to select prototype. Equations below are for filters in the form of Fig. 1(a), but they are readily converted to the form in Fig. 1(c) or (d) by use of Fig. 4. Using these equations, sections S_{01} and $S_{n,n+1}$ are omitted, and there will be $n-1$ parallel-coupled sections for an n-reactive-element prototype.

Sections S_{12} to $S_{n-1,n}$

$$\frac{K_{12}}{Z_0} = \frac{K_{n-1,n}}{Z_0} = \frac{\sqrt{2g_0 g_1}}{\sqrt{g_1 g_2}},$$

$$\left.\frac{K_{k,k+1}}{Z_0}\right|_{k=2 \text{ to } n-2} = \frac{K_{n-k,n-k+1}}{Z_0} = \frac{2g_0 g_1}{\sqrt{g_k g_{k+1}}},$$

$$\theta_1 = \frac{\pi}{2}\frac{\omega_1}{\omega_0}, \qquad N_{k,k+1} = \sqrt{\left(\frac{K_{k,k+1}}{Z_0}\right)^2 + (\omega_1' g_0 g_1 \tan\theta_1)^2}$$

$$(Z_{oe})_{k,k+1} = (Z_{oe})_{n-k,n-k+1} = Z_0\left(N_{k,k+1} + \frac{K_{k,k+1}}{Z_0}\right)$$

$$(Z_{oo})_{k,k+1} = (Z_{oo})_{n-k,n-k+1} = Z_0\left(N_{k,k+1} - \frac{K_{k,k+1}}{Z_0}\right)$$

where $k = 1, 2, \cdots, n-1$.

TABLE III

Design Equations for Filters of the Form in Fig. 3

Use mapping (5) and Fig. 6 or 7 to select prototype.

$$\theta_1 = \frac{\pi\omega_1}{2\omega_0}, \qquad \theta_\infty = \frac{\pi\omega_\infty}{2\omega_0},$$

where ω_∞ is a frequency of infinite attenuation as indicated in Fig. 11. Referring to Fig. 3:

$$a = \cot^2\theta_\infty, \qquad Z_1 = Z_n = \frac{[a(\tan\theta_1)^2 - 1]\omega_1' g_0 g_1}{Y_0(a+1)\tan\theta_1},$$

$$Z_1' = Z_n' = aZ_1, \qquad C_a = 2dg_2,$$

where $d \leq 1$ is a constant (typically one-half or somewhat larger), which may be chosen to give a desired impedance level in the interior of the filter.

$$\frac{J_{23}}{Y_0} = \frac{J_{n-2,n-1}}{Y_0} = \frac{\sqrt{g_2 C_a}}{g_0\sqrt{g_2 g_3}}, \qquad \left.\frac{J_{k,k+1}}{Y_0}\right|_{k=3 \text{ to } n-3} = \frac{C_a}{g_0\sqrt{g_k g_{k+1}}},$$

$$M_{k,k+1} = \sqrt{\left(\frac{J_{k,k+1}}{Y_0}\right)^2 + \left(\frac{\omega_1' C_a \tan\theta_1}{2g_0}\right)^2},$$

$$\left.Y^s_{k,k+1}\right|_{k=2 \text{ to } n-2} = Y^s_{n-k,n-k+1} = Y_0\left(M_{k,k+1} - \frac{J_{k,k+1}}{Y_0}\right).$$

Then for the shunt stubs:

$$Y_2 = Y_{n-1} = \frac{Y_0\omega_1'(1-d)g_2}{g_0}\tan\theta_1 + Y^s_{23},$$

$$\left.Y_k\right|_{k=3 \text{ to } n-2} = Y_{n-k+1} = Y^s_{k-1,k} + Y^s_{k,k+1}.$$

And for the connecting lines:

$$\left.Y_{k,k+1}\right|_{k=2 \text{ to } n-1} = Y_{n-k,n-k+1} = J_{k,k+1}.$$

TABLE IV

SUMMARY OF EVEN-MODE AND ODD-MODE IMPEDANCE VALUES FOR THE FILTERS OF FIG. 8(a)–(c) DESIGNED BY USE OF TABLE I AND REALIZED IN THE FORM IN FIG. 1(a)

	Fig. 8(a) (5% Band-width)	Fig. 8(b) (30% Band-width)	Fig. 8(c) (2 to 1 Band-width)
$(Z_{oe})_{01}=(Z_{oe})_{67}$	1.251	1.540	1.716
$(Z_{oe})_{12}=(Z_{oe})_{56}$	0.996	1.023	1.142
$(Z_{oe})_{23}=(Z_{oe})_{45}$	0.981	0.937	0.954
$(Z_{oe})_{34}$	0.980	0.927	0.933
$(Z_{oo})_{01}=(Z_{oo})_{67}$	0.749	0.460	0.284
$(Z_{oo})_{12}=(Z_{oo})_{56}$	0.881	0.491	0.208
$(Z_{oo})_{23}=(Z_{oo})_{45}$	0.895	0.536	0.250
$(Z_{oo})_{34}$	0.896	0.542	0.255

All values normalized so that $Z_o=1$.

TABLE V

ELEMENT VALUES FOR THE FILTER OF FIG. 9 REALIZED AS SHOWN IN FIG. 1(d)

Filter designed using Table II from a 0.10-db ripple, $n=8$, Tchebycheff prototype using $\omega_1/\omega_0=0.650$.

$Y_1=Y_8=1.042$	$Y_3=Y_6=2.049$
$Y_{12}=Y_{78}=1.288$	$Y_{34}=Y_{56}=1.292$
$Y_2=Y_7=2.050$	$Y_4=Y_5=2.087$
$Y_{23}=Y_{67}=1.364$	$Y_{45}=1.277$

All values normalized so $Y_0=1$.

TABLE VI

ELEMENT VALUES FOR THE FILTER OF FIG. 10 REALIZED AS SHOWN IN FIG. 2

Filter designed from a 0.10-db ripple, $n=8$, Tchebycheff prototype using $\omega_1/\omega_0=0.850$ and $\omega_\infty/\omega_0=0.500$. This, then, calls for $a=1$ so that $Y_k'=Y_k''$ throughout.

$Y_1'=Y_8'=1.806$	$Y_3'=Y_6'=3.584$
$Y_{12}=Y_{78}=1.288$	$Y_{34}=Y_{56}=1.292$
$Y_2'=Y_7'=3.585$	$Y_4'=Y_5'=3.614$
$Y_{23}=Y_{67}=1.364$	$Y_{45}=1.277$

All values normalized so that $Y_0=1$.

TABLE VII

ELEMENT VALUES FOR THE FILTER OF FIG. 11 REALIZED AS SHOWN IN FIG. 3

Filter designed using Table III from a 0.10-db ripple, $n=8$, Tchebycheff prototype using $\omega\ /\omega_0=0.650$ and $\omega_\infty/\omega_0=0.500$.

$Z_1=Z_8=0.606$	$Y_3=Y_6=1.235$
$Z_1'=Z_8'=0.606$	$Y_{34}=Y_{56}=0.779$
$Y_2=Y_7=1.779$	$Y_4=Y_5=1.258$
$Y_{23}=Y_{67}=0.823$	$Y_{45}=0.770$

NOVEL MICROWAVE INTEGRATED LOWPASS FILTERS

Indexing terms: Filters, Microwave techniques, Networks

The procedure is described for synthesising Cauer Chebŷshev lowpass filters of the third order as rectangular microwave integrated structures. The synthesis procedure is based on a two-mode approximation and leads to structures with very small dimensions compared with the usual realisations of such type of filters. The experimental behaviour is shown to be quite satisfactory, particularly in the passband, where the filters show a better performance than the corresponding lowpass prototypes.

The filtering properties of rectangular two-port planar structures have been illustrated by many authors.[1,2] In particular, the existence of different types of transmission zeros has been stressed both theoretically and experimentally.[3,4] An accurate description of the behaviour of such structures, including fringe field effects, has been obtained by expanding the electromagnetic field in terms of resonant modes of the structure.[3] From such an analysis, an equivalent lumped-element network of the planar structure can be derived, in which each resonant mode is represented by an antiresonant LC cell;[5] in a limited frequency rànge, however, and by properly choosing the structure's geometry, only a few resonant cells may be taken into account. Starting from such a result, in this letter the procedure is described for synthesising Cauer-Chebŷshev (C.C.) lowpass filters of the 3rd order as rectangular two-port planar structures. The synthesis procedure is based on a two-mode approximation and leads to structures with much smaller dimensions than those of the usual realisations of such type of microwave filters. The experimental behaviour is shown to be quite satisfactory.

Fig. 1*a* shows the geometry of a planar rectangular structure; by expanding the electromagnetic field in terms of resonant modes and retaining only the first two modes, one obtains,[3] assuming $b > 1$, the following expression of the impedance parameters:

$$Z_{mn} = \frac{h}{l_{00} b_{00} \varepsilon_0 \varepsilon_{d,00}} \left(\frac{1}{j\omega} + \frac{l_{00} b_{00} \varepsilon_{d,00}}{l_{01} b_{01} \varepsilon_{d,01}} \frac{2j\omega g_m g_n}{\left(\frac{\pi c_0}{b_{01}\sqrt{\varepsilon_{d,01}}} \right)^2 - \omega^2} \right) \qquad m, n = 1, 2 \quad (1)$$

h is the substrate's thickness; l_{00}, b_{00} and l_{01}, b_{01} are the effective structure's dimensions relative to the TM_{00} and TM_{01} resonant modes, respectively, calculated using Reference 6; $\varepsilon_{d,00}$ and $\varepsilon_{d,01}$ are the dynamic permittivities of such modes;[6] ε_0 and c_0 are the vacuum dielectric constant and light velocity, respectively; and finally

$$g_m = -\sin\frac{\pi p_m}{b_{01}} \sin\frac{\pi w_{eff,m}}{2b_{01}} \Big/ \left(\frac{\pi w_{eff,m}}{2b_{01}} \right) \qquad (2)$$

where $w_{eff,m}$ is the effective width of the mth feeding line. Since only the first two resonant modes are taken into account in eqn. 1, this expression is well approximated when the contribution of higher-order modes can be neglected; if $1 < 2b$ this happens in a range of frequency from zero up to about 1·5 times the second resonant frequency ω_{01}. When the frequency approaches the third resonant frequency $\omega_{02} \approx 2\omega_{01}$, expr. 1 is no more valid. It should be observed that the dynamic permittivities are a function of frequency; nevertheless, in the range of validity of eqn. 1, these quantities may be assumed to be independent of frequency and to be given by the values calculated at the reference frequency f_r of the C.C. filter to be synthesised.

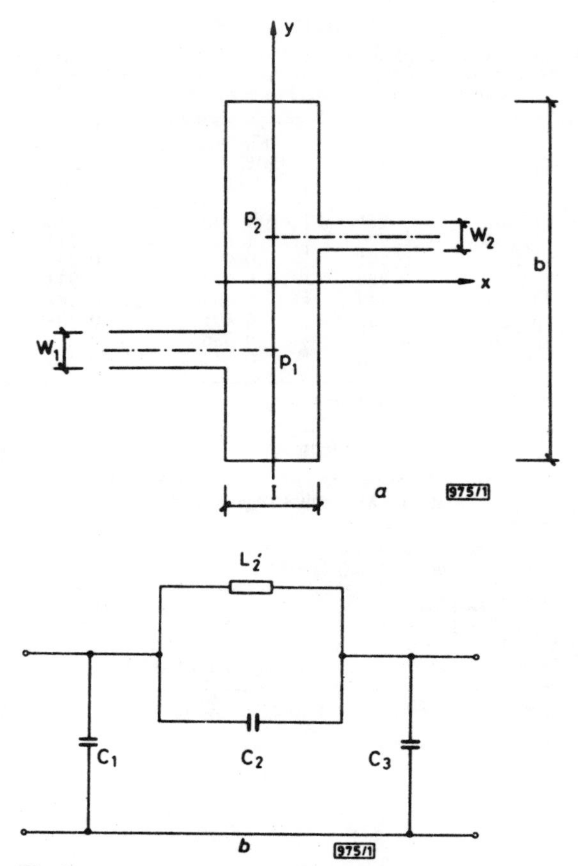

Fig. 1

a Geometry of the new type of lowpass filter
b Equivalent circuit obtained on the basis of a two-mode approximation

The equivalent two-port network in Fig. 1*b* is then easily obtained from eqn. 1. When the proper values of C_1, C_2, L_2 and C_3 are chosen, such a network, as is known, is simply a Cauer-Chebŷshev lowpass filter of the 3rd order.

For the sake of simplicity, let us consider the case of symmetrical structures for which $w_2 = w_1$ and $p_2 = -p_1$, and, therefore, $g_2 = -g_1$ and $C_3 = C_1$. Equating the impedance parameters of the equivalent network in Fig. 1*b* to those given by eqn. 1, one obtains

$$C_3 = C_1 = \frac{\varepsilon_0}{h} \frac{l_{00} b_{00} \varepsilon_{d,00}}{2} \qquad (3a)$$

$$C_2 = \frac{\varepsilon_0}{h} \frac{l_{01} b_{01} \varepsilon_{d,01} - 2 l_{00} b_{00} \varepsilon_{d,00} g_1^2}{8 g_1^2} \qquad (3b)$$

$$L_2 = \mu_0 h \frac{8 b_{01} g_1^2}{\pi^2 l_{01}} \qquad (3c)$$

The resonant frequency of the TM_{01} mode of the rectangular structure

$$\omega_{01} = \frac{\pi c_0}{b_{01}\sqrt{\varepsilon_{d,01}}}$$

corresponds to the resonance of the inductor L_2 with the three capacitors C_1, C_2, $C_3 = C_1$; we have therefore

$$\omega_{01}^2 = \frac{\pi^2 c_0^2}{b_{01}^2 \varepsilon_{d,01}} = \left[L_2 \left(\frac{C_1}{2} + C_2 \right) \right]^{-1} \qquad (4)$$

The above expressions, together with those giving l_{00}, b_{00}, l_{01}, b_{01}, $\varepsilon_{d,00}$, $\varepsilon_{d,01}$ as a function of l and b,[6] are used to evaluate the geometrical parameters l, b, $p_1 = -p_2$ of the planar structure. This can be done once the C.C. filter to be realised, the reference frequency f_r, the substrate's characteristics (h, ε_r) and the feeding-line impedance have been chosen.

It should be observed, however, that the evaluation of l, b and p_1 is not straightforward, since the relations between the effective parameters, the dynamic permittivities and l and b can be reversed only numerically. However, although l_{00}, b_{00}, b_{01} and $\varepsilon_{d,00}$ depend on both l and b, l_{01} and $\varepsilon_{d,01}$ are functions only of l. As a consequence, starting from a trial value of l, b_{01} and then b can be calculated from eqn. 4; afterwards, b_{00} and $\varepsilon_{d,00}$ can be calculated from these values of l and b; a new value of l is finally obtained from expr. 3a of C_1. This is, basically, the procedure we have adopted for calculating l and b; the positions of the ports can be then evaluated through, for instance, the expr. 3c of L_2. The overall computation time for calculating the structure's geometrical parameters starting from the lowpass C.C. filter elements is about 30 s on our HP9830 desk calculator.

Several lowpass filters have been designed through the above procedure and have been realised as microstrips on alumina substrate ($h = 0{\cdot}0635$ cm, $\varepsilon_r = 10$). Fig. 2 shows the measured scattering parameters of one of these filters as a function of frequency in the range 2–12·4 GHz. The lowpass prototype is a C.C. 032041[7] with reference frequency $f_r = 5$ GHz, whose characteristics are also shown in the same Figure. The performance of the filter may be considered highly satisfactory up to 10 GHz. To explain the differences between the prototype characteristics (corresponding to a two-mode approximation of the structure behaviour) and the measured ones, the computed results of a five-mode approximation are also plotted in Fig. 2. As can be seen, the computed results are in good agreement with the measurements. On the other hand, it is apparent that the contribution of higher-order modes results in a wider 30 dB stop band (1·55 GHz instead of 0·65 GHz), and over $\approx$ 10 GHz it produces a second passband. With regard to the passband behaviour, it can be noted that the experimental $|s_{11}|$ is about 5 dB less than that of the C.C. prototype; this better matching is due in part to the contribution of higher-order modes. Accurate measurements have demonstrated a passband attenuation less than 0·5 dB, essentially due to the feeding lines, which have an overall length of $\approx$ 2·5 cm.

Let us finally point out the very small dimensions of the filter; typically, l is of the order of one hundred micrometres, and b is $\gtrsim$ 1 cm for frequencies $f_r \approx$ 4–8 GHz.

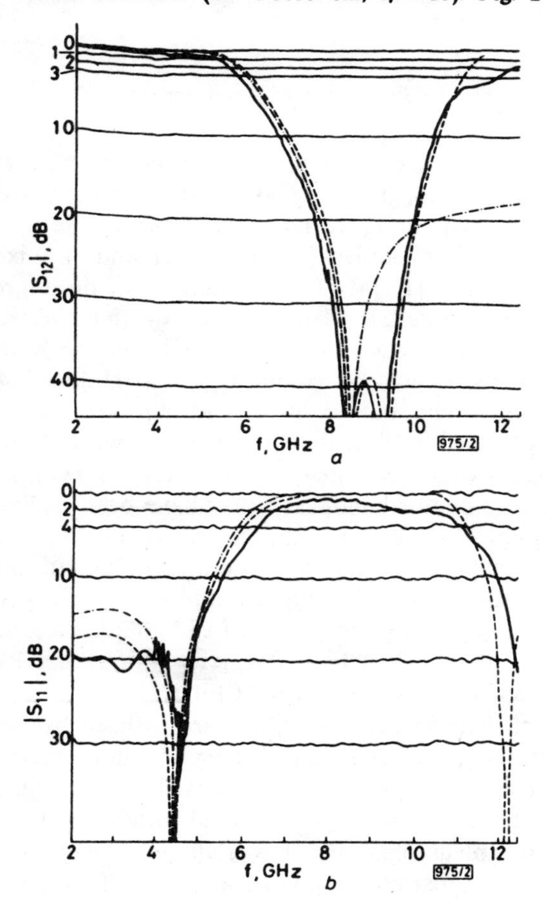

Fig. 2 *Comparison of filter scattering parameters*

——— measured
—·— lowpass CC 032041 prototype
- - - - computed

Filter dimensions: $l = 0{\cdot}0260$ cm, $b = 0{\cdot}995$ cm, $p_2 = -p_1 = 0{\cdot}176$ cm, $w_1 = w_2 = 0{\cdot}06$ cm

Acknowledgments: This work was partially supported by CNR, Italy. The authors are indebted to Servizio Microonde, Elettronica S.p.A., Via Tiburtina, Roma, for assistance with the measurements.

GUGLIELMO D'INZEO
FRANCO GIANNINI
ROBERTO SORRENTINO

Istituto di Elettronica
Università di Roma
Via Eudossiana 18, 00184 Roma, Italy

26th March 1979

References

1 BIANCO, B., and RIDELLA, S.: 'Nonconventional transmission zeros in distributed rectangular structures', *IEEE Trans.*, 1972, **MTT-20**, pp. 297–303

2 KOMPA, G.: 'S-matrix computation of microstrip discontinuities with planar waveguide model', *Arch. Elektron. & Ubertragungstech.*, 1976, **30**, pp. 58–64

3 D'INZEO, G., GIANNINI, F., SODI, C. M., and SORRENTINO, R.: 'Method of analysis and filtering properties of microwave planar networks', *IEEE Trans.*, 1978, **MTT-26**, pp. 462–471

4 D'INZEO, G., GIANNINI, F., MALTESE, P., and SORRENTINO, R.: 'On the double nature of transmission zeros in microstrip structures', *Proc. IEEE*, 1978, **66**, pp. 800–802

5 D'INZEO, G., GIANNINI, F., and SORRENTINO, R.: 'A lumped constant approach to the study of microwave planar networks'. Proceedings of the 2nd Riunione Nazionale di Elettromagnetismo Applicato, Pavia, Italy, 1978, pp. 337–344

6 WOLFF, I., and KNOPPIK, N.: 'Rectangular and circular microstrip disk capacitors and resonators', *IEEE Trans.*, 1974, **MTT-22**, pp. 857–864

7 ZVEREV, A. I.: 'Handbook of filter synthesis' (Wiley, New York, 1967)

0013-5194/79/090258-03$1.50/0

Design and Performance of Coplanar Waveguide Bandpass Filters

DYLAN F. WILLIAMS AND S. E. SCHWARZ, SENIOR MEMBER, IEEE

Abstract—End-coupled resonator bandpass filters built in coplanar waveguide are investigated. The admittance inverter parameters of the coupling gaps between resonant sections are deduced from experiment, and bandpass filter design rules are developed. This allows easy filter synthesis from "prototype" low-pass designs. Measurements of single section resonator quality factors are used to predict filter insertion losses. Several examples of filters realized in coplanar waveguide are presented. Odd-mode coplanar waveguide filter elements that shortcircuit the even coplanar waveguide mode are investigated. Filter tuning, accomplished by adjusting the height of conducting planes above the resonant filter sections, is demonstrated.

I. Introduction

DEVICES FOR operation at millimeter wavelengths have small dimensions. It is convenient to fabricate such devices using photolithography, but this requires that they be planar, or as nearly so as possible. Four guides that are easily produced photolithographically are microstrip, slotline, coplanar strips, and coplanar waveguide (CPW) [1], as shown in Fig. 1. These guides are open structures, and do not require precisely machined metallic enclosures.

Recently there has been considerable interest in using coplanar waveguide in millimeter-wave integrated circuits [2]–[4]. CPW is planar, permits both series and shunt connection of circuit elements, and has low radiation losses in the odd mode (opposing electric fields). CPW parameters are not sensitive functions of substrate thickness, and a wide range of impedance is achievable on reasonably thick substrates. Also, circuits can be built using both the odd and the even (electric fields in the same direction) CPW modes. Microstrip, the usual choice for integrated circuits, possesses some of the desirable properties of CPW. It has the advantage of familiarity; many well-characterized microstrip circuits are available. Microstrip, however, is not a truly planar guide, as the ground plane is on the bottom surface of the dielectric. While it is usually not difficult to construct the required ground plane, shunt connection of circuit elements is quite awkward, especially in the millimeter-wave region. Moreover, microstrip impedance and guide wavelength are undesirably sensitive functions of substrate thickness.

Manuscript received October 19, 1982; revised February 15, 1983. This work was supported in part by the U. S. Army Research Office under Contract DAAG29-82-K-0166, in part by the National Science Foundation under Grant ECS-8116018, in part by the Joint Services Electronics Program under AFOSR Grant F49620-79-C-0178, and in part by the U. S. Army MERADCOM under Grant DAAK 70-80-C-0134.

The authors are with the Department of Electrical Engineering and Computer Sciences and the Electronics Research Laboratory, University of California, Berkeley, CA 94720.

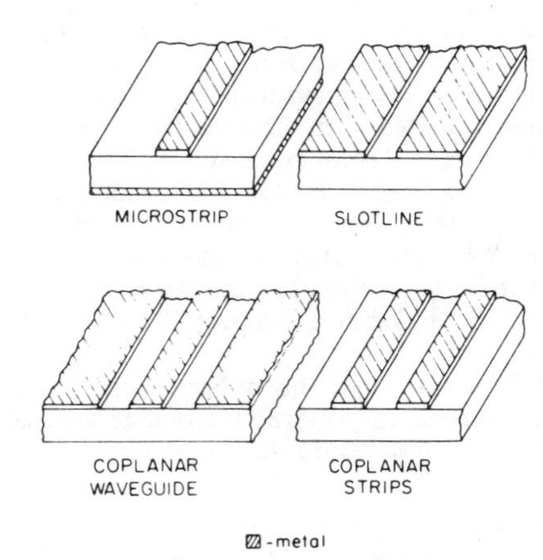

Fig. 1. Four open guiding structures.

In contrast to microstrip, there are fewer well-known CPW circuits, although the guide itself has been well characterized [1]–[10]. There has been considerable work on CPW directional couplers [1], [2], [7]–[9], and on mixer circuits using CPW [1]–[4], [11]–[20], and some on nonreciprocal CPW devices [21], planar antennas with CPW feed lines [22], and a magic T in CPW [23]; but with the exception of the papers by Houdart [2] and Holder [24], which present some mixer, filter, and diplexer circuits utilizing CPW and slotline, there has been no work, to the authors' knowledge, on filters using CPW. Previously, end-coupled resonator bandpass filters have been realized in many guiding structures including conventional waveguide and coaxial lines [25]–[27], microstrip [25], stripline [25], [27], and finline [28]–[30]. In this paper, we shall discuss the design and performance of end-coupled resonator bandpass filters realized in CPW. As will be seen, CPW is a guide well suited for this type of filter.

End-coupled resonant CPW filters are realized by cutting gaps in the inner conductor of the guide, thus creating capacitively coupled resonant sections as shown in Fig. 2. This filter structure retains all of the advantages of CPW including complete planarity, low radiation losses, and insensitivity to substrate thickness, and is well suited to monolithic millimeter-wave integrated circuitry. Filter design is accomplished by a synthesis technique [25]–[27] applicable to bandpass filters with fractional bandwidth less than 20 percent, utilizing the concept of admittance inverters (ideal quarter-wavelength transformers). This procedure is reviewed in Section II. Realization of the desired admittance inverters using gaps in the center conductor of CPW is discussed in Section III. To facilitate determina-

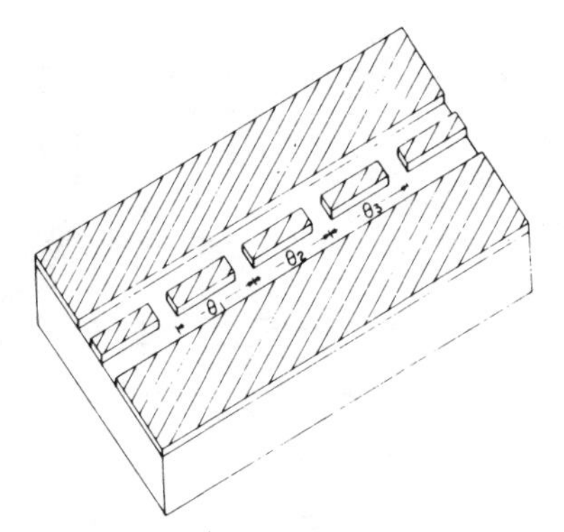

Fig. 2. Three-section bandpass filter in CPW.

tion of gap geometry and spacing, design information is presented in graphical form. A filter coupling element that presents a short circuit to the even mode propagating in the CPW is also described. Measurements of the unloaded quality factors of single resonant sections of CPW are used to predict filter insertion losses. In Section IV, the performance of several CPW bandpass filters is described. Filter tuning, accomplished by the use of conducting planes suspended at adjustable heights above the guide, is also demonstrated in this section. Performance at near-millimeter wavelengths is considered in Section V.

II. Design Principles

The bandpass CPW filters demonstrated in this work are designed using filter synthesis techniques for gap-coupled resonators as outlined by Matthaei, Young, and Jones [25] and Collins [26], and developed by Cohn [27]. We begin with a "prototype" low-pass filter as shown in Fig. 3(a), with element values g_i and the response shown in Fig. 3(b). The quantity g_i is the inductance of a series coil or the capacitance of a shunt capacitor for $i = 1$ to n. The quantities g_0 and g_{n+1} are the generator and load impedances, respectively, when g_1 corresponds to a capacitor and the designs are symmetrical, as they are here. The g_i are normalized to make $g_0 = 1\ \Omega$ and $\omega_1' = 1$ rad/s, where ω_1' is the prototype filter cutoff frequency, as shown in Fig. 3(b). The element values g_i are defined for more general circuit configurations and are conveniently tabulated for many desired responses in [25]. Here they were chosen to give a 0.2-dB Chebyshev response. The "prototype" low-pass filter of Fig. 3(a) is transformed to the lumped element bandpass filter of Fig. 3(c) with response shown in Fig. 3(d). The passbands are transformed according to

$$\omega' = \frac{\omega_1'}{w}\left(\frac{\omega}{\omega_0} - \frac{\omega_0}{\omega}\right) \tag{1}$$

$$w = \frac{\omega_2 - \omega_1}{\omega_0} \tag{2}$$

$$\omega_0 = \sqrt{\omega_1 \omega_2} \tag{3}$$

where ω and ω' are the angular frequencies in the bandpass and low-pass domains, respectively, and ω_0, ω_1, and ω_2 are the center, lower cutoff, and upper cutoff angular frequencies in the bandpass domain, as shown in Fig. 3(d). The

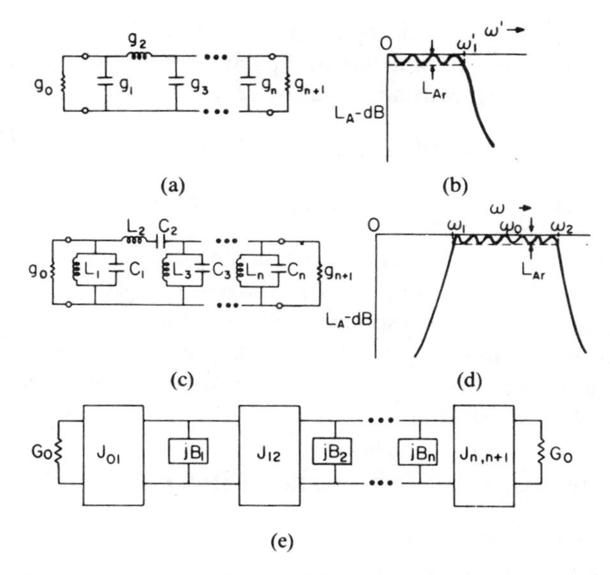

Fig. 3. Prototype low-pass, lumped element bandpass, and admittance inverter bandpass filters. (a) The prototype low-pass circuit and (b) its frequency response. (c) The lumped-element bandpass circuit and (d) its frequency response. (e) A schematic of a bandpass filter using admittance inverters. L_A and L_{Ar} are the filter attenuation and passband ripple, respectively.

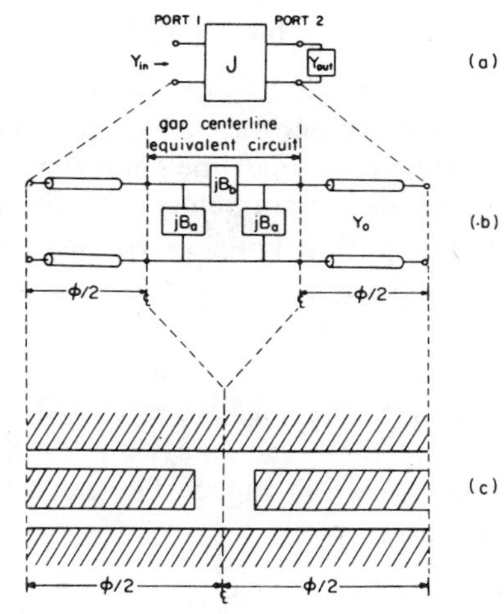

Fig. 4. Admittance inverters. (a) An ideal schematic representation. (b) A circuit representation. (c) The realization in CPW.

quantity w, defined by (2), is the fractional bandwidth of the bandpass filter.

The lumped-element circuit of Fig. 3(c) can be transformed to the circuit of Fig. 3(e), which has the same frequency response and is in a form that can be easily realized in CPW. All of the susceptances $B_j(\omega)$ were chosen to be identical in this work. This results in a considerable simplification, allowing the $B_j(\omega)$ to be realized as sections of CPW which are one-half wavelength long at the filter center frequency and of characteristic admittance Y_0, the characteristic admittance of the system. The boxes marked $J_{j,j+1}$ are admittance inverters. An admittance inverter is an ideal quarter-wavelength transformer. The admittance Y_{in} seen at port one is related to the admittance Y_{out} at port two (see Fig. 4(a)) by

$$Y_{in} = J^2 / Y_{out}. \tag{4}$$

With the choice of the $B_j(\omega)$ described above, the admittance inversion parameters J/Y_0 required to produce the response of Fig. 3(d) are given by [25]

$$J_{01}/Y_0 = J_{n,n+1}/Y_0 = \sqrt{\pi w/(2g_0g_1\omega'_1)} \quad (5)$$

$$J_{j,j+1}/Y_0 = \pi w/\left(2\omega'_1\sqrt{g_jg_{j+1}}\right), \quad j \neq 0, n \quad (6)$$

for symmetrical designs, where n is the number of resonant sections. The J's, like the g's in the low-pass domain, now determine the filter response in the bandpass domain. The admittance inverters are realized as adjustable gaps between the half-wavelength sections of CPW, as described in the following section.

III. Realization of Admittance Inverters in CPW

A. Circuit Description

The ideal admittance inverters just introduced can be approximated by the equivalent circuit of Fig. 4(b). The electrical line length ϕ is chosen to be [25]

$$\phi = -\tan^{-1}(2B_b/Y_0 + B_a/Y_0) - \tan^{-1}(B_a/Y_0). \quad (7)$$

The admittance parameter J is then given by

$$J/Y_0 = |\tan(\phi/2 + \tan^{-1}(B_a/Y_0))|. \quad (8)$$

The portion of Fig. 4(b) labeled "gap centerline equivalent circuit" is realized as the centerline equivalent circuit of the gap shown in Fig. 4(c). The centerline equivalent circuit of the gap is defined by its S-parameters with the reference planes of port 1 and port 2 lying in coincidence at the centerline position, marked ℄ in Fig. 4(c). Two sections of CPW waveguide complete the circuit. The electrical length of these CPW sections computed from (7) is negative for most gap configurations. The negative electrical lengths are realized by combining these sections with the half-wavelength resonators, as shown in Fig. 5. The electrical length of the jth section is given by

$$\theta_j = \pi + (\phi_{j-1,j} + \phi_{j,j+1})/2 \quad (9)$$

where $\phi_{j,j+1}$ is computed from (7) for the gap that separates resonator j from resonator $j+1$.

B. Physical Configurations

The physical configurations of the gaps are sketched in Fig. 6. Actual dimensions are listed in Table I. Large values of J were achieved through the use of interleaved fingers (Fig. 6(a) and (b)), as suggested by Houdart [2], while small values of J were obtained with simple gaps (Fig. 6(c)). As will be seen, the interleaved fingers give lower radiation loss for the same value of J.

The inverters shown in Fig. 6 were built in 50-Ω CPW with internal conductor width (x_4) of $22.7 \times 10^{-3}\lambda_0$, where λ_0 is the free-space wavelength. The spacing between the center conductor and the outer conductor was $13.41 \times 10^{-3}\lambda_0$ in all cases. The substrate's low-frequency dielectric constant was found from low-frequency capacitance measurements to be approximately 11.4, close to those of the silicon or GaAs substrates that might be used for monolithic integrated circuits in the millimeter-wave region. At millimeter wavelengths, thick substrates, which are easier to process, are desirable. The maximum allowable substrate thickness is that at which the lowest order TE surface-wave mode begins to propagate. This maximum thickness was calculated to be $0.077\lambda_0$ for the dielectrics used in this work [3]. The first evanescent surface mode was experimentally observed at a thickness of $0.066\lambda_0$. The substrate thickness chosen for these experiments was $0.054\lambda_0$.

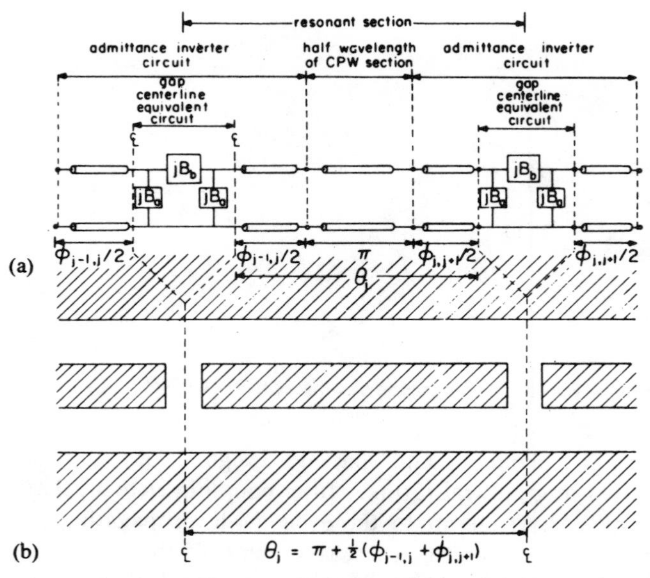

Fig. 5. A resonant section of CPW with gaps. (a) The circuit representation and (b) its realization in CPW.

TABLE I
DIMENSIONS FOR FIG. 6, NORMALIZED TO THE FREE-SPACE WAVELENGTH

i	$10^3\, x_i/\lambda_0$
1	4.13
2	41.28
3	10.32
4	22.70
5*	6.19
6*	4.13
7	16.51
8	30.96
9	66.04
10	49.53

Note: The "bulge" in Fig. 6(b) associated with x_5 and x_6 results from the technique of fabrication and probably contributes no useful effect.

Another type of admittance inverter structure is shown in Fig. 6(d) and (e). These structures, which we shall call "overlaid gaps," have a metallic bridge connecting the two outer conductors of the CPW. The bridge is insulated from the center conductor by a dielectric layer. The purpose of these overlaid gaps is to short-circuit the even CPW mode.

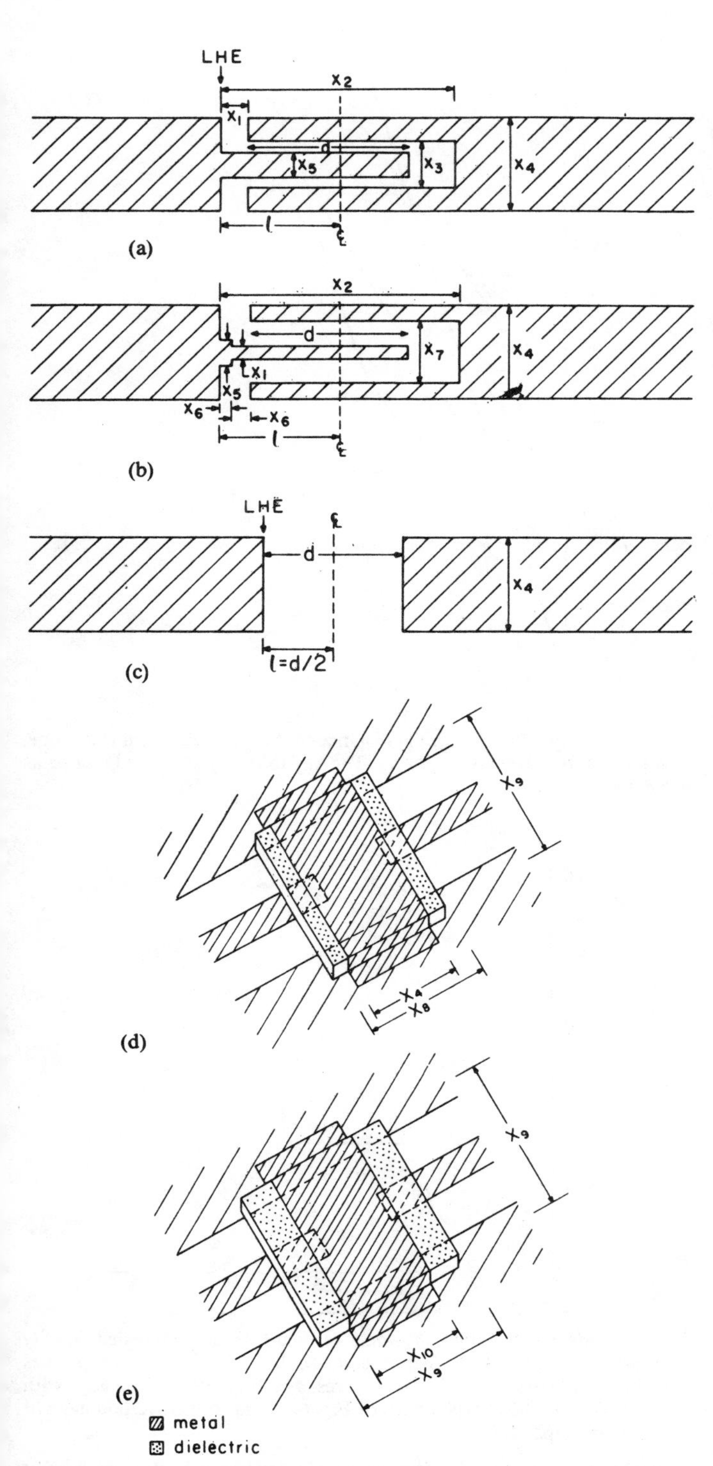

Fig. 6. Physical configurations of the admittance inverters. Only the center conductor is shown. Table I gives the normalized values of the x_i. The distance d is varied to give different values of the admittance inverter parameters J, ϕ, and l. The quantity l is the distance of the centerline equivalent circuit reference plane from the edge of the gap and is found from Fig. 9. Junction type b^* is the same as type b except that $x_2 = 24.76 \times 10^{-3} \lambda_0$. (d) and (e) depict overlaid gaps. The overlay dielectric is of thickness $3.1 \times 10^{-3} \lambda_0$, and has a dielectric constant of 7.3.

A dielectric of thickness $0.0031\lambda_0$, and dielectric constant 7.3 is placed over the active sections of the inverter gaps. The metal bridge is then placed over the dielectric and connected at its ends to the two ground planes. The distances separating the left-hand edges of the gaps of Fig. 6(a) and Fig. 6(c) (marked LHE in the figures) from the centers of the overlay structures are $x_1 + d/2$ and $d/2$, respectively. The even CPW mode is short-circuited, while the normal odd CPW mode is transmitted with high efficiency, so long as its frequency is within the filter passband. We note that although a single overlaid gap would suffice to reject the even mode, there would also be large reflections of the odd mode. In a filter, reflections of the odd mode can be made to cancel over the filter passband, so that nearly perfect transmission is obtained.

C. S-Parameter Measurements

Measurements of the junction's S-parameters were made as functions of d. From these we calculate the equivalent circuit elements B_b and B_a. The imaginary parts of B_b and B_a are small and, for now, are neglected. We then calculate J and ϕ from (7) and (8). The condition $\angle S_{11} = \angle S_{22}$ was used to determine l, the distance between the left-hand edge of the gap and the reference plane defining the gap's electrical centerline, as shown in Fig. 6. Plots of J/Y_0, ϕ, and l/λ_0 versus the normalized length d/λ_0 are given by the solid curves in Figs. 7, 8, and 9, respectively. (The data points indicated by circles, squares, and triangles will be considered later.) These curves can be used for filter design as follows. After calculating the values of J/Y_0 from the procedure in Section II, suitable gap types and their corresponding values of d/λ_0 are found from Fig. 7. Values of ϕ for each gap are then found from Fig. 8 and the physical distance between gap centerlines calculated from (9). Physical gap positions with respect to the centerline positions are determined from Fig. 9.

D. Excess Filter Loss

The excess filter loss L is defined as the extra loss at the center frequency, due to radiation, metallic, and dielectric losses, in a real filter that is not present in the ideal filter built with lossless elements. The data of Figs. 7, 8, and 9 do not allow prediction of the excess filter loss. In fact, the imaginary parts of B_b and B_a were neglected in the calculations leading to Figs. 7, 8, and 9. In any case, the S-parameter measurements are not sufficiently precise for accurate determination of the imaginary parts of B_b and B_a or the excess filter loss. The excess loss at the filter center frequency can be estimated, however, by the formulas due to Cohn [31], [25]

$$L = 4.343 \sum_{k=1}^{n} d_k g_k \text{ (dB)} \tag{10}$$

and

$$d_k = \omega_1'/(wQ_{u,k}) \tag{11}$$

where $Q_{u,k}$ is the unloaded quality factor of the kth resonant section, and n, g, w, and ω_1' are as defined earlier. The unloaded quality factor Q_u is the quality factor of the resonant section of Fig. 5, with all energy dissipation in the circuit due to radiation, ohmic, or dielectric losses, and with no external loading. To obtain accurate values of Q_u, we have performed transmission measurements on single resonant sections like those of Fig. 5, with several kinds of

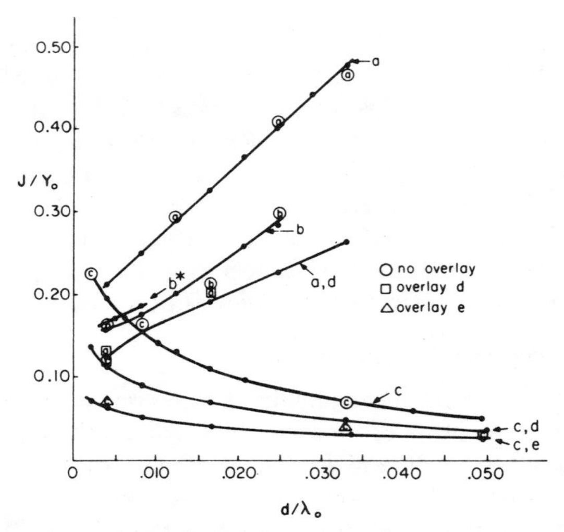

Fig. 7. J/Y_0 as a function of d/λ_0. Letters on solid curves refer to the gap types of Fig. 6. (For example, "a" means gap of Fig. 6(a) with no overlay; "a, d" means gap of Fig. 6(a) with the overlay of Fig. 6(d).) The solid curves represent data derived from S-parameter measurements. Letters inside circles, squares, and triangles refer to gaps with no overlay, to the overlaid gaps of Fig. 6(d), and to the overlaid gaps of Fig. 6(e), respectively, and represent data derived from resonant section measurements.

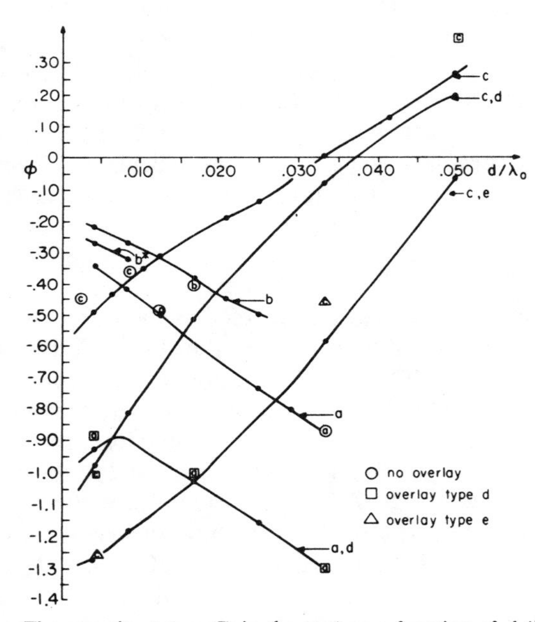

Fig. 8. The quantity ϕ (see (7) in the text) as a function of d/λ_0. The key to the symbols is the same as for Fig. 7.

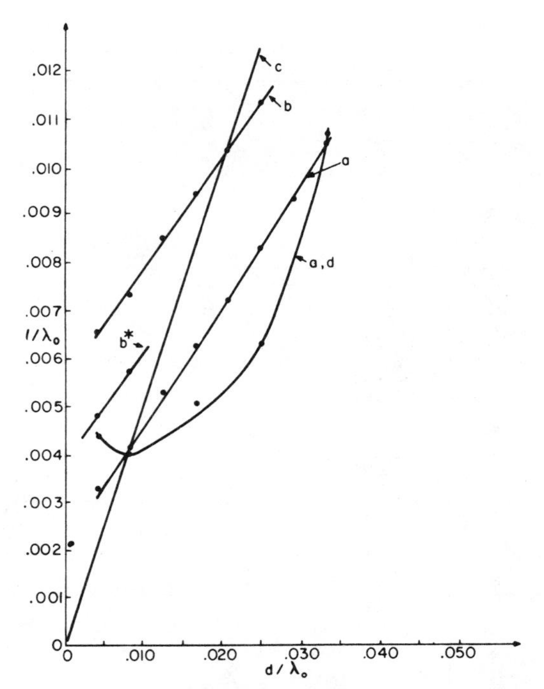

Fig. 9. The quantity l/λ_0, the distance to the gap's electrical centerline, is plotted as a function of d/λ_0. The key to the symbols is the same as for Fig. 7.

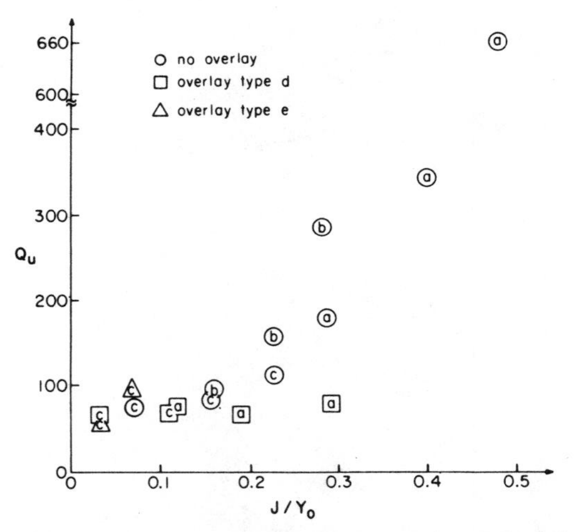

Fig. 10. Measured values of single resonant section unloaded quality factors are plotted as a function of J/Y_0. Letters refer to the gap types of Fig. 6. Letters inside circles, squares, and triangles refer to gaps with no overlay, to the overlaid gaps of Fig. 6(d),and to the overlaid gaps of Fig. 6(e), respectively.

terminating gaps. This was done by determining the center frequency f_s, the 3-dB bandwidth $f_{3\text{dB}}$, and the center frequency excess loss L_s of a single resonant section and using the relations [25]

$$Q_L = f_s / f_{3\text{ dB}} \tag{12}$$

$$Q_e^2 = 4Q_L^2 10^{L_s/10L_s} \tag{13}$$

$$Q_u^{-1} = Q_L^{-1} - 2Q_e^{-1} \tag{14}$$

where L_s is in decibels. The external quality factor Q_e is the quality factor that the resonant section would have if there were no radiation, ohmic, or dielectric losses, all damping in that case being due to the external circuit. The loaded quality factor Q_L is the quality factor of the resonant section including radiation, ohmic, and dielectric losses, as well as the external loading of the measurement apparatus.

Fig. 10 shows the resulting values of Q_u for different gap configurations as a function of J/Y_0. The measurements were performed at $f_0 = 0.78$ GHz, where the measured Q_u were dominated by radiation losses. To obtain minimum-loss filters, the gap type with the highest Q_u for a desired J/Y_0 should be chosen. Reference to Fig. 10 shows that the type b gap is preferable to either type a or c gaps for comparable values of J/Y_0. This can be explained qualitatively in the following way. Type c gaps have the largest radiation loss because the electric fields in the gaps radiate as two simple dipoles, one at each end of the resonant section. In the type b gap, the electric fields are roughly in opposite directions and radiate as two quadrupoles, dissipating less energy. As J/Y_0 increases, the gap center conductor length d increases, and the fields become more nearly opposite in direction, lowering the radiation losses further. For values of J/Y_0 of approximately 0.3, the center conductor length d of the type a gap is still short, and fields are not completely opposite, resulting in higher radiation losses than the type b gap, which has a long center conductor length for $J/Y_0 = 0.3$. For larger values of J/Y_0 in type a gaps, d increases, the fields become more nearly opposite in direction, and radiation losses decrease.

The synthesis technique outlined in Section II will not give filters with precise equiripple characteristics or minimum achievable losses. This is because the finite resonant section unloaded quality factors were not considered in the synthesis procedure. Precise minimum-loss, equiripple, or maximally flat filters can be designed using the unloaded quality factors from Fig. 10 and the synthesis techniques presented by Taub and Bogner [32], Fubini and Guillemin [33], and Dishal [34]. Cohn [31] presents a useful comparison of these synthesis techniques.

E. Comparision of Measurements

We are now in position to verify the gap admittance parameters J and ϕ using the single-resonant-section transmission measurements. J is calculated from [25]

$$J/Y_0 = \sqrt{\pi/2Q_e} \tag{15}$$

and ϕ is calculated from

$$\phi = \phi_s + \pi(f_s - f_0)/f_0 \tag{16}$$

where f_0 is the design center frequency and ϕ_s is the value of ϕ used in the design of the resonant section. The quantity ϕ_s was found from Fig. 8 and was derived from the S-parameter measurements described above.

Figs. 7 and 8 show good agreement between J and ϕ calculated from S-parameters (solid lines) and J and ϕ calculated from resonant section measurements (circled letters) for gaps without overlays. Fig. 7 also shows the good agreement between J calculated from S-parameters and J calculated from resonant section measurements (letters in squares or triangles) for the overlaid gaps. Experimental difficulties with the overlaid gaps limited the accuracy of the phase measurements of S_{11} and S_{22}, reducing the accuracy of the overlaid gap data derived from S-parameter measurements shown in Figs. 8 and 9. The values of ϕ derived from resonant section measurements for overlaid gaps are believed to be more accurate than those values of ϕ derived from S-parameter measurements for the overlaid gaps in Fig. 8.

IV. CPW Bandpass Filter Examples

In order to verify the design data given in the previous sections, several 3-section 0.2-dB Chebyshev filters were built with different bandwidths. The filter design parameters are summarized in Table II. The filters were built with a center frequency of 0.78 GHz. Predicted excess losses

TABLE II
Filter Design Parameter Summary

		1ST ADMITTANCE INVERTER			2ND ADMITTANCE INVERTER			L	
Fig.	w	Type	J_{01}/Y_0	Q_u	Type	J_{12}/Y_0	Q_u	Predicted	Measured
11[1]	.177	Fig. 6(a)	.476	660	Fig. 6(b)	.234	160	.41 dB	.45 dB
12[1]	.13	Fig. 6(a)	.408	350	Note 4	.172	110	.84 dB	.93 dB
13(a)[1]	.047	Fig. 6(a)	.245	190	Fig. 6(c)	.062	75	3.5 dB	5.5 dB
13(b)[2]	.047	Fig. 6(b)	.245	190	Note 5	.062	95	2.9 dB	6.0 dB
13(c)[3]	.047	Fig. 6(b)	.245	190	Fig. 6(c)	.062	75	3.5 dB	2.7 dB

For the 3-section 0.2-dB Chebyshev filters in this paper, $g_0 = g_4 = 1.0$, $g_1 = g_3 = 1.2275$, and $g_2 = 1.1525$.
Notes: [1]Untuned, no overlay. [2]Untuned, with overlay. [3]Tuned, no overlay. [4]Same as Fig. 6(b) but with $x_2 = 24.7 \times 10^{-3}\lambda_0$. [5]Gap of Fig. 6(c) with overlay of Fig. 6(e).

were calculated using Fig. 10 and (10), and are presented in Table II. Unloaded quality factors for resonant sections with different gaps on either end were estimated to be

$$Q_u = 2/\left(Q_{u1}^{-1} + Q_{u2}^{-1}\right) \tag{17}$$

where Q_{u1} and Q_{u2} are the single-section resonant radiation quality factors associated with the two gaps.

Figs. 11 and 12 show the measured and ideal transmission characteristics of filters with $w = 0.177$ and 0.13, respectively. The predicted and measured transmission characteristics are in good agreement. In the filter transmission characteristic of Fig. 11, even the 0.2-dB Chebyshev ripples are apparent. The minimum filter losses of 0.45 dB and 0.93 dB are quite low, and are close to the predicted excess losses of 0.41 dB and 0.84 dB shown in Table II. Equations (10) and (11) predict even lower excess loss for wider bandwidth filters. This is because the term wQ_u appears in the denominator of (11) and, as can be seen from (5), (6), and Fig. 10, is an increasing function of w.

Fig. 13 shows the response curves of three narrow-band filters with $w = 0.047$. The filter of Fig. 13(a) is built without using overlaid gaps. The filter of Fig. 13(b) was built with overlaid gaps, and short-circuits the even CPW mode. While the fractional bandwidths and out-of-band attenuation characteristics of the filters in Fig. 13(a) and (b) are roughly as predicted, the center frequencies and midband transmission losses are not. It is apparent from a comparison of Figs. 11, 12, and 13 that the moderate bandwidth filters of Figs. 11 and 12 perform adequately as designed with no further adjustments necessary, while the narrow bandwidth filters of Fig. 13(a) and (b) require tuning of the resonant sections to achieve the predicted performance.

Tuning of CPW resonant sections, as suggested by Wang and Schwarz [35], can be accomplished by placing metallic conducting planes above the CPW circuits. Fig. 13(c) shows the transmission loss for the filter of Fig. 13(a) when a conducting plane over the third resonant section was adjusted to a height of $0.026\lambda_0$ above the dielectric surface.

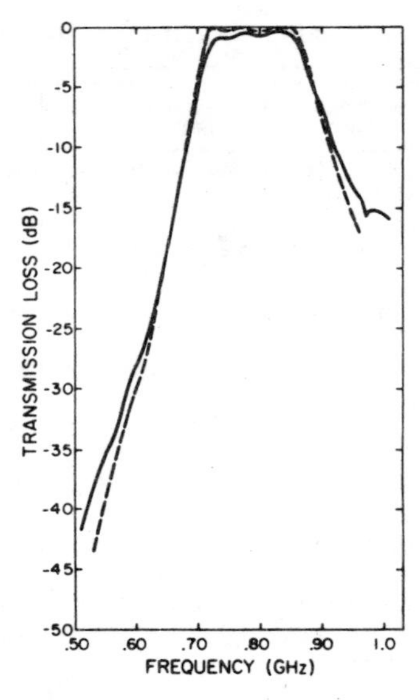

Fig. 11. Measured (solid line) and ideal (dashed lines) transmission curves for a 3-section CPW bandpass filter ($w = 0.177$).

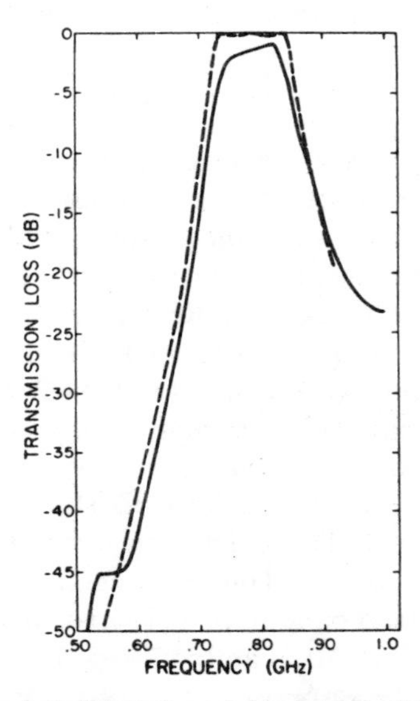

Fig. 12. Measured (solid line) and ideal (dashed lines) transmission curves for a 3-section CPW bandpass filter ($w = 0.13$).

The excess loss of the tuned filter of Fig. 13(c) was 2.7 dB, considerably less than the 5.5-dB excess loss of the similar, but untuned, filter of Fig. 13(a). The excess loss of the tuned filter of Fig. 13(c) was even lower than the 3.5-dB excess loss predicted in Table II. By placing adjustable conducting planes above all three resonant sections, the passband center frequency could be adjusted upward by 7 percent while maintaining the low filter loss and the passband shape of Fig. 13(c). Attempts to shift the center frequency further, however, resulted in distortion of the shape of the filter passband and increased excess loss.

V. Predicted Performance at Higher Frequencies

We envision the use of CPW filters in planar near-millimeter-wave technology. Thus, the question of ohmic losses at frequencies up to perhaps 100 GHz must be considered.

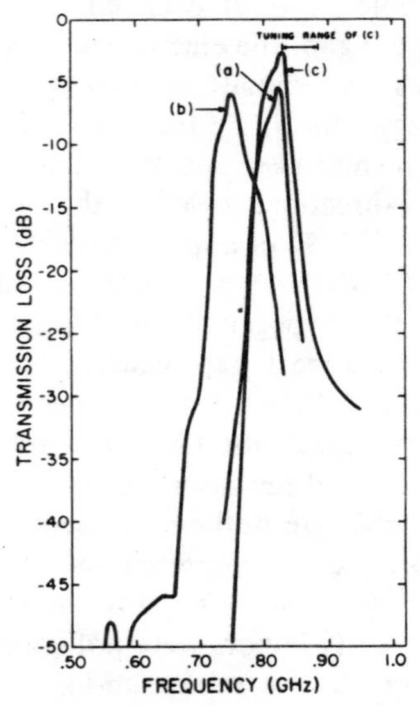

Fig. 13. Measured transmission curves for 3-section CPW bandpass filters ($w = 0.047$). (a) The response of an untuned filter with no overlay. (b) The response of an untuned filter with overlaid gaps. (c) The response of the filter of Fig. 13(a) after tuning.

Ohmic losses in CPW have been studied by a number of authors [1], [3], [4], [36]–[39]. Let us define an additional unloaded quality factor Q_{u0} for single resonant sections as the value that Q_u would take if ohmic losses, but not radiation losses, were present. Similarly, we define Q_{ur} as the unloaded quality factor including radiation losses, but not ohmic losses. Because the low frequency losses measured in the last section were dominated by radiation losses, for CPW we identify Q_{ur} with the Q_u plotted in Fig. 10. In estimating Q_{ur} we have assumed that the tolerances of photolithographic millimeter-wave structures will be at least as good as those of our microwave models. This assumption is valid for frequencies up to at least 150 GHz if a photolithographic resolution of one micron is used. The high-frequency unloaded Q, Q_{uh}, is then given by $Q_{uh}^{-1} = Q_{ur}^{-1} + Q_{u0}^{-1}$. Once the Q_{uh} are known, the excess filter loss can be obtained from (10).

Using data from Denlinger [36], we estimate Q_{u0} to be 350 at 75 GHz, although the actual value will depend on the smoothness of the metal surfaces and of the edges defined by the photolithographic process. Hence, at 75 GHz the filters of Figs. 11, 12, and 13 would have excess losses 0.25 dB, 0.34 dB, and 0.95 dB greater than those shown for 0.78 GHz, respectively. The excess filter losses would be 0.7 dB, 1.3 dB, and 3.7 dB, respectively. These losses are reasonably low for an open structure, and recommend CPW filters for use in the near-millimeter-wave region.

Bandpass filters at millimeter frequencies are most commonly realized in closed structures such as rectangular waveguide and coaxial line. Bandpass filters realized in finline [28], [29], a closed guiding structure, are particularly interesting as the filter elements are defined photolithographically. Losses of finline bandpass filters with fractional bandwidths less than 0.05 are at least 2 dB lower [28], [29] than those of comparable CPW filters in the

75-GHz range. (The transition loss necessary for integration of semiconductor devices with finline bandpass filters has been included.) At moderate fractional bandwidths (0.1–0.2), however, the losses of finline and CPW become comparable. From the results of Meier [30], we estimate the loss of a three-resonator finline bandpass filter with fractional bandwidth of 0.125, 75-GHz center frequency, and the appropriate transitions for semiconductor device integration to be 1.7 dB. This is to be compared with the 1.3-dB loss estimated above for a similar CPW bandpass filter. The great advantage of CPW over finline is, of course, its simplicity of manufacture and its compatibility with fully planar structures.

It is also interesting to compare the losses of CPW at near-millimeter wavelengths with those of microstrip, the most popular planar open guiding structure. Using data from Denlinger [36], Q_{u0} for microstrip is estimated to be 850 at 75 GHz. This is to be compared with the value of 350 for CPW. The microstrip resonant section has lower ohmic losses than the CPW resonant section because the fields in microstrip are not as concentrated at the conductor edges as they are in CPW. Radiation losses of gaps in microstrip, on the other hand, are somewhat larger, with the thick substrates desirable for millimeter-wave circuits. Assuming the same dielectric constant and substrate thickness, the value of Q_{ur} for a 50-Ω half-wavelength resonant section of microstrip is calculated by [36, eq. (15)] to be 22, if simple gaps such as those shown in Fig. 6(c) are assumed. This is to be compared with the value of 75 measured for a large simple-gap resonant section of CPW in this work. In order to obtain a comparison, we calculate the combined unloaded single-resonant-section quality factors Q_{uh} for resonant sections terminated in simple gaps. These are calculated to be approximately 62 for CPW sections and 21 for microstrip sections. Thus, at least for the case of simple gaps, the CPW filter is seen to have lower loss than its microstrip equivalent. This is due to the dominance of radiation losses in the case of simple gaps on thick substrates. With the gap types of Fig. 6(a) and (b), however, ohmic losses may be relatively more significant, and the advantage of CPW may become smaller or nonexistent.

VI. Conclusions

Our results show that high-efficiency bandpass filters can readily be built in planar form. Design is straightforward and leads to predictable results. Excess loss can also be estimated accurately in most cases. The minimum insertion loss of 0.45 dB measured at 0.78 GHz for a filter with a 17.7-percent fractional bandwidth is quite satisfactory for an open structure. Filters with fractional bandwidths smaller than 5 percent are also feasible, but require tuning. Special filters intended to block the even CPW mode have been demonstrated. Loss estimates indicate that CPW filters will continue to be useful at frequencies as high as 100 GHz.

The low radiation loss of CPW recommends it for use in planar integrated circuits. Integrated circuits with low-loss guides and tunable components may eventually become nearly as efficient as conventional waveguide systems.

Acknowledgment

The authors thank Nan-lei Wang for his assistance and encouragement.

References

[1] K. C. Gupta, R. Garg, and I. J. Bahl, *Microstrip Lines and Slotlines*. Dedham, MA: Artech House, 1979.

[2] M. Houdart, "Coplanar lines: Application to broadband microwave integrated circuits," in *Proc. Sixth Eur. Microwave Conf.*, 1976, pp. 49–53.

[3] R. A. Pucel, "Design considerations for monolithic microwave circuits," *IEEE Microwave Theory Tech.*, vol. MTT-29, pp. 513–534, June 1981.

[4] D. R. Ch'en and D. R. Decker, "MMIC's: The next generation of microwave components," *Microwave J.*, pp. 67–78, May 1980.

[5] T. Hatsuda, "Computation of coplanar-type strip-line characteristics by relaxation method and its application to microwave circuits," *IEEE Microwave Theory Tech.*, vol. MTT-23, pp. 795–802, Oct. 1975.

[6] T. Kitazawa and Y. Hayashi, "Coupled slots on an anistropic sapphire substrate," *IEEE Microwave Theory Tech.*, vol. MTT-29, pp. 1035–1040, Oct. 1981.

[7] J. B. Knorr and B. Kuchler, "Analysis of coupled slots and coplanar strips on dielectric substrate," *IEEE Microwave Theory Tech.*, vol. MTT-23, pp. 541–548, July 1975.

[8] C. P. Wen, "Coplanar-waveguide directional couplers," *IEEE Microwave Theory Tech.*, vol. MTT-18, pp. 318–332, June 1970.

[9] R. N. Simons, "Suspended broadside-coupled slot line with overlay," *IEEE Microwave Theory Tech.*, vol. MTT-30, pp. 76–81, Jan. 1982.

[10] T. Kitazawa and Y. Hayashi, "Quasi-static characteristics of coplanar waveguide on a sapphire substrate with its optical axis inclined," *IEEE Microwave Theory Tech.*, vol. MTT-30, pp. 920–922, June 1982.

[11] L. E. Dickens and D. W. Maki, "An integrated-circuit balanced mixer image and sum enhanced," *IEEE Microwave Theory Tech.*, vol. MTT-23, pp. 276–281, Mar. 1975.

[12] S. Dixon, R. J. Malik, J. Paul, P. Yen, T. R. Aucoin, and L. T. Yaun, "Subharmonic mixer using planar doped barrier diodes," in *Proc. IEEE MTT-S Int. Microwave Symp.*, 1982, pp. 27–29.

[13] L. Bui and D. Ball, "Broadband planar balanced mixers for millimeter-wave applications," in *Proc. IEEE MTT-S Int. Microwave Symp.*, 1982, pp. 204–205.

[14] L. Yuan, J. Paul, and P. Yen, "140 GHz quasi-optical planar mixers," in *Proc. IEEE MTT-S Int. Microwave Symp.*, 1982, pp. 374–375.

[15] J. K, Hunton and J. S. Takeuchi, "Recent developments in microwave slotline mixers and frequency multipliers," in *Proc. IEEE MTT-S Int. Microwave Symp.*, 1970, pp. 196–199.

[16] H. Ogawa, M. Akaike, M. Aikawa, T. Karaki, and J. Watanabe, "A 26-GHz band integrated circuit of a double-balanced mixer and circulators," *IEEE Microwave Theory Tech.*, vol. MTT-30, pp. 34–41, Jan. 1982.

[17] A. Cappello and J. Pierro, "A 22 to 24 GHz cryogenically cooled low noise FET amplifier in coplanar waveguide," in *Proc. IEEE MTT-S Int. Microwave Symp.*, 1982, pp. 19–22.

[18] J. K. Hunton, "A microwave integrated circuit balanced mixer with broad-bandwidth," in *Proc. IEEE MTT Microelectronics Symp.*, 1969, pp. A3.1–A3.2.

[19] B. J. Clifton, G. D. Alley, R. A. Murphy, and W. J. Piacentini, "Cooled low noise GaAs monolithic mixers at 110 GHz," in *Proc. IEEE MTT-S Int. Microwave Symp.*, 1981, pp. 444–446.

[20] J. Kohler and B. Schiek, "Broadband microwave frequency doublers," *Radio Electron. Eng.*, vol. 48, pp. 29–32, Jan./Feb. 1978.

[21] C. P. Wen, "Coplanar waveguide: A surface strip transmission line suitable for nonreciprocal gyromagnetic device applications," *IEEE Microwave Theory Tech.*, vol. MTT-17, pp. 1087–1090, Dec. 1969.

[22] A. Nesic, "Slotted antenna array excited by a coplanar waveguide," *Electron. Lett.*, vol. 18, no. 6, pp. 275–276, Mar. 1982.

[23] M. Aikawa and H. Ogawa, "A new MIC magic-T using coupled slotlines," *IEEE Microwave Theory Tech.*, vol. MTT-28, pp. 523–528, June 1980.

[24] P. A. R. Holder, "*X*-band microwave integrated circuits using slotline and coplanar waveguide," *Radio Electron. Eng.*, vol. 48, pp. 38–42, Jan./Feb. 1978.

[25] G. L. Matthaei, L. Young, and E. M. T. Jones, *Microwave Filters, Impedance-Matching Networks, and Coupling Structures*. New York: McGraw-Hill, 1964.

[26] R. E. Collin, *Foundations for Microwave Engineering*. New York: McGraw-Hill, 1966.

[27] S. B. Cohn, "Direct-coupled-resonator filters," *Proc. IRE*, vol. 45, pp. 187–196, Feb. 1957.

[28] F. Arndt, J. Bornemann, D. Grauerholz, and R. Vahldieck, "Theory and design of low-insertion loss fin-line filters," *IEEE Microwave Theory Tech.*, vol. MTT-30, pp. 155–163, Feb. 1982.

[29] A. M. K. Saad and K. Schunemann, "Design and performance of fin-line bandpass filters," in *Proc. Tenth European Microwave Conf.*, Sept. 1980, pp. 397–401.

[30] P. J. Meier, "Integrated fin-line millimeter components," *IEEE Microwave Theory Tech.*, vol. MTT-22, pp. 1209–1216, Dec. 1974.

[31] S. B. Cohn, "Dissipation loss in multiple-coupled-resonator filters," *Proc. IRE*, vol. 47, pp. 1342–1348, Aug. 1959.

[32] J. J. Taub and B. F. Bogner, "Design of three-resonator band-pass filters having minimum insertion loss," *Proc. IRE*, vol. 45, pp. 681–687, May 1957.

[33] E. G. Fubini and E. A. Guillemin, "Minimum insertion loss filters," *Proc. IRE*, vol. 47, pp. 37–41, Jan. 1959.

[34] M. Dishal, "Design of dissipative band-pass filters producing desired exact amplitude-frequency characteristics," *Proc. IRE*, vol. 37, pp. 1050–1069, Sept. 1949.

[35] N. Wang and S. E. Schwarz, "Planar oscillators for monolithic integration" *Int. J. Infr. Millimeter Waves*, vol. 3, pp. 771–782, Nov. 1982.

[36] E. J. Denlinger, "Losses of microstrip lines," *IEEE Microwave Theory Tech.*, vol. MTT-28, pp. 513–522, June 1980.

[37] A. Gopinath, "Losses in coplanar waveguides," *IEEE Trans. Microwave Theory Tech.*, vol. MTT-30, pp. 1101–1104, July 1982.

[38] B. E. Spielman, "Dissipation loss effects in isolated and coupled transmission lines," *IEEE Microwave Theory Tech.*, vol. MTT-25, pp. 648–655, Aug. 1977.

[39] J. A. Higgins, A. Gupta, G. Robinson, and D. R. Ch'en, "Microwave GaAs FET monolithic circuits," in *Int. Solid State Circuits Conf. Dig.*, 1979, pp. 20–21.

Junction Reactance and Dimensional Tolerance Effects on X-Band 3-dB Directional Couplers

WILLIAM H. LEIGHTON, JR., MEMBER, IEEE, AND ARTHUR G. MILNES, FELLOW, IEEE

***Abstract*—Theoretical characteristics are presented for *X*-band 3-dB rat-race and branch-line couplers using gold microstrip lines with a semi-insulating GaAs dielectric. The rat-race configuration is shown to be less influenced by junction reactances and dimensional tolerances and has a greater bandwidth than the two-branch coupler. However, the rat-race coupler has the disadvantage that the output arms are not adjacent. Three-branch couplers are shown to have bandwidth comparable to the rat-race coupler but are much more sensitive to junction reactances and dimensional tolerances.**

Manuscript received November 25, 1970; revised March 15, 1971. This work was supported in part by the U. S. Army Electronics Command, Ft. Monmouth, N. J., under Contract DAAB07-67-C-0583, and in part by a National Science Foundation graduate fellowship.

W. H. Leighton, Jr., was with Carnegie-Mellon University, Pittsburgh, Pa. He is now with Sandia Laboratories, Albuquerque, N. Mex. 87115.

A. G. Milnes is with Carnegie-Mellon University, Pittsburgh, Pa. 15213.

Introduction

Typical 3-dB microstrip directional couplers are shown in Fig. 1. Applications of such couplers include balanced mixers, frequency discriminators, and phase shifters. In the low-frequency approximation these couplers are considered as interconnected transmission lines and the effects of the junctions are neglected. When the size of the junctions are not negligible compared to a wavelength, however, there can be appreciable equivalent reactances at the junctions. In this paper the behavior of three types of 3-dB coupler are calculated using the low-frequency approximation and also including the effects of junction reactances. In addition, the effect of small deviations in coupler dimensions from nominal is considered.

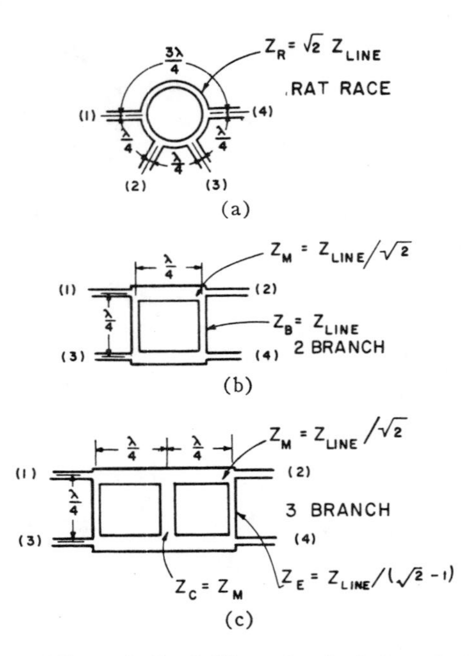

Fig. 1. Microstrip-line 3-dB couplers for balanced mixers.

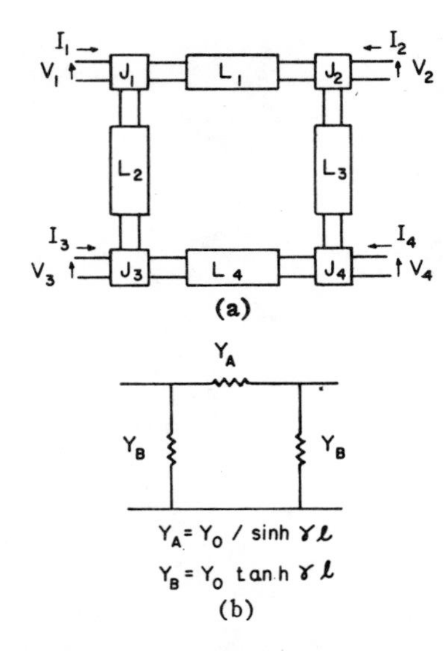

Fig. 2. Equivalent circuit for two-branch or rat-race couplers. (a) Schematic showing line and junction components. (b) Transmission-line equivalent circuit.

The important characteristics of directional couplers are the following.

1) *Coupling Amplitude and Phase:* When a signal is applied to terminal 1 of either of the branch-line couplers in Fig. 1, outputs should appear at terminals 2 and 4 that are equal in amplitude and differ in phase by 90°. For the rat-race coupler [Fig. 1(a)], outputs at terminals 2 and 4 due to an input at 1 should appear 180° out of phase, while those due to an input at 3 should appear in phase. The difference between the actual phase relationship and the correct phase angle between the two outputs will be called phase error.

2) *VSWR:* The standing-wave ratio is related to the amount of power, assumed to be coming from a matched 50-Ω source, that is reflected by the coupler when matched loads are connected to the coupler outputs. A VSWR of 1.9 corresponds to 10-percent reflected power.

3) *Isolation:* Isolation characterizes the amount of power coupled into the theoretically decoupled arm. An isolation factor of 10 dB means that 10 percent of the incident power is coupled into the isolated arm.

4) *Insertion Loss:* In *X*-band Au–GaAs microstrip, attenuation is caused primarily by resistive loss in the microstrip conductors. At higher frequencies, radiation loss may also be significant. The attenuation is a function of line impedance and standing-wave ratio in the line.

The suitability of a coupler for use in a given application depends on all of the above characteristics. In comparing different couplers, the passband of a coupler will be arbitrarily defined as that frequency range in which the total signal loss due to reflected power and power coupled to the isolated terminal does not exceed 10 percent of the incident power, inequality of the coupling amplitudes into thé two output arms is less than 1 dB, and phase error is less than 11°. Either a phase error of 11° or a coupling amplitude inequality of 1 dB is sufficient to limit the AM local oscillator noise suppression of an otherwise perfectly balanced mixer to 20 dB. This definition of bandwidth is reasonable in an investigation of couplers for use in balanced mixers. If the couplers are to be used for other purposes, the importance attached to different parameters may be different. For example, in a balanced duplexer using two identical couplers, phase errors in the two couplers cancel while the effects of VSWR and poor isolation add.

The study that follows is more extensive than those previously available because allowance is made for the reactance of the microstrip-line junctions. This is significant when the dimensions of the lines are not negligible compared to a wavelength in the line. Furthermore, the study examines the effects of dimensional tolerances which can become critical at high frequencies.

Coupler Analysis with Junction Effects

An equivalent circuit for the two-branch coupler, with junction effects, is given in Fig. 2(a). The same circuit can be used for the rat-race coupler if terminals 1 and 2 are interchanged. L represents a section of microstrip line and J represents any junction effects. Assuming that only the quasi-TEM mode described by Wheeler [1] can propagate, each section of line can be represented by the π equivalent circuit in Fig. 2(b) where Y_0 is the characteristic admittance, γ is the propagation constant, which is a weak function of line admittance, and l is the length of the line measured from the appropriate reference planes at the junctions. The usual analytical treatments of directional couplers neglect the junction effects represented by J in Fig. 2(a). With this simplification each line can be replaced by its π equivalent, and the normal mode analysis described by Reed and Wheeler [2] can be used to determine the coupler properties.

In determining a junction equivalent circuit, an approximate model that is similar to a model previously used by Oliner [3] and Altschuler and Oliner [4] to calculate junction effects in symmetric strip lines is used. The cross section of a microstrip line is shown in Fig. 3(a). The line may be approximated by the model shown in Fig. 3(b), which represents a section of parallel-plate TEM transmission line with the same impedance and propagation constant as the actual line. The required value of the effective relative dielectric constant is

$$\epsilon_e = \left(\frac{\lambda_0}{\lambda_g}\right)^2 \tag{1}$$

where λ_0 is the free-space wavelength and λ_g is the wavelength in the microstrip. The effective linewidth D is

$$D = \frac{h}{Z_0}\sqrt{\frac{\mu_0}{\epsilon_e \epsilon_0}} \tag{2}$$

where h is the dielectric thickness and Z_0 is the characteristic impedance. Both ϵ_e and Z_0 have been calculated for a wide range of w/h ratios and dielectric constants by Wheeler [1]. Fig. 3(c) shows the Babinet equivalent of the model in Fig. 3(b), obtained by interchanging the conductors with the magnetic walls. The equivalent circuit of a T in this model, which represents the dual of the microstrip line, has been determined by Marcuvitz [5]. The equivalent circuit of a symmetric T junction in microstrip line can be obtained by taking the dual of the circuit derived by Marcuvitz. The results, analogous to those obtained by Altschuler and Oliner [4], are given in Fig. 4, where

$$n = \frac{\sin(\pi D_2/\lambda_g)}{\pi D_2/\lambda_g} \tag{3}$$

$$\frac{X_A}{Z_0} = -\frac{D_2}{\lambda_g}\left(n\frac{\pi}{4}\right)^2 \tag{4}$$

and

$$\frac{X_B}{Z_0} = -\frac{X_A}{2Z_0} + \frac{2D_1}{n^2\lambda_g}\left[\ln\left(\frac{1.43D_1}{D_2}\right) + 2\left(\frac{D_1}{\lambda_g}\right)^2\right], \quad \text{for } \frac{D_2}{D_1} > 0.5. \tag{5}$$

X_A/Z_0, X_B/Z_0, and n are all functions of D_1/λ_g and D_2/λ_g, as D_1 and D_2 depend only upon line impedance and substrate dielectric constant; they are independent of frequency. Junction effects thus become more significant at high frequencies and disappear entirely in the low-frequency limit as D_1/λ_g and D_2/λ_g approach zero.

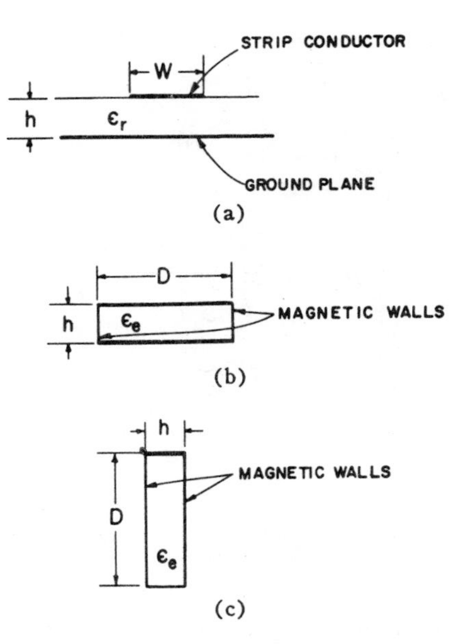

Fig. 3. Microstrip-line models used for junction-effect calculations. (a) Microstrip line. (b) Microstrip-line model with fringing eliminated. D is an effective linewidth and ϵ_e is an effective dielectric constant. (c) Babinet equivalent (dual) of (b).

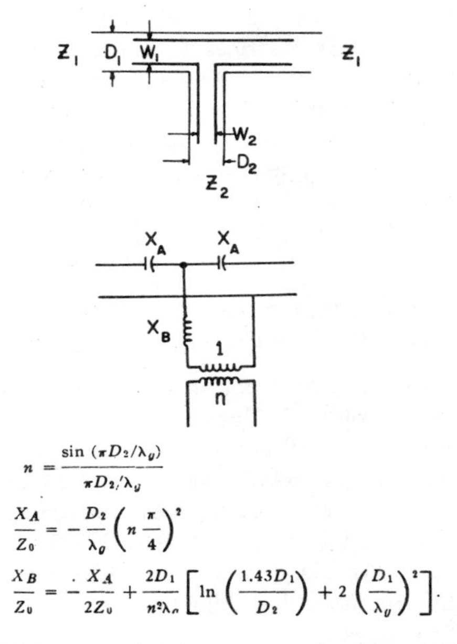

Fig. 4. Equivalent circuit for a symmetric microstrip-line T.

The circuit includes no allowance for radiation loss. Lewin [6] has calculated radiation loss in symmetric strip line. The approximations used are equally appropriate to microstrip when the correct value of effective linewidth (D in Fig. 3) is used. Based on these results, it appears that radiation loss at the junctions is less than the resistive loss of 9-GHz Au–GaAs microstrip lines. Calculations have shown that even substantially higher losses have little effect on the shape of the coupler characteristics other than adding an insertion loss; so radiation from junctions can be neglected.

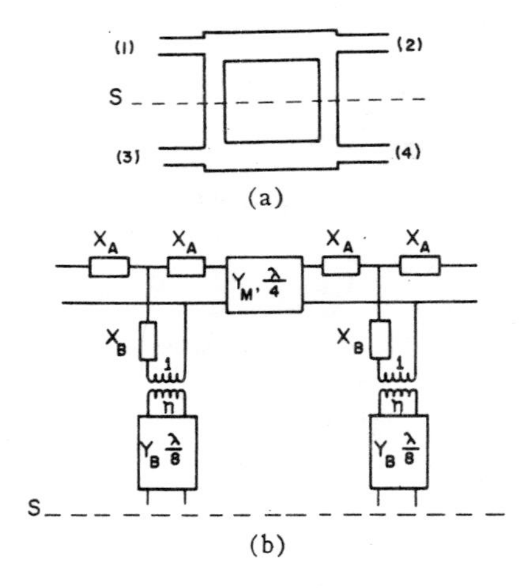

Fig. 5. Two-branch coupler and equivalent circuit with junction components.

The equivalent circuit of the two-branch coupler including junction reactances is given in Fig. 5 where S represents the symmetry plane. This circuit can be analyzed by the method of Reed and Wheeler [2], who used the same circuit but without junction effects. The even- and odd-mode (open and short circuits at the symmetry plane) $ABCD$ matrices of the two-port in Fig. 5(b) are determined, and the even- and odd-mode solutions are superimposed to obtain a complete solution for the four-port coupler. The appropriate $ABCD$ matrices are given in the Appendix. The rat-race coupler and couplers with more than two branches can be treated in a similar fashion. Details are given elsewhere [7].

Theoretical Characteristics of the Two-Branch Coupler

In Figs. 6–10 the isolation, coupling, and VSWR of various couplers are plotted. Power is assumed to be applied to terminal 1. In all cases, the nominal center frequency f_0 is 9 GHz. For 50-Ω lines on a 0.025-cm semi-insulating GaAs substrate (relative dielectric constant 13), $\lambda_g/4$ is 0.275 cm at 9 GHz, and linewidth is 0.02 cm. The effective linewidth (D in Fig. 3) is 0.06 cm. For a line impedance of $50/\sqrt{2}$ Ω, the figures are 0.268, 0.032, and 0.083 cm.

Fig. 6 shows the performance of a two-branch coupler. The bandwidth, using the arbitrary definition in the Introduction, is 18 percent of the center frequency if no allowance is made for junction effects and 20 percent when junction effects are included. It is seen that junction effects shift the center of the band down in frequency by 4 percent. Phase error is less than 2° at all frequencies within the band if junction effects are neglected and reaches 8° when they are included.

Examination of the effects of constructional tolerances shows that if the main-line impedance is 10 percent high, as in Fig. 7, the bandwidth is increased at the expense of unequal coupling at the center frequency. When

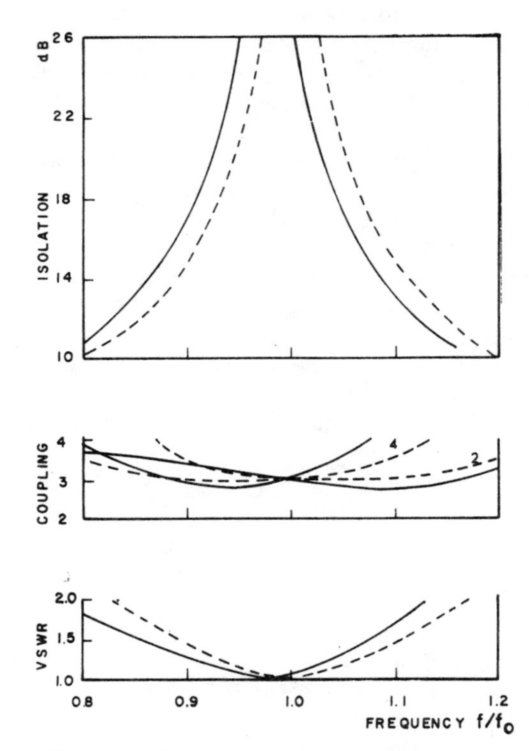

Fig. 6. Theoretical isolation, coupling, and VSWR of a lossless two-branch 9-GHz 3-dB coupler with nominal dimensions, with (solid line) and without (broken line) allowance for junction effects.

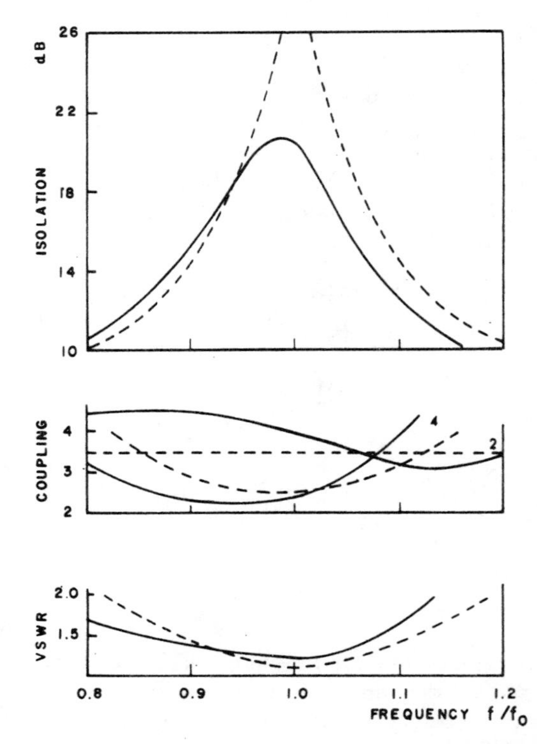

Fig. 7. Theoretical performance of 9-GHz two-branch coupler with the main-line impedance 10 percent high or the branch-line impedance 10 percent low, with (solid line) and without (broken line) junction effects.

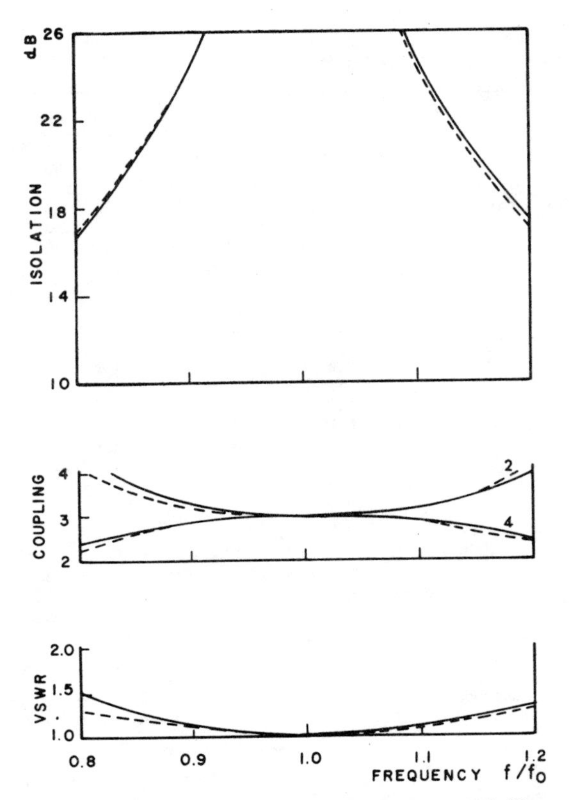

Fig. 8. Theoretical performance of a 9-GHz rat-race 3-dB coupler with nominal dimensions, with (solid line) and without (broken line) junction effects.

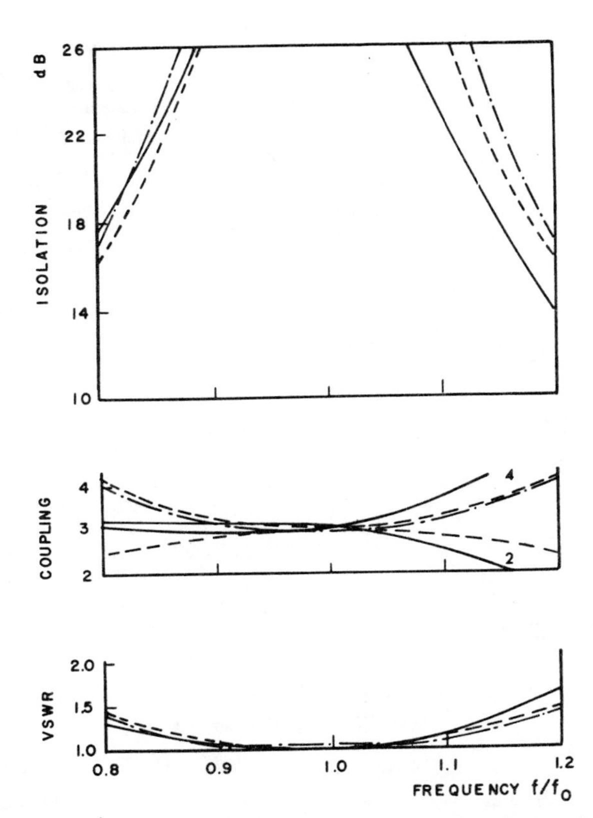

Fig. 10. Theoretical 9-GHz three-branch coupler characteristics. ———, Butterworth coupler with junction effects. - - - - - - -, Butterworth coupler without junction effects. - · - · - · -, Chebyshev coupler without junction effects.

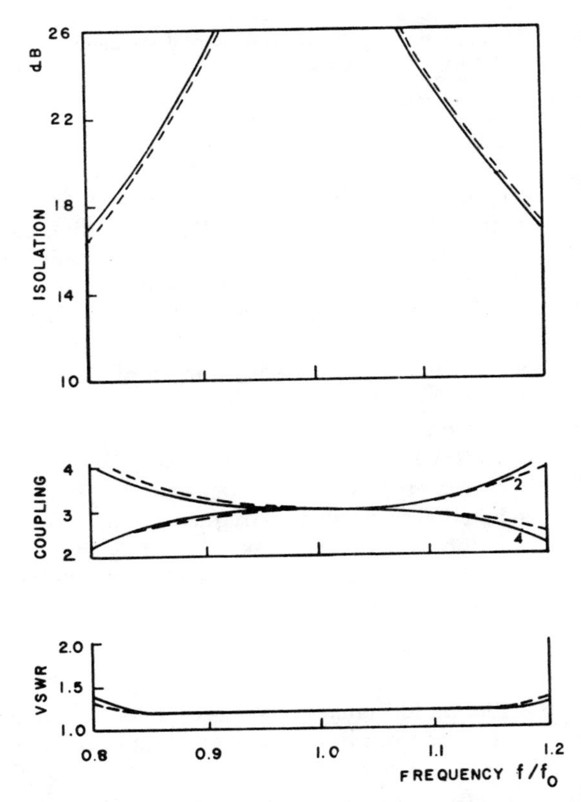

Fig. 9. Characteristics of a 9-GHz rat-race coupler with the ring impedance 10 percent high, with and without junction effects.

junction effects are included, the sensitivity of the coupling curves to line impedance is twice as great as when they are neglected. Decreasing the main-line impedance below $Z_{\text{line}}/\sqrt{2}$ has the effect of moving the two coupling curves away from each other so that coupling into the two output arms is not equal at any frequency. A decrease in the branch-arm impedance [Z_B in Fig. 1(b)] has the same effect as an increase of the same magnitude in the main line. Decreasing the length of the branch arms by 10 percent raises the center frequency slightly, as expected, and the bandwidth when junction effects are included is increased from 20 to 27 percent. Coupling inequality at midband is about 1/4 dB.

For a 9-GHz coupler on a GaAs dielectric 0.025 cm thick and a 50-Ω nominal line impedance, the length of a branch arm is 0.275 cm. It is therefore easy to hold dimensional tolerances of lengths to a few percent. However, impedances are somewhat more difficult to control, especially at higher frequencies where dimensions are still smaller and variations in substrate thickness and surface conditions are important. On some substrates the dielectric constant may also differ slightly from sample to sample.

Including the theoretical loss of Au–GaAs microstrip at 9 GHz has little effect on the shape of the curves and introduces only 0.1-dB insertion loss. Kurzrok [8] has calculated the effect of losses on isolation using a simpli-

TABLE I

COMPARISON OF THREE TYPES OF 9-GHz 3-dB COUPLERS

Coupler	Frequency (GHz)	Junction Effects Neglected				Junction Effects Included			
		VSWR	Coupling (dB)		Isolation (dB)	VSWR	Coupling (dB)		Isolation (dB)
			C_2	C_4			C_2	C_4	
Two-branch	8	1.5	3.0	3.6	14	1.3	3.4	2.9	16
	9	1.0	3.0	3.0	∞	1.1	3.0	3.0	26
	10	1.5	3.0	3.6	14	1.8	2.7	4.7	13
Three-branch	8	1.1	2.8	3.4	27	1.1	3.2	3.0	27
	9	1.0	3.0	3.0	>30	1.0	3.0	3.0	>30
	10	1.2	2.8	3.4	27	1.1	2.5	3.8	23
Rat-race	8	1.1	3.3	2.9	24	1.2	3.4	2.9	24
	9	1.0	3.0	3.0	∞	1.0	3.0	3.0	>30
	10	1.1	3.2	2.9	24	1.1	3.2	2.9	24

fied method that neglects junction effects and is valid only at the coupler design frequency. His results are in agreement with the present theory, neglecting junction effects.

THEORETICAL CHARACTERISTICS OF THE RAT-RACE AND THREE-BRANCH COUPLERS

The theoretical isolation, coupling, and VSWR for the rat-race coupler are given in Figs. 8 and 9. Junction effects are much less significant than in the two-branch coupler, and the line impedances are much less critical. The bandwidth of the rat-race coupler, using the same arbitrary definition given in the Introduction, is about 30 percent. The theoretical loss of a Au–GaAs 9-GHz rat-race coupler is 0.1 dB.

Considering now the three-branch coupler, the calculations become more involved and there is a larger number of design parameters available. For perfect coupling at midband, the line admittances must satisfy the relations

$$\frac{Y_C}{(Y_M)^2} = \frac{1}{\sqrt{2}}$$
$$Y_E = \sqrt{2} \pm 1 \qquad (6)$$

where Y_M, Y_C, and Y_E are the main-line, center-branch, and end-branch admittances normalized to the nominal line admittance outside the coupler. The impedances in Fig. 1(c) represent a special case of these relations. A method has been developed by Levy and Lind [9] for giving the VSWR and isolation, but not the coupling of a branch-line coupler, a maximally flat (Butterworth) or approximate equal ripple (Chebyshev) characteristic. The synthesis procedure neglects junction reactances.

Fig. 10 shows characteristics of three-branch couplers with Butterworth and Chebyshev characteristics and with ideal performance at midband. Performance of the Butterworth coupler is indistinguishable on the graph from that of the coupler with ideal midband performance.

The effect of junction reactances on the three-branch couplers is qualitatively the same as on the two-branch coupler, but smaller in magnitude. The three-branch couplers are as sensitive to variations in line dimensions as the two-branch coupler. The main-line, end-branch, and center-branch impedances are equally important. The theoretical loss of this type of gold on GaAs couplers at 9 GHz is 0.4 dB. This loss is larger than for the two-branch and rat-race couplers because the three-branch form is physically larger and because it uses microstrip lines of higher impedance, which have higher resistive loss.

Tables I and II summarize some of the information from the graphs. Coupler behavior at three frequencies is listed using the low-frequency approximation with junction effects neglected, including junction effects, and for some selected deviations of line impedances from their nominal values.

TABLE II

COUPLER COMPARISON INCLUDING JUNCTION EFFECTS AND SOME INCORRECT IMPEDANCE LEVELS

Coupler	Frequency (GHz)	VSWR	Coupling (dB)		Isolation (dB)
			C_2	C_4	
Two-branch[a]	8	1.4	4.5	2.4	15
	9	1.2	4.0	2.4	21
	10	1.7	3.1	4.0	12
Three-branch[b]	8	1.2	4.1	2.3	23
	9	1.1	3.8	2.5	23
	10	1.0	3.1	3.0	29
Rat-race[c]	8	1.2	3.2	2.9	25
	9	1.2	3.0	3.0	>30
	10	1.2	3.2	3.0	25

[a] Main line impedance 10 percent above nominal.
[b] Butterworth-type coupler with main line impedance 10 percent above nominal.
[c] Ring impedance 10 percent above nominal.

CONCLUSIONS

The performances of rat-race, two-branch, and three-branch microstrip couplers at X-band frequencies have been calculated with and without junction effects. The rat-race configuration has a bandwidth about 1/3 wider than the two-branch coupler and is considerably less sensitive to junction effects and to the effects of variations of geometry because of dimensional tolerances. The principal disadvantage of the rat-race coupler is that the output arms are not adjacent and therefore a crossover connection may be needed.

The three-branch coupler has bandwidth comparable to the rat-race coupler but has higher losses. Branch-line couplers with more than three branches would have broader bandwidth and higher losses. Sensitivity of the two- and three-branch couplers to variations in parameters is comparable, and junction effects are significant in both.

Appendix

Coupling, VSWR, and isolation of any of the couplers discussed can be determined using their symmetry as described by Reed and Wheeler [2]. Consider the equivalent circuit in Fig. 5(b). *ABCD* matrices can be written for each element in the equivalent circuit. Equations (7)–(9) give matrices for a series impedance X_A, a shunt admittance Y_S, and a section of transmission line.

$$[M_1] = \begin{bmatrix} 1 & X_A \\ 0 & 1 \end{bmatrix}, \quad \text{for a series impedance } X_A \tag{7}$$

$$[M_2] = \begin{bmatrix} 1 & 0 \\ Y_S & 1 \end{bmatrix}, \quad \text{for a shunt admittance } Y_S \tag{8}$$

$$[M_3] = \begin{bmatrix} \cosh \gamma l & Z_0 \sinh \gamma l \\ \dfrac{1}{Z_0} \sinh \gamma l & \cosh \gamma l \end{bmatrix}, \quad \text{for a transmission line of length } l \text{ and characteristic impedance } Z_0. \tag{9}$$

The overall matrix for the equivalent circuit is given by (10):

$$[M_0] = [M_1]\cdot[M_2]\cdot[M_1]\cdot[M_3]\cdot[M_1]\cdot[M_2]\cdot[M_1] \tag{10}$$

where in $[M_2]$

$$Y_S = 1 \bigg/ \left(X_B + \frac{1}{n^2} (Z_B \coth \gamma l) \right), \quad \text{even mode}$$

$$Y_S = 1 \bigg/ \left(X_B + \frac{1}{n^2} (Z_B \tanh \gamma l) \right), \quad \text{odd mode}$$

Z_B = characteristic impedance of branch line

l = length of branch line to the symmetry plane.

From the overall *ABCD* matrix $[M_0]$, the transmission and reflection coefficients T and Γ can be determined for the even- and odd-mode two-ports:

$$T = \frac{2}{A + B + C + D}.$$

$$\Gamma = (A + B - C - D) \frac{T}{2} \tag{11}$$

(coefficients normalized to the line impedance outside the coupler, i.e., 50 Ω).

The even mode represents the solution for the complete coupler when $V_1 = V_3$, and the odd mode represents the case when $V_1 = -V_3$. By superimposing the two solutions, the complete response to the source at port 1 is obtained.

$$B_1 = \tfrac{1}{2}(\Gamma_E + \Gamma_O) A_1$$

$$B_2 = \tfrac{1}{2}(T_E + T_O) A_1$$

$$B_3 = \tfrac{1}{2}(\Gamma_E - \Gamma_O) A_1$$

$$B_4 = \tfrac{1}{2}(T_E - T_O) A_1 \tag{12}$$

where A_1 is the input at port 1, B_n is the output at port n, and subscripts E and O refer to the even and odd modes.

Any desired values of line lengths and impedances can be substituted into (7)–(9), and the results evaluated numerically. The three-branch and rat-race couplers are treated in the same manner.

References

[1] H. A. Wheeler, "Transmission-line properties of parallel strips separated by a dielectric sheet," *IEEE Trans. Microwave Theory Tech.*, vol. MTT-13, Mar. 1965, pp. 172–185.

[2] J. Reed and G. J. Wheeler, "A method of analysis of symmetrical four-port networks," *IRE Trans. Microwave Theory Tech.* (Special Issue: Symp. Microwave Techniques), vol. MTT-4, Oct. 1965, pp. 246–252.

[3] A. A. Oliner, "Equivalent circuits for discontinuities in balanced strip transmission line," *IRE Trans. Microwave Theory Tech.* (Special Issue: Symp. Microstrip Circuits), vol. MMT-3, Mar. 1955, pp. 134–143.

[4] H. M. Altschuler and A. A. Oliner, "Discontinuities in the center conductor of symmetric strip transmission lines," *IRE Trans. Microwave Theory Tech.*, vol. MTT-8, May 1960, pp. 328–339.

[5] N. Marcuvitz, *Waveguide Handbook* (MIT Radiation Laboratory Series, vol. 10). Lexington, Mass.: Boston Technical Publishers, 1950, p. 363.

[6] L. Lewin, "Radiation from discontinuities in strip line," *Proc. Inst. Elec. Eng.*, vol. 107, pt. C, Feb. 1960, pp. 163–170.

[7] W. Leighton, "Monolithic X-band microstrip line mixers on semi-insulating gallium arsenide," Ph.D. dissertation, Carnegie-Mellon Univ., Pittsburgh, Pa., 1970.

[8] R. M. Kurzrok, "Isolation of lossy transmission line hybrid circuits," *IEEE Trans. Microwave Theory Tech.* (Corresp.), vol. MTT-15, Feb. 1967, pp. 127–128.

[9] R. Levy and L. F. Lind, "Synthesis of symmetrical branch-guide directional couplers," *IEEE Trans. Microwave Theory Tech.*, vol. MTT-16, Feb. 1968, pp. 80–89.

Interdigitated Microstrip Coupler Design

ADOLPH PRESSER, MEMBER, IEEE

***Abstract*—A design procedure for four-line interdigitated couplers is presented which provides excellent agreement between performance and actual coupler dimensions. The inclusion of a correction term for the finite metal thickness of the microstriplines is significant. Using existing odd-and-even mode impedance data of only two coupled lines in the array actual coupling coefficients in the 2.5–6.5-dB range are predictable to within ±0.05 dB. Graphs are shown which relate fabrication tolerances of dielectric constant and physical line dimensions to deviations in coupling and characteristic coupler impedance. The design was verified on 3-, 5-, and 6-dB couplers in the 1–5-GHz frequency range.**

I. Introduction

THE INTERDIGITATED 3-dB coupler as described by Lange [1] is a quadrature coupler and is well-suited for realization in microstrip form. The main advantages are its small size and the relatively large line separation when compared with the gaps of a conventional two-coupled line device and its relatively large bandwidth when compared with branch-line couplers. In the 3-dB form, it is an ideal component for balanced MIC amplifiers and mixers, and for binary power divider trees. Interdigitated couplers can be fabricated with coupling coefficients other than 3 dB and, therefore, can be used as components for serial type dividers with power divisions other than binary. There is a need for reliable design procedures that lead to producible couplers and predictable performance.

The original description of the interdigitated coupler [1] did not provide any design information in terms of the known coupled line parameters of a line pair or the parameters derived from a rigorous charge distribution of the four-line set. A more recent publication [2] presents design equations for such couplers with an arbitrary even number of coupled lines. The equations are written in terms of even- and odd-mode impedances of only two adjacent coupled lines in the array which are identical to any other pair in the structure. These equations together with published [3] microstrip data were used in a coupler design. The basic design assumes zero conductor thickness. The physical dimensions as determined by the basic design resulted, however, in overcoupled responses of fabricated couplers in the 3- to 6-dB range on two types of substrates, namely, alumina and BeO. A metallization thickness correction applied to the line and gap dimensions, similar to those described in [4], gave better results.

Manuscript received October 14, 1977. This work was supported in part by the U.S. Army ECOM, Fort Monmouth, NJ, under Contract DAAB07-75-C-1359.

The author is with the David Sarnoff Research Center, RCA Laboratories, Princeton, NJ 08540.

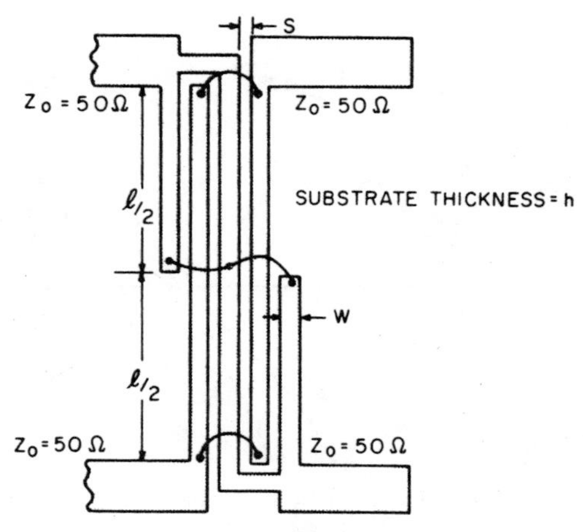

Fig. 1. Interdigitated coupler.

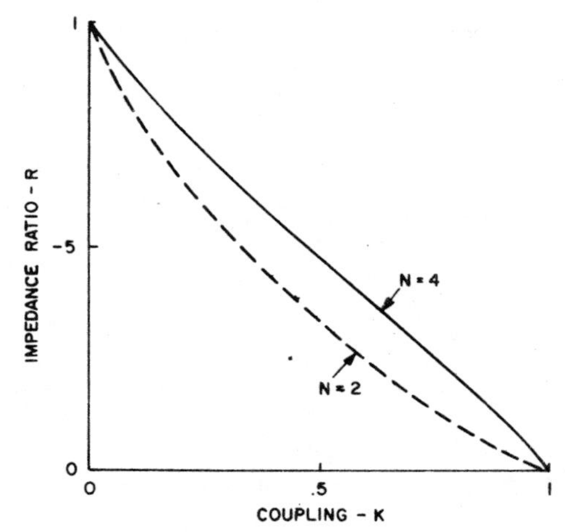

Fig. 2. Impedance ratio versus coupling.

The design accuracy was demonstrated with the check of at least 100 couplers with coupling coefficients ranging from 2.5 to 6.5 dB. These coefficients were predictable to within ±0.05 dB when actual line and gap dimensions were considered.

II. Coupler Design

The physical layout of a four-line coupler is shown in Fig. 1. The design of the coupler proceeds from the specification of the desired coupling coefficient (k) and the characteristic impedance (Z_0). The coupling region (l) is a quarter wavelength at the center frequency of the operating band. The objective now is to find the gap spacing (s) and the line width (w) for a given substrate of thickness (h) and with dielectric constant (ϵ_r).

The two basic equations for an N-line coupler (N even) can be expressed as

$$K=\frac{(N-1)(1-R^2)}{(N-1)(1+R^2)+2R} \tag{1}$$

$$Z=\frac{Z_{0o}}{Z_0}\,\frac{\sqrt{R[(N-1)+R][(N-1)R+1]}}{(1+R)} \tag{2}$$

$$R=\frac{Z_{0o}}{Z_{0e}}$$

in which Z_{0o} is the odd-mode impedance and Z_{0e} is the even-mode impedance of two-coupled lines. The impedance ratio R is plotted as a function of the coupling coefficient in Fig. 2 and the normalized ($Z_0=50\ \Omega$) odd-mode impedance Z is plotted in Fig. 3. Knowing the impedances Z_{0o} and Z_{0e}, the shape ratios w/h and s/h can be obtained from known coupled-line data [3] for a given dielectric. There exists one unique set of shape ratios for which both the coupling and the system impedance relationships are met simultaneously. The necessary shape ratios for 50-Ω couplers on $\epsilon_r=10$ material were collected as a function of coupling and are shown in Fig. 4. Also computed and shown in Fig. 5 are the shape ratios for a 50-Ω 3-dB coupler as a function of substrate dielectric constant over the ϵ_r range from 2 to 16.

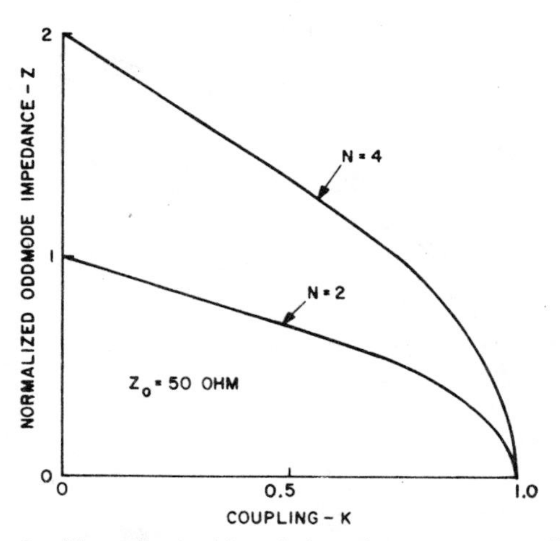

Fig. 3. Normalized odd-mode impedance versus coupling.

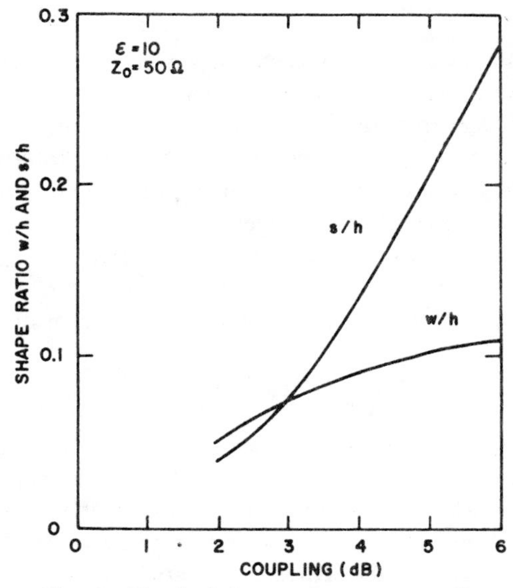

Fig. 4. Nominal shape ratios versus coupling.

Applications of this zero thickness conductor design procedure described so far consistently resulted in couplers with overcoupled characteristics. It was then experimentally determined that conductor metallization thick-

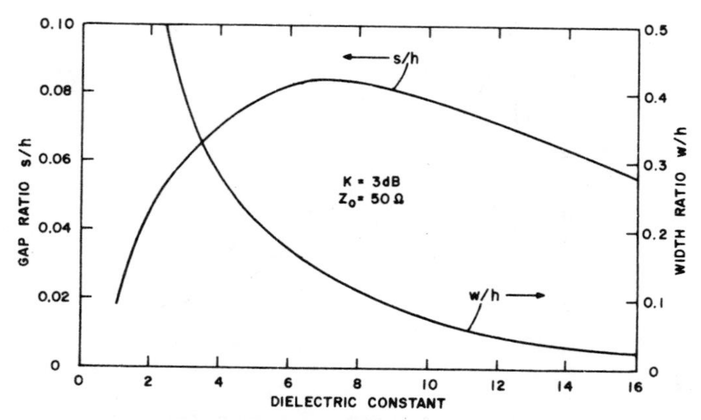

Fig. 5. Nominal 3-dB shape ratios versus dielectric constant.

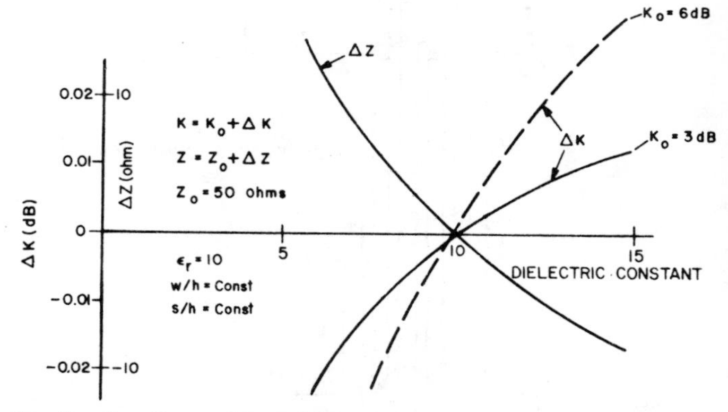

Fig. 7. Coupling and impedance deviation versus dielectric constant (shape ratio constant).

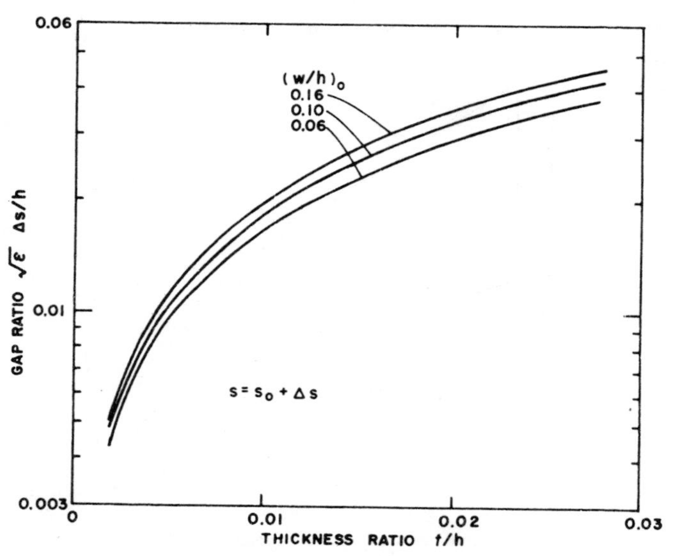

Fig. 6. Gap correction ratio versus thickness ratio.

ness has a significant influence upon coupling coefficient. A further review of the design procedure led to the use of a thickness correction Δs as described by Wheeler [4] for a single strip. However, we found that the interpolation factor $\sqrt{\varepsilon}$ fitted our experimental results better than the factor ε_r suggested by Wheeler. The ε is the effective odd-mode dielectric constant, as tabulated in [3], which corresponds to the zero thickness shape ratios. Thus the correction factor Δs was expressed in the form of

$$\Delta s/h = \frac{t/h}{\pi\sqrt{\varepsilon}}\left(1+\log_e \frac{4\pi w_0/h}{t/h}\right) \tag{3}$$

where t/h is the actual thickness ratio of the metallization. The major effect of t is that it reduces effectively the zero thickness design gap s_0 by Δs and increases the zero thickness design width w_0 by the same amount. The plot in Fig. 6 shows the correction ratio as a function of practical thickness ratios for a wide range of zero thickness width ratios. If a tabulated value of ε is not available, it can be substituted by the effective dielectric constant ε_{eff} of a single strip with a shape ratio w_0/h; a correction factor error of at most 5 percent results for all practical coupling coefficients and substrate materials.

The described procedure was used in the design of 3-, 5-, and 6-dB couplers on alumina and on BeO substrates with a thickness of both 0.635 and 1.27 mm. Photomasks and fabrication processes were coordinated to result in actual line and gap dimensions for a nominal metallization thickness of 4.5 μm. The described coupling deviation from design values on about 150 couplers constructed was never larger than ± 0.25 dB. The larger deviations were always traceable to unwanted dimensional variations that were introduced during processing. A cross check between actual dimensions and the design procedure showed agreement to within ± 0.05 dB when measured dissipative losses were accounted for. Couplers at center frequencies between 1.3 and 4.5 GHz had typically over 40-percent bandwidth isolations of 25 dB, return losses greater than 20 dB, and insertion losses of 0.2 dB$\pm$.05 dB. Attempts to compare these results with four-strip impedance solutions [5] failed since no thickness correction data for the latter approach were available.

III. Fabrication Tolerances

The effects of fabrication tolerances are expressible in terms of coupling (k) and characteristic impedance (Z_0) sensitivities. Generally, sensitivity functions [6] are easily derivable from (1) and (2). However, they would relate to the odd- and even-mode impedance changes only and not directly to the manufacturable dimensions. Therefore, coupling and impedance changes were calculated, using the available odd- and even-mode impedance data [3], as a function of dielectric constant and of fractional changes in gap and linewidth. One parameter was changed at a time, while all other parameters stayed fixed at their nominal values.

The graph in Fig. 7 shows both coupling and impedance deviations as a function of dielectric constant over the range of $\varepsilon_r = 5$ to $\varepsilon_r = 15$. The initial designs are assumed to be for 50-Ω couplers on alumina for 3- and 6-dB coupling. The impedance variations are essentially independent of coupling and near the desired value of $\varepsilon_r = 10$; a 10-percent change in dielectric constant corresponds to a 5-percent change in characteristic impedance. Coupling deviations are extremely small since for a given

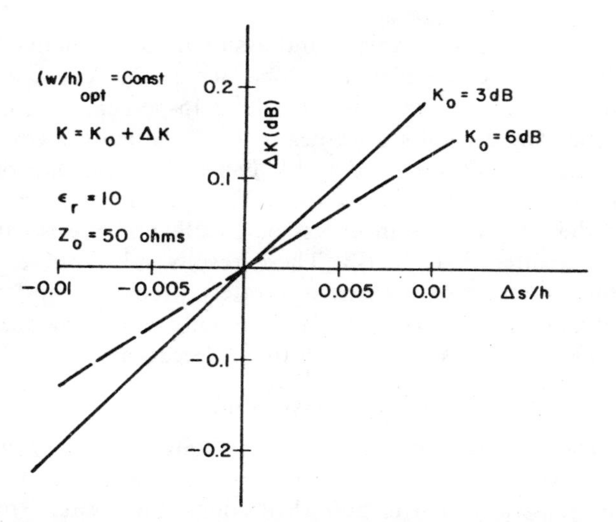

Fig. 8. Coupling deviation versus gap deviation (width ratio constant).

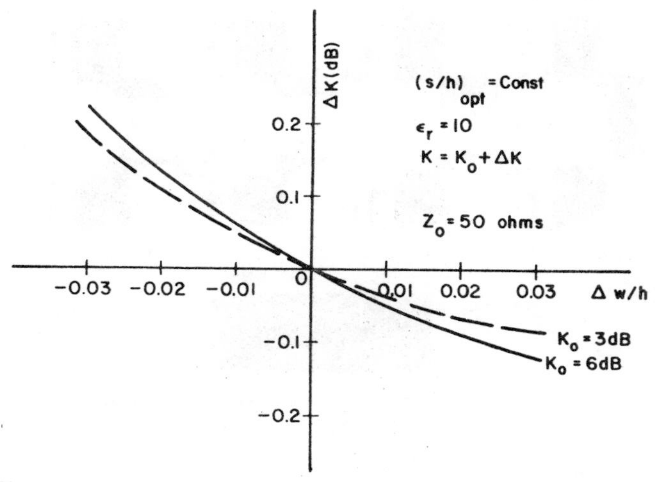

Fig. 10. Coupling deviation versus gap deviation (gap ratio constant).

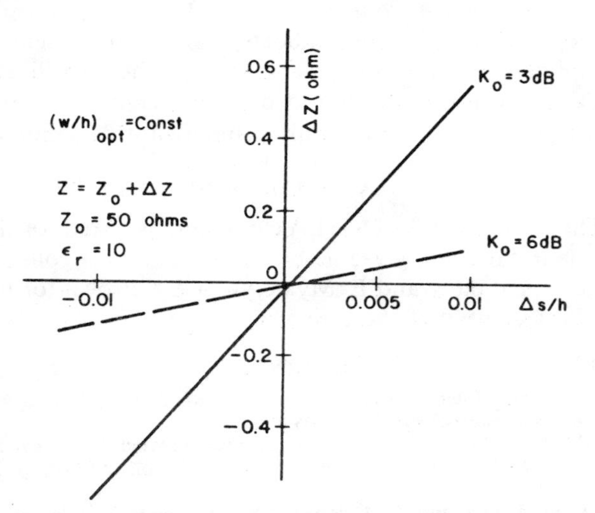

Fig. 9. Impedance deviation versus gap deviation (width ratio constant).

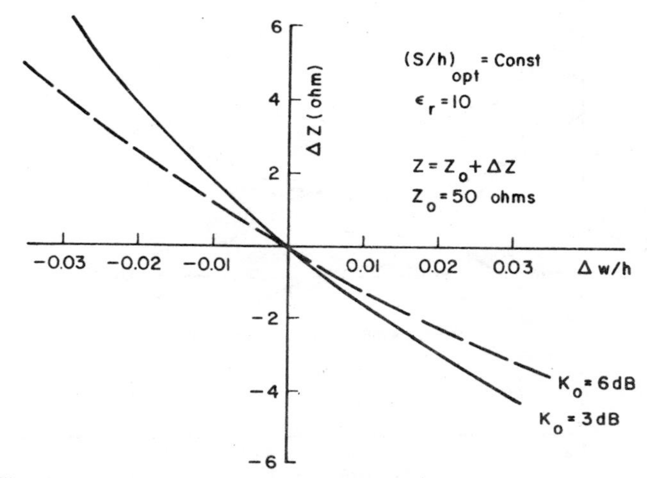

Fig. 11. Impedance deviation versus gap deviation (gap ratio constant).

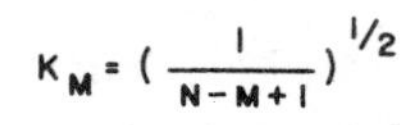

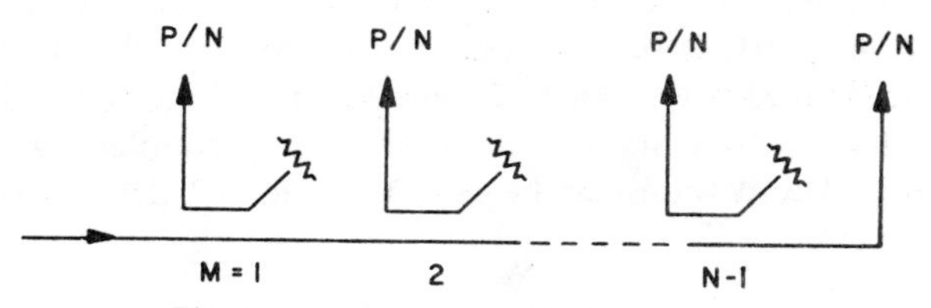

Fig. 12. Serial power divider schematic.

shape ratio pair (w/h and s/h) the impedance ratio R is essentially independent of ε_r over the range of interest, and coupling is dependent upon R only (see (1)).

Figs. 8 and 9 depict the coupling deviation and impedance variation, respectively, as a function of the normalized gap change from nominal while the width remains unchanged. The dominant effect here is the coupling deviation. Assuming a 0.635-mm thick substrate the coupling sensitivity is about 0.03-dB/μm gap variation for a 3-dB coupler and 0.02 dB/μm for a 6-dB coupler. Impedance deviations from 50 Ω are extremely small amounting to 80 mΩ/μm for a 3-dB coupler.

For the case in which the gap remains constant and the line width is allowed to vary, coupling deviations are negligible (0.01 dB/μm), whereas impedance deviations are high (250 mΩ/μm). Figs. 10 and 11 show the corresponding plots for this case. It is worthwhile to note that for a 3-dB coupler a 40-percent increase in line width only changes the coupling by about 0.1 dB whereas the impedance decreases to 45 Ω causing a 1.1 VSWR.

IV. Design Example

The above described design procedure was used on the design of a four-way serial divider. A serial divider [7] for N equal power divisions consists of a serial cascade of $(N-1)$ couplers each having a different coupling coefficient. This scheme, as depicted in Fig. 12, provides N integer power divisions with all desired performance features of quadrature couplers when four-line interdigitated couplers are used as building blocks. The four-way divider requires three couplers with power coupling coef-

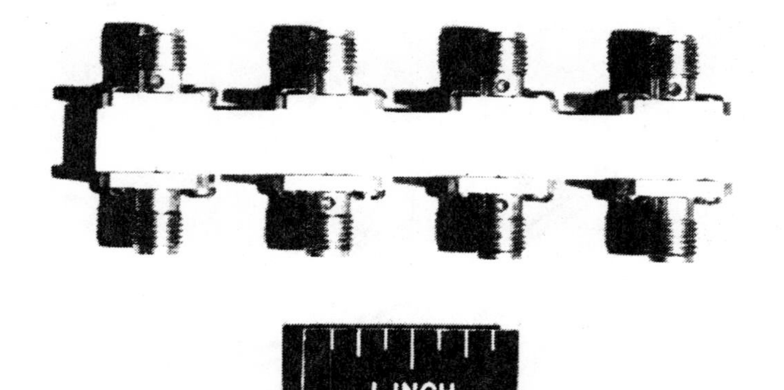

Fig. 13. Photograph of four-way serial divider.

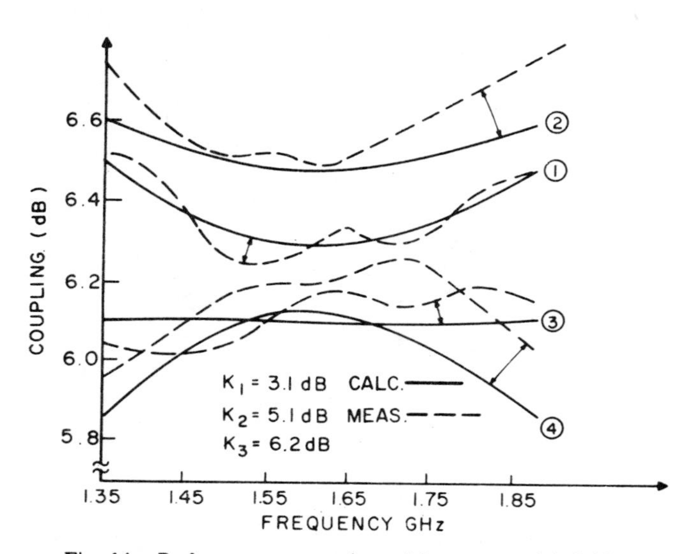

Fig. 14. Performance comparison of four-way serial divider.

ficients (K^2) of 1/4, 1/3, and 1/2, respectively. The coupler was fabricated on a single 1.27-mm thick alumina substrate with all couplers directly interconnected. Fig. 13 shows a photograph of such a coupler for the 1.35–1.85-GHz frequency range. From the final dimensions the coupling coefficients of the component couplers were calculated and found to be 3.1, 5.1, and 6.2 dB, respectively. Using these values and assuming a dissipative loss of 0.1 dB per coupler, the responses of the four outputs were calculated over the 1.6-GHz ± 15-percent frequency band. These results, together with the actually measured values, are shown in Fig. 14. Especially near the band center, agreement is very good. The measured return loss of the coupler was in excess of 28 dB, and the isolation was greater than 30 dB. These results substantiate that coupler responses can be accurately predicted, and that deviations from design goals are mainly caused by dimensional variations that arise during fabrication.

V. Conclusion

The described procedure, even though based upon an approximate description of a four-line interdigitated coupler [2], together with published coupled-line data [3] and an empirical thickness correction term, can be used to design producible couplers in the 2.5–6.5-dB coupling range. Tolerance studies indicate that the most sensitive parameters are the gap dimensions and the metallization thickness, whereas width and dielectric constant changes of 10 percent cause practically insignificant deviations.

Acknowledgment

The author thanks Dr. H. Veloric and W. Sked for their efforts in fabricating the many couplers and for collecting dimensional data, and E. Mykietyn and J. Brown for their skillful assembly of the couplers.

References

[1] J. Lange, "Interdigitated stripline quadrature hybrid," in *G-MTT Int. Microwave Symp. Dig.*, May 1969.

[2] W. P. Ou, "Design equations for an interdigitated directional coupler," *IEEE Trans. Microwave Theory Tech.*, vol. MTT-23, p. 253, 1975.

[3] T. G. Bryant and J. A. Weiss, "Normal mode impedance of a coupled pair of microstrip transmission lines," in *G-MTT Int. Microwave Symp. Dig.*, pp. 117–122, May 1968.

[4] H. A. Wheeler, "Transmission-line properties of parallel strips separated by a dielectric sheet," *IEEE Trans. Microwave Theory Tech.*, vol. MTT-13, p. 172, 1965.

[5] D. D. Paolino, "Design more accurate interdigitated couplers," *Microwaves*, vol. 15, no. 5, May 1976.

[6] J. Gorski-Popiel, "Classical sensitivity—A collection of formulas," *IEEE Trans. Circuit Theory*, vol. CT-10, June 1963.

[7] R. J. Mohr, "A microwave power divider," *IRE Trans. Microwave Theory Tech.*, vol. MTT-9, p. 573, 1961.

INTERDIGITATED COPLANAR DIRECTIONAL COUPLERS

Indexing terms: Microwave networks, Directional couplers

A new coplanar coupler is presented which is suitable both for hybrid and monolithic i.c. applications. Design charts deduced from a theoretical analysis are given and experimental results concerning X- and J-band quadrature hybrids manufactured on alumina substrates are presented and discussed.

Introduction: Microwave planar networks are studied with increasing interest[1] due to the rapid growth of GaAs hybrid and monolithic i.c. technology. Though coplanar directional couplers have been known[2] for some years, in practice they are only used as low-coupling devices. For high couplings, in fact, extremely small spacings s between the coupled conductors are required to obtain total device widths allowing low radiation losses.[3] Such narrow gaps are not reproducible on commercial dielectrics and also give problems in monolithic circuits, where the loss increase limits the coupler width reduction. Nonplanar coupler solutions, e.g. microstrip Lange hybrids, are also unsuitable for monolithic integration, leading to unacceptable losses when constructed on small thickness (~ 100 μm) GaAs substrates.

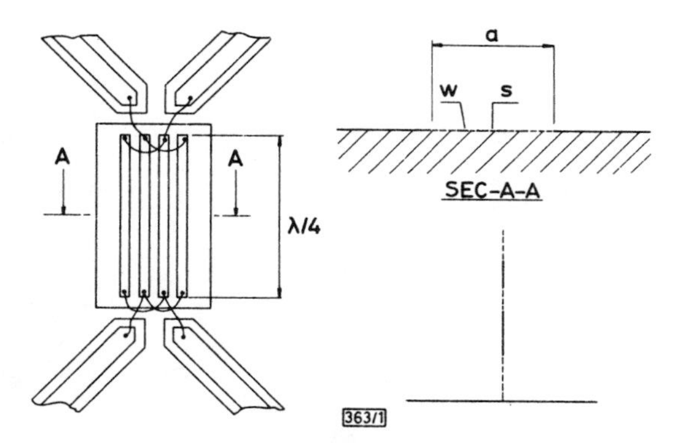

Fig. 1 *Diagram of coplanar coupler*

This letter describes new interdigital planar couplers, where the ratio between the total device width a and the minimum coupled conductor gap s is greatly reduced. Consequently, high coupling sections can be easily manufactured on commercial dielectrics and lower losses can be obtained in miniaturised circuits for a given total coupler width. In comparison with Wen's hybrids[2] wider bandwidths are achieved, whereas in comparison with Lange's microstrip couplers better directivities are usually obtained thanks to the lower difference between the even and odd mode phase velocities.

Coupler analysis and design data: A sketch of the coupler we propose is given in Fig. 1.† The device coupling factor k and the input/output impedance level Z_0 can be written, as is well known, in terms of the coupled lines even and odd mode impedances Z_{oe} and Z_{oo}:

$$k = (Z_{oe} - Z_{oo})(Z_{oe} + Z_{oo})^{-1}; \quad Z_o = (Z_{oe}Z_{oo})^{1/2} \qquad (1)$$

It is therefore sufficient, for the coupler design, that the impedances Z_{oe} and Z_{oo} are provided as functions of the device dimensions and of the substrate relative dielectric constant ε_r.

† BASTIDA, E. M., and FANELLI, N.: Italian patent 20486A/80, March 1980

Z_{oe} and Z_{oo} were calculated for an infinitely thick dielectric support. A sequence of conformal mappings was first applied to the even and odd mode configurations and the geometry shown in the right-hand side of Fig. 1 was obtained in both cases; the related Dirichlet problem was finally solved by a finite subinterval method. In Fig. 2, Z_{oe} and Z_{oo} are reported for an $\varepsilon_r = 10$ substrate. The impedance values for different ε_r can be deduced by just scaling the vertical axes in Fig. 2 by $[(\varepsilon_r + 1)/11]^{1/2}$. Z_{oe} and Z_{oo} were also calculated for 6 and 8 finger couplers.

Experimental results: To test the validity of theoretical results, 3 dB couplers were constructed on 0·625 mm thick Al_2O_3 substrates with 0·05 μm surface finish and 6 μm gold metallisation. For $k = 0{\cdot}707$ and $Z_o = 50$ Ω, eqn. 1 gives $Z_{oe} = 120{\cdot}7$ Ω and $Z_{oo} = 20{\cdot}7$ Ω, corresponding to $w/a = s/a = 0{\cdot}053$; a coupler with $a = 1$ mm, $s = w = 0{\cdot}053$ was then constructed, and the even and odd mode impedances were measured as described in Reference 2. A good agreement was found between theoretical and experimental results for Z_{oo}, while the measured odd impedances were $\sim 7\%$ higher than the theoretical values. This discrepancy was ascribed to the finite substrate thickness, and could be easily overcome by setting a lower Z_{oe} value (-7%) in Fig. 2.

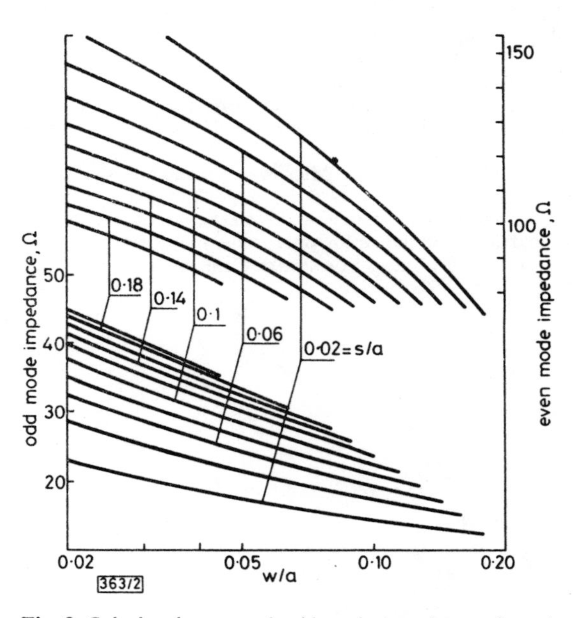

Fig. 2 *Calculated even and odd mode impedances for substrate with $\varepsilon_r = 10$*

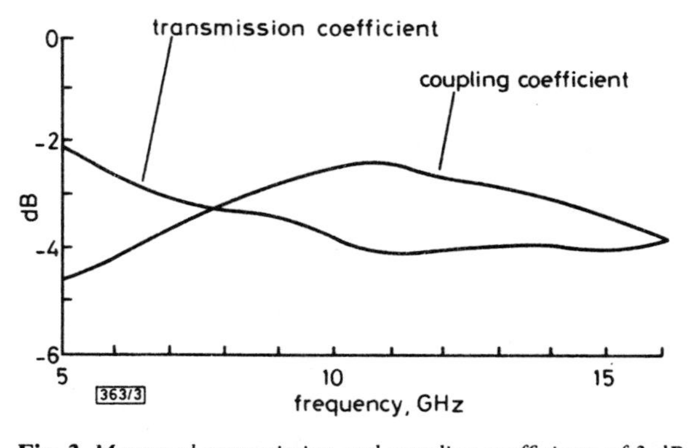

Fig. 3 *Measured transmission and coupling coefficients of 3 dB Al_2O_3 coplanar coupler*

To exploit the coupler broadband capability, a 2·5 dB coupling, 11 GHz centre frequency device was then designed with the mentioned correction accounted for. Cross dimensions were $a = 1$ mm; $w = 68$ μm; $s = 50$ μm. The measured frequency response (Fig. 3) outlines the 1·3 octave bandwidth capability of the coupler. Less than 0·5 dB insertion loss was obtained and, although no attempt was made to optimise for directivity, an isolation better than 20 dB was measured over the whole frequency band. No spurious slot modes which could occur for asymmetric coupler excitation were noticed, since they were avoided by suitable conductor connections.

Similar J-band couplers, with 0·5 dB insertion loss, have been recently used as input/output matching networks in monolithic balanced amplifier modules.[5]

In conclusion, a new coplanar coupler suitable for hybrid and monolithic circuit applications has been described. The reported results evidence the broadband capability and the excellent operation of the proposed device up to J-band frequencies.

E. M. BASTIDA
N. FANELLI

CISE SpA
PO Box 12081, 20100 Milan, Italy

7th July 1980

References

1 PENGELLY, R. S.: 'Monolithic GaAs ICs technology task', *Microwave*, 1979, **18**, pp. 56–65

2 WEN, C. P.: 'Coplanar-waveguide directional couplers', *IEEE Trans.*, 1970, **18**, pp. 518–522

3 GOPINATH, A.: 'A comparison of coplanar waveguide and microstrip for GaAs monolithic circuits'. MTT Int. Mic. Symp. Dig., 1979, pp. 109–111

4 CAULTON, M., and SOBOL, H.: 'Microwave I.C. technology: a survey', *IEEE J. Solid-State Circ.*, 1970, **SC-5**, pp. 292–303

5 BASTIDA, E. M., DONZELLI, G. P., and FANELLI, N.: 'Cascadable monolithic balanced amplifiers for microwave frequencies'. To be presented at 10th European Microwave Conf., Warsaw, Sept. 1980

HIGH FREQUENCY MICROSTRIP BRANCH-LINE COUPLER DESIGN WITH T-JUNCTION DISCONTINUITY COMPENSATION

Indexing terms: Microstrip, Microwave devices

A design procedure has been developed for high frequency microstrip branch-line couplers. The performance of these couplers is improved when T-junction discontinuity effects are compensated.

At frequencies below X-band, microstrip branch-line couplers can be designed with acceptable performance using either alumina substrate or RT Duroid substrates. However, at frequencies above 10 GHz, such devices designed on 0·6 mm alumina substrates may not perform as predicted, and in some cases a practical design cannot be realised in a 50 Ω environment. The reasons for these design problems are now explained.

The design of a branch-line coupler requires accurate modelling of the T-junction discontinuity. Fig. 1*a* shows a symmetrical microstrip T-junction with the reference planes of the junction defined as T_1 and T_2, and the equivalent line widths defined as D_1 and D_2. The equivalent circuit for Fig. 1*a*, which uses the same reference planes T_1 and T_2, is shown in Fig. 1*b*.

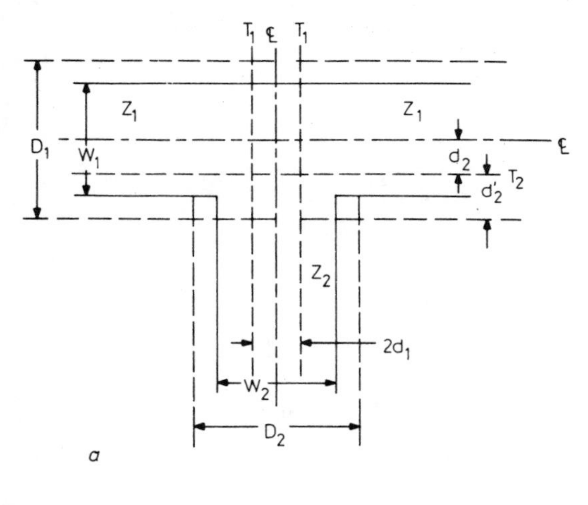

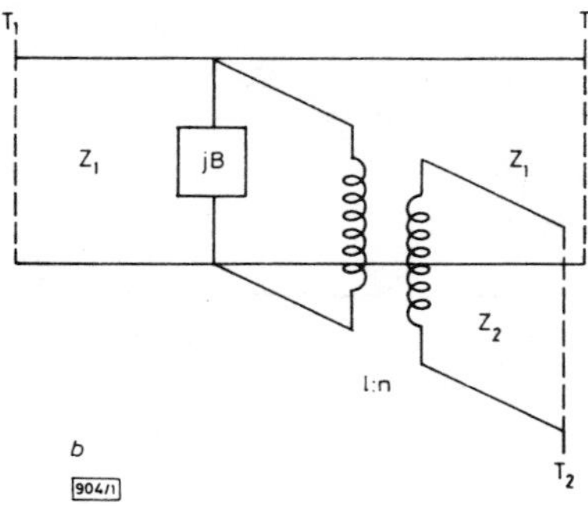

Fig. 1 (*a*) *Microstrip T-junction (T_1, T_2 are the phase reference planes) and* (*b*) *T-junction equivalent circuit*

At frequencies below X-band, the guided wavelength λ_g in the microstrip structure is much greater than either of the line widths W_1 and W_2, and the thickness h of the substrate. Also the value of the normalised junction susceptance B in the T-junction equivalent circuit can be ignored in most cases. Thus the only compensation necessary is to transform the branch impedance Z_2 using the transformer turns ratio n in the equivalent circuit of Fig. 1*b*. However, at frequencies above X-band, the use of the normal procedure to obtain a transformed impedance Z_2 does not necessarily provide a convergent solution. Even if it did, the corresponding line width would either approach or be greater than $\lambda_g/4$ which is equal to the required separation of the branch lines. Therefore, on a 0·6 mm alumina substrate, a 3 dB branch-line coupler is not readily realisable in a 50 Ω environment. In addition, the value of the normalised junction susceptance B is no longer negligible (i.e. $B \geq 0{\cdot}1$) and therefore compounds the problem.

The following presents a design technique whereby microstrip branch-line couplers for frequencies above X-band can be designed and realised with good resulting directivity without iterative trials.

Various authors[1–3] have studied the subject of T-junction discontinuity in some detail. In particular, good design data are available for the symmetrical case. These design data are used as a starting point for the present design procedure which is illustrated using the examples below.

First, the value of the junction normalised susceptance B can be calculated according to Franco and Oliner's formula:[1]

$$B/Y_1 = 2\tan(2\pi d/\lambda_g) - n^2(Z_1/Z_2)\tan(2\pi d_2/\lambda_g) \quad (1)$$

Then values for n, d_1 and d_2 can be obtained from Hammerstad's[3] equations:

$$d_2/D_1 = [0{\cdot}076 + 0{\cdot}2(2D_1/\lambda_g)^2 + 0{\cdot}663\exp[-1{\cdot}71(Z_1/Z_2)] - 0{\cdot}172\ln(Z_1/Z_2)](Z_1/Z_2) \quad (2)$$

$$d_1/D_2 = 0{\cdot}5n^2(Z_1/Z_2) \quad (3)$$

$$n^2 = \left|\frac{\sin\{(\pi/2)(2D_1/\lambda_g)(Z_1/Z_2)\}}{(\pi/2)(2D_1/\lambda_g)(Z_1/Z_2)}\right|^2 \left|1 - \left(\pi\frac{2D_1}{\lambda_g}\frac{d_2'}{D_1}\right)^2\right| \quad (4)$$

$$D_i = \eta_0(h/Z_i) \qquad (i = 1, 2) \quad (5)$$

where η_0 is intrinsic wave impedance. Values for these parameters are essential to the design of the microstrip branch-line coupler.

The following two design examples will serve to illustrate the rest of the design procedure, that is the compensation techniques. First, it is assumed that the coupling ratios are 3 dB and 4·77 dB, and the normalised branch impedances can be determined.[4] To realise the transformed Z_2 and maintain an approximately symmetric T-junction, when the coupling ratio is other than 3 dB, the branch-line coupler must be designed for an impedance environment Z_0' higher than 50 Ω. Impedance transforming sections will be required to interconnect the coupler with the standard $Z_0 = 50\,\Omega$ interface. Eqns. 1 to 4 can now be used to determine the T-junction parameters. Second, the junction susceptance can be cancelled with short stubs placed approximately $\lambda_g/4$ away from the junction, or directly at the junction, depending on the sign of B. The same T-junction compensating procedure is applied to calculate the length of the short stubs. Figs. 2*a* and 2*b* show the configurations of a compensated 3 dB and a 4·77 dB coupler, respectively. The 3 dB coupler was designed for a 70·7 Ω environment whereas the 4·77 dB coupler was designed for a 69 Ω environment. The $\lambda_g/4$ transformer section for the 4·77 dB coupler (59 Ω to reduce the coupler impedance level to the 50 Ω interface) was connected directly to the coupler to form an almost symmetrical T-junction. In general, the T-junction can be made exactly symmetrical if (i) the impedance level of the coupler Z_0' is chosen so that $Z_0' = Z_0/|S_{12}|^2$, where Z_0 is the external impedance level, usually 50 Ω, and $|S_{12}|^2$ is the coupling ratio between ports 1 and 2; and (ii) the single $\lambda_g/4$ transformer section is connected directly to the T-junction of the coupler. However, in this particular case, fabrication tolerances dictate an upper impedance level for the high impedance lines, i.e. the high impedance lines can become too narrow to fabricate with precision. To circumvent this problem, a slightly asymmetrical T-junction was used in the design. This junction was modelled using the symmetrical case without degrading the coupler performance. Figs. 3 and 4 show the measured performance of these two couplers.

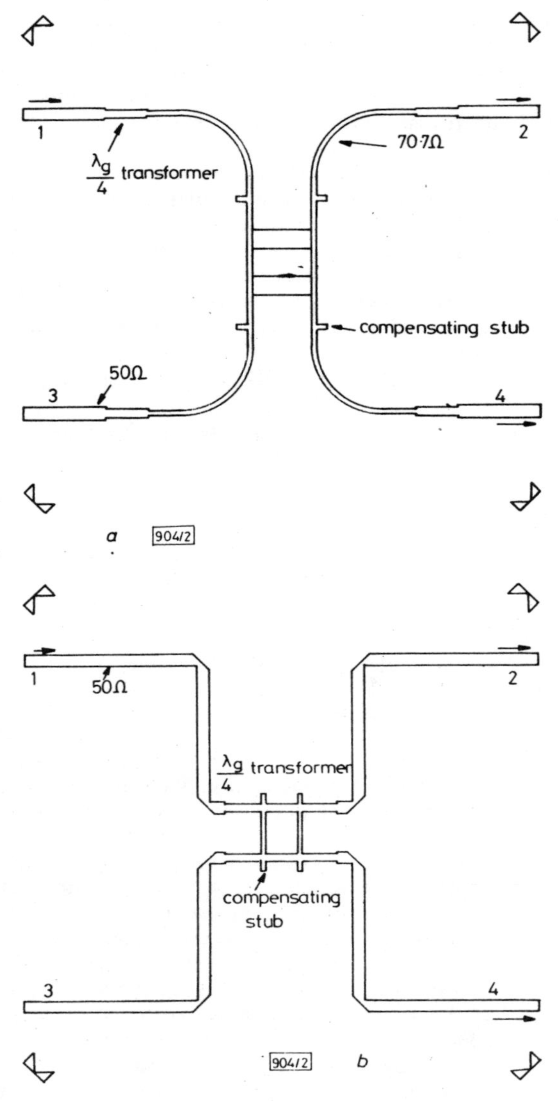

Fig. 2

(*a*) 12 GHz 3 dB coupler
(*b*) 14 GHz 4·77 dB coupler
$\varepsilon_r = 10$, $h = 0{\cdot}64$ mm

For the 3 dB coupler, the results for a coupler designed without junction susceptance cancellation are included to illustrate the improvement in performance when stubs are used to cancel the junction susceptance *B*.

In conclusion, the compensation techniques used in the above design procedure allow practical realisation with improved performance of microstrip branch-line couplers on standard substrates.

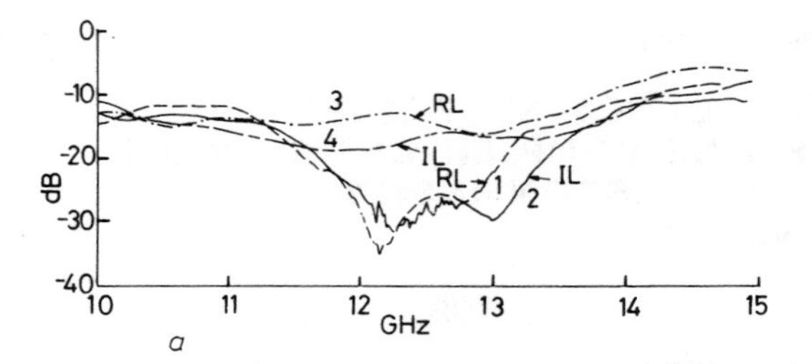

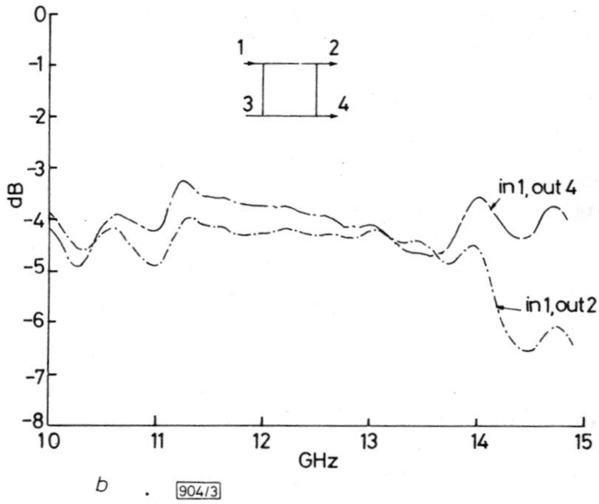

Fig. 3 *3 dB coupler measured results*

a Return loss (RL) and isolation (IL) for junction susceptance *jB* compensated (1, 2) and uncompensated (3, 4) couplers
b Power split for compensated case

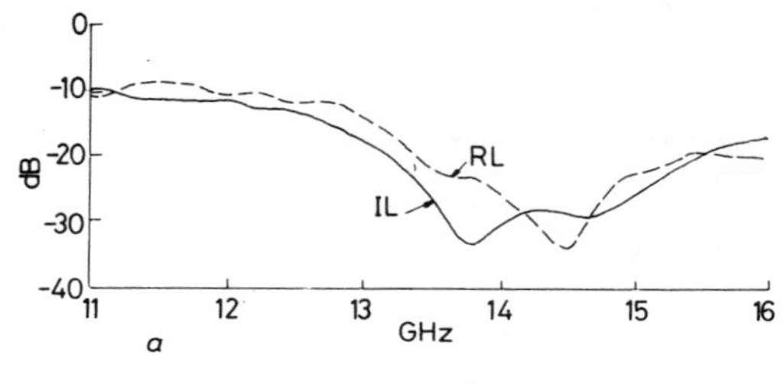

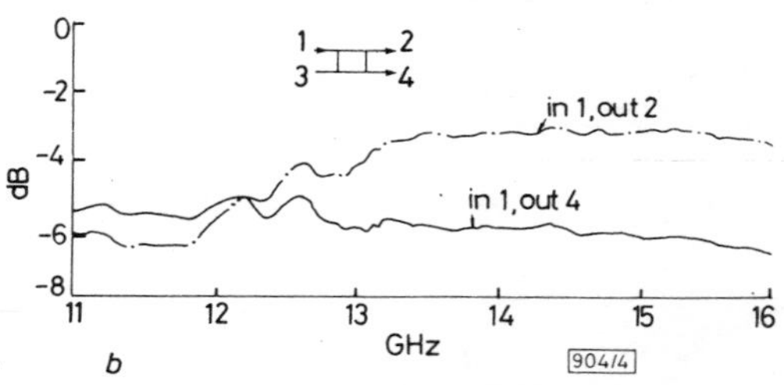

Fig. 4 *4·77 dB coupler measured results*

a Return loss (RL) and isolation (IL)
b Power split

Acknowledgment: The authors wish to thank B. Clarke and R. J. P. Douville for helpful discussions.

M. CUHACI G. J. P. LO

Department of Communications
Communications Research Centre
Shirley Bay, Ottawa, Canada

18th December 1980

References

1 FRANCO, A. G., and OLINER, A. A.: 'Symmetric strip transmission line tee junction', *IRE Trans.*, (MTT), March 1962
2 VOGEL, R. W.: 'Effects of the T-junction discontinuity on the design of microstrip directional couplers', *IEEE Trans.*, (MTT), March 1973
3 HAMMERSTAD, E. O.: 'Equations for microstrip circuit design'. 5th European Microwave Conference Digest, 1975
4 ALTMAN, J. L.: 'Microwave circuits' (Van Nostrand, 1964), pp. 157–160

MICROSTRIP BANDPASS FILTER USING DEGENERATE MODES OF A MICROSTRIP RING RESONATOR

Indexing terms: Striplines, Microwave filters, Cavity resonators

It is shown that two degenerate modes can be excited on a microstrip ring resonator. These modes can be used to realise a double-tuned circuit bandpass filter in microstrip technique.

Recently, we published a theory for calculating the resonance frequencies of the microstrip ring resonator,[1] a magnetic-wall model being assumed to take into account the curvature of the microstrip ring line. The edge effects of the electric field could be described to a first approximation by the effective relative permittivity ε_{eff} defined by Wheeler.[2] As has been shown in Reference 1, a solution of Maxwell's equations for the field components of the electromagnetic field is

$$\left.\begin{aligned} E_z &= \{A\,\mathrm{J}_n(kr) + B\mathrm{N}_n(kr)\}\cos(n\phi) \\ H_r &= \frac{n}{j\omega\mu_0 r}\{A\,\mathrm{J}_n(kr) + B\,\mathrm{N}_n(kr)\}\sin(n\phi) \\ H_\phi &= \frac{k}{j\omega\mu_0}\{A\,\mathrm{J}_n'(kr) + B\,\mathrm{N}_n'(kr)\}\cos(n\phi) \end{aligned}\right\} \quad (1)$$

where J_n is the Bessel function of the first kind of order n,

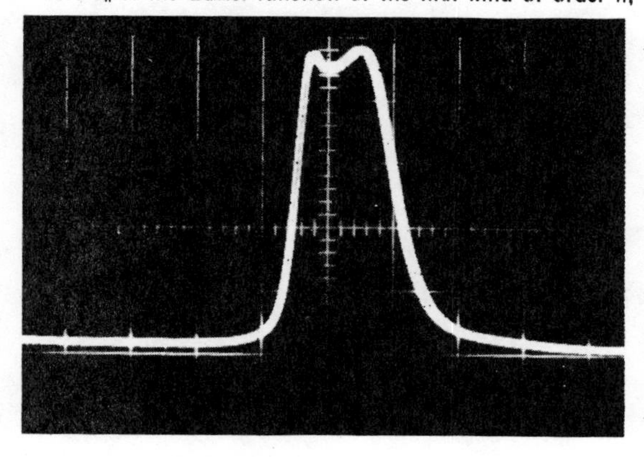

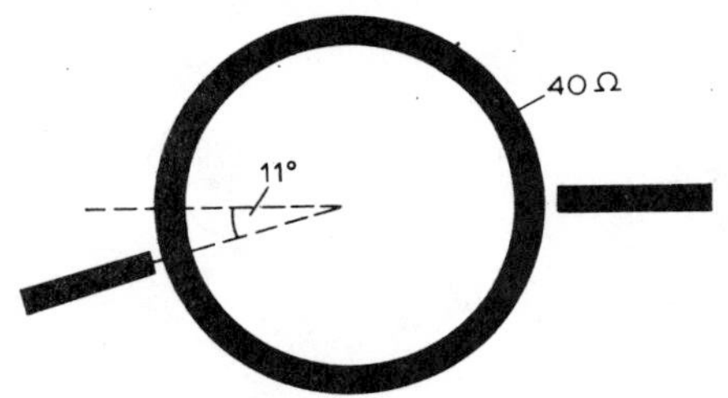

Fig. 1 *Asymmetrically coupled microstrip ring resonator and resonance curve of the structure*

The substrate material is Polyguide, with $\varepsilon_r = 2{\cdot}33$
Mean diameter of the ring $D = 11{\cdot}6$ cm

N_n is the Bessel function of the second kind of order n and $k = \omega\sqrt{(\varepsilon_0\,\varepsilon_{eff}\,\mu_0)}$ is the wavenumber. From these field equations, the eigenvalue equation of the microstrip ring resonator can be calculated, as shown in Reference 1. As can be easily shown with the help of Maxwell's equations, the solution for the field components can also be written in the form

$$\left.\begin{aligned} E_z &= \{A\,\mathrm{J}_n(kr) + B\,\mathrm{N}_n(kr)\}\sin(n\phi) \\ H_r &= -\frac{n}{j\omega\mu_0 r}\{A\,\mathrm{J}_n(kr) + B\,\mathrm{N}_n(kr)\}\cos(n\phi) \\ H_\phi &= \frac{k}{j\omega\mu_0}\{A\,\mathrm{J}_n'(kr) + B\,\mathrm{N}_n'(kr)\}\sin(n\phi) \end{aligned}\right\} \quad (2)$$

i.e. the cosine functions, as well as the sine functions, are solutions for the field dependence on the azimuthal angle ϕ. As is known from microwave cavity resonators, this means that two degenerate modes occur at the resonance frequency. If the ring resonator is excited by symmetrical coupling lines, only one of the degenerate modes will be excited. Both modes are orthogonal to each other, and hence, in circular symmetrical ring resonators, no coupling occurs between the two modes. The two modes can be interpreted as two waves, travelling clockwise and anti-clockwise on the microstrip ring resonator.

As is known from the filter techniques of microwave cavity resonators, the two degenerate modes can be coupled if the symmetry of the resonator is disturbed. The same principle can be used for the microstrip ring resonator. If, for example, the coupling lines of the resonator are not arranged symmetrically, both modes should be excited. Experiments show that this is true. Fig. 1 shows the microstrip ring resonator and the arrangement of the coupling lines, and the resonance curve of this resonator. The splitting of the resonance frequency, which occurs if the two degenerate modes are excited, can be well detected. The two modes are excited with different amplitudes, which depend on the arrangement of the coupling lines. The arrangement shown in Fig. 1 produced a symmetrical resonance curve, i.e. both modes are excited with the same amplitude.

Another way of exciting the two degenerate modes is to use a symmetrical arrangement of the coupling lines and to disturb the symmetry of the ring resonator. This can be done easily if a notch is applied in the ring. Fig. 2 shows the arrangement which has been examined experimentally. The width of the notch was $w = 3{\cdot}0$ mm, and the depth was $t = 2$, 3 and 4 mm. Fig. 2 also shows the resonance curve of a

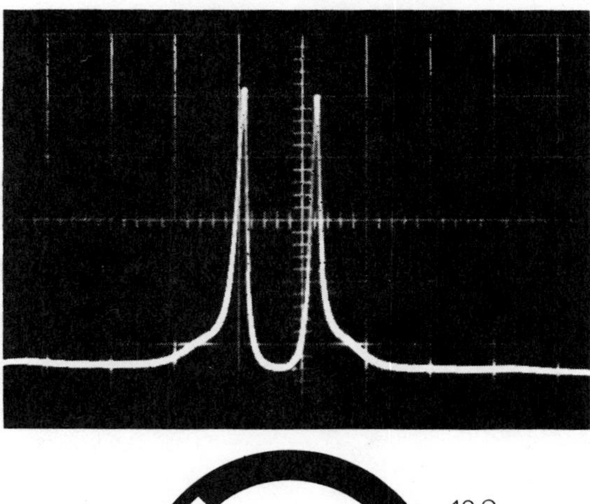

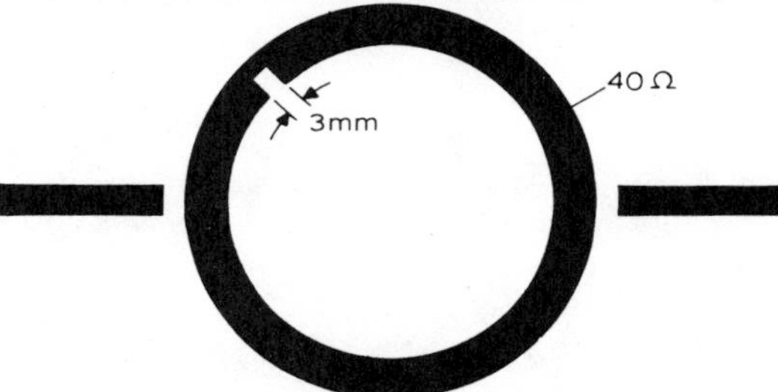

Fig. 2 *Microstrip ring resonator disturbed by a notch of width w and depth t and the resonance curve of the structure for w = 3 mm and t = 4 mm*

The substrate material is Polyguide, with $\varepsilon_r = 2{\cdot}33$
Mean diameter of the ring $D = 11{\cdot}6$ cm

ring resonator with a 4 mm-deep notch. The two modes are excited with different amplitudes, which depend on the position of the notch.

Fig. 3 shows the measured resonance frequency of the ring resonator as a function of the depth of the notch. It can be seen that, without the notch ($t = 0$), no splitting of the resonance frequency occurs. For a notch with $t = 4$ mm, a frequency splitting of 53 MHz (see resonance curve of Fig. 2) can be measured.

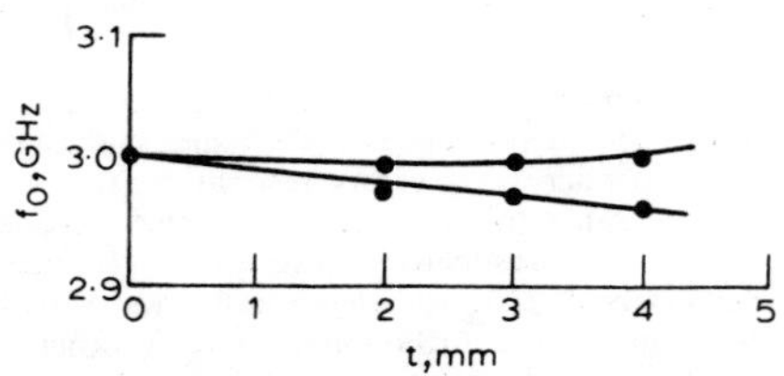

Fig. 3 *Dependence of the frequency splitting on the depth of the notch*

● measured frequencies

The coupling between the two degenerate modes can be used to build a bandpass filter. The coupling can be realised by every type of asymmetry of the resonator structure, e.g. an asymmetrical coupling or an asymmetrical disturbance of the ring resonator.

I. WOLFF

25th April 1972

Institut für Hochfrequenztechnik
Technische Hochschule Aachen
51 Aachen, W. Germany

References

1 WOLFF, I., and KNOPPIK, N.: 'Microstrip ring resonator and dispersion measurement on microstrip lines', *Electron. Lett.*, 1971, **7**, pp. 779–781

2 WHEELER, H. A.: 'Transmission-line properties of parallel strips separated by a dielectric sheet', *IEEE Trans.*, 1965, **MTT-13**, pp. 173–185

Reprinted from IEEE TRANSACTIONS
ON *MICROWAVE THEORY AND TECHNIQUES*
Volume MTT-19, Number 7, July, 1971
pp. 643-652

Dielectric Resonator Filters for Application in Microwave Integrated Circuits

TOR DAG IVELAND

***Abstract*—Design of bandpass filters for microwave integrated circuits (MICs) utilizing dielectric resonators is discussed. Synthesis methods for both Tschebycheff and Butterworth responses are derived. Experimental results with *S*- and *X*-band filters are presented, and the agreement between theory and experiments is shown to be fairly good. Limitations on this technique due to poor temperature stability are also discussed.**

I. INTRODUCTION

THE USE of dielectric resonators in microwave bandpass filters is discussed. By a dielectric resonator we refer to any dielectric object having free-space boundaries, but for resonator purposes only materials of fairly high dielectric constant will be of interest.

By appropriate choice of resonator materials, extremely high-Q values can be obtained. High-Q resonators are valuable elements in every kind of filter design, but especially in microwave integrated circuits (MICs) this technique seems attractive due to the lack of alternative solutions.

It has been known for many years that dielectric objects can resonate in various modes. In 1939 it was proved by Richtmeyer [1] that with a finite dielectric constant the resonant frequencies must be complex, regardless of geometrical shape. With the exception of the spherical resonator, calculations of the resonant frequencies involve approximations. Okaya and Barash [2] have treated the case of rectangular disks, including the complexity of dielectric anisotropy. Their approximations have been applied by other authors to calculate resonances of cylindrical disks and rods [3], [4].

When situated in a propagating waveguide, a dielectric resonator offers bandstop properties. Equivalent circuits for waveguide-mounted resonators have been calculated by variational methods [5]. Multielement bandstop filters have been designed by Hansen [6], and a waveguide bandpass synthesis, employing dielectric resonators and lumped reactances, has been reported by Pettersen [7]. Harrison [8] and Cohn [9] have reported design methods for bandpass filters based on coupling

Manuscript received November 16, 1970; revised February 5, 1971. This work was supported by the Royal Norwegian Council for Scientific and Industrial Research.
The author was with the Microwave Section, Norwegian Institute of Technology, University of Trondheim, Trondheim, Norway. He is now with the Electronics Research Laboratory, Trondheim, Norway.

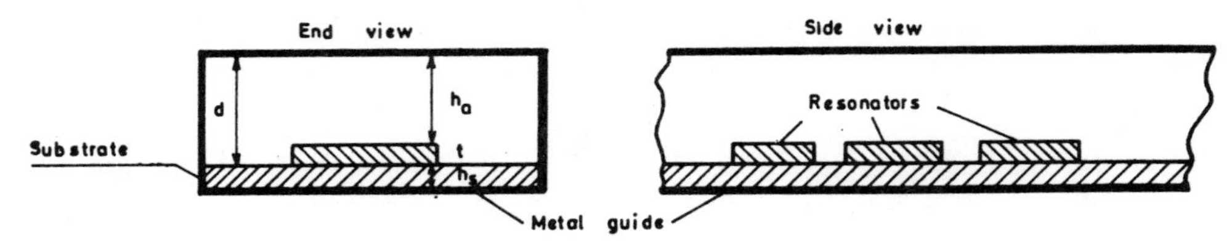

Fig. 1. Basic filter geometry.

between resonators within metal waveguides below cutoff. This technique permits a more easily achieved bandpass response and a considerable size reduction compared to the propagating guide technique.

The object of this paper is to present a design technique which is suited for MICs. The introduction of MICs has reinforced the need for a high-Q resonator element of small size, which is easily integrated in the circuit geometry. The coupling mechanism is essentially based on the evanescent guide technique, but apart from Harrison's design, the coupling structure is kept in the plane of the substrate, containing both the filter and the connected circuits.

II. Filter Design Considerations

A. Basic Filter Geometry

A brief sketch of the filter structure to be examined will now be given. Although some of the expressions to be developed are more generally valid, we will concentrate on the actual design which was used in the experimental filters. The main parts are shown in Fig. 1. The metal waveguide is operating below cutoff for all modes in the frequency band of interest. The substrate at the bottom of the guide supports the resonators, as well as the microstrip circuit, to which the end resonators of the filter are coupled. At resonance, the resonators will excite the normal modes of the waveguide, and coupling between resonators is achieved via the evanescent fields of these modes. The microstrip structures, which provide the coupling to the end resonators, will be described later. Since the guide is cutoff, the modes excited by the resonators will be almost vanishing at some distance beyond the end resonators, and the guide may be opened to permit connection to other microstrip components on the same substrate.

Although the resonators are not of infinitesimal size and thus partly extend into the coupling region between the resonators, the coupling modes are taken to be those of a uniform dielectric loaded waveguide as shown in Fig. 2. These modes are most conveniently separated into orthogonal sets, the LSE modes and the LSM modes, as shown by Collin [10]. Collin also gives the complete expressions for the fields which are needed in the calculation of coupling. Calculation of the fields involves the solution of two independent transcendental equations which, however, are easily solved by a computer to any desired accuracy.

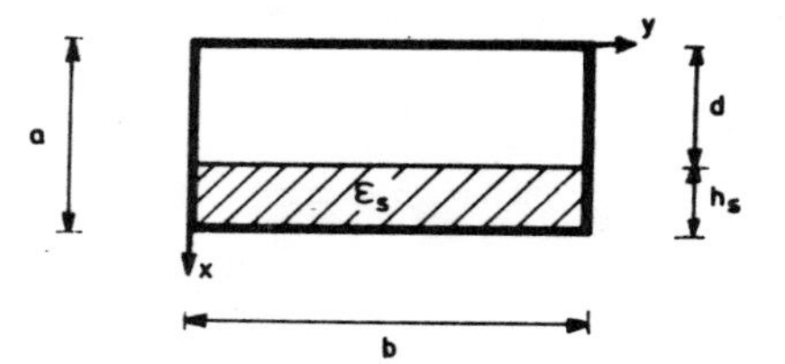

Fig. 2. Dielectric loaded rectangular waveguide.

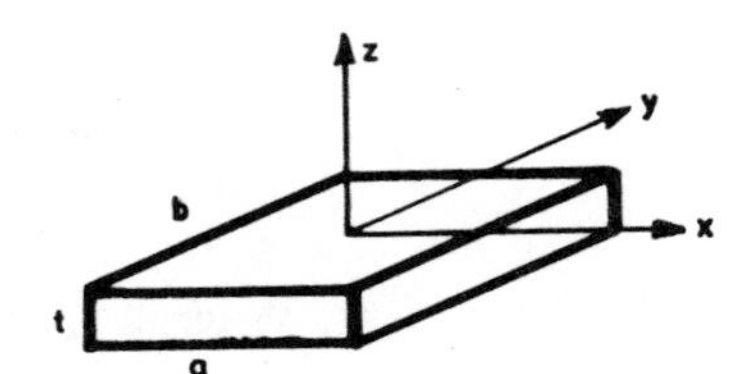

Fig. 3. Dielectric resonator.

With the given structure only the LSE modes will be excited by the resonator fields and contribute to the coupling.

The LSM modes will, however, be excited, e.g., by the end coupling structure. Thus it is essential that these modes also are evanescent; otherwise resonance effects will occur in the filter box, causing unwanted spurious passbands. The requirement that the LSM modes also should be evanescent normally imposes a stronger restriction on the maximum allowable value of the dimension b than the LSE modes alone.

B. Resonator Properties

The resonators used in this paper were shaped as rectangular (including square) disks, as shown in Fig. 3. It has been shown [4], [5] that if the dielectric constant is high, an open-circuit boundary condition applies at the small surfaces of the resonator. This is defined by

$$\boldsymbol{E}\cdot\boldsymbol{n} = 0 \tag{1}$$

where $\boldsymbol{E}$ is the electric field vector, and $\boldsymbol{n}$ the surface normal. A boundary with this property is often called a magnetic wall. An approximate solution for the resonance frequencies is obtained by extending the magnetic walls to form an infinite tube (Fig. 4). The problem is now a straightforward waveguide problem. In the dielectric region the guide is above cutoff and a standing wave exists at resonance, while in the air region the fields exhibit an exponential decay since the waveguide is

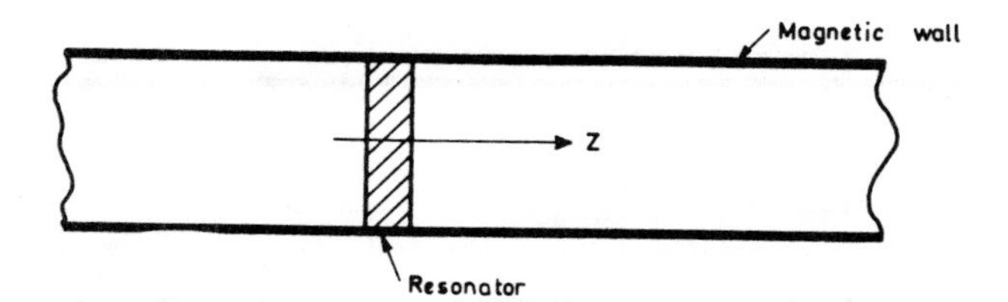

Fig. 4. Second-order approximation for calculation of resonance frequencies.

below cutoff. Assuming dielectric isotropy, the resonant frequencies are given by the following equation [5]:

$$p = k_z \begin{Bmatrix} \tan \\ -\cot \end{Bmatrix} \left(k_z \cdot \frac{t}{2} \right) \tag{2}$$

where

$$k_z = \sqrt{\omega^2 \mu_0 \epsilon_0 \epsilon_r - k_x^2 - k_y^2} \tag{3}$$

$$p = \sqrt{k_x^2 + k_y^2 - \omega^2 \mu_0 \epsilon_0} \tag{4}$$

ϵ_0 = permittivity of air (vacuum)

ϵ_r = relative permittivity of resonator

$$\left.\begin{aligned} k_x &= \frac{n \cdot \pi}{a} \\ k_y &= \frac{m \cdot \pi}{b} \end{aligned}\right\} \quad n, m = 1, 2, 3, \cdots.$$

The fundamental mode is obtained by putting $m=n=1$ and choosing the tan function in (2).[1]

The open-circuit boundary approximation has been used by several authors, and its validity has been experimentally confirmed. The filter structure to be described, however, claims a formula which takes into account the influence of a dielectric substrate, a ground plane, and a top cover. The actual configuration is obtained from Fig. 2 by introducing these parts, as shown in Fig. 5.

Assuming $\epsilon_s \ll \epsilon_r$, the effect of the metallic walls is to modify the exponential decay of the field components into a hyperbolic z dependence of the form

$$\sinh\left(\left(z + h_s + \frac{t}{2}\right) p_s\right) \quad \text{in the substrate region} \tag{5}$$

$$\sinh\left(\left(h + \frac{t}{2} - z\right) p\right) \quad \text{in the air region} \tag{6}$$

where h_s and h are defined by Fig. 5. In the resonator region the trigonometric behavior is retained with the addition of a phase shift ϕ in the z direction.

[1] The fundamental mode has no component of the electric field in the z direction. As a consequence of this, the outlined design formulas, based on the assumption of isotropy, also apply to uniaxial crystals, exhibiting dielectric isotropy in the plane normal to the optical axis, provided the crystal is oriented with this axis in the z direction. More complicated orientations have been treated by Okaya and Barash [2].

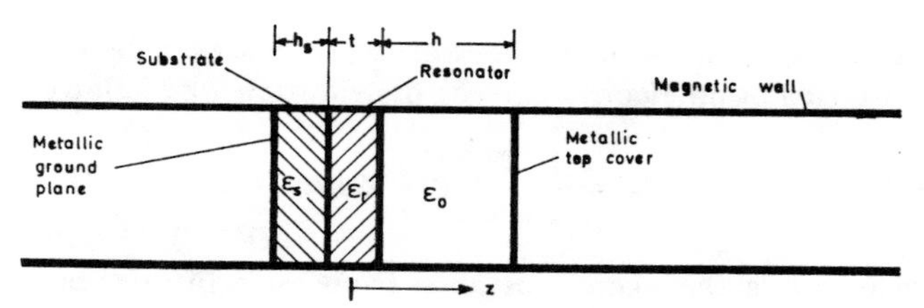

Fig. 5. Geometry for calculating resonance frequencies of actual filter.

The equations determining the resonances and the quantities p_s, p, ϕ, and k_z are now

$$\frac{p_s}{\tanh(p_s h_s)} = k_z \tan\left(k_z\left(\frac{t}{2} + \phi\right)\right) \tag{7}$$

$$\frac{p}{\tanh(ph)} = k_z \tan\left(k_z\left(\frac{t}{2} - \phi\right)\right) \tag{8}$$

where p and k_z are as defined by (3) and (4), and

$$p_s = \sqrt{k_x^2 + k_y^2 - \omega^2 \mu_0 \epsilon_0 \epsilon_s} \tag{9}$$

ϵ_s being the dielectric constant of the substrate.

When ϵ_s, ϵ_r, a, b, h_s, h, and the desired resonance frequency are known, (7) and (8) may be solved for $(t/2)+\phi$ and $(t/2)-\phi$, respectively, and the appropriate thickness of the resonator is determined by summation.

Calculations of coupling coefficients between the resonators also require calculation of stored energy and dipole moment.

The stored energy is given by

$$W = \frac{\epsilon_0}{2} \cdot \iiint \epsilon(z) \, |\boldsymbol{E}|^2 \, dv. \tag{10}$$

The volume of integration is the magnetic-wall tube of Fig. 3, with the range of z being limited by the two metallic planes. $\epsilon(z)$ is the dielectric constant, which takes the values ϵ_s, ϵ_r and 1, corresponding to the three different media. Substitution of the field components gives, by carrying out the integration in the x and y direction,

$$W = \frac{H_0^2 \cdot \omega^2 \mu_0^2 \epsilon_0 \cdot ab}{16(k_x^2 + k_y^2)} \left\{ \epsilon_s \left[\frac{\cos\left(k_z \frac{t}{2} + \phi\right)}{\sinh(p_s h_s)} \right]^2 \cdot \left(\frac{\sinh(2p_s h_s)}{2p_s} - h_s \right) + \left[\frac{\cos\left(k_z \frac{t}{2} - \phi\right)}{\sinh(ph)} \right]^2 \cdot \left(\frac{\sinh(2p_s)}{2p} - h \right) + \epsilon_r \left(\frac{1}{k_z} \sin(k_z t) \cos(2\phi) + t \right) \right\}. \tag{11}$$

The magnetic dipole moment of the resonator is defined in terms of an electric current distribution i as follows:

$$M = \frac{1}{2}\iiint r \times i\, dv \tag{12}$$

where r is the vector distance from an arbitrary but fixed point. The volume of integration is the same as for the stored energy. This formula also applies to the dielectric resonator, by substituting the displacement current $j\omega\epsilon_0\epsilon E$ for the current vector as follows:

$$M = \frac{j\omega\epsilon_0}{2}\iiint_V \epsilon(z)\cdot r \times E\, dv \tag{13}$$

which integrates to

$$|M| = \frac{4\omega^2\mu_0\epsilon_0 H_0 ab}{(k_x^2 + k_y^2)\pi^2}\cdot F \tag{14}$$

where

$$F = \frac{\epsilon_s}{p_s}\,\frac{\cos\left(k_z\frac{t}{2} + \phi\right)}{\sinh(p_s h_s)}(\cosh(p_s h_s) - 1) + 2\frac{\epsilon_r}{k_z}\sin\left(k_z\frac{t}{2}\right)\cos\phi + \frac{1}{p}\,\frac{\cos\left(k_z\frac{t}{2} - \phi\right)}{\cosh(ph)}(\cosh(ph) - 1). \tag{15}$$

From a far-field point of view, the radiation from the resonator is a magnetic dipole field, and (13) shows from symmetry considerations that the dipole moment is in the z direction.

Experiments have shown, however, that the far-field approximation does not apply in the calculations of coupling between resonators. This difficulty has been overcome by introducing a distributed dipole moment. The dipole moment per unit volume is, however, not uniquely defined. From (13) the assumption that the dipole moment is proportional to $\epsilon(z)\cdot(\nabla\times E)$ seems to be reasonable, or by neglecting the transversal components which integrate to zero, we define a dipole moment per unit volume

$$m(x, y, z) = \frac{\epsilon(z)\cdot H_z(x, y, z)}{\iiint_V \epsilon(z)\cdot H_z(x, y, z)\, dV} M. \tag{16}$$

C. Coupling Between Resonators in Waveguides

The coupling between resonators in a waveguide will now be given. The analysis follows that of Cohn [9]. If the resonators are small, the coupling coefficients are conveniently described in terms of the dipole moment of the resonators. Otherwise we define a distributed dipole moment as shown in (16) and calculate the coupling by integration. Let the resonators be represented by infinitesimally small current loops, separated in the waveguide by a distance s, as shown in Fig. 6.

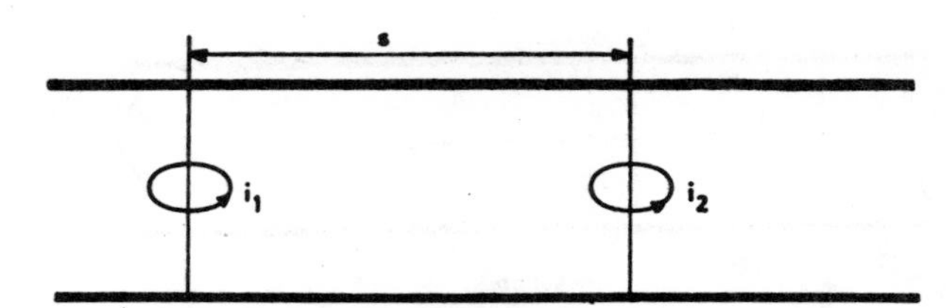

Fig. 6. Current loops in waveguide.

Loop 1 is carrying a current I_1, thus having a dipole moment

$$M_1 = A_1\cdot I_1 \tag{17}$$

A being the area of the loop.

The stored energy is

$$W_1 = \tfrac{1}{2}LI_1^2 \tag{18}$$

where L is the loop inductance.

The EMF induced in loop 2 is

$$V_2 = -\oint E_2 dl = j\omega L_m I_1 \tag{19}$$

where L_m is the mutual inductance between the loops.

By Stokes' theorem we have

$$j\omega L_m I_1 = -\iint_{A_2} n_2\cdot(\nabla\times E_2)\, dS = A_2\cdot j\omega\mu_0 H_2 \tag{20}$$

where H_2 is the field value at the location of loop 2.

The coupling coefficient is defined as

$$k = \frac{L_m}{L} \tag{21}$$

which by (18) and (20) gives

$$k = \frac{\mu_0 H_2 I_1 A_2}{2W_1}. \tag{22}$$

For identical loops

$$k = \frac{\mu_0 H_2 M_1}{2W_1}. \tag{23}$$

The magnetic field H_2 is the field at position 2, arising from a dipole M_1 at position 1. This can be expressed in terms of the normal modes of the waveguide.

Let the field vectors of a certain mode, denoted by q, be

$$E_q^{\pm}(x, y, z) = (e_{tq}(x, y) \pm e_{zq}(x, y))\exp(\mp\Gamma_q z) \tag{24a}$$

$$H_q^{\pm}(x, y, z) = (\pm h_{tq}(x, y) + h_{zq}(x, y))\exp(\mp\Gamma_q z) \tag{24b}$$

where subscripts t and z refer to transverse and longitudinal components, respectively, Γ_q is the propagation constant, and upper and lower signs refer to propagation in positive and negative direction, respectively.

The normal mode field components are normalized subject to the condition

$$\iint (e_q \times h_q)\, dS = 1 \tag{25}$$

where the integration is over the cross section of the guide.

It has been shown [10] that a magnetic dipole of strength $\boldsymbol{M}$ will excite a certain waveguide mode with an amplitude

$$a_q^{\pm} = \tfrac{1}{2} j\omega\mu_0 (\boldsymbol{H}_q^{\pm} \cdot \boldsymbol{M}). \tag{26}$$

Now assume dipole 1 to be positioned at $z=0$ and dipole 2 to be at $z=s$. In the case of interest all waveguide modes are cut off, i.e., all the Γ_q are real. Further, the dipoles are transverse oriented. The field H_2 is then

$$\boldsymbol{H}_2(x_2, y_2, z_2) = \tfrac{1}{2} j\omega\mu_0 \sum_q (\boldsymbol{h}_q(x_1, y_1) \cdot \boldsymbol{M}_1) \cdot \boldsymbol{h}_q(x_2, y_2) \exp(-\Gamma_q s). \tag{27}$$

When calculating the actual coupling between dielectric resonators in a practical filter structure, the assumption of infinitesimally small dipoles is violated. In this case the total coupling is found by integration.

Let dV_1 be a volume element of resonator 1 and dV_2 an element of resonator 2. The dipole moment per unit volume of resonator 1 is $\boldsymbol{m}(x_1, y_1, z_1)$.

From (23) and (26) we get the following expression for the coupling:

$$k = j \frac{\mu_0^2 \omega}{4W_1} \sum_q \iiint_{V_1} \iiint_{V_2} (\boldsymbol{h}_q(x_1, y_1) \cdot \boldsymbol{m}(x_1, y_1, z_1)) \boldsymbol{h}_q(x_2, y_2) \boldsymbol{m}(x_2, y_2, z_2) \cdot \exp(-\Gamma_q(z_1 - z_2))\, dV_1\, dV_2. \tag{28}$$

The stored energy is given by (11) and the dipole moment by (14), (15), and (16).

D. External Coupling

The coupling between the end resonators and the microstrip circuit will now be described. Fig. 7 shows the magnetic field of a resonator and a current carrying microstrip, respectively. From the field configuration it is evident that a coupling will occur when the resonator is positioned close to the microstrip. A stronger coupling is obtainable by placing a microstrip on each side of the resonator, feeding them 180° out of phase. This arrangement is shown in Fig. 8.

Besides the possibility of stronger coupling, the balanced arrangement of Fig. 8 has another advantage. The resonator field expressions are alternately symmetrical and antisymmetrical with respect to x and y, corresponding to factors like

$$\sin\left(\frac{n\pi x}{a}\right), \qquad n = 1, 2, 3, \cdots.$$

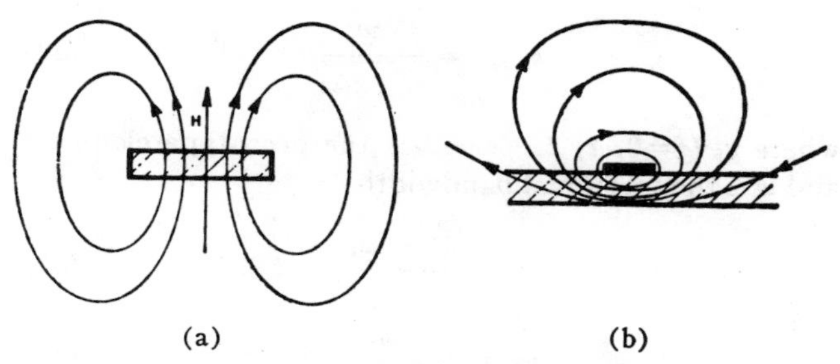

Fig. 7. (a) Magnetic field of dielectric resonator. (b) Magnetic field of current-carrying microstrip.

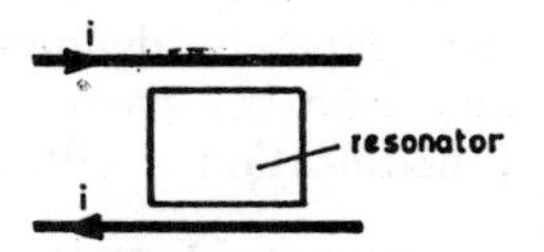

Fig. 8. Balanced coupling to end resonators.

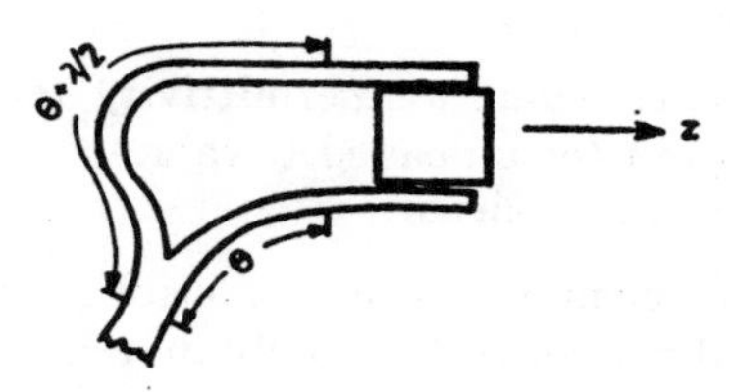

Fig. 9. Practical realization of coupling.

It follows that only half of the possible modes will be excited by the balanced coupling arrangement. Fig. 9 shows a practical realization of the coupling arrangement. The 180° phase shift is obtained by means of a power splitter and a path difference of $\lambda/2$ between the two signal paths. This constitutes a very simple balun. The coupling is now easily adjusted by moving the resonator in the z direction.

Some effort has been made in order to calculate the coupling as a function of position for a given geometry. However, the expressions were not found accurate enough for actual filter design. Instead this relationship was established by measurements. These measurements were accomplished using a method described by Sucher and Fox [11]. The method is based on a plot of reflection coefficient in the Smith chart as a function of frequency. At resonance this plot describes a circle, which contains all information on both external and unloaded Q, as well as losses due to the coupling structure.

E. Filter Synthesis

The filter synthesis is based on the well-known low-pass prototype elements and a low-pass to bandpass mapping, as described, e.g., by Matthaei *et al.* [12]. This permits synthesis of both Tchebyscheff and Butterworth responses. The design is completely determined by the following formulas [12, p. 432]:

$$Q_{\text{ext}} = \frac{g_0 g_1}{w} \tag{29}$$

$$k_{j,j+1} = \frac{w}{\sqrt{g_j g_{j+1}}} \tag{30}$$

where g_j ($j=0, 1, 2, \cdots$) are the prototype elements and w is the fractional bandwidth

$$w = \frac{\omega_2 - \omega_1}{\omega_0} \tag{31}$$

$$\omega_0 = \sqrt{\omega_2 \omega_1}. \tag{32}$$

The passband edges ω_2 and ω_1 are for Tchebyscheff filters defined by the passband ripple level, while the bandwidth of Butterworth filters is defined by the 3-dB points. However, any arbitrary passband definition is possible by a slight modification of (29) and (30).

III. Resonator Materials

When choosing the resonator material, the following properties are of interest:

1) dielectric constant (or permittivity tensor);
2) loss tangent (or unloaded Q value);
3) temperature coefficient.

The dielectric constant is not a critical factor, but should be of the order of 100 to obtain reasonable resonator dimensions in the microwave region. The loss tangent and the temperature coefficient should of course be as small as possible. Both crystals and ceramics are usable for resonator purposes. To some extent the parameters of the ceramics can be controlled during the manufacturing process, but a simultaneous optimization of both loss tangent and temperature coefficient seems to be difficult. Thus, with materials available at the present time, a compromise has to be made.

The highest unloaded Q values ($Q_0 \simeq 1/\tan\delta$) have been observed with single crystals of TiO_2 (rutile), $SrTiO_3$, and ThBr–Tl. At room temperatures and microwave frequencies the unloaded Q values of these materials are in the order of 10^4. The Q value is strongly dependent on crystal purity and may be further increased by annealing processes. The dielectric constant is for rutile ~ 80 (transverse to optical axis), and for $SrTiO_3$ (isotropic) ~ 250. The temperature sensitivities of these crystals are, however, strong. For rutile the variations in permittivity with temperature is

$$\Delta\epsilon_r/\epsilon_r \simeq 1000 \text{ ppm/}^\circ\text{C}$$

which implies a frequency change

$$\Delta f/f = 500 \text{ ppm/}^\circ\text{C}$$

since the resonance frequency is approximately proportional to $1/\sqrt{\epsilon_r}$. For $SrTiO_3$ the temperature coefficient is even 3–4 times greater. Ceramics have the advantage of being isotropic (thus eliminating orientation effort) and cheap. A great spectrum of permittivity values are available, but Q values are in general lower than for single crystals. The following ceramics have been measured:

1) Eccoceram K-90 (Emerson & Cuming, Inc.);
2) AlSiMag 192 (American Lava Corporation);
3) AlSiMag NPO T96 (American Lava Corporation).

Ceramics 1) and 2) have nearly the same properties

$$\epsilon_r = 80\text{–}90; \qquad Q_0 \sim 2000; \qquad \Delta\epsilon_r/\epsilon_r \simeq 1000 \text{ ppm/}^\circ\text{C}.$$

Ceramic 3) has an extremely low temperature coefficient,

$$\Delta\epsilon_r/\epsilon_r \sim 6 \text{ ppm/}^\circ\text{C}$$

but the Q value is low ($Q_0 \sim 300\text{–}400$), and $\epsilon_r \simeq 32$. Except for the last one, which is not very usable because of its low Q value, the temperature dependence of all these materials is too strong for narrow-band microwave filter applications. Until materials with better performance have been developed, stabilization is required. The temperature of the resonators depends on both signal power and environment temperature. In the actual filter structure, the resonators are in thermal contact with the substrate which, at least for alumina substrates, provides a quite effective heat sink, but the dissipation of course still restricts this type of filter to low or medium power applications. Stabilization of the environment temperature is a quite trivial problem which has not been dealt with in this work. More sophisticated stabilization methods, utilizing parasitic or composite resonators have been suggested,[2] but the complexity of these arrangements reduces greatly their benefit.

IV. Experimental Results

A. 3-GHz Bandpass Filter with Polyolefin Substrate

The first experimental filter was designed with the following parameters:

center frequency	3 GHz
response	Butterworth (maximum flat)
3-dB bandwidth	70 MHz (2.3 percent)
number of resonators	3
resonator material	Eccoceram K-90
substrate	Rexolene P, 1/8 in (Polyolefin, $\epsilon_r = 2.32$)
box dimensions	125 by 60 by 11.6 mm
box material	Aluminum.

The resonator dimensions were calculated to be 18 by 18 by 2.77 mm, with $\epsilon_r = 80$. Prototype elements for a

[2] Two resonators separated by a small air gap may act as a single resonator with a fundamental resonant frequency which depends on gap spacing [15]. Thermal expansion of the mounting fixture may be utilized to adjust this gap in such a manner that the temperature dependence of ϵ is partly compensated.

Butterworth filter with three resonators are

$$g_0 = g_1 = g_3 = g_4 = 1$$
$$g_2 = 2.$$

From (29) and (30)

$$Q_{ext} = \frac{3000}{70} = 43$$

$$k_{12} = k_{23} = \frac{70}{3000\sqrt{2}} = 1.65 \times 10^{-2}.$$

Using a coupling program based on methods described earlier, the appropriate distance between resonators (center to center) was calculated to be $s = 21$ mm.

Coupling to the external circuit was performed by two 100-Ω microstrips, separated by 18 mm and fed 180° out of phase. The structure is shown on Fig. 10. Measurements showed that the required external Q, $Q_{ext} = 43$, was the maximum achievable coupling with this structure, corresponding to a resonator position which is observable on the photograph. This picture also shows the tuning screws which were mounted in the top cover to compensate for unequalness in resonator dimensions. The screws perturbate the radiation field of the resonators and have the effect of slightly increasing the resonant frequency.

The passband response of the filter is shown on Fig. 11. The center frequency is slightly higher than predicted, which is probably due to inaccurate data for the dielectric constant of the resonators. The insertion loss is 0.5 dB, from which 0.1–0.15 dB is due to the omni spectra miniature (OSM) microstrip transitions, which are mounted beneath the ground plane. By Cohn's formula [14]

$$Q_0 = \frac{4.343}{w \cdot A} \sum_{1}^{n} g_i \tag{33}$$

where A is the insertion loss, w is the fractional bandwidth, and the resonators are assumed equal; the resultant filter losses correspond to an unloaded Q value of the resonators; $Q_0 \simeq 2000$.

The first filter was designed to test the passband response. In a practical filter the waveguide (box width) should be more narrow. With the chosen dimensions, the first cavity resonance in the box occurs at 3.9 GHz. The next resonator mode was observable at 3.45 GHz. By placing a simple mode filter, consisting of a centered cross of thin copper wire on the broad surface of each resonator (Fig. 12), the insertion loss at this frequency was increased by 25 dB. The resonators were simply fastened to the substrate by means of double-sided tape. In a practical filter, a more mechanically rigid construction is recommended. The resonators could either be glued to the substrate, or the whole box simply filled with polyfoam.

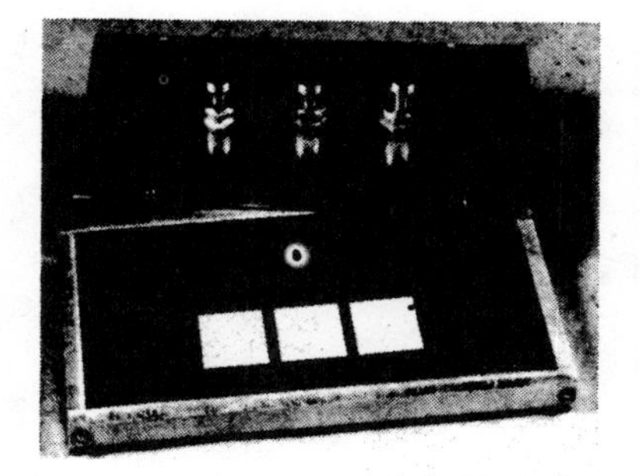

Fig. 10. Disassembled 3-GHz filter.

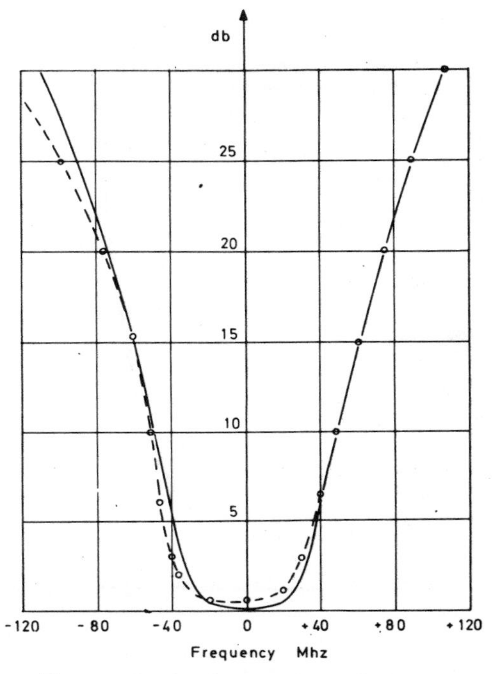

Fig. 11. Passband response of 3-GHz filter.

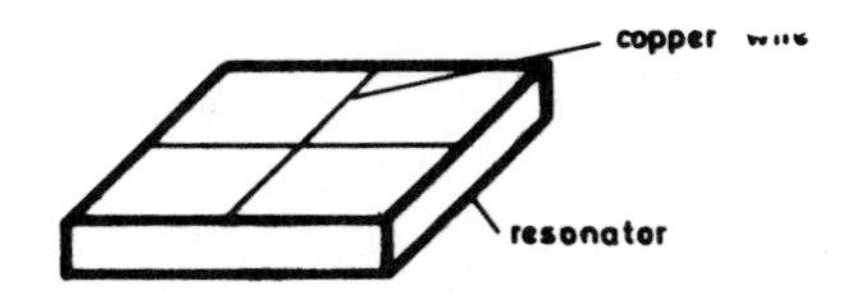

Fig. 12. Dielectric resonator with mode supression filter.

B. 9-GHz Bandpass Filter with Polyolefin Substrate

Design parameters for this filter were as follows:

center frequency	9 GHz
response	Tchebycheff
ripple level	0.2 dB
0.2-dB bandwidth	70 MHz (0.78 percent)
number of resonators	4
resonator material	TiO_2 (single crystal rutile)

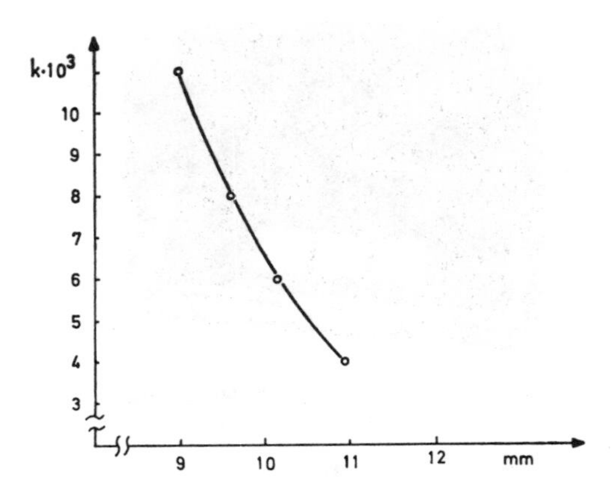

Fig. 13. Coupling between resonators versus center-to-center separation (9-GHz filter).

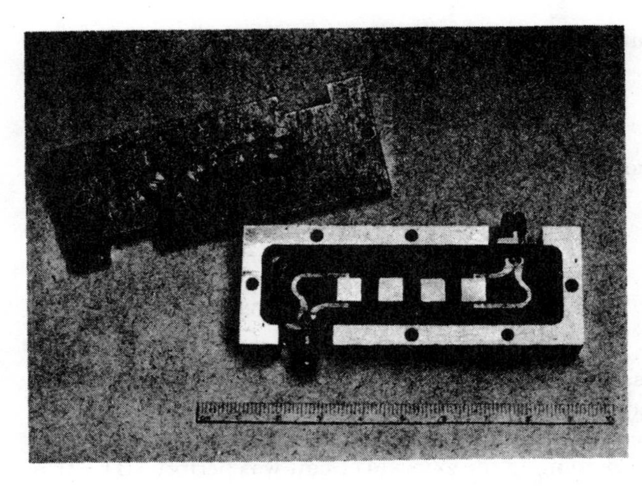

Fig. 15. Disassembled 9-GHz filter.

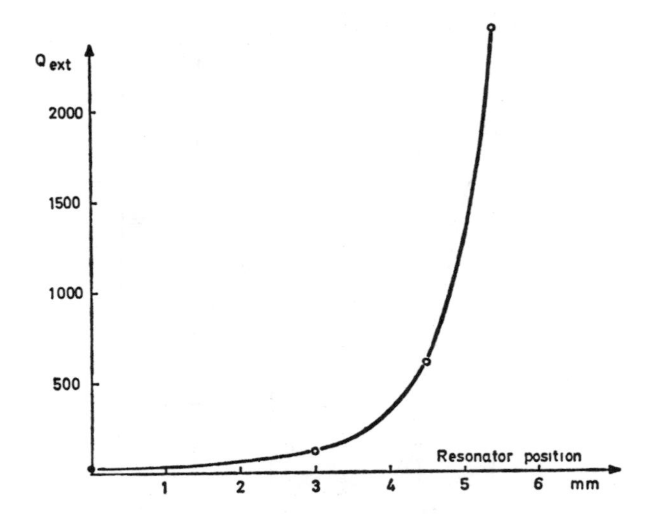

Fig. 14. External Q value versus resonator position (9-GHz filter).

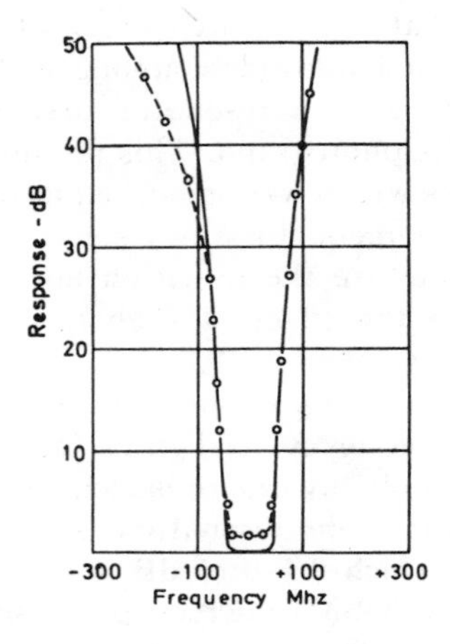

Fig. 16. Theoretical (-) and measured (- -o- -) response of 9-GHz filter.

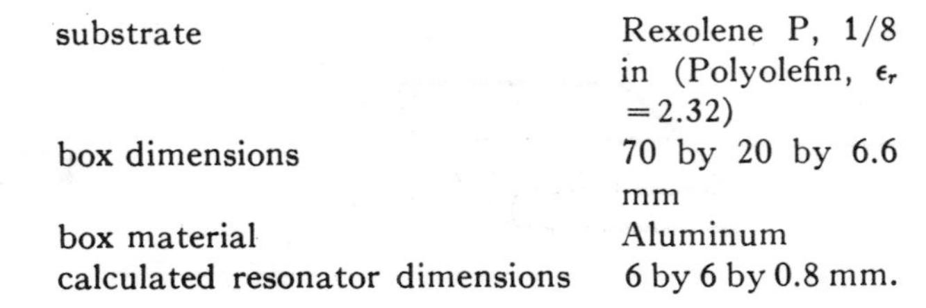

substrate	Rexolene P, 1/8 in (Polyolefin, $\epsilon_r = 2.32$)
box dimensions	70 by 20 by 6.6 mm
box material	Aluminum
calculated resonator dimensions	6 by 6 by 0.8 mm.

With the prototype elements

$$g_0 = 1; \quad g_1 = 1.3028; \quad g_2 = 1.2844$$

$$g_3 = 1.9761; \quad g_4 = 0.8464; \quad g_5 = 1.5386$$

the coupling parameters are, by (29) and (30),

$$Q_{ext} = 167$$

$$k_{12} = k_{34} = 6 \times 10^{-3}$$

$$k_{23} = 5.5 \times 10^{-3}.$$

Figs. 13 and 14 show the coupling parameters as a function of resonators positions. The filter was constructed according to these curves which resulted in the layout shown in Fig. 15.

The theoretical and measured responses are shown in Fig. 16. The ripple level (and the corresponding VSWR) was as predicted, while the slope of the lower skirt became less than the theoretical above the 30-dB level.

The passband attenuation was 1.5 dB. Approximately 0.4 dB of this is due to the coaxial microstrip transitions and the microstrip. The resultant 1.1-dB resonator loss corresponds to an unloaded Q value of 3200. The Q value of the resonators, measured in a waveguide, was 6000. The reduction is due to the ground plane, the coupling structure, and the tuning screws. It is conceivable that these losses could be reduced by improved coupling design.

Fig. 17 shows the spurious responses in the frequency range 8–12 GHz. It was originally believed that the spurious responses were higher order resonator modes. A mode filter, similar to one which is shown in Fig. 12, had no effect, however. All the spurious responses have been identified as cavity resonances of the LSM_{11} mode of the coupling guide. Since the LSM mode theoretically

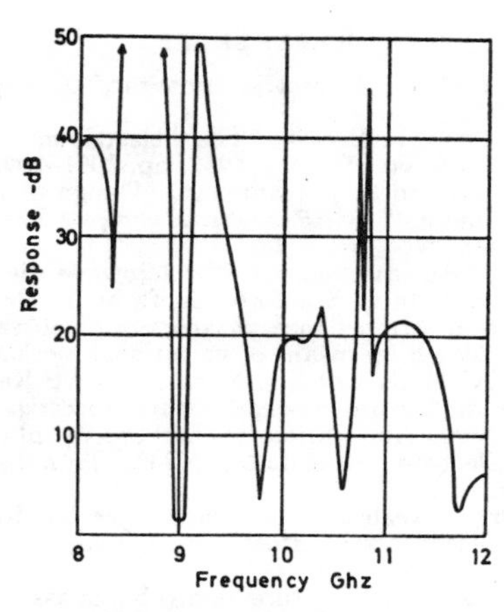

Fig. 17. Measured principal and spurious responses of 9-GHz filter.

Fig. 18. Disassembled 9.9-GHz filter.

does not couple to the resonator field, the propagation properties of these modes were not checked when designing the filter. The response, however, shows that these modes are easily excited, e.g., by the coupling structure.

C. 9.9-GHz Bandpass Filter with Alumina Substrate

Design parameters for this filter were as follows:

center frequency	9.9 GHz
response	Tchebycheff
ripple level	0.01 dB
0.01-dB bandwidth	32 MHz (0.32 percent)
number of resonators	3
resonator material	TiO_2 (single crystal rutile)
substrate	AlSiMag 772 (alumina, 0.25 in $\epsilon_r = 9.7$)
box dimensions	12 by 40 by 5.63 mm
box material	Aluminum.

The resonators were the same as for the filter described in Section IV-B. The frequency is increased from 9 to 9.9 GHz because of the change in dielectric constant and thickness of the substrate.

$$g_0 = g_4 = 1$$

$$g_1 = g_3 = 0.6291$$

$$g_2 = 0.9702$$

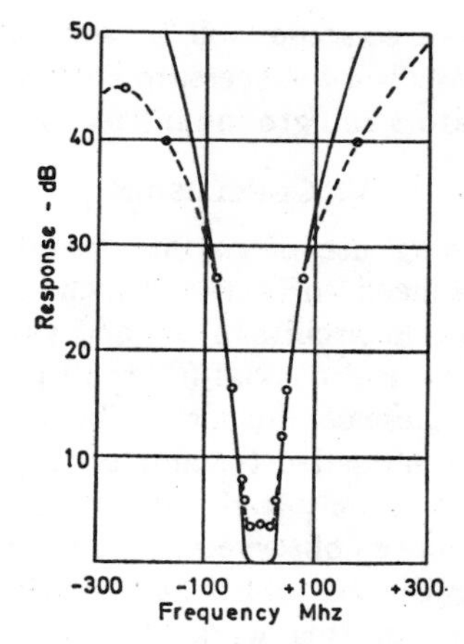

Fig. 19. Theoretical (-) and measured (--o--) response of 9.9-GHz filter.

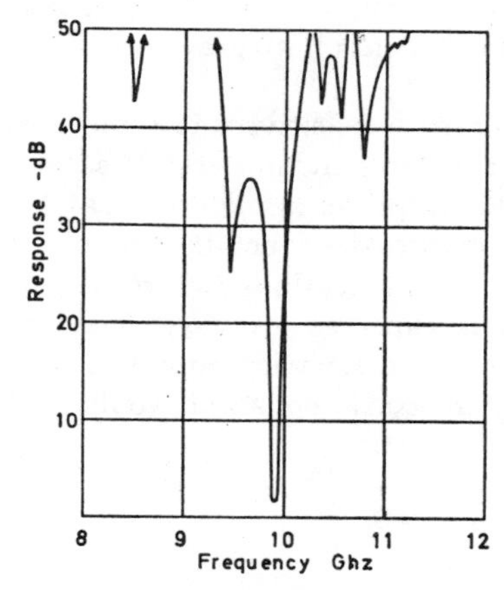

Fig. 20. Measured principal and spurious responses of 9.9-GHz filter.

which by (43) and (44) yield

$$Q_{ext} = 195$$

$$k_{12} = k_{23} = 4.14 \times 10^{-3}.$$

As shown in Fig. 18, $Q_{ext} = 195$ corresponds to the maximum achievable coupling with the given structure and the coupling program calculated the resonator distance to be $s = 10$ mm. Figs. 19 and 20 show the theoretical and measured responses. Note that reduction of the box width has reduced the presence of spurious responses.

Passband insertion loss was 3.7 dB. With 0.5 dB due to the transitions, the resultant resonator losses correspond to an unloaded Q value $Q_0 = 935$. It is seen that the Q value is greatly reduced, mainly because of the reduced thickness of the substrate, which results in strong induced currents in the ground plane and correspondingly increased dissipation losses. The Q value of this resonator is, however, still superior to a half-wave microstrip resonator by a factor of 3. Mounting the resonators with their dipole axis colinear with the waveguide axis, as in Harrison's design [8], would greatly reduce these losses. Considerable reduction of induced current losses is also achievable by supporting the resonators on lowloss, low-ϵ spacers, to increase the distance between resonators and ground plane.

V. Conclusion

With increasing use of microstrip circuits there is undoubtedly a need for filters which are compatible with the microstrip circuits in size and with the conventional waveguide and coaxial filters in performance. It is obvious that these conditions can be met by dielectric filters, since the unloaded Q value of the resonator element itself is extremely high. The reduction of the Q value which has been observed in the constructed filters is mainly due to dissipations in surrounding metal parts.

The objective of this work has been primarily to prove that an accurate filter design is possible on a synthesis basis. Design improvements in order to reduce the dissipation losses are obviously possible without renouncing the benefit of integration with the microstrip circuit.

The temperature sensitivity is a more serious problem, which at the present time restricts this type of filter to low or medium power applications, and filter designs using the techniques described here require temperature stabilization in applications where the environment temperature is expected to vary. Development of a material with the dielectric properties of rutile and a less sensitive dielectric constant would certainly solve this problem.

References

[1] R. D. Richtmeyer, "Dielectric resonator," *J. Appl. Phys.*, vol. 10, June 1939.

[2] A. Okaya and L. F. Barash, "The dielectric microwave resonator," *Proc. IRE*, vol. 50, Oct. 1962, pp. 2081–2092.

[3] J. C. Sethares and S. J. Naumann, "Design of microwave dielectric resonators," *IEEE Trans. Microwave Theory Tech.*, vol. MTT-14, Jan. 1966, pp. 2–7.

[4] H. Y. Yee, "An investigation of microwave dielectric resonators," Stanford Univ., Stanford, Calif., M. L. Rep. 1065, 1963.

[5] T. D. Iveland, "Impedance parameters of obstacles in waveguides, calculated by means of variational methods," Electron. Res. Lab., NTH, Trondheim, Norway, ELAB Rep. TE-78.

[6] T. Hansen, "A theoretical-experimental investigation of dielectric resonators. Application to microwave filters" (in Norwegian), Electron. Res. Lab., NTH, Trondheim, Norway, ELAB Rep. TE-68.

[7] T. Pettersen, "Realization of microwave bandpass filters by means of dielectric resonators" (in Norwegian), *ETT-Elektro*, vol. 81, Aug. 1968.

[8] W. H. Harrison, "A miniature high-Q bandpass filter employing dielectric resonators," *IEEE Trans. Microwave Theory Tech.*, vol. MTT-16, Apr. 1968, pp. 210–218.

[9] S. B. Cohn, "Microwave bandpass filters containing high-Q dielectric resonators," *IEEE Trans. Microwave Theory Tech.*, vol. MTT-16, Apr. 1968, pp. 218–227.

[10] R. E. Collin, *Field Theory of Guided Waves.* New York: McGraw-Hill, 1960.

[11] M. Sucher and J. Fox, *Handbook of Microwave Measurements*, vol. 2, 3rd ed. Polytechnic Inst. Brooklyn, Brooklyn, N. Y.: Polytechnic Press.

[12] G. L. Matthaei, L. Young, and E. M. T. Jones; *Microwave Filters, Impedance-Matching Networks and Coupling Structures.* New York: McGraw-Hill, 1964.

[13] T. D. Iveland, "Microstrip bandpass-filters with dielectric resonators," Electron. Res. Lab., NTH, Trondheim, Norway, Tech. Publ. 49 (presented at the European Microwave Conference, London, England, Sept. 8–21, 1969).

[14] S. B. Cohn, "Dissipation loss in multiple-coupled-resonator filters," *Proc. IRE*, vol. 47, Aug. 1959, 1342–1348.

[15] M. R. Stiglitz: "Frequency tuning of rutile resonators," *Proc. IEEE* (Lett.), vol. 54. Mar. 1966, pp. 413–414.

Design of Cylindrical Dielectric Resonators in Inhomogeneous Media

RENÉ R. BONETTI AND ALI E. ATIA, MEMBER, IEEE

Abstract—**An iterative analytical method is presented for computing resonant frequencies of dielectric cylindrical resonators in inhomogeneous media. Normalized design charts are presented including a wide range of practical geometrical and physical parameters. Numerical results, when compared to three independent sets of experimental data, show an accuracy of better than 1 percent.**

I. Introduction

INTEREST in the utilization of high-dielectric-constant resonators has been revived recently because of the availability of low-loss temperature-stable materials [1], [2]. Among the many possible applications of these resonators are temperature-compensated oscillators [3], [4], low-noise microwave synthesizers [5], and narrow-bandpass filters [6].

Several approximate methods have been presented for determining the resonant frequency of a dielectric cylinder in the presence of either one [7] or two [8] conductor planes perpendicular to its axis. In practice, when a resonator is used in a microwave circuit employing a microstrip transmission medium, the microstrip substrate as well as other dielectric supports and metallic boundaries can significantly alter the resonant frequency predicted from the idealized conditions usually assumed.

This paper describes an accurate analytical method to compute the resonant frequency of a high-dielectric-constant cylinder inside a metallic cylindrical cavity, which includes a microstrip dielectric support and several options for supporting the resonator (Fig. 1). The basic assumptions are as follows.

a) All dielectric materials involved are isotropic and lossless.

b) The metallic boundaries are perfectly conducting.

c) The electromagnetic field distribution is that of the dominant $TE_{10\delta}$ mode. (The subscripts refer to the cylindrical coordinates r, θ, and z, respectively.)

II. Method of Analysis

Fig. 2 shows the configuration to be analyzed, which consists of a cylindrical high-dielectric-constant material (region 3) positioned between three layers of different dielectrics (regions 1, 2, and 4). The $TE_{10\delta}$-mode field components in the ith region can be written as [9]

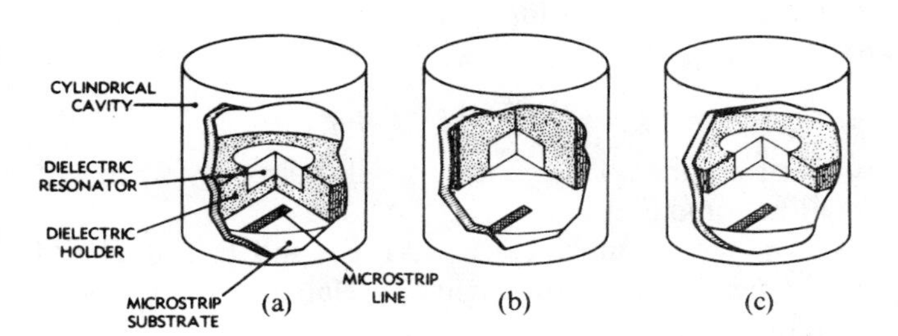

Fig. 1. Three possible ways for supporting a dielectric resonator coupled to a microstrip line. (a) From below. (b) From above. (c) From the side edge.

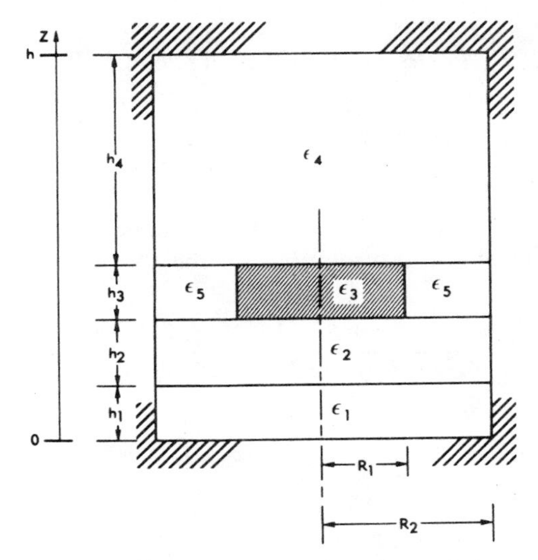

Fig. 2. Cross section of cavity under analysis.

$$H_z^{(i)} = C_0(k_i r) g_i(z) \tag{1}$$

$$H_r^{(i)} = \frac{1}{k_i} C_0'(k_i r) g_i'(z) \tag{2}$$

$$E_\phi^{(i)} = \frac{j\omega\mu_0}{k_i} C_0'(k_i r) g_i(z) \tag{3}$$

$$H_\phi^{(i)} = E_r^{(i)} = E_z^{(i)} = 0 \tag{4}$$

with

$$C_0(k_i r) = J_0(k_i r), \qquad r \leq R_1$$

$$C_0(k_i r) = K_0(k_i r) - \frac{K_0'[k_i R_2] I_0(k_i r)}{I_0'[k_i R_2)]}, \qquad R_1 \leq r \leq R_2$$

Manuscript revised December 1, 1980. This paper is based upon work performed at COMSAT Laboratories under the sponsorship of the International Telecommunications Satellite Organization (INTELSAT). A condensed version of this paper was presented at the 1980 IEEE-MTT International Microwave Symposium, Washington, DC.

The authors are with COMSAT Laboratories, Clarksburg, MD 20734.

where J_0, K_0, and I_0 are the appropriate Bessel functions that describe the field distribution in the cylindrical region $r \leqslant R_1$ and the radially decaying fields for $r > R_1$. Also

$$g_i(z) = A_i \sinh \zeta_i z + B_i \cosh \zeta_i z, \qquad i = 1,2,4 \qquad (5a)$$

$$g_i(z) = A_i \sin \zeta_i z + B_i \cos \zeta_i z, \qquad i = 3,5. \qquad (5b)$$

The radial and axial wavenumbers (k_i and ζ_i) are related by the wave equation as

$$k_i^2 = \omega^2 \mu_0 \epsilon_i \pm \zeta_i^2 \qquad (6)$$

where the minus sign holds for $i=3$ and 5. The field decay in the radial direction for $r > R_1$ implies that the wavenumber

$$(jk_5)^2 = \zeta_5^2 - \omega^2 \mu_0 \epsilon_5 \qquad (7)$$

is a real number. This condition will hold only when ϵ_5 is small as compared to ϵ_3.

Of the ten unknown constants (A_i's and B_i's) in (1)–(4) for the field components, eight are related by the boundary conditions

$$E_\phi^{(i)}(r,z) = 0, \qquad i = 1,4, \quad z = 0, h \qquad (8)$$

$$\frac{d^m E_\phi^{(1)}(r,h_1)}{dz^m} = \frac{d^m E_\phi^{(2)}(r,h_1)}{dz^m} \qquad (9)$$

$$\frac{d^m E_\phi^{(2)}(r,h_1+h_2)}{dz^m} = \frac{d^m E_\phi^{(3)}(r,h_1+h_2)}{dz^m} \qquad (10)$$

$$\frac{d^m E_\phi^{(3)}(r,h_1+h_2+h_3)}{dz^m} = \frac{d^m E_\phi^{(4)}(r,h_1+h_2+h_3)}{dz^m} \qquad (11)$$

with $m = 0,1$, totaling a set of eight linear equations. The existence of nonzero solutions for the above system implies that

$$\frac{\zeta_3/\zeta_4 \tanh\theta_4 \tan\theta_3 - 1}{\zeta_3/\zeta_4 \tanh\theta_4 + \tan\theta_3} + \frac{p\zeta_3/\zeta_2 \tan\theta_3 - 1}{p\zeta_3/\zeta_2 + \tan\theta_3} = 0 \qquad (12)$$

where

$$p = \frac{\zeta_2/\zeta_1 \tanh\theta_1 + \tanh\theta_2}{1 + \zeta_2/\zeta_1 \tanh\theta_1 \tanh\theta_2}$$

$$\theta_i = \zeta_i h_i, \qquad i = 1, \cdots, 4.$$

The relationship between the ζ_i follows from

$$k_1 = k_2 = k_3 = k_4 \qquad (13)$$

$$\zeta_5 = \zeta_3. \qquad (14)$$

Since

$$\zeta_3 = \frac{\delta\pi}{h_3}$$

where δ defines the mode, (6) and (13) yield

$$\theta_i = \left[\omega^2 \mu_0 (\epsilon_3 - \epsilon_i) - \left(\frac{\delta\pi}{h_3}\right)^2\right]^{1/2} h_i, \qquad i = 1,2,4. \qquad (15)$$

Equation (12), therefore, has two unknowns, δ and ω. Another equation follows from the continuity of the fields, which at the resonator's edge can be written in terms of the wall admittance matching

$$\vec{Y} + \overleftarrow{Y} = 0 \qquad (16)$$

where

$$\vec{Y} = \left.\frac{H_z^{(5)}}{E_\phi^{(5)}}\right|_{r=R_1}, \qquad \overleftarrow{Y} = -\left.\frac{H_z^{(3)}}{E_\phi^{(3)}}\right|_{r=R_1}$$

Equation (16), together with (1)–(3), yields

$$k_3 \frac{J_0(k_3 R_1)}{J_0'(k_3 R_1)} + jk_5 \frac{C_0(jk_5 R_1)}{C_0'(jk_5 R_1)} = 0. \qquad (17)$$

A natural way of solving the system [(12) and (17)] is to iteratively start with the solution of (17) using an assumed value between 0 and 1 for δ (e.g., $\delta = 0.5$), and continue by correcting this value from the solution of (12) and the value of the resonant frequency from (17). This technique can be easily implemented even on a small computer. However, the number of iterations necessary to converge to a stationary result strongly depends on the starting value. The computations presented in this paper required no more than six iterations, when the starting frequency was taken as

$$f_0 = \frac{1.2}{\pi\sqrt{\mu_0 \epsilon_3}\, R_1}$$

computed via the first root of

$$J_0(k_3 R_1) = 0 \qquad (18)$$

with ($\delta = 0$) only. It should be noted that when $h_3 \ll \lambda_0/\sqrt{\epsilon_5}$ and $R_2 \gg R_1$, the second term in (17) approaches zero and the equation becomes equivalent to (18), which corresponds to a magnetic wall boundary condition at $r = R_1$.

III. Numerical Results

The pair of eigenvalue equations, (12) and (17), can be solved in a universal form, independent of the absolute values of the parameters involved, if the following normalizations are introduced:

$$\hat{\epsilon}_i = \frac{\epsilon_i}{\epsilon_3}, \quad \hat{h}_i = \frac{h_i}{h_3}, \qquad i = 1,2,4,5$$

$$\hat{R}_1 = \frac{R_1}{h_3}, \quad \hat{R}_2 = \frac{R_2}{R_1}.$$

Equation (15) can then be rewritten as

$$\theta_i = \left[\left(\frac{\hat{\omega}}{\hat{R}_1}\right)^2 (1 - \hat{\epsilon}_i) - (\delta\pi)^2\right]^{1/2} \hat{h}_i \qquad (19)$$

in which

$$\hat{\omega} = \omega\sqrt{\mu_0 \epsilon_3}\, R_1.$$

The arguments of the Bessel function in (17) becomes

$$k_3 R_1 = \left[\hat{\omega}^2 - (\delta\pi\hat{R}_1)^2\right]^{1/2} \qquad (20)$$

$$jk_5 R_1 = \left[(\delta\pi\hat{R}_1)^2 - \hat{\omega}^2 \hat{\epsilon}_5\right]^{1/2}. \qquad (21)$$

The resonant normalized frequency $\hat{\omega}$ of the dielectric resonator placed in free space can be computed from (12) and (15) with $\hat{h}_1 = 0$, $\hat{h}_2 = \hat{h}_4 \to \infty$; $\epsilon_i = \epsilon_0$ $(i = 1,2,4,5)$; and $R_2/R_1 \to \infty$. Under these conditions, (12) and (17) become

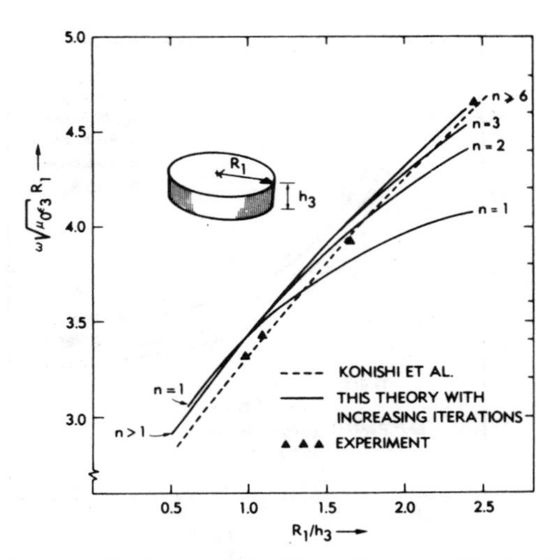

Fig. 3. Normalized resonant frequency of a cylindrical dielectric resonator in free space for an increasing number of iterations compared to the theoretical and experimental results of [9].

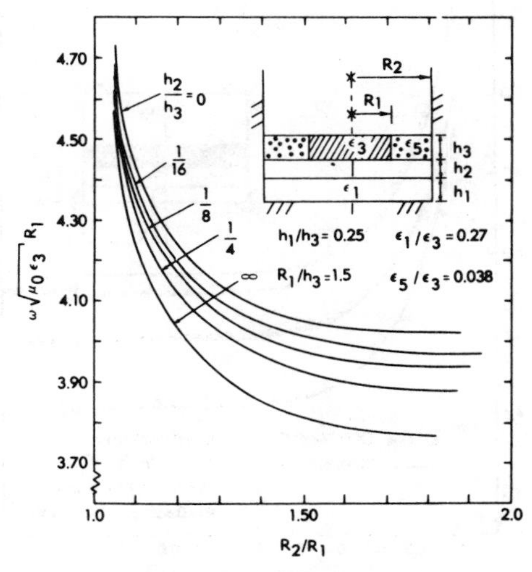

Fig. 5. Normalized resonant frequency as affected by the sidewalls.

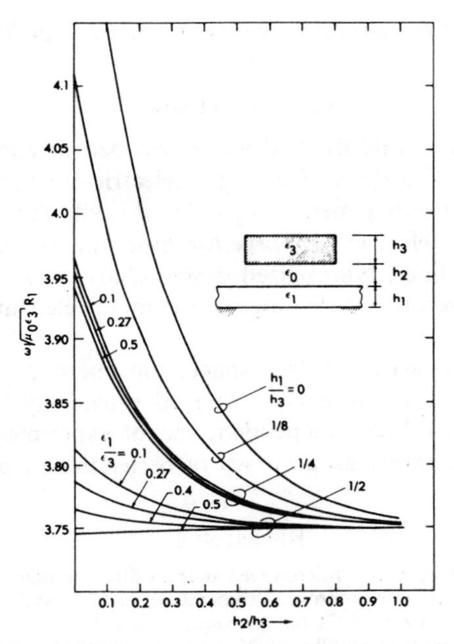

Fig. 4. Normalized resonant frequency of a dielectric disk in the presence of a dielectric-coated conductor plane.

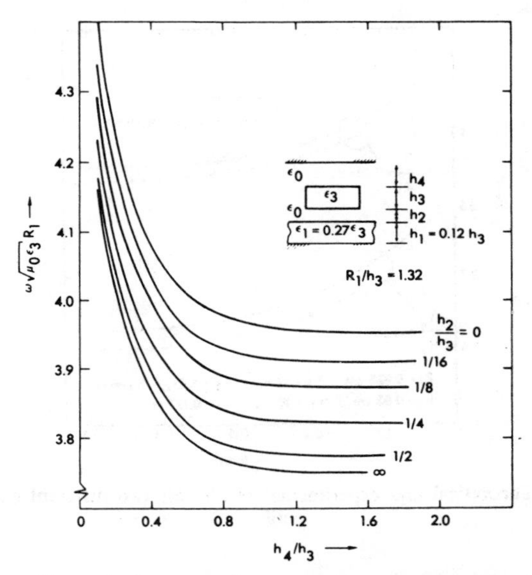

Fig. 6. Normalized resonant frequency dependence on the proximity of two conductor planes (one supporting a microstrip substrate).

$$\tan(\delta\pi)=\frac{\zeta_2}{\zeta_3} \tag{22}$$

$$k_3\frac{J_0(k_3R_1)}{J_0'(k_5R_1)}+jk_5\frac{K_0(jk_5R_1)}{K_0'(jk_5R_1)}=0 \tag{23}$$

which are the same equations derived by Itoh and Rudokas [7] for this particular case.

Fig. 3 compares the convergence of the method discussed in this paper with the theoretical and experimental results of Konishi *et al.* [10]. The small error between these two approaches is that open resonators couple energy into free space; therefore, the analysis must include radiation modes. As pointed out by Itoh [7], this error decreases for higher dielectric constants. However, radiation effects are not present in closed structures, as will be exemplified in the next section.

Fig. 4 shows the effects of the proximity of a microstrip substrate on free-space resonance ($\hat{h}_{2,4}\rightarrow\infty$) for four different substrate thicknesses and a normalized dielectric constant between 0.1 and 0.5. It should be noted that the slope of these curves can be controlled by adjusting either the substrate thickness or its dielectric constant; however, for thin substrates ($\hat{h}_2<1/4$), a variation of 500 percent in its dielectric constant will cause less than 5-percent variation on the resonant frequency.

Fig. 5 exemplifies the dependence on the cavity radius for a dielectric resonator placed at several different positions from the substrate. It shows that the side boundaries must be placed at a minimum distance from the resonator of one and a half times its radius if they are not accounted for in the analysis. (This ratio holds for the set of parameters depicted in the insert.)

Fig. 6 gives an idea of the tunability range of a resonator

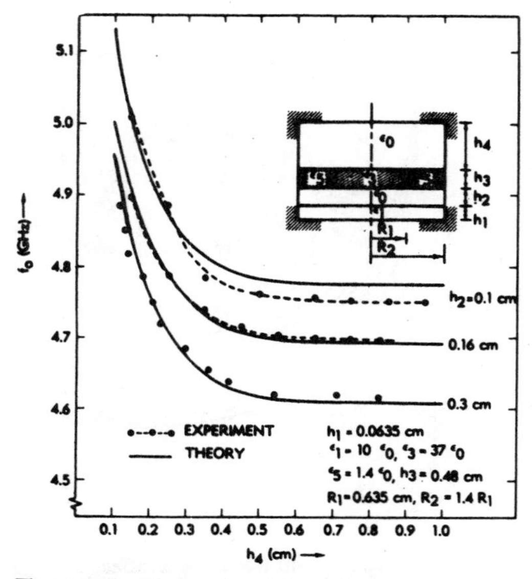

Fig. 7. Theoretical and experimental results for a prototype cavity as depicted in the insert.

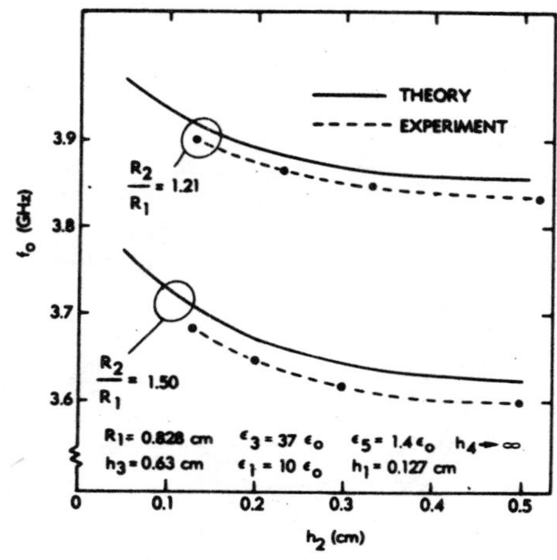

Fig. 8. Theoretical and experimental results for two different external radii.

enclosed in a flat box in which the sidewalls satisfy the condition specified above, and is useful for the design of tunable oscillators and filters. The normalized substrate dielectric constant ($\hat{\epsilon}_1 = 0.27$) corresponds, for example, to an alumina substrate ($\epsilon_1 \cong 10$) and a barium tetratitanate resonator ($\epsilon_3 \cong 37$). The ratio $R_1/h_3 = 1.32$ is close to some standard, commercially available sizes.

IV. Experimental Results

Three sets of experimental data were taken with two samples of barium tetratitanate placed within different cavities and dielectric boundaries. In the first two sets (Figs. 7 and 8) the theoretical data were computed assuming 37.0 for the resonator's dielectric constant, as measured by an independent method. The maximum error was of the order of 0.6 percent in both cases. In the third experiment, one of the theoretical curves was fitted to the experimental data to find the dielectric constant of the sample, and the result was 36.8. With this value in theoretical computations, the remaining curves show an error of 0.2 percent (Fig. 9).

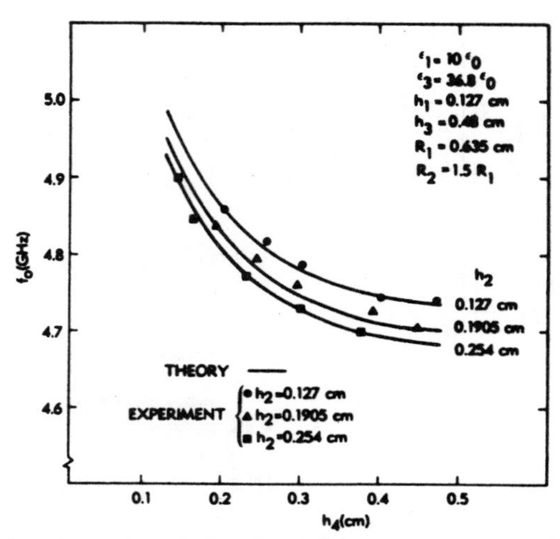

Fig. 9. Experimental results compared to theoretical computations with a dielectric constant of 36.8 (obtained from curve fitting the data set of $h_2 = 0.254$ cm).

V. Conclusions

A very accurate method was developed to compute the frequency of a cylindrical high-dielectric-constant resonator placed inside a metallic cylindrical cavity containing all necessary dielectric supports for both the resonator and microstrip lines. Normalized design charts have been presented, covering a wide range of the more relevant parameters.

For a resonator in free space, this method yields the same analytical expressions derived previously [7]. When compared to three independent sets of experimental data, the method shows an accuracy of better than 1 percent in all cases.

References

[1] W. Wakino *et al.*, "Microwave bandpass filters containing dielectric resonators with improved temperature stability and spurious response," in *Proc. 1975 Int. Microwave Symp.*, pp. 63–65, May 1975.

[2] J. K. Plourde *et al.*, "Ba_2TigO_2 as a microwave dielectric resonator," *J. Amer. Ceramic Soc.*, vol. 58, no. 9–10, pp. 418–420, 1975.

[3] ——, "A dielectric resonator oscillator with 5 ppm long term frequency stability at 4 GHz," in *IEEE MTT-S Int. Microwave Symp. Dig.*, pp. 273–276, June 1977.

[4] S. Tatsuguchi *et al.*, "An integrated 18 GHz receiver front end using a dielectric resonator stabilized generator," in *ICC 79, Conf. Rec.*, vol. 2, pp. 26.2.1–5.

[5] G. D. Alley and H. C. Wang, "An ultra low noise microwave synthesizer," in *Dig. 1979 Int. Microwave Symp.* (Orlando, FL), pp. 147–149.

[6] J. K. Plourde and D. F. Linn, "Microwave dielectric resonator filters utilizing $BA_2TI_2O_{20}$ ceramics," in *Dig. 1977 Int. Microwave Symp.* (San Diego, CA), pp. 290–293.

[7] T. Itoh and R. Rudokas, "New method for computing the resonant frequency of dielectric resonators," *IEEE Trans. Microwave Theory Tech.*, vol. MTT-25, pp. 52–54, Jan. 1977.

[8] M. Jaworski and M. W. Pospieszalski, "An accurate solution of the cylindrical dielectric resonators problem," *IEEE Trans. Microwave Theory Tech.*, vol. MTT-27, pp. 639–642, July 1979.

[9] J. C. Sethares and S. J. Naumann, "Design of microwave dielectric resonators," *IEEE Trans. Microwave Theory Tech.*, vol. MTT-14, pp. 2–7, Jan. 1966.

[10] Y. Koniski, N. Hoshino, and Y. Utsum, "Resonant frequency of a $TE_{01\delta}$ dielectric resonator," *IEEE Trans. Microwave Theory Tech.*, vol. MTT-24, pp. 112–114, Feb. 1976.

Corrections to "Design of Cylindrical Dielectric Resonators in Inhomogeneous Media"

RENÉ R. BONETTI

In the above-referenced paper,[1] the following corrections should be made:

On page 176, column one, two lines below (12) the definition of θ_i is

$$\theta_i = \zeta_i h_i, \qquad i = 1,2,4$$

$$\theta_3 = \zeta_3 h_3 / 2.$$

On page 325, (22) should read

$$\tan \frac{\delta \pi}{2} = \frac{\zeta_2}{\zeta_3}.$$

Manuscript received July 1, 1981.

The author is with COMSAT Laboratories, Clarksburg, MD 20734.

[1] R. R. Bonetti and A. E. Atia, *IEEE Trans. Microwave Theory Tech.*, vol. MTT-29, pp. 323–326, Apr. 1981.

Design of Digital Loaded-Line Phase-Shift Networks for Microwave Thin-Film Applications

FRANCIS L. OPP AND W. F. HOFFMAN, MEMBER, IEEE

***Abstract*—This paper describes the design approach, fabrication techniques, and electrical performance for two types of microwave hybrid thin-film phase shifters. Emphasis is placed on the practical aspects of the overall design and fabrication.**

A simplified set of design equations for loaded-line phase-shift networks is presented and divided into three categories based on the type of loading employed. The two circuits presented are a 4-bit 90° network employing single-section multibits to minimize physical size, and a 4-bit 360° network employing the 45° section as a basic building block.

Introduction

The increased use of phased-array radars and electronically steerable antennas has led to the requirement for small, highly reliable phase-shift networks compatible with large-scale production. One way of meeting this need is through the use of hybrid integrated microwave circuits. Various approaches were considered; the two networks discussed in this paper use the diode-loaded line.

Analysis

The theory of operation of the diode-loaded-line phase-shift network is well documented in the literature.[1] It is not the purpose of this paper to extend this theory, but rather to extend its application to the design of low-power multibit phase-shift networks which are compatible with thin-film techniques.

A typical diode-loaded-line section and its electrical equivalent is shown in Fig. 1. Here, two elements of approximately $\frac{1}{4}$-wavelength spacing shunt the main transmission line. The loading susceptances of these elements are controlled with switching diodes to electrically shorten or lengthen the transmission line. The general expressions for the electrical length θ' and the characteristic admittance Yo' are given in (1) and (2), assuming lossless elements. Using these equations, the desired performance is therefore set by specifying B, Yo, and θ:

$$\theta' = \cos^{-1}(\cos\theta - Zo\,B\sin\theta) \quad (1)$$

$$Yo' = Yo[1 - (B/Yo)^2 + 2(B/Yo)\cot\theta]^{1/2}. \quad (2)$$

Manuscript received February 26, 1968; revised April 4, 1968. This work was supported in part by the U. S. Air Force Avionics Laboratory under Contract AF 33(615)-2525.

This special issue on Microwave Integrated Circuits is published jointly with the IEEE JOURNAL OF SOLID-STATE CIRCUITS, June 1968, and IEEE TRANSACTIONS ON MICROWAVE THEORY AND TECHNIQUES, July 1968.

The authors are with Texas Instruments Incorporated, Dallas, Tex. 75222

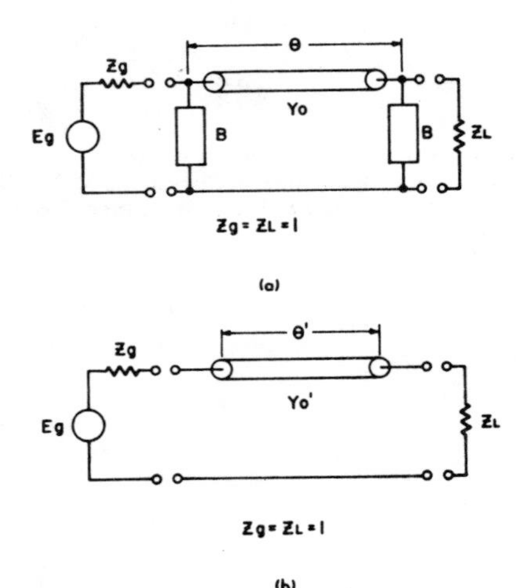

Fig. 1. Typical loaded-line section and electrical equivalent.

Two special loading conditions further simplify these equations (which are only exact at a single frequency) and allow closed-form solutions for B_n, Yo_n,[1] and θ in terms of the differential phase shift. For purposes of explanation, three classes of loaded-line sections will be defined. Class I is the general case in which the two values of B are nonzero and unequal. Class II is the special case in which one value of B is zero. An additional constraint in this instance is that the input VSWR be equal to unity for both diode states. A closed-form solution yields the following results:

$$B_n = -2\tan\psi/2 \quad (3)$$

$$\theta = \psi/2 + \pi/2 \quad (4)$$

$$\psi = \theta_0' - \theta_{B_1}' \quad (5)$$

where θ' is defined in (1). The subscripts refer to the loading condition.

Class III is another special case in which B is switched between values of equal magnitude but of opposite sign. Again, with the same constraint that the input VSWR be equal to unity, the design equations are

$$B_n = \tan\psi/2 \quad (6)$$

$$Yo_n = \sec\psi/2 \quad (7)$$

$$\theta = 90°$$

[1] B_n and Yo_n are normalized to the load admittance.

where $$\psi = \theta_-' - \theta_+' \tag{8}$$

and θ' is defined in (1). The subscripts refer to the condition of $+B$ or $-B$ loading.

These sets of equations assume lossless elements. The loss can be considered separately and consists of

1) mismatch loss,
2) transmission line loss, and
3) dissipative loss associated with the shunt elements.

An approximate loss expression for the shunt elements is given by

$$I_L = -20 \log \left[1 + \left(\frac{Rs}{Z_L} \right) \tan^2 (\psi/2) \right] \tag{9}$$

under the following assumptions:

1) $Zg \doteq Z_L$;
2) the shunting elements can be represented by a lumped resistance in series with a lumped reactance;
3) the section input and output VSWR are made equal to one;
4) the total loss is low;
5) Rs = diode resistance, lumped inductor resistance, and lumped bypass capacitor resistance.

Although the previous sets of equations can be used for initial design values, a general analysis of a phase-shift network constructed by cascading these sections is accomplished with computer-aided programs. Any circuit modifications due to the interaction of sections, loss, or bandwidth requirements are best determined in this manner.

The general factors to be considered in any such application are:

1) electrical performance
2) [illegible]bility
3) si[illegible]
4) circuit complexity
5) diode requirements
6) diode driver requirements
7) process considerations.

The particular order depends on the specific application. In the case of the two circuits discussed in this paper, the primary considerations were electrical performance, reliability, and size, within the constraints of a specified process using 20-mil glazed ceramic substrate. In addition, the diode drivers were to be compatible with standard Series 5400 logic. The particular approaches chosen are a direct result of the required bit size.

Differential phase shifts of 22.5° or less can be achieved satisfactorily using Class I and II configurations. This usually required one section per differential phase bit. Since one of the primary considerations is physical size, the loaded-line theory was extended to include multiple

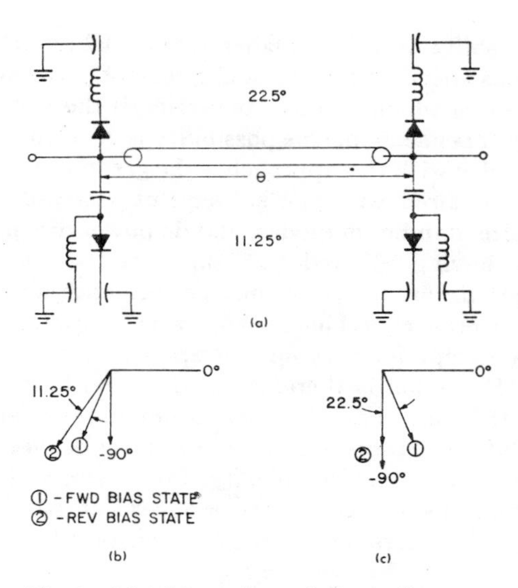

Fig. 2. Multibit section and phaser diagrams.

phase shifts within a single section, shown in Fig. 2 (e.g., for our application, the shunted elements are switched to four loading values rather than two).

Although this approach reduces the size to 70 percent of that required using conventional sections, the phase errors and VSWR have greater variations, as a function of frequency. In addition, careful attention must be given to the physical layout.

Since no closed-form solution was available for the analysis of this type section, the approach used to arrive at the final design values consisted of the following steps.

1) The initial design values were obtained using the previously mentioned design equations.

2) The final design values were determined making iterative computer calculations until the desired performance was achieved.

One section, which was analyzed [shown in Fig. 2(a)] provided differential phase shifts of 11.25°, 22.5°, and 33.75°. Fig. 2(b) and (c) shows a vector diagram of the phase steps.

The following table indicates the computed results, which pointed out that a separation of 75°, rather than 90°, would yield the better performance. The same analysis was performed for combining a 5.6° and 45° bit with similar results.

Desired Phase	VSWR	Loss	Phase
For a 90° separation:			
min	1.007	0.28 dB	0
11.25°	1.018	0.38 dB	12.39°
22.5 °	1.099	0.18 dB	22.71°
33.75°	1.309	0.37 dB	35.99°
For a 75° separation:			
min	1.051	0.28 dB	0
11.25°	1.053	0.37 dB	12.30°
22.5 °	1.070	0.17 dB	22.04°
33.75°	1.011	0.27 dB	34.15°

Phase shifts of 45° or higher require Class III configurations strictly from the standpoint of performance. The question which requires answering is the maximum phase shift per section. One possibility is 22.5°; however, the difficulty with this approach is the greater number of sections required with the subsequent increase in the circuit size, number of diodes, and dc power dissipation. Sections having 90° and 180° phase shifts have been investigated, but the frequency performance and component tolerance problems make this approach unacceptable except for very special applications.[2]

The 45° section is therefore used as the basic block for the 45°, 90°, and 180° bits. In our judgement, this phase shift represents a good compromise between performance and circuit complexity. For example, sample calculations using (1) over a ±5 percent bandwidth show the phase error compared to a constant time delay to be within 2°.

Microwave Components

The requirement for small size and large quantities emphasizes the use of hybrid integrated microwave circuits. Here, thin-film techniques are used to construct microstrip transmission lines, capacitors, and resistors on Al_2O_3 substrates.[3],[4] Beam-lead diodes and capacitors can be added to the substrate by a variety of bonding techniques. The following paragraphs briefly outline the geometry and electrical characteristics of the beam-lead devices used for these applications.

Beam-Lead Diodes

Two types of beam-lead diodes were designed to be used in these applications. The first uses standard planar geometries fabricated on double epitaxial material to achieve junction capacitances in the 0.2 to 1.0 pF range. The surface-oriented diode is used to achieve lower junction capacitance.[5] Fig. 3 is a graph of the forward characteristics for these devices. These curves show the desired characteristic for low RF power applications, which is the combination of low resistance at low drive currents.

The small size (typically, less than 1/100λg at 3.0 GHz), combined with the absence of a package, reduces the parasitics to a second-order effect.

Beam-Lead Capacitors

The fabrication is similar to that of the beam-lead diode except that SiO_2 is grown in the area where the junction is normally formed. These devices were made with a capacitance of 0.2 to 0.5 pF and a series resistance of less than 3 ohms.

The need for these capacitors stemmed from the physical limitations of thin-film geometries.

Fabrication

The fabrication of hybrid integrated microwave circuits can be divided into two basic operations. The first is the preparation of the substrate on which the micro-

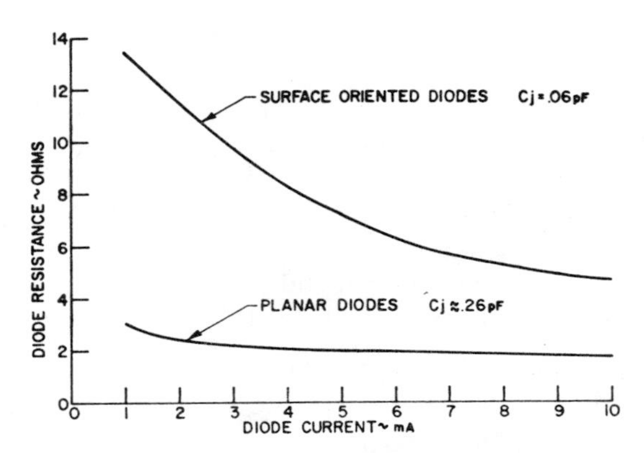

Fig. 3. Diode resistance versus diode current.

strip transmission lines, capacitors, and resistors are formed. The second is the assembly operation where the beam-lead devices and interconnections are made to produce an operating circuit.

Thin-Film Process

The major steps in the thin-film process are the following.

1) Aluminum evaporation and selective removal: the aluminum is left in those areas where capacitors will be formed in order to lower the plate resistance.

2) Tantalum evaporation and selective removal: the tantalum is left in the areas where capacitors and resistors will be formed; it also is used as an adhesive between the substrate and the microstrip lines.

3) Selective anodization for resistors and capacitor dielectrics.

4) Selective gold plating of microstrip lines and capacitor top plates.

5) Drilling of holes for ground plane connections; this is achieved with either a pulsed laser or by sand blasting.

6) Plating of the bottom ground plane and ground feedthroughs.

Assembly Procedure

The major steps in the assembly operation are the following.

1) Sawing operation: since the substrates are processed containing more than one circuit, the first step is the separation of these circuits using a diamond saw.

2) Bonding of the necessary interconnections.

3) Mounting of beam devices: three techniques can be used for device mounting—split tip welder, hot chisel bonder, and ultrasonic bonder.

4) Final test.

Circuit Performance

After a detailed computer analysis was completed, two diode-loaded-line phase shifters were constructed on 20-mil glazed ceramic. The first circuit to be evaluated was a 4-bit 90° phase-shift network for use in the

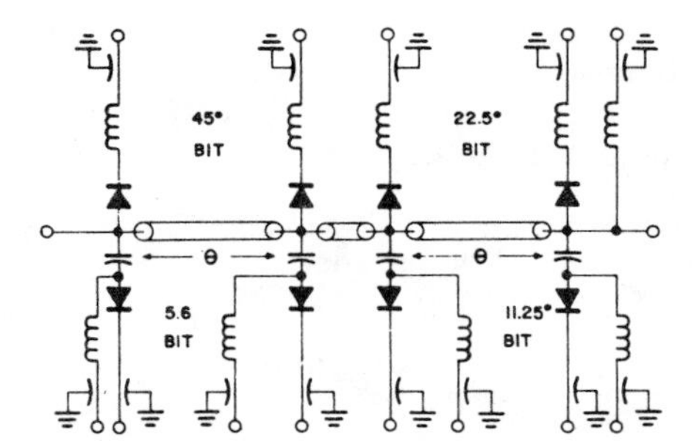

Fig. 4. Schematic diagram for a 4-bit 90° phase-shift network.

MERA Modular Radar.[6] The requirements for this phase shifter were as follows:

1) Frequency 2.25 GHz ± 2.5 percent
2) Bit size 5.625°, 11.25°, 22.5°, and 45°
3) Phase error ± 2.5° maximum
4) Insertion loss 1.5-dB maximum, ± 0.25-dB variation
5) Input VSWR less than 1.5:1
6) Diode logic serial input compatible with Series 5400 logic
7) Physical size small as possible.

Due to the size requirement and narrow bandwidth, it was decided to use the multibit approach for the 5.6°–45° bits and the 11.25°–22.5° bits. An electrical schematic of this circuit is shown in Fig. 4. The 5.6° and the 11.25° bits operate Class I in that a 0.35-pF capacitor is in series with a *p-i-n* diode which, in turn, is paralleled with an inductor. When the diode is forward biase, the transmission line is loaded with the capacitor or approximately $-j200$ ohms. When the diode is reverse biased (0.06 pF), it appears as an open circuit and the transmission line is loaded by the capacitor in series with the inductor. For the 11.25° bit, referring to (1), when the line is loaded by $-j200$ ohms, $\theta' = -104.5°$. In the second state, if the inductor is 6 nH at 2.25 GHz, the resultant impedance would be $-j115$ ohms and $\theta' = -115.8°$. Therefore, $\Delta\theta' = 11.3°$. One advantage for this type of phase shifter is the realization of inductors when compared to the 35 nH required for Class III operation.

The 22.5° bit is an example of Case II in that when the diode is forward biased, an inductive loading is obtained, while the reverse bias condition approaches an open circuit. All that is required to extend the 22.5° bit to a 45° increment is to change the diode reverse bias capacitance from that of 0.06 pF to 0.28 pF ± 5 percent. Although this was the basic approach for the 45° bit, an evaluation of the planar diode revealed a higher loss condition in the reverse bias state due to the low voltages available from standard 5400 logic. Therefore, in order to balance the loss, it became necessary to achieve 30° of phase shift in the forward condition and only 15° in the reverse condition.

Fig. 5 shows the constructed circuit. The physical size is 0.760 by 0.270 inch. The circuit was fabricated using the techniques previously described, including hole drilling, which is not shown in this figure.

Fig. 5. Constructed 4-bit 90° phase-shift network.

TABLE I

PERFORMANCE DATA FOR A 90° MULTIBIT PHASE SHIFTER

Desired Phase	Measured Phase	Phase Error	Loss (dB)	VSWR
0°	0°	—	1.3	1.19
5.6°	4.0°	−1.60°	1.3	1.21
11.25°	12.1°	+0.85°	1.3	1.21
16.18°	16.0°	−0.87°	1.3	1.16
22.5°	21.9°	−0.60°	0.9	1.12
28.12°	25.9°	−2.22°	0.95	1.10
33.75°	34.8°	+1.05°	1.0	1.06
39.37°	38.5°	−0.87°	1.05	1.15
45.0 °	45.4°	+0.40°	1.05	1.06
50.62°	50.0°	−0.62°	1.05	1.07
56.25°	57.0°	+0.75°	1.05	1.07
61.87°	63.0°	+1.13°	1.05	1.06
67.5 °	67.0°	−0.5 °	0.8	1.08
73.12°	72.5°	−0.62°	0.8	1.06
78.75°	79.0°	+0.25°	0.85	1.11
84.37°	84.8°	+0.43°	0.85	1.19

Table I is a listing of the performance data for a typical unit operated at 2.25 GHz. It can be seen that the maximum phase error is within ± 2° and could be reduced further with additional trimming of inductors. The average loss was 1.1 dB with a ± 0.2-dB variation. The input VSWR reached a maximum of 1.21:1. The results obtained agreed with the computed analysis with the exception of insertion loss, which was on the order of 0.4 dB too high. However, this difference can be explained by the higher diode series resistance which existed in the circuit versus the assumed value of 4 to 5 ohms used in the computer analysis.

In order to minimize the dc power requirement for the MERA radar, it was decided that the forward bias current level for the phase-shifter diodes would not exceed 2.5 mA. Fig. 3 shows that the series resistance for the surface-oriented diodes runs around 10 ohms for 2.5 mA.

An increase in the diode current level to 10 mA would decrease the insertion loss to that obtained in the computer analysis. However, such an increase would double the dc power presently required for each module. This

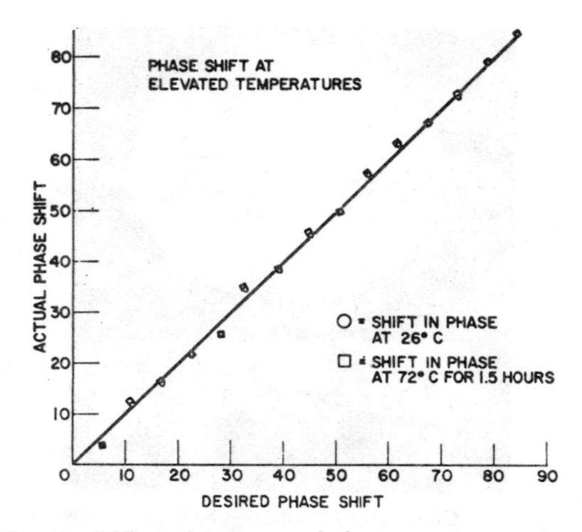

Fig. 6. Differential phase variation versus temperature.

represents a sizeable increase when figured on a basis of 604 modules.

Further tests were performed to determine if any undesirable characteristics would appear for phase shifts at elevated temperatures. Fig. 6 is a graph of phase shift at 26°C and 72°C. It can be seen that there was virtually no change in phase at the elevated temperature.

The second phase-shift network was developed to meet the following requirements.

Electrical:

1) Frequency range	2.675 to 2.775 GHz
2) Bit size	22.5°, 45°, 90°, and 180°
3) Insertion loss	3-dB maximum 1-dB variation
4) VSWR	1.5:1 maximum
5) Phase error	±10° maximum
6) Operation	receive only
7) Diode control	serial input compatible with Series 5400.

Mechanical:

1) Package size should be as small as possible.
2) Phase shift and logic circuitry must be contained within the same package
3) The RF input and output must mate with OSM coaxial connectors.

Since this application required 360° phase shift, the 45°, 90°, and 180° bits are constructed using the 45° section as a basic block. The required susceptance is realized in each leg by a diode in series with a short-circuited transmission line. The "on state" of the diode allows inductive loading determined by the length of the shorted line. The "off state" provides capacitive loading determined by the difference in reactance between the diodes' junction capacitance and the shorted line. Of the many realizations possible for the shunt elements, this particular one was chosen for two primary reasons.

1) Low network loss can be achieved at very low diode current.

2) The required component performance is well within the process limitations.

The initial design values for the 45° section are obtained from the Class III equations:

$$B = \pm j8.3 \text{ mmho}$$
$$Yo = 21.7 \text{ mmho}$$
$$\theta = 90°.$$

Further evaluation using "real" component values indicated that a slight increase in the inductive loading and a subsequent decrease in the capacitive loading effected a reduction in both the loss unbalance and the phase error. The primary reasons for this improvement were the lower diode loss in its forward bias state and the reduced electrical length required to achieve the series inductance. The modified values are

$$B = +j6.9 \text{ or } -j10.0 \text{ mmho}$$
$$Yo = 22.2 \text{ mmho}$$
$$\theta = 93°.$$

The diodes used in this application are the same beam-lead planar type which were discussed previously, except $C_j = 0.24$ pF ±5 percent.

The 22.5° bit is a Class II configuration. The reasons for using this type section are 1) the diodes operate as switches to either load or unload the line, and 2) all the phase shift is achieved with inductive loading, thereby reducing the line length for the shunt inductance.

The section values using (3) and (4) are

$$B = -j8.0 \text{ mmho}$$
$$\theta = 101.3°$$
$$Yo = 20 \text{ mmho}.$$

The diodes used in this section are the surface-oriented type with $C_j \leq 0.06$ pF and with the resistance characteristic shown in Fig. 3.

The complete phase-shift network, which consists of seven 45° sections and one 22.5° section in cascade, was analyzed using the computer to verify that its performance met the required specifications. The computed performance over the bandwidth is as follows.

1) Phase characteristics
   a) The insertion phase (minimum phase state) variation with frequency is basically linear.
   b) The differential phase error, compared to constant phase, was less than ±7°.
2) The VSWR was less than 1.3:1.
3) The maximum loss was 2.4 dB with the loss variation equal to 0.7 dB.

Fig. 7 shows the packaged phase-shift assembly. The phase-shift network is built on a 1.6- by 0.54-inch glazed ceramic substrate. The line switch is a single surface-oriented diode located in series with the main transmission line. The two large spirals are RF chokes. One is

Fig. 7. A 4-bit 360° phase-shift network with logic.

Fig. 8. Capacitor bypass and ground strap geometry.

TABLE II

4-Bit 360° Phase-Shift Network Performance

Bit Position (deg)	2.675 GHz θ Error (deg)	2.675 GHz Loss (dB)	2.675 GHz VSWR	• 2.725 GHz θ Error (deg)	• 2.725 GHz Loss (dB)	• 2.725 GHz VSWR	2.775 GHz θ Error (deg)	2.775 GHz Loss (dB)	2.775 GHz VSWR
min	—	2.4	1.11	—	2.4	1.16	—	2.4	1.23
22.5	−1	2.3	1.24	0	2.3	1.19	1	2.3	1.22
45	0	2.6	1.24	−0.5	2.6	1.21	0	2.7	1.14
67.5	2	2.4	1.23	1	2.4	1.17	2	2.5	1.39
90	−0.5	2.7	1.39	−1.5	2.7	1.39	−1.5	2.8	1.33
112.5	−2	2.5	1.34	−3.5	2.4	1.32	−3.5	2.5	1.22
135	0	2.7	1.16	−2.5	2.6	1.19	−3	2.6	1.33
157.5	0	2.7	1.18	−2	2.5	1.23	−2	2.5	1.30
180	0	2.5	1.14	−1.5	2.4	1.23	0.5	2.4	1.32
202.5	−1	2.4	1.20	−2	2.3	1.27	1	2.3	1.30
225	0	2.7	1.18	−2.5	2.5	1.20	−1	2.5	1.23
247.5	2	2.5	1.17	−0.5	2.4	1.15	1.5	2.4	1.21
270	−0.5	2.7	1.40	−3	2.7	1.37	−1.5	2.6	1.32
292.5	−1.5	2.5	1.37	−4	2.5	1.30	−2	2.5	1.28
315	0.5	2.9	1.28	−3	2.7	1.19	−2	2.5	1.23
337.5	0.5	2.8	1.19	−2	2.6	1.25	0	2.4	1.27

used to supply the control voltages to the line switch, and the other supplies a common voltage of +1.3 volts to the diodes to allow on–off controls from nonpolar logic. The paralleled shunt elements resulting from the cascading of identical sections are combined into single elements. However, diodes with twice the capacitance for use in these paralleled elements were not available at the time of assembly. Therefore, it was necessary to use two diodes of the same capacitance in parallel. A total of 14 planar- and 3 surface-oriented diodes are required for each circuit. Fig. 8 shows an enlarged picture of the bypass capacitor and strapping used to connect to the bottom ground plane. The reactive parasitics contributed by this geometry are less than 10 percent of the total reactance required in each shunt element. The control bar is 1.6 by 0.25 inches and contains two SN5400 driver bars and one SN7493 ripple-through counter. Also included is the low-voltage regulation to supply the common diode voltage and diode limiting and pullup resistors. This circuit requires +5 and +10 volt supplies with all the dc and logic inputs contained within the same connector. The overall package size is 1.9 by 1.4 by 0.375 inches excluding connectors.

Table II shows typical performance data of a packaged unit. These results agree very well with that predicted. The slightly higher insertion losses caused by the two chokes and line switch were not included in the original estimate. An approximate breakdown of the center frequency loss (minimum phase condition) is:

1) Line loss 0.6 dB
2) Seven 45° sections 1.2 dB
3) Two chokes 0.2 dB
4) Line switch 0.2 dB
5) One 22.5° section 0.2 dB.

The 0.6-dB loss variation over the frequency band is well within the specifications.

These circuits have been fabricated on glazed ceramic which had a thickness tolerance of ± 2 mils due to variations in both the glazed and unglazed portions. The differential phase error caused by this variation was compensated by minor phase trimming. However, the overall insertion phase was found to vary between 1 to $1\frac{1}{2}$ percent.

The junction capacitance of the diodes used in Class I and III configurations required a ± 5 percent tolerance.

Measurement Techniques

A brief comment should be made concerning the coaxial to microstrip-line transitions which are required for the testing of hybrid integrated circuits. The test fixtures built for these applications, shown in Fig. 9, used transitions which started with the GR900 geometry and tapered to a geometry with a center conductor of 0.020 inch. This tapered line was partially teflon loaded for support. Measurements in the 2 to 3 GHz range showed typical VSWR's of 1.05:1. The RF ground continuity is maintained between the circuit and test fixture by using "gold fuzz" in the transition area.

Conclusion

The information presented in this paper describes two successful applications of thin-film hybrid circuitry. Any comparison between this approach and other possible approaches to meet this and other system requirements must consider the physical size, reliability, ease of production, and electrical performance. Further improvements in the electrical performance can be made by the choice of dielectric, dielectric thicknesses, and additional improvements in the diode characteristics. Although the phase errors and VSWR's presented were well within the design requirements, strict process controls are required to maintain this performance on a production basis.

Fig. 9. Test fixture.

The approach presented in this paper is presently being used for the design of high-power phase-shifter applications. The primary differences are the diode and the dc driver requirements.

Acknowledgment

The authors wish to express their appreciation to H. F. McQuarie and L. P. Walton for their patient assistance, and to J. E. Austin for his helpful discussions.

References

[1] J. F. White, "High power, *p-i-n* diode controlled, microwave transmission phase shifters," *IEEE Trans. Microwave Theory and Techniques*, vol. MTT-13, pp. 233–242, March 1965.

[2] J. E. Austin, "Development of integrated microwave components for ground-based phased arrays," Rept. submitted to Lincoln Labs., Lexington, Mass., January 1968.

[3] B. T. Vincent, Jr., "Ceramic microstrip for hybrid integrated circuitry," presented at the 1966 G-MTT Symp., Palo Alto, Calif.

[4] C. E. Earhart, "Microwave integrated circuit technology," presented at the 2nd Internat'l Symp. on Micro-Electronics, Munich, Germany, 1966.

[5] B. Battershall and S. Emmons, "Optimization of diode structures for monolithic integrated circuits," this issue, page 507.

[6] N. Sclater, "Civilian markets beckon microwave IC's," *Electronic Design*, vol. 25, p. 34, December 6, 1967.

Thin Ferrite Devices for Microwave Integrated Circuits

GERARD T. ROOME, MEMBER, IEEE, AND HUGH A. HAIR

Abstract—This paper is intended as a review of developments which allow ferrite materials in a planar geometry to be used in the realization of magnetic devices which are compatible in form with other microwave integrated circuits. These devices include phase shifters (reciprocal and nonreciprocal), latching circulators, isolators, and phase and amplitude modulators. The application of some of these devices is demonstrated in the form of electronically steerable array antennas.

I. INTRODUCTION

MICROWAVE semiconductor integrated circuits are currently being successfully developed using microstrip transmission line as the principal waveguide. For compatibility in complex ferrite-semiconductor integrated systems, it would seem appropriate to investigate the feasibility of ferrite devices using this same transmission-line type. It may not be possible, of course, to realize efficient ferrite devices of all types using microstrip line, but a sufficient number of functions do appear possible so as to warrant an intensive development in this area.

This paper is concerned with only the simplest form of device realization. That is, a ferrite substrate (of a commercially available material) in the form of a thin plate (20 mils thick) with a conducting ground plane deposited on one side and a signal-guiding conductor on the other side. Various RF magnetic-field configurations (which are required to realize different types and magnitudes of interaction) are obtained by a suitable design of the signal-conductor circuit.

Most ferrite materials have relative dielectric constants in the range 9 to 16, and dielectric loss tangents are normally small (<0.001). The difference between these media and dielectric substrates is, of course, the permeability of the ferrite, which depends on the RF magnetic-field configuration in the medium relative to the static magnetization state of the ferrite.

II. RECIPROCAL PHASE SHIFTERS

Wheeler[1] has obtained approximate solutions for the impedance and propagation constant for microstrip line on dielectric substrates. The solutions were based on the determination of an effective filling factor (q) for the dielectric medium. The effective dielectric constant for the transmission line is therefore obtained by a weighted combination of the dielectric constants for air and the substrate, where q is the weighting factor.

$$\epsilon_{eff} = (1 - q) + q\epsilon_r = 1 + q(\epsilon_r - 1). \qquad (1)$$

The filling factor (q) is strongly dependent on the ratio of the strip width to ground plane spacing and varies only slightly with the relative dielectric constant of the substrate. To a very good approximation one may use the same filling factor obtained by Wheeler ($q=0.6$) to

Manuscript received February 6, 1968. This work was supported by the Molecular Electronics Branch, Air Force Avionics Lab., Wright-Patterson AFB, Ohio.

This special issue on Microwave Integrated Circuits is published jointly with IEEE TRANSACTIONS ON ELECTRON DEVICES, July 1968, and the IEEE JOURNAL OF SOLID-STATE CIRCUITS, June 1968.

G. T. Roome is with Syracuse University Research Corporation, Syracuse, N. Y. 13210

H. A. Hair was with Syracuse University Research Corporation. He is now with ANAREN, Inc., Syracuse, N. Y.

determine the effective permeability for the transmission line. The result is a weighted parallel combination of the relative permeabilities:

$$\frac{1}{\mu_{eff}} = 1 - q + \frac{q}{\mu_r},$$

i. e.,

$$\mu_{eff} = \frac{1}{1 + q\left(\frac{1}{\mu_r} - 1\right)}. \tag{2}$$

Thus, the characteristic impedance for microstrip line on a ferrite substrate is

$$Z_0 = \frac{Z_{01}}{\left|\left[1 + q(\epsilon_r - 1)\right]\left[1 + q\left(\frac{1}{\mu_r} - 1\right)\right]\right|^{1/2}} \tag{3}$$

where

Z_{01} = characteristic impedance for microstrip line in air only

μ_r = ferrite relative permeability.

The transmission-line wavelength is given by

$$\frac{\lambda}{\lambda_0} = \left[\frac{1 + q\left(\frac{1}{\mu_r} - 1\right)}{1 + q(\epsilon_r - 1)}\right]^{1/2}. \tag{4}$$

where λ_0 = free-space wavelength.

In the above equations, it was assumed that the ferrite permeability is a scalar quantity. This cannot be exactly the case with microstrip transmission line. However, with certain restrictions, the gyromagnetic interaction can be approximated with a scalar permeability.

These restrictions can be stated simply as follows. The RF field configuration must be determined principally by the conducting boundaries of the structure. This is achieved if the substrate thickness is electrically small (i.e., $\epsilon_r h \ll \lambda$), and the ferrite interaction is small (i.e., $\delta\mu_r < 20$ percent). A more exact discussion of this problem is found in Suhl and Walker[2] under the topic "Parallel Plane Cable."

The easy direction of magnetization is in the plane of the substrate, and only devices with the magnetization in this direction will be discussed. Fig. 1 shows a sketch of the RF magnetic-field configuration in the microstrip transmission line together with the magnetization direction in the ferrite.

When the ferrite sample is magnetized to saturation in its plane in a direction perpendicular to the center conductor (i.e., parallel to the RF magnetic field $\phi = 0°$), then for small RF signal strengths there is a minimum interaction between the ferrite and the RF magnetic field. That is, the effective RF relative permeability is approximately unity. When the ferrite sample is magnetized to saturation in its plane in a direction parallel to the center conductor (i.e., perpendicular to the RF magnetic field $\phi = 90°$), maximum interaction is obtained between the ferrite medium and the RF magnetic field such that the effective RF relative permeability is given by[2]

$$\mu_r = \frac{\mu^2 - K^2}{\mu} \tag{5}$$

where μ and K are the components of the permeability tensor.

In the frequency range of interest ($\omega_m/\omega < 1$), and with small applied magnetic field, it can be shown that the above equation reduces to

$$\mu_r \approx 1 - \left(\frac{\omega_m}{\omega}\right)^2 \tag{6}$$

where

$\omega_m = \gamma 4\pi M_s$

$4\pi M_s$ = ferrite magnetization

γ = gyromagnetic ratio (2.8 MHz/Oe).

When the ratio ω_m/ω approaches unity, the magnetic loss becomes significant and modifies (6). Thus, the propagation constant of the TEM-limit mode is given by

$$\beta = \omega\sqrt{\epsilon_{eff}\mu_{eff}\mu_0\epsilon_0}. \tag{7}$$

If the transmission line has a filling factor of 0.5, then substitution from (6) and (7) yields

$$\beta \approx \omega\sqrt{\mu_0\epsilon_0\epsilon_{eff}}\left[\frac{2 - 2\left(\frac{\omega_m}{\omega}\right)^2}{2 - \left(\frac{\omega_m}{\omega}\right)^2}\right]^{1/2}. \tag{8}$$

With the ferrite magnetized in the noninteracting state, the propagation constant is given by

$$\beta_d = \omega\sqrt{\mu_0\epsilon_0\epsilon_{eff}}. \tag{9}$$

Thus, the fractional differential change in propagation constant obtained when the ferrite magnetization direction is changed between the two states described above is given by

$$\frac{\Delta\beta}{\beta_d} = \frac{\beta_d - \beta}{\beta_d} = 1 - \left[\frac{2 - 2\left(\frac{\omega_m}{\omega}\right)^2}{2 - \left(\frac{\omega_m}{\omega}\right)^2}\right]^{1/2} \tag{10}$$

This equation is shown graphically in Fig. 2 together with experimental results. Note that a significant deviation occurs when the fractional change in propagation constant exceeds 0.1.

Analog control of the insertion phase can be achieved by either varying the magnitude of the magnetization vector in the direction of the center conductor, or by rotation of the direction of the magnetization vector in the plane of the substrate, as indicated in Figs. 3 and 4.

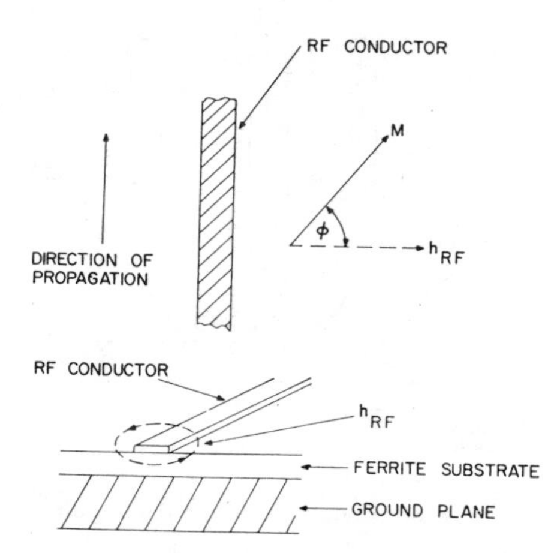

Fig. 1. RF magnetic field and magnetization direction in ferrite.

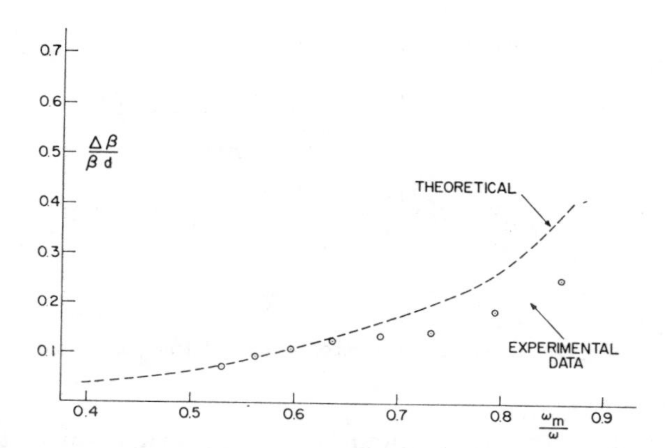

Fig. 2. Correlation of experimental and theoretical propagation characteristics for microstrip S-band phase shifter.

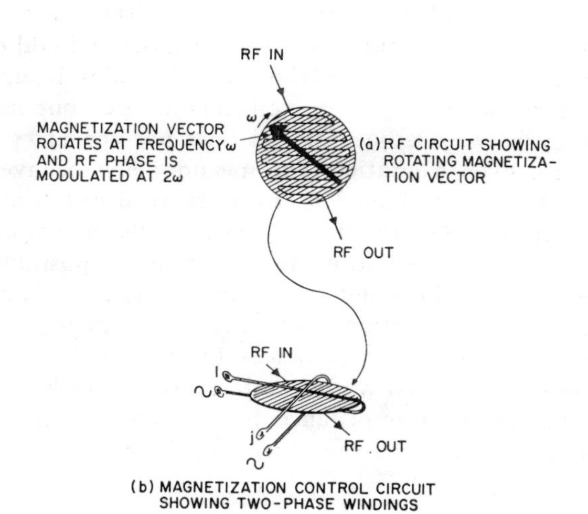

Fig. 3. Cyclic phase control.

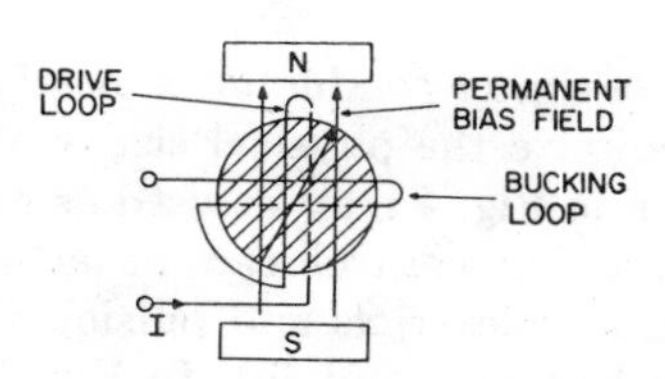

Fig. 4. Saw-tooth phase control.

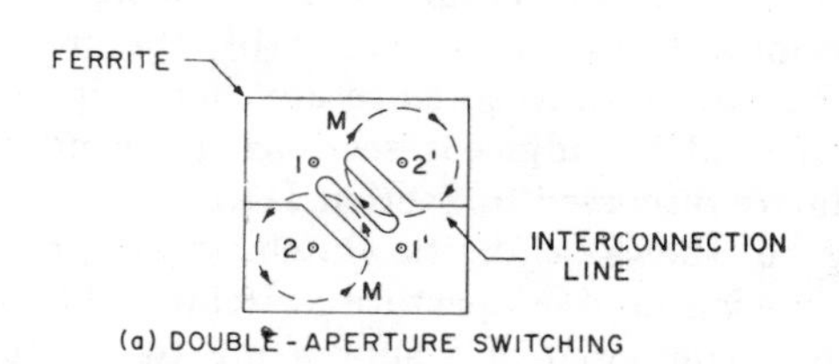

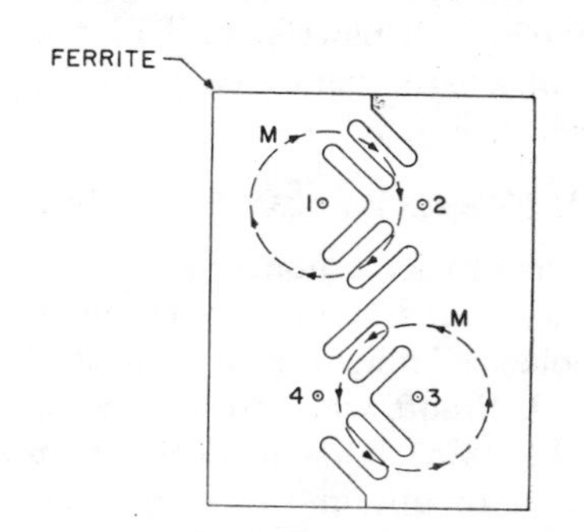

Fig. 5. Latching configurations for reciprocal phase shifter

Fig. 6. Latching reciprocal phase shifter.

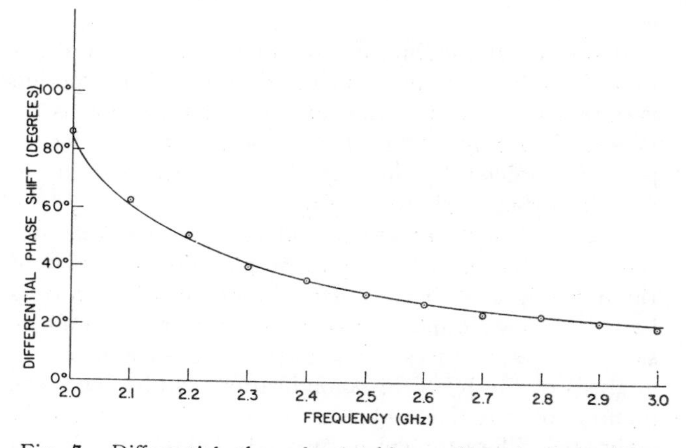

Fig. 7. Differential phase for latching reciprocal phase shifter.

Note that the center conductor is loosely meandered in order to minimize the physical size of the device. The device shown in Fig. 4 may be used as a serrodyne.

Digital latching control can be achieved by using high remanence materials and pulsing the substrate as indicated in Fig. 5(a) and (b). In Fig. 5(a), the meandered RF center conductors must be separated by at least five times the ground plane spacing to minimize nonreciprocal effects. In Fig. 5(b), the meander line may be tightly coupled since any nonreciprocal effects are canceled by adjacent sections. (The nonreciprocal effects are discussed in Section III.)

Fig. 6 shows a digital latching reciprocal phase shifter using double aperture switching. The device as shown is composed of a supporting test fixture and a 1 by 1 by 0.020 inch platelet of TTI-414[3] ferrite. The differential phase/frequency characteristic for this device is shown in Fig. 7.

III. Nonreciprocal Phase Shifters

In order to obtain a nonreciprocal interaction with the ferrite medium, a microwave circuit which produces circularly polarized magnetic fields in the ferrite medium is required. A circuit which produces such a condition is shown in Fig. 8(a). This meander line is similar to the structure used to obtain the reciprocal phase shifters except that the line lengths are a quarter wavelength at the center frequency, and the adjacent lines are spaced sufficiently close together so that a strong line-to-line coupling is obtained. Fig. 8(b) shows a sketch of the RF magnetic fields produced by currents flowing in two adjacent lines. At point A, the RF magnetic fields are spatially orthogonal. Since the lines are a quarter wavelength long, the current flowing at the center of line 2 is delayed by 90° in time relative to the current flowing at the center of line 1. Thus, at point A, the resultant RF magnetic field is circularly polarized relative to the direction into the paper. At sections off-center, the relative time-phase between the currents falls off (or increases) linearly with distance from the center. The sense of polarization therefore varies from circular at the center of the lines through eliptical to linear at the ends.

If the ferrite medium is magnetized along the direction of the lines, a nonreciprocal differential interaction is obtained if the direction of the magnetization is reversed. A latching device can be obtained if the ferrite plate is sufficiently thin, or if the ferrite plate is in toroidal form, as shown in Fig. 9.

A satisfactory theoretical model has not yet been obtained for the impedance and propagation constant of the nonreciprocal phase shifter. Practical phase shifters have too few coupled lines to be considered infinite slow-wave structures, and until a reasonable exact analysis of the RF field configurations is obtained, the quality of circular polarization cannot be properly estimated. The problem is currently being investigated in our laboratory.

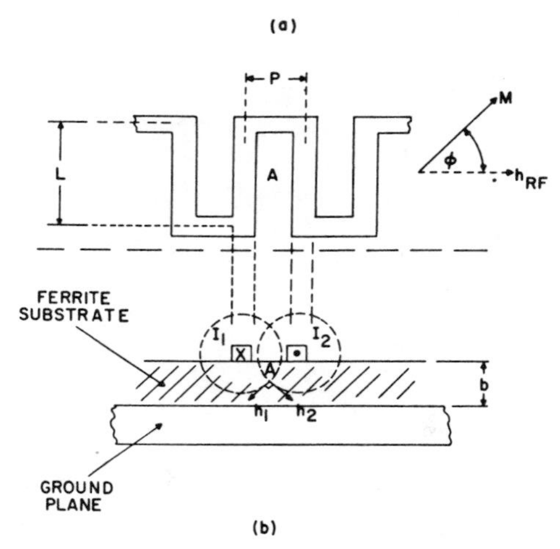

Fig. 8. Coupled meander-line circuit.

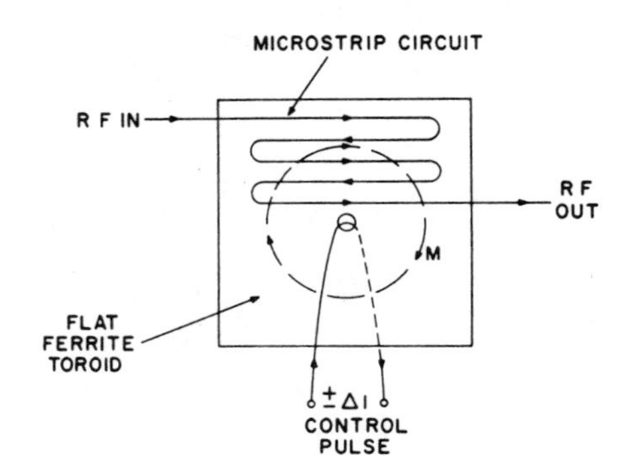

Fig. 9. Latching nonreciprocal phase shifter (flat toroid).

It is possible to obtain a first approximation to the impedance by assuming the device to be an infinite slow-wave structure. Then at the center frequency (i.e., where the coupled line lengths are $\lambda/4$), the two normal modes of the structure are set up by even and odd excitation at the extremes (the normal modes being defined as those modes of excitation where coupling of energy between adjacent lines does not occur).

With even excitation, the meander line behaves as though it were divided up into identical cells isolated by means of electric and magnetic walls, as shown in Fig. 10. With the odd-mode excitation the positions of the electric and magnetic walls are simply interchanged. Each cell cross section appears as shown in Fig. 11(a). The characteristic impedances for the even and odd modes are denoted by Z_{oe} and Z_{oo}, respectively.

The resultant impedance for the coupled meander line is then given by the usual expression,

$$Z_0 = \sqrt{Z_{oe}Z_{oo}}.$$

By inspection, the even- and odd-mode impedances are equal, and only one need be calculated. (Note that the even- and odd-mode propagation constants are also equal for the quarter-wavelength coupled meander line.)

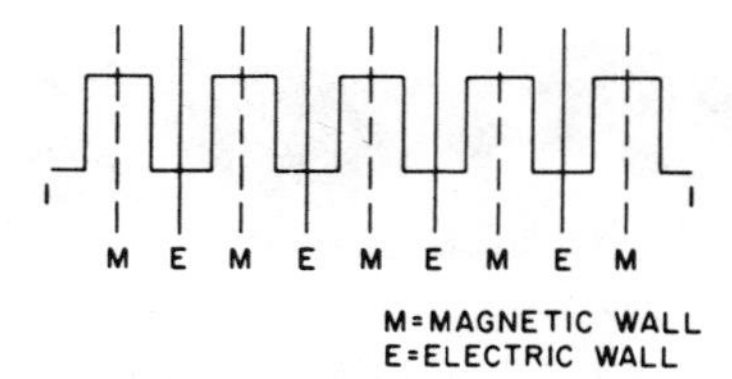

Fig. 10 Coupled meander line with even excitation.

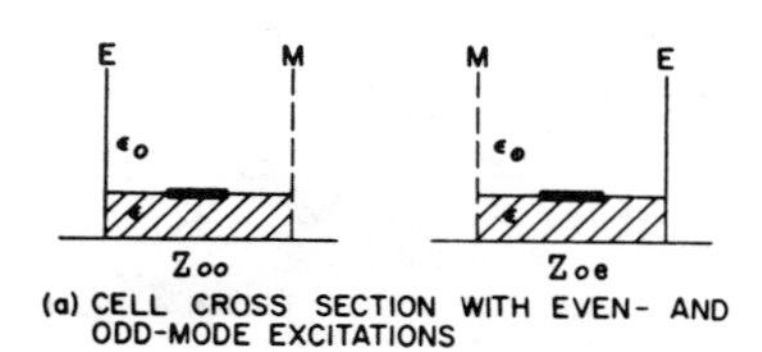

(a) CELL CROSS SECTION WITH EVEN- AND ODD-MODE EXCITATIONS

E M
C_1 W g
C_2 C_4 C_3 h
1,2,3: FRINGING CAPACITANCES
4: PARALLEL-PLATE CAPACITANCE

(b) CAPACITIVE REGIONS OF CELL STRUCTURE

Fig. 11. Elemental cell structure.

In Fig. 11(b) the pertinent capacities and dimensions are defined for the impedance calculation:

$$Z_0 = \sqrt{\frac{L}{C}} = \frac{1}{vC},$$

where

v = phase velocity
C = capacitance.

In terms of the material properties and assuming the permeability to be that of free space, the impedance is

$$Z_0 = \frac{\sqrt{\epsilon_{eff}}}{vC},$$

where

$$v = \text{velocity of light in free space}$$

$$= \sqrt{\epsilon_{eff}}\, v = \frac{1}{\sqrt{\mu_0 \epsilon_0}}$$

ϵ_{eff} = effective relative dielectric constant
ϵ = intrinsic relative dielectric constant.

$$Z_0 = \frac{\sqrt{\mu_0\epsilon_0}\sqrt{\epsilon_{eff}}}{\epsilon_0\left|\frac{C_{01}}{\epsilon_0} + \epsilon_2\frac{C_{02}}{\epsilon_0} + \epsilon_3\frac{C_{03}}{\epsilon_0} + \epsilon_4\frac{C_{04}}{\epsilon_0}\right|},$$

where C_0 = capacitance in free space, and with $\epsilon_2 = \epsilon_3 = \epsilon_4 = \epsilon$, we have

$$Z_0 = \frac{377\sqrt{\epsilon_{eff}}}{\frac{C_{01}}{\epsilon_0} + \epsilon\left[\frac{C_{02}}{\epsilon_0} + \frac{C_{03}}{\epsilon_0} + \frac{W}{h}\right]}. \qquad (11)$$

The individual capacitances can be determined from the following references:

$$\frac{C_{01}}{\epsilon_0}, \text{ reference [5]}$$

$$\frac{C_{02}}{\epsilon_0}, \text{ reference [4]}$$

$$\frac{C_{03}}{\epsilon_0}, \text{ reference [6]} \qquad (C_{fe}).$$

In most applications of the nonreciprocal phase shifter, the design of the meander line is based on the satisfaction of specific goals such as peak phase shift, bandwidth, and loss. After these requirements have been met, the problem of matching this preshaped circuit remains. The meander-line circuit impedance can be calculated for the interior lines using the elemental cell structure shown in Fig. 11 and by solving (11). The impedance of the two outermost line elements (end line) can also be computed by using (11), but a pair of unequal cell structures must now be used to represent the appropriate capacitances. This modification of the cell structure occurs because of the lack of symmetry about the end lines. Referrring to Fig. 11, one cell structure will be bounded by an electric wall on one side and unbounded on the other (Z_{oe}). The second will be bounded by a magnetic wall on one side and unbounded on the other (Z_{oo}). In short, either an electric or magnetic wall is removed from Fig. 11(a). It is worth noting that since the end-line elements are already $\lambda/4$ long, they may be used as matching transformers.

A nonreciprocal latching phase shifter is shown in Fig. 12. This device is controlled by means of a current pulse applied to a control wire which passes through the hole in the center of the ferrite (refer to Fig. 9). The circuit was designed for operation at S-band using a 1 by 1 by 0.020 inch sample of TTI-414[3] ferrite. The differential phase-frequency characteristic for this device is shown in Fig. 13.

Multibit devices[7] may be realized by either cascading individual phase-shifter bits or by partially switching[8] a single large (360°) phase shifter. A two-bit (180°, 90°) cascaded digital phase shifter is shown in Fig. 14. More bits may be added by simply increasing the size of the substrate and adding the desired circuit elements at appropriate control aperture spacings. Care must be taken in the relative spacing of bits and in the amplitude of the control switching pulses in order to insure adequate isolation between adjacent bits while switching.

The second technique for achieving a multibit function involves the partial switching of a single 360° phase shifting element. If the volt-time product of the control pulse is variable, the phase shifter can be partially switched to any one of a large number of phase settings from 0° to 360°. If a constant voltage pulse is applied

Fig. 12. Nonreciprocal phase shifter (one bit).

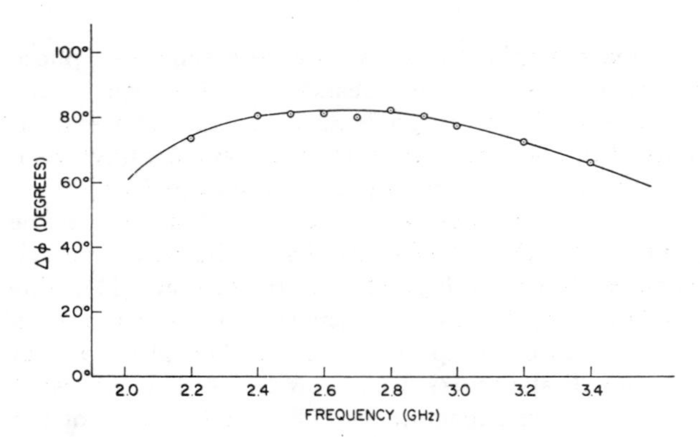

Fig. 13. Phase characteristic (latching nonreciprocal).

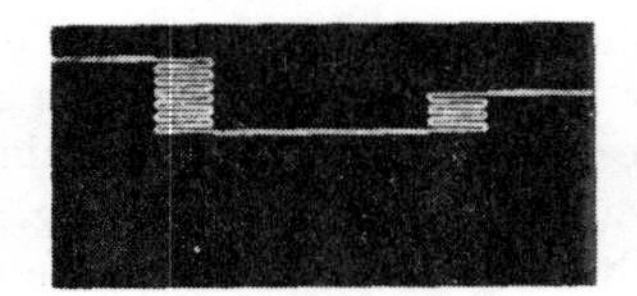

Fig. 14. *X*-band digital phase shifter (two-bit cascaded).

to the control wire, the magnetization is reversed in concentric circles around the control wire with a time course such that a wave of flux-reversal spreads radially outwards from the hole. In essence this arrangement places the sophistication of multibit performance on the drive circuit. The benefits of this approach are found in a significant reduction of the size of the ferrite substrate and some reduction in insertion loss due to the elimination of interconnecting lines between bits. The total insertion loss for the 360° device is approximately 3 dB.

IV. Integrated Devices and Subsystems

Using the phase shifters as building blocks, many other useful signal-processing devices and systems can be realized.

A four-port latching circulator[9] (or DPDT switch) is shown in Fig. 15. This is the well-known waveguide phase-shift circulator[10] in microstrip form. A branch-line hybrid performs as a side-wall coupler, and a hybrid together with a 90° line length at one port behaves as a magic tee. Two 90° nonreciprocal phase shifters complete the network. The performance of this device is illustrated in Fig. 16.

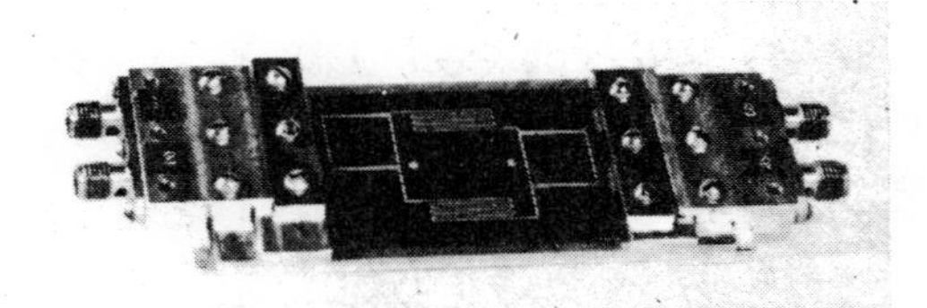

Fig. 15. Four-port switchable circulator.

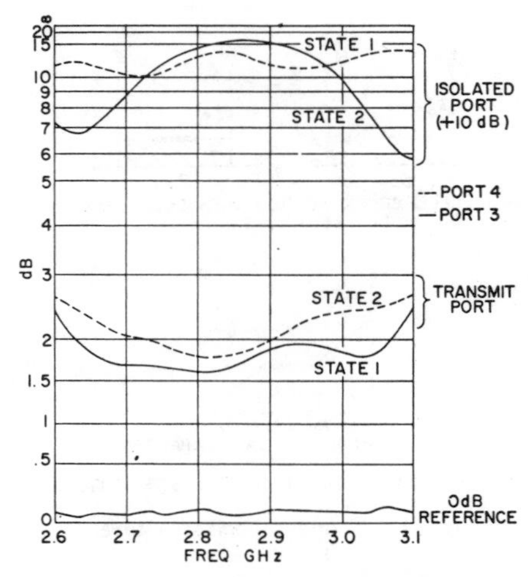

Fig. 16. Switchable four-port circulator characteristic.

An equivalent of the field displacement isolator is shown schematically in Fig. 17. With the phase shifters set as shown, energy propagating from left to right is transmitted as an odd mode in the coupled-line region. This results in a maximum electric field parallel to the resistance sheet and a high insertion loss is experienced. Energy propagating in the opposite direction appears as an even mode in the coupled line region. For this condition the electric field is at a minimum across the resistance sheet, and a minimum insertion loss is experienced. An isolator using this principle is shown in Fig. 18. This device had a reverse loss of 20 dB and a forward loss of about 2.0 dB over a 25 percent bandwidth at *X*-band. An additional improvement in the bandwidth capability should be possible if the 90° line length used to balance the bridge were replaced by a Schiffman phase shifter.[11]

Another form of isolator is obtained by using an appropriately terminated circulator, as shown in Fig. 19. Here two ports of the previously mentioned four-port circulator are terminated by depositing a resistive film over a short meandered line. Due to the narrow-band nature of the branch line hybrids, the useful isolation bandwidth is of the order of 15 percent. Both isolators may also be considered to be self-latching variable attenuators and can be controlled by partially switching the ferrite.

A steerable array antenna can be easily fabricated by the integration of many ferrite control elements on a common ferrite substrate. Fig. 20 shows an *X*-band, eight-port corporate feed with nonreciprocal phase

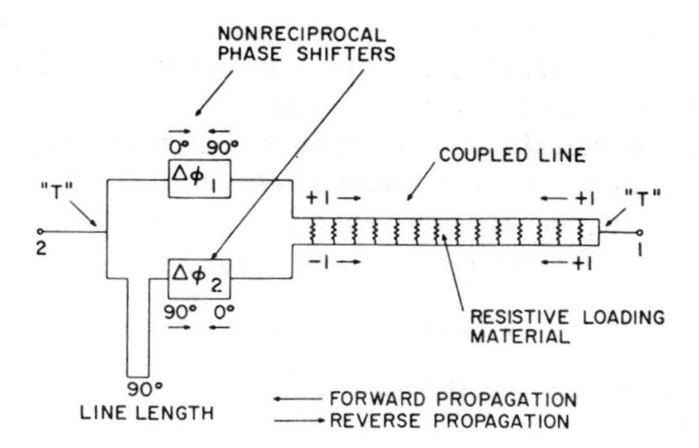

Fig. 17. Planar field displacement isolator.

Fig. 18. Planar field displacement isolator (*X*-band).

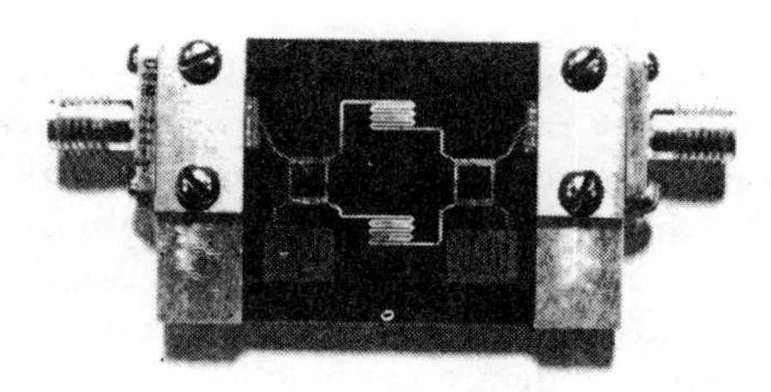

Fig. 19. *X*-band isolator/variable attenuator (latching).

Fig. 20. Eight-port corporate feed with nonreciprocal phase shifters (*X*-band).

Fig. 21. *X*-band eight-element linear array antenna.

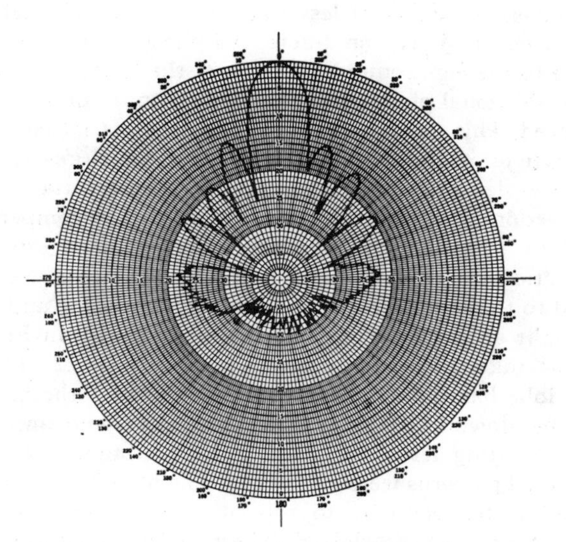

Fig. 22. Boresight pattern for eight-element linear array (amplitude in dB).

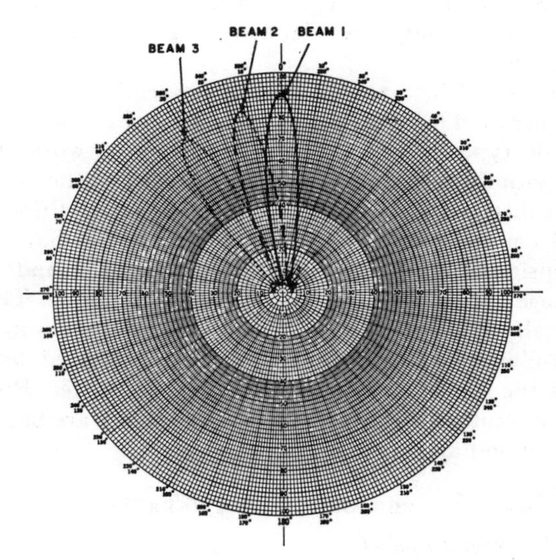

Fig. 23. Linear plot of steered beams.

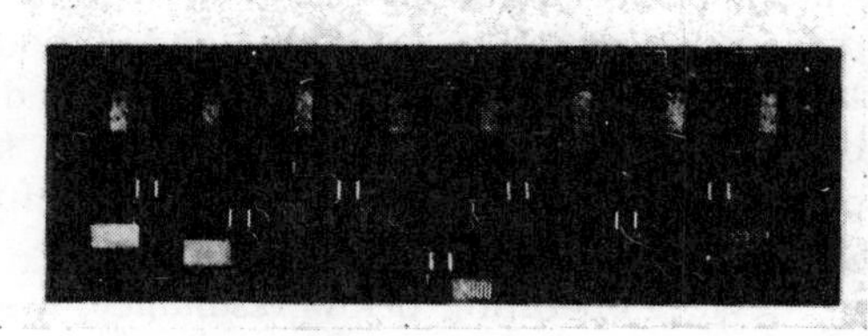

Fig. 24. Eight-element linear array with printed dipole radiators.

shifters. The corporate feed consists of appropriately placed 3-dB branch line couples and short-phase compensating line lengths which provide a maximum relative phase variation of less than 3° between all eight output ports. When the differential phase shifters were added to the eight equiphase ports of the feed network, some additional phase errors between output ports were observed. This was apparently due to local variations in the state of magnetization of the ferrite, which resulted from the size and shape of the sample. These variations in insertion phase are reproducible and can be compensated by suitably adjusting the corporate feed interconnections. Coaxial dipole radiating elements were added to the structure at half-wavelength spacing and a boresight antenna pattern for the array shown in Fig. 21 was taken. This pattern is shown in Fig. 22. The main lobe has a 3-dB beamwidth of 12° with the first sidelobes down 13 dB. This is as expected with no amplitude weighting across the array. Some preliminary data on steered patterns were also taken. The main beam was steered off boresight by appropriate partial switch settings of each phase shifter. These results conformed quite well with the theory and are shown in Fig. 23. These antenna patterns (linear plot) correspond to the conditions where the progressive increment in phase setting between adjacent elements was 0° (boresight), 45°, and 90°.

This type of integrated linear array lends itself well to another modification, which is shown in Fig. 24. Here the same type of feed and phase-shifting network are shown with the radiating elements deposited on the same ferrite substrate. This eliminates the need for additional coaxial connections and the attachment of radiators. The topside of the ferrite substrate shows the meanderline phase shifter and one-half the dipole antenna. The other half of the dipole is etched from the deposited ground-plane side. A balanced two-wire printed line couples the dipole antenna and the phase shifter. Preliminary results for this type of array antenna are being evaluated and appear to show promise.

V. Peak and Average Power Characteristics

A. Peak Power Capability

The peak power-handling capability is determined by the nonlinear effects in the ferrite material. Although the exact mechanisms producing the nonlinear loss in unsaturated ferrites are not yet fully understood, a great deal of experimental work[8],[12],[15] has been done (and is continuing) to determine the threshold field strength of commercially available materials as a function of (ω_m/ω).

In ferrite devices operating below resonance, a sudden linear increase in insertion loss is observed as the incident power level is increased beyond a certain threshold level. This effect is indicative of frequency down conversion. Schloman[13] has shown that the generation of the first subharmonic is the most easily obtained nonlinear effect if the ferrite sample has unequal transverse demagnetizing factors and is subjected to a parallel pumping RF magnetic field.

For the generation of the subharmonic, it is necessary that the system have a natural resonance at the subharmonic frequency. In an unsaturated ferrite, domain resonances exit over the frequency range

$$\gamma H_{\text{ANIS}} < \omega < \omega_m$$

where H_{ANIS} is the effective anisotropy field in the material

$$\omega_m = \gamma(4\pi M_s).$$

Within these domains, many possible resonance modes can exist. The lowest-order mode is the uniform precession ($k=0$). The higher-order modes ($k \geq 1$) are the magnetostatic modes and spin-wave modes. In general, however, the larger the wave number (k), the greater is the damping of the mode (i.e., ΔH_k increases with k). Thus, if many modes exist simultaneously, the mode with the lowest wave number will be most easily excited.

For subharmonic excitation of only the $k=0$ mode, over the frequency range described by the above equation, it is possible to obtain a reasonable estimate of the critical field strength required for the onset of instabilities. The results obtained by this approach become less valid as the frequency extremes for excitation of the zero-order mode are approached.

Using this approach to the problem, it has been shown[8] that the critical field strength can be calculated as a function of (ω_m/ω) by using the following relationship:

$$\frac{h_{\text{crit}}}{\Delta H_k} = \frac{4}{\frac{\omega_m}{\omega}\left[3 - \sqrt{1 + 2\left(\frac{\omega}{\omega_m}\right)^2}\right]}. \tag{12}$$

It should be stressed that for values of $(\omega_m/\omega) < 0.6$, this equation does not apply. The linewidth of the uniform precession in the domain (ΔH_k) was in the range of one to three Oe for the materials mentioned in this paper.

The power flow is approximately

$$P = I^2 Z_0 \tag{13}$$

where

I = current on the center strip

Z_0 = characteristic impedance of the line.

The RF magnetic field strength at the conductor–ferrite interface is approximately

$$H = \frac{I}{2W} \tag{14}$$

and

$$P = 4W^2 H^2 Z_0. \tag{15}$$

For W in inches, and the critical field level H_c in oersteds, the critical power level is

$$P_c = 16.3\, W^2 H_c^2 Z_0 \text{ (watts)}. \tag{16}$$

An experimental circuit was printed on a 0.020 inch thick ferrite (TTI-414) and had a strip width of 0.012 inch (which is approximately a 50-ohm line). The theoretical critical power levels for this circuit are as follows:

Frequency	P_c
2.2 GHz	2.76 watts
2.4 GHz	4.87 watts
2.6 GHz	6.85 watts
3.0 GHz	>10 watts

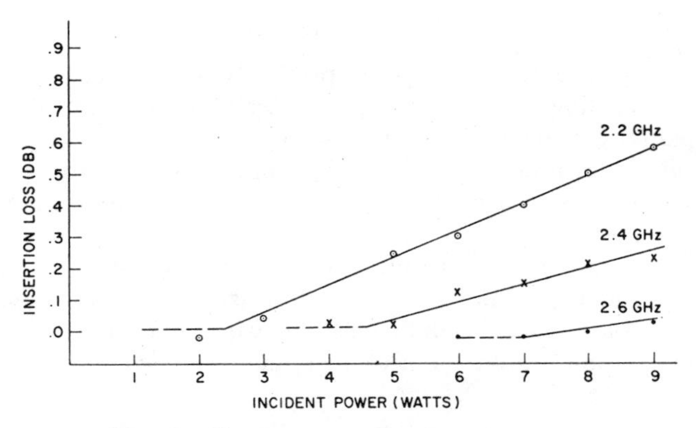

Fig. 25. Nonlinear loss effect (experimental).

Fig. 25 shows the experimental results of the critical power experiment. In this figure, the low-level losses have been factored out and only the nonlinear magnetic losses are shown as a function of peak incident power level with frequency as a parameter. As frequency is increased, the threshold level increases and the slope of the nonlinear loss characteristic decreases. The break point in nonlinear loss is more difficult to determine for the higher frequencies, but a reasonable correlation with theory has been attained. Although these data were for a simple uncoupled line, they compare quite well with the results obtained for the coupled meander-line circuits which are used for the nonreciprocal phase shifters.

For a given impedance and ferrite, the critical power level increases as the square of the strip width (16). This, of course, requires an increase in the ground-plane spacing. The peak power-handling capability can also be increased by separating the center strip from the ferrite by means of a dielectric spacer.

B. Average Power-Handling Capability

The average power-handling capability of the devices investigated is a function of the maximum allowable temperature rise in the ferrite, device insertion loss, and the heat transfer efficiency of the structure.

Efficient heat transfer is obtained because of the planar geometry of the ferrite, which is in immediate contact with a heat sink (ground plane). Assuming that the predominant heat source in the devices is copper loss in the center conductor, this is the worst case, since the heat flow has a maximum path length through the ferrite.

The heat transfer per unit time (Q watts) is given by

$$Q = -kA\frac{\Delta T}{h} \tag{17}$$

where

k = thermal conductivity of the ferrite (watts/cm²/cm/°C)
A = cross-sectional area normal to the direction of heat flow (cm²)
ΔT = temperature differential between center conductor and ground plane (°C)
h = ferrite thickness (cm)

For most ferrites, the thermal conductivity is approximately

$$k \approx 4.10^{-2} \text{ watts/cm}^2\text{/cm/°C}.$$

A conservative estimate for the temperature differential in the devices can be obtained by assuming the area normal to the direction of heat flow to be the product of the width and length of the center conductor. (In reality, this area is somewhat larger by at least a factor of two.) Using this heat transfer area, an estimate for the temperature differential is as follows.

Strip width to ground-plane spacing:

$$\frac{W}{h} = 0.65 \text{ (50–ohm line)}.$$

Power loss per centimeter length $= Q/l$:

$$\Delta T \approx 40\frac{Q}{l}\,°\text{C} \tag{18}$$

where

Q = watts dissipated
l = length of center strip (cm).

This expression can be written in terms of average input power and insertion loss per centimeter, i.e.,

$$\frac{\Delta T}{W} = 9.2\alpha\ °\text{C/watt input} \tag{19}$$

where

α = dB/cm
W = input power (watts).

At S-band frequencies, the temperature differential is approximately 1°C/watt input. The allowed temperature rise depends, of course, on the stability of the ferrite material being used.

VI. Conclusion

This program has been primarily concerned with establishing the feasibility of ferrite devices in the planar geometry. Some of these devices have shown considerable promise and further optimization will be achieved with a continued refinement of the technique involved.

It appears at this time that certain microwave control functions can be performed utilizing thin magnetic materials, which should be compatible with the integrated microwave circuit concepts envisioned.

Acknowledgment

The authors wish to thank C. W. Gerst, C. AuMiller, L. Lu, E. E. Des-Jardins, and W. E. Parfitt for their contributions during this program.

References

[1] H. A. Wheeler, "Transmission-line properties of parallel strips separated by a dielectric sheet," *IEEE Trans. Microwave Theory and Techniques*, vol. MTT-13, pp. 172–185, March 1965.

[2] H. Suhl and R. L. Walker, "Topics in guided wave propagation through gyromagnetic media," *Bell Sys. Tech. J.*, vol. 33, September 1954.

[3] Trans-Tech, Inc., Gaithersburg, Md.

[4] C. R. Cruzan and R. V. Garver, "Characteristic impedance of rectangular coaxial transmission lines," *IEEE Trans. Microwave Theory and Techniques*, vol. MTT-12, pp. 488–495, September 1964.

[5] G. L. Matthaei, L. Young, and E. M. T. Jones, *Microwave Filters, Impedance-Matching Networks and Coupling Structures.* New York: McGraw-Hill, 1964, p. 207.

[6] *Ibid.*, p. 188.

[7] Fifth Quart. Rept., Contract AF 33 (615)-3332, sponsored by AF Avionics Lab., Research and Technology Div., AF Systems Command.

[8] "Development of helical phase-shifters," General Electric Company, Final Rept. to M.I.T. Lincoln Labs., Subcontract 250, Prime Contract AF 19 (628)–500, December 1964.

[9] G. T. Roome, H. A. Hair, and C. W. Gerst, "A planar four-port switchable circulator for microwave integrated circuits," presented at the 1967 Internat'l Solid-State Circuits Conf., Philadelphia, Pa., February 1967.

[10] L. Levy and L. M. Silber, "Fast switching X-band circulator utilizing ferrite toroids," *1960 IRE Wescon Rec.*

[11] B. M. Schiffman, "A new class of broad-band microwave 90-degree phase shifters," *IRE Trans. Microwave Theory and Techniques*, vol. MTT-6, pp. 232–237, April 1958.

[12] E. A. Killick, "High power limitations in low field ferrite devices," *1964 ESATA Symp. Proc.* RADC-TDR-64-255, vol. 1, pp. 224–241.

[13] E. Schloman, J. J. Green, and U. Milano, "Recent development in thorough magnetic resonance at high power levels," *J. Appl. Phys.*, vol. 31, pp. 386S–395S, 1960.

[14] J. J. Green, J. A. Hillier, and J. H. Saunders, "Dependence of peak power threshold upon ω_m/ω," *1967 IEEE PG–MTT Symp.*, pp. 100–102.

[15] E. Stern, "Non-linear threshold in remanent ferrite," *1967 IEEE PG-MTT Symp.*, pp. 103–106.

Planar Meanderline Ferrite-Dielectric Phase Shifter

E. R. BERTIL HANSSON, SHEEL ADITYA, MEMBER, IEEE, AND MATS A. LARSSON

Abstract—This paper presents the design of meanderline circuits with multilayer ferrite-dielectric embedding. New expressions are developed for the even- and the odd-mode admittances for an infinite meanderline in such a structure. It is shown that the effective dielectric constants and the effective relative permeabilities for some of the multilayer structures are simply related. An efficient synthesis routine for the design of meanderline circuits is described. Effect of different parameters on the phase shift has been studied experimentally. It is indicated that the present structure can result in a compact phase shifter with an improved figure of merit, peak power-handling capability, and temperature stability.

I. INTRODUCTION

FERRITE phase shifters based on meander-folded lines have been known for several years. In 1966, Jones described the design of a stripline phase shifter [1] by using the theories of Bolljahn and Matthaei [2]. A couple of years later, Roome and Hair [3] gave a first-order theory for the functioning of reciprocal as well as nonreciprocal phase shifters using microstrip techniques. In separating the meanderline from the ferrite by a thin dielectric sheet, the peak power capability was shown to increase [4]; also the total losses and the differential phase shift were found to decrease. However, by choosing a proper combination of materials and geometry, a net improvement of the figure of merit was achieved [5]. Thus experimental results indicate that optimal performance of the meanderline phase shifter demands a multilayer structure. Accordingly, the multilayer ferrite-dielectric structure shown in Fig. 1(a) has been investigated for its application in meanderline phase shifters.

II. DESIGN OF AN INFINITE MEANDERLINE EMBEDDED IN A MULTILAYER FERRITE-DIELECTRIC STRUCTURE

For a meanderline surrounded by layers of different media, Weiss [6] showed, under the quasi-TEM approximation, that the dispersion law and the image admittance for

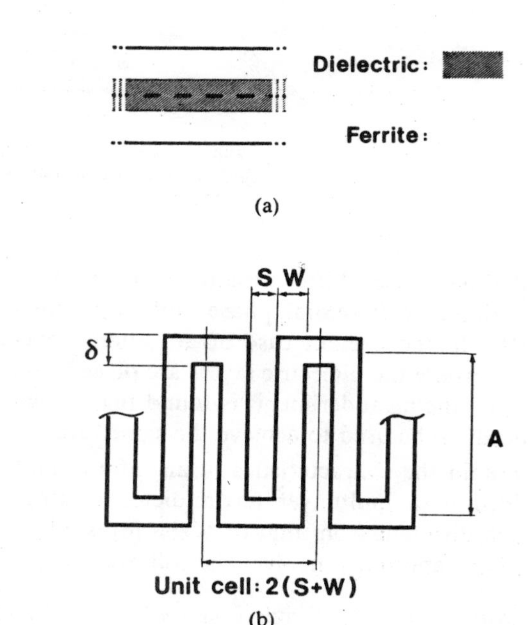

Fig. 1. (a) Meanderline embedded in a ferrite-dielectric composite. (b) Meanderline pattern showing the unit cell and other dimensions of the meanderline.

the forward-wave propagation are given by

$$\tan^2 \frac{\Phi}{4} = \frac{Y_e(\Phi)}{Y_o(\Phi)} \tan\{k_e(\Phi)A/2\} \tan\{k_o(\Phi)A/2\} \quad (1)$$

$$Y_{\text{im}}(\Phi) = \sqrt{Y_e(\Phi)Y_o(\Phi)\frac{\tan\{k_e(\Phi)A/2\}}{\tan\{k_o(\Phi)A/2\}}} \quad (2)$$

where

$$k_i^2(\Phi) = \frac{\omega^2}{C^2}\epsilon_{\text{eff}\,i}(\Phi)\mu_{\text{eff}\,i}(\Phi), \qquad i=e,o. \quad (3)$$

In these equations, Φ is the phase increment per unit cell of the periodic meanderline structure and Y_e and Y_o are the even- and the odd-mode admittances corresponding to the two normal modes assumed to propagate on an array of infinitely long strips. The dimensional parameter A is the length of the meanderlines which are obtained by connecting alternate strips (Fig. 1(b)). For an even mode, the phase difference between adjacent strips is $\Phi/2$, and for an odd mode, it is $\Phi/2+\pi$, or $(\Phi+2\pi)/2$ [6]. For the special case of $\Phi=0$, the phase difference per unit cell for the even and the odd mode is 0 and 2π, respectively.

Appearance of Φ following a parameter is meant to emphasize the fact that the parameter changes with Φ. For

Manuscript received September 30, 1980; revised October 13, 1980. A condensed version of this paper has been presented at the 1980 IEEE-MTTS International Microwave Symposium, Washington, DC. This work was supported in part by the Swedish Board for Technical Development. A full length version is found in the internal report [15].

E. R. B. Hansson was with the Division of Network Theory, Chalmers University of Technology, Gothenburg, Sweden. He is now with Microwave Development Laboratories, Inc., Natick, MA, 01760.

S. Aditya was with the Division of Network Theory, Chalmers University of Technology, Gothenburg, Sweden, under a collaboration program supported by Swedish International Development Agency. He is now with the Department of Electrical Engineering, Indian Institute of Technology, Delhi, India.

M. A. Larsson is with the Division of Network Theory, Chalmers University of Technology, Gothenburg, Sweden.

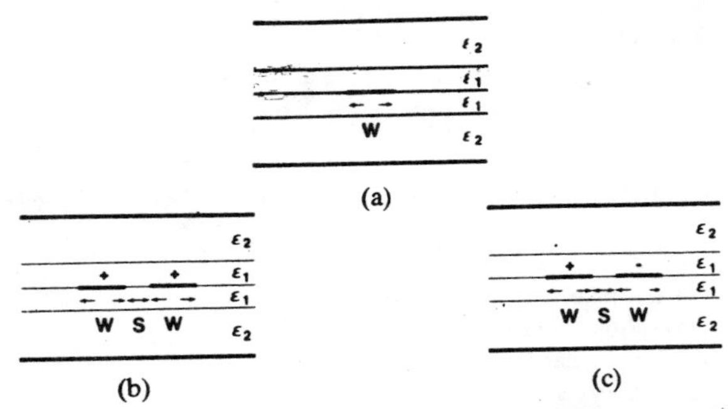

Fig. 2. Basic four-layer structures involving two dielectrics. (a) Single line. (b) Double line with even excitation. (c) Double line with odd excitation.

meanderline phase shifter structures reported previously [7], maximum differential phase shift was obtained for $\Phi=180°$. In the present case of an inhomogeneous construction where the dielectric layers are placed between the ferrite and the meanderline, it is found that a higher value of Φ needs to be used to achieve the same result.

To obtain the characteristics of an infinite meanderline embedded in a multilayer ferrite-dielectric structure, an approach different from that of Weiss [6] is adopted here. The present approach involves the following steps.

A. Characteristics of a Single Line and Two Coupled Lines

The characteristics of the single line and the double line in the four-layer dielectric–dielectric structure, shown in Fig. 2, are worked out by the method of Lennartsson [8]. In this method, the lines are described in terms of filling factors α_s, α_{de}, and α_{do} and characteristic admittances Y_{sv}, Y_{dev}, and Y_{dov}, the latter for the lines in vacuum. The indices s, de, and do indicate, respectively, the parameters corresponding to the single line and the even- and the odd-mode excitation of the double line.

B. Algorithm for Efficient Analysis

By considering the linewidth W as a variable and the other parameters of the structure as constants we can expand each one of the six characterizing parameters in a power series in W, thereby approximating the actual behavior over a limited linewidth interval. If the structure is analyzed for N different values of $W, W_1 \cdots W_N$, one can fit polynomial approximations of the order $N-1$ to the obtained parameter values resulting in the following equation system:

$$[W_a][C]=[S] \tag{4}$$

where

$$[W_a]=\begin{bmatrix} W_1^0 & W_1^1 & \cdots & W_1^{N-1} \\ W_2^0 & W_2^1 & \cdots & W_2^{N-1} \\ \vdots & \vdots & & \vdots \\ W_N^0 & W_N^1 & & W_N^{N-1} \end{bmatrix}$$

$[C]$ is a coefficient matrix and $[S]$ is the matrix formed by the N analysis result vectors.

By solving (4) for the coefficient matrix $[C]$ one gets

$$[C]=[W_a]^{-1}[S]. \tag{5}$$

Using $[C]$, the structure can be analyzed for an arbitrary linewidth W in the interval according to

$$[R]=[W_b][C] \tag{6}$$

where

$$[W_b]=[W^0 W^1 \cdots W^{N-1}]$$

and

$$[R]=[\alpha_e(W) \quad \alpha_o(W) \quad \alpha_s(W) \quad Y_{vde}(W) \quad \cdot Y_{vdo}(W) \quad Y_{vs}(W)].$$

Based on the coefficient matrix $[C]$ and (6), the analysis can be performed several orders of magnitude faster than by direct use of, for instance, a finite difference method [8].

C. Characteristics of an Infinite Meanderline

Leblond *et al.* [9] derived, for the admittance of an infinite coupled line, an expression which, under the present definition of Φ, is written as

$$Y(\Phi)=2y_{oo}+4\sum_{n=1}^{\infty} y_{on}\sin^2(n\Phi/4) \tag{7}$$

in which y_{on} are the mututal admittances to the ground (y_{oo}) and to the neighboring conductors ($y_{on}, n\neq 0$), respectively. For $\Phi=0$ and $\Phi=2\pi$, (7) simplifies considerably. Since these values of Φ correspond to the even- and the odd-mode excitation, respectively, for the special case of zero phase increment per unit cell, one can write

$$Y(0)=Y_e \tag{8}$$

$$Y(2\pi)=Y_o. \tag{9}$$

Thus from (7)

$$Y_e=2y_{oo} \tag{10}$$

$$Y_o=2y_{oo}+4\sum_{n=1}^{\infty} y_{on}, \quad \text{where } n \text{ takes on odd values.} \tag{11}$$

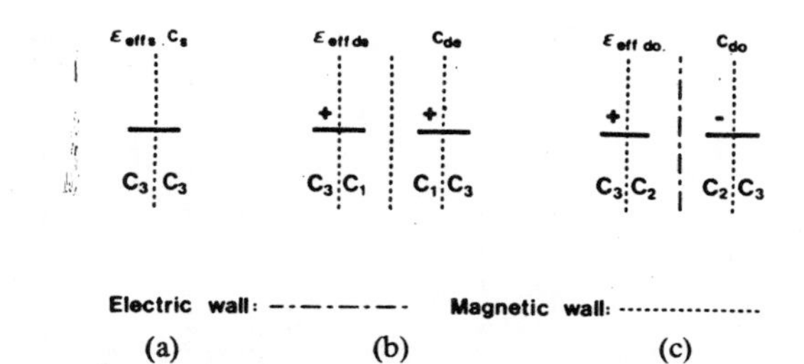

(a) (b) (c)

Fig. 3. Schematic representation of single- and double-line configurations, with associated capacitances and effective dielectric constants. (a) Single line. (b) Double line with even excitation. (c) Double line with odd excitation.

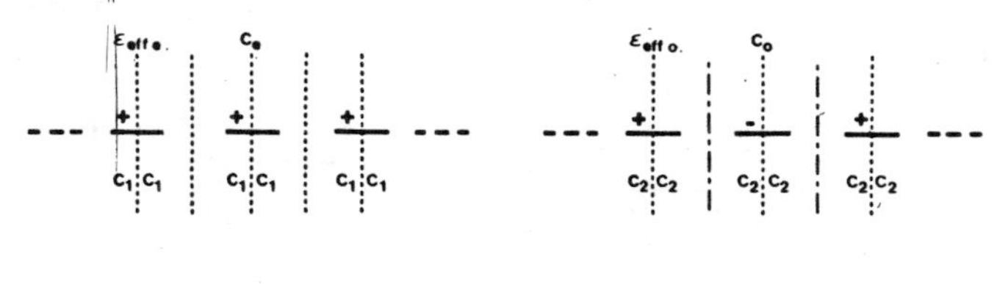

(a) (b)

Fig. 4. Schematic representation of infinite coupled line configuration, with associated capacitances and effective dielectric constants. (a) Even excitation. (b) Odd excitation.

Next, retaining only the first two terms in (7), i.e., neglecting the coupling between nonadjacent strips, one obtains

$$Y(\Phi) = Y_e + (Y_o - Y_e)\sin^2(\Phi/4). \qquad (12)$$

Consider the single- and the double-line configurations represented by Fig. 3(a), (b), and (c), with the associated capacitances C_s, C_{de}, and C_{do}, and the effective dielectric constants $\epsilon_{\mathrm{eff}\,s}$, $\epsilon_{\mathrm{eff}\,de}$, and $\epsilon_{\mathrm{eff}\,do}$. The corresponding infinite coupled line case is represented by Fig. 4(a) and (b), with C_e and C_o as the associated capacitances and $\epsilon_{\mathrm{eff}\,e}$ and $\epsilon_{\mathrm{eff}\,o}$ as the associated effective dielectric constants. In Figs. 3 and 4, electric and magnetic walls are centered between the lines. Also, magnetic walls are assumed to pass through the middle of the lines. These assumptions involve a first-order approximation for the cases of Fig. 3(b) and (c). From Figs. 3 and 4

$$C_e = 2C_1 = 2C_{de} - C_s \qquad (13)$$

$$C_o = 2C_2 = 2C_{do} - C_s. \qquad (14)$$

In the following, subscript i is used in place of both e and o. For the vacuum case

$$C_{iv} = 2C_{div} - C_{sv}, \qquad i = e, o. \qquad (15)$$

Recognizing that

$$Y_{div} = c_o C_{div} \qquad (16)$$

$$Y_{sv} = c_o C_{sv} \qquad (17)$$

where c_o is the speed of light in vacuum, from (15)

$$Y_{iv} = 2Y_{div} - Y_{sv}. \qquad (18)$$

Defining

$$\epsilon_{\mathrm{eff}\,i} = C_i / C_{iv} \qquad (19)$$

$$\epsilon_{\mathrm{eff}\,di} = C_{di} / C_{div} \qquad (20)$$

$$\epsilon_{\mathrm{eff}\,s} = C_s / C_{sv} \qquad (21)$$

one gets

$$\epsilon_{\mathrm{eff}\,i} = (2\epsilon_{\mathrm{eff}\,di} Y_{div} - \epsilon_{\mathrm{eff}\,s} Y_{sv}) / (2Y_{div} - Y_{sv}). \qquad (22)$$

Also, using

$$Y_i / Y_{iv} = (\epsilon_{\mathrm{eff}\,i})^{1/2} \qquad (23)$$

one obtains

$$Y_i = \{(2\epsilon_{\mathrm{eff}\,di} Y_{div} - \epsilon_{\mathrm{eff}\,s} Y_{sv})(2Y_{div} - Y_{sv})\}^{1/2}. \qquad (24)$$

Substitution of (18) and (24) in (12) yields $Y_{iv}(\Phi)$ and $Y_i(\Phi)$, respectively. Thus for instance

$$Y_e(\Phi) = Y(\Phi) = Y_e + (Y_o - Y_e)\sin^2(\Phi/4) \qquad (25)$$

$$Y_o(\Phi) = Y(\Phi + 2\pi) = Y_e + (Y_o - Y_e)\cos^2(\Phi/4). \qquad (26)$$

Then, from (23)

$$\epsilon_{\mathrm{eff}\,e}(\Phi) = \left[\frac{Y_e + (Y_o - Y_e)\sin^2(\Phi/4)}{Y_{ev} + (Y_{ov} - Y_{ev})\sin^2(\Phi/4)}\right]^2 \qquad (27)$$

$$\epsilon_{\mathrm{eff}\,o}(\Phi) = \left[\frac{Y_e + (Y_o - Y_e)\cos^2(\Phi/4)}{Y_{ev} + (Y_{ov} - Y_{ev})\cos^2(\Phi/4)}\right]^2. \qquad (28)$$

For the special case of $\Phi = \pi$

$$Y_e(\pi) = Y_o(\pi) \qquad (29)$$

$$\epsilon_{\mathrm{eff}\,e}(\pi) = \epsilon_{\mathrm{eff}\,o}(\pi). \qquad (30)$$

The above simplification is not possible in the case of $\Phi \neq \pi$.

D. Effective Permeability

Based on the duality of ϵ and μ in the Maxwell's equations, Pucel and Massé [10] derived a relationship between the effective dielectric constant ϵ_{eff} and the effective relative permeability μ_{eff} of a microstrip on a dielectric/mag-

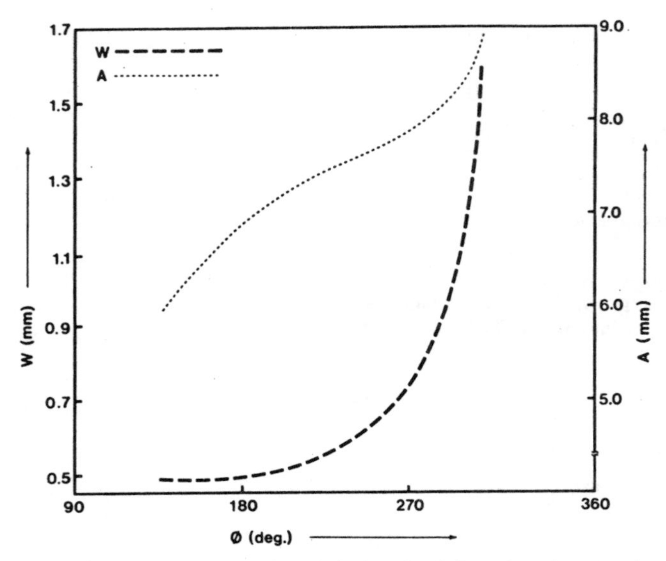

Fig. 5. Variation of the width and the length of the strips of a meanderline for different values of Φ. Impedance level $1/Y_{im}=50\ \Omega$, spacing $s=0.4$ mm, dielectric constant of the dielectric $=2.22$.

netic substrate. Under similar restrictions, an extension of that relation for the case when two media, dielectric or magnetic, are present, has been derived [15]

$$\mu_{\text{eff}}(\mu_1,\mu_2)=\left[\epsilon_{\text{eff}}(\mu_1^{-1},\mu_2^{-1})\right]^{-1}. \tag{31}$$

For gyromagnetic media, expressions given by Massé and Pucel [11] for μ_{dem} and μ_{mag}, corresponding to the demagnetized and "latched" states, are used. Thus the effective relative permeability can also be computed using the filling factors described in the previous subsection.

In summary, for the structure of Fig. 1, the effective dielectric constants are calculated using (27) and (28). The corresponding effective relative permeabilities are given by (31). These results are substituted in (3) to obtain $k_e(\Phi)$ and $k_o(\Phi)$. Then, using $Y_e(\Phi)$ and $Y_o(\Phi)$ calculated from (25) and (26), the length of the meander strips A is computed from (1). Finally, (2) yields Y_{im}, the image admittance of the infinite meanderline structure. To arrive at a particular admittance level one may vary the strip width w while holding the spacing s constant. For an infinite meanderline centered in the four-layer ferrite-dielectric structure of Fig. 1, the widths and the lengths of the strips, obtained for different values of Φ, are shown in Fig. 5. These results are obtained for an impedance level of 50 Ω, a spacing of 0.4 mm between the strips and for a dielectric constant of the dielectric to be 2.22. Beyond $\Phi=270°$, the width and the length of the strips increase rapidly. This is a consequence of the fact that the argument of tangent function on the left-hand side in (1) approaches 90°.

III. Design of Edge Lines

If the coupling between nonadjacent lines is neglected, the edge meander sections can be treated as C-sections. It is known that in microstrip, i.e., in an inhomogeneous environment, a C-section is not well matched [12]. Also, as shown in the case of ferrite microstrip, a C-section

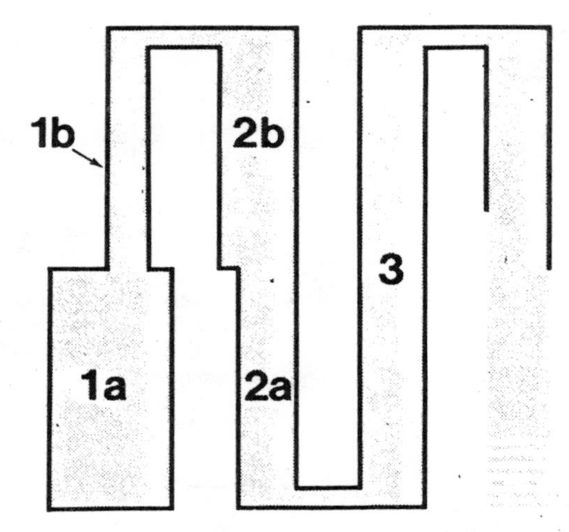

Fig. 6. Stepped admittance design of the meanderline edge sections.

designed for a nominal phase difference of $\pi/2$ between the strip centers, is cut off in the vicinity of design frequency [13]. These problems are overcome by adopting the stepped impedance design suggested in [12]. The edge strips are divided into two sections (Fig. 6), with their characteristic admittances given by

$$Y_{ea}\cdot Y_{oa}=(\theta_{ea}/\theta_{oa})\,Y_{\text{im}}^{\;2} \tag{32}$$

$$Y_{eb}\cdot Y_{ob}=(\theta_{eb}\tan^2\theta_{ob}/\theta_{ob}\tan^2\theta_{eb})\,Y_{\text{im}}^{\;2} \tag{33}$$

where

$$\theta_{ea}+\theta_{oa}=\theta_{eb}+\theta_{ob}=\pi/2. \tag{34}$$

In the above equations, Y_{im} is the matching admittance and the subscripts a and b refer to the corresponding strip sections. In principle, widths of sections $2a$ and $2b$ can be different, but, in practice, the difference is negligibly small.

IV. Synthesis Routine

The synthesis of the phase shifter structure shown in Fig. 1 starts by the calculation of the coefficient matrix $[C]$ given by (5). The concept of filling factors implies that $[C]$ is independent of the material properties. Thus the same coefficient matrix can be used for the optimization of phase shifter structures with different ferrite/dielectric combinations if the geometry is maintained. The effective dielectric constants and the corresponding relative permeabilities are obtained from (27), (28), and (31). The widths of the strips in the meander are then varied until the matching conditions are satisfied. This gives the width and the length of the internal strips. These correspond to a particular spacing between the strips which, for an optimum phase shift, is determined experimentally. Finally, the edge strips are designed according to the method outlined in the previous section.

V. Experimental Results

For the experiments, 0.125-mm-thick RT-Duroid is used as the dielectric. In each case, a 50-Ω meanderline pattern, printed on one of the two dielectric pieces, is sandwiched in a structure similar to the one shown in Fig. 1(a). The

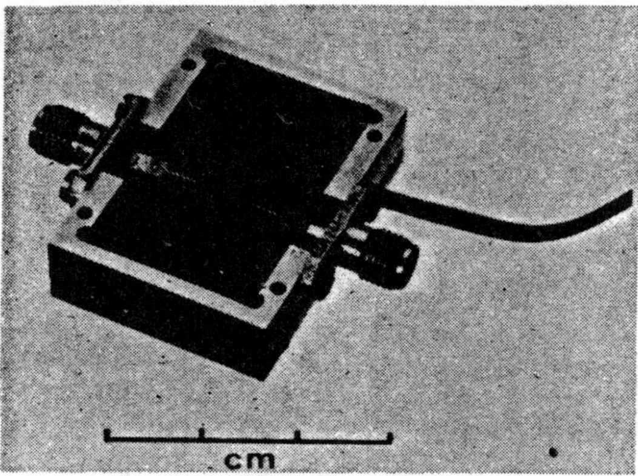

Fig. 7. Phase shifter prototype.

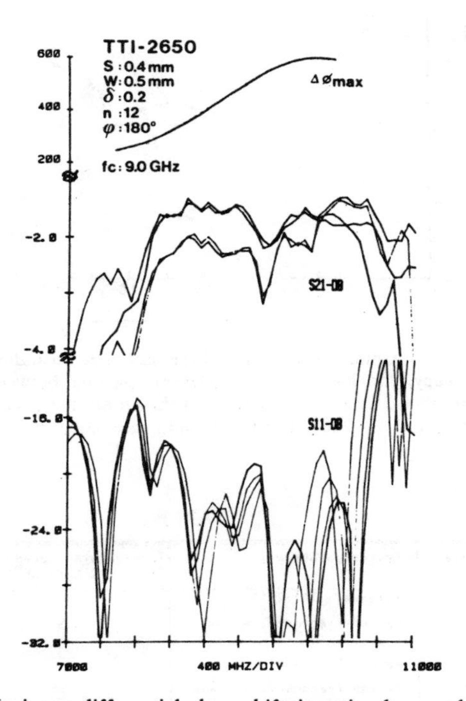

Fig. 8. Maximum differential phase shift, insertion loss, and reflections for different magnetizations, as a function of frequency. Design frequency for the meanderline circuit: 9.0 GHz.

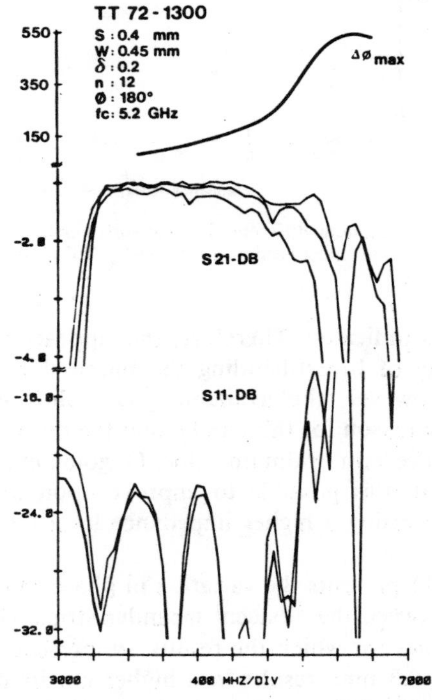

Fig. 9. Same as Fig. 8. Design frequency for the meanderline circuit: 5.2 GHz.

magnetic circuit consists of 1.6-mm-thick ferrite pieces and thin rectangular iron pieces, accurately machined to the required thickness, the latter sitting in slots made in the dielectric pieces. The four-piece toroid so formed is latched to various magnetizations with the help of a magnetizing coil printed on the dielectric piece itself. Trans-Tech ferrites and garnets are used in the experiments. A photograph of the phase shifter is shown in Fig. 7.

Figs. 8 and 9 show the maximum differential phase shift ($\Delta\Phi_{max}$) along with insertion loss and reflections in the case of circuits designed for operation at 9.0 and 5.2 GHz, respectively. In the vicinity of the design frequency the matching is good. While at higher frequencies, the reflections increase sharply due to the approaching stopband of the meander circuit [7]; at lower frequencies, the same occurs due to the rapid change in the impedance of the lines, arising from the frequency dependence of the permeability as ω approaches ω_m [11]. As regards the phase shifts, one can achieve a mean figure of merit of 310°/dB, as seen in the X-band case, from 9.4 to 10.0 GHz. On the other hand, there is a considerable variation in phase shift with frequency.

Meanderline circuits represented by Figs. 8 and 9 are designed for $\Phi = 180°$. In these cases, the maximum differential phase shift occurs at a frequency higher than the design frequency. Thus it can be expected that using a somewhat higher value of Φ will bring down the frequency of maximum differential phase shift. Results presented in Fig. 10 verify this. Here, the differential phase shift for a single meander section for three successively higher values of Φ is plotted. For the $\Phi = 260°$ case, allowing for a 5-percent variation in the phase shift, a 16-percent band-

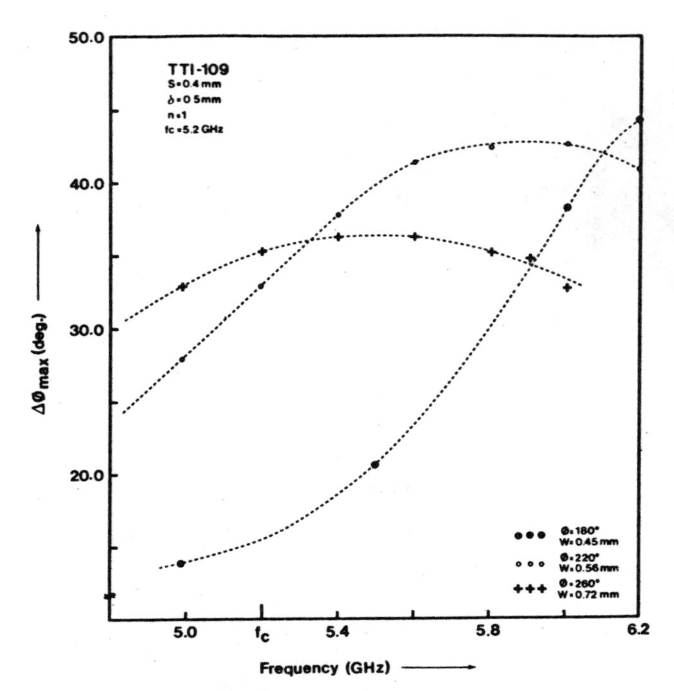

Fig. 10. Maximum differential phase shift versus frequency per single meander section for $\Phi = 180°$, $220°$, and $260°$.

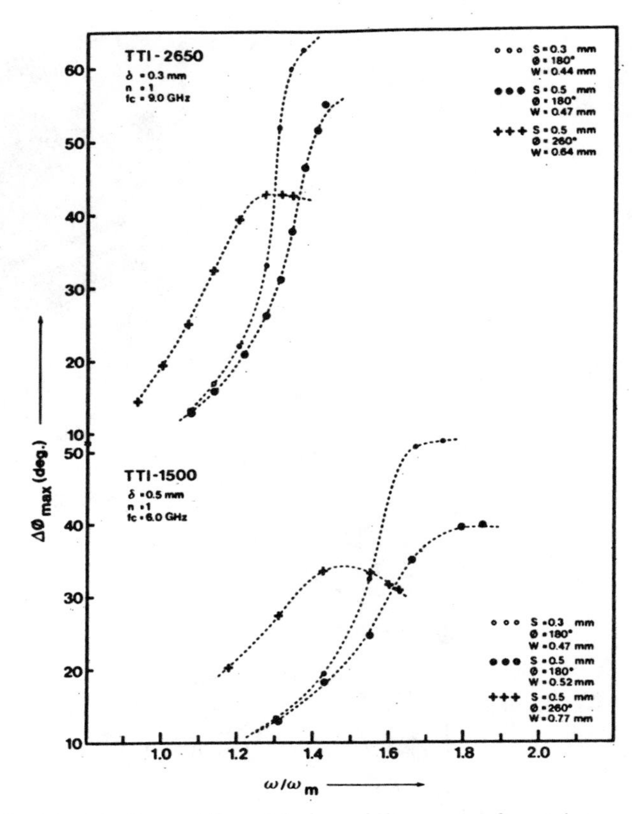

Fig. 11. Maximum differential phase shift per meander section versus frequency, for $\Phi = 180°$, for different spacings between the meander strips: $s = 0.3$ and $s = 0.5$ mm. Also shown are the results for the latter spacing and $\Phi = 260°$. For the X-band case, ω/ω_m values are lower.

width is indicated. Therefore, this appears to be an effective way of broad-banding the phase shift. At the same time, however, the available phase shift is lowered. A possible reason for this can be that the ratio s/w is lowered below a certain optimum value. Ongoing experiments indicate that it is possible to improve upon this phase shift value by using a higher impedance level for the meanderline.

Fig. 11 presents the variation in phase shift for different gaps between the adjacent meander strips. Out of the two gap values for which the results are presented, the smaller gap, $s = 0.3$ mm, results in a higher maximum differential phase shift. This trend is similar to that for other ferrite phase shifters based on the meanderline circuit, for instance [7]. For the present structure, it is also observed that reflections from the device are higher for $s = 0.3$ than for $s = 0.5$. This is attributed to the presence of air gaps between the adjacent meander strips, since for a smaller gap these are more difficult to fill in. Also presented in Fig. 10 are the results for $s = 0.5$ mm and $\Phi = 260°$ for X- and C-band. For these two cases, mean figures of merit of 280°/dB and 250°/dB, respectively, have been achieved. The corresponding bandwidths are approximately 10 and 14 percent.

The peak power threshold, for the parameters given in Fig. 8 ($\omega_m/\omega = 0.82$ at 9 GHz), has been measured to be 40 W at 9 GHz and 60 W at 9.3 GHz. It is felt that this threshold could be significantly raised by choosing a lower ω_m/ω [14] or by using a material with a larger spin wave linewidth. The measured values are, however, significantly higher than those expected for a similar structure without the dielectric inserts. Temperature dependence of the phase shift has also been measured in two cases. The results are given in Table I.

TABLE I

Device	Device parameters	Temperature dependence in deg./°C (from -10°C to 60°C)
1.	Material: TT1-2650 Design frequency: 9 GHz	0.5
2.	Material: G-1002 Design frequency: 4.5 GHz	0.24

Before concluding this section, it may be mentioned that optimization with respect to the thickness and the dielectric constant of the dielectric, as well as the impedance level of the meanderline, remains to be done.

VI. Conclusions

A method has been given for designing well-matched meanderline circuits for use in planar multilayer ferrite-dielectric phase shifters. Experimental results at C- and X-band have been presented to illustrate the effects of varying different circuit parameters. The results indicate a good figure of merit, which may exceed 300°/dB. For a somewhat lower figure of merit, an operating bandwidth of 10 percent of the design frequency can be easily achieved. This configuration is attractive also for improving peak power threshold and temperature stability.

Acknowledgment

The authors wish to thank Prof. E. F. Bolinder for his encouragement and support. The peak power threshold measurements were done at Telefonaktiebolaget L M Ericsson, Mölndal, Sweden. J. -O. Yxell photo-etched the meanderline patterns, and Miss C. Eliasson typed the manuscript.

References

[1] R. R. Jones, "A slow wave digital ferrite strip transmission line phase shifter," *IEEE Trans. Microwave Theory Tech.*, vol. MTT-14, pp. 684–688, Dec. 1966.

[2] J. T. Bolljahn and G. L. Matthaei, "A study of the phase and filter properties of arrays of parallel conductors between ground planes," *Proc. IRE*, vol. 50, pp. 299–311, Mar. 1962.

[3] G. T. Roome and H. A. Hair, "Thin ferrite devices for microwave integrated circuits," *IEEE Trans. Microwave Theory Tech.*, vol. MTT-16, pp. 411–420, July 1968.

[4] C. G. Aumiller, D. H. Harris, M. C. Willson, Y. S. Wu, F. J. Rosenbaum, and D. L. LaCombe, "Ferrite dielectric composite integrated microwave circuit development," in *IEEE G-MTT Int. Microwave Symp. Dig.*, pp. 60–69, 1971.

[5] W. Schilz, "Miniaturized microstrip ferrite phasers," in *Proc. European Microwave Conf.*, vol. 2, paper B. 10.5, 1973.

[6] J. A. Weiss, "Dispersion and field analysis of a microstrip meanderline slow-wave structure," *IEEE Trans. Microwave Theory Tech.*, vol. MTT-22, pp. 1194–1201, Dec. 1974.

[7] F. J. Rosenbaum, "Integrated ferrimagnetic devices," in *Advances in Microwaves*, vol. 8, L. Young and H. Sobol, Eds. New York: Academic Press, 1974, ch.V.

[8] B. Lennartsson, "A network analogue method for computing the TEM characteristics of planar transmission lines," *IEEE Trans. Microwave Theory Tech.*, vol. MTT-20, pp. 586–591, Sept. 1972.

[9] A. Leblond and G. Mourier, "Etude des lignes à barraux à structures periodique pour tubes electronique U.H.F.," *Ann. Radioélect.*, vol. 9, pp. 311–328, 1954.

[10] R. A. Pucel and D. J. Massé, "Microstrip propagation on magnetic substrates—Part I: Design theory," *IEEE Trans. Microwave Theory Tech.*, vol. MTT-20, pp. 304–308, May 1972.

[11] D. J. Massé and R. A. Pucel, "Microstrip propagation on magnetic substrates—Part II: Experiment," *IEEE Trans. Microwave Theory Tech.*, vol. MTT-20, pp. 309–313, May 1972.

[12] B. Schiek and J. Köhler, "A method for broad-band matching of microstrip differential phase shifters," *IEEE Trans. Microwave Theory Tech.*, vol. MTT-25, pp. 666–671, Aug. 1977.

[13] W. M. Libbey, "Characteristics of a microstrip two-meander ferrite phase shifter," *IEEE Trans. Microwave Theory Tech.*, vol. MTT-21, pp. 483–487, July 1973.

[14] W. H. Ince and D. H. Temme, "Phasers and time-delay elements," in *Advances in Microwaves*, vol. 4, L. Young, Ed. New York: Academic Press, 1969, ch. I.

[15] B. Hansson, S. Aditya, and M. Larsson, "Planar meanderline ferrite-dielectric phase shifters," Chalmers University of Technology, Division of Network Theory, Gothenburg, Sweden, Report TR 8004, May 1980.

CHAPTER III

COMPUTER AIDED DESIGN

By making circuit design easier, faster, and cheaper, computer aided design techniques have become essential to the development of MIC technology. The survey article by Monaco and Tiberio is followed by examples from Arai and Tokumitse; Besser; and Bandler, *et al.* Nonlinear circuits are presented in the article by Rizzoli, *et al.*; an example is given by Besser. The synthesis approach is discussed by Liu and Ku.

Computer-Aided Analysis of Microwave Circuits

VITO A. MONACO, MEMBER, IEEE, AND PAOLO TIBERIO, MEMBER, IEEE

(*Invited Paper*)

Abstract—**The most relevant techniques that have either found or should find useful application in analyzing microwave circuit performances in the frequency domain are surveyed. The particular needs of the microwave engineer are briefly discussed. Circuit equation formulations in terms of voltages and currents and wave variables are presented and the solution of the set of circuit equations by sparse-matrix techniques is illustrated. Methods based on multiport connection are also reviewed.**

The techniques for computing the first- and second-order sensitivity are illustrated and a comparison is made between the direct method and the transpose-matrix method, which is in certain cases similar to the method based on the adjoint circuit.

I. Introduction

THE PROGRESS registered in recent years in the field of computer-aided design has been considerable and conceptually important, so much so that the computer is no longer considered an auxiliary aid for checking the validity of a solution obtained in other ways, but rather as an indispensable instrument during all circuit design phases. Present-day computer programs, in fact, permit determination not only of the component parameter nominal values but also their maximum permitted spreads in relation to given tolerances on circuit response functions and to the required production yield when a large number of identical circuits must be realized. This is made possible by the availability of analysis programs that, besides being rapid, also allow precise determination of network functions without limitations on component composition or on circuit topology.

This paper describes the methods and algorithms that are the basis for the most important and known programs for analyzing linear circuits in frequency domain. Though giving most attention to the methods specially conceived for microwave circuits with distributed elements, a description is also given of those that are the basis for lumped-element circuit analysis programs since, with appropriate artifices and modifications, they could be adapted for the analysis of distributed component circuits. A comparison between the various methods is also made with a view, above all, to advising the reader of the different limitations deriving from them regarding circuit topology and component composition.

No indications are given on the structure and use of the programs since, being well aware that the employment of a program is strictly conditioned by its simplicity in use, we do not believe this is essential for this paper. In fact, there are no theoretical difficulties that prevent programs from meeting the user's requirements when these are clearly defined [1]. An analysis program, whether used as a routine of larger programs (optimization and tolerance assignment programs) or as an independent instrument for the designer, must have rapid execution, easy input data preparation, and clear output data presentation. Fast execution above all is required when a number of analyses have to be made of one circuit with different component values, as happens in optimization processes and in component tolerance assignment. The other requirement, that is, the simplicity of man–machine interaction, is desirable both to overcome the designer's natural reluctance to use something new and to reduce the time spent in input–output operations [2]. It must be possible, in particular, to modify component values and circuit topology without changing the complete data file. Besides, the printed output data must contain not only the required network functions but also the input data describing the circuit so that it is possible to recognize even some time afterwards the circuit to which they refer. The possibility of obtaining results graphically by means of the same printer or, even better, by means of a plotter or a cathode ray tube display is, finally, a useful though not indispensable convenience.

To analyze a circuit means computing a certain number of response functions in terms of the component parameters, circuit topology, and independent excitations being given. The response functions may be determined both in terms of voltages and currents in some nodes and branches of the circuit, as is usually done with circuits composed of lumped components, and in terms of incident and reflected waves at some ports, as is often done with microwave circuits. Correspondingly, circuit equations may be formulated either in terms of voltages and currents or of normalized wave variables. In the first case, the components are defined by means of admittance, impedances, or dependent generators; each constitutes a branch that is connected between the nodes. In the second case, the components are multiports connected through pairs of ports. The circuit description is effected by means of topological matrices that indicate the nodes between which the branches are connected or the pairs of adjacent ports.

Circuit analysis, that is, determination of the voltages and currents or of the normalized waves, implies the solution of a system of equations whose number, according

Manuscript received July 20, 1973; revised December 7, 1973. This work was supported by the National Research Council of Italy.
The authors are with the Istituto di Elettronica, Università di Bologna, Centro Interazione Operatore-Calcolatore (CNR), Bologna, Italy.

to the method adopted, depends on the number of nodes and branches of the network or on the number of component ports. This might cause limitations in the maximum number of circuit components in relation to computer memory capacity and to the maximum running time imposed.

The classical solution methods require a number of operations proportional to the cube of the number of equations [3]. Various methods have been proposed to reduce computing time by taking advantage of the sparsity of the coefficient matrices of the equation system. There are two basic approaches. The first consists of progressive elimination of all variables not needed for the requested network functions. This approach has been most widely used in microwave circuit analysis since only the external port variables are generally of interest With the second approach, computing time reduction is obtained by carrying out only the arithmetical operations with nonzero operands. It is based on examination of the sparsity structure of the coefficient matrix and on generation of a code or of a set of pointers and indices that provide the "key" to execution of the arithmetical operations. It was first used for power distribution network analysis and subsequently for lumped and distributed circuit analysis.

A limitation on the use of many existing programs for analyzing microwave circuits derives from the fact that only two-terminal components are permitted. Because of this, all the circuit components must be described by means of lumped-element equivalent circuits. For transistors at high frequency, numerous models have been proposed [4]–[7]. However, it is not always easy in the microwave field to characterize active and passive components by means of lumped-element equivalent circuits, but it is always possible to determine the parameters of any component by direct measurements at its ports. In this regard it is observed that both manual and automatic instruments exist today that permit measurements of scattering parameters on broad frequency bands both precisely and very quickly [8]. In the opinion of the authors, shared also by others [1], [9] the possibility of defining circuit components by means of measured parameters must therefore be considered as a necessary property of programs for microwave circuit analysis.

Alternatively, the port parameters of many passive components (microstrip transmission lines, etc.) can be determined in terms of their geometrical dimensions and the electrical characteristics of the materials forming them. In this case it is enough to insert appropriate routines in the analysis program to calculate the component parameters. In this paper, however, no indication is given regarding the operation of these routines since we consider only the problem of determining circuit performance in terms of the electrical parameters.

In Section II, the formulation of circuit equations is described when branch voltages and currents and node voltages are considered as unknowns, and the tableau method and the nodal admittance matrix are explained along with the modified tableau and the mixed method. In Section III, the circuit equation formulation is given when normalized waves at component ports are considered as unknowns and the connection scattering matrix is described. Subsequently, in Section IV, the methods based on multiport connection and, therefore, on the computation of the port matrix of the complete circuit are given. A comparison is also made between the methods, bringing out the inconveniences of some, particularly in relation to accuracy in calculation and the difficulties that might arise in describing the circuits. In Section V, the sparse-matrix techniques for solving the system of the equations are discussed. The method based on execution code generation is dealt with in detail; this is particularly suitable for microwave circuits since their dimensions are not usually very great. A comparison is also made between the computation times required to analyze a single circuit by means of two programs, one being based on the method of connecting components in pairs, the other on the generation and execution of the code that solves the system of the equations describing the circuit.

Finally, Section VI is devoted to computation of network function sensitivities with respect to component parameters.

The direct and the transpose-matrix methods are described and a discussion is presented on the computing effort required by each one. The equivalence that in certain cases exists between the transpose-matrix method and the adjoint circuit method is also shown.

To conclude, the results of analyses on some circuits are given and the problem of component tolerance assignment in relation to permitted performance tolerances is briefly described. This problem is of particular interest to industry, since circuit cost and mass production yield are often greatly dependent on component value spreads.

II. Circuit Analysis in Terms of Voltages and Currents

The solution of an electrical circuit in terms of voltages and currents may be achieved in several ways depending on the variables assumed as unknowns. In lumped-element circuits the variables to be computed are the branch voltages and currents and the voltages between each node and the reference node.

Allowing only one circuit component per branch and applying Ohm's law for each branch, a set of b equations is obtained between vectors $\boldsymbol{V}_b$ and $\boldsymbol{I}_b$ of branch voltages and currents at the b branches:

$$\overset{\longleftarrow b \longrightarrow \quad \longleftarrow b \longrightarrow}{} \\ b \updownarrow \begin{bmatrix} \boldsymbol{Y}_b & -\boldsymbol{Q}_I \\ -\boldsymbol{Q}_V & \boldsymbol{Z}_b \\ \boldsymbol{\mu} & \boldsymbol{0} \\ \boldsymbol{0} & \boldsymbol{\beta} \end{bmatrix} \cdot \begin{bmatrix} \boldsymbol{V}_b \\ \boldsymbol{I}_b \end{bmatrix} = \begin{bmatrix} \boldsymbol{J}_0 \\ \boldsymbol{E}_0 \\ \boldsymbol{0} \\ \boldsymbol{0} \end{bmatrix} \tag{1}$$

where $\boldsymbol{E}_0$ and $\boldsymbol{J}_0$ are the vectors of independent voltage and current generators; the $\boldsymbol{Q}_V$ and $\boldsymbol{Q}_I$ matrices are made up of rows whose elements are all 0 except for the 1 in the entry relative to the branch to which the row refers. The four groups of equations derive from branches containing, respectively: y elements, independent current sources, and voltage-controlled current sources; z elements, independent voltage sources, and current-controlled voltage sources; voltage-controlled voltage sources; current-controlled current sources. By way of example, the set of equations describing the circuit in Fig. 1 is

$$\begin{bmatrix} 0 & y_m & 0 & 0 & 0 & 0 & 0 & 0 & -1 & 0 \\ 0 & 0 & 0 & 0 & y_5 & 0 & 0 & 0 & 0 & -1 \\ -1 & 0 & 0 & 0 & 0 & 0 & 0 & 0 & 0 & 0 \\ 0 & -1 & 0 & 0 & 0 & 0 & z_2 & 0 & 0 & 0 \\ 0 & -1 & 0 & 0 & \mu & 0 & 0 & 0 & 0 & 0 \end{bmatrix} \cdot \begin{bmatrix} V_1 \\ V_2 \\ V_3 \\ V_4 \\ V_5 \\ I_1 \\ I_2 \\ I_3 \\ I_4 \\ I_5 \end{bmatrix} = \begin{bmatrix} 0 \\ 0 \\ E_{10} \\ 0 \\ 0 \end{bmatrix}.$$

The constraints imposed by the topology supply the other equations necessary to define the circuit completely. Applying the Kirchhoff voltage law to all circuit branches and the Kirchhoff current law to all the circuit nodes, except the reference node, the following two topological relations can be obtained:

$$\boldsymbol{A}\boldsymbol{V}_N - \boldsymbol{V}_b = \boldsymbol{0} \tag{2}$$

$$\boldsymbol{A}^T\boldsymbol{I}_b = \boldsymbol{0} \tag{3}$$

where $\boldsymbol{V}_N$ is the vector of the node voltages, $\boldsymbol{A}$ the branch node incidence matrix [10], and $\boldsymbol{A}^T$ its transpose. System (2) contains b equations, each specifying the nodes between which each branch is connected. Each row of $\boldsymbol{A}$ thus contains 1 and -1 in the entries corresponding to the two nodes, all the other elements being 0. System

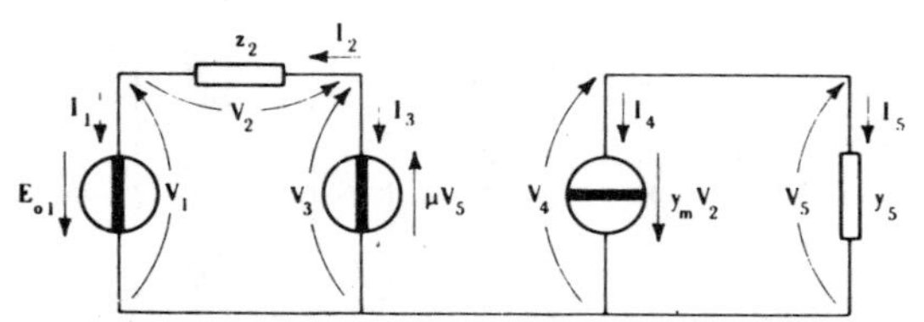

Fig. 1. Circuit chosen as example to show set of equations obtained by applying Ohm's law to each branch.

(3) contains n equations indicating which are the branches connected to each of the n nodes excluding the reference one. Each a_{ij} of $\boldsymbol{A}$ has $\pm$ 1 in the entries corresponding to the branches connected to the node, the sign depending on the branch orientation.

Collecting together systems (1)–(3) and indicating by $\boldsymbol{1}$ a $(b \times b)$ unit matrix, one obtains the set

$$\boldsymbol{T}\cdot\begin{bmatrix} \boldsymbol{V}_N \\ \boldsymbol{I}_b \\ \boldsymbol{V}_b \end{bmatrix} = \begin{array}{c} \\ b \updownarrow \\ n \updownarrow \\ \\ b \\ \\ \end{array} \overset{\begin{array}{ccc} n & b & b \end{array}}{\begin{bmatrix} \boldsymbol{A} & \boldsymbol{0} & -\boldsymbol{1} \\ \boldsymbol{0} & \boldsymbol{A}^T & \boldsymbol{0} \\ \boldsymbol{0} & -\boldsymbol{Q}_I & \boldsymbol{Y}_b \\ \boldsymbol{0} & \boldsymbol{Z}_b & -\boldsymbol{Q}_V \\ \boldsymbol{0} & \boldsymbol{0} & \boldsymbol{\mu} \\ \boldsymbol{0} & \boldsymbol{\beta} & \boldsymbol{0} \end{bmatrix}} \cdot \begin{bmatrix} \boldsymbol{V}_N \\ \boldsymbol{I}_b \\ \boldsymbol{V}_b \end{bmatrix} = \begin{bmatrix} \boldsymbol{0} \\ \boldsymbol{0} \\ \boldsymbol{J}_0 \\ \boldsymbol{E}_0 \\ \boldsymbol{0} \\ \boldsymbol{0} \end{bmatrix} \tag{4}$$

where $\boldsymbol{T}$ is the tableau matrix of the circuit [11].

The application of sparse-matrix techniques to the circuit equations of system (4) is the sparse-tableau method, which has recently met with much approval, particularly for the analysis of nonlinear circuits in the time domain.

A method based on the solution of a system with a smaller number of equations consists in assuming only the node voltage vector $\boldsymbol{V}_N$ as unknown and in expressing system (3) in terms of these and of branch admittances:

$$\boldsymbol{Y}\boldsymbol{V}_N = \boldsymbol{J}_{N0} \tag{5}$$

where $\boldsymbol{J}_{N0}$ is the node impressed current vector and $\boldsymbol{Y}$ the nodal admittance matrix. The kth equation derives from the application of Kirchhoff's current law to node k. Referring to the circuit in Fig. 2(a), one gets, for example, the following equation for node 2:

$$-y_2V_1 + (y_2 + y_3 + y_8)V_2 - y_3V_4 = J_{10}. \tag{6}$$

$\boldsymbol{Y}$ may be obtained by means of the following rules easily deduced from (3).

1) Each diagonal term y_{ii} is the sum of all the admittances connected to node i.

2) Each off-diagonal term y_{ij} is the negative sum of all the transadmittances relative to current generators connected to node i, controlled by node-j voltage, and of all the admittances connected between node i and j.

The nodal admittance matrix does not lend itself to describing circuits including current-dependent current generators and dependent or independent voltage generators except by using special artifices such as the introduction of extra dummy nodes and dummy components [12]–[14]. By way of example, Fig. 3 shows that a current-dependent voltage generator may be represented by introducing two extra nodes and positive and negative impedances [12]. These artifices, however, besides pro-

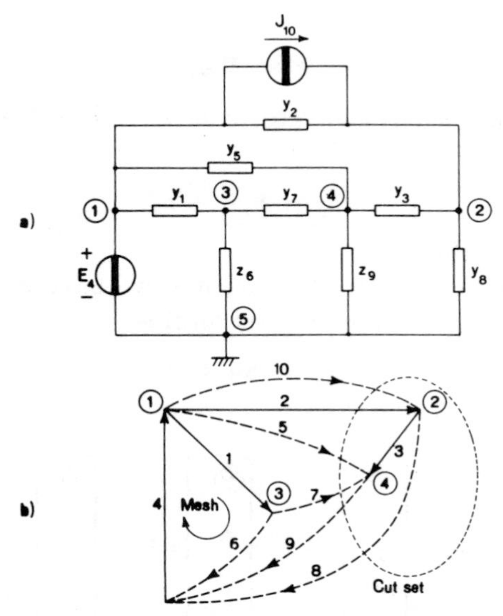

Fig. 2. (a) Lumped-element circuit. (b) Lumped-element circuit graph.

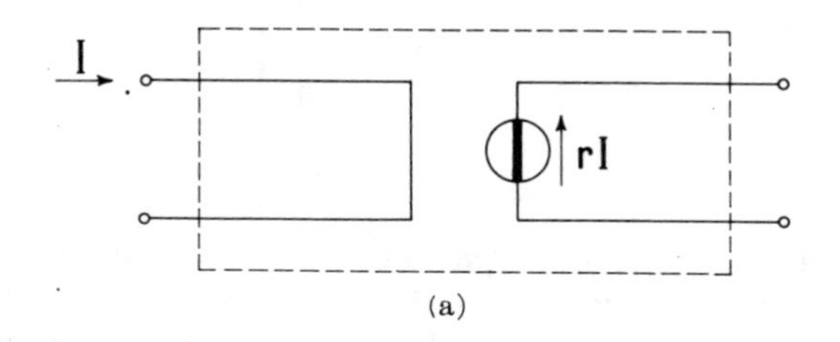

(a)

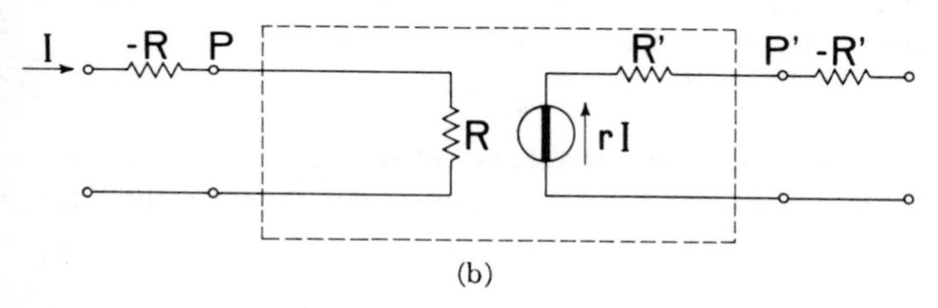

(b)

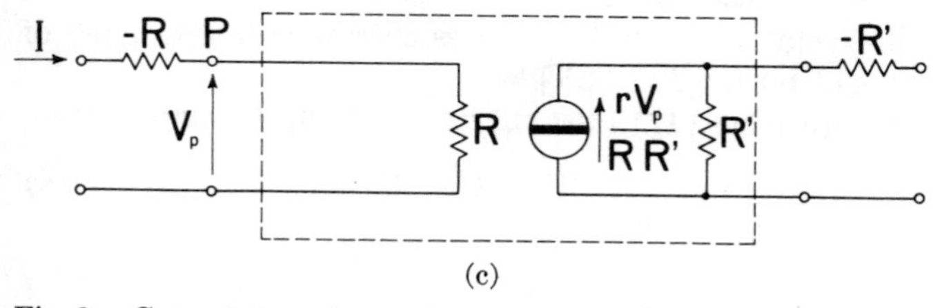

(c)

Fig. 3. Current-dependent voltage generator and its modeling with dummy nodes and components.

ducing an increase in the Y-matrix size, cause the presence of coefficients equal to 0 on the main diagonal; this second fact, as we shall see later, must be kept in mind when solving system (5). Moreover, roundoff errors might arise in the solution of (5) when, for example, the voltages of two nodes connected by one or more branches assume values very close to each other or when the Y coefficients assume widely different values.

These inconveniences are not manifested with the previously described tableau method. For the same reasons the modified tableau method [15], [16] and the mixed method [17], which are described hereunder, are, in some cases, preferable. In both these methods, in order to describe the topology, circuit branches are classified as tree branches and links.[1] Each link identifies a mesh composed of the link itself and those specific tree branches required to close the circuit. Each tree branch identifies a cut set that consists of this tree branch itself and the set of links cut by a closed line [see Fig. 2(b)]. Kirchhoff's voltage law applied to the meshes and Kirchhoff's current law applied to the cut sets give the topological relations

$$[C \quad 1_l]\begin{bmatrix} V_t \\ \\ V_l \end{bmatrix} = 0 \tag{7}$$

$$[1_t \quad -C^T]\begin{bmatrix} I_t \\ \\ I_l \end{bmatrix} = 0 \tag{8}$$

where V_t, I_t, and V_l, I_l are the voltage and current vectors of the tree branches and links, respectively; 1_l and 1_t are unit matrices, C is the branch-mesh matrix in which $c_{ij} = \pm 1$ if the branch j is in the mesh defined by link i, the sign depending on the branch and mesh orientation; $c_{ij} = 0$ if the tree branch is not in the mesh i; C^T is the transpose of C.

Separating the variables relative to the tree branches and the links, system (1) may be rewritten in the following form:

$$[H_1 \quad H_2]\begin{bmatrix} I_t \\ V_l \\ V_t \\ I_l \end{bmatrix} = [K] \tag{9}$$

where the meaning of the symbols H_1, H_2, and K can be deduced immediately from (1).

Collecting together the topological systems (7), (8), and the branch constitutive relations expressed by (9), one obtains the following system:

$$\left[\begin{array}{cc|cc} 1_t & 0 & 0 & -C^T \\ 0 & 1_l & C & 0 \\ \hline & H_1 & & H_2 \end{array}\right]\begin{bmatrix} I_t \\ V_l \\ \hline V_t \\ I_l \end{bmatrix} = \begin{bmatrix} 0 \\ 0 \\ \hline K \end{bmatrix} \tag{10}$$

whose coefficient matrix is the modified tableau.

The method based on this approach, which has recently been proposed, allows shorter computation time in its authors' opinion [16] compared to that required by the complete tableau, without loss of solution accuracy.

[1] A tree is made up of a set of branches that, in the circuit graph, make it possible to reach all the nodes without forming closed paths.

Another method requiring tree search and the consequent subdivision of the circuit branches into tree branches and links is the well-known mixed method on which ECAP II program is based [17]. The circuit branches are subdivided into two types, y and z: generally, y type with low admittance values and z type with low impedance values. A tree is built up by choosing the circuit branches in the following order: independent voltage generators, dependent voltage generators, y branches, and z branches. Independent voltage generators may not be chosen as links, nor current generators as tree branches, since these choices might imply a violation of the Kirchhoff laws. Thus the branches are classified in four categories: tree admittance branches, tree impedance branches, admittance links, and impedance links. The tree admittance branch voltages and the impedance link currents are assumed to be independent variables, and the circuit equations are written by applying the Kirchhoff current law for the cut sets identified by the tree admittance branches, and the Kirchhoff voltage law for the meshes identified by the impedance links.

By way of example for the cut set identified by branch 2 and for the mesh identified by link 6 in the circuit of Fig. 2(b), the following equations can be written:

$$y_2V_2 + y_5(V_2 + V_3) + y_7(V_2 + V_3 - V_1) - I_8 - I_9 = J_{10}$$

$$V_1 + Z_6I_6 = -E_4. \tag{11}$$

For the complete circuit the system can be written

$$\begin{bmatrix} \boldsymbol{Y}_t & \boldsymbol{N}_{yz} \\ \boldsymbol{N}_{zy} & \boldsymbol{Z}_l \end{bmatrix} \cdot \begin{bmatrix} \boldsymbol{V}_{yt} \\ \boldsymbol{I}_{zl} \end{bmatrix} = \begin{bmatrix} \boldsymbol{J}_{yt} \\ \boldsymbol{E}_{zl} \end{bmatrix} \tag{12}$$

where $\boldsymbol{V}_{yt}$ and $\boldsymbol{I}_{zl}$ are, respectively, the tree admittance branch voltage vector and the impedance link current vector; $\boldsymbol{Y}_t$ and $\boldsymbol{N}_{yz}$ are the coefficient matrices deriving from the cut-set equations, $\boldsymbol{N}_{zy}$ and $\boldsymbol{Z}_l$ the coefficient matrices from the mesh equations; $\boldsymbol{J}_{yt}$ is the vector of the cut-set equivalent independent current generators, and $\boldsymbol{E}_{zl}$ the vector of the mesh equivalent independent voltage generators.

System (12) cannot generally be obtained by simple rules without searching the tree or using the topological matrices. This is not, however, the proper place to go into greater detail and the reader is referred to the works by Branin [10], [17].

III. Circuit Analysis in Terms of Wave Variables

The behavior of a microwave circuit may also be described in terms of the normalized wave variables at the ports of the component multiports.[2] Given a circuit with m component multiports, for each component with scattering matrix $\boldsymbol{S}_i$ the vectors $\boldsymbol{a}_i$ and $\boldsymbol{b}_i$ of incident and reflected waves at its n_i ports are related by the following equation:

$$\boldsymbol{b}_i = \boldsymbol{S}_i\boldsymbol{a}_i. \tag{13}$$

An independent generator is described, instead, by the relation

$$b_g = S_ga_g + c_g \tag{14}$$

where c_g is the impressed wave.

Considering all the components, we have a system of linear equations whose matrix form is

$$\boldsymbol{b} = \boldsymbol{S}\boldsymbol{a} + \boldsymbol{c} \tag{15}$$

where

$$\boldsymbol{a} = \begin{bmatrix} \boldsymbol{a}_1 \\ \boldsymbol{a}_2 \\ \vdots \\ \boldsymbol{a}_m \end{bmatrix}, \quad \boldsymbol{b} = \begin{bmatrix} \boldsymbol{b}_1 \\ \boldsymbol{b}_2 \\ \vdots \\ \boldsymbol{b}_m \end{bmatrix}, \quad \boldsymbol{c} = \begin{bmatrix} \boldsymbol{c}_1 \\ \boldsymbol{c}_2 \\ \vdots \\ \boldsymbol{c}_m \end{bmatrix}$$

and

$$\boldsymbol{S} = \begin{bmatrix} \boldsymbol{S}_1 & \cdot & 0 & \cdot & 0 \\ \cdot & \cdot & \cdot & \cdot & \cdot \\ 0 & \cdot & \boldsymbol{S}_i & \cdot & 0 \\ \cdot & \cdot & \cdot & \cdot & \cdot \\ 0 & \cdot & 0 & \cdot & \boldsymbol{S}_m \end{bmatrix}. \tag{16}$$

The connections between the m components impose constraints on the vectors $\boldsymbol{a}$ and $\boldsymbol{b}$; in fact, incident and reflected waves at ports j and k connected together must satisfy the following relations (see Fig. 4):

$$a_j = b_k \qquad a_k = b_j$$

if the normalization numbers are the same. The relations for all the circuit component ports may be put in the form

$$\boldsymbol{b} = \boldsymbol{\Gamma}\boldsymbol{a} \tag{17}$$

where $\boldsymbol{\Gamma}$ is the connection matrix whose elements are all null except the 1's in the entries corresponding to pairs of adjacent ports [22]–[25].[3]

Substituting (17) into (15) and solving for $\boldsymbol{a}$ by setting

$$\boldsymbol{W} = \boldsymbol{\Gamma} - \boldsymbol{S} \tag{18}$$

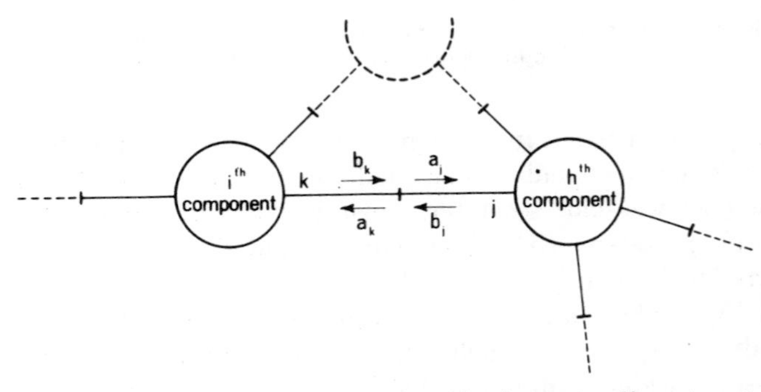

Fig. 4. Constraints imposed by connection between adjacent ports.

[2] It is always possible to transform a lumped-element network into a circuit made up of multiports connected through pairs of ports [18]–[21].

[3] It would be easy to define the connection matrix, also, when different normalization numbers are chosen for adjacent ports [26].

we have

$$Wa = c \tag{19}$$

where c is the vector of the impressed waves and W is the connection scattering matrix. Its main diagonal elements are the reflection coefficients at component ports; the other W elements are all null except those relative to ports belonging to the same component (the transmission coefficients) and those relative to ports connected together (the Γ elements). Numerical values of nonzero elements change with the frequency except the 1's indicating connections.

IV. Multiport Connection Methods

Considerable reduction of computing time and memory space requirements in analyzing large circuits can be achieved by dividing the circuit into subcircuits and calculating for each of them one of its port matrices. Subsequently, the subcircuits are interconnected and, finally, the matrix relative to the ports of the complete circuit is determined.

A method based on these principles has been proposed by Murray-Lasso for the BELLNAP program [12], [27] employing the indefinite admittance matrix, which is simply the nodal admittance matrix defined in Section II, but referred to a datum node outside the circuit. The nodes of every subcircuit are divided into internal and external. By eliminating the variables relative to the internal nodes, one obtains the indefinite admittance matrix relative to the external nodes.

Every indefinite admittance matrix is subdivided as follows:

$$\begin{bmatrix} I_e \\ \\ I_i \end{bmatrix} = \begin{bmatrix} Y_{ee} & Y_{ei} \\ \\ Y_{ie} & Y_{ii} \end{bmatrix} \begin{bmatrix} V_e \\ \\ V_i \end{bmatrix} \tag{20}$$

where I_e and V_e are the vectors of the currents and voltages relative to the external nodes, and I_i and V_i are those relative to the internal nodes. Since no generators are connected to the internal nodes, we can take $I_i = 0$ and, solving with respect to V_i in the second set of equations of (20), one has

$$V_i = -Y_{ii}^{-1} Y_{ie} V_e. \tag{21}$$

Substituting (21) in the first set of (20) one gets

$$I_e = Y_e V_e \tag{22}$$

with

$$Y_e = Y_{ee} - Y_{ei} Y_{ii}^{-1} Y_{ie} \tag{23}$$

which represents the indefinite admittance matrix with respect to the external ports of each subcircuit. When the subcircuits are connected together, the indefinite admittance matrix for the external nodes of the complete circuit is calculated using the same procedure.

Some programs that use the S-matrix formulation [23], [24] are also based on the same principle, that is, on determining the port matrix of the circuit obtained by interconnecting a number of components. These programs are mainly microwave circuit oriented.

Evaluation of the scattering matrix of a circuit composed of multiports connected through pairs of ports in terms of component S parameters is effected by dividing component ports into connected and nonconnected ones. Then by partitioning system (15) and letting $c = 0$, since independent generators will be considered connected to external ports, one obtains

$$\begin{bmatrix} b_p \\ \\ b_c \end{bmatrix} = \begin{bmatrix} S_{pp} & S_{pc} \\ \\ S_{cp} & S_{cc} \end{bmatrix} \begin{bmatrix} a_p \\ \\ a_c \end{bmatrix} \tag{24}$$

where a_p, b_p and a_c, b_c are the normalized waves at the p external ports and at the c internal connected ones. The constraints between connected ports yield

$$b_c = \Gamma a_c \tag{25}$$

where Γ is the connection matrix previously defined in Section III. From (24) and (25), by first eliminating b_c, one obtains

$$a_c = (\Gamma - S_{cc})^{-1} S_{cp} a_p. \tag{26}$$

Then, by eliminating a_c,

$$b_p = S_p a_p \tag{27}$$

where

$$S_p = S_{pp} + S_{pc}(\Gamma - S_{cc})^{-1} S_{cp} \tag{28}$$

is the scattering matrix of the microwave circuit at its p external ports. It can be determined in terms of the S matrices of its component multiports by relation (28). For a circuit comprising many components, the computing time is, however, too long due primarily to the inversion of a matrix with order equal to the number of connected ports.

Great running time reduction is obtained in the program SCAMAT [23] by connecting the m component multiports of the complete circuit two at a time and determining the S matrix of the resulting subcircuit every time. In such a manner, after (m-1) applications of (28), the S matrix of the complete network is computed. The number of arithmetical operations necessary to compute the S matrix for a given circuit topology depends on the order according to which the components are connected to each other.

In order to minimize computing time a connection sequence based on an easily programmable rule has been proposed that implies a number of algebraic operations at all times very near to the minimum, whatever the circuit topology. The rule consists of connecting every time the two components whose resultant multiport has the smallest number of ports.

The application of this method to circuits including lumped elements is done by transforming every component having n terminals into a multiport with n ports. The transformation is carried out by associating a ground terminal with each component terminal, and these terminal pairs are considered as ports [19], [20]. When a component has one of its n terminals connected to ground, it is considered a multiport having (n-1) ports; all the ports in such a case derive by pairing the ground terminal with the other (n-1) terminals. The multiports thus obtained are connected together to form the network. Since the program connects only pair of ports, auxiliary multiports that transform every node with k branches into a multiport with k ports are introduced. These auxiliary multiports are parallel tees (Fig. 5) introduced at the rate of (k-2) tees for every node connecting k branches. The introduction of the auxiliary multiports and the transformation of every n-terminal component into an (n-1) port or n port is made automatically by the program through interpretation of the input data.

In addition to the characterizing parameters, the data for every component indicate to which nodes its terminals are connected. The interconnection modalities between real and auxiliary components are then found and the connection sequence stated. After this preliminary phase, which is performed only once for a given circuit with m components, the execution phase begins and consists of applying (28) (m-1) times for every frequency point.

A similar formulation has been adopted in the program General [9]. It requires the user to decompose the circuit into wire-coupling multiports and original components, then a formula similar to (28) is applied repeatedly, starting from the last subnetwork. The circuit decomposition required appears, however, too cumbersome for the user.

Determination of the matrix of the multiport resulting from the connection of two components can be effected with more simple rules than (23) or (28) if matricial representation of the components is suitably chosen. Indeed, rules that determine the matrix of the multiport resulting from the connection of two multiport components are well known [28]. For the various types of connections, they require the components to be defined according to different matricial representations. The simplicity of these connection rules has brought about their widespread use in a number of general and special-purpose programs [9], [29]–[35]. In these programs the matrix relative to the external ports of the complete circuit is determined by connecting the components in twos, each time determining the matrix of the resulting multiports in accordance with rules codified in library routines. Table I shows, by way of example, some of the most widely used rules in the case of connections between 2-port components. It may, however, happen that the matricial representation required by the type of the connection to be made may not exist for some components. Besides, the method may call for numerous matrix transformations, which sometimes cause a loss of accuracy.

The types of connections and the sequence in which they are made are generally decided by the user. This last, apparently difficult, operation is considerably simplified by using high-level languages for circuit description. A particularly interesting one is MARTHA, proposed by Penfield [21], [35]. It consists of defining a certain number of wiring operators by means of which connections between components may be simply and concisely identified and described. The order of writing the operators establishes the order for carrying out the connections by the program. By way of example the simple circuit in Fig. 6 is described using the wiring operators shown in Table I. The number of wiring operators permitted by

TABLE I
VARIOUS TYPES OF CONNECTION BETWEEN TWO PORTS—MATRIX OPERATIONS INVOLVED AND MARTHA WIRING OPERATORS

CONNECTION TYPE		Matrix Operation	MARTHA Wiring Operator
Parallel	(Y: Y_1, Y_2)	$Y = Y_1 + Y_2$	WPP
Series	(Z: Z_1, Z_2)	$Z = Z_1 + Z_2$	WSS
Series-parallel	(H: H_1, H_2)	$H = H_1 + H_2$	WSP
Parallel-series	(G: G_1, G_2)	$G = G_1 + G_2$	WPS
Cascade	(T_1, T_2)	$T = T_1 \times T_2$	WC

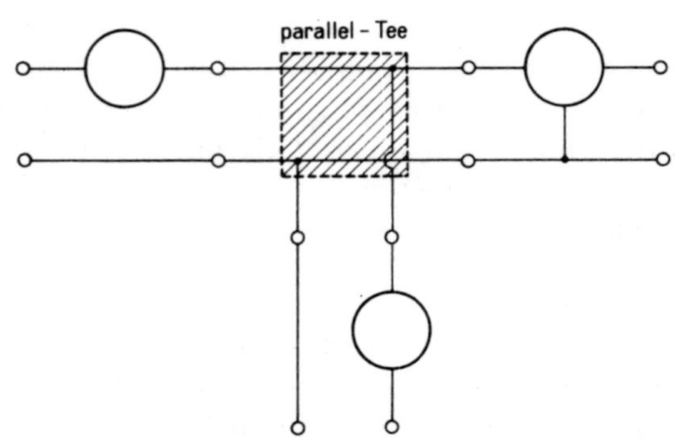

Fig. 5. Parallel tee as auxiliary multiport.

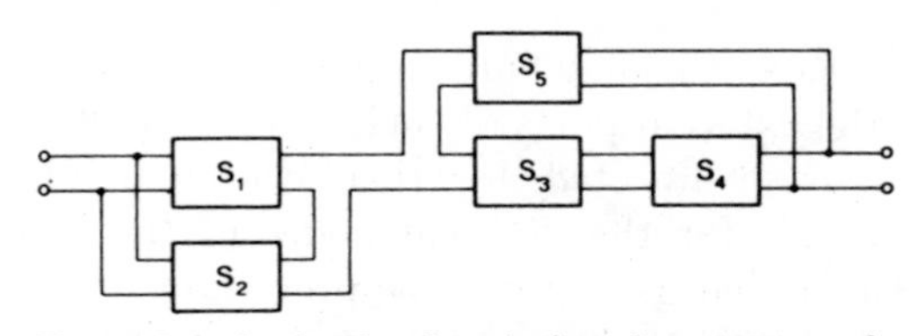

Fig. 6. Example of circuit description by means of MARTHA language. MARTHA description: (S_1 WPS S_2)WC((S_3 WC S_4)WSP S_5).

MARTHA is such as to allow considerable generality in the type of circuit that may be analyzed.

V. Sparse-Matrix Approach

Many methods have been proposed for the solution of linear systems with sparse coefficient matrices [36]–[39]. Evaluation of their efficiency is not, however, one of the aims of this work, so the description, though brief, is limited to the LU-factorization method [3], which is most frequently applied in the field of electric networks. According to this method the solution of the system $\boldsymbol{Mx} = \boldsymbol{c}$ is carried out first by factoring $\boldsymbol{M}$ into the product of two matrices, a lower triangular matrix $\boldsymbol{L}$ and an upper triangular matrix with 1's on the diagonal $\boldsymbol{U}$:

$$\boldsymbol{M} = \boldsymbol{LU} = \begin{bmatrix} l_{11} & \cdot & 0 & \cdot & 0 & \cdot & 0 \\ \cdot & \cdot & \cdot & \cdot & \cdot & \cdot & \cdot \\ l_{k1} & \cdot & l_{kk} & \cdot & 0 & \cdot & 0 \\ \cdot & \cdot & \cdot & \cdot & \cdot & \cdot & \cdot \\ l_{i1} & \cdot & l_{ik} & \cdot & l_{ii} & \cdot & 0 \\ \cdot & \cdot & \cdot & \cdot & \cdot & \cdot & \cdot \\ l_{n1} & \cdot & l_{nk} & \cdot & l_{ni} & \cdot & l_{nn} \end{bmatrix} \cdot \begin{bmatrix} 1 & \cdot & u_{1k} & \cdot & u_{ij} & \cdot & u_{1n} \\ \cdot & \cdot & \cdot & \cdot & \cdot & \cdot & \cdot \\ 0 & \cdot & 1 & \cdot & u_{kj} & \cdot & u_{kn} \\ \cdot & \cdot & \cdot & \cdot & \cdot & \cdot & \cdot \\ 0 & \cdot & 0 & \cdot & 1 & \cdot & u_{jn} \\ \cdot & \cdot & \cdot & \cdot & \cdot & \cdot & \cdot \\ 0 & \cdot & 0 & \cdot & 0 & \cdot & 1 \end{bmatrix}. \tag{29}$$

The elements of $\boldsymbol{L}$ and $\boldsymbol{U}$ are determined by recurrence formulas as follows:

$$l_{ik} = m_{ik} - \sum_{\mu=1}^{k-1} l_{i\mu}u_{\mu k}, \qquad i \geq k$$

$$u_{kk} = 1$$

$$u_{kj} = (m_{kj} - \sum_{\mu=1}^{k-1} l_{k\mu}u_{\mu j})/l_{kk}, \qquad j > k \tag{30}$$

for $k = 1,2,\cdots,n$, where n is the matrix dimension. Then by solving the two triangular systems

$$\boldsymbol{Ly} = \boldsymbol{c} \qquad \boldsymbol{Ux} = \boldsymbol{y} \tag{31}$$

using "forward elimination" on $\boldsymbol{Ly} = \boldsymbol{c}$ and "back substitution" on $\boldsymbol{Ux} = \boldsymbol{y}$, the unknown vector $\boldsymbol{x}$ is obtained [3]. This is performed by applying the recurrence formulas:

$$y_j = (c_j - \sum_{\mu=1}^{j-1} l_{j\mu}y_\mu)/l_{jj}, \qquad j = 1,2,\cdots,n$$

$$x_j = y_j - \sum_{\mu=j+1}^{n} u_{j\mu}x_\mu, \qquad j = n,n-1,\cdots,1. \tag{32}$$

All the elements of $\boldsymbol{L}$ and $\boldsymbol{U}$ can be stored in a matrix:

$$\boldsymbol{Q} = \boldsymbol{L} + \boldsymbol{U} - 1 \tag{33}$$

1 being unit matrix. Any q_{jk} of $\boldsymbol{Q}$ is 0 if both m_{jk} of $\boldsymbol{M}$ and all the products $q_{ji}q_{ik}$, $1 \leq i \leq \min\{j-1,k-1\}$ are 0. Therefore, the number of nonzeros in $\boldsymbol{Q}$ depends on the ordering of rows and columns in $\boldsymbol{M}$, as is discussed later. The nonzeros in $\boldsymbol{Q}$ in the entries corresponding to zeros in $\boldsymbol{M}$ are currently called "fills."

A great reduction in execution time is obtained with the reduced Crout method [40], according to which only the nonzero operands are considered in computing the nonzeros of $\boldsymbol{Q}$. Two different strategies are used to this end. The first consists of creating a sequence of indices and pointers that establish the type of operation to be carried out and the position of the operands in the tables where the operands are stored [41]–[43]. The second method consists of generating a no-loop no-branch code containing the instructions to perform all the necessary operations.

The second method is very fast in execution but requires large memory space due to the need to store the generated code and high central processing unit time to generate the code itself. On the other hand, the first method, though slower in execution, requires less time for preparation of the sequence of indices and pointers and much less memory space. Memory requirements make the code generation method unsuitable for very large networks like power distribution networks [44], while it is widespread for electronic circuit analysis both with lumped [11], [16] and distributed elements [25].

The solution code may be generated either in machine language or in a high-level language such as Fortran. In the first case it requires shorter execution time but has the inconvenience of being machine dependent. Generation time, execution time, and storage requirements depend on the length of the code, which depends in turn on the number of nonzeros in $\boldsymbol{Q}$ and $\boldsymbol{c}$ and, therefore, on the number and position of nonzeros in $\boldsymbol{M}$.

With the aim of minimizing code length, numerous reordering algorithms of the $\boldsymbol{M}$-matrix coefficients have been proposed. In all these algorithms the accuracy problem must be kept in mind; this requires the rows and the columns of the $\boldsymbol{M}$ matrix to be rearranged so that the diagonal elements are nonzero, since they are used as divisors in (30) and (32). To this end, depending on the circuit matrix adopted, some rules are established to avoid pivoting on the critical elements.

For circuits described by the nodal admittance matrix ($\boldsymbol{M} \equiv \boldsymbol{Y}$), the diagonal term m_{ii} represents the sum of admittances connected to the ith node and, therefore, it is different from 0 except in particular cases.[4] For this reason the reordering algorithms for $\boldsymbol{Y}$ matrix keep these terms on the diagonal while ordering the rows and columns to minimize the code length. This is equivalent to circuit node renumbering. This procedure is based on the supposition that nonzero elements on the $\boldsymbol{Y}$ diagonal are a sufficient guarantee that the elements on the $\boldsymbol{Q}$ diagonal

[4] When certain components are modeled by introducing extra dummy nodes or dummy components, the corresponding diagonal positions cannot be pivoted [13].

will be nonzero. The node renumbering algorithms most frequently used for the Y matrix are reported in the following [41], [43], [44].

1) The nodes are ordered so that the number of nonzeros in the corresponding rows are nondecreasing.

2) At every jth step the node is selected whose corresponding row has fewer nonzeros on the right of the $(j-1)$th entry.

3) Select as jth step the node whose corresponding row and column, when used in factorization, would cause the smallest number of fills.

For the connection scattering matrix $\boldsymbol{W}$, on the other hand, as described in Section III, the diagonal elements represent the reflection coefficients of the circuit component ports and, therefore, being very near to 0 in matched conditions, cannot be chosen as pivots. However, in system (19) every row of $\boldsymbol{W}$ contains the constant 1, deriving from $\boldsymbol{\Gamma}$, which could be an ideal pivot because it allows great precision, independent of frequency, and, at the same time, divisions are avoided. In reality, roughly half the 1's are modified in the course of the factorization process, but rarely do the modified values become 0 and only in anomalous cases. This method has been adopted in a recently realized program for microwave circuit analysis [25] with the following ordering strategy: the pair of rows relative to adjacent ports are considered together and ordered so that each pair has a number of nonzeros not greater than that of the successive one; in every pair the row with fewer nonzeros precedes the other; the columns are then ordered to place all the 1's of $\boldsymbol{\Gamma}$ on diagonal.

The programs adopting the code generation techniques are, therefore, structured in two phases. In the first, after data input and interpretation, coefficient matrix row and column ordering is established according to the algorithm used and the solution code is generated. In the second phase the matrix coefficient values are determined for every frequency point and then the code is executed, giving the unknown variable values in terms of which the requested network functions are determined.

The time required for the first phase is generally very high, but it should be remembered that for a given circuit the code is generated only once, while the code itself is executed many times and may be repeated at any later time if it is stored in a permanent file. Analogous considerations may be done for the structure of the programs creating a sequence of pointers and indices.

However, for very simple circuits not requiring many analysis repetitions, it may be more convenient both for computing time and memory space to use programs of the type described in Section IV, whose preliminary phase is less complex. In order to supply quantitative information the circuit in Fig. 7, representing a thin-film strip-line branching filter [25], has been analyzed with two programs realized by the authors: the BMT program adopting a sparse-matrix technique and the SCAMAT program effecting connection of multiports two at a time. The relative computing time versus the number of executions is shown in Fig. 8.

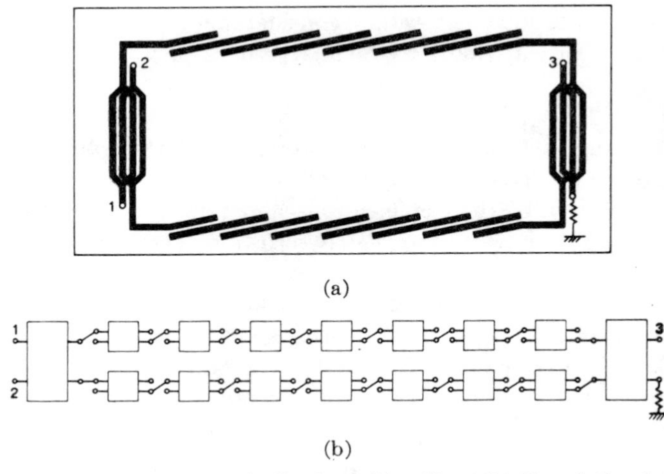

(a)

(b)

Fig. 7. (a) Thin-film strip-line branching filter. (b) Description for analysis program.

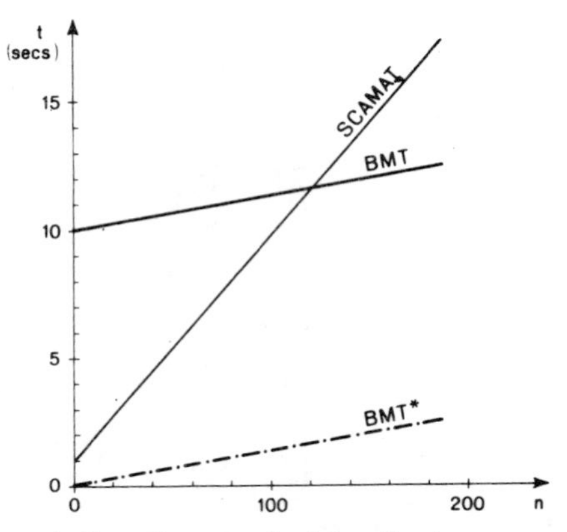

Fig. 8. Computation time required by the two programs SCAMAT and BMT versus number of analyses effected for branching filter in Fig. 6. Dotted line refers to case for which execution code has already been generated and compiled.

This figure shows that for the circuit analyzed, the first phase of the BMT program is ten times slower, while the second phase is seven times faster. Then, when more than 120 executions (different frequency points or parameters values) are required, the code generation method is more convenient. However, when the code is already available, the dotted line must be considered and the convenience of the BMT program is evident.

VI. First- and Second-Order Sensitivity

A performance generally required of circuit analysis programs is the computation of the partial derivatives (sensitivities) of the network functions with respect to the variables on which the component parameters depend. It is useful for the designer to know them both in order to have an indication of circuit criticality relative to the variables themselves, and in order to utilize the sensitivities in calculating particular network functions (group delay, for example) and in optimization processes.

Simple determination of the sensitivities by means of the variational method may cause computation errors that depend on the intrinsic precision of the program and the increment chosen for the independent variables. Computing time may, besides, be too high when derivatives with respect to many parameters are requested. It is for these reasons that other techniques are used in the important programs; among these the adjoint circuit method has met with much favor in recent years [45]–[61]. It must, however, be noted that the most convenient technique depends on the analysis method used by the program. The best known among recently proposed methods are illustrated below, and a comparison is made between them in relation to the adopted method of analysis.

Where circuit analysis consists of the solution of a system of the type

$$\boldsymbol{M}\boldsymbol{x} = \boldsymbol{c} \tag{34}$$

where $\boldsymbol{x}$ is the circuit variable vector (voltages, currents, or normalized waves) and $\boldsymbol{M}$ is a matrix that takes topology and circuit composition into account (nodal admittance, matrix, mixed matrix, connection scattering matrix, etc.), computation of the partial derivatives of the vector $\boldsymbol{x}$ with respect to any single parameter p on which the circuit components depend may be carried out by differentiating (34):

$$\boldsymbol{M}\frac{\partial \boldsymbol{x}}{\partial p} = -\frac{\partial \boldsymbol{M}}{\partial p}\boldsymbol{x} + \frac{\partial \boldsymbol{c}}{\partial p}. \tag{35}$$

This equation may be solved for $\partial \boldsymbol{x}/\partial p$ by evaluating the right-hand side vector:

$$\boldsymbol{c}' = -\frac{\partial \boldsymbol{M}}{\partial p}\boldsymbol{x} + \frac{\partial \boldsymbol{c}}{\partial p} \tag{36}$$

which may be calculated when $\partial \boldsymbol{M}/\partial p$ and $\partial \boldsymbol{c}/\partial p$ are known and $\boldsymbol{x}$, by solving (34), has been determined.

Determination of vector $\partial \boldsymbol{x}/\partial p$ by means of (35) requires only forward and back (FB) substitution since the LU factorization already done for the solution of (34) may be utilized. If sparse-matrix techniques are adopted, FB substitution may be performed by executing the same code (or the same set of pointers and indices) as that generated for the analysis, provided that the code has been generated without considering the sparsity of vector $\boldsymbol{c}$, since its sparseness structure is generally different from that of $\boldsymbol{c}'$.

This direct method permits determination of the sensitivity of all the elements of $\boldsymbol{x}$ with respect to a single parameter p, and the computing effort involved is only slightly higher than that of the original analysis. If the sensitivities of all elements of $\boldsymbol{x}$ are requested with respect to several parameters, as many FB substitutions are required as there are parameters.

If the sensitivities of only one element of $\boldsymbol{x}$ are requested with respect to many parameters, it may be convenient to adopt the adjoint network method proposed by Director and Rohrer [45], [46], deriving it from Tellegen's theorem [62], [63]. This method has in recent years been subject of numerous studies [45]–[61] and the reader is referred to them for detailed information. Here, a method is presented that provides (in certain cases) results similar to the adjoint method. The derivation is quite straightforward and involves only matrix operations [25], [65].

Indicating by

$$\boldsymbol{\gamma}_j^T = [0 \quad 0 \cdots 0 \quad 1 \quad 0 \cdots 0] \tag{37}$$

a row vector whose elements are all null except a 1 in position j, we have

$$\frac{\partial x_j}{\partial p} = \boldsymbol{\gamma}_j^T \frac{\partial \boldsymbol{x}}{\partial p}. \tag{38}$$

Keeping (35) in mind this becomes

$$\frac{\partial x_j}{\partial p} = -\boldsymbol{\gamma}_j^T \boldsymbol{M}^{-1}\left(\frac{\partial \boldsymbol{M}}{\partial p}\boldsymbol{x} - \frac{\partial \boldsymbol{c}}{\partial p}\right) = \boldsymbol{\xi}_j^T\left(\frac{\partial \boldsymbol{M}}{\partial p}\boldsymbol{x} + \frac{\partial \boldsymbol{c}}{\partial p}\right) \tag{39}$$

having indicated by

$$\boldsymbol{\xi}_j = (\boldsymbol{\gamma}_j^T \boldsymbol{M}^{-1})^T = (\boldsymbol{M}^T)^{-1}\boldsymbol{\gamma}_j \tag{40}$$

the vector of the unknowns of a system of equations whose coefficient matrix is equal to the transpose of that characterizing the circuit being analyzed and having $\boldsymbol{\gamma}_j$ as its right-hand side vector.

Supposing for simplicity $\partial \boldsymbol{c}/\partial p = 0$, (39) is reduced to

$$\frac{\partial x_j}{\partial p} = -\boldsymbol{\xi}_j^T \frac{\partial \boldsymbol{M}}{\partial p}\boldsymbol{x} \tag{41}$$

which can be used to compute sensitivity of variable x_j with respect to any p parameter when vectors $\boldsymbol{x}$ and $\boldsymbol{\xi}_j$ have been computed by solving systems (34) and (40).

This method, which in the following is called the transpose-matrix method, is in some cases similar to the adjoint method. In fact considering, for instance, the connection scattering matrix (that is, letting $\boldsymbol{M} \equiv \boldsymbol{W}$) we have from (18)

$$\boldsymbol{W}^T = (\boldsymbol{\Gamma} - \boldsymbol{S})^T = \boldsymbol{\Gamma} - \boldsymbol{S}^T$$

being $\boldsymbol{\Gamma} = \boldsymbol{\Gamma}^T$; thus $\boldsymbol{W}^T$ may be interpreted as the connection scattering matrix of a new circuit with the same topology as the one being examined and components whose scattering matrices are the transposes of the corresponding ones in the original circuit. In this case, $\boldsymbol{\xi}_j^T$ represents the vector of the incident waves at the new circuit component ports with excitations stated by $\boldsymbol{\gamma}_j$. The equivalence between this method and the adjoint circuit method is then evident [48].

The same consideration can be made with reference to the nodal admittance matrix. Indeed, $\boldsymbol{\xi}_j$ in this case may be interpreted as the nodal voltage vector of the adjoint circuit, which, as it is known, has a matrix equal to the transpose of the original one and is excited as established by $\boldsymbol{\gamma}_j$ [51].

When the mixed method is adopted for analysis, the transpose of the coefficient matrix in (12) does not coincide with the matrix of the adjoint circuit due to the sign reversals of its off-diagonal submatrices. However, the transpose matrix method can be equally adopted and the results are identical to those derived by means of the adjoint network.[5]

In order to make the reader aware of the computing effort in determining sensitivity with (41), we observe that computation of $\boldsymbol{\xi}_j$ involves only a single FB substitution [14], [64] for the following reason. Since

$$M^T = (LU)^T = U^T L^T = \mathcal{L}\mathcal{U}$$

it is not necessary to repeat factorization in order to compute $\mathcal{L}$ and $\mathcal{U}$, as these are obtainable through transposition of U and L, respectively. When sparse-matrix techniques are used with code generation it should be noted that the FB-substitution code generated for the analysis cannot be utilized; thus a modified code should be generated for the FB substitution applied to $\mathcal{L}$ and $\mathcal{U}$. If, however, M^T has the same sparseness structure as M, differing at the most in the values of some nonzero coefficients, then $\boldsymbol{\xi}_j$ can be determined starting from M^T by executing the LU-factorization and FB-substitution codes already generated for the analysis. When M represents the connection scattering matrix W and if all the parameters of the components are considered to be different from 0 the analysis code may be used; the same thing takes place with the nodal admittance matrix if we consider as nonzero the coefficients in locations symmetrical to those of the dependent generators. Thus with two complete code executions in addition to the supplementary operations[6] required by (41), the sensitivity of one variable x_j may be computed for many parameters.

A quantitative comparison between this method and the direct one cannot be effected in general. It is, however, noted that the direct method is preferable when the derivatives of many variables with respect to few parameters are required, while the transpose-matrix method is more convenient when the derivatives of few variables with respect to many parameters are to be calculated. However, it is observed that if sparse-matrix techniques are used, the choice between the two methods may be conditioned by other factors such as, for example, general organization of the program.

Calculation of sensitivity by the direct method and the adjoint circuit are not equally convenient when multiport connection methods, described in Section IV, are adopted for the analysis. In this case, in fact, the variables relative to internal nodes or ports of the circuit are not normally calculated. It is, however, always possible to include routines in the program that, on the basis of suitable algorithms [56], [57], [66], make it possible to calculate the voltage and currents or the wave variables relative to the internal ports in terms of component parameters and of the impressed vectors. These routines may, however, bring about a considerable increase in program complexity and thus, considering also that these programs are usually utilized for analyzing circuits that are not too large and that have a particular topology, it may be convenient to do the sensitivity computation by means of variational techniques. These techniques have the advantage of directly supplying the sensitivity of the required network functions, which are often complicated functions of the derivatives $\partial \boldsymbol{x}/\partial p$.

To compute second-order sensitivity, (35) may be differentiated with respect to a new variable q and, for simplicity, supposing $\boldsymbol{c}$ independent of p and q, one obtains the second-order sensitivity expression

$$\frac{\partial^2 \boldsymbol{x}}{\partial p \partial q} = -M^{-1}\left(\frac{\partial^2 M}{\partial p \partial q} x + \frac{\partial M}{\partial p}\frac{\partial \boldsymbol{x}}{\partial q} + \frac{\partial M}{\partial q}\frac{\partial \boldsymbol{x}}{\partial p}\right). \qquad (42)$$

As in the first-order sensitivity case, by introducing vector $\boldsymbol{\gamma}_j$ the following relation is obtained:

$$\frac{\partial^2 x_j}{\partial p \partial q} = -\boldsymbol{\xi}_j^T \frac{\partial^2 M}{\partial p \partial q} x - \boldsymbol{\xi}_j^T\left(\frac{\partial M}{\partial p}\frac{\partial \boldsymbol{x}}{\partial q} - \frac{\partial M}{\partial q}\frac{\partial \boldsymbol{x}}{\partial p}\right) \qquad (43)$$

which allows computation of the second-order sensitivity of variable x_j with respect to parameters p and q.

The application of (43) in determining the second-order sensitivity is very convenient, especially when the analysis program is based on the generation of the LU-factorization and FB-substitution codes. In fact it involves two complete code executions for determining vectors $\boldsymbol{x}$ and $\boldsymbol{\xi}_j$ and two more executions of the FB-substitution code for evaluating $\partial \boldsymbol{x}/\partial p$ and $\partial \boldsymbol{x}/\partial q$. When the second-order sensitivities of the same variable x_j with respect to m different parameters have to be computed, the FB-substitution code must be executed m times. For a more detailed discussion the reader is referred to [78].

VII. Results of Some Analyzed Circuits

The analysis programs based on the methods described in the preceding sections allow determination for every assigned set of component parameter values and for every frequency point the values of the circuit variables considered as unknowns. In terms of these variables, the response functions of the circuit required by the user must be computed. For this reason, programs usually contain library routines for computation of the most common functions such as: voltage and current insertion gain; input and output impedances; loss attenuation; reflection coefficients at circuit ports; etc. It is often interesting also to determine group delay and/or the sensitivities of the above functions with respect to certain parameters; to this end one must also know the partial derivatives of the circuit variables with respect to the parameters themselves. When the functions to be calculated are not contained in the library, it must be possible for the user to insert new specially written routines into the program.

In order to give the reader an idea of the functions that

[5] See Branin [65] for a detailed discussion.
[6] The sparsity of $\partial \mathbf{M}/\partial p$ and $\partial \mathbf{c}/\partial p$ may be taken into account.

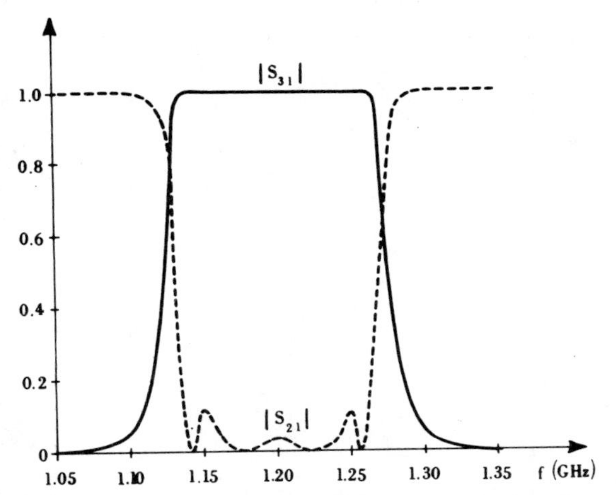

Fig. 9. Computed transmission coefficients S_{31} and S_{21} of branching filter in Fig. 6.

may be requested, the results of the analyses carried out by the authors on some circuits are reported. Numerous other examples of considerable interest are described in the works mentioned in the References.

With reference to the circuit already shown in Fig. 7 representing a branching filter implemented on an alumina ceramic substrate by thin-film technology, the amplitudes of the transmission coefficients S_{31} and S_{21} have been computed and plotted versus frequency in Fig. 9. The analysis was done with the BMT program, which utilizes the connection scattering matrix $\boldsymbol{W}$ to describe the circuit and adopts the sparse-matrix technique with code generation to determine the normalized wave vector. The circuit has been described for the program as shown in Fig. 6(b), connecting port 1 to a matched generator with impressed wave $c_g = 1$, ports 2 and 3 to matched loads, and all the other ports to open-circuit terminations. The transmission coefficients S_{21} and S_{31} coincide, in this case, with the waves b_2 and b_3 reflected by ports 2 and 3:

$$S_{21} = (b_2)_{a_1=1} \qquad S_{31} = (b_3)_{a_1=1}.$$

The condition $a_1 = 1$ is imposed by the generator connected to port 1. The S parameters of the coupled-transmission microstrip have been computed by means of routines [67] associated to the program in terms of the geometric dimensions and electrical characteristics. For the same circuit, using the direct method illustrated in Section VI, computations have been made for group delay:

$$\tau_{31} = \frac{\partial \beta_{31}}{\partial \omega} = \mathrm{Im}\left(\frac{1}{b_3}\frac{\partial b_3}{\partial \omega}\right)$$

where $\beta_{31} = \measuredangle b_3$ and the magnitude sensitivity M_ϵ with respect to the permittivity ϵ of the ceramic substrate is

$$M_\epsilon = \frac{\partial \ln |b_3|}{\partial \ln \epsilon} = \epsilon \,\mathrm{Re}\left[\frac{1}{b_3}\frac{\partial b_3}{\partial \epsilon}\right].$$

The computed results are shown in Fig. 10.

The circuit in Fig. 11 has been analyzed by the SCAMAT program, which is based on the multiport connection method after transformation of the circuit components

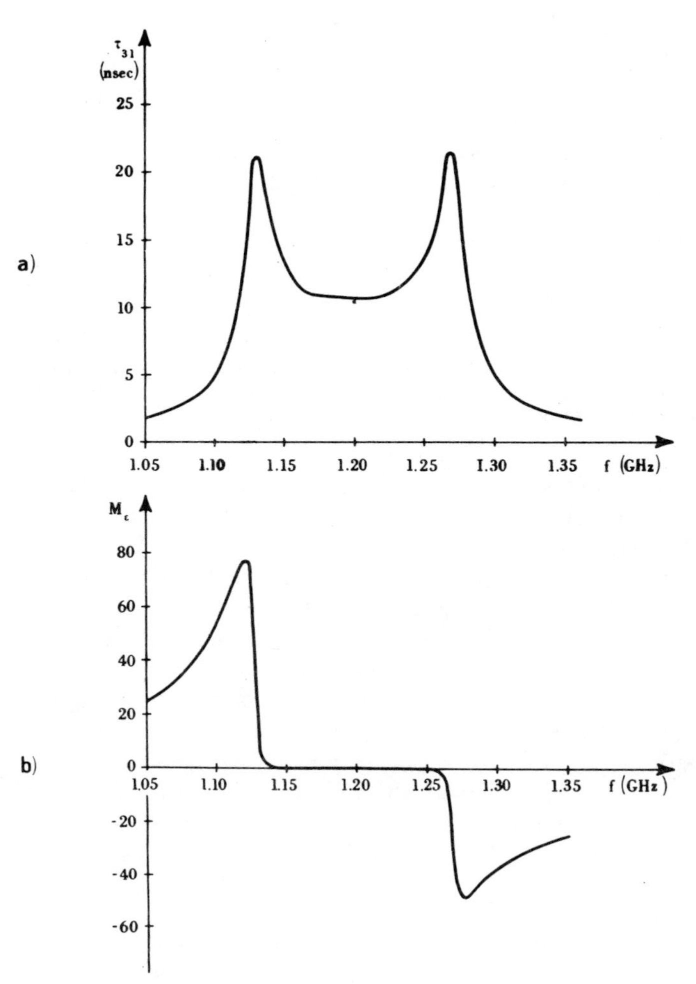

Fig. 10. (a) Group delay τ_{31} and (b) sensitivity M_ϵ, with respect to permittivity ϵ of transmission coefficient S_{31} of filter in Fig. 6 versus frequency.

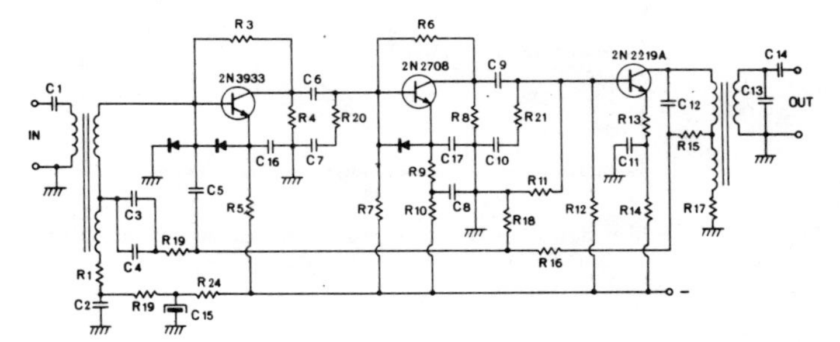

Fig. 11. Broad-band transistor amplifier for 960-channel FDM system (courtesy of Telettra Laboratory).

into multiports by means of the introduction of auxiliary multiports. It represents a broad-band transistor amplifier for a 360-channel frequency division multiplexing (FDM) system. Transistors and transformers have been characterized by measured parameters. The computed voltage insertion gain G and return losses ρ_i and ρ_0 at input and output ports are shown in Fig. 12. In the same figure the values measured at several frequency points are also given; the discrepancy between computed and measured values are due to the inability of the instrument to measure very high values of return loss.

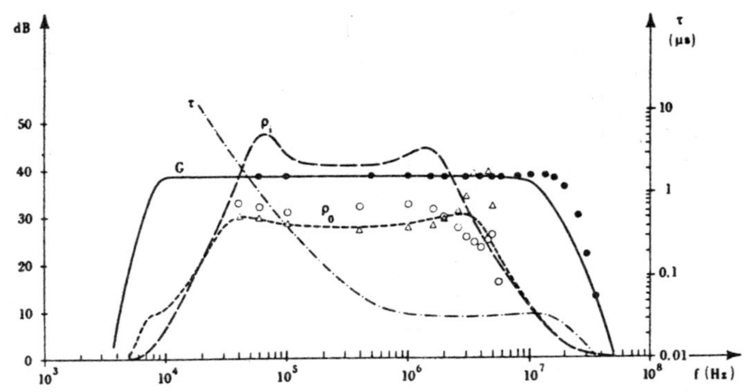

Fig. 12. Computed voltage insertion gain G and reflection coefficients at input and output ports of amplifier in Fig. 10. Experiment points—●: G; ○: ρ_i; Δ: ρ_o.

An application of analysis programs as routines of larger programs is supplied with reference to the circuit in Fig. 13, which represents a microstrip negative-resistor transistor amplifier tunable in the band 2.05–2.35 GHz, the envelope of its computed tuned voltage insertion gain being shown in Fig. 14. For this amplifier the transistor parameter tolerances and the production yield of a large number of circuits had to be determined given the assigned tolerances of permittivity ϵ and thickness δ of the ceramic substrate and the specified circuit performance [75]. These are expressed by the following relations: a) tuned insertion gain G = 12–16 dB in the RF band B = 2.05–2.35 GHz; b) 1-dB bandwidth $B_w \geq 50$ MHz at any tuning frequency; c) tunability in the whole RF band by a trimmer capacitor C_{tun} = 0.2–2 pF.

To this end, the acceptable regions have been determined in the plane (ϵ,δ) and for three transistors T_1, T_2, and T_3 with a program that, by means of repeated analyses (effected with BMT) searches for the contours of these regions. These contours are shown in Fig. 15 where the region of the possible values of ϵ and δ is shaded. It is seen from the same figure that since the whole area lies within the acceptable region relative to T_1, the production yield is 100 percent, while it is almost completely nonexistent for transistors T_2 and T_3. In this way it has been possible to determine the admissible tolerances for the transistor parameters.

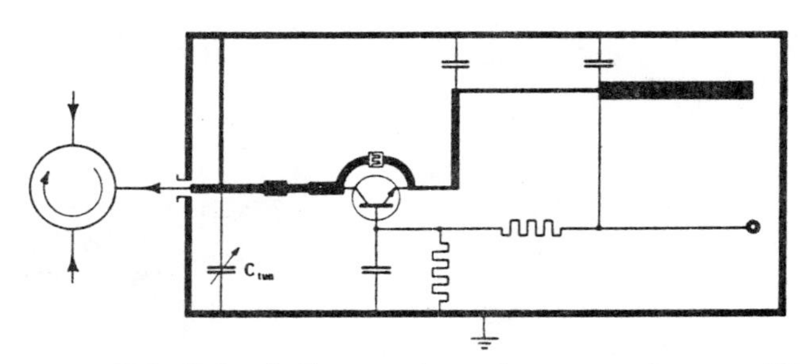

Fig. 13. Thin-film strip-line negative-resistance transistor amplifier (courtesy of Telettra Laboratory).

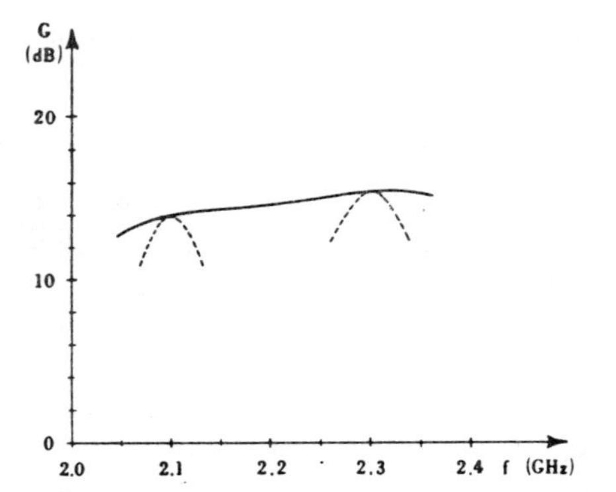

Fig. 14. Envelope of computed tuned voltage insertion gain of amplifier in Fig. 12.

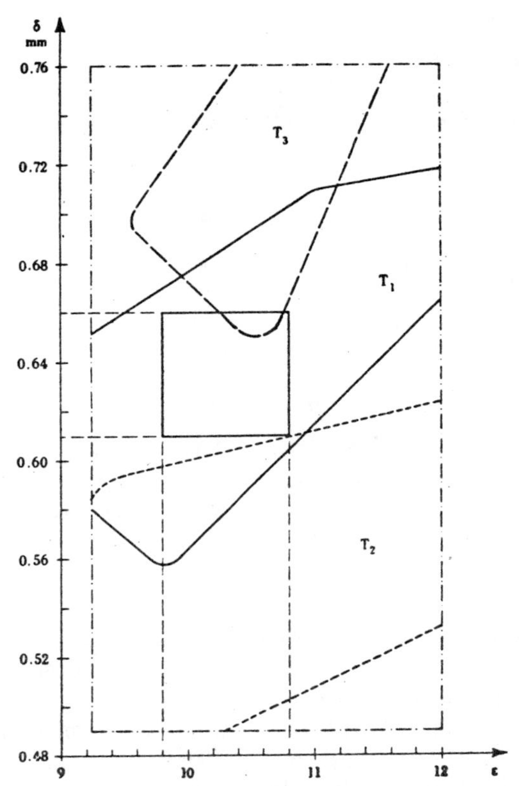

Fig. 15. Contours of acceptable regions in (ϵ,δ) plane for circuit in Fig. 12, with three different transistors.

The component tolerance assignment in relation to a given production yield is a problem being studied at present, as can be seen from recently published works [68]–[77]. For this, as in the case of optimization problems, it is very important that the programs for network function computation and the respective sensitivity be particularly fast, as is possible by adopting solution methods based on the sparse-matrix techniques described above.

VIII. Conclusions

The methods most frequently adopted by analysis programs of linear circuits in frequency domain have been described, giving greater attention to those best suited for use in microwave circuits. A comparison of the methods has been made emphasizing execution speed as well as limitations imposed on the component nature and the circuit topology.

Section V has been dedicated to the solution methods based on sparse-matrix techniques.

Determination of sensitivity by the direct and the transpose-matrix methods has been dealt with, and the convenience of using one or the other method in relation to the number of parameters and analysis methods has been discussed.

In Section VII some examples of analyzed circuits have been shown, referring, in particular, to the problem of component tolerance assignment.

Acknowledgment

The authors wish to thank the reviewers and Dr. M. Blasgen of the IBM T. J. Watson Center, Visiting Professor of the University of Bologna, for useful suggestions, and Prof. G. Vannucchi, Director of Telettra Laboratory, for giving permission to publish the analyzed circuits.

References

[1] P. E. Green, M. K. McPhun, M. A. Murray-Lasso, and A. E. Smoll, "Automatic general-purpose microwave circuit analysis programs (*Panel Discussion*)," *IEEE Trans. Microwave Theory Tech.* (*Special Issue on Computer-Oriented Microwave Practices*), vol. MTT-17, pp. 527–533, Aug. 1969.

[2] M. L. Dertouzos, G. P. Jessel, and J. R. Stinger, "CIRCAL-2: General-purpose on-line circuit design," *Proc. IEEE* (*Special Issue on Computers in Design*), vol. 60, pp. 39–48, Jan. 1972.

[3] D. A. Calahan, *Computer Aided Circuit Design*. New York: McGraw-Hill, 1972.

[4] W. Baechtold, W. Kotyczka, and M. J. O. Strutt, "Computerized calculation of small signal and noise properties of microwave transistors," *IEEE Trans. Microwave Theory Tech.* (*Special Issue on Computer-Oriented Microwave Practices*), vol. MTT-17, pp. 614–619, Aug. 1969.

[5] G. J. Herskovitz and R. B. Shilling, Ed., *Semiconductor Device Modeling for Computer-Aided Design*. New York: McGraw-Hill, 1972.

[6] R. I. Ollins and S. J. Ratner, "Computer-aided design and optimization of a broad-band high-frequency monolithic amplifier," *IEEE J. Solid-State Circuits* (*Special Issue on Analog Integrated Circuits*), vol. SC-7, pp. 487–492, Dec. 1972.

[7] *Proc. Symp. Essential Characteristics of Semiconductor Devices and Methods of Measurements* (Palermo, Italy, Dec. 1972) (in Italian).

[8] Hewlett-Packard, Application Note 117-1, 1969.

[9] P. Bodharamik, L. Besser, and R. W. Newcomb, "Two scattering matrix programs for active circuit analysis," *IEEE Trans. Circuit Theory* (*Special Issue on Active and Digital Networks*), vol. CT-18, pp. 610–619, Nov. 1971.

[10] F. H. Branin, Jr., "Computer methods of network analysis," *Proc. IEEE* (*Special Issue on Computer-Aided Design*), vol. 55, pp. 1787–1801, Nov. 1967.

[11] G. D. Hatchel, R. K. Brayton, and F. G. Gustavson, "The sparse tableau approach to network analysis and design," *IEEE Trans. Circuit Theory* (*Special Issue on Computer-Aided Circuit Design*), vol. CT-18, pp. 101–113, Jan. 1971.

[12] M. A. Murray-Lasso, "Black-box models for linear integrated circuits," *IEEE Trans. Educ.* (*Special Issue on Educational Aspects of Circuit Design by Computer—I*), vol. E-12, pp. 170–180, Sept. 1969.

[13] D. A. Calahan, "Numerical considerations for implementation of a nonlinear transient circuit analysis program," *IEEE Trans. Circuit Theory* (*Special Issue on Computer-Aided Circuit Design*), vol. CT-18, pp. 66–73, Jan. 1971.

[14] L. Nagel and R. A. Rohrer, "Computer analysis of nonlinear circuits, excluding radiation (CANCER)," *IEEE J. Solid-State Circuits* (*Special Issue on Computer-Aided Circuit Analysis and Device Modeling*), vol. SC-6, pp. 166–182, Aug. 1971.

[15] W. T. Weeks, A. J. Jimenez, G. W. Mahoney, H. Qassemzadah, and T. R. Scott, "Network analysis using a sparse tableau with tree selection to increase sparseness," in *Proc. 1973 IEEE Int. Symp. Circuit Theory* (Toronto, Canada, 1973), pp. 165–168.

[16] W. T. Weeks *et al.*, "Algorithms for ASTAP—A network-analysis program," *IEEE Trans. Circuit Theory* (*Special Issue on Computer-Aided Design*) (Corresp.), vol. CT-20, pp. 628–634, Nov. 1973.

[17] F. H. Branin, Jr., G. R. Hogsett, R. L. Lunde, and L. E. Kugel, "ECAP II—A new electronic circuit analysis program," *IEEE J. Solid-State Circuits* (*Special Issue on Computer-Aided Circuit Analysis and Device Modeling*), vol. SC-4, pp. 146–166, Aug. 1971.

[18] E. DeCastro, *Applied Electronics* (in Italian), preliminary ed. Torino, Italy: UTET, 1974.

[19] V. A. Monaco and P. Tiberio, "A method for automatic scattering matrix computation of a lumped, linear network," *Alta Freq.*, vol. 38, pp. 906–912, Nov. 1969.

[20] ——, "On the transformation of a lumped element linear network into a circuit composed of multiports," *Alta Freq.*, vol. 38, pp. 1013–1014, Nov. 1970.

[21] P. Penfield, Jr., "Description of electrical networks using wiring operators," *Proc. IEEE* (*Special Issue on Computers in Design*), vol. 60, pp. 49–53, Jan. 1972.

[22] G. C. Corazza. "Scattering matrix," (in Italian), *Alta Freq.*, vol. 32, pp. 393–414, June 1963.

[23] V. A. Monaco and P. Tiberio, "Automatic scattering matrix computation of microwave circuits," *Alta Freq.*, vol. 39, pp. 59–64, Feb. 1970.

[24] ——, "A computer program for circuit analysis from dc to microwave using scattering parameters," in *Dig. Tech Papers IEEE Symp. Circuit Theory* (Dec. 1970), pp. 119–120.

[25] F. Bonfatti, V. A. Monaco, and P. Tiberio, "Microwave circuit analysis by sparse matrix techniques," presented at the IEEE G-MTT Int. Microwave Symp., Boulder, Colo., June 1973; also this issue, pp. 264–269.

[26] H. J. Carlin, "The scattering matrix in network theory," *IRE Trans. Circuit Theory* (*Scattering Matrix Issue*), vol. CT-3, pp. 88–97, June 1956.

[27] M. A. Murray-Lasso, "Analysis of linear integrated circuits by digital computer using black-box techniques," in *Computer-Aided Integrated-Circuit Design*, G. J. Herskowitz, Ed. New York: McGraw-Hill, 1968, pp. 113–159.

[28] L. P. Huelsman, *Circuits, Matrices, and Linear Vector Spaces*. New York: McGraw-Hill, 1963.

[29] L. Besser, "Combine S parameters with time-sharing," *Electron. Des.*, vol. 16, pp. 62–68, Aug. 1968.

[30] W. N. Parker, "DIPNET, a general distributed parameter network analysis program," *IEEE Trans. Microwave Theory Tech.* (*Special Issue on Computer-Oriented Microwave Practices*), vol. MTT-17, pp. 495–505, Aug. 1969.

[31] P. L. Green, "General purpose programs for the frequency domain analysis of microwave circuits," *IEEE Trans. Microwave Theory Tech.* (*Special Issue on Computer-Oriented Microwave Practices*), vol. MTT-17, pp. 506–514, Aug. 1969.

[32] T. N. Trick and J. Vlach, "Computer-aided design of broadband amplifiers with complex loads," *IEEE Trans. Microwave Theory Tech.*, vol. MTT-18, pp. 541–547, Sept. 1970.

[33] M. E. Mokari-Bolhassan and T. N. Trick, "Computer aided design of distributed-lumped-active networks," *IEEE Trans. Circuit Theory* (*Special Issue on Computer-Aided Circuit Design*) (Corresp.), vol. CT-18, pp. 187–190, Jan. 1971.

[34] V. G. Gelnovatch and I. L. Chase, "DEMON: An optimal seeking computer program for the design of microwave circuits," *IEEE J. Solid-State Circuits* (*Special Issue on Microwave Circuits*), vol. SC-5, pp. 303–309, Dec. 1970.

[35] P. Penfield, Jr., *MARTHA Users' Manual*. Cambridge, Mass.: M.I.T. Press, 1971.

[36] *Sparse Matrix Symp. Proc.* Yorktown Heights, N. Y.: IBM, Rep. RA-1, Mar. 1969.

[37] J. K. Reid, Ed., *Large Sparse Sets of Linear Equations*. New York: Academic, 1970.

[38] D. J. Rose and R. A. Willoughby, Ed., *Sparse Matrices and Their Applications*. New York: Plenum, 1972.

[39] I. DeLotto, G. Pierini, and P. Tiberio, "Sparse matrix techniques in computer-aided design," in *Proc. Int. Computing Symp. European Ass. Comput. Mach.* (Davos, Switzerland, Oct. 1973).

[40] F. G. Gustavson, W. Liniger, and R. A. Willoughby, "Symbolic generation of an optimal Crout algorithm for sparse system of linear equations," *J. Ass. Comput. Mach.*, vol. 17, pp. 87–109, Jan. 1970.

[41] W. F. Tinney and J. W. Walker, "Direct solutions of sparse network equations by optimally ordered triangular factorization," *IEEE Proc.* (*Special Issue on Computer-Aided Design*), vol. 55, pp. 1801–1809, Nov. 1967.

[42] A. Chang, "Application of sparse matrix methods in electric power system analysis," in *Sparse Matrix Symp. Proc.* Yorktown Heights, N. Y.: IBM, Rep. RA-1, Mar. 1969.

[43] R. D. Berry, "An optimal ordering of electronic circuit equa-

tions for a sparse matrix solution," *IEEE Trans. Circuit Theory* (*Special Issue on Computer-Aided Circuit Design*), vol. CT-18, pp. 40–50, Jan. 1971.
[44] A. M. Erisman and G. E. Spies, "Exploiting problem characteristics in the sparse matrix approach to frequency domain analysis," *IEEE Trans. Circuit Theory*, vol. CT-19, pp. 260–265, May 1972.
[45] S. W. Director and R. A. Rohrer, "Automated network design—The frequency-doman case," *IEEE Trans. Circuit Theory*, vol. CT-16, pp. 330–337, Aug. 1969.
[46] ——, "The generalized adjoint network and network sensitivities," *IEEE Trans. Circuit Theory*, vol. CT-16, pp. 318–323, Aug. 1969.
[47] G. A. Richards, "Second-derivative sensitivity using the concept of the adjoint network," *Electron. Lett.*, vol. 5, pp. 398–399, Aug. 1969.
[48] V. A. Monaco and P. Tiberio, "On linear network scattering matrix sensitivity," *Alta Freq.*, vol. 39, pp. 193–195, Feb. 1970.
[49] G. C. Temes, "Exact computation of group delay and its sensitivities using adjoint-network concepts," *Electron. Lett.*, vol. 6, pp. 483–485, July 1970.
[50] G. C. Temes and R. N. Gadenz, "Simple technique for the prediction of dissipation-induced loss distortion," *Electron. Lett.*, vol. 6, pp. 836–837, Dec. 1970.
[51] J. W. Bandler and R. E. Seviora, "Current trends in network optimization," *IEEE Trans. Microwave Theory Tech.* (*1970 Symposium Issue*), vol. MTT-18, pp. 1159–1170, Dec. 1970.
[52] G. Iuculano, V. A. Monaco, and P. Tiberio, "Network sensitivities in terms of scattering parameters," *Electron. Lett.*, vol. 7, pp. 53–55, Jan. 1971.
[53] J. W. Bandler and R. E. Seviora, "Computation of sensitivities for noncommensurate networks," *IEEE Trans. Circuit Theory* (*Special Issue on Computer-Aided Circuit Design*) (Corresp.), vol. CT-18, pp. 174–178, Jan. 1971.
[54] R. N. Gadenz and G. C. Temes, "Computation of dissipation induced loss distortion in lumped/distributed networks," *Electron. Lett.*, vol. 7, pp. 258–260, May 1971.
[55] R. A. Rohrer, L. Nagel, R. Meyer, and L. Weber, "Computationally efficient electronic-circuit noise calculations," *IEEE J. Solid-State Circuits* (*Special Issue on Computer-Aided Circuit Analysis and Device Modeling*), vol. SC-6, pp. 204–213, Aug. 1971.
[56] G. Iuculano, V. A. Monaco, and P. Tiberio, "Automatic computation of microwave circuit sensitivity coefficients," in *Proc. 1971 European Microwave Conf.* (Stockholm, Sweden, Aug. 1971).
[57] ——, "A computer program for sensitivity and group-delay evaluation of linear networks," *Alta Freq.*, vol. 40, pp. 873–880, Nov. 1971.
[58] J. W. Bandler and R. E. Seviora, "Wave sensitivities of networks," *IEEE Trans. Microwave Theory Tech.*, vol. MTT-20, pp. 138–147, Feb. 1972.
[59] R. N. Gadenz and G. C. Temes, "Efficient hybrid and state space analysis of the adjoint network," in *Proc. 1972 IEEE Int. Symp. Circuit Theory* (Los Angeles, Calif., Apr. 1972), pp. 184–188.
[60] V. A. Monaco and P. Tiberio, "Two properties for circuit sensitivity in terms of scattering parameters," *Electron. Lett.*, vol. 8, pp. 382–383, Aug. 1972.
[61] G. C. Temes, R. M. Ebers, and R. N. Gadenz, "Some applications of the adjoint network concept in frequency domain analysis and optimization," *Comput. Aided Des.*, pp. 129–134, Apr. 1972.
[62] B. D. H. Tellegen, "A general network theorem, with applications," *Philips Res. Rep.*, vol. 7, pp. 259–269, Aug. 1952.
[63] P. Penfield, Jr., R. Spence, and S. Duinker, "A generalized form of Tellegen's theorem," *IEEE Trans. Circuit Theory*, vol. CT-17, pp. 302–305, Aug. 1970.
[64] S. W. Director, "*LU* factorization in network sensitivity computations," *IEEE Trans. Circuit Theory* (*Special Issue on Computer-Aided Circuit Design*) (Corresp.), vol. CT-18, pp. 184–185, Jan. 1971.
[65] F. H. Branin, Jr., "Network sensitivity and noise analysis simplified," *IEEE Trans. Circuit Theory* (*Special Issue on Large-Scale Networks*), vol. CT-20, pp. 285–288, May 1973.
[66] C. Rauscher, "A fast evaluation of *S*-parameter sensitivities," private communication.
[67] V. Rizzoli, "The calculation of scattering parameters for coupled microstrip arrays of any cross section," *Alta Freq.*, vol. 42, pp. 191–199, Apr. 1973.
[68] E. M. Butler, "Realistic design using large-change sensitivities and performance contours," *IEEE Trans. Circuit Theory* (*Special Issue on Computer-Aided Circuit Design*), vol. CT-18, pp. 58–66, Jan. 1971.
[69] E. DeCastro, G. Iuculano, and V. A. Monaco, "Component value spread and network function tolerances: An optimal design procedure," *Alta Freq.*, vol. 40, pp. 867–872, Nov. 1971.
[70] J. W. Bandler, "Optimization of design tolerances using nonlinear programming," in *Proc. 6th Annu. Princeton Conf. Information Sciences and Systems*, 1972, pp. 655–659; also, to be published in *J. Optimiz. Theory Appl.*
[71] J. F. Pinel and K. A. Roberts, "Tolerance assignment in linear networks using nonlinear programming," in *Proc. 1972 Int. Symp. Circuit Theory* (Los Angeles, Calif., Apr. 1972), pp. 129–183.
[72] B. J. Karafin, "The optimum assignment of component tolerances for electrical networks," *Bell Syst. Tech. J.*, vol. 50, pp. 1225–1242, Apr. 1972.
[73] J. W. Bandler and P. C. Liu, "Automated network design with optimal tolerances," *IEEE Trans. Circuits Syst.*, vol. CAS-21. pp. 219–222, Mar. 1974.
[74] A. R. Thorbjornsen and S. W. Director, "Computer-aided tolerance assignment for linear circuits with correlated elements," in *Proc. 1973 Int. Symp. Circuit Theory* (Toronto, Canada, Feb. 1973).
[75] E. Marazzi, V. A. Monaco, A. M. Brini, and V. Solaro, "Computer-aided realistic design of a thin-film microwave reflection-amplifier and production yield optimization," in *Proc. 1973 European Microwave Conf.* (Brussels, Belgium, Sept. 1973).
[76] J. W. Bandler, "The tolerance problem in optimal design," in *Proc. 1973 European Microwave Conf.* (Brussels, Belgium, Sept. 1973).
[77] R. N. Gadenz, G. Rezai-Fakhr, and G. C. Temes, "A method for the computation of large tolerance effects," *IEEE Trans. Circuit Theory* (*Special Issue on Computer-Aided Design*), vol. CT-20, pp. 704–708, Nov. 1973.
[78] F. Bonfatti, V. A. Monaco, and P. Tiberio, "Fast computation of microwave circuit response functions and sensitivities," in *Proc. 5th Colloq. Microwave Communication* (Budapest, Hungary), June 1974.

Reprinted by permission from IEEE TRANSACTIONS ON MICROWAVE THEORY AND TECHNIQUES
Vol. MTT-22, No. 3, March 1974, pp. 249-263

CAD Optimizes Broadband Amplifiers

By **Youichi Arai** and **Y. Tokumitse**, Fujitsu Laboratories

Large-signal characterization for computer optimization yields 5 W in 4–8-GHz amp, 6 W in 8-GHz amp and a 12-GHz, 1-W circuit.

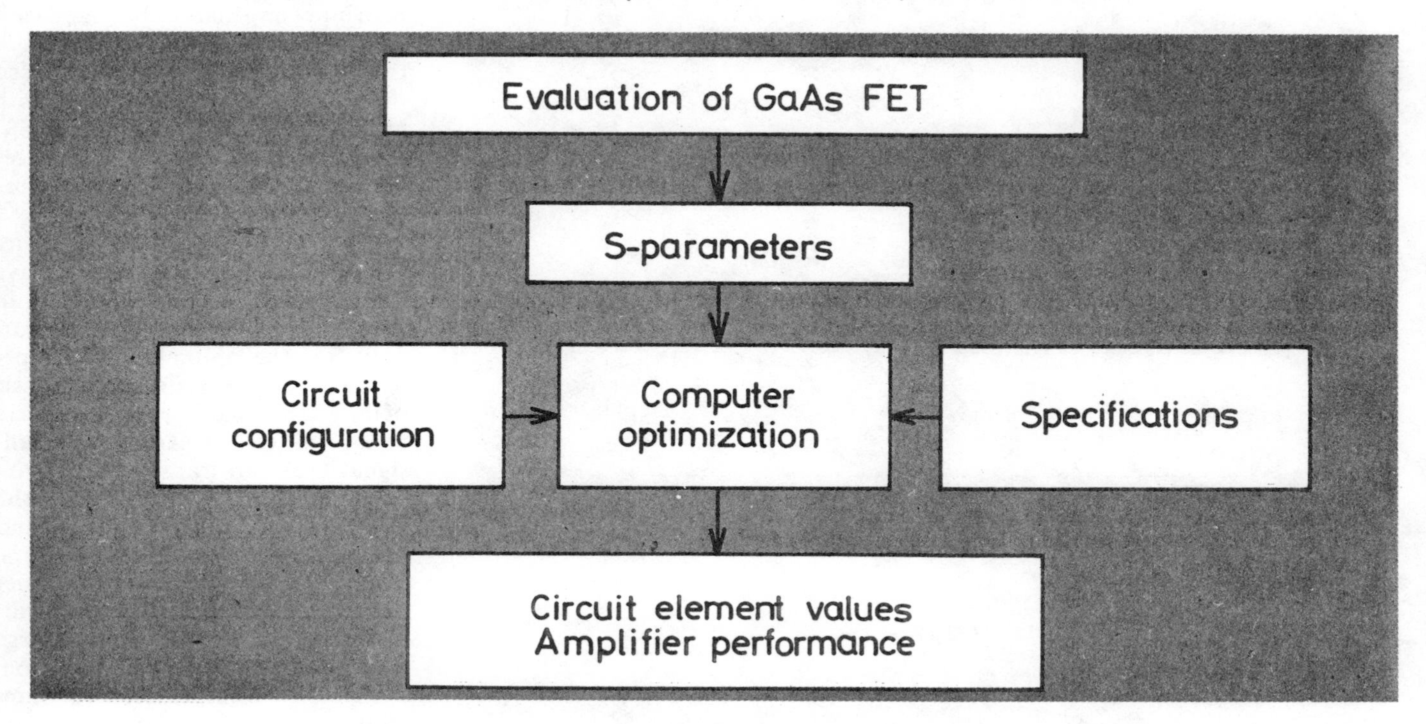

1. Several steps are required for the CAD process of amplifier circuit design: the GaAs Fets evaluated and S-parameters obtained, then the S-parameters, circuit configuration, and amplifier specifications are fed into the computer, where circuit optimization is carried out, resulting in data on the circuit's element values and amplifier performance.

Broadband operation and the need for circuit simplicity when GaAs Fets are used in amplifiers make use of computer-aided design imperative. There are many CAD programs presently in use throughout the microwave industry; one of these, COMAC (Computerized Optimization of Microwave Amplifier Circuits), has been developed by Fujitsu Laboratories to assist in the design of amplifier circuits using GaAs Fets.

The CAD process of amplifier circuit design[1] requires several steps (Fig. 1). First, the GaAs Fets must be evaluated and S-parameters obtained. Then these S-parameters together with the circuit configuration and amplifier specifications are fed into the computer as input data. Optimization of the circuit is carried out by the computer with the element values of the circuit and the amplifier performance printed out as output data.

Evaluating GaAs Fets

To evaluate the performance of a small-signal Fet in the microwave region, the S-parameters of the device are commonly measured. S-parameters can be measured accurately with an automatic network analyzer (ANA) using a test circuit. The test circuit has the same construction around the Fet as the envisaged amplifier. Measured S-parameters can be input to a computer to provide quick design of low-power amplifiers.

However, other problems arise in the evaluation of a high-power Fet with a total gate width of more than 1,800 microns.

First, it is difficult to measure S-parameters of high-power Fets with a total gate width of more than 1,800 microns at small-signal level, because input impedance becomes lower as gate width increases. Using the ANA for impedance measurements, which can be as low as 4 ohms, degrades measurement accuracy.

Second, since the Fet is nonlinear at high-power operation, optimum load impedance for maximum output power varies when the drive level changes. This nonlinearity presents many problems in the high-power amplifier design.

The authors are with the Fujitsu Transmission Systems Laboratory, Kawasaki, Japan. For further information regarding these amplifiers contact: Fujitsu America, 2945 Kifer Road, Santa Clara, CA 95051, (408) 727–1700.

Table 1.
Telecommunication Bandwidth Amplifiers
(Preliminary Specifications April 13, 1979)

Model No.	Frequency Range (MHz) Min.	Gain at Nominal Saturated Output Power (dB) Min.	Power Output Saturated (dBm) Min.	Power Output 1 dB GCP (dBm) Typ.	Gain Flatness (dB/20MHz) Max.
CGB596405-01	5925 - 6425	37	37	36	0.2
CGB596403-01	5925 - 6425	34	34	33	0.2
CGB596401-01	5925 - 6425	31	31	30	0.2
CGB5964P3-01	5925 - 6425	25	25	24	0.2
CGB647105-01	6425 - 7125	37	37	36	0.2
CGB647103-01	6425 - 7125	34	34	33	0.2
CGB647101-01	6425 - 7125	31	31	30	0.2
CGB6471P3-01	6425 - 7125	25	25	24	0.2
CGB717705-01	7100 - 7700	37	37	36	0.2
CGB717703-01	7100 - 7700	34	34	33	0.2
CGB717701-01	7100 - 7700	31	31	30	0.2
CGB778205-01	7700 - 8200	37	37	36	0.2
CGB778203-01	7700 - 8200	34	34	33	0.2
CGB778201-01	7700 - 8200	31	31	30	0.2

Octave Bandwidth Amplifiers
(Preliminary Specifications April 13, 1979)

Model No.	Frequency Range (MHz) Min.	Linear Gain (dB) Min.	Power Output at 1 dB GCP (dBm) Min.	Gain Flatness (dB) Max.
CGB204001-01	2000 - 4000	32	30	1.0
CGB408001-01	4000 - 8000	31	30	1.0
CGB408003-01	4000 - 8000	36	35	1.0

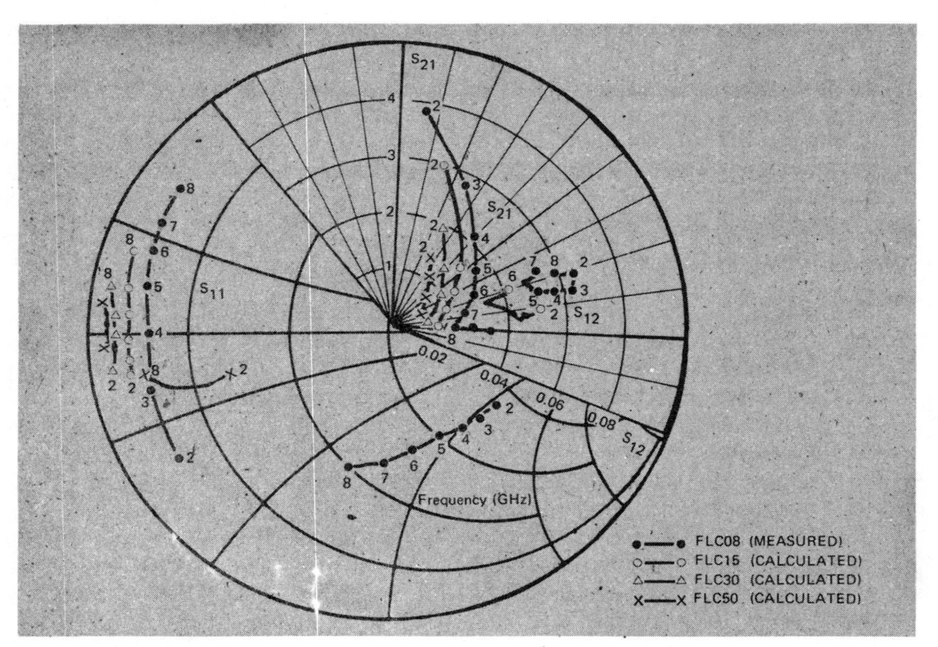

2. Measured S-parameters can be input to the computer to provide data for the quick design of low-power amplifiers. Difficulties arise in the evaluation of high-power Fets with total gate widths above 1,800 microns, since input impedance becomes lower as the gate width increases. These are measured S-parameters (S_{11}, S_{12}, and S_{21}) of the FLC 08 device, and synthesized results for the FLC 15, FLC 30, and FLS 50 with gate widths of 3,600, 7,200, and 10,400 μm, respectively.

Solutions to these problems are based on the facts that input impedance changes very little against drive level and that output impedance is the most sensitive parameter of a high-power Fet against drive level (Table 1).

First, small-signal S-parameters are measured. The FLC 08 has a relatively high input impedance compared with a Fet with a total gate width of more than this device's 1,800 microns, so the measurement can be made with greater accuracy. S-parameters (S_{11}, S_{12}, and S_{21}) of the other large devices are calculated by synthesizing measured S-parameters of FLC 08.

To achieve these results large devices are considered as if they have several small unit cells connected in parallel. S_{11}, S_{12}, and S_{21} are linear; only S_{22}, the optimum load impedance, is not linear. For the synthesis of the S_{11}, S_{12}, and S_{21}, the parameters of the unit cell—measured at small-signal level—are transformed into Y-parameters. Y-parameters of the required numbers are then added and again converted into S-parameters. This method is in use in amplifier design and has given no problems. Gate leakage currents in the large drive are not taken into consideration.

Figure 2 shows measured S-parameters (S_{11}, S_{12}, and S_{21}) of the FLC 08 and synthesized results for the FLC 15, FLC 30, and FLS 50, which have gate widths of 3,600, 7,200, and 10,400 μm, respectively.

Second, optimum output load impedances for maximum output power of the device under large-signal operation are measured by a conventional substitution method which does not take into account harmonic termination loading. The optimum load impedance of large devices can be obtained by connecting in parallel the required number of small devices. In this substitution method, the test circuit previously mentioned and two slug tuners with two dielectric rings inserted into a coaxial air line are used. In this measurement, key parameters are drive level and operating frequency.

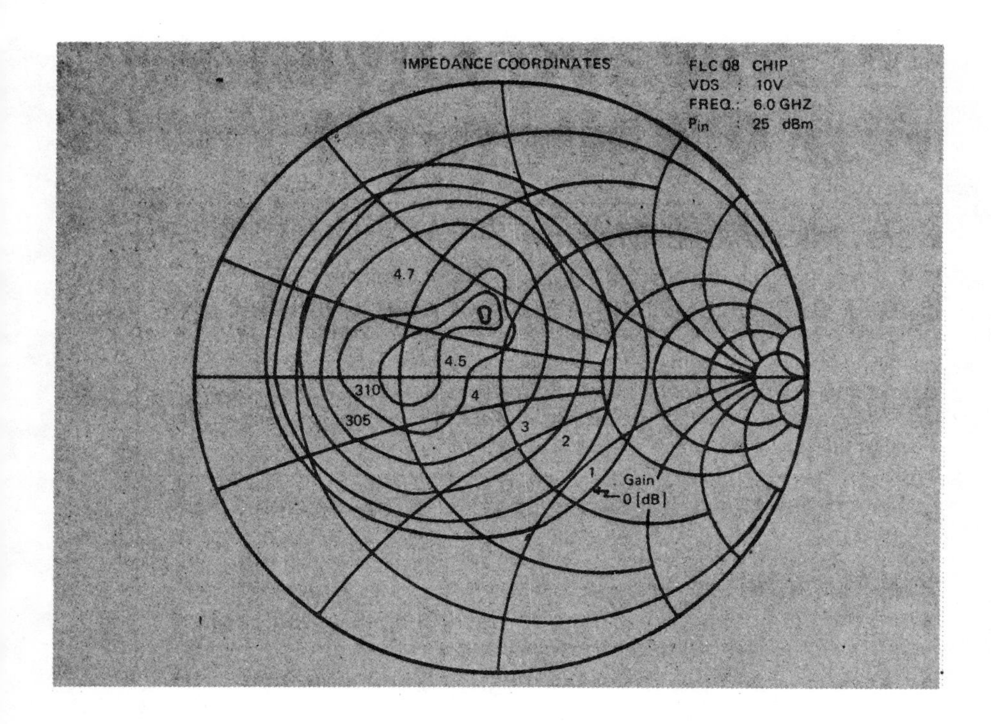

3. **Constant gain circles** for FLC 08 at 6 GHz with an input power of 25 dBm were measured at five frequency points and nine different power levels, obtaining optimum load impedance by combining the centers of the circles. This was used to calculate optimum load impedances for FLC 15, FLC 30, and FLS 50, by synthesizing measured impedance of FLC 08.

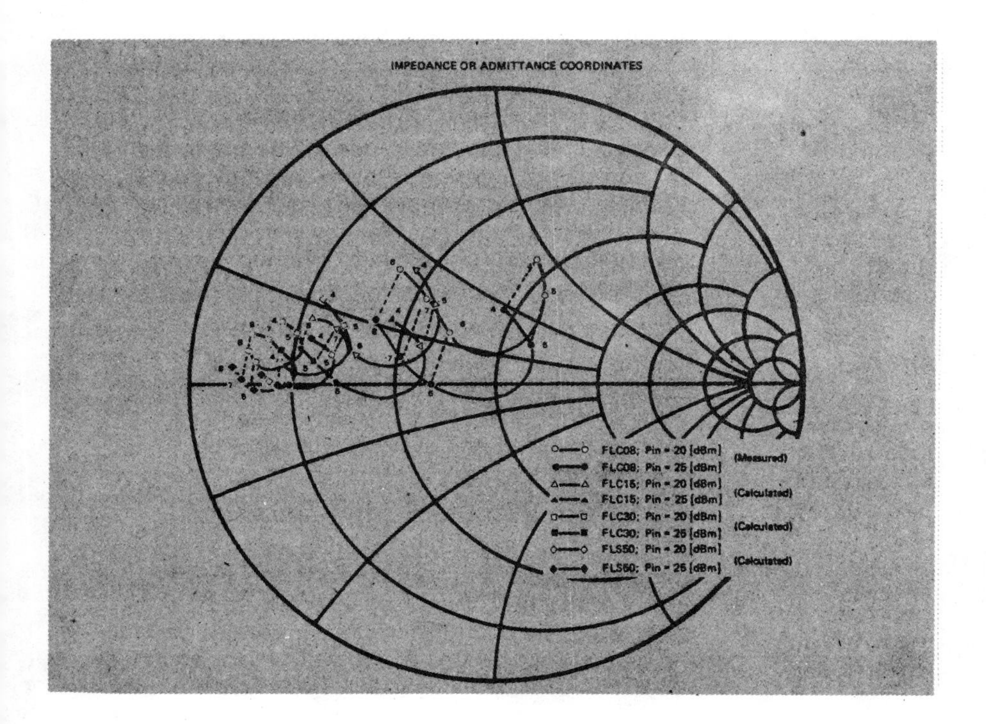

4. **From the measured optimum load** impedance of FLC 08, results were calculated for FLC 15, FLC 30, and FLS 50. In order to validate the synthesizing method, the optimum load impedance for FLC 30 was measured, and calculated results agreed well with measurements, demonstrating the practicality of synthesizing procedures.

FLC 08 is also used for this measurement, as it was in the small-signal input impedance measurement. Figure 3 shows constant gain circles of FLC 08 at 6 GHz, and an input power of 25 dBm. Many constant gain circles of FLC 08 were measured at five frequency points and nine different power levels. Optimum load impedance is obtained by combining the centers of the circles. The optimum output load impedances for FLC 15, FLC 30, and FLS 50 are calculated by synthesizing the measured impedance of FLC 08. The measured optimum load impedances of FLC 08 and the calculated results of FLC 15, FLC 30, and FLS 50 are shown in Figure 4.

In order to validate this synthesizing method, the optimum load impedance of FLC 30 was measured. Calculated results agree well with the measured ones (Fig. 5), showing that these synthesizing methods are a practical way to obtain input and output impedances of high-power Fets.

Circuit Optimization

Data input into a computer are the S-parameters of GaAs Fets previously mentioned, the specifications of the amplifier to be designed, and the circuit configuration. The amplifier's specifications are: the gain; input and output impedances; the stability condition; the variation of element values; and, in the case of a low-noise amplifier, the impedance of the input circuit providing the minimum noise figure.

The configuration of the circuit is free, its topology chosen to simplify design, not because of program considerations (Fig. 6). Circuits consisting of both some lumped elements and distributed circuits are used. From these input data, COMAC determines matching circuit elements using in the optimization process the gradient search method, chosen because it is faster than other available procedures.

Data printed out from the computer are element values, input and output impedances of matching circuits, the gain flatness against frequency, the stability circle, and group delay.

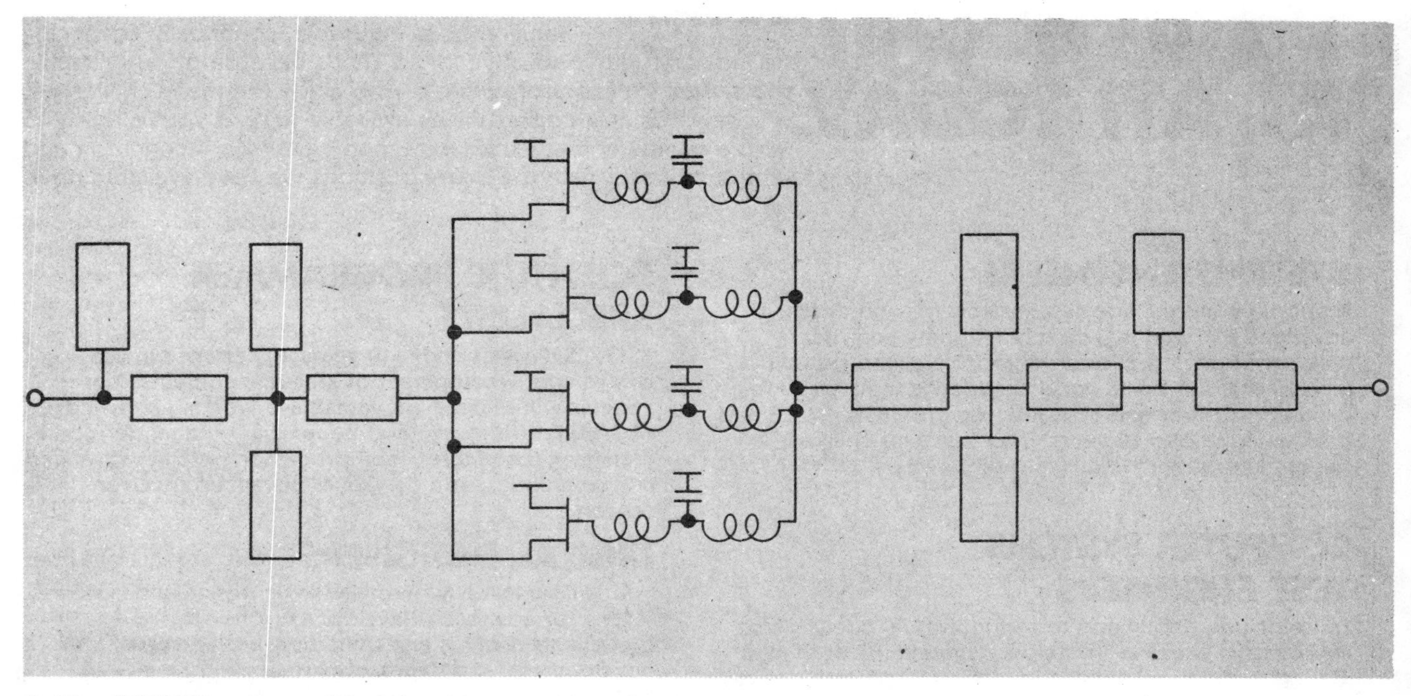

5. The COMAC program determines the matching circuit elements using a gradient search method in the optimization process, from the data fed into the computer: S-parameters of GaAs Fets, specifications of the amplifier to be designed, and the circuit configuration. No stub is used in the matching section because it is difficult to shoot the stub through the large capacitor and give good performance at microwave frequencies.

In the case of lumped elements, element values are printed out; with distributed circuits, the size of a microstrip line. COMAC can also calculate variations in amplifier performance, such as gain flatness and input and output impedances, depending on circuit element variation.

6. The COMAC program can also calculate variations in an amplifier's performance, such as gain flatness and input and output impedances. By applying this method, a 5-W amplifier with an octave bandwidth from 4 to 8 GHz was made. Shown here are the power responses and input VSWR of the integrated amplifier.

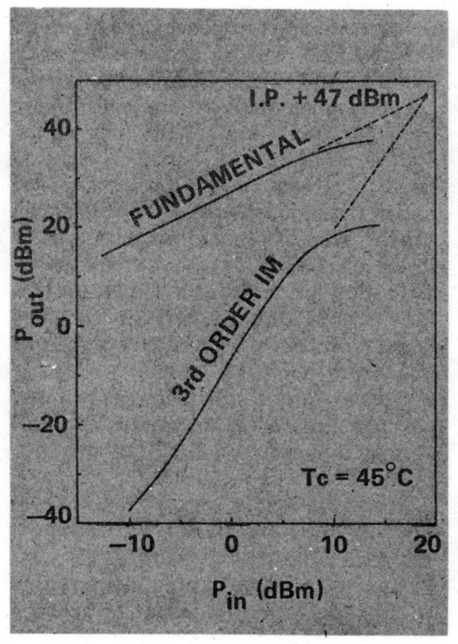

7. Five-unit, 4-8-GHz amplifier has relatively low third-order intermodulation products and high fundamental power response at 6 GHz.

Using this method, a 5-W GaAs Fet amplifier[3] with an octave bandwidth from 4 to 8 GHz, a 6-GHz 8-W amplifier from 5.9 to 6.4 GHz, and a 12-GHz 1-W amplifier have been developed.

Many GaAs Fet amplifiers have been developed with the COMAC program, showing that the use of CAD for the generation of amplifier circuits is both a sound and practical way to go. ■

References

1. Y. Arai et al., "A 4-GHz TWT Replaceable GaAs MESFET Amplifier," *1978 EuMC Digest*, pp. 468–472.
2. Y. Arai et al., "High Power GaAs Fet Amplifier for TWT Replacement," *Fujitsu Scientific Technical Journal*, Vol. 15, No. 3, September 1979.
3. K. Ohta et al., "A 5-W 4-to-8-GHz GaAs Fet Integrated Amplifier with One-V DC Bias Supply," *Microwave Journal*, to be published November 1979.

Synthesize Amplifiers Exactly

By Les Besser, Compact Engineering, Inc.

Design of distributed matching networks is complex, requiring intelligent, efficient use of synthesis and optimization. Payoff is impressive broadband performance.

Exact synthesis of circuit elements is no longer limited to filters. It can now be performed for such active microwave circuits as transmission line networks where both terminations are complex.

A principal application is design of transistor amplifiers, which through computer synthesis will yield flat gain across broad bandwidths. An example examined here is a prototype single-stage Fet amplifier to be built this fall. According to projections from its computer-aided design (CAD), it should attain gain that varies only from 7.0 to 7.6 dB across the full 6–12-GHz octave.

Exact synthesis and intelligent use of optimization are keys to cost-effective CAD of this and other circuits.

Traditionally, broadband amplifier design has been based on approximations from Smith-chart constant gain circles[1] and lots of "brute-force" computer optimization. A few years ago a lumped matching network technique was introduced[2] that offers exact synthesis of LC networks with arbitrary gain-slope to compensate the inherent gain rolloff of transistors. This approach works extremely well at the VHF-UHF range, where the circuit elements can be conveniently realized in lumped form. At the higher microwave frequencies, where the components must be in distributed form, this software offers an approximated "lumped-to-distributed" conversion, based on the terminal impedances of the components. The approximations introduce relatively small error in the case of transmission line stubs, but cascade transmission lines (unit elements) may cause significant errors.

Transmission line matching networks can be synthesized by the CADSYN™ program providing exact synthesis of transmission line networks with user selectable circuit topology, gain-slope, ripple, and insertion loss. In the case of passive circuit design, the program provides the final solution to the problem, while in amplifier design, a follow-up optimization is still needed to correct the input/output interaction of the active devices. This approach is based on the principles developed by Ku and Petersen.[3]

Specific Example

The single-stage amplifier is a case study in efficient, step-by-step CAD. The procedure includes modeling and analysis of the Fet's stability, synthesis of the input and output matching networks, and finally, the optimization of the complete circuit.

GaAs Fets display high usable gain at microwave frequencies. Contrasted with the bipolar devices, the maximum gain of a Fet is not apparent by viewing the transducer gain (S_{21}) alone; most of the available gain is due to the existing large mismatch at the input and output terminals. For example, at 6 GHz, the HP5001 Fet has a transducer gain (in the 50-ohm system) of 5.9 dB, while its $G_{max.}$ is 12.9 dB. This means that an additional 7 dB is gained when the mismatch is eliminated by simultaneously matching the device to 50 ohms at its input and output.

While the large mismatch is helpful in getting extra gain, it provides a challenging circuit design task for the engineer and also represents potential instability that may lead to unwanted oscillation. Steps in the design are:

a. Establish the desired specifications
b. Obtain the S-parameters of the Fet
c. Analyze stability
d. Model the Fet with distributed elements
e. Synthesize the input/output networks
f. Optimize the complete amplifier stage
g. Evaluate the circuit

The details of the bias network will not be discussed here; References 4, 5, and 6 will be helpful for the interested reader.

Design Procedure

• *Target Specifications* The amplifier stage we are designing in this example should have a gain flatness of ±0.5 dB within the 6-to-12-GHz passband. The active device to be used is the HP5001 GaAs Fet chip, in common source configuration, biased at V_{DS}=5 V and I_D=0.5I_{DSS}. The maximum gain capability of the device should be used to the fullest extent possible.

• *S-Parameters of the Fet* The COMPACT™ transistor databank is

---

Inquiries on use of the software described here should be directed to: Compact Engineering, Inc., 1088 Valley View Court, Los Altos, CA 94022, U.S.A., Tel. (415) 941-6223, TWX 910-370-7457. Mr. Besser, president of Compact, is contributing a series of articles on specific applications of CAD to be published in MSN.

used to retrieve the S-parameters of the device. However, since Hewlett-Packard's devices are characterized without parasitic inductances, the device parameters should be re-computed after adding realistic compensation for bondwires at all three terminals. Based on past experience, 0.2 nH will be used at the input/output and 0.1 nH in the common (source) terminal. These figures are based on 20-nH/inch inductance and assume two sets of parallel grounding at the source terminal. The resultant S-parameters and the computed simultaneous conjugate source and load impedances are shown in Figure 1.

The feedback caused by the source lead inductor increases S_{12} of the device and also affects the stability.[7] At 6 GHz, the inductance actually improved the k-factor (1.24 from 0.89), while at 12 GHz, the k-factor became significantly worse (1.06 from 1.64). The cascaded inductors at the input and output have no effect on the stability factor.

S-PARAMETERS AND CONJUGATE MATCHED SOURCE/LOAD FOR THE ACTUAL CHIP

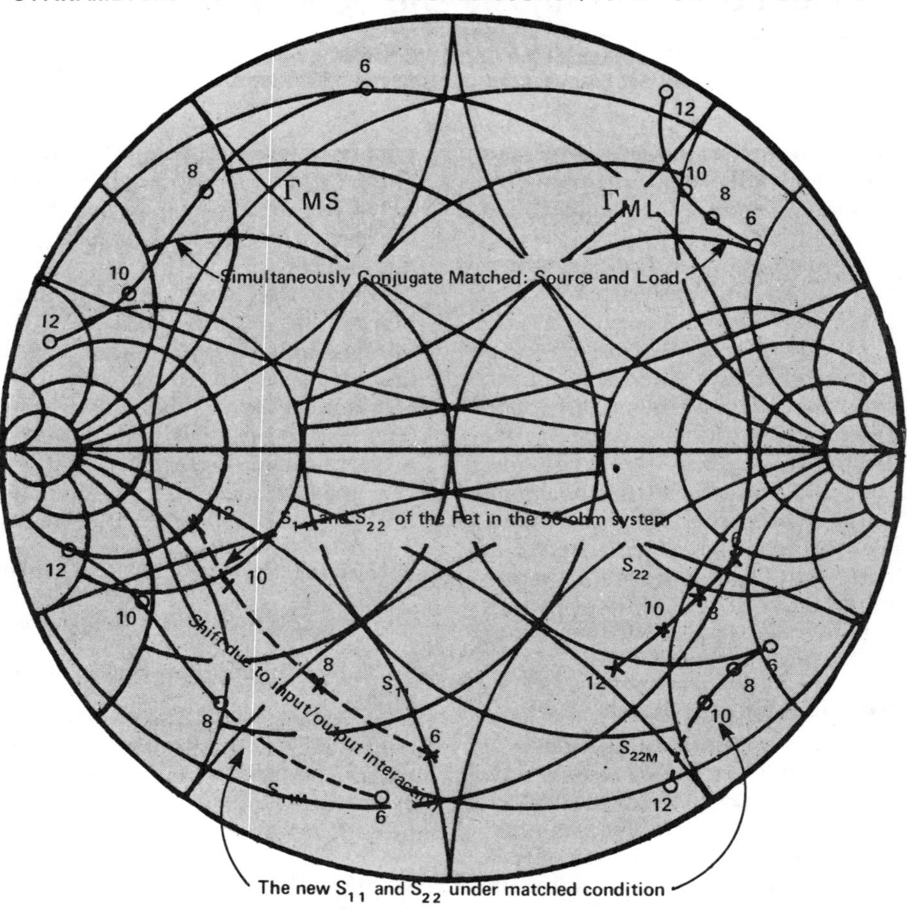

POLAR S-PARAMETERS IN 50.0 OHM SYSTEM

FREQ.	S11 MAGN	S11 ANGL	S21 MAGN	S21 ANGL	S12 MAGN	S12 ANGL	S22 MAGN	S22 ANGL	S21 DB	K FACT.
6000.00	.73	-96	1.97	99.3	.051	69.8	.64	-26	5.89	1.25
7000.00	.69	-110	1.84	88.2	.059	70.3	.63	-30	5.30	1.30
8000.00	.67	-124	1.71	78.4	.066	73.2	.62	-35	4.66	1.29
9000.00	.65	-136	1.56	69.8	.073	77.2	.61	-40	3.86	1.33
10000.00	.62	-147	1.45	61.7	.081	82.7	.61	-45	3.23	1.36
11000.00	.61	-155	1.38	53.7	.093	87.5	.60	-50	2.80	1.27
12000.00	.62	-160	1.33	44.6	.108	90.7	.60	-58	2.48	1.07

POLAR COORDINATES OF SIMULTANEOUS CONJUGATE MATCH

F MHZ	SOURCE REFL. COEFF. MAGN.	SOURCE REFL. COEFF. ANGLE	LOAD REFL. COEFF. MAGN.	LOAD REFL. COEFF. ANGLE	GMAX DB
6000.0	.85	104	.80	38	12.83
7000.0	.82	118	.79	40	11.64
8000.0	.82	131	.79	43	10.91
9000.0	.81	141	.79	46	9.85
10000.0	.79	151	.79	49	8.96
11000.0	.81	157	.80	52	8.57
12000.0	.89	161	.88	59	9.25

.2 nH
.2 nH
.1 nH

1. S-parameters and the simultaneous conjugate match for the HP 5001 GaAs Fet include the computed effect of bondwire inductances. S_{11}, S_{22}, S_{11M}, S_{22M}, and the simultaneous conjugate matched source and load impedances of the Fet are plotted from 6 to 12 Ghz.

● *Modeling the Fet* The stability factors indicate unconditional stability (k>1) through the 6–12-GHz band, although it becomes marginal at the high end. The simultaneous conjugate matched impedances, S_{11M} and S_{22M}, are well behaved until 10 GHz, then suddenly move toward the edge of the Smith chart as the potential instability approaches. Another interesting fact is the sudden increase of G_{max}. As the device becomes less and less stable. There is only a little over 3 dB gain rolloff through the octave frequency range, instead of the customarily expected 6 dB/octave. The difference is due to the decreased stability of the device at 12 GHz, and if the analysis were carried out to the higher frequency where the device becomes potentially unstable (k=1), the theoretical maximum gain reaches infinity.

In order to synthesize the matching networks, the input and output impedances of the Fet must be described by equivalent circuits where the resistive and reactive components can be clearly separated. The synthesis is carried out between resistive terminations and the reactive parts will be "absorbed" in the matching networks.

The input impedance behaves similarly to a series RC network, while the output is closer to a parallel RC network. In distributed network theory, the capacitors can be approximated by series and open parallel stubs; therefore, the Fet input device can be modeled by a resistor in series with an open stub, while the output model consists of a resistor and a parallel open stub (Fig. 2). Adding series inductance by series shorted stubs would improve the accuracy of the model; however, for practical purposes, the simpler model is sufficient. Having more elements in the model also

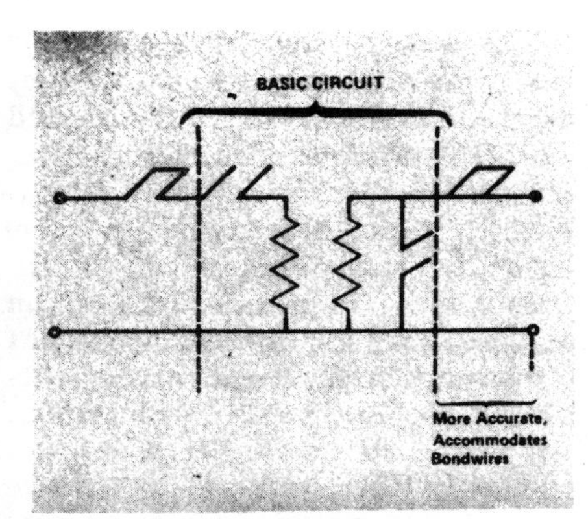

2. Use of a more accurate model (bondwire compensation, outside dotted lines) also places more constraints on the synthesis procedure.

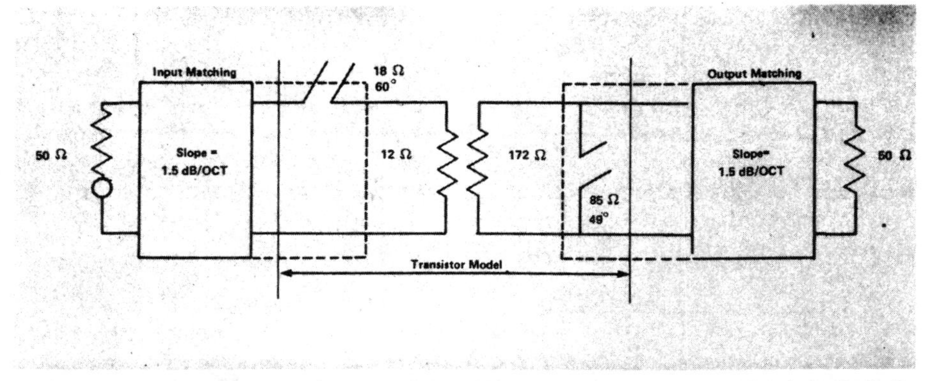

3. Source and load terminations for the CADSYN matching network synthesis include the reactive portions of the Fet input/output impedances which are treated as parts of the networks.

places more restriction on the topology selection and the synthesis because there are more elements to be absorbed in the matching networks.

If the amplifier is designed for flat gain, using lossless matching elements, the Fet must be mismatched at the low end of the passband, and conjugate matched at the high end for maximum gain. Under simultaneous conjugate match condition, the device input and output impedances (S_{11M} and S_{22M}) can be computed and can be used for modeling purposes. However, the device impedances cannot be determined under the mismatched conditions. Therefore, the impedances of the models can only be approximated, and they can either be based on S_{11} and S_{22} or S_{11M} and S_{22M}. Neither method provides an exact solution. In our example, the impedances are based on S_{11} and S_{22} because they present more continuous responses than S_{11M} and S_{22M}.

The resistive parts of the device model can be directly read off the constant resistance and constant reactance circles of the Smith chart. At a single frequency, the reactive portions can be represented by an infinite number of combinations, since the reactance X, of an open stub is

$$X = -jZ_o \operatorname{ctn} \theta$$

where Z_o is the characteristic impedance of the stub, and θ is the electrical length.

Therefore, different combinations of Z_o and θ can result in the same reactance. For the broadband case, the optimum variables may be

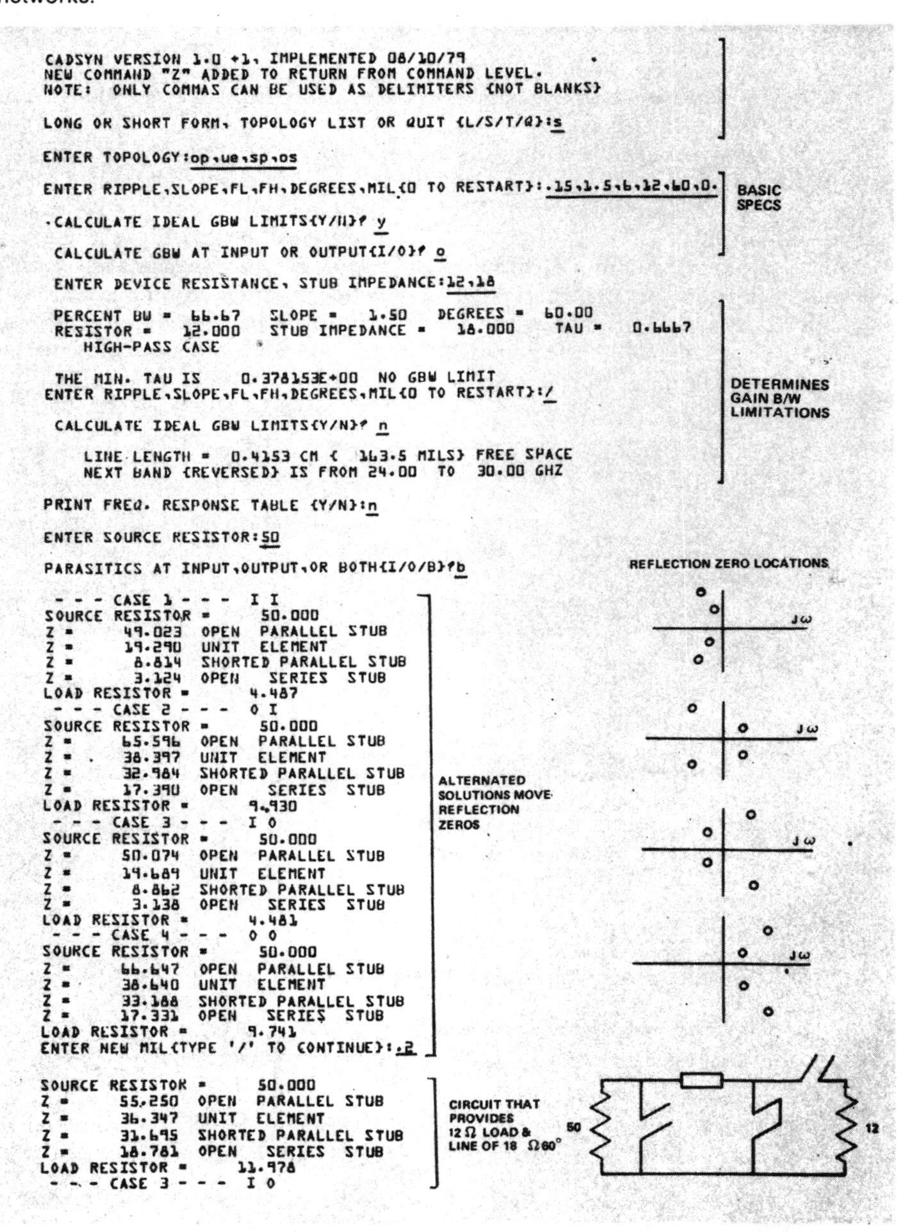

```
CADSYN VERSION 1.0 +1, IMPLEMENTED 08/10/79
NEW COMMAND "Z" ADDED TO RETURN FROM COMMAND LEVEL.
NOTE:  ONLY COMMAS CAN BE USED AS DELIMITERS (NOT BLANKS)

LONG OR SHORT FORM, TOPOLOGY LIST OR QUIT (L/S/T/Q):s

ENTER TOPOLOGY:op,ue,sp,os

ENTER RIPPLE,SLOPE,FL,FH,DEGREES,MIL(0 TO RESTART):.15,1.5,6,12,60,0.

.CALCULATE IDEAL GBW LIMITS(Y/N)? y

 CALCULATE GBW AT INPUT OR OUTPUT(I/O)? o

 ENTER DEVICE RESISTANCE, STUB IMPEDANCE:12,18

 PERCENT BW =  66.67   SLOPE =   1.50   DEGREES =  60.00
 RESISTOR =   12.000   STUB IMPEDANCE =   18.000     TAU =    0.6667
    HIGH-PASS CASE

 THE MIN. TAU IS     0.378153E+00  NO GBW LIMIT
ENTER RIPPLE,SLOPE,FL,FH,DEGREES,MIL(0 TO RESTART):/

 CALCULATE IDEAL GBW LIMITS(Y/N)? n

    LINE LENGTH =  0.4153 CM (  163.5 MILS) FREE SPACE
    NEXT BAND (REVERSED) IS FROM 24.00  TO  30.00 GHZ

PRINT FREQ. RESPONSE TABLE (Y/N):n

ENTER SOURCE RESISTOR:50

PARASITICS AT INPUT,OUTPUT,OR BOTH(I/O/B)?b

 - - - CASE 1 - - -   I I
SOURCE RESISTOR =      50.000
Z =      49.023  OPEN   PARALLEL STUB
Z =      19.290  UNIT   ELEMENT
Z =       8.814  SHORTED PARALLEL STUB
Z =       3.124  OPEN    SERIES  STUB
LOAD RESISTOR =       4.487
 - - - CASE 2 - - -   O I
SOURCE RESISTOR =      50.000
Z =      65.596  OPEN   PARALLEL STUB
Z =      38.397  UNIT   ELEMENT
Z =      32.984  SHORTED PARALLEL STUB
Z =      17.390  OPEN    SERIES  STUB
LOAD RESISTOR =       9.930
 - - - CASE 3 - - -   I O
SOURCE RESISTOR =      50.000
Z =      50.074  OPEN   PARALLEL STUB
Z =      14.689  UNIT   ELEMENT
Z =       8.862  SHORTED PARALLEL STUB
Z =       3.138  OPEN    SERIES  STUB
LOAD RESISTOR =       4.481
 - - - CASE 4 - - -   O O
SOURCE RESISTOR =      50.000
Z =      66.647  OPEN   PARALLEL STUB
Z =      38.640  UNIT   ELEMENT
Z =      33.188  SHORTED PARALLEL STUB
Z =      17.331  OPEN    SERIES  STUB
LOAD RESISTOR =       9.741
ENTER NEW MIL(TYPE '/' TO CONTINUE):.2

SOURCE RESISTOR =      50.000
Z =      55.250  OPEN   PARALLEL STUB
Z =      36.347  UNIT   ELEMENT
Z =      31.695  SHORTED PARALLEL STUB
Z =      18.781  OPEN    SERIES  STUB
LOAD RESISTOR =      11.978
 - - - CASE 3 - - -   I O
```


4. The interactive response of the matching network synthesis shows four alternative networks for the same frequency response. Case No. 2 will result in full parasitic response at the load side.

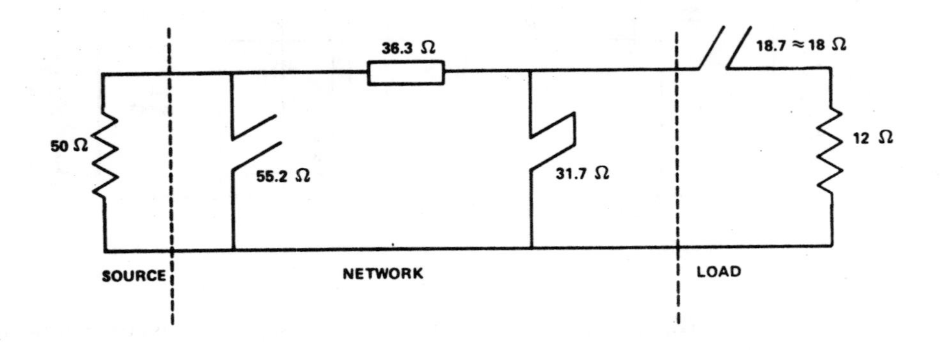

5. Input network provided by CADSYN. All transmission lines are of commensurate lengths of 60 degrees at 12 GHz.

reached by computer optimization.[8] (A convenient design chart that is helpful in approximating the solution for various stub lengths and impedances will be published in a future issue of *MSN*.)

The optimized Fet model and the block diagram of the matching synthesis are shown in Figure 3. The 3-dB gain rolloff of the Fet will be compensated equally between the input and output networks.

• *Synthesis of the Matching Networks* The interactive response of the CADSYN program is shown in Figure 4. Following the network topology, the specifications of the network, such as ripple and bandwidth, are presented to the program. All network elements will be realized in microstrip form, except the series open stub that is to be fully absorbed as the reactive part of the Fet input. Next, CADSYN is asked to approximate the necessary minimum insertion loss at 12 GHz for full absorption. It was found that the absorption may even be achieved at zero loss. At that point, the network was synthesized, and scaled to a source resistance of 50 ohms. Since this bandpass network is a fourth-order one, there are four possible combinations, $(N/2)^2$, of reflection zero locations, yielding four different sets of component values, without changing the magnitude of the gain response.[9] It should be noted that all transmission lines have equal lengths of 60 degrees.

In bandpass synthesis, the desired load resistance cannot be achieved directly and it is usually obtained through the application of Norton's transformations or Kuroda's identities.[10] In our example, the load consists of a 12-ohm resistor in series with an 18-ohm open stub, and the reader should notice that Case Numbers 2 and 4 of Figure 4 provide results quite close to the desired load. Increasing the minimum insertion loss to 0.2 dB yields four new sets of component values. Case Number 2 of the new synthesis provides impedances within a few percent of the desired load and eliminates the need for impedance transformation (Fig. 5). The series open stub portion of the load is now fully absorbed in the network.

The output network was synthesized next with 1.5 dB gain slope, 0.15 dB ripple, and 0.1 dB minimum insertion loss. The topology is somewhat different from that of the previous network, since here the input side of the network is where the parasitic absorption should take place. The source impedance, as represented by the output of the Fet, consists of a 172-ohm resistor, parallel with a 49-degree-long open stub of 85-ohm impedance. In this case, all transmission lines will have 49-degree lengths at 12 GHz.

The last section of the output work synthesis is shown in Figure 6. Case Number 1 of the available options was previously selected to maximize parasitic absorption at the input. When the network was scaled to a

```
   * - IN THE FOLLOWING LIST THE VARIABLES N,M,V, AND Y
       REPRESENT NUMBERS TO BE SUPPLIED BY THE USER - *
COMMAND    DESCRIPTION

Q          QUIT
B          BEGIN NEW DESIGN
Z          RETURN TO PARASITIC ABSORPTION SECTION
P          PRINT CIRCUIT
R,V        RENORMALIZE INPUT TO V OHMS
R,-V       RENORMALIZE OUTPUT TO V OHMS
D,V        CREATE DUAL NETWORK, V OHMS INPUT
D,-V       CREATE DUAL NETWORK, V OHMS OUTPUT
C,N        COMBINE ELEMENTS N AND N+1
S,N,V      SPLIT ELEMENT N TO V OHMS
               FOLLOWED BY REMAINDER
A,V        ADD UNIT ELEMENT AT INPUT AND EXECUTE R,V
A,-V       ADD UNIT ELEMENT AT OUTPUT AND EXECUTE R,-V
X,N,M,V    EXCHANGE N AND M, SET INPUT TO V OHMS
X,N,M,V,Y  SPLIT N AND EXCHANGE PART WITH M
               SUCH THAT INPUT IS V OHMS, OUTPUT IS Y OHMS
     NOTE: FOR THE X COMMAND, M AND N MUST BE ADJACENT
             172.000 SOURCE RESISTOR
  1) Z =      57.668 OPEN PARALLEL STUB
  2) Z =     115.608 SHORTED PARALLEL STUB
  3) Z =     165.092 UNIT ELEMENT
  4) Z =     115.107 OPEN PARALLEL STUB
             136.970 LOAD RESISTOR
READY
(1) x,2,3,172,50
             172.000 SOURCE RESISTOR
  1) Z =      57.668 OPEN PARALLEL STUB
  2) Z =     213.596 SHORTED PARALLEL STUB
  3) Z =      99.747 UNIT ELEMENT
  4) Z =     152.258 SHORTED PARALLEL STUB
  5) Z =      42.019 OPEN PARALLEL STUB
              50.000 LOAD RESISTOR
READY
(2) s,1,85
             172.000 SOURCE RESISTOR
  1) Z =      85.000 OPEN PARALLEL STUB
  2) Z =     179.345 OPEN PARALLEL STUB
  3) Z =     213.596 SHORTED PARALLEL STUB
  4) Z =      99.747 UNIT ELEMENT
  5) Z =     152.258 SHORTED PARALLEL STUB
  6) Z =      42.019 OPEN PARALLEL STUB
              50.000 LOAD RESISTOR
READY
```

172 137 172 50 172 50 SOURCE NETWORK LOAD

6. High-pass Kuroda transformation and element splitting in the output network. Figure 6c shows the final output network.

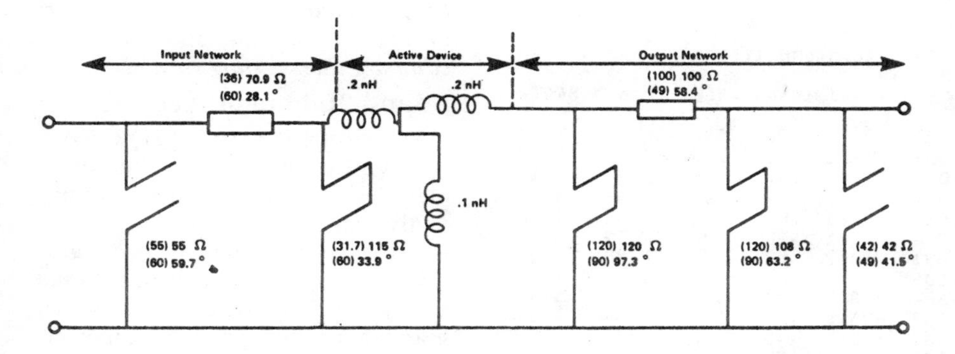

7. Circuits schematics of the Fet amplifier stage. Component values in parenthesis indicate the initial values prior to the first optimizations. Boldfaced numbers indicate the final values after the second optimization.

```
                    CIRCUIT OPTIMIZATION WITH  7 VARIABLES
 INITIAL CIRCUIT ANALYSIS

                   POLAR S-PARAMETERS IN   50.0 OHM SYSTEM
  FREQ.       S11          S21          S12          S22        S21     K
           (MAGN ANGL) ( MAGN ANGL) ( MAGN ANGL) (MAGN ANGL)    DB    FACT.

  6000.00  .76      0  1.84  129.3  .048   99.8  .74    -15    5.31   1.39
  7000.00  .65    -66  1.96   74.6  .063   56.7  .71    -54    5.86   1.38
  8000.00  .60   -115  1.88   31.3  .073   26.1  .70    -84    5.49   1.34
  9000.00  .54   -147  1.80   -5.2  .084    2.2  .70   -108    5.12   1.38
 10000.00  .40   -169  1.86  -41.9  .104  -20.9  .69   -130    5.39   1.40
 11000.00  .20    171  2.08  -83.0  .140  -49.2  .59   -156    6.38   1.32
 12000.00  .25    -39  2.47 -142.9  .200  -96.8  .19    131    7.85   1.12

 OPTIMIZATION BEGINS WITH FOLLOWING VARIABLES AND GRADIENTS

     VARIABLES                           GRADIENTS
  ( 1): 60.000                        ( 1):  97.415
  ( 2): 60.000                        ( 2):  4.6392
  ( 3): 60.000                        ( 3): -36.271
  ( 4): 90.000                        ( 4): -114.66
  ( 5): 49.000                        ( 5): -102.43
  ( 6): 90.000                        ( 6):  52.489
  ( 7): 49.000                        ( 7):  99.584
 ERR. F.=     51.281
        ----****----
 HOW MANY ITERATIONS BEFORE NEXT STOP  '0' RESULTS IN FINAL ANALYSIS.
 WANT INTERMEDIATE PRINTS (YES=1,NO=0)? TYPE TWO NUMBERS: I,J ? 10,0
 ERR. F.=     13.281
 ERR. F.=     10.607
 ERR. F.=      9.957
 ERR. F.=      9.592
  ( 1):  47.854.                       ( 1): -.16102
  ( 2):  57.351.                       ( 2): -.74098
  ( 3):  68.353.                       ( 3):  .42881
  ( 4):  103.82.                       ( 4): -.17902
  ( 5):  60.418.                       ( 5):  .91677
  ( 6):  69.047.                       ( 6):  .78250
  ( 7):  35.607.                       ( 7): -1.3762
 ERR. F.=      9.503
        ----****----
 FRACTIONAL TERMINATION WITH ABOVE VALUES. FINAL ANALYSIS FOLLOWS

  6000.00  .73     -8  2.15  134.8  .056  105.3  .67     10    6.65   1.36
  7000.00  .61    -78  2.40   77.8  .077   59.9  .56    -34    7.60   1.37
  8000.00  .58   -130  2.35   31.6  .091   26.4  .48    -76    7.43   1.33
  9000.00  .53   -167  2.25   -8.1  .105    -.7  .41   -116    7.05   1.37
 10000.00  .40    159  2.26  -47.6  .126  -26.6  .34   -163    7.08   1.40
 11000.00  .26    110  2.30  -90.5  .155  -56.7  .28    125    7.22   1.32
 12000.00  .24     14  2.14 -141.5  .173  -95.4  .48     35    6.59   1.13
```

8. Optimization of the amplifier stage by COMPACT. The initial gain ripple of 2.5 dB is reduced to less than 1 dB by COMPACT.

source resistance of 172 ohms, the impedance of the first parallel open stub was 57.7 ohms; that is somewhat greater capacitance than the minimum required 85 ohms. This indicates that the source parasitics can be absorbed in the network, with some extra capacitance left over. There is only one problem in the network: the load resistance is 137 ohms, instead of the desired 50 ohms, and here a transformation is necessary.

A high-pass Kuroda transformation between element numbers 2 and 3 of Figure 6a achieves the desired 50-ohm load. Next, element number 1 of Figure 6b is split to two parts by CADSYN to separate the 85-ohm source parasitics. The resultant network is shown in Figure 6c.

Inspection of the final output circuit reveals that the characteristic impedance of three elements (##2, 3, and 5) are too high for conventional microstrip realization. The impedances could be altered by additional network transformations, but since the complete circuit will be optimized anyway, the following adjustments can be made:

a. The two-short-circuited parallel stub (#3 and #5) impedances are reduced to 120 ohms, which can be realized on microstrip. To compensate for the impedance changes, the lengths of the stubs are arbitrarily increased to 90 degrees.

b. The 179-ohm parallel open stub can be eliminated from the circuit; the effect will be compensated during the optimization.

In the input network the 34-degree-long short-circuited stub will be difficult to realize, and it may have to be fabricated in lumped form. The rest of the input and output circuits are realizable, and the complete circuit is optimized.

- *Optimization of the Circuit*

Computerized optimization is one of the most powerful design tools available to the microwave engineer. Optimization helps to find the answer iteratively to problems where the exact solution may not exist in closed form, or if it exists, it is not solvable by practical means. However, optimization is often misused and is expected to replace common sense and engineering judgment, which should be exercised before the problem is

POLAR S-PARAMETERS IN 50.0 OHM SYSTEM

	FREQ.	S11		S21		S12		S22		S21	K
		MAGN	ANGL	MAGN	ANGL	MAGN	ANGL	MAGN	ANGL	DB	FACT.
	2000.00	.99	138	.15	-54.7	-58.2DB	-125.6	.98	146	-16.40	2.72
	3000.00	.98	110	.41	-86.3	.005	-148.3	.95	125	-7.81	1.32
	4000.00	.94	73	.92	-126.0	.016	-177.8	.91	99	-.73	1.13
	5000.00	.82	21	1.68	-176.7	.037	142.4	.82	66	4.52	1.24
	6000.00	.68	-40	2.25	128.0	.058	98.5	.69	24	7.03	1.38
	7000.00	.60	-94	2.39	78.1	.076	60.1	.56	-22	7.57	1.40
PASS	8000.00	.56	-135	2.34	36.0	.091	30.7	.49	-67	7.40	1.35
BAND	9000.00	.48	-166	2.24	-1.5	.105	5.9	.44	-106	7.02	1.41
	10000.00	.36	160	2.25	-39.4	.126	-18.5	.38	-147	7.04	1.42
	11000.00	.22	111	2.33	-82.2	.157	-48.5	.27	151	7.36	1.34
	12000.00	.30	-9	2.24	-139.4	.182	-93.3	.41	36	7.00	1.16
	13000.00	.65	-78	1.39	156.7	.137	-146.7	.74	-36	2.86	1.03
	14000.00	.83	-114	.63	107.4	.075	173.7	.87	-73	-3.96	1.03
	15000.00	.92	-137	.26	69.7	.039	145.7	.92	-45	-11.61	1.19
	16000.00	.96	-154	.10	40.3	.019	125.5	.95	-110	-20.08	1.78

9. Broadband analysis of the final amplifier circuit. Component values are shown by boldfaced numbers in Figure 7. Note that the amplifier is unconditionally stable at all frequencies and the gain falls off smoothly on both sides of the passband.

presented to the computer. Otherwise a lot of time and money may be expended without getting anything in return.

Our Fet amplifier stage as shown in Figure 7 has seven transmission line matching elements. Since each transmission line has two parameters (Z_0, θ) that may be optimized, the total number of variables would be fourteen and, depending on the initial response, the optimization may be a costly one. A more cautious approach is to optimize all lengths first and look at the other variables when the performance is already near optimum.

The maximum gain of the device at 12 GHz is 9.4 dB. Allowing for circuit losses and broadbanding effects, a conservative target of 8 dB is set for the gain response between 6 and 12 GHz. A frequency dependent loss of 0.1 dB/in. will be added to all transmission lines during the optimization. The optimization is performed by the general-purpose program COMPACT™ on the UCS Timeshare System. The response of the program is shown in Figure 8.

● *Interpreting the Optimization* The initial analysis in Figure 8 shows an average gain of 6 dB with a maximum of 2.5 dB ripple for the octave frequency range, which is an excellent starting point for the optimization. In five iterations COMPACT brought up the average gain to 7 dB and reduced the ripple to 1 dB. At this point the program could not improve the response any further, and a sensitivity analysis was performed to see if some of the line impedances could also be included among the variables. The sensitivity analysis indicated that three of the seven impedances could also be optimized, increasing the total number of variables to ten. An additional optimization was performed to the complete circuit, with a reduced target gain of 7.5 dB. The resultant gain variation was held between 7 and 7.6 dB, and all the component values were at practical, realizable values (Fig. 9).

● *Providing DC Bias to the Fet* a practical realization, the short-circuited parallel stubs of the input and output networks are grounded through bypass capacitors only and they can be used to provide the appropriate DC bias to the device. The effect of the bypass capacitors on gain and low-frequency stability must be considered, and it may be necessary to create additional compensating networks to provide stability. DC blocking should be inserted into the 50-ohm microstrip lines at the input/output terminals.

(A follow-on article will be published in MSN, *next year, that will discuss the construction by Hewlett-Packard's Microwave Semiconductor Division of this Fet amplifier as well as the potential and actual problems associated with the circuit realization. Our readers are invited to analyze the circuit presented here and anticipate the solutions necessary to realize the high impedances and small capacitors on the real, alumina substrate, then compare their results with H-P's.)*

Sound Judgment Needed

Distributed matching network theory is a relatively new and complex design technique that requires analytical preparation that most microwave engineers have forgotten—or may not have been exposed to. Very few, if any, standard graduate or undergraduate engineering programs include applicable material, and in most cases the related courses so heavily emphasized electromagnetic field theory they are of little practical value. Most of the published material on this subject has been written to impress rather than to inform, a fact that forces the practicing engineer to learn things the hard way—by trial and error.

The optimum design approach combines graphical approximations, computer-aided circuit synthesis and optimization, and sound engineering judgment. The last, being just as important, is often underemphasized because the computer is expected to do all the work. The old saying is quite applicable here: "It is not what you got that counts, but how you use it." ■

References

1. "S-Parameter Design," *HP Applications Notes No. 95 and 154,* 1968 and 1972.
2. D.J. Mellor and J.G. Linvill, "Synthesis of Interstage Networks of Prescribed Gain vs. Frequency Slopes," *IEEE Trans. Microwave Theory and Techniques,* Vol. MTT-23, December 1975.
3. W.H. Ku and W.C. Petersen, "Optimum Gain-Bandwidth Limitations of Transistor Amplifiers as Reactively Constrained Active Two-Port Networks," *IEEE Trans. on Circuits and Systems,* Vol. CAS-22, June 1975, pp. 523–533.
4. "GaAs Power Fets," *Fujitsu Application Note FG-005,* July 1978.
5. "Transistor Bias Considerations," *HP Application Notes 944-1 and 949-1,* 1974.
6. K. Richter, "Design DC Stability into Your Transistor Circuits," *Microwaves*, Dec. 1973.
7. L. Besser, "Stability Considerations of Low-Noise Amplifiers with Simultaneous Noise and Power Match," *IEEE MTT International Symp. Digest*, Palo Alto, CA, May 1975.
8. "Microwave Circuit Design," *Class Notes from UCLA and U. of Maryland Continuing Education Courses*, March 1979.
9. CADSYN User Manual, 1979, Compact Engineering, Inc., Los Altos, CA 94022.
10. A. Matsumoto, "Microwave Filters and Circuits," *Academic Press*, 1970.

Integrated Approach to Microwave Design

JOHN W. BANDLER, SENIOR MEMBER, IEEE, PETER C. LIU, MEMBER, IEEE, AND HERMAN TROMP

Abstract—**A new, integrated approach to microwave design is presented involving concepts such as optimal design centering, optimal design tolerancing, optimal design tuning, parasitic effects, uncertainties in models and reference planes, and mismatched terminations. The approach is of the worst case type, and previously published design schemes fall out as particular cases of the ideas presented. The mathematical and computational complexity as well as the benefits realized by our approach is illustrated by transformer examples, including a realistic stripline circuit.**

I. Introduction

THE use of nonlinear programming techniques for the design of microwave circuits has been well established. Applications hitherto reported by the authors, for example, fall into two categories. 1) The improvement of a response in the presence of parasitics [1], [2], in which case the function to be minimized is of the error function type and the constraints, if any, are normally imposed on the design parameters. 2) Design centering and tolerance assignment to yield a minimum cost circuit that satisfies certain specifications, usually imposed on the frequency response, for all possible values of the actual parameters [3]. The function to be minimized is of the cost function type and the constraints are due to the specifications. Tuning elements may be introduced to further increase possible unrealistic tolerances and thus decrease the cost or make a circuit meet specifications [4].

No consideration, however, of optimal tolerancing or tuning of microwave circuits has been reported where parasitic effects were taken into account. A major complication is introduced here, since the models available for common parasitic elements normally include uncertainties on the value of the model parameters. These uncertainties are due to the fact that the model is usually only approximate and that approximations have to be made in the implementation of existing model formulas. A typical example of the latter is the relationship between the characteristic impedance and width of a symmetric stripline, where the formula involves elliptic integrals.

The model uncertainties can well be of the same order of magnitude as the tolerances on the physical network parameters so that a realistic design, including tolerances, can only be found when allowance is made for them. In the approach adopted, an attempt is made to deal with the model uncertainties in the same way as with the other tolerances. This involves, however, a complication in the formulation of the problem. The physical tolerances affect the physical parameters, whereas the model parameter uncertainties affect a set of intermediate parameters (which will be called the model parameters) in the calculation of the response.

In the present paper we consider design of microwave circuits with the following concepts treated as an integral part of the design process: optimal design centering, optimal design tolerancing, optimal design tuning, parasitic effects, uncertainties in the circuit modeling, and mismatches at the source and the load.

Manuscript received November 14, 1975; revised March 15, 1976. This work was supported by the National Research Council of Canada under Grant A7239 and by a Graduate Fellowship of the Rotary Foundation to one of the authors (H.T.). This paper is based on material presented at the 1975 IEEE International Microwave Symposium, Palo Alto, CA, May 12–14, 1975.

J. W. Bandler is with the Group on Simulation, Optimization, and Control and the Department of Electrical Engineering, McMaster University, Hamilton, Ont., Canada.

P. C. Liu was with the Group on Simulation, Optimization, and Control and the Department of Electrical Engineering, McMaster University, Hamilton, Ont., Canada. He is now with Bell-Northern Research, Verdun, P.Q., Canada.

H. Tromp was with the Group on Simulation, Optimization, and Control and the Department of Electrical Engineering, McMaster University, Hamilton, Ont., Canada. He is now with the Laboratory of Electromagnetism and Acoustics, University of Ghent, Ghent, Belgium.

II. Theory

The Tolerance-Tuning Problem

In this section we introduce some of the notation and briefly review the parameters involved in the tolerance-tuning problem.

We consider first a vector of nominal design parameters ϕ^0 and a corresponding vector containing the manufacturing tolerances ε. Thus, for k variables,

$$\phi^0 \triangleq \begin{bmatrix} \phi_1^0 \\ \phi_2^0 \\ \vdots \\ \phi_k^0 \end{bmatrix} \qquad \varepsilon \triangleq \begin{bmatrix} \varepsilon_1 \\ \varepsilon_2 \\ \vdots \\ \varepsilon_k \end{bmatrix}. \tag{1}$$

A possible outcome of a design is then

$$\phi = \phi^0 + E\mu_\varepsilon \tag{2}$$

where

$$\mu_\varepsilon \triangleq \begin{bmatrix} \mu_{\varepsilon_1} \\ \mu_{\varepsilon_2} \\ \vdots \\ \mu_{\varepsilon_k} \end{bmatrix} \tag{3}$$

and

$$E \triangleq \begin{bmatrix} \varepsilon_1 & & & \\ & \varepsilon_2 & & \\ & & \ddots & \\ & & & \varepsilon_k \end{bmatrix}. \tag{4}$$

The vector μ_ε determines the actual outcome and can, for example, be bounded by

$$-1 \leq \mu_{\varepsilon_i} \leq 1, \qquad i = 1,2,\cdots,k. \tag{5}$$

It is assumed that the designer has no control over μ_ε. This leads to the concept of the tolerance region R_ε, namely, the set of points ϕ of (2) subject to, for example, (5). An untuned design implies ϕ as given by (2). Consider a vector t containing tuning variables corresponding to (1). Thus

$$t \triangleq \begin{bmatrix} t_1 \\ t_2 \\ \vdots \\ t_k \end{bmatrix}. \tag{6}$$

A design outcome with tuning implies

$$\phi = \phi^0 + E\mu_\varepsilon + T\mu_t \tag{7}$$

where

$$\mu_t \triangleq \begin{bmatrix} \mu_{t_1} \\ \mu_{t_2} \\ \vdots \\ \mu_{t_k} \end{bmatrix} \tag{8}$$

and

$$T \triangleq \begin{bmatrix} t_1 & & & \\ & t_2 & & \\ & & \ddots & \\ & & & t_k \end{bmatrix}. \tag{9}$$

The vector μ_t determines the setting of the tuning elements and we consider, for convenience,

$$-1 \leq \mu_{t_i} \leq 1, \qquad i = 1,2,\cdots,k. \tag{10}$$

Hence, we have a tuning region R_t centered at $\phi^0 + E\mu_\varepsilon$ for each outcome μ_ε.

The worst case tolerance-tuning problem is to obtain an optimal set $\{\phi^0,\varepsilon,t\}$ such that all possible outcomes (controlled by μ_ε) can be tuned so as to satisfy the design specifications (by adjusting μ_t) if tuning is available. If tuning is not available all outcomes must satisfy the design specifications. A detailed discussion has been presented [4].

Model Uncertainties

Taking ϕ as the vector of physical design parameters which have to be determined and appear in the cost function, we may consider an n-dimensional vector p containing the model parameters, e.g., the parameters appearing in an electrical equivalent circuit. In general, $n \neq k$. We have an associated vector of nominal model parameters p^0 and a vector of model uncertainties δ, where

$$p^0 \triangleq \begin{bmatrix} p_1^0 \\ p_2^0 \\ \vdots \\ p_n^0 \end{bmatrix} \qquad \delta \triangleq \begin{bmatrix} \delta_1 \\ \delta_2 \\ \vdots \\ \delta_n \end{bmatrix}. \tag{11}$$

A possible model can then be described by

$$p = p^0 + \Delta\mu_\delta \tag{12}$$

where

$$\mu_\delta \triangleq \begin{bmatrix} \mu_{\delta_1} \\ \mu_{\delta_2} \\ \vdots \\ \mu_{\delta_n} \end{bmatrix} \tag{13}$$

and

$$\Delta \triangleq \begin{bmatrix} \delta_1 & & & \\ & \delta_2 & & \\ & & \ddots & \\ & & & \delta_n \end{bmatrix}. \tag{14}$$

Thus μ_δ determines the particular model under consideration. We will assume

$$-1 \leq \mu_{\delta_i} \leq 1, \qquad i = 1,2,\cdots,n \tag{15}$$

and also the functional dependence on ϕ implied by

$$p = p^0(\phi) + \Delta(\phi)\mu_\delta. \tag{16}$$

Given a tolerance region in the ϕ space it would be hard, in general, to envisage its effect in the p space, even if $\delta = 0$. The selection of worst case p is complicated by the modeling uncertainties. Especially, when $n < k$ more than one $\{\mu_\varepsilon,\mu_\delta\}$ may give the same worst case p. In selecting candidates we will assume, intuitively, that the following is sufficient:

$$\mu_{\varepsilon_i},\mu_{\delta_j} = \pm 1, \qquad i = 1,2,\cdots,k, \quad j = 1,2,\cdots,n. \tag{17}$$

Mismatch Considerations

We consider environmental influences in the form of mismatches at the source and load. The situation is depicted in Fig. 1. The discussion is directed towards handling terminations with prescribed maximum reflection-coefficient amplitudes and arbitrary reference planes, the

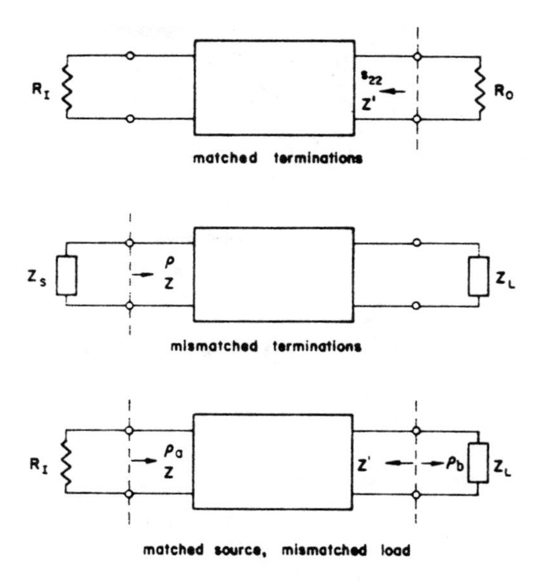

Fig. 1. Two-port circuit viewed with respect to three sets of terminations for defining impedances Z and Z' and reflection coefficients ρ, ρ_a, ρ_b, and s_{22}.

mismatches at different frequencies being, pessimistically, taken as independent.

Fig. 1(a) shows the ideal situation of matched resistive terminations R_I and R_0. Assume that the actual complex terminations as seen by the circuit are Z_S and Z_L, as shown in Fig. 1(b). Then the reflection coefficient

$$\rho_S = \frac{Z_S - R_I}{Z_S + R_I} \tag{18}$$

at the source, and

$$\rho_L = \frac{Z_L - R_0}{Z_L + R_0} \tag{19}$$

at the load. The actual reflection coefficient ρ at the source is given by

$$\rho = \frac{Z - Z_S^*}{Z + Z_S} \tag{20}$$

using the notation of Fig. 1(b). The asterisk denotes the complex conjugate.

Consider the situation depicted in Fig. 1(c). We have, for a matched source and mismatched load, the input impedance Z with the reflection coefficients

$$\rho_a = \frac{Z - R_I}{Z + R_I} \tag{21}$$

and

$$\rho_b = \frac{Z_L - Z'^*}{Z_L + Z'} \tag{22}$$

where Z' is the impedance at the output when the input is matched. Associated with the latter situation is the parameter s_{22} given by [Fig. 1(a)]

$$s_{22} = \frac{Z' - R_0}{Z' + R_0}. \tag{23}$$

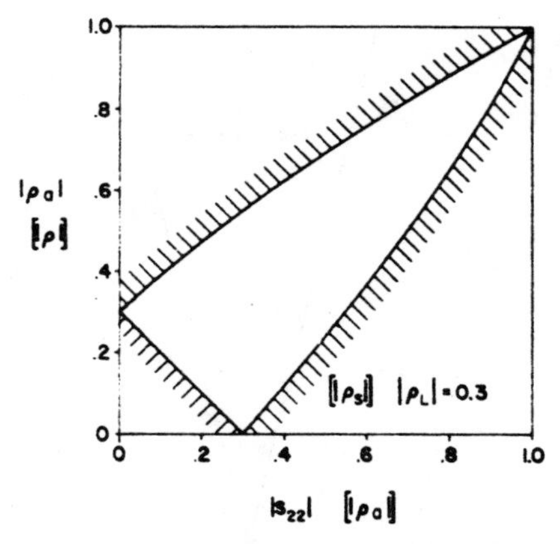

Fig. 2. Feasible region of reflection coefficients given that $|\rho_S| = |\rho_L| = 0.3$.

From (18), (20), and (21) we can obtain ρ in terms of ρ_S and ρ_a. Similarly, from (19), (22), and (23) we can obtain ρ_b in terms of s_{22} and ρ_L. Using Carlin and Giordano [5] we may readily derive the following expressions. For all possible phases

$$\frac{||\rho_a| - |\rho_S||}{1 - |\rho_a||\rho_S|} \le |\rho| \le \frac{|\rho_a| + |\rho_S|}{1 + |\rho_a||\rho_S|} \tag{24}$$

where, assuming a lossless circuit, $|\rho_a| = |\rho_b|$ and

$$\frac{||\rho_L| - |s_{22}||}{1 - |\rho_L||s_{22}|} \le |\rho_b| \le \frac{|\rho_L| + |s_{22}|}{1 + |\rho_L||s_{22}|}. \tag{25}$$

A particular example showing the extreme values of $|\rho_a|$ and $|\rho|$ is shown in Fig. 2.

Explicit upper and lower bounds on $|\rho|$ may be derived. Simplest is the upper bound, given for all possible phases of ρ_S and ρ_L and constant amplitude by

$$\max |\rho| = \frac{K_p + |s_{22}|}{1 + K_p|s_{22}|} \tag{26}$$

where

$$K_p = \frac{|\rho_L| + |\rho_S|}{1 + |\rho_L||\rho_S|}. \tag{27}$$

Let

$$K_q = \frac{|\rho_L| - |\rho_S|}{1 - |\rho_L||\rho_S|} \tag{28}$$

and

$$K_r = -K_q. \tag{29}$$

Assuming all possible phases of ρ_S and ρ_L, but constant amplitude as before, we obtain the following lower bounds.

$$\min |\rho| = \begin{cases} \dfrac{|s_{22}| - K_p}{1 - K_p|s_{22}|}, & \text{if } K_p < |s_{22}| \\ \dfrac{K_q - |s_{22}|}{1 - K_q|s_{22}|}, & \text{if } K_p > |s_{22}|,\ |\rho_L| > |\rho_S|,\ K_q > |s_{22}| \\ \dfrac{K_r - |s_{22}|}{1 - K_r|s_{22}|}, & \text{if } K_p > |s_{22}|,\ |\rho_L| < |\rho_S|,\ K_r > |s_{22}| \\ 0, & \text{otherwise.} \end{cases} \tag{30}$$

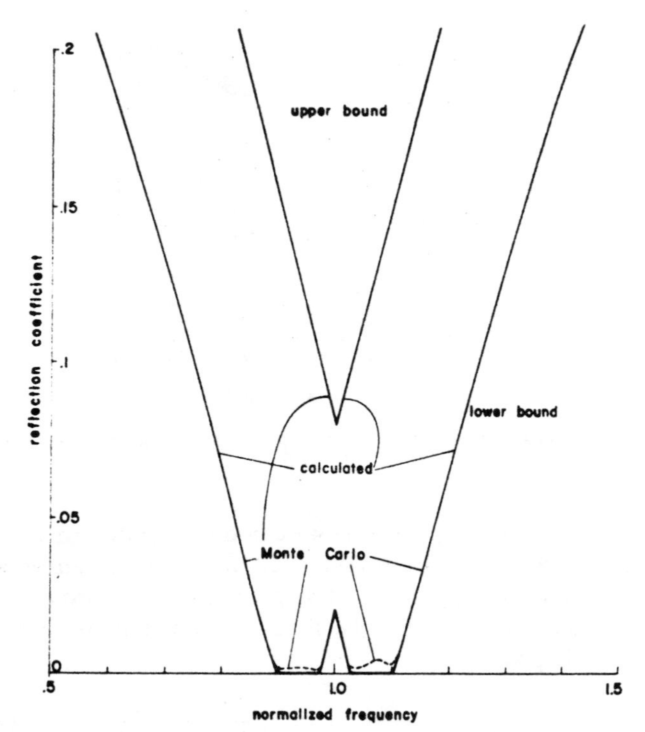

Fig. 3. Upper and lower bounds on reflection coefficient calculated from (26) and (30) and checked by a Monte Carlo analysis (1000 points) for an ideal one-section transformer from 50 to 20 Ω with $|\rho_S| = 0.05$ and $|\rho_L| = 0.03$.

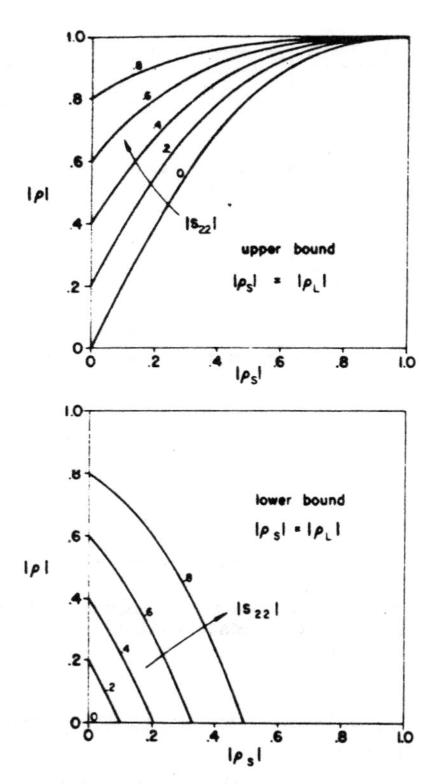

Fig. 4. Upper and lower bounds on $|\rho|$ for $|\rho_S| = |\rho_L|$.

Fig. 3 shows a comparison of these relations with the results of a Monte Carlo analysis with 1000 uniformly distributed values for the phases of ρ_S and ρ_L on $[0,2\pi]$ for a particular example of an ideal one-section transformer from 50 to 20 Ω with $|\rho_S| = 0.05$ and $|\rho_L| = 0.03$.

Assume now all possible amplitudes up to $|\rho_S|$ and $|\rho_L|$ in addition to all possible phases. The upper bound remains the same as (26) but the lower bound becomes

$$\min |\rho| = \begin{cases} \dfrac{|s_{22}| - K_p}{1 - K_p|s_{22}|}, & \text{if } K_p < |s_{22}| \\ 0, & \text{if } K_p \geq |s_{22}|. \end{cases} \tag{31}$$

An illustration for $|\rho_S| = |\rho_L|$ is shown in Fig. 4. We note that under this restriction, the results are not affected by whether all possible amplitudes are considered or not.

Design Specifications

Let all the performance specifications and constraints be expressed in the form

$$g_i \geq 0 \tag{32}$$

where g_i is, in general, an ith nonlinear function of $\boldsymbol{p}(\boldsymbol{\phi})$. Thus we may consider mismatches by an expression of the form

$$g_i = g_i^0(\boldsymbol{p}) + \mu_{\rho_i}(\boldsymbol{p},\rho_{S_i},\rho_{L_i}) \tag{33}$$

where subscript i may denote a sample point and where ρ_S represents the source mismatch and ρ_L the load mismatch. The function μ_{ρ_i} has the effect of shifting the constraint.

Given mismatches, model uncertainties, and so on, obviously influence the nominal design parameters and manufacturing tolerances. An objective, for example, is to find an optimal set $\{\boldsymbol{\phi}^0,\boldsymbol{\varepsilon},\boldsymbol{t}\}$ such that all possible outcomes (controlled by $\boldsymbol{\mu}_\varepsilon$), all possible models (controlled by $\boldsymbol{\mu}_\delta$), and all possible mismatches (controlled by $\boldsymbol{\mu}_\rho$) are accommodated in satisfying the design specifications.

III. Examples

To illustrate some of the ideas presented, we consider two simple circuits. The first includes tuning, the second considers possible model uncertainties, parasitic effects, and mismatched terminations.

Two-Section Transformer

An upper specified reflection coefficient of 0.55 for a two-section lossless transmission-line transformer with quarter-wave-length sections and an impedance ratio of 10:1 was considered at 11 uniformly spaced frequencies on 100-percent relative bandwidth.

Table I shows some results of minimizing certain objective (cost) functions of relative tolerances and tuning ranges. The functions are chosen to penalize small tolerances and large tuning ranges. The design parameters are the normalized characteristic impedances of the two sections, namely, Z_1 and Z_2. The problem has already been considered from the purely tolerance point of view [3]. The parameter ε_i' is the effective tolerance [4] of the ith parameter, i.e.,

$$\varepsilon_i' \triangleq \varepsilon_i - t_i \quad \text{for} \quad \varepsilon_i > t_i. \tag{34}$$

TABLE I
TWO-SECTION 10:1 QUARTER-WAVE TRANSFORMER DESIGN CENTERING, TOLERANCING, AND TUNING

Cost Function*	C_1	C_1	C_1	C_2	C_3	C_4	C_5
Z_1^0	2.1487	2.0340	2.2754	2.5025	1.8748	2.1487	2.1487
Z_2^0	4.7307	4.5355	4.9467	5.3337	4.2642	4.7307	4.7307
$\epsilon_1/Z_1^0 \times 100\%$	12.74	17.83	17.60	25.08	31.62	31.62	12.74
$\epsilon_2/Z_2^0 \times 100\%$	12.74	17.60	17.83	31.62	25.08	31.62	12.74
$t_1/Z_1^0 \times 100\%$	-	10.00	-	-	31.62	18.88	0.00
$t_2/Z_2^0 \times 100\%$	-	-	10.00	31.62	-	18.88	0.00
$\epsilon_1'/Z_1^0 \times 100\%$	-	7.83	-	-	0.00	12.74	12.74
$\epsilon_2'/Z_2^0 \times 100\%$	-	-	7.83	0.00	-	12.74	12.74

$^*C_1 = Z_1^0/\epsilon_1 + Z_2^0/\epsilon_2$

$C_2 = Z_1^0/\epsilon_1 + Z_2^0/\epsilon_2 + 10(t_2/Z_2^0)$

$C_3 = Z_1^0/\epsilon_1 + Z_2^0/\epsilon_2 + 10(t_1/Z_1^0)$

$C_4 = Z_1^0/\epsilon_1 + Z_2^0/\epsilon_2 + 10(t_1/Z_1^0 + t_2/Z_2^0)$

$C_5 = Z_1^0/\epsilon_1 + Z_2^0/\epsilon_2 + 500(t_1/Z_1^0 + t_2/Z_2^0)$

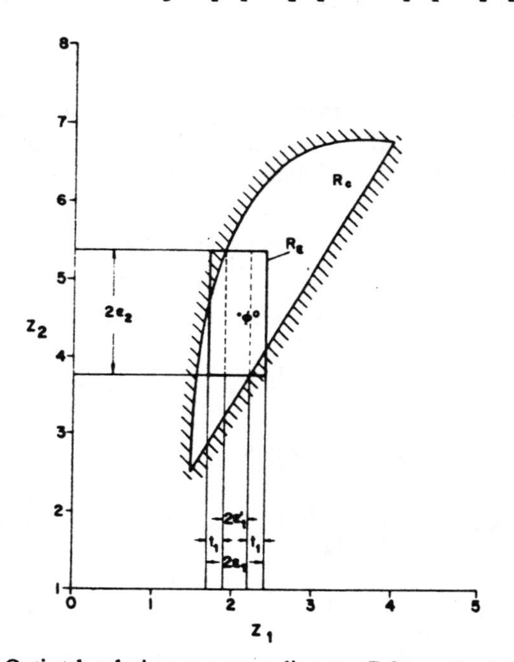

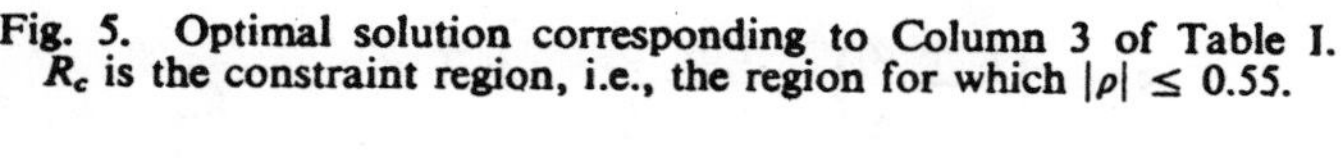
Fig. 5. Optimal solution corresponding to Column 3 of Table I. R_c is the constraint region, i.e., the region for which $|\rho| \leq 0.55$.

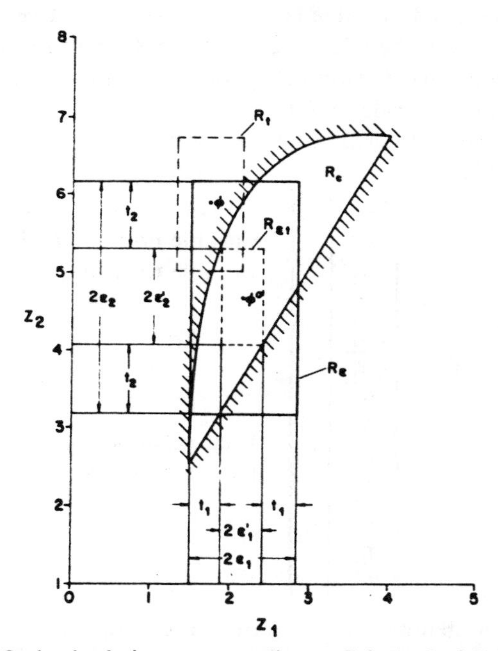

Fig. 6. Optimal solution corresponding to Column 7 of Table I. $R_{\epsilon t}$ is the *effective* tolerance region.

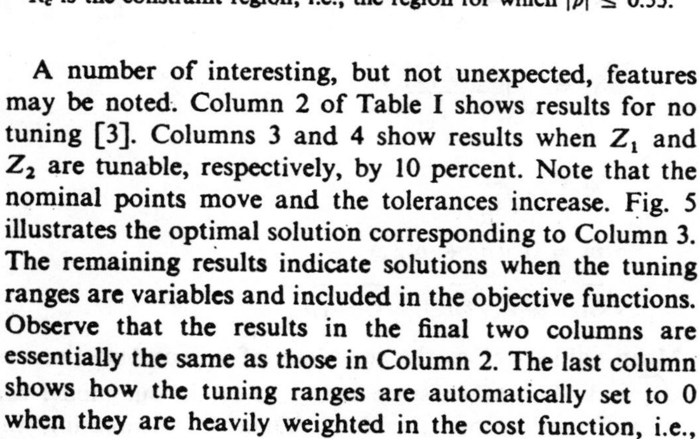
A number of interesting, but not unexpected, features may be noted. Column 2 of Table I shows results for no tuning [3]. Columns 3 and 4 show results when Z_1 and Z_2 are tunable, respectively, by 10 percent. Note that the nominal points move and the tolerances increase. Fig. 5 illustrates the optimal solution corresponding to Column 3. The remaining results indicate solutions when the tuning ranges are variables and included in the objective functions. Observe that the results in the final two columns are essentially the same as those in Column 2. The last column shows how the tuning ranges are automatically set to 0 when they are heavily weighted in the cost function, i.e., they are assumed to be expensive. Fig. 6 corresponds to the situation of Column 7.

Tuning of any component enhances all the tolerances, as expected. Furthermore, if tuning is expensive, it is rejected by the general formulation, which is useful if the designer has a number of possible alternative tunable components and is not sure which components should be effectively tuned ($t_i \geq \epsilon_i$) and which should be effectively toleranced.

One-Section Stripline Transformer

A more realistic example of a one-section transformer on stripline from 50 to 20 Ω is now considered. The physical

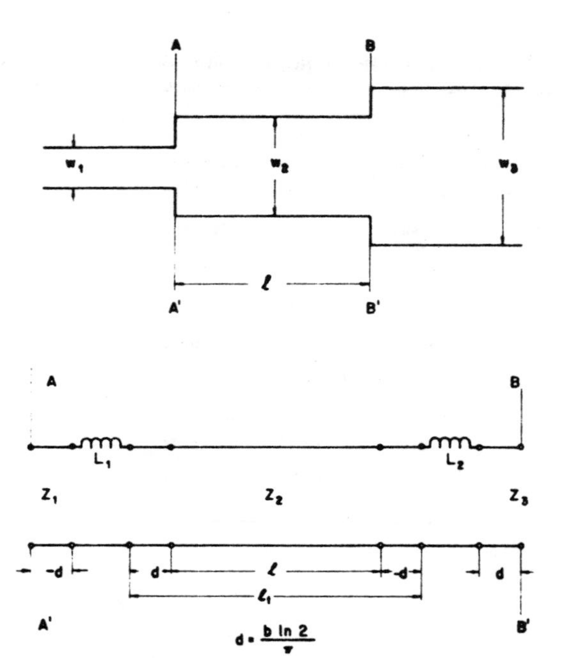

Fig. 7. Stripline transformer and equivalent circuit.

circuit and its equivalent are depicted in Fig. 7. The specifications are listed in Table II. Also shown are source and load mismatches to be accounted for as well as fixed tolerances on certain fixed nominal parameters and assumed uncertainties in model parameters.

Thirteen physical parameters implying 2^{13} extreme points are

$$\phi = \begin{bmatrix} w_1 \\ w_2 \\ w_3 \\ l \\ \sqrt{\varepsilon_{r1}} \\ \sqrt{\varepsilon_{r2}} \\ \sqrt{\varepsilon_{r3}} \\ b_1 \\ b_2 \\ b_3 \\ t_{s1} \\ t_{s2} \\ t_{s3} \end{bmatrix} \begin{matrix} \left.\right\} \text{variable nominal and variable tolerances} \\ \left.\right\} \text{fixed nominal and fixed tolerances} \end{matrix} \tag{35}$$

where w denotes strip width, l the length of the middle section, ε_r the dielectric constant, t_s the strip thickness, and b the substrate thickness. Tolerances on ε_r, b, and t_s were imposed independently for the three lines allowing independent outcomes. Nominal values for corresponding parameters were the same throughout.

Six model parameters implying 2^6 extreme points are

$$p = \begin{bmatrix} D_1 \\ D_2 \\ D_3 \\ L_1 \\ L_2 \\ l_t \end{bmatrix} \tag{36}$$

where D denotes effective linewidth, L the junction parasitic inductance, and l_t the effective section length.

TABLE II
ONE-SECTION STRIPLINE TRANSFORMER

Center Frequency	5 GHz
Frequency Band	4.5 - 5.5 GHz
Reflection Coefficient Specification	0.25 (upper)
Source Impedance	50 Ω (nominal)
Load Impedance	20 Ω (nominal)
Source Mismatch (Maximum)	0.025 (reflection coeff.)
Load Mismatch (Maximum)	0.025 (reflection coeff.)
ε_r	2.54 ± 1%
b	6.35 mm ± 1%
t_s	0.051 mm ± 5%
Uncertainty on L_1, L_2	3%
D_1, D_2, D_3	1%
ℓ_t	1 mm

The formula for D_i used is [6]

$$D_i = w_i + \frac{2b_i}{\pi} \ln 2 + \frac{t_{si}}{\pi}\left[1 - \ln \frac{2t_{si}}{b_i}\right], \qquad i = 1,2,3. \tag{37}$$

The formula is claimed to be good for $w_i/b_i > 0.5$. A 1-percent uncertainty was rather arbitrarily chosen for D_i. The characteristic impedance Z_i is then found as

$$Z_i = \frac{30\pi(b_i - t_{si})}{D_i\sqrt{\varepsilon_{ri}}}. \tag{38}$$

The values of L_i were calculated as [7]

$$L_i = \frac{30\bar{b}_i}{c} K_i, \qquad i = 1,2 \tag{39}$$

where c is the velocity of light *in vacuo* and

$$K_i = \ln\left[\left(\frac{1-\alpha_i^2}{4\alpha_i}\right)\left(\frac{1+\alpha_i}{1-\alpha_i}\right)^{\{[\alpha_i + (1/\alpha_i)]/2\}}\right] + \frac{2}{A_i}$$

$$\alpha_i = \frac{D_i}{D_{i+1}} < 1$$

$$A_i = \left(\frac{1+\alpha_i}{1-\alpha_i}\right)^{2\alpha_i} \frac{1+S_i}{1-S_i} - \frac{1+3\alpha_i^2}{1-\alpha_i^2}$$

$$S_i = \sqrt{1 - \frac{D_{i+1}^2}{\bar{\lambda}_{gi}^2}}$$

$$\bar{\lambda}_{gi} = \frac{c}{f\sqrt{\bar{\varepsilon}_{ri}}}$$

$$\bar{b}_i = 0.5(b_i + b_{i+1})$$

$$\sqrt{\bar{\varepsilon}_{ri}} = 0.5(\sqrt{\varepsilon_{ri}} + \sqrt{\varepsilon_{r(i+1)}}).$$

Mean values across the junctions of adjacent sections of $\sqrt{\varepsilon_r}$ and b are taken since actual values in our model can be different across junctions. Data for estimating the

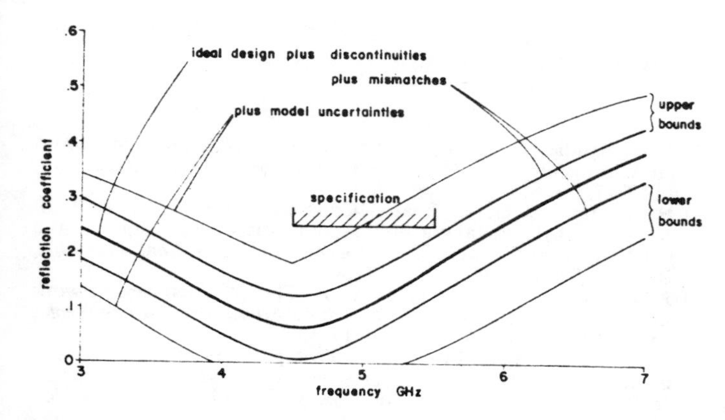

Fig. 8. Worst case analyses for the stripline transformer. Note that physical parameter tolerances are not included.

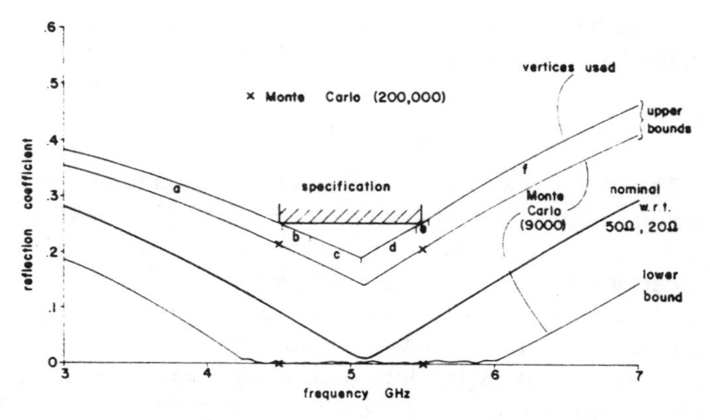

Fig. 9. Final results for the stripline transformer. The letters $a, b, \cdots, f$ indicate different vertices (designs) determining the worst case in different frequency bands.

uncertainties on L_i are available [6], [7]. Other approximations have, however, been introduced due to the tolerancing. A 3-percent uncertainty on L_i was adopted.

The length l_t is nominally the same as l. Experimental results [6] indicate possibly large inaccuracies in d (see Fig. 7) and that it depends at least on α, so that it is actually different for the two junctions. A rather pessimistic estimated error of 1 mm on l_t was chosen.

Maximum mismatch reflection coefficients of 0.025 were chosen for the source and load. Note that these values are assumed with respect to 50 and 20 Ω, respectively. The relevant formulas developed in Section II cannot be applied directly, since Z_1 and Z_3, which are affected by tolerances, must be considered for normalization. We take, most pessimistically,

$$|\rho_S| = \frac{0.025 + |\rho_1|}{1 + 0.025|\rho_1|} \tag{40}$$

where

$$\rho_1 = \frac{50 - Z_1}{50 + Z_1}$$

and

$$|\rho_L| = \frac{0.025 + |\rho_3|}{1 + 0.025|\rho_3|} \tag{41}$$

where

$$\rho_3 = \frac{20 - Z_3}{20 + Z_3}.$$

Fig. 8 summarizes some of the results obtained from worst case analyses. Depicted are curves of the ideal design with discontinuity (parasitic) effects taken into account; upper and lower bounds on the response with source and load mismatches also added; finally, upper and lower responses with model uncertainties further deteriorating the situation.

A worst case study was made to select a reasonable number of constraints from the possible $2^{19} = 2^{13} \times 2^6$, since 2^{19} would have required about 5000 s of CDC 6400 computing time per frequency point. The vertex selection procedure for the 13 physical parameters follows Bandler *et al.* [3]. From each of the selected vertices the worst values of the modeling parameters are chosen. Only the band edges are used during optimization. After each optimization the selection procedure is repeated, new constraints being added, if necessary.

TABLE III
RESULTS FOR ONE-SECTION STRIPLINE TRANSFORMER

Cost Function	$\frac{1}{100}\left(\frac{w_1^0}{\varepsilon_{w_1}} + \frac{w_2^0}{\varepsilon_{w_2}} + \frac{w_3^0}{\varepsilon_{w_3}} + \frac{\ell^0}{\varepsilon_\ell}\right)$		
Sample Points	4.5, 5.5		GHz
Number of Variables	8		
State of Solution	Intermediate	Final	
Number of Final Constraints	18	21	
Number of Optimizations	7	9	
CDC 6400 Time	2	4	min
Minimal Cost	4.82	4.93	
w_1^0	4.660	4.642	mm
w_2^0	8.968	8.910	mm
w_3^0	15.463	15.442	mm
ℓ^0	8.494	8.437	mm
$\varepsilon_{w_1}/w_1^0 \times 100$	0.94	0.92	%
$\varepsilon_{w_2}/w_2^0 \times 100$	1.20	1.13	%
$\varepsilon_{w_3}/w_3^0 \times 100$	0.74	0.70	%
$\varepsilon_\ell/\ell^0 \times 100$	0.64	0.65	%

Results on centering and tolerancing using DISOPT [8] are shown in Table III. The final number of constraints used is 21 after 9 optimizations required to identify the final constraints. Less than 4 min on the CDC 6400 was altogether required. (An intermediate, less accurate, solution is obtained using 18 constraints after 7 optimizations requiring 2 min on the CDC 6400.) To verify that the solution meets the specification, the constraint selection procedure was repeated at 21 points in the band.

Fig. 9 presents final results for this example. The reason for the discrepancy between the worst cases when vertices are used and when the Monte Carlo analysis is used is that the Monte Carlo analysis does not employ the pessimistic approximations of (40) and (41).

IV. Conclusions

The concepts we have described and the results obtained are promising. Our approach is the most direct way of currently obtaining minimum cost designs under practical situations, at least in the worst case sense. It is felt that this work is a significant advance in the art of computer-aided design, since the approach permits the inclusion of all realistic degrees of freedom of a design and all physical phenomena that influence the subsequent performance.

The approach automatically creates a tradeoff between physical tolerances (implying the cost of the network), model parameter uncertainties (implying our knowledge of the network), the quality of the terminations, and, eventually, the cost of tuning. Our approach to mismatches permits input and output connecting lines of arbitrary length—an important step towards modular design.

The conventional computer-aided design process, which seeks a single nominal design or its extension which attempts to find a design center influenced by sensitivities (see, for example, Rauscher and Epprecht [9]), would normally be a preliminary investigation to find a starting point for the work we have in mind.

References

[1] J. W. Bandler, "Computer optimization of inhomogeneous waveguide transformers," *IEEE Trans. Microwave Theory Tech.*, vol. MTT-17, pp. 563–571, Aug. 1969.

[2] H. Tromp and G. Hoffman, "Computer optimization of 3 dB microstrip hybrids taking into account dispersive, coupling and junction effects," *Proc. 1973 European Microwave Conf.* (Brussels, Belgium, Sept. 1973), Paper A.12.4.

[3] J. W. Bandler, P. C. Liu, and J. H. K. Chen, "Worst case network tolerance optimization," *IEEE Trans. Microwave Theory Tech.*, vol. MTT-23, pp. 630–641, Aug. 1975.

[4] J. W. Bandler, P. C. Liu, and H. Tromp, "A nonlinear programming approach to optimal design centering, tolerancing and tuning," *IEEE Trans. Circuits and Systems*, vol. CAS-23, pp. 155–165, March 1976.

[5] H. J. Carlin and A. B. Giordano, *Network Theory*. Englewood Cliffs, N.J.: Prentice-Hall, 1964, pp. 331–334.

[6] H. M. Altschuler and A. A. Oliner, "Discontinuities in the center conductor of symmetric strip transmission line," *IRE Trans. Microwave Theory Tech.*, vol. MTT-8, pp. 328–339, May 1960.

[7] V. Nalbandian and W. Steenaart, "Discontinuities in symmetric striplines due to impedance steps and their compensations," *IEEE Trans. Microwave Theory Tech.*, vol. MTT-20, pp. 573–578, Sept. 1972.

[8] J. W. Bandler and J. H. K. Chen, "DISOPT—A general program for continuous and discrete nonlinear programming problems," *Int. J. Systems Science*, vol. 6, pp. 665–680, 1975.

[9] C. Rauscher and G. Epprecht, "Simplified approach to sensitivity optimization by use of scattering parameters," in *Proc. 1974 European Microwave Conf.* (Montreux, Switzerland, Sept. 1974), pp. 394–398.

A General-Purpose Program for Nonlinear Microwave Circuit Design

VITTORIO RIZZOLI, MEMBER, IEEE, ALESSANDRO LIPPARINI, AND ERNESTO MARAZZI

Abstract —The paper describes the basic philosophy and the general structure of a user-oriented program package capable of designing broad classes of nonlinear microwave subsystems. Some of the peculiar aspects of the nonlinear design problem and the computer solutions adopted are discussed in detail. The application to a practical medium-power oscillator shows that the program is numerically efficient and yields well-defined and accurate results. Furthermore it provides full coverage of several aspects of circuit performance that were previously treated by empirical approaches, such as detailed effects of higher harmonics, active device operating temperatures, and circuit regulations.

I. Introduction

THE COMPUTER-AIDED design (CAD) of linear microwave circuits can be considered a well-settled matter, as is shown by the extensive technical literature on this subject, and by the commercial availability of powerful general-purpose CAD programs [1]. On the other hand, the general problem of nonlinear circuit design still represents a challenge for the microwave engineer, owing to its much higher difficulty: in fact, in this case, carrying out a design means finding a network and a nonsinusoidal electrical regime which satisfies the design specifications, that this network must be able to support.

The primary purpose of this paper is to describe the structure and basic philosophy, and to illustrate an example of the practical application of a program package allowing straightforward MIC designs to be carried out within a class of active nonlinear subsystems having the general topology shown in Fig. 1. In the current version of this program the nonlinearity is confined to the presence of a user-defined nonlinear "component" having a maximum of 3 ports and usually consisting of a set of semiconductor chips: possible combinations are, for example, one transistor (either bipolar or FET), one or two diodes, or one transistor and one diode. The remaining blocks are representative of linear subnetworks and are labeled according to their physical meaning:

- *L* linear elements (if any) of chip equivalent circuits;
- *S* set of movable short-circuit connections allowing any chip mount configuration to be selected (e.g., common source or gate for an FET chip);
- *P* package or mounting parasitics;
- *M* MIC (usually microstrip) network including load, dc bias, and possibly a number of independent sinusoidal sources harmonically related to the fundamental frequency of operation (e.g., the pump in a frequency divider).

Manuscript received February 28, 1983; revised May 3, 1983. This work was partly sponsored by the Italian National Research Council [CNR].

V. Rizzoli and A. Lipparini are with the Dipartimento di Elettronica, Informatica e Sistemistica, University of Bologna, Villa Griffone, Pontecchio Marconi, Bologna, Italy.

E. Marazzi is with the SIAE Microelettronica, S.p.A., Via Buonarroti 21, Cologno Monzese, Milano, Italy.

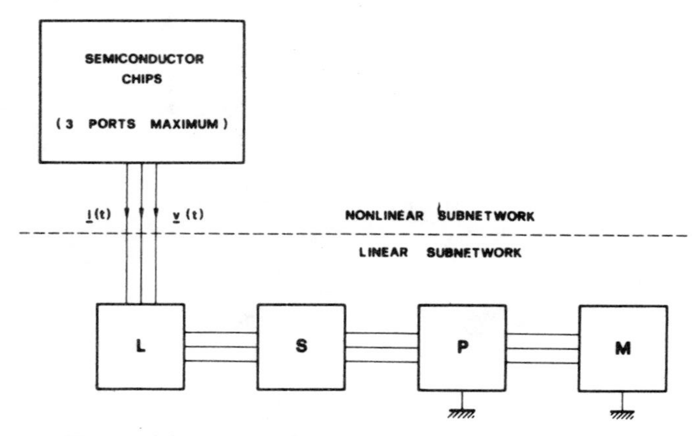

Fig. 1. Schematic topology of microwave nonlinear network.

The topology of the linear subnetwork is completely arbitrary and can be specified by the user in the input data file; in the same way, one can also select a number of physical or electrical parameters of the microstrip network to be used as design variables. Thus despite the limitations on the nonlinear subnetwork, the program is general enough to cover a number of applications of practical interest, including frequency dividers, microwave oscillators both free-running and voltage-controlled, active multipliers, and so on. Furthermore, the basic discussion is equally valid for any number of ports of the nonlinear subnetwork.

The design method is based on the assumption that the semiconductor devices can be described by a reliable nonlinear circuit model, the availability of such models at present being well established as a result of the work of several research teams throughout the world [2]–[5]. Otherwise the formulation is rigorous, at least in principle, and is probably more advanced than many previous approaches to the same problem under several respects. As a first point, all relevant harmonics of the fundamental frequency of operation are exactly accounted for, so that the intrinsic limitations of most available design techniques (e.g., those based on large-signal S-parameters [6], [7]) are overcome. This may be of special importance in the case of power devices acting in a frequency-selective environment such as microstrip circuitry. Furthermore, a straightforward computer solution of the basic problem—designing the nonlinear network for a given set of electrical specifications—becomes feasible and cost-effective thanks to a special optimization strategy [8]. The unknown circuit parameters and the signal waveforms are simultaneously determined by minimizing a unique objective function, thus avoiding the nesting of nonlinear analysis and network optimization loops. The application example presented—concerning the design of a medium-power microstrip oscillator—clearly shows how deep an insight into circuit performance can be obtained by the present approach. The available information includes voltage and current waveforms, junction temperatures, effects of harmonic components, and compensation of the spread of active device parameters by circuit trimming.

II. Design Philosophy

As in any circuit design problem, the starting information is represented by a set of electrical specifications which define the desired network performance. In order to meet the design objectives, a first obvious requirement is that a suitable number of degrees of freedom be available in the linear subnetwork. This is accomplished in the usual way, by selecting a topology of the microstrip network and by choosing some of its electrical or physical parameters as a first set of problem unknowns, namely $\boldsymbol{P}$. Since the network is nonlinear, however, its performance is not only determined by physical configuration, but also depends on the electrical regime that takes place in the circuit. Thus to obtain a complete description we must introduce a further set of unknowns, which generally speaking consist of the voltage and current waveforms. In practical cases one is mostly concerned with the steady-state behavior, so that we may restrict our search to those electrical regimes that the network can support which are periodic in time. The unknowns describing the electrical regime may then be reduced to the vector of (complex) voltage harmonics at the ports of the nonlinear subnetwork, namely $\boldsymbol{V}$. On the other hand, semiconductor devices are usually best simulated in terms of time-domain voltage and current vectors $\boldsymbol{v}(t), \boldsymbol{i}(t)$. A general time-domain representation of the nonlinear subnetwork could be of the form

$$\boldsymbol{i}(t) = \boldsymbol{f}\left\{\boldsymbol{i}(t), \frac{d\boldsymbol{i}}{dt}, \boldsymbol{v}(t), \frac{d\boldsymbol{v}}{dt}\right\} \tag{1}$$

where $\boldsymbol{f}$ is nonlinear and analytically known. Equation (1) is most common, but higher order derivatives could appear as well without affecting the validity of the following discussion. Fig. 2 shows an example drawn from the literature [3] of a nonlinear circuit model for an active device (MSC-3000 chip), leading by inspection to a set of time-domain equations of the form (1).

For any given vector $\boldsymbol{P}$ the frequency-domain equations of the linear subnetwork can be written down as

$$\boldsymbol{I}(\omega) = \boldsymbol{Y}(\omega, \boldsymbol{P})\boldsymbol{V}(\omega) + \boldsymbol{J}(\omega, \boldsymbol{P}) \tag{2}$$

where $\boldsymbol{V}, \boldsymbol{I}$ are vectors of voltage and current phasors at the subnetwork ports, $\boldsymbol{Y}$ represents its admittance matrix, and $\boldsymbol{J}$ is a vector of Norton's equivalent current sources. Assuming a periodic regime with fundamental angular frequency ω_0 we also have

$$\boldsymbol{i}(t) = \mathrm{Re}\left\{\sum_{k=0}^{N} \boldsymbol{I}_k \exp(jk\omega_0 t)\right\}$$

$$\boldsymbol{v}(t) = \mathrm{Re}\left\{\sum_{k=0}^{N} \boldsymbol{V}_k \exp(jk\omega_0 t)\right\} \tag{3}$$

N being the number of significant harmonics. At $\omega = k\omega_0$, (2) is rewritten as

$$\boldsymbol{I}_k = \boldsymbol{Y}(k\omega_0, \boldsymbol{P})\boldsymbol{V}_k + \boldsymbol{J}_k(\boldsymbol{P}). \tag{4}$$

Now we replace (4) into (3) and (3) into (1), and take the

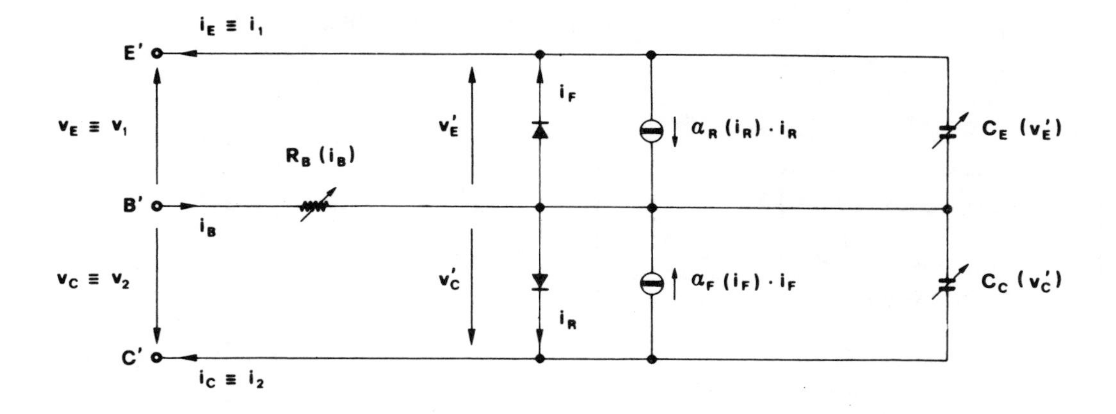

Fig. 2. Nonlinear equivalent circuit of microwave transistor chip (after [3]).

Fourier expansion of the currents to obtain

$$i(t) = \mathrm{Re}\left\{ \sum_{k=0}^{N} F_k(V) \exp(jk\omega_0 t) \right\} \tag{5}$$

where F_k may actually be computed by the FFT. A comparison of (5) and (4) leads to the nonlinear solving system

$$F_k(V) - Y(k\omega_0, P)V_k - J_k(P) = O, \qquad k = 0, 1, \cdots, N. \tag{6}$$

The above approach is a straightforward application of the well-known harmonic-balance technique [9], [10]. Once a solution of (6) has been found, all quantities used to describe circuit performance (network functions) may be determined by conventional linear network analysis, to be carried out, if required, at several harmonic frequencies.

In summary, the problem to be solved consists of finding the unknowns P, V in such a way that both (6) and the design specifications be satisfied.

It should be noted that the above considerations implicitly assume an order of priority between the two sets of unknowns, in that physically significant network functions and thus an objective function for optimization can only be found after solving the nonlinear system (6). This leads to a solution scheme consisting of two nested iteration loops, the inner one providing the objective function for the outer.

Now one of the key ideas underlying the present design approach is that this apparent hierarchy of variables can be bypassed. As a first point, we observe that solving the nonlinear system (6) is conceptually equivalent to minimizing the harmonic-balance error

$$e_B(P, V) = \left\{ \sum_{k=0}^{N} |F_k(V) - Y(k\omega_0, P)V_k - J_k(P)|^2 \right\}^{1/2} \tag{7}$$

with respect to the voltage harmonics (note that from a physical standpoint a solution is only acceptable when the corresponding minimum is zero). On the other hand, the network functions can be computed (in the way described in detail in Section III) starting from *any* given set of design variables (P, V) even though not satisfying the network equations (6). In such cases, of course, they are devoid of physical meaning, since the network defined by P cannot support the steady-state regime represented by V. They can, nevertheless, be used to define in a purely mathematical sense an objective function encompassing the design specifications. We may thus carry out a simultaneous search for the network parameters and the voltage harmonics by minimizing a suitable combination of such a function and of the harmonic-balance error (7). After a successful optimization the harmonic balance will be restored, and the network functions will get back their original physical meaning, thus providing a significant design with a dramatic saving of computer time.

In fact, there are also very good reasons why the above mentioned hierarchy of variables *should* be bypassed. In several cases of practical interest—usually circuits providing power transfer from one frequency to another such as oscillators or frequency dividers—the solving system (6) turns out to be impossible for a wide variety of linear subnetworks. In such cases a conventional optimization scheme might be severely inefficient or even useless at all unless a starting point close enough to the final solution were available. On the contrary, the present method simply starts with a large harmonic-balance error thus compelling the minimization algorithm to approach network configurations compatible with the desired electrical performance.

III. Formulation of the Objective Function

A considerable effort has been spent in order to make the program as general and flexible as possible, while preserving its user-oriented character. Of course, the standard definitions of the function to be minimized, which are used in conventional linear CAD programs, are not applicable, due to the peculiar aspects of the nonlinear design problem. In this section, we illustrate the solutions that were adopted to cope with such peculiar requirements. The topics to be covered include the computation of network

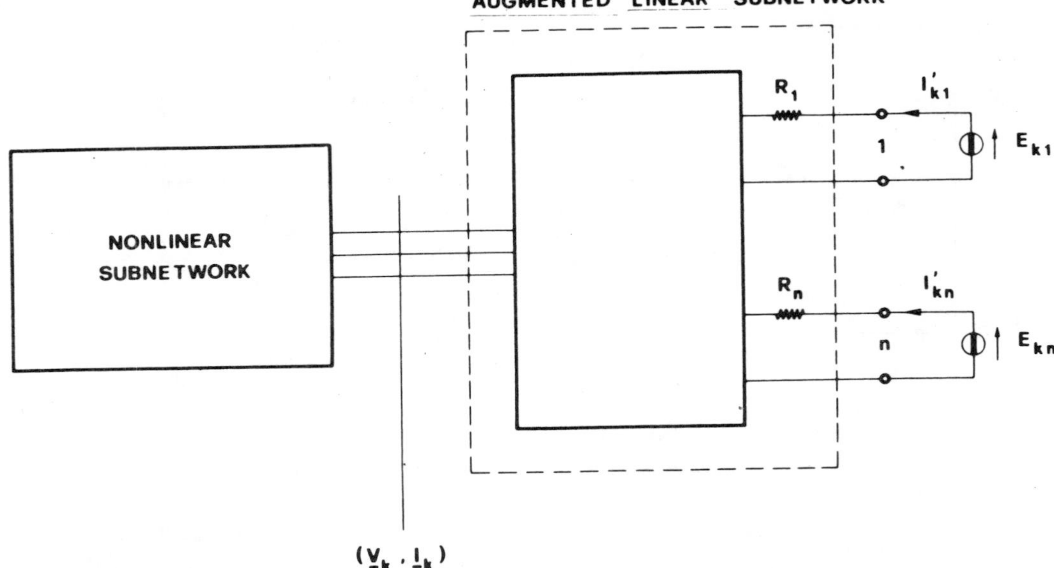

Fig. 3. Modified network topology for computation of network functions.

functions, the formulation of the objective, and the search for operating temperatures of the semiconductor devices. In any case, the starting point will be represented by a set of problem unknowns $(\boldsymbol{P}, \boldsymbol{V})$ provided by the minimization algorithm at any iteration of the search loop.

A. Network Functions

The calculation of network functions usually requires a knowledge of the current harmonics in a number of branches of the linear subnetwork which may, or may not, contain a sinusoidal source (including dc bias for $\omega = 0$). To obtain this, we first modify the topology of the linear subnetwork in such a way that all branches containing free generators and all branches used to compute the network functions are explicitly put into evidence, as shown in Fig. 3. The number of these branches (which will be named "external" branches) is denoted by n, and the number of ports of the nonlinear subnetwork (device ports) by n_D. In this way, we generate an $(n_D + n)$-port circuit which will be referred to as the "augmented" linear subnetwork. To define circuit topology at the data-entry level, we separately input a description of the augmented linear subnetwork to be handled by a general-purpose linear multiport analysis routine, and a set of vectors $\boldsymbol{E}_k$ $(k = 0, 1, \cdots, N)$, each containing the free generator voltages at $\omega = k\omega_0$ ($\boldsymbol{E}_k$ is an n-element vector). It is essential that the linear-analysis subprograms allow the circuit to be described on a node basis, since some of the device ports may be floating (e.g., Fig. 4).

In order to carry out one function evaluation, the augmented linear subnetwork is first analyzed at all harmonics of interest, that is, for $\omega = k\omega_0$ $(k = 0, 1, \cdots, N)$ to find its admittance matrix $\boldsymbol{Y}_A(k\omega_0, \boldsymbol{P})$. We may write

$$\boldsymbol{Y}_A(k\omega_0, \boldsymbol{P}) = \left[\begin{array}{c|c} \boldsymbol{Y} & \boldsymbol{Y}_{12} \\ \hline \boldsymbol{Y}_{21} & \boldsymbol{Y}' \end{array}\right](k\omega_0, \boldsymbol{P}) \tag{8}$$

where $\boldsymbol{Y}(k\omega_0, \boldsymbol{P})$ is the same admittance matrix appearing in (4). From the augmented subnetwork equations we further get

$$\boldsymbol{J}_k(\boldsymbol{P}) = \boldsymbol{Y}_{12}(k\omega_0, \boldsymbol{P})\boldsymbol{E}_k$$
$$\boldsymbol{I}_k'(\boldsymbol{P}, \boldsymbol{V}) = \boldsymbol{Y}_{21}(k\omega_0, \boldsymbol{P})\boldsymbol{V}_k + \boldsymbol{Y}'(k\omega_0, \boldsymbol{P})\boldsymbol{E}_k \tag{9}$$

where $\boldsymbol{I}_k'$ is the vector of currents in the external branches at $\omega = k\omega_0$; from $\boldsymbol{I}_k'$ and $\boldsymbol{E}_k$ one can derive all network functions which are usually of interest. Note that (8) and (9) also provide a complete description of the linear subnetwork, thus allowing the harmonic-balance error to be computed in the way shown in the previous section.

As an example, let the nonlinear network be a free-running sinusoidal oscillator, whose performance is described in terms of output power (P_o), dc to RF conversion efficiency (η), and harmonic content of the output waveform. In this case, we take $n = 3$, and let the first of the external branches be the load branch and the remaining ones be bias branches (e.g., Fig. 4). Since no free generators other than dc act in the circuit, we have $\boldsymbol{E}_k = 0$ $(k > 0)$ and

$$\boldsymbol{E}_0 = \begin{bmatrix} 0 \\ E_{02} \\ E_{03} \end{bmatrix}. \tag{10}$$

Thus, the network functions may be computed as

$$P_0 = \frac{1}{2}R_1|I_{11}'|^2$$
$$\eta = \frac{R_1|I_{11}'|^2}{2(E_{02}I_{02}' + E_{03}I_{03}')}$$
$$S = 10\log_{10}\frac{|I_{11}'|^2}{\sum_{k=2}^{N}|I_{k1}'|^2} \tag{11}$$

where S is the harmonic output power expressed in decibels below the fundamental.

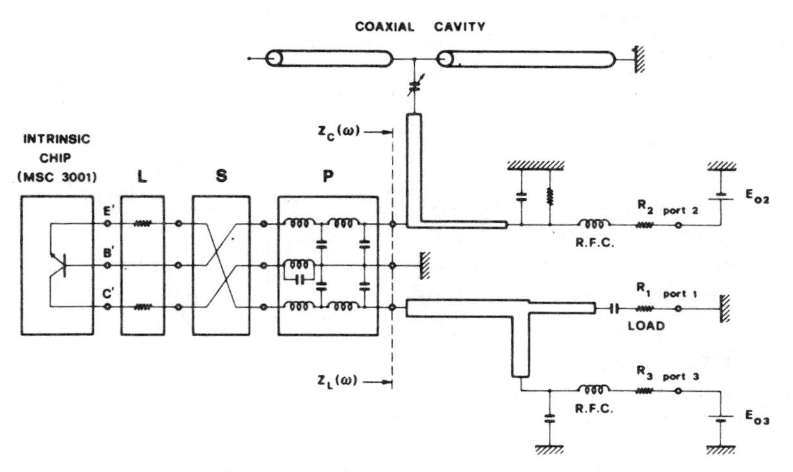

Fig. 4. Circuit diagram of MIC medium-power oscillator.

In conclusion, for any set of design variables $(\boldsymbol{P}, \boldsymbol{V})$ the analysis of the augmented linear subnetwork through (8) and (9) provides all the information required to find the network functions. In practice the program performs this analysis automatically and makes the vectors $\boldsymbol{I}_k'$ available to the user via a COMMON block; the functions are then computed in a user-defined subroutine to ensure maximum flexibility.

B. Objective

For a given set $(\boldsymbol{P}, \boldsymbol{V})$, let $f_i(\boldsymbol{P}, \boldsymbol{V})$ denote any network function used to specify the design goals. The performance specifications will be of the general form

$$f_i(\boldsymbol{P}, \boldsymbol{V}) \geqslant f_{i\min} \qquad i = 1, 2, \cdots, M \tag{12}$$

where $f_{i\min}$ is a suitably selected lower bound. While (12) represents the most commonly encountered case, it is occasionally required that some of the network functions be optimized in a strict sense, i.e., take the maximum possible value in the final circuit, the exact amount being *a priori* unknown. In such cases, we must combine (12) with the further requirements

$$f_i(\boldsymbol{P}, \boldsymbol{V}) \text{ as large as possible}, \qquad i = 1, 2, \cdots, T \quad (T \leqslant M). \tag{13}$$

Besides (12) and (13) the harmonic-balance condition $e_B = 0$ must be imposed. For practical purposes, this is replaced by

$$e_B \leqslant e_{\max} \tag{14}$$

where $e_{\max}$ is a threshold value to be established by experience in relation with the given problem.

In order to define the objective, we first introduce the weighted errors

$$E_0 = W_B(e_B - e_{\max})$$
$$E_i = W_i(f_{i\min} - f_i), \qquad i = 1, 2, \cdots, M \tag{15}$$

(all W's are positive quantities), and let

$$E = \max(E_i), \qquad i = 0, 1, \cdots, M \tag{16}$$

$$\delta_i = \begin{cases} 1, & (E_i > 0) \\ 0, & (E_i \leqslant 0). \end{cases} \tag{17}$$

Now we take as the objective function to be minimized the quantity

$$F_{OB}(\boldsymbol{P}, \boldsymbol{V}) = \begin{cases} \sum_{i=0}^{M} \delta_i E_i^2, & (E > 0) \\ -\sum_{i=1}^{T} E_i^2, & (E \leqslant 0) \end{cases} \tag{18}$$

When $E \leqslant 0$ the harmonic-balance condition (14) is met, and so are the electrical specifications (12); thus the efforts of the optimization algorithm are entirely devoted to increasing the magnitude of the errors E_i $(i = 1, 2, \cdots, T)$, that is, to making the network functions (13) as large as possible. Note that the introduction of a harmonic-balance threshold $e_{\max} > 0$ is essential whenever design specifications of the kind (13) are to be dealt with. Otherwise one always has $E_0 > 0$, so that any network function exceeding the prescribed lower bound has no further effect on the objective; thus in the long run the program will only try to minimize the harmonic-balance error while keeping all network functions essentially constant at their lower bounds. The above approach has proven effective in optimizing some aspects of circuit performance such as the output power and/or efficiency of an oscillator..

C. Device Temperatures

The temperature of operation usually affects the performance of semiconductor devices in a significant way. This results in temperature-dependent parameters appearing in the chip equivalent circuits, such as the voltage–current relationships of the emitter and collector junctions for the bipolar transistor of Fig. 2. Thus especially for CW operation of power devices, the actual device temperature must be evaluated, in order that the final design be practically significant. Of course a possible approximate solution would be to give rough *a priori* estimates of the device temperatures and use these to model the equivalent circuits throughout the optimization. However, an accurate determination of the actual temperatures is possible within the present framework at virtually no extra cost in terms of CPU time.

Let us consider any one of the semiconductor devices included in the nonlinear subnetwork, and let V_{Dk}, I_{Dk} be the vectors of voltage and current harmonics at the device ports for $\omega = k\omega_0$ $(k = 0, 1, \cdots, N)$, the positive directions for currents being specified in Fig. 1. V_{Dk}, I_{Dk} are obviously subsets of V_k, I_k as defined by (3). Prior to each evaluation of the objective, starting from the given set of design variables (P, V) we compute the quantity

$$P_{DJ} = -V_{D0}^T I_{D0} - \frac{1}{2} \sum_{k=1}^{N} \mathrm{Re}\{V_{Dk}^T I_{Dk}^*\} \tag{19}$$

(we denote by ^{T} a transposed matrix and by $*$ the complex conjugate). If (P, V) were a solution of (4) and (6), P_{DJ} would obviously represent the power dissipated inside the device being considered. In general, this will not be the case during the search, but will become true after a successful optimization. Based on (19) we may now introduce the quantity

$$T_D = \begin{cases} T_A, & P_{DJ} \leq 0 \\ T_A + R_D \cdot P_{DJ}, & P_{DJ} > 0 \end{cases} \tag{20}$$

where T_A is room temperature and R_D the known thermal resistance of the device being considered. T_D is conventionally used as the current device temperature to compute the temperature-dependent features of the equivalent circuit. Once again, after a successful optimization T_D will represent the actual steady-state temperature of the chip, so that the nonlinear constraints imposed by the device will be exactly formulated in the final description of the circuit.

IV. A Design Example

In this section we report a few numerical and experimental results concerning a medium-power low-noise microstrip oscillator that was designed by means of the computer program described above. This oscillator had to be mechanically tunable over the 2.25 to 2.50-GHz band with a minimum output power of 0.5 W and harmonics lower than −25 dBc. In order to meet the tuning requirements and the very stringent specifications on noise, a tunable coaxial cavity was used and was connected to the transistor base via a capacitive coupling and a microstrip transformer. The selected transistor was an MSC 3001 chip (consisting of two MSC 3000's connected in parallel) in a grounded-bar package for which an accurate circuit model was available. Mainly for the sake of thermal dissipation, a common-collector configuration was adopted; on the emitter side the transistor was matched to the load by a simple microstrip stub network. A complete circuit diagram is shown in Fig. 4, where the main building blocks are labeled according to Fig. 1 and the network topology is arranged according to Fig. 3. A unique bias voltage $E_{02} = E_{03} = -16$ V was used due to system requirements.

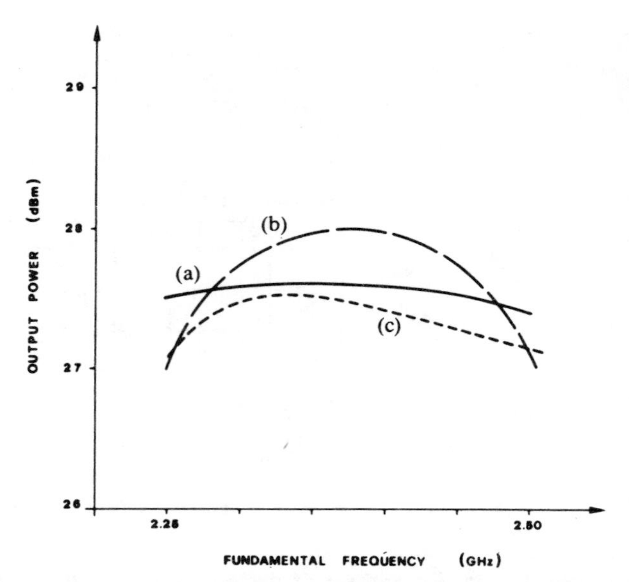

Fig. 5. Oscillator output power versus frequency. (a) Nominal design. (b) Same with a different chip. (c) Measured on prototype.

The design was carried out by optimizing all significant parameters of the passive network (including the bias circuit) as well as three voltage harmonics besides the fundamental and dc components. A circuit model of the chip was obtained by connecting in parallel two identical networks, each having the topology given in Fig. 2. The oscillator performance in terms of output power versus frequency (the latter being determined by mechanical tuning) is shown in Fig. 5. Curve (a) in this figure represents the nominal design, while curve (b) was obtained by dropping the nonlinear model of a different chip [3] into the same linear network. Finally curve (c) is experimental, and was measured on a prototype oscillator built on the basis of the theoretical design. The agreement among these curves gives a clear check of the reliability of our design approach. Other features of the oscillator were a minimum efficiency of 25 percent and a harmonic output power of less than −26.5 dBc across the tuning band, closely corresponding to the predicted values.

The power output capabilities of this circuit were investigated in some detail both numerically and experimentally. Some results concerning the center-band frequency are reported below. In Fig. 6 we plot the load impedance at the fundamental $Z_L(\omega_0)$ (see Fig. 4), which is required to produce a prescribed output power (thick solid curves). This impedance is taken as representative of the microstrip network topology. The interesting point is that $Z_L(\omega_0)$ is almost power-independent in a broad range of power values, roughly 15–28 dBm, while it changes rapidly outside this range. Fig. 7 shows that the cavity impedance $Z_c(\omega_0)$ (see Fig. 4) is virtually a short circuit irrespective of output power, while the solid line in Fig. 8 gives the computed relationship between the output power and the emitter bias resistance (R_3 in Fig. 4). In Fig. 6 we also report the actual $Z_L(\omega_0)$ measured on the prototype oscillator, which is obviously represented by a couple of horizontal straight lines since it is power independent. This

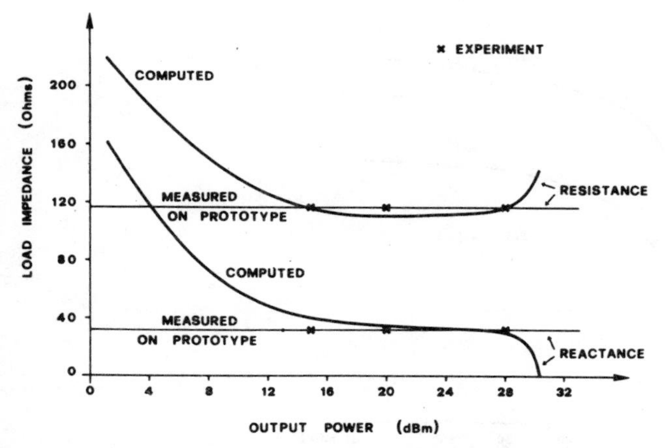

Fig. 6. Load impedance at the fundamental versus output power.

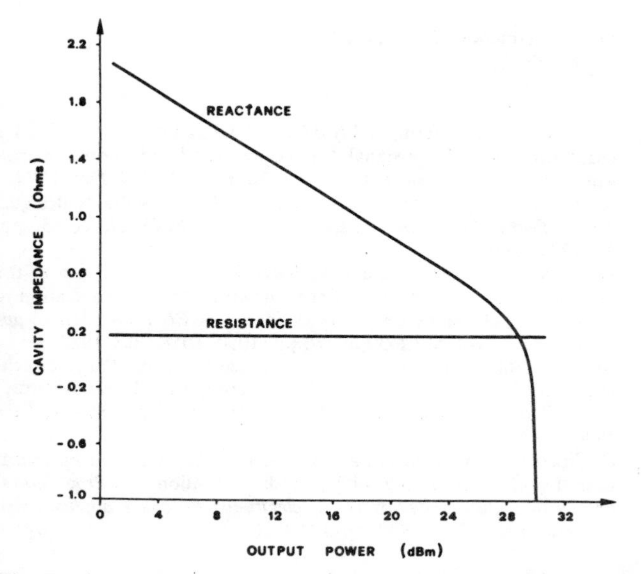

Fig. 7. Cavity impedance at the fundamental versus output power (computed).

impedance is practically the same as the load required for oscillation between 15 and 28 dBm. As a consequence, the oscillator output power could actually be varied throughout the range of constant impedance by simply changing the emitter bias resistance (see the experimental points reported in Figs. 6, 8, and 9): outside the oscillation would cease or else be transferred to spurious frequencies unrelated to ω_o. The above behavior allowed the output power fluctuations due to the spread of the active devices to be compensated by simply trimming the emitter resistor in a production series of about 200 similar oscillators. Finally, Fig. 9 shows the degradation of the spectral purity of the output signal as a function of the fundamental-frequency power output.

The importance of taking into account several harmonics in the design is demonstrated by the data collected in Table I still concerning oscillation and center band. The $N = 4$ column in this table represents the nominal design, which is seen to reproduce very accurately the measured performance, also given in the table. On the other hand,

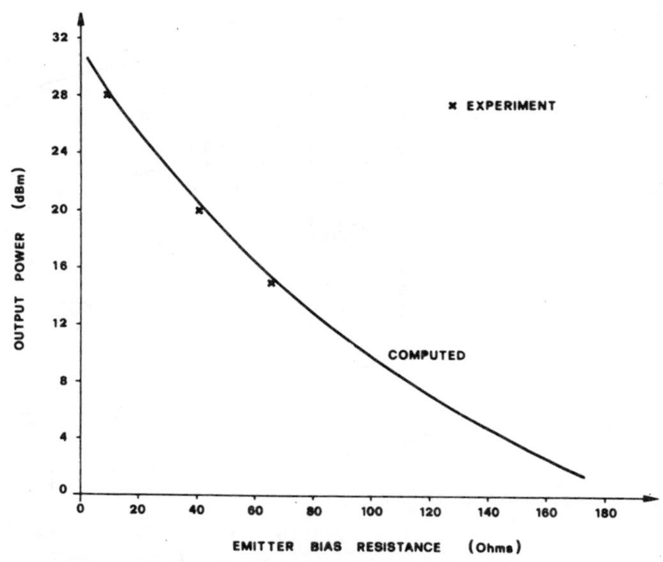

Fig. 8. Dependence of output power on emitter bias resistance.

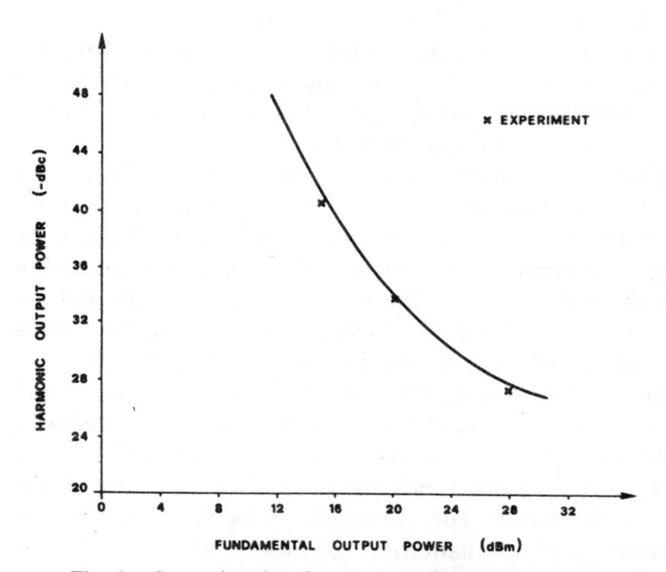

Fig. 9. Spectral purity of output waveform versus power.

TABLE I

	Measured	Computed, N = 4	Computed, N = 1
DC to RF conversion efficiency	26%	26.5%	47%
Fundamental power output	27.5 dBm (560 mW)	27.6 dBm (575 mW)	29.4 dBm (870 mW)
Load impedance at ω_o	115 + j 35 Ω	116 + j 33 Ω	95 + j 50 Ω

the $N = 1$ column displays the computed performance when the network is optimized (with the bias circuit kept fixed) while considering only the fundamental and dc components. The results show that the single-frequency design is only moderately misleading concerning the microstrip net-

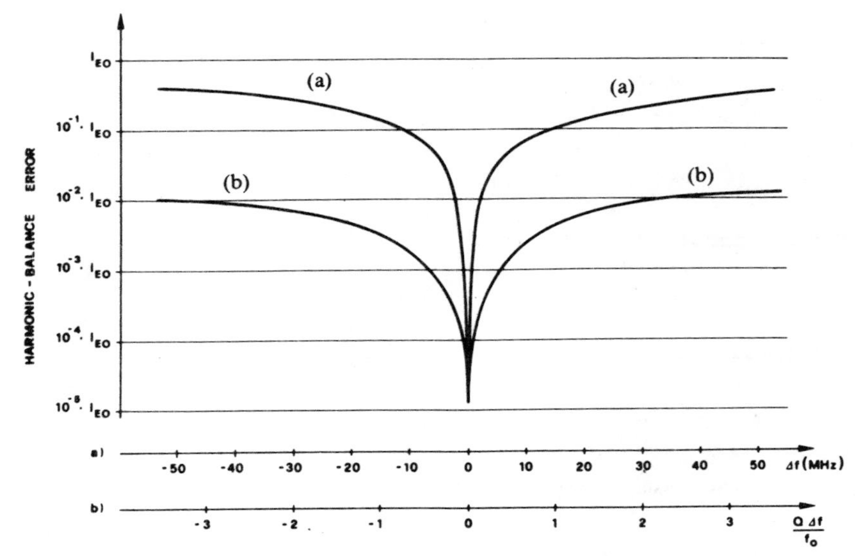

Fig. 10. Minimum harmonic-balance error versus frequency offset. (a) Upper frequency scale. (b) Lower scale.

work, but does not allow the oscillator output power and efficiency to be predicted with practically useful accuracy.

Finally, Fig. 10 shows that the numerical solutions are very well defined with respect to frequency changes. In this figure we plot the minimum harmonic-balance error that the search algorithm can achieve by optimizing the voltage harmonics only with a fixed linear subnetwork (corresponding to the nominal design of the oscillator). Since the error is dimensionally a current, the e_B axis is graduated in terms of fractions of the dc component of the emitter current (I_{E0}) for ease of comparison. Curve (a), corresponding to the upper frequency scale, shows the error as a function of frequency offset from the nominal center-band in megahertz. Curve (b) is the same as (a) but is redrawn with an expanded frequency scale (lower scale) for which one division corresponds to the 3-dB bandwidth of the oscillator cavity. The minimum error (at the nominal frequency of oscillation) is obviously not zero due to numerical roundoff. However, e_B increases by about 2 orders of magnitude in $\pm$ one half of the 3-dB bandwidth and by almost 3 orders of magnitude in ± 2.5 MHz. Thus the design shows no appreciable numerical uncertainty on the actual frequency of oscillation.

References

[1] L. Besser *et al.*, "Computer-aided design for the 1980's," in *1981 IEEE MTT-S Int. Microwave Symp. Tech. Dig. Papers*, Los Angeles, CA, June 1981, pp. 51–53.

[2] H. A. Willing, C. Rauscher and P. De Santis, "A technique for predicting large-signal performance of a GaAs MESFET," *IEEE Trans. Microwave Theory Tech.*, vol. MTT-26, no. 12, pp. 1017–1023, Dec. 1978.

[3] S. Benedetto *et al.*, "Simulation models for microwave power transistors under large-signal operating conditions," ESA-ESTEĆ Contract 3334/77, Final Rep., Noordwijk, Dec. 1979.

[4] R. S. Tucker, "RF characterization of microwave power FET's," *IEEE Trans. Microwave Theory Tech.*, vol. MTT-29, no. 8, pp. 776–781, Aug. 1981.

[5] G. P. Bava *et al.*, "Modeling and performance simulation techniques of GaAs MESFET's for microwave power amplifiers," ESA Contract 4043/79/NL/PP, Final Rep., Oct. 1981.

[6] Y. Mitsui, M. Nakatani, and S. Mitsui, "Design of GaAs MESFET oscillators using large-signal *S*-parameters," *IEEE Trans. Microwave Theory Tech.*, vol. MTT-25, no. 12, pp. 981–984, Dec. 1977.

[7] K. M. Johnson, "Large signal GaAs MESFET oscillator design," *IEEE Trans. Microwave Theory Tech.*, vol. MTT-27, no. 3, pp. 217–227, Mar. 1979.

[8] A. Lipparini, E. Marazzi, and V. Rizzoli, "A new approach to the computer-aided design of nonlinear networks and its application to microwave parametric frequency dividers," *IEEE Trans. Microwave Theory Tech.*, vol. MTT-30, no. 7, pp. 1050–1058, July 1982.

[9] M. S. Nakhla and J. Vlach, "A piecewise harmonic-balance technique for determination of periodic response of nonlinear systems," *IEEE Trans. Circuits Syst.*, vol. CAS-23, no. 2, pp. 85–91, Feb. 1976.

[10] F. Filicori, V. A. Monaco, and C. Naldi, "Analysis and optimization of non-linear circuits with periodic excitation," in *Proc. Spacecad 79 (Computer-aided design of electronics for space applications)*, Bologna, Italy, Sept. 1979, pp. 171–176.

CAD Techniques Improve Microwave Switch Design Efficiency

By
Les Besser
Microwave Educational Programs

Linear approximations can be effectively applied to non-linear problems in the computer-aided design of microwave switches.

The past two decades have brought major improvements in the design of linear steady-state microwave circuits. The introduction of S-parameter design techniques, acceptance of computer-aided design (CAD), and availability of powerful, small computers, has contributed to increased design efficiency and accurate prediction of performance before building circuits. However, non-linear circuit design and device modeling are still in an infant state and typically carried out through an empirical approach. There are cases, however, when linear approximations can be successfully applied to non-linear problems. The following is an outline of one such application in the design of microwave switches.

Microwave switches stop or change the direction of energy flow in communication systems. Due to obvious limitations of mechanical structures (bulk, switching time, and so forth), PIN-diode switches are widely used in a "multistate mode" where the active device is turned "ON" or "OFF" by changing its bias condition. When properly used, a PIN diode can exhibit a large impedance variation vs. bias to either transmit or attenuate incoming signals.

Numerous publications have already presented information on basic switch design theory,[1-4] without suggesting a practical approach to handle both "ON" and "OFF" specifications simultaneously. Exact synthesis of the complete physical circuit (with losses and parasitics) is prohibitively complex, so the only practical solution lies in computerized optimization. This article emphasizes the CAD approach using a typical linear circuit design package.[5]

Two basic configurations of microwave switches are shown in Figure 1. In the series mode, the diode is turned OFF (reverse biased) to stop transmission, while in the shunt mode it is turned ON (forward biased) to accomplish the same. Conversely, in the series mode the diode is turned ON, and in the shunt mode it is turned OFF to pass signals.

If the diode was ideal—zero Ohms series resistance in the ON mode or an infinite series resistance in the OFF mode—a switch could be built displaying zero insertion loss and infinite isolation. Instead, a real PIN diode will have some non-zero forward resistance and a finite, lossy open-circuit capacitance, in addition to internal and package parasitics. Simplified equivalent circuits of a PIN diode in the forward- and reverse-bias modes are shown in Figure 2; typical values for the circuit parameters are also given.

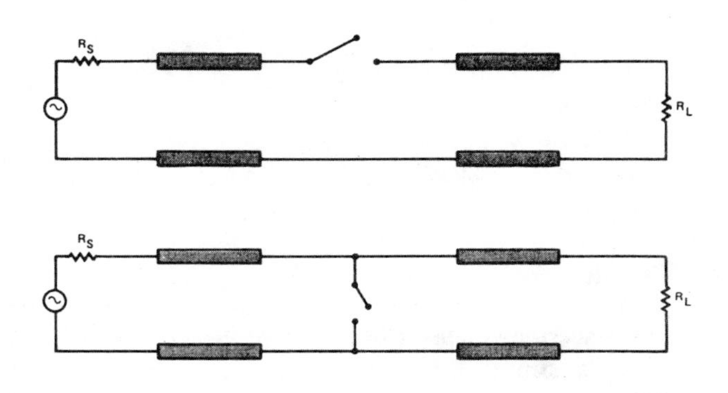

1. Series and shunt configurations are shown for the SPST switches.

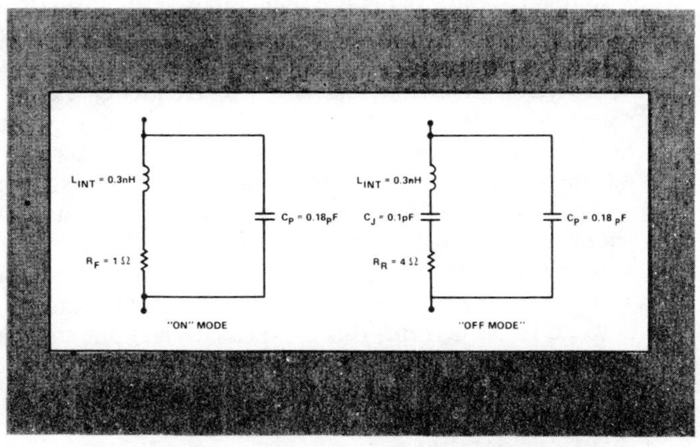

2. In tnese simplified equivalent circuits of an MA47899-030 PIN diode in the forward (ON) and reverse (OFF) biased conditions, $\tau = 0.5$ sec. and $F_{CS} = 800$ GHz.

Les Besser heads his own consulting firm, Microwave Educational Programs, 1109 Russell Ave., Lcs Altos, CA 94022; (415) 960-0536.

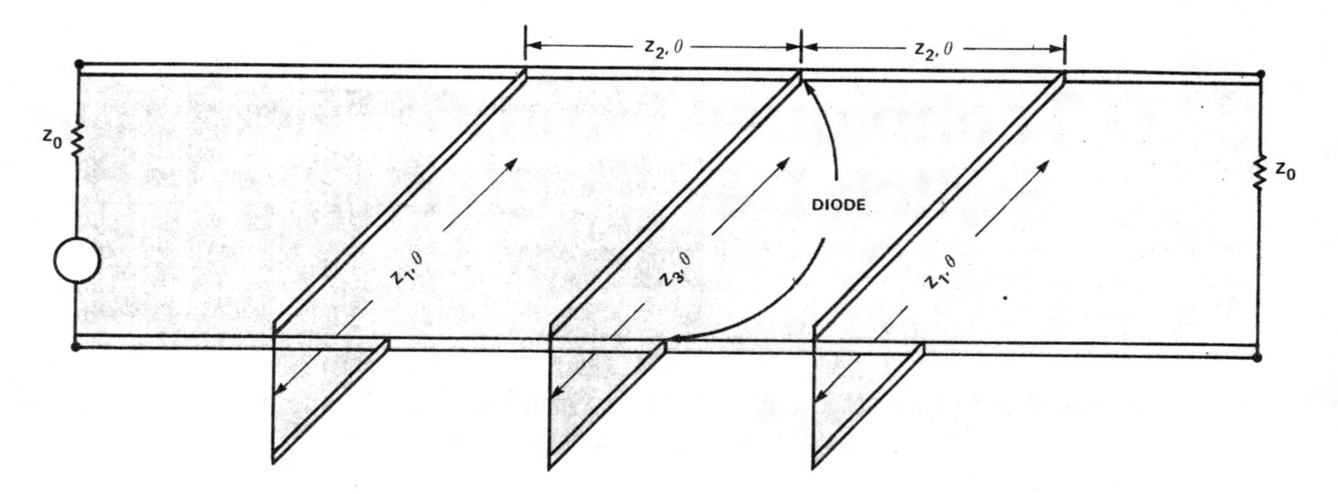

3. In this microwave bandpass filter structure, the diode is connected to the junction of the center stub through an appropriate bias circuit.

The loss created by a single diode is defined[6] as,

a) Series configuration:

$$\text{Loss} = 1 + \frac{R}{Z_o} + \left(\frac{R}{2Z_o}\right)^2 + \left(\frac{X}{2Z_o}\right)^2 \quad (1)$$

b) Shunt configuration:

$$\text{Loss} = 1 + GZ_o + \left(\frac{GZ_o}{2}\right)^2 + \left(\frac{BZ_o}{2}\right)^2 \quad (2)$$

where R, X, G and B are the real and reactive components of the diode, and the appropriate bias condition Z_o is the characteristic impedance of the system.

Circuit Considerations

The design philosophy is illustrated here through a single-section single-pole, single-throw (SPST) configuration using a shunt diode. The principles, however, can be extended to design multisection switches using cascaded series and shunt-diode sections.

Since the real diode represents some shunt capacitance and dissipative loss, the switch's actual insertion loss will be non-zero and frequency dependent. For a single frequency, this internal capacitance can be parallel resonated by an inductor or a parallel short-circuited stub, reducing the switch's insertion loss. As the frequency range increases, the resonating task becomes more complicated. One practical solution is to place the diode across the appropriate inductive stub of a microwave filter, shown in Figure 3. The original length of the short-circuited stub can be adjusted to compensate for the effect of diode capacitance without significantly changing performance of the filter in a narrow frequency range. For bandwidths above 20 to 30 percent, this compensation is not sufficient and the complete filter needs to be re-optimized to improve performance.

CAD Considerations

To optimize the circuit, both the ON and OFF mode specifications need to be included in the error function. In the general form, for a frequency range of f_1 to f_N in N discrete steps,

$$EF = \frac{1}{N}\sum_{f_1}^{f_N}\left[W_{ON}\left|IL - GOAL_{IL}\right|^2 + W_{OFF}\left|ISO - GOAL_{ISO}\right|^2\right] \quad (3)$$

defines the least-squared error function for the switch, where IL is the insertion loss and ISO is the isolation. Actually, they are represented by S_{21} in the ON and OFF modes. The weighting factors, W_{ON} and W_{OFF}, emphasize or de-emphasize the importance of performance in the appropriate mode; selecting a larger weight places more importance on the particular specification in a given mode.

The weights are also used to eliminate any contribution to the error function once the associated parameter attains some acceptable limit. For example, the requirements of the single-section switch are as follows: insertion loss of less than 0.15 dB (−0.15 dB GT) in the ON mode and at least 15-dB (−15 dB LT) isolation in the OFF mode, the error function would then be

$$EF = \frac{1}{N}\sum_{f_1}^{f_N}\left[W_{ON}\left|IL_{dB} - 0.15\right|^2 + W_{OFF}\left|ISO_{dB} - 15\right|^2\right] \quad (4)$$

where

$$W_{ON} = \begin{cases} 0 \text{ if } IL \leq 0.15 \text{ dB} \\ 1 \text{ if } IL > 0.15 \text{ dB} \end{cases}$$

and

$$W_{OFF} = \begin{cases} 0 \text{ if } ISO \geq 15 \text{ dB} \\ 1 \text{ if } ISO < 15 \text{ dB} \end{cases}$$

Insertion Loss Mode Compensation

An ideal PIN diode in the forward bias mode ($R_F = 0$, $L_{INT} = 0$) would exhibit an infinite isolation in the shunt configuration. The actual physical device can only achieve a finite isolation since neither R_F nor L_{INT} are zero. The forward diode resistance, R_F, is set by the basic characteristics and the bias conditions of the diode and, therefore, cannot be changed. However, the parasitic inductance,

L_{INT}, can be tuned out by a series-resonant capacitor C_S (see Fig. 4) such that

$$j\omega L_{INT} = \frac{1}{j\omega C_s}$$

ω is the radian center frequency of the passband for a single-section switch; multisection circuits may be "stagger-tuned" for improved wideband isolation.

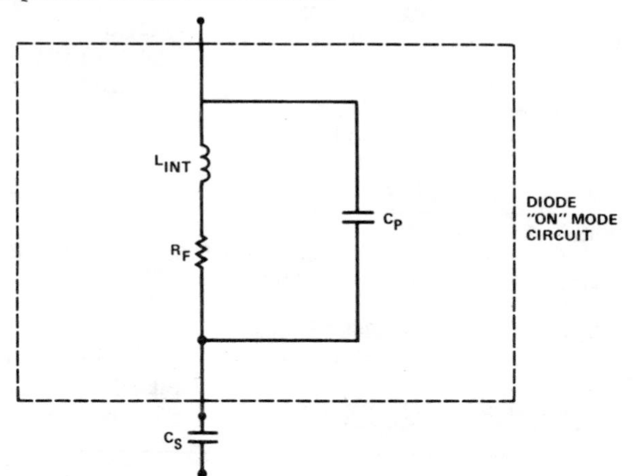

4. Isolation of the shunt diode is improved by adding C_S to resonate the package inductance.

Tolerance Analysis

Once the circuit simulation shows promising performance, effects of bias elements and component tolerances should be evaluated. By using statistical design tools, the tolerance effects can be investigated. Depending on the results of the statistical analysis, tolerances may have to be tightened or the circuit may have to be tuned to meet the required specifications.

Unfortunately, a thorough statistical evaluation, such as a Monte Carlo analysis, requires a large sampling of circuit components to find tolerance distributions; these are not readily available in most cases. In the absence of statistical sampling, the designer may assume a uniform distribution, in which case, component values are assigned equal probabilities within the tolerance limits (Fig. 5). If sampled data is available, it should definitely be used.

Generally speaking (at least in the author's experience), statistical analysis is rarely performed for most microwave circuits. The problems do not surface until the units are already in production. At that point, fixing problems can become prohibitively expensive.

For the above microwave switch, tolerance limits and distribution types need to be assigned for both passive and active components, including the dimensions and parameters of the dielectric media. Dielectric variations will probably affect all transmission lines equally.

Design Outline

The major steps of a switch design can be illustrated through a 2- to 4-GHz single-section shunt-diode circuit, as follows:

Selecting the active device. A suitable diode is selected to meet both insertion loss and isolation specifications using Equations 1 or 2. The device must also be able to handle the RF power present at the terminals of the diode. Individual switch sections or diodes may be combined to meet higher-power or isolation requirements.

Substituting the real and reactive component values of Table I into Equation 1 at the center frequency results in the following:

$$\text{IL} < 0.1 \text{ dB and ISO} > 12 \text{ dB}$$

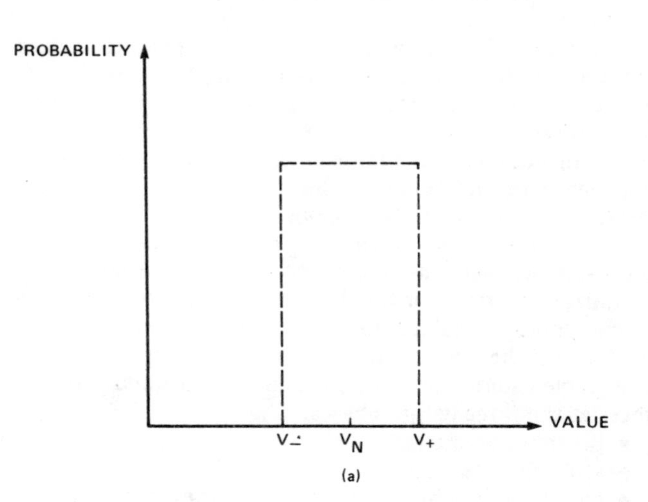

Table I
Impedances and Lengths of Filter Elements at Various Stages of Optimization of the 2- to 4-GHz Switch

	Stub 1		Stub 2		Cascade Line		C Series	Insertion Loss	Isolation
No.	Impedance or width	Electr or phys. length	Impedance or width	Electr or phys. length	Impedance or width	Electr or phys. length	pF	dB max	dB min
1	50Ω	90°	25Ω	90°	50Ω	90°	—	1.6	12.8
2	66Ω	90°	57Ω	90°	100Ω	58°	—	0.16	15.2
3	64Ω	90°	51Ω	90°	111Ω	66°	10.59	0.09	19.9
4	13.5 mil	366 mil	23.3 mil	400 mil	1.93 mil	337 mil	10.50	0.20	20.0

Case 4 indicates physical dimensions and includes losses, dispersion and junction effects.

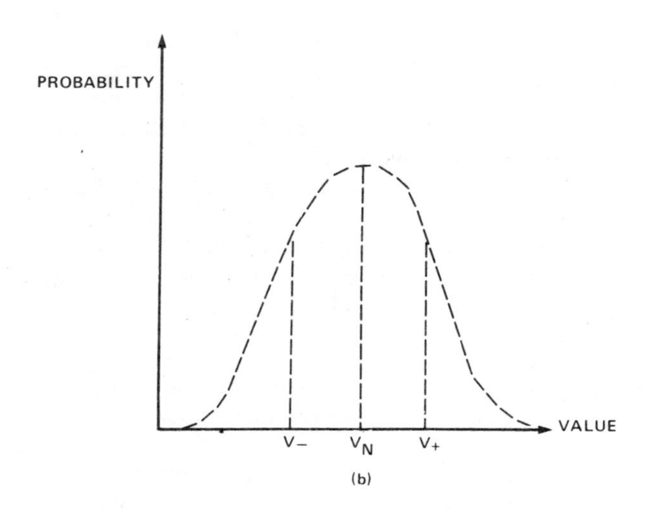

5. Two possible distribution forms between tolerance limits V_+ and V_+ are shown: a) uniform distribution, and b) standard distribution. It should be noted that the nominal value, V_N, may not be exactly halfway between the two limits. Other distributions may also exist, depending on the sampled data.

Selection of the filter structure. With the aid of filter synthesis,[7] or filter tables,[8] find the appropriate filter network that includes at least one parallel inductor or short-circuited stub.

A distributed filter prototype with three parallel-shorted stubs was selected for the passive circuit. All transmission-line lengths were quarter wavelength at center frequency. Impedances of the input/output stubs and connecting cascade transmission lines (unit elements) were Z = 50 Ohms. Impedance of the center stub is 25 Ohms. This design results in a maximally flat response.

Initial analysis of the switch. Insert the PIN diode into the filter structure as shown on Figure 3. Analyze and optimize the circuit for the desired performance by varying all component variables. Insert the series resonator capacitor C_S into the circuit and re-optimize for improved isolation. Table I summarizes the component values and performances at the three design phases:

- before optimization
- after optimization
- re-optimized with a series compensating capacitor

Convert to physical dimensions. Using transmission-line synthesis[5] or charts,[9] convert from the electrical transmission-line parameters to physical dimensions. Include the effects of junctions, conductive and dielectric losses, dispersion, surface roughness and top cover to get the best possible predicted performance. Re-optimize the circuit, if necessary, until the specifications are met.

Line 4 of Table I indicates performance with the transmission lines in the final circuit described by physical parameters. Figure 6 lists the corresponding SUPER-COMPACT™ data file.

```
F1: 3 GHz

QWT:  ?365 mil 0.1%?
QWS:  ?399 mil 0.1%?                        VARIABLE
LCS:  ?337 mil 0.1%?                        INITIALIZATION
W51:  ?13.4 mil 2.5%?
W5260:  ?23.3 mil 1.3%?
W61:  ?1.64 mil  1.94 mil  2.24 mil?
BLK
  LINT:  IND 12 13 L=? 0.3NH 5%?
  CP:  CAP 12 0 C=? 0.18PF 5%?              DIODE
  RES  13 0 R=1                             EQUIVALENT
  DFOR:  1POR 12 0                          CIRCUITS
  LINT  22 23
  SRC  23 0 R=4 C=0.1PF
  CP  22 0
  DREV:  1POR 22 0

  SST  51 0 W=W51 P=QWS SUB
  TEE  50 52 51 W1=24.2 mil W2=W5260 W3=W51 SUB
  TRL  52 60 W=W5260 P=QWT SUB
  HALF:  2POR 50 60
  SST  61 0 W=W61 P=LCS SUB
  TEE  60 62 61 W1=W5260 W2=5260 W3=W61 SUB
  HALF  3 62                                FILTER
  CAP  61 92 C=?10.5PF 5%?                  STRUCTURE
  LINES:  3POR 50 92 3
END
  LINES  10 20 30                           OFF-MODE
  DFOR  20 0                                SWITCH
  SOFF:  2POR 10 30

  LINES  40 50 60                           ON-MODE
  DREV  50 0                                SWITCH
  SON:  2POR 40 60
END
FREQ                                        FREQUENCY
  STEP 2 GHz 4 GHz 5E8                      SPECS
END
OUT
  PRI SON S                                 OUTPUT
  PRI SOFF S                                SPECS
END
OPT
  SOFF MS21=-20dB LT                        OPTIMIZATION
  SON MS21=0dB                              TARGETS
  TERM =0.01
END
STAT                                        STATISTICAL
  SOFF MS21=-18dB LT                        LIMITS
  SON  MS21=0dB -0.25dB
END
DATA
  SUB: MS H=?25 mil 5%? ER=?9.8 5%? TAND=0.001
+ MET1=CR 100A MET2=AU 0.2 mil              SUBSTRATE AND
END                                         METALIZATION
                                            DATA
```

6. In this SUPER-COMPACT™ data file of the final circuit, the entries between question marks indicate variables and statistical limits.

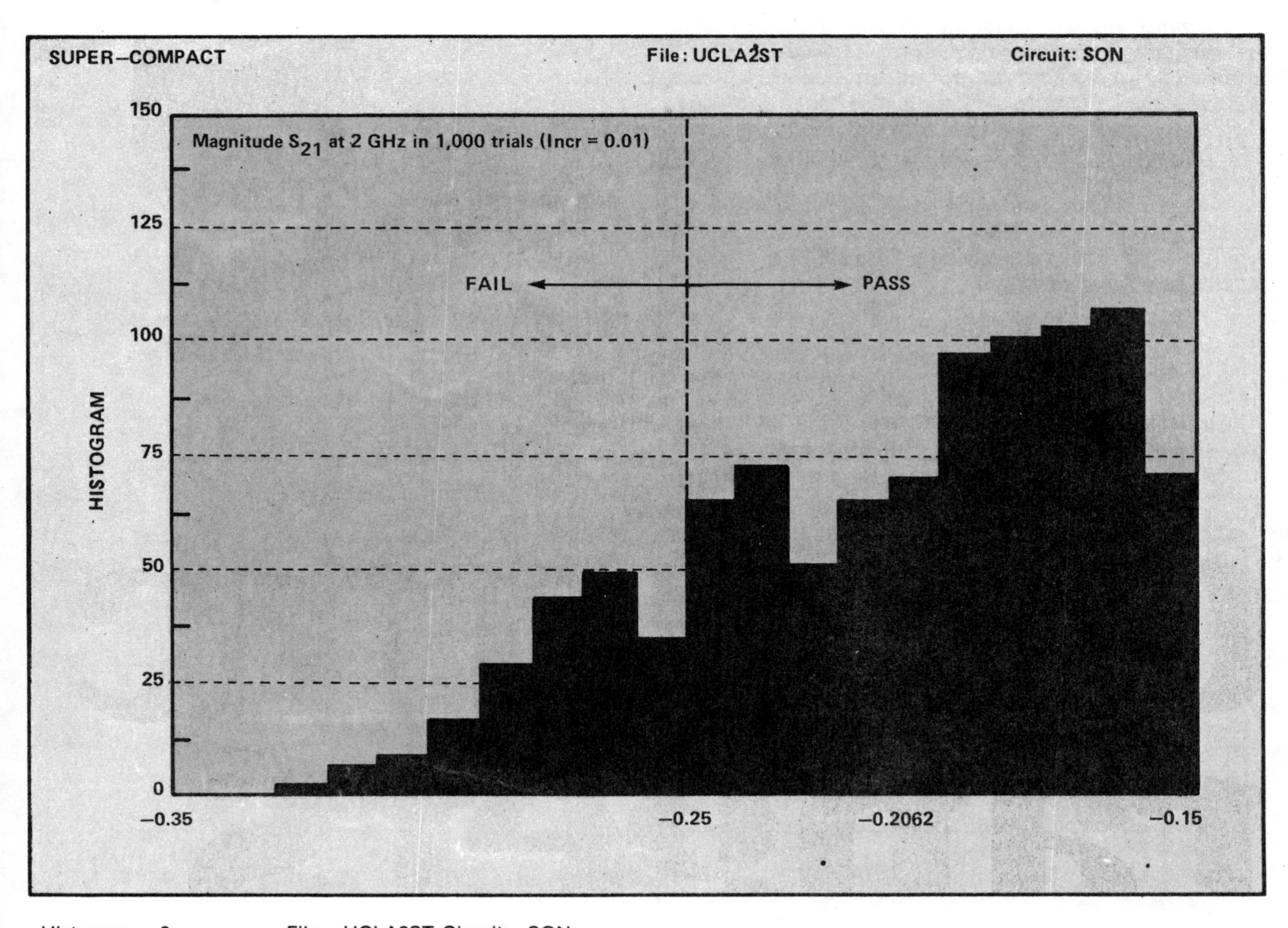

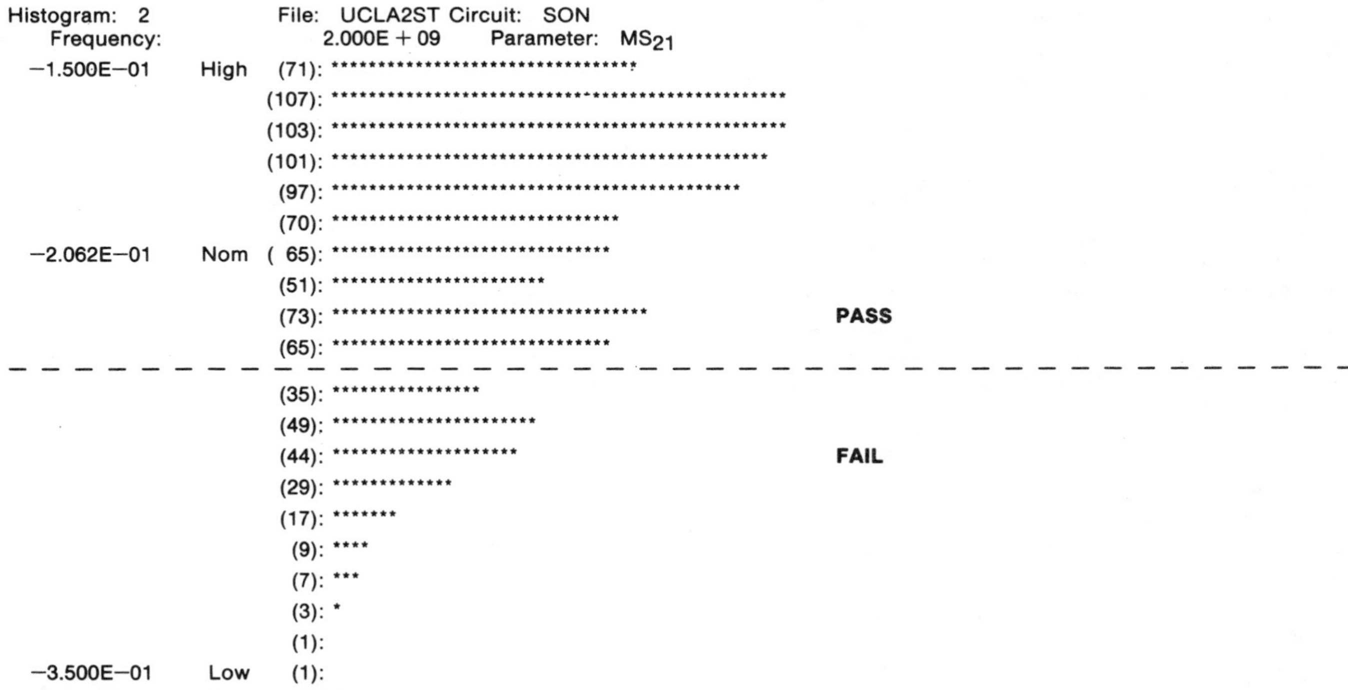

```
Histogram:  2                File:  UCLA2ST Circuit:  SON
    Frequency:                   2.000E + 09       Parameter:  MS21
  –1.500E–01     High    (71): ***********************************
                        (107): *****************************************************
                        (103): ***************************************************
                        (101): **************************************************
                         (97): ************************************************
                         (70): ***********************************
  –2.062E–01     Nom    ( 65): ********************************
                         (51): *************************
                         (73): ************************************        PASS
                         (65): ********************************
– – – – – – – – – – – – – – – – – – – – – – – – – – – – – – – – – – – – – – – – –
                         (35): *****************
                         (49): ************************
                         (44): **********************                      FAIL
                         (29): **************
                         (17): *******
                          (9): ****
                          (7): ***
                          (3): *
                          (1):
  –3.500E–01     Low      (1):
0.00% of samples below and 0.20% above histogram limits
```

7. At the "weakest" frequency of the design—2 GHz— statistical distribution predicts that 185 of the 1,000 samples will not meet the IL 0.25-dB specification. Fifteen additional samples also failed the isolation requirements at various frequencies, lowering the predicted yield to 80 percent.

Tolerance analysis. Input all tolerance limits and types of distributions. If sample data is not available, assume a uniform distribution for the components. Perform a Monte Carlo analysis to estimate expected yield. If necessary, tighten tolerances on most sensitive components (use *statistical* sensitivities instead of nominal sensitivities) until the yield becomes acceptable.

With ±5-percent tolerances on all passive components and dimensions, ±5-percent tolerances on the diode parameters, ±3-mil etching tolerances, 80 percent of the circuits would meet specifications of

$$\text{IL} \leq 0.25 \text{ dB}$$
$$\text{ISO} \geq 18 \text{ dB}$$

over the 2- to 4-GHz frequency range.

Circuit layout. Create physical drawing and mask, produce and test prototypes.[10] Compare predicted and measured data and store information for next design. ■

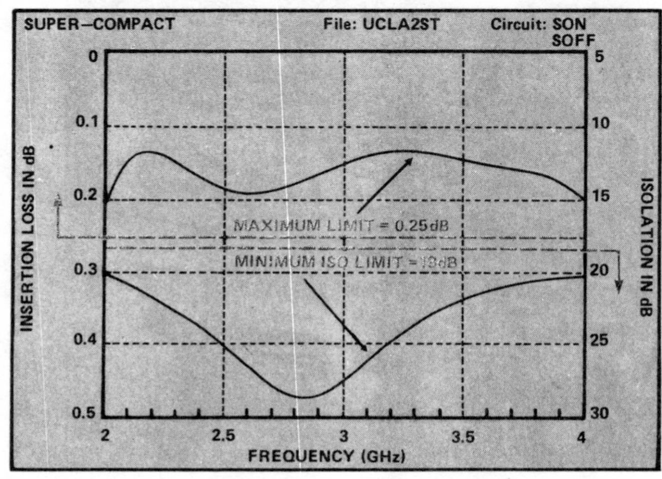

8. Response of the switch in the ON and OFF modes is shown using nominal design values. The heavy, dotted lines indicate performance limits for the statistical Monte Carlo analysis.

References

1. Hines, Marion, "Fundamental Limitations in RF Switching and Phase Shifting Using Semiconductor Diodes," *Proc. of IEEE*, Vol. 52, 1964.
2. Fisher, R.E., "Broadbanding of Microwave Diode Switches," *IEEE Trans. on MTT*, Vol. 13, Sept. 1965.
3. Chafin, Roger, "Microwave Semiconductor Devices," John Wiley & Sons, 1973.
4. Lepoff, J., "Selection and Use of Microwave Diode Switches and Limiters," *Hewlett-Packard Application Note* No. 932, May 1973.
5. "SUPER-COMPACT User's Manual," Version 1.7, Compact Software, Inc., Palo Alto, Calif., May 1984.
6. Gupta, K.C., "PIN Diode Circuits," Section II of Class Notes, "*Microwave Circuit Design—Non-linear Circuits*," UCLA Extension, April 1983.
7. "S/FILSYN User Manual," Version 1.6, DGS Associates, Santa Clara, Calif., 1983.
8. Mumford, W.W., "Tables of Stub Admittances for Maximally Flat Filters Using Shorted Quarter Wave Stubs," *IEEE Trans. MTT*, Vol. 13, No. 5, Sept. 1965. pp. 695-696.
9. Stinehelfer, Harold, *Microwave Engineers' Handbook*, Vol. 1, 1971, pp. 115-128.
10. March, S.L. and L. Besser, *Proc. 14th European Microwave Conference*, Sept., 1984.

Computer-Aided Synthesis of Lumped Lossy Matching Networks for Monolithic Microwave Integrated Circuits (MMIC's)

LOUIS C. T. LIU, MEMBER, IEEE, AND WALTER H. KU, MEMBER, IEEE

Abstract —A systematic computer-aided synthesis (CAS) technique of lumped lossy matching networks is presented in this paper. This exact synthesis procedure can take arbitrary finite quality factor Q for each lumped element in the matching network and therefore facilitate the circuit design for monolithic microwave integrated circuits (MMIC's) where the loss of the passive elements is too large to be neglected. The gain–bandwidth limitations of some useful lumped lossy matching networks are discussed in detail and are summarized in a set of gain–bandwidth constraint plots. An interactive computer program LUMSYN is developed to solve this lumped lossy synthesis problem. LUMSYN is a general-purpose CAS program which can be used by microwave circuit designers with limited background in network synthesis to carry out low-noise and power amplifier designs in MMIC's. Finally, a design example of broad-band monolithic microwave low-noise amplifier using a state-of-the-art low-noise submicron gate-length GaAs MESFET is presented to illustrate the computer-aided synthesis of MMIC amplifiers.

I. Introduction

THE ADVANCES IN GaAs material development and wafer processing achieved in the past few years have made the monolithic microwave integrated circuits (MMIC's) practical [1], [2]. These integrated circuits have potential applications in the low-cost transmit–receive modules for phased array radars and in the X-band receivers for satellite direct-broadcast television. This paper is intended to provide a systematic computer-aided synthesis and design (CAS/CAD) procedure, which forms part of the basic technology for the development of MMIC's.

In the design of MMIC's, the matching networks consist of lumped reactive elements and/or transmission-line elements. Lumped elements are often essential since they occupy less GaAs chip area and have broader bandwidth capability. Unfortunately, the lumped elements fabricated on the semi-insulating GaAs substrates have losses which are too large to be neglected. Due to the lack of a lossy synthesis technique, most circuit designers will first synthesize a lossless matching network and then simply add loss elements to each lumped circuit component. Since the loss elements added have different effects to the transducer power gain at different frequencies, the gain response will be out of control. The development of a lumped lossy matching network synthesis technique is therefore very desirable for MMIC's.

Manuscript received August 11, 1983; revised December 29, 1983. This work was supported in part by the Joint Services Electronics Program at Cornell University under AFOSR Contract F49620-81-C-0082, monitored by Dr. G. Witt.

L. C. T. Liu is with the Torrance Research Center, Hughes Aircraft Co., Torrance, CA, 90509.

W. H. Ku is with the School of Electrical Engineering and National Submicron Facility, Cornell University, currently on sabbatical leave as Distinguished Visiting Professor at the Department of Electrical Engineering and Computer Sciences, University of California, San Diego, La Jolla, CA 92093.

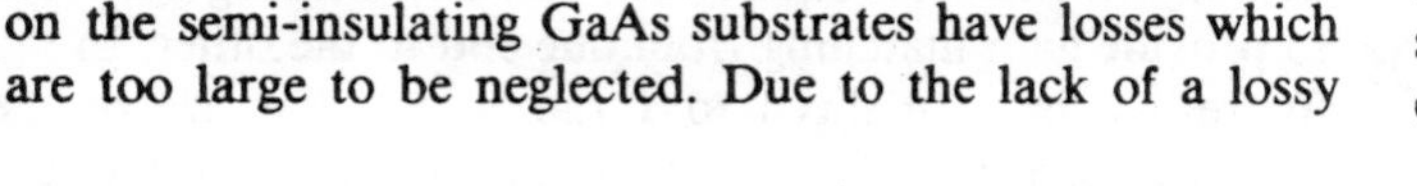

Fig. 1. Block diagram of a single-stage GaAs FET amplifier.

The exact synthesis of lumped networks with lossy elements has been an open problem with long standing for the general case of arbitrary nonuniform dissipation. Using both analytical and CAS techniques, we have solved the lossy synthesis problem for the case of unequal inductor and capacitor losses with arbitrary circuit topology and realizable gain functions. This new result is directly applicable to the synthesis of the matching networks for MMIC's. Presently, the new theory we have developed does not take the parasitic reactances of the lossy circuit elements into account, and CAD and optimization techniques must be used to "fine-tune" the synthesized amplifier response, thus modifying the element values of the actual lossy L's and C's of the matching network. Our preliminary study indicates that the integrated analytical and CAD approach we have used for the successful synthesis of lossy matching networks for MMIC's can also be extended to the more general problem.

II. Exact Synthesis of Lumped Lossy Matching Networks

In MMIC's, the matching network should be synthesized to provide a desired impedance match between the output of one stage and the input of the next stage. For example, Fig. 1 is the block diagram of a basic single-stage GaAs MESFET amplifier. The matching networks M_1 and M_2 should provide a good impedance match which includes

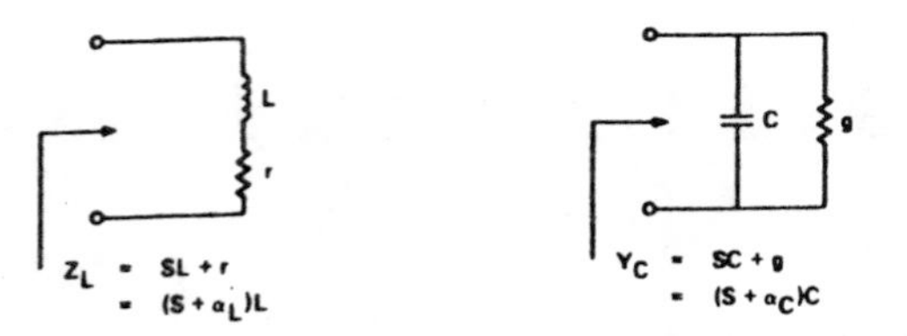

Fig. 2. Simplified equivalent circuit for lumped reactive elements.

the compensation of the gain roll-off of the FET between R_g and the input of the FET, and the output of the FET and R_L, respectively. While trying to match the input or output of the FET, simplified models for the FET are usually used to avoid complicated network synthesis. For instance, the input equivalent circuit of a lumped GaAs FET model is a series capacitor terminated with a resistor, and the output equivalent circuit is a parallel capacitor terminated with a resistor. The matching networks will then absorb the reactances of these simplified equivalent circuits while providing the specific gain response.

In order to synthesize a matching network, a realizable gain function should be obtained first. In this paper, only the lumped lossy matching network is considered. The transducer power gain function of a lumped lossy matching network must contain the lossy element which accompanies each lossy reactance of the matching network. As shown in Fig. 2, the simplified model of a monolithic lumped inductor is considered as an ideal inductor in series with a resistor r, which is then specified in terms of the quality factor Q_L defined as

$$r = \frac{\omega_0 L}{Q_L} \tag{1}$$

where L is the value of the ideal lossless inductor and ω_0 is the frequency at which the Q_L is defined. The impedance of the lossy inductor is then given by

$$Z_L = r + sL = \frac{\omega_0 L}{Q_L} + sL = (s + \alpha_L)L \tag{2}$$

where $\alpha_L = \omega_0 / Q_L$ is the inductor loss or dissipation factor. Similarly, a simplified model of a lossy capacitor is considered as an ideal lossless capacitor C in parallel with a resistor with conductance g. If this conductance is specified in terms of the quality factor Q_c as

$$g = \frac{\omega_0 C}{Q_c} \tag{3}$$

then the admittance of the lossy capacitor is given by

$$Y_c = g + sC = \frac{\omega_0 C}{Q_c} + sC = (s + \alpha_c)C \tag{4}$$

where $\alpha_c = \omega_0 / Q_c$ is the capacitor loss factor. Consider the appropriate impedance and admittance presented in (2) and (4). It is clear that the basic transformation of variable from s to $(s + \alpha)$ will incorporate the losses of the L's and C's, and the gain function of a lossy matching network is given by

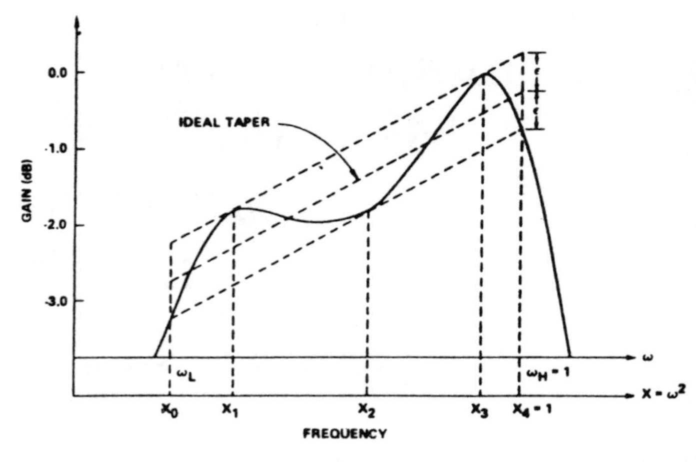

Fig. 3. Ideal taper and its equiripple approximation of a matching network.

$$G_M(\omega^2) = \frac{k(\omega^2 + \alpha_1^2)(\omega^2 + \alpha_2^2)\cdots(\omega^2 + \alpha_m^2)}{P_n(\omega^2)} = \frac{k \prod_{j=1}^{m} (x + \alpha_j^2)}{P_n(x)} \tag{5}$$

where

$x = \omega^2$,

m = number of high-pass elements,

$P_n(x)$ = an nth order polynomial which will be derived to provide an equiripple or maximally-flat gain function,

k = gain constant,

α_j = loss factor of jth high-pass element.

The equiripple error gain function provides a better initial overall gain response of the amplifier. In addition, it is much more flexible in the reactive element absorption and impedance ratio transformation. Therefore, in the following discussion only the equiripple error gain function will be considered. It is the task now to derive the polynomial $P_n(x)$ such that the gain function will be realizable and meet certain requirements. The same approach used by Petersen [3] to derive a lossless equiripple gain function is adopted here.

Fig. 3 shows a typical tapered equiripple gain function with $n = 4$, which is required for certain matching networks to provide gain matching from one end to the other. In the figure, ω_H is normalized to 1 rad/s, ϵ is the size of the maximum error in decibels, and x_0, x_1, x_2, x_3, and x_4 are called critical points since the approximate gain function has maximum error at those points. To solve for the general nth-order gain function, the value of the $n-1$ critical points (since x_0 and x_n are known) and the n coefficients of $P_n(x)$ have to be solved. Let $G_M(x)$ and $\hat{f}(x)$ represent the equiripple approximation and ideal gain function (e.g., the center dotted line in Fig. 3), respectively; then the error function $E(x)$ on a log–log scale can be written as

$$E(x) = \ln[G_M(x)] - \ln[\hat{f}(x)]. \tag{6}$$

If the passband is normalized to the interval $[x_0, 1]$, as shown in Fig. 3, the equiripple conditions can be written as

$$E(x_i) = (-1)^i \epsilon, \qquad i = 0, 1, \cdots, n \tag{7}$$

$$\left.\frac{dE(x)}{dx}\right|_{x=x_i} = 0, \qquad i = 0, 1, \cdots, n \tag{8}$$

where $x_0 < x_1 < \cdots < x_n$ are the points of maximum error. The ideal tapered gain function is given by

$$\hat{f}(x) = x^{\hat{\alpha}} \tag{9a}$$

where

$$\hat{\alpha} = \frac{\text{SLOPE(dB/OCTAVE)}}{20 \log_{10} 2}. \tag{9b}$$

Define

$$f(x) = \frac{1}{\hat{f}(x)} = x^{-\hat{\alpha}} \tag{10}$$

and

$$B^i = \begin{cases} e^{\epsilon}, & i \text{ even} \\ e^{-\epsilon}, & i \text{ odd} \end{cases}. \tag{11}$$

From (6) and (7), it can be derived that

$$\ln\left[\frac{\prod_{j=1}^{m}(x_i + \alpha_j^2)}{P_n(x_i)}\right] + \ln[f(x_i)] + \ln B_i = 0,$$

$$i = 0, 1, \cdots, n. \tag{12}$$

Since the gain constant k only changes the gain level and not the shape of the gain response, it can be set to 1 at this moment. Then from (12), it can be seen that

$$B_i \prod_{j=1}^{m}(x_i + \alpha_j^2) f(x_i) = P_n(\underset{\sim}{a}, x_i), \qquad i = 0, 1, \cdots, n \tag{13a}$$

where

$$P_n(\underset{\sim}{a}, x_i) = P_n(x_i) = a_0 + a_1 x_i + \cdots a_n x_i^n. \tag{13b}$$

Invoking (13), the first equiripple condition, or (7), becomes

$$\underset{\sim}{a} = \boldsymbol{X}^{-1} \underset{\sim}{R}(\underset{\sim}{x}) \tag{14a}$$

where

$$\underset{\sim}{a} = [a_0 \; a_1 \cdots a_n]^T \tag{14b}$$

$$\underset{\sim}{x} = [x_0 \; x_1 \cdots x_n]^T \tag{14c}$$

$$\boldsymbol{X} = \begin{bmatrix} 1 & x_0 & x_0^2 & \cdots & x_0^n \\ 1 & x_1 & x_1^2 & \cdots & x_1^n \\ \vdots & & & & \vdots \\ 1 & x_n & x_n^2 & \cdots & x_n^n \end{bmatrix} \tag{14d}$$

$$\underset{\sim}{R}(\underset{\sim}{x}) = \begin{bmatrix} B_0 \prod_{j=1}^{m}(x_0 + \alpha_j^2) f(x_0) \\ B_1 \prod_{j=1}^{m}(x_1 + \alpha_j^2) f(x_1) \\ \vdots \\ B_n \prod_{j=1}^{m}(x_n + \alpha_j^2) f(x_n) \end{bmatrix}. \tag{14e}$$

Let $F(x_i)$ be the numerator of $E'(x_i)$, where the prime denotes the differentiation with respect to x. Then from (6) and the second equiripple condition, or (8), it can be shown that

$$F(x_i) = P_n(x_i)\left[\sum_{j=1}^{m} \frac{1}{x_i + \alpha_j^2} f(x_i) + f'(x_i)\right] - f(x_i) P_n'(x_i)$$

$$= 0, \qquad i = 1, 2, \cdots, (n-1). \tag{15}$$

Equations (14) and (15) are now the equivalent conditions for the equiripple error gain function. Newton's iteration method [4] can be used to solve for x_i's by inserting (14) into (15). The iteration formula in Newton's method is given by

$$\underset{\sim}{x}^{(k+1)} = \underset{\sim}{x}^{(k)} - \beta \boldsymbol{J}^{-1}(\underset{\sim}{x}^{(k)}) \underset{\sim}{F}(\underset{\sim}{x}^{(k)}) \tag{16a}$$

where

$$\beta = 1 \tag{16b}$$

$$F(x^{(k)}) = [F(x_1^{(k)}) \; F(x_2^{(k)}) \cdots F(x_{n-1}^{(k)})]^T \tag{16c}$$

$$\boldsymbol{J}(\underset{\sim}{x}^{(k)}) = \left.\frac{\partial F(x)}{\partial \underset{\sim}{x}}\right|_{\underset{\sim}{x} = \underset{\sim}{x}^{(k)}} = \begin{bmatrix} \frac{\partial F(x_1)}{\partial x_1} & \frac{\partial F(x_1)}{\partial x_2} & \cdots & \frac{\partial F(x_1)}{\partial x_{n-1}} \\ \frac{\partial F(x_2)}{\partial x_1} & \frac{\partial F(x_2)}{\partial x_2} & \cdots & \frac{\partial F(x_2)}{\partial x_{n-1}} \\ \vdots & \vdots & & \vdots \\ \frac{\partial F(x_{n-1})}{\partial x_1} & \frac{\partial F(x_{n-1})}{\partial x_2} & \cdots & \frac{\partial F(x_{n-1})}{\partial x_{n-1}} \end{bmatrix}_{\underset{\sim}{x} = \underset{\sim}{x}^{(k)}} \tag{16d}$$

and the superscripts (k) refer to the number of iterations. In order to calculate the Jacobian matrix J, (15) is expanded as

$$F(x_i) = \left(\sum_{j=0}^{n} a_j x_i^j\right)\left[\sum_{j=1}^{m} \frac{1}{x_i + \alpha_j^2} f(x_i) + f'(x_i)\right] - f(x_i)\left(\sum_{j=1}^{n} j a_j x_i^{j-1}\right). \quad (17)$$

Differentiating (17) with respect to one of the critical points, e.g., x_l, gives

$$J_{il} = \frac{\partial F(x_i)}{\partial x_l}$$
$$= \left\{ P_n(x_i)\left[f''(x_i) + f'(x_i) \sum_{j=1}^{m} \frac{1}{x_i + \alpha_j^2} - f(x_i) \sum_{j=1}^{m} \frac{1}{\left(x_i + \alpha_j^2\right)^2} \right] + P_n'(x_i) f(x_i) \sum_{j=1}^{m} \frac{1}{x_i + \alpha_j^2} - f(x) P_n''(x) \right\} \delta_{il}$$
$$+ \left[\sum_{j=1}^{m} \frac{1}{x_i + \alpha_j^2} f(x_i) + f'(x_i)\right]\left(\sum_{j=0}^{m} \frac{\partial a_j}{\partial x_l} x_i^j\right) - f(x_i)\left(\sum_{j=1}^{m} j \frac{\partial a_j}{\partial x_l} x_i^{j-1}\right) \quad (18a)$$

where

$$\delta_{il} = \begin{cases} 0, & i \neq l \\ 1, & i = l \end{cases}. \quad (18b)$$

Furthermore, $\partial a_j / \partial x_l$ can be calculated by differentiating (14) with respect to x_l as

$$\frac{\partial \underset{\sim}{a}}{\partial \underset{\sim}{x}} = X^{-1} \operatorname{diag}\left[\underset{\sim}{R}'(\underset{\sim}{x}) - \underset{\sim}{P}_n(\underset{\sim}{x})\right] \quad (19a)$$

where

$$\frac{\partial \underset{\sim}{a}}{\partial \underset{\sim}{x}} = \begin{bmatrix} \frac{\partial a_0}{\partial x_0} & \frac{\partial a_0}{\partial x_1} & \cdots & \frac{\partial a_0}{\partial x_n} \\ \frac{\partial a_1}{\partial x_0} & \frac{\partial a_1}{\partial x_1} & \cdots & \frac{\partial a_1}{\partial x_n} \\ \vdots & \vdots & & \vdots \\ \frac{\partial a_n}{\partial x_0} & \frac{\partial a_n}{\partial x_1} & \cdots & \frac{\partial a_n}{\partial x_n} \end{bmatrix} \quad (19b)$$

and

$$\underset{\sim}{P}_n'(\underset{\sim}{x}) = \left[P_n'(x_0)\ P_n'(x_1) \cdots P_n'(x_n)\right]. \quad (19c)$$

In order to start Newton's iteration, an initial vector $\underset{\sim}{x}^{(0)}$ has to be selected. One of the natural selections is the vector consisting of equi-distance points between x_0 and x_n, or

$$\underset{\sim}{x}^{(0)} = \left[x_1^{(0)} x_2^{(0)} \cdots x_n^{(0)}\right]^T \quad (20a)$$

where

$$x_i^{(0)} = x_0 + i\left[\frac{x_n - x_0}{n}\right]. \quad (20b)$$

The coefficient vector $\underset{\sim}{a}$ can then be calculated from (14). This result is used to calculate the next $\underset{\sim}{x}$ vector, or $\underset{\sim}{x}^{(1)}$, through (16). This procedure continues until $\underset{\sim}{x}^{(k+1)}$ converges to $\underset{\sim}{x}^{(k)}$. The final $\underset{\sim}{x}$ and $\underset{\sim}{a}$ will provide a gain function which meets the requirements specified earlier.

After the shape of the gain response is determined, the gain constant k can be used to adjust the gain level in order to satisfy other specifications, for example, the realizability of the gain function, gain–bandwidth limitation, impedance transformation ratio, and realizability of the element values. For a lossless matching network, the reflection coefficient can be calculated from $G_M(\omega^2)$ according to the following equations:

$$|S_{11}(j\omega)|^2 = 1 - |S_{12}(j\omega)|^2 = 1 - G_M(\omega^2) \quad (21)$$

and

$$|S_{11}(j\omega)|^2 = S_{11}(s) S_{11}(-s)|_{s=j\omega}. \quad (22)$$

Therefore, the element value of the matching network can be obtained through the reflection coefficient or the input impedance function. However, in a lossy matching network synthesis, (21) is no longer valid, and there is no simple relation between $S_{21}(s)$ and $S_{11}(s)$. In order to derive the element values, the problem has to be solved by another method. The topology of the matching network can be determined first, and then the loss factor or quality factor Q of each element is assigned according to practical considerations. The transducer power gain function $G_M(\omega^2)$ of the matching network can be calculated in terms of all the L's, C's, and α's associated with each element. By equating the coefficients of $P_n(\underset{\sim}{a}, x)$ and the gain constant obtained from both Newton's iteration and circuit calculation, $n+2$ nonlinear equations are formed (but since one of these can be absorbed by the others, only $n+1$ equations are needed). By solving these $n+1$ nonlinear equations, n reactive element values and the load resistance R can be obtained.

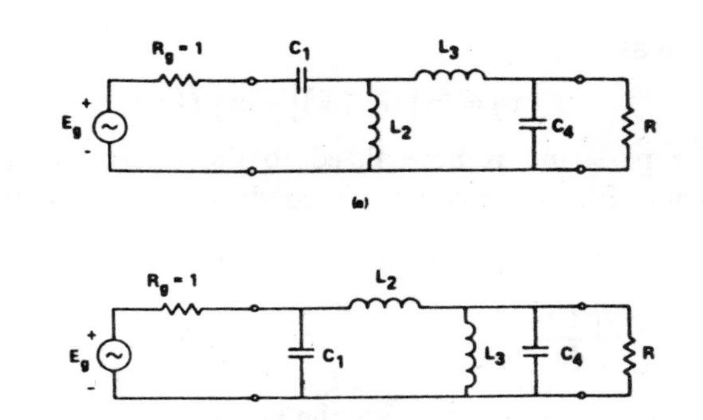

Fig. 4. Two possible topologies of the lumped lossy matching network. (a) $N=4$, $N_L=2$, $N_H=2$. (b) $N=4$, $N_L=3$, $N_H=1$.

To illustrate the above procedure, an output matching network example is employed. Fig. 4(a) and (b) shows two possible topologies for input and output matching networks, respectively. The $S_{21}(s)$ of the output lossy matching network shown in Fig. 4(b) can be calculated as

$$S_{21}(s)=\frac{2RL_3(s+\alpha_3)}{b_0+b_1s+b_2s^2+b_3s^3+b_4s^4} \tag{23a}$$

where

$$\begin{aligned} b_0 = {} & (\alpha_1C_1+1)(\alpha_2L_2R+\alpha_2\alpha_3\alpha_4L_2L_3C_4R+\alpha_2\alpha_3L_2L_3 \\ & +\alpha_3L_3R)+R+\alpha_3\alpha_4L_3C_4R+\alpha_3L_3 \end{aligned} \tag{23b}$$

$$\begin{aligned} b_1 = {} & C_1(\alpha_2L_2R+\alpha_2\alpha_3\alpha_4L_2L_3C_4+R+\alpha_2\alpha_3L_2L_3 \\ & +\alpha_3L_3R)+(\alpha_1C_1+1)[L_2R+L_2L_3C_4R(\alpha_2\alpha_3 \\ & +\alpha_2\alpha_4+\alpha_3\alpha_4)+L_2L_3(\alpha_2+\alpha_3)+L_3R] \\ & +L_3C_4R(\alpha_3+\alpha_4)+L_3 \end{aligned} \tag{23c}$$

$$\begin{aligned} b_2 = {} & C_1[L_2R+L_2L_3C_4R(\alpha_2\alpha_3+\alpha_2\alpha_4+\alpha_3\alpha_4) \\ & +L_2L_3(\alpha_2+\alpha_3)+RL_3] \\ & +(\alpha_1C_1+1)[L_2L_3C_4R(\alpha_2+\alpha_3+\alpha_4) \\ & +L_2L_3]+L_3C_4R \end{aligned} \tag{23d}$$

$$\begin{aligned} b_3 = {} & (\alpha_1C_1+1)L_2L_3C_4R \\ & +C_1[L_2L_3C_4R(\alpha_2+\alpha_3+\alpha_4)+L_2L_3] \end{aligned} \tag{23e}$$

$$b_4 = C_1L_2L_3C_4R. \tag{23f}$$

Therefore, the transducer power gain is given by

$$G_M(\omega^2)=\frac{4RL_3^2(\omega^2+a_3^2)}{b_0^2+(b_1^2-2b_0b_2)\omega^2+(b_2^2+2b_0b_4-2b_2-2b_4)\omega^4+(b_3^2-2b_2b_4)\omega^6+b_4^2\omega^8} \tag{24}$$

By comparing the above equation with the lossy gain function (5), it can be shown that

$$\frac{k}{a_0}=\frac{4RL_3^2}{b_0^2} \tag{25a}$$

$$\frac{a_1}{a_0}=\frac{b_1^2-2b_0b_1}{b_0^2} \tag{25b}$$

$$\frac{a_2}{a_0}=\frac{b_2^2+2b_0b_4-2b_1b_3}{b_0^2} \tag{25c}$$

$$\frac{a_3}{a_0}=\frac{b_3^2-2b_2b_4}{b_0^2} \tag{25d}$$

$$\frac{a_4}{a_0}=\frac{b_4^2}{b_0^2}. \tag{25e}$$

By solving the above set of nonlinear equations, the element values for C_1, L_2, L_3, L_4, and R can be obtained.

The nonlinear equation set (25) can be solved most easily by the help of a digital computer. Either Brown's derivative-free method [5] or Marquardt's algorithm [6] can be used for this purpose. Both methods need a good initial guess to start the iteration for a solution. The element values generated from a lossless matching network synthesis procedure turn out to be a natural and good choice. The reason is that the lossy matching network desired should have exactly the same shape as that of the lossless one, only the gain level should be lower. Consequently, a solution from lossless matching network synthesis can be used as an initial guess for the lossy matching network with certain gain reduction (e.g., 0.5 dB) added to the gain function to compensate for the gain reduction due to the losses in the matching network. The result turns out to be very good as will be shown in the next section. Once a set of solutions for the lossy matching network is obtained, it can serve as an initial guess for other lossy matching networks with similar gain slope, gain reduction, or gain ripple. Since the gain constant k changes only the gain level and not the general shape of the gain response, it will be very convenient to solve a specified gain function first and then to change just the k to obtain a set of matching networks with different gain levels. This is the way the matching network tables are generated in the next section.

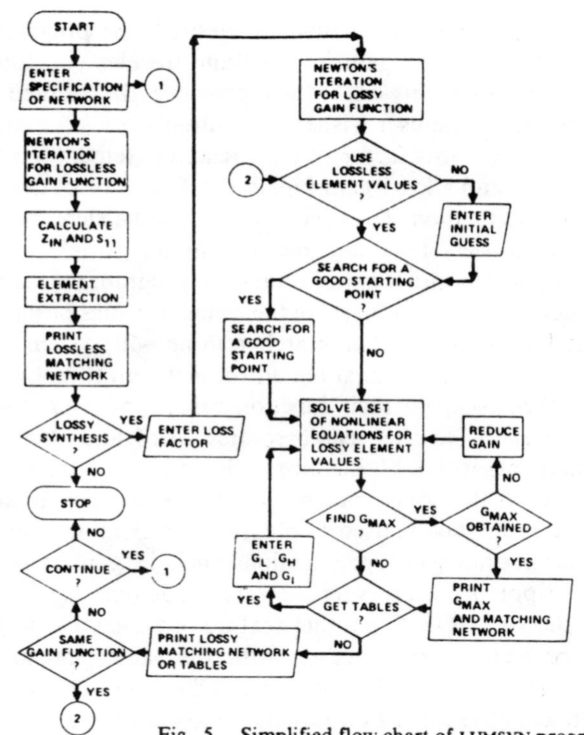

Fig. 5. Simplified flow chart of LUMSYN program.

III. LUMSYN PROGRAM

An interactive program called LUMSYN written in FORTRAN has been developed to solve the lumped lossy synthesis formulation discussed in the previous section. It is the hope of the authors that people who do not specialize in network synthesis can still use it as a design tool for MMIC design. Therefore, a considerable amount of time and effort has been put into the program design to make it easier to understand and use.

Fig. 5 shows a simplified flow chart of the LUMSYN program. In this flow chart, it can be seen that after the user specifies the gain function desired, the program will solve for a lossless gain function and the element values of the matching network which provides the desired gain response. If the user wishes to synthesize a lossy matching network, the loss factor of each reactive element has to be specified and a lossy gain function will then be obtained by Newton's method. The user now can use the element values of the lossless matching network as an initial guess, or enter his own initial guess, or ask the program to search for a good initial guess, to solve the element values of the lossy matching network. The search routine will systematically search an n-dimensional region for different initial guesses and then compare their function values and pick the best initial guess. In this search routine, Aird and Rice's systematic algorithm [7] has been adopted. After the element values of the lossy matching network are acquired, an iteration method is used to obtain the maximum gain G_{max} under certain gain specifications such as gain slope and gain ripple by decreasing the gain reduction step by step. As shown in Fig. 5, another feature of LUMSYN is to get a set of element value tables with the same general gain response shape but different gain reductions. The user can then keep the same gain function and vary the gain reduction, or solve for another gain function, or terminate the running section by entering the appropriate commands.

One thing that might be interesting to the circuit designer is the uniqueness of the solution. It has been proved that the equiripple gain function is unique under a certain frequency bandwidth, gain slope, and gain ripple [3]. However, the element values with specified loss factors are obtained by solving a set of nonlinear equations. Theoretically, this kind of solution cannot be proved to be unique. Fortunately, a systematic search routine is available, and it is used to find all the possible solutions. It is found that with lots of different initial guesses, the entire set of solutions converge to $2^{(n/2)-1}$ practical solutions, where n is the order of the matching network. These $2^{(n/2)-1}$ solutions correspond to the $2^{(n/2)-1}$ different distributions of the zeros of the reflection coefficient, or $S_{11}(s)$, in the lossless matching network synthesis [3]. It can be concluded, therefore, that the lossy matching network solved by the above method is unique. This conclusion will be demonstrated further in the next section when the gain-bandwidth limitations are discussed.

IV. Gain-Bandwidth Limitations for Lossy Matching Networks

The general gain-bandwidth limitation of the lossless matching networks was introduced by Bode [8] in 1945, and was extended by Fano [9] and Youla [10]. Applying this theory to the typical simplified FET model, two integral inequalities can be obtained. Ku and Petersen [11] used ideal tapered gain functions to derive the optimum gain-bandwidth limitations which yield an upper bound of the capability of reactive element absorption under the specific gain slope, gain reduction, and bandwidth. Therefore, before a matching network is synthesized for a certain

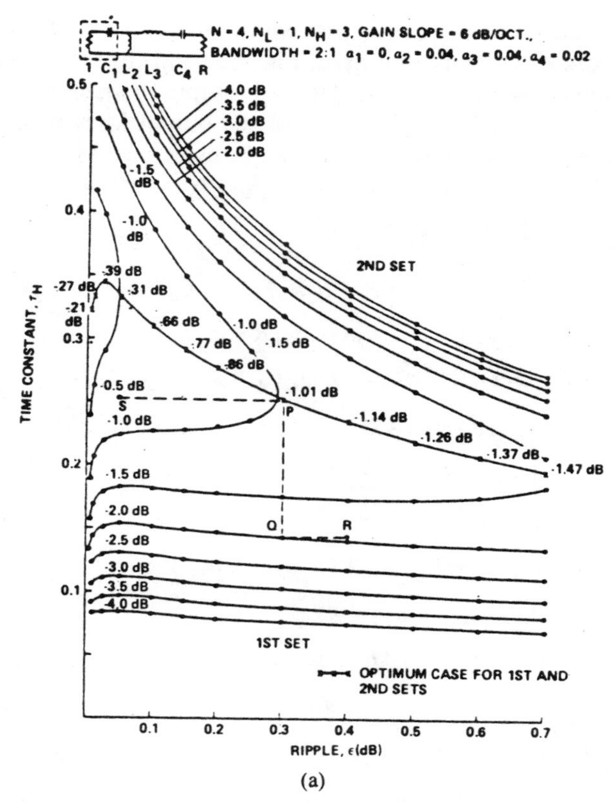

(a)

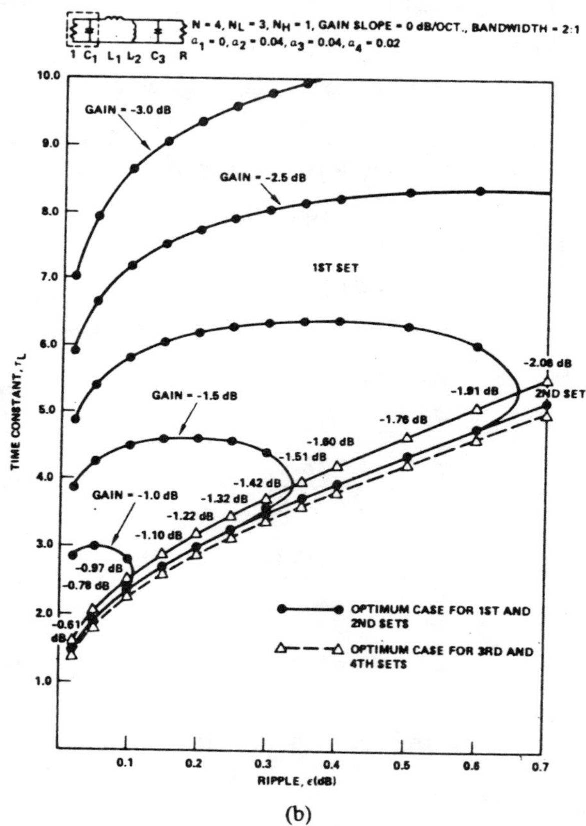

(b)

Fig. 6. (a) Gain-bandwidth constraint for lumped lossy input matching networks. (b) Gain-bandwidth constraint for lumped lossy output matching networks.

FET, the optimum gain-bandwidth limitations of the FET simplified model can be checked first to determine the appropriate gain slope, gain reduction, and bandwidth. For the actual design of the GaAs FET amplifiers, the gain–bandwidth limitation of practical gain functions must be employed. The practical gain–bandwidth constraint plots for a lossy input and output matching network are shown in Fig. 6(a) and (b), respectively.

For a lossy matching network with some prescribed gain slope and gain ripple, there is a minimum gain reduction which has to be put into the gain function in order to obtain a realizable network. This is the minimum gain reduction introduced by the element losses in the matching network, and the gain level in this situation is called G_{max}. Any matching network with a gain level lower than G_{max} is realizable while any matching network with a gain level higher than G_{max} is unrealizable. In addition, this G_{max} is a function of both gain slope and gain ripple for a certain topology of a matching network. Due to the nonlinearity of the lossy matching network, there is no analytical method to calculate the G_{max}. As a result, an iteration method is employed to determine the G_{max}. The gain–bandwidth limitation curves with G_{max} are plotted in Fig. 6 as the optimum cases. These optimum cases correspond to the 0-dB gain reduction states in the lossless matching network. Each of these states has a zero of the reflection coefficients on the $j\omega$-axis. The other zeros may be either in the left-half plane (LHP) or in the right-half plane (RHP), or in a mixed distribution form. Each different distribution of zeros has a different G_{max}, and hence generates a new set of optimum curves in the gain–bandwidth constraint plots. For the $n = 4$ case, one set of complex conjugated zeros is on the $j\omega$-axis and another set of zeros can be either in the LHP or RHP in the complex S-plane. Therefore, two optimum curves are generated as shown in Fig. 6. Beginning with an optimum case, when some gain reduction is added to the matching network, the zeros on the $j\omega$-axis will move away from the $j\omega$-axis. Since there are two directions that the zeros can take, i.e., move into LHP or RHP, there are two solutions with the same gain response but different gain–bandwidth constraints. The result is that there are two sets of curves with the same gain reduction as shown in Fig. 6(a) and (b). The gain–bandwidth constraint curves with a certain gain reduction have to merge to the optimum curves; therefore, these will have different shapes than those of the lossless case.

Two possible input and output matching networks for a GaAs MESFET are shown in Fig. 6(a) and (b), respectively. In the figure, N is the order of the matching network, N_L and N_H are the number of the low-pass and high-pass elements, respectively. The loss factors, α_i's, for inductor and capacitor are defined in (2) and (4), with their values being normalized at $\omega_H = 1$. The gain reduction at the optimum case is the maximum gain that the matching network can have under certain gain slope and ripple, and was defined as G_{max}. The reactance absorption capability will increase with higher gain reduction. The first set of curves in Fig. 6(a) illustrate this property if the element C_1 is considered as the reactive element to be absorbed.

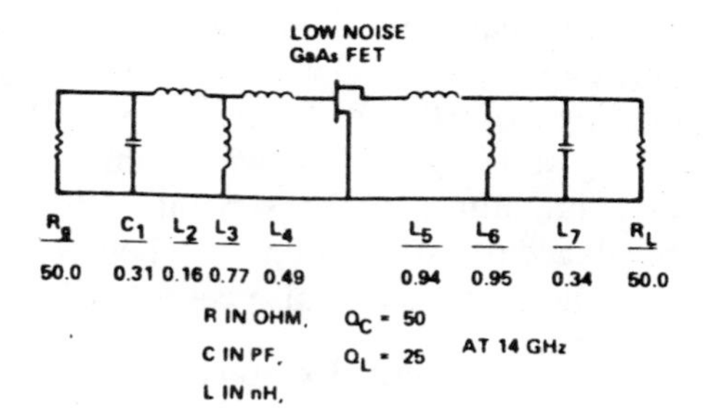

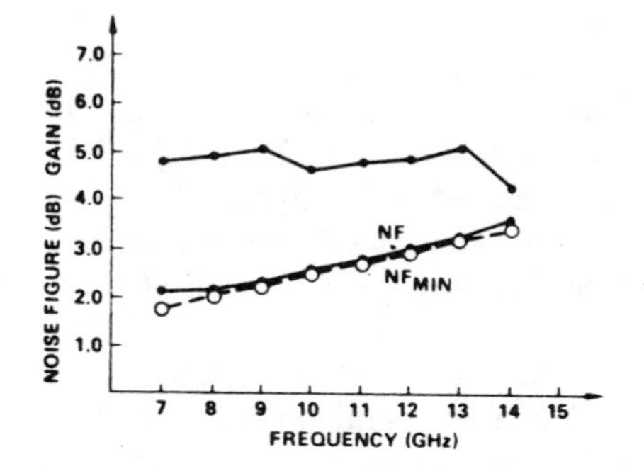

Fig. 7. Amplifier design, gain response, and noise figure of the low-noise amplifier using Hughes GaAs MESFET.

TABLE I
MEASURED S-PARAMETERS OF THE 0.5-μm GATE GaAs MESFET BIASED AT $V_D = 3$ V AND $I_D = 12$ mA

FREQ. (GHz)	S11 MAG	S11 <ANG	S12 MAG	S12 <ANG	S21 MAG	S21 <ANG	S22 MAG	S22 <ANG
7.00	0.888	-57.677	0.063	61.479	1.254	115.379	0.764	-40.284
8.00	0.828	-67.075	0.064	54.445	1.147	104.645	0.727	-47.946
9.00	0.817	-72.691	0.056	56.424	1.118	99.724	0.769	-49.660
10.00	0.812	-80.151	0.067	54.262	1.052	92.062	0.773	-53.840
11.00	0.819	-84.816	0.068	55.187	1.029	87.187	0.777	-58.916
12.00	0.815	-88.303	0.068	54.049	0.991	79.249	0.787	-62.362
13.00	0.775	-93.012	0.073	55.581	1.006	74.181	0.750	-70.123
14.00	0.732	-100.767	0.070	51.608	0.925	62.308	0.777	-80.259

To illustrate the use of these gain–bandwidth plots, it is assumed that an input matching network is to be synthesized and the time constant of the input port of the FET is found out to be 0.25. If a gain ripple of 0.3 dB is acceptable, then from Fig. 6(a), point P on the optimum curve can absorb the reactive element of the input port of the FET. The gain reduction is 1.01 dB in this case. On the other hand, if an input matching network is desired for a FET with more strict input gain–bandwidth limitations, e.g., with a time constant of 0.14, then only point Q in Fig. 6(a) can absorb the reactive element if the gain ripple is kept at 0.3 dB. The gain reduction is increased to 2 dB in order to match this FET. A higher gain level can still be used if the gain ripple is larger. For example, point R in Fig. 6(a) has 0.4-dB gain ripple, but a higher gain of -1.9 dB can also absorb the reactive element of the FET.

It may be noted that point S in Fig. 6(a) has the same reactive element absorption capability as point P but with a smaller gain ripple of 0.05 dB. Therefore, point S is more desirable as long as the gain–bandwidth limitation is the only consideration. But sometimes point P is preferred when the impedance transformation ratio between the two ends of the matching network is also considered.

V. Design Example

A Hughes 0.5-μm low-noise GaAs MESFET [13] is used as a broad-band low-noise amplifier design example covering the octave frequency band from 7 to 14 GHz. The S-parameters of this FET are shown in Table I. Based on the input RC-series model ($R_{\text{in}} = 12.23\ \Omega$, $C_{\text{in}} = 0.27$ pF) of the FET and the measured noise figure of 2.53 dB at 10 GHz, the simplified noise model developed by Podell, Ku, and Liu [12] can be used to predict the noise figure and the optimum source impedance at each frequency. The calculation shows that in order to obtain a minimum noise figure of 3.43 dB at 18 GHz, a RC-parallel equivalent circuit with $R_{\text{in}} = 59.56\ \Omega$ and $C_{\text{in}} = 0.25$ pF has to be matched at the input side. A lumped lossy input matching network with $n = 4$, flat gain, a 0.78-dB gain reduction, and a 0.05-dB gain ripple covering 2:1 band is synthesized through LUMSYN. The output model of the circuit cascading input noise matching network and the FET is calculated to be a RC-parallel circuit with $R_0 = 321.31\ \Omega$ and $C_0 = 0.17$ pF. A lumped lossy matching network is then synthesized to absorb this output model. The output matching network has $n = 4$, flat gain, 1.57-dB gain reduction, 0.2-dB gain ripple, and covers 2:1 band. Some optimization iterations are then used to make the overall gain response flatter. The final amplifier design and its gain response together with the noise figure are shown in Fig. 7. Note that the lumped inductors in the matching network are assumed to have Q's of 25 while capacitors have Q's of 50 to 14 GHz.

VI. Conclusion

Systematic computer-aided synthesis techniques for matching networks in MMIC's have been developed and presented in this paper. The synthesis of the lumped matching network can incorporate the arbitrary loss factor associated with each reactive element and provide a very good initial design for a practical MMIC network. The application of this synthesis technique in the low-noise broad-band GaAs MESFET amplifier design is also presented to illustrate the general applicability of our computer-aided synthesis technique for broad-band GaAs MESFET MMIC amplifiers.

References

[1] R. A. Pucel, "Design considerations for monolithic microwave circuits," *IEEE Trans. Microwave Theory Tech.*, vol. MTT-29, pp. 513–534, June 1981.

[2] W. R. Wisseman, "GaAs technology in the 80's," *Microwave J.*, vol. 24, pp. 16–18, Mar. 1981.

[3] W. C. Petersen, "Analytic and computer aided design techniques for bipolar and FET transistor amplifiers," Ph.D. thesis, Cornell Univ., Jan. 1976.

[4] A. Ralston, *Mathematical Method for Digital Computers*. New York: Wiley, 1966.

[5] K. M. Brown, "A quadratically convergent Newton-like method based upon Gaussian elimination," *SIAM J. Numerical Anal.*, vol. 6, pp. 560–569, Dec. 1969.

[6] D. W. Marquardt, "An algorithm for least-squares estimation of nonlinear parameters," *SIAM J. Appl. Math.*, vol. 11, pp. 431–441, 1963.

[7] T. J. Aird and J. R. Rice, "Systematic search in high dimensional sets," *SIAM J. Numerical Anal.*, vol. 14, pp. 296–312, Apr. 1977.

[8] H. W. Bode, *Network Analysis and Feedback Amplifier Design*. New York: Van Nostrand, 1945.

[9] R. M. Fano, "Theoretical limitations on the broadband matching of arbitrary impedances," *J. Franklin Inst.*, vol. 249, pp. 57–83, Jan. 1950; pp. 139–155, Feb. 1950.

[10] D. C. Youla, "A new theory of broadband matching," *IEEE Trans. Circuits Theory*, vol. CT-11, pp. 30–50, Mar. 1964.

[11] W. H. Ku and W. C. Petersen, "Optimum gain–bandwidth limitations of transistor amplifiers as reactively constrained active two-port networks," *IEEE Trans. Circuits Syst.*, vol. CAS-22, pp. 523–533, June 1975.

[12] A. Podell, W. H. Ku, and L. Liu, "Simplified noise model and design of broadband low-noise MESFET amplifiers," in *Proc. 7th Biennial Conf. on Active Microwave Semiconductor Devices and Circuits*, (Cornell University), Aug. 1979, pp. 429–443.

[13] D. W. Maki, R. Esfandiari, H. Yamasaki, M. Siracusa, and W. F. Marx, "A monolithic low noise amplifier," in *Proc. 8th Biennial Conf. on Active Microwave Semiconductor Devices and Circuits*, (Cornell University), pp. 27–36, Aug. 1981.

CHAPTER IV

FABRICATION TECHNIQUES

The technology involved in the fabrication of microwave integrated circuits is constantly developing to meet the requirements of increasing frequency of operation, higher yield, and reduction of costs. A large body of literature which covers the details of relevant thin-film technology is available. Consequently, the general aspects of hybrid MIC and monolithic fabrication technology are considered here, in the articles by Caulton and by Andrade.

Film Technology in Microwave Integrated Circuits

MARTIN CAULTON, SENIOR MEMBER, IEEE

Abstract—A review of the material technology for microwave integrated circuits (MICs) is presented. The types of microwave circuit media that have been used are described and classified as a function of the amount of size reduction or integration which corresponds to the effective dielectric constant of the media. The materials used for substrates, conductors, dielectrics, and resistors are considered in terms of the requirements for microwave circuits. The fabrication of multilayered thin-film circuits and the various thin-film combinations that have been used in MICs are discussed. The various loss contributions for microstrip circuits produced by thin- and thick-film technology and substrate material are compared with each other as a function of frequency. It is concluded that microwave circuits operating at frequencies 2 GHz and above require thin-films on pure smooth substrates.

I. Introduction

MICROWAVE integrated circuits (MICs) have been under active investigation since 1965 and are now in production to a limited extent all over the world. The circuit techniques to permit size reduction of microwave elements has been a reality since 1952 [1], but the impetus to provide a state-of-the-art technology stemmed from the availability of 1) solid-state devices of small size operating at microwave frequencies and 2) techniques for integration that were developed for low-frequency integrated circuits. The realization that many of the advantages of solid-state devices could only be achieved by circuitry of comparable size also played a major role in the decision to pursue the technology.

A large part of the technology is concerned with materials; microwave integrated circuits pose different requirements on materials than do low-frequency integrated circuits. The properties of metal and dielectric films, as well as substrates, are of particular importance, and for this reason a paper on these aspects is of interest.

We will discuss the circuit types presently used in MICs and develop the necessary design information so that the material requirements can be developed. Material technology, including substrates, dielectrics, conductors, and resistors will be described. We will then go into fabrication schemes, consider the pros and cons of thick and thin films, monolithic versus hybrid integration, and will attempt to survey the types of film technologies now being used in MICs.

II. Circuits for MICs

In this section we describe the ways of integrating microwave circuits and point out the characteristics which determine the film technology.

A. Size Reduction

In order to use solid-state devices with microwave circuits, it is necessary to transform the large world of conventional circuits into the miniature one of solid-state. Size reduction is accomplished by using distributed or lumped circuits. Normally, sections of microwave transmission lines, usually less than a wavelength, are used for the circuitry and a significant size reduction is achieved by shortening the guide wavelength λ_g of these distributed circuits. The other technique is to use lumped-element inductors, capacitors, and resistors as in conventional low-frequency circuitry. By keeping the size of these components much smaller than a wavelength through the use of photolithographic techniques, the elements remain lumped through X band (10 GHz) [2], [3].

Manuscript received March 25, 1971; revised May 11, 1971.
The author is with RCA Laboratories, David Sarnoff Research Center, Princeton, N. J. 08540.

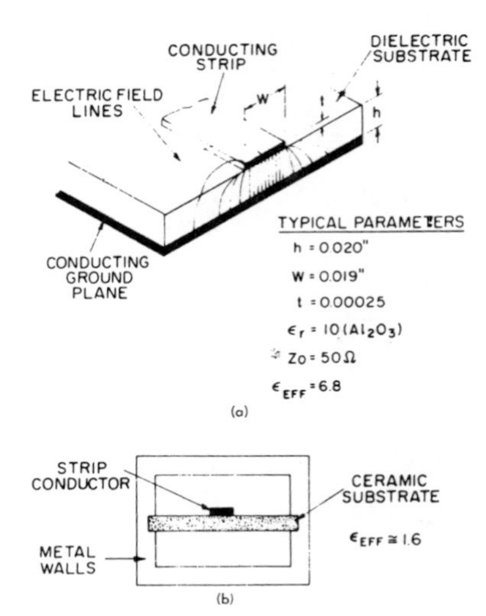

Fig. 1. (a) Microstrip transmission line, indicating nature of electric-field lines and typical parameters. (b) Suspended substrate line. Metalization is on only one side of substrate.

The guide wavelength λ_g of *distributed circuits* is reduced by high-dielectric-constant ε_r materials and circuitry to lower the propagation velocity. Because of the nature of the fields in typical integrated structures, the system has an effective dielectric constant ε_{eff} which is lower than ε_r and is defined [4] as a measure of the degree of integration and size reduction. (The guide wavelength λ_g is given by

$$\lambda_g = \frac{\lambda_0}{\sqrt{\varepsilon_{eff}}} \tag{1}$$

where λ_0 is the free-space wavelength). Fig. 1(a) illustrates the most common MIC transmission line, microstrip. Typical parameters are listed. As may be seen from the electric field lines shown, some of the field is in air and only a fraction q is in the substrate. The propagation is quasi-TEM. The effective dielectric constant ε_{eff} is made up of the dielectric constant of air ($\varepsilon_r = 1$) plus the dielectric constant of the substrate in excess of that of air ($\varepsilon_r - 1$), times the filling fraction q or

$$\varepsilon_{eff} = 1 + q(\varepsilon_r - 1). \tag{2}$$

This [4], [5] expression holds true for all the media to be discussed. For microstrip using the most common substrate material, alumina ($\varepsilon_r = 10$), the filling fraction q [6] is ~ 0.64, the $\varepsilon_{eff} \sim 6.8$, and the size reduction compared to free space is ~ 2.5. Larger size reduction can be achieved using higher-dielectric-constant materials. Here other problems can occur, such as excitation of higher order surface waves, too narrow a line width required for 50-Ω impedance, and temperature variations of ε_r.

Fig. 1(b) illustrates the suspended substrate line. Here metal surrounds the system and acts as a ground plane while the ceramic is

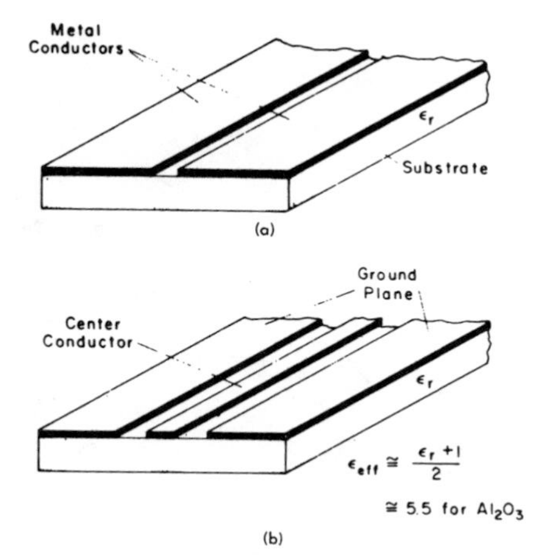

Fig. 2. (a) Slot Line. (b) Coplanar waveguide. Metalization for both lines are on only one side of substrate.

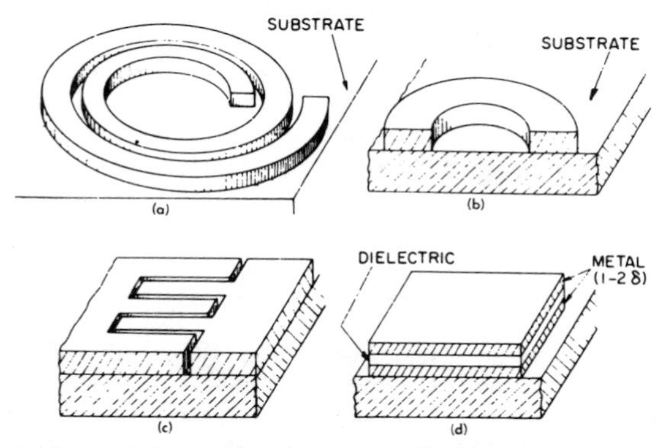

Fig. 3. Lumped elements for microwave applications. (a) Spiral inductor. (b) Strip inductor. (c) Interdigitated capacitor. (d) Metal-oxide-metal capacitors.

more of a support. The degree of integration is low (typical $\varepsilon_{eff} \sim 1.6$), but the system has been used by Bell Laboratories [7] with high reliability. Because the loss α of the suspended-substrate circuits is proportional to $(\varepsilon_{eff})^{1/2}$, the performance can be very good.

Fig. 2 shows two other types of transmission lines that are being considered for MIC applications. The finite slot line [8] of Fig. 2(a) is a geometrical and electrical dual of the coplanar line [9] of Fig. 2(b). The propagation is not TEM, and there are longitudinal as well as transverse RF magnetic fields. Hence nonreciprocal devices can be fabricated with magnetic material placed on the surface of the substrate. Shunt mounting of devices without requiring holes through the substrate is possible since all of the circuit is on one side of the dielectric. The filling fraction q for the coplanar and slot lines is about $\frac{1}{2}$ (half of the field is in air) and $\varepsilon_{eff} = (1 + \varepsilon_r)/2$. Typical $\varepsilon_{eff} \cong 5$ to 8.5 for alumina and magnetic materials.

Fig. 3 illustrates the types of *lumped elements* that are used at microwave frequencies. Fig. 3(a) is a spiral inductor useful up to ~ 8 GHz, Fig. 3(b) a strip inductor that gives reasonable performance to X band and suffices for the few nanohenries required at these frequencies. Fig. 3(c) is an interdigitated capacitor that can be used to 3 GHz or higher, depending on its size. Fig. 3(d) is a metal-oxide-metal capacitor that is lumped to frequencies above X band. The components of Fig. 3(a)–(c) require only one metalization layer, while that of Fig. 3(d) requires 3 layers (metal, dielectric, metal).

B. Current Flow and Loss Considerations

The current distribution in the various circuits determines the required conductor thicknesses. From a consideration of the RF magnetic fields tangential to the conductors, we see that most of the fields of the circuits of Figs. 1(a) and 3(d) are in the dielectric and the currents lie on the dielectric sides of the conductors. Only 2–3 skin depths of metal are needed. With the other circuits, such as Figs. 1(b), 2(a), and 2(b), current can flow on both sides of the conductors. Because of the nonuniform current distribution [10] the inductors of Fig. 3(a) and (b) need thicknesses on the order of 10 skin depths to reduce losses. Similar current crowding considerations for the circuits of Figs. 2(a), 2(b), and 3(c) suggest that thicker conductors are also desirable.

The losses in MICs are generally divided into two parts: 1) that caused by current flow in lossy conductors, the conducting loss α_c, and 2) that contributed by the dielectric material through which the fields propagate, the dielectric loss α_d.

$$\alpha = \alpha_c + \alpha_d. \tag{3}$$

The loss α can be normalized in terms of decibels per wavelength, so that $\alpha'\ (\mathrm{dB}/\lambda_g) = \lambda_g \alpha$.

The conductive loss for distributed lines and lumped elements depends on the nature of the conductor system, i.e., the current flow distribution, the conductivity, and the smoothness of the conductor. The dielectric loss is generally related to the tan δ or $1/Q$ of the material and is weighted by the relative amount of field in the dielectric compared to that in air. Interestingly, the relative contributions of each vary little with the integration figure $(\varepsilon_{eff})^{1/2}$, but are very dependent on the frequency as will be described later. The total loss or $1/Q$ does vary with the amount of integration $(\varepsilon_{eff})^{1/2}$ of distributed circuits. For suspended-substrate systems, $\varepsilon_{eff} \cong 1.6$, both α_d and α_c are about $\frac{1}{2}$ of that of an alumina microstrip system.

First let us review the loss contribution of conductors and dielectrics.

1) *Conductive Losses:* The conductive loss α_c (nepers/length) of microstrip can be written as [11], [12]

$$\alpha_c = \frac{R}{2Z_0} = \frac{R_{gp} + R_{st}}{2Z_0}. \tag{4}$$

In Fig. 4 the resistance of the line R is shown divided into the resistance of the ground plane R_{gp}, and the resistance of the strip conductor R_{st}, all per unit length. It is found that the current distribution in the microstrip ground plane [13] normally extending to the edges, can be equated to a uniform current which extends a substrate thickness h on each side of the center strip's projection on the ground plane (Fig. 4). Thus $R_{st} \cong R_s/W$, $R_{gp} \cong R_s/(2h + W)$, and Z_0 is a function of W/h. The resultant conductor loss α_c' can be expressed as

$$\alpha_c'(\mathrm{dB}/\lambda_g) = 8.68\pi R_s \lambda_g f\left(\frac{W}{h}\right)\frac{\alpha_{cR}}{\alpha_{c0}}. \tag{5}$$

It is interesting to note that these approximations lead to results very close to that of a more exact analysis [12]. The last term α_{cR}/α_{c0} of (5) is the ratio of surface-loss contribution because of surface roughness to the loss of a smooth surface. This term, the effect of surface roughness of microwave current loss, has been evaluated by Morgan [14] twenty years ago. He did this by considering theoretical eddy current losses for equilateral triangular grooves. These considerations are for losses transverse to the direction of induced current flow, and neglect grooves parallel to current flow. Basically the loss is increased by 60 percent when the surface roughness Δ is equal to a skin depth δ. This has been compared with experiment by Lend-

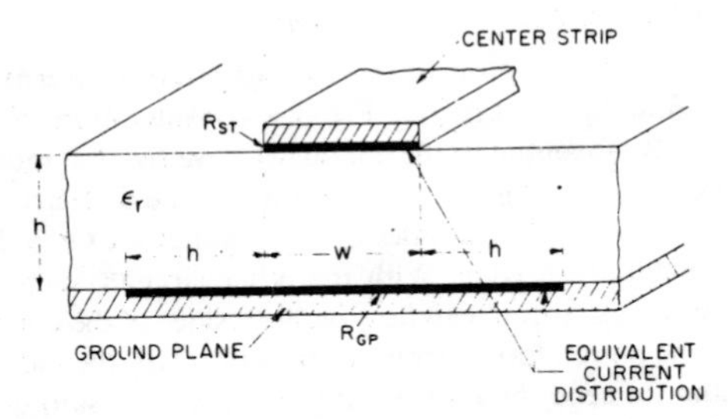

Fig. 4. The equivalent current distribution in microstrip. The current in the ground plane extending to infinity replaced by a limited uniform current distribution. This equivalence similar to replacement of the static charge distribution of two electrodes by the uniform one.

ing [15] using waveguides. More recently Sobol [16] applied Morgan's theory to microstrip and his results are displayed in Fig. 5. As described by Lending, the frequency dependence of the increase in loss is taken into account by the term Δ/δ. If the ratio is less than 0.4 the increase in loss is only 10 percent. Thus for higher microwave frequencies where δ is small the surface roughness is much more critical than at frequencies below 1 GHz.

The conductor loss from (5) is found to vary as $\lambda_g^{1/2}$, $\sqrt{\varepsilon_{\text{eff}}}$, and is inversely proportional to substrate thickness.

2) *Dielectric Loss:* The effect of dielectric loss is simply the tan δ of the media, weighted by the amount of flux lines in the lossy dielectric. Thus

$$\alpha_d'(\text{dB}/\lambda_g) = 8.68\pi \frac{\varepsilon_r}{\varepsilon_{\text{eff}}} q \tan \delta. \tag{6}$$

This expression is modified from Schneider [4] and is relatively independent of frequency.

With lumped elements many of the previous arguments regarding surface roughness are valid [10]. The dielectric loss considerations also apply [2], depending on the amount of fields in the substrate or the dielectric.

III. Material Technology

We wish to describe the materials that are being used or considered for MICs and list the properties that affect the circuit performance. These materials are classified according to their usage: substrates, conductors, dielectrics, and resistive materials.

A. Substrates

Substrates to be considered for use with MICs should have certain properties. Low RF dielectric loss or tan δ is important where most of the RF field is confined to the substrate. The surface finish is very important since it determines 1) the definition of circuit patterns, 2) yield in thin-film metal-oxide capacitors, and 3) RF conductor loss and surface finish. The substrate should be able to maintain mechanical and electric integrity during processing. The dielectric constant ε_r should be in the 8–16 range for normal integrated circuit size reduction for integration applications. Too high an ε_r leads to the problems discussed earlier. Heat conductivity is an important consideration where high-power devices are used.

Table I lists substrates that have been used for MICs along with some properties and applications. Glass is the most lossy and has the poorest thermal conductivity, while beryllia with one of the highest thermal conductivities is difficult to handle. We list it as a compound substrate, as it is used in conjunction with other material. Rutile, a high ε_r material, is also used for slot and coplanar lines. Ferrite and garnet are used for nonreciprocal components, and semi-insulating GaAs and silicon are being studied for use in monolithic integration.

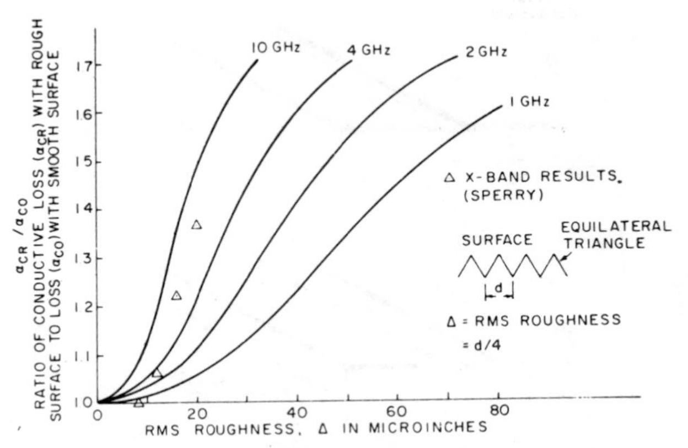

Fig. 5. Increase of RF loss α_c versus surface roughness. Figure reproduced from Sobol [16].

The insulating properties of high-resistivity silicon are difficult to maintain during processing. We have also listed fused quartz, a pure material now being used for MIC substrates [17].

Most of the substrate material of Table I can be supplied with a very high polish (less than 2-μin center line average (CLA) but the cost can be prohibitive. Other ceramics, such as the 85-percent and 96-percent alumina, and higher ε_r material such as the magnesium titanates, have been used. The less pure aluminas are rougher due to the impurities. The RF loss limits their frequency range and circuit application.

B. Conductors

Some considerations for conductors of MICs are the RF resistance and skin depth (parameters determining the thickness required), deposition technique, substrate adherence, and the thermal expansion during processing. The ability to define the conductor circuit must play a role and will be discussed separately.

Conductors can be divided into several categories as indicated in Table II: I Good conductors, low resistivity, but with poor adhesion to dielectrics. Aluminum is an anomaly since it has fair adhesive properties. The second category II is that of poorer conductors, but with good adherence to dielectrics. We have listed the more popular ones: Cr, Ta, Ti. Thin flashes of these provide adhesive layers for category I conductors. The metals of the first two categories are generally deposited by vacuum evaporation, resistance boat, or electron beam heating. The third category III contains fair conductors with fair adherence to dielectrics. Tungsten and molybdenum are refractive materials and vacuum evaporation using electron beam heating is required for deposition. Sputtering, however, works with all of these conductors, and is particularly useful for category III materials. We have also listed a fourth category in which we have placed barrier metals, platinum and palladium. In order for the system to withstand heat and corrosion, platinum or palladium are often used to isolate the good conductors I from the glues II and avoid diffusion and alloying.

The relative resistivity ρ of the metals are also listed in Table II. (These are normalized to that of copper 1.7×10^6 $\Omega \cdot$cm). The RF conductivity or surface resistance, R_s (ohms per square), varies as $\sqrt{\rho}$. As discussed earlier, several skin depths of conductors or thicknesses greater than several micrometers of metal are required.

C. Dielectrics and Resistors

Dielectrics for isolation and for capacitors in MICs require the properties of reproducibility, capability of withstanding high volt-

TABLE I

PROPERTIES OF SUBSTRATES

Material	Surface Roughness Δ (μm)	tan $\delta \times 10^4$ (10 GHz)	ε_r	K (W/cm^2-C°)	MIC Applications
Alumina (99.5%)	2–8	1–2	10	0.3	microstrip, suspended substrate
(96%)	20	6	9	0.28	
(85%)	50	15	8	0.20	
Sapphire	1	1	9.3–11.7	0.4	microstrip, lumped element
Glass	1	20	5	0.01	lumped element quasi-monolithic MICs
Quartz (fused)	1	1	3.8	0.01	microstrip, lumped element
Beryllia	2–50	1	6.6	2.5	compound substrates
Rutile	10–100	4	100	0.02	microstrip, slot-line coplanar
Ferrite/garnet	10	2	13–16	0.03	microstrip, coplanar compound substrates nonreciprocal components
GaAs (high resistivity)	1	16	13	0.3	high-frequency microstrip, monolithic MICs
Si (high resistivity)	1	10–100	12	0.9	monolithic MICs

TABLE II

CHARACTERISTICS OF CONDUCTOR FOR MICs

Material	Dc Resistivity ρ(relative to Cu)	Skin Depth δ at 2 GHz (μm)	α_T Thermal Expansion (/ C × 10^6)	Adherence to Dielectric
I (Ag, Cu, Au, Al)	0.95 to 1.6	1.4 to 1.9	15–26	poor
II (Cr, Ta, Ti)	7.6 to 48	4.0 to 10.5	8.5 to 9.0	good
III (Mo, W)	3.3	2.6	6.0, 4.6	fair
IV (Pt, Pd)	6.2	3.6	9–11	

ages, and the ability to undergo processing without developing pin holes, and for some applications, low RF dielectric loss. Some of these properties are difficult to achieve in thin films.

Several dielectrics used with MICs are shown in Table III. SiO, SiO_2, and tantalum pentoxide are the most widely used. It is now possible to obtain thin-film SiO_2 with high dielectric Q's or low tan δ. This is obtained by the pyrolytic deposition of silane and densification of the resultant SiO_2 layer by heat treatment [2]. Silicon dioxide can also be deposited by sputtering.

Resistive films for use in MICs should have resistivities in the range of 10–500 Ω/□, a low temperature coefficient of resistivity, TCR, and good stability. Some resistive materials are shown in Table IV. Nichrome and tantalum have good stability and low temperature coefficients, and are the most widely used.

TABLE III

PROPERTIES OF DIELECTRIC FILMS

Material	ε_r	Dielectric Strength V/cm	Microwave Q Dielectric
SiO (evaporated)	6–8	4×10^5	30
SiO_2 (deposited)	4–5	10^7	20–5000
Al_2O_3 (anodized or evaporated)	7–10	4×10^6	
Tantalum oxide (Ta_2O_5) anodized and sputtered	22–25	6×10^6	<100
Si_3N_4			
Vap phase	7.6	10^7	
Sputtered	6.5	10^7	

TABLE IV

PROPERTIES OF RESISTIVE FILMS

Material	Resistivity Ω/□	TCR, % per °C	Stability
Cr (evaporated)	10–1000	−0.1 to +0.1	poor
NiCr (evaporated)	40–400	+0.002 to +0.1	good
Ta (sputtered in A–N)	5–100 +	−0.01 to +0.01	excellent
Cr–SiO (evaporated) (Cermet)	up to 600	−0.005 to −0.02	fair
Ti (evaporated)	5–2000	−0.1 to +0.1	fair

IV. FILM APPLICATIONS AND FABRICATION

A. Adherence

Metals adhere to ceramics by either a mechanical or chemical bond. The mechanical bond requires a rough surface, defeating the precise definition of metals. The chemical bond is therefore required for surface finishes better than 5 μin. Fig. 6 indicates the mechanism for a chemical bond of thin films to ceramics and many other substrates. A reducing material, such as chrome or titanium, is oxidized by the heated substrate. Pure chrome without oxide will then adhere to a pure metal of category I if it is deposited in the same vacuum run. The required thickness of good conductor metal can be built up by either evaporating in the same vacuum run or by plating over the seed metal later.

B. Pattern Definition

Two techniques to define patterns (metal layers, several skin-depths thick) are illustrated in Fig. 7. By using only a thin seed of evaporated metal one can plate through a thick photoresist form as shown in Fig. 7(a) and obtain a line 5 μ thick or more with rather precise definition. This is possible because only a thin seed metal less than 1 μ thick is etched and the undercut is reduced. On the other hand, straight etching of thick metal as shown in Fig. 7(b) leaves one with an undercut which is of the order of twice the line thickness, or in this case about a half a mil. The plating–etching technique allows more precise definition, although the latter provides smoother metal with bulk conductivity.

1) Thick-Film Techniques: Metal films may also be deposited and defined by so-called "thick-film" techniques often involving silk screening through a mask. The term "thick film" refers to the process used and not the film thickness. (Microwave "thin-film" metals are several micrometers to 15 μm thick, thicker than those of low-frequency integrated circuits.) The thick-film process usually involves the printing and screening of silver or gold in a glass frit which is applied on the ceramic and fired at 850°C. Silk screening the material ($\frac{1}{2}$ mil or more) through a metal mask gives a coarse line definition. After firing, the initial layer may be plated with gold. The problem with thick films is that the material is of two constituents, metal or dielectric, interdispersed with glass. Because of this, a well-defined etch pattern, such as obtained with thin-film processing, is not possible although etching and eliminating the screening procedure improves the definition. The dc resistance of the fired conductor is higher than that of pure evaporated films, and the RF conductivity is partially degraded. The propagating electromagnetic wave appears to penetrate the glass suspension and mainly see the pure metal, as will be described later. Thick-film dielectrics can be applied by screening and firing high-dielectric constant

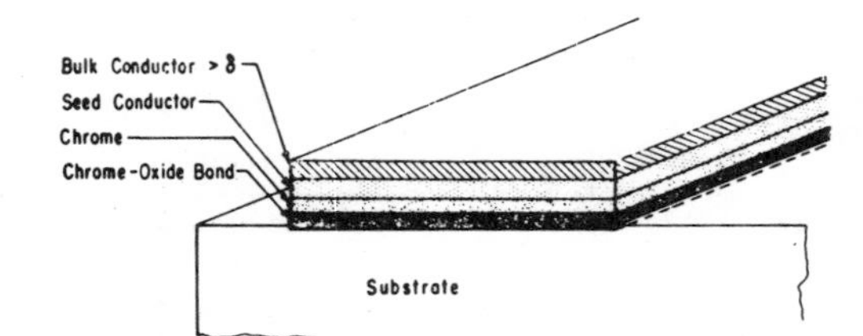

Fig. 6. Schematic representation of the metal-ceramic bond for thin-film depositions.

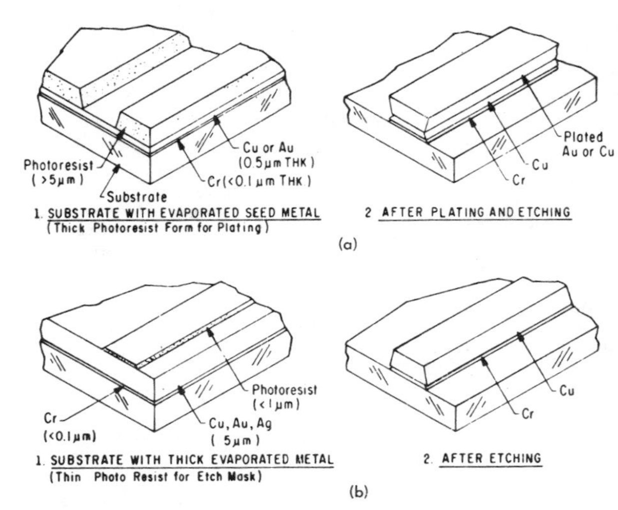

Fig. 7. Techniques for defining patterns in several micrometers of metal. (a) Circuit fabrication by plating and etching. (b) Circuit fabrication by etching thick metal.

Fig. 8. (a) Scanning electron microphotograph of thick film lines on 96-percent alumina. The lines are 4 mils wide. Device shown has beam leads 0.5 mil thick. (b) Scanning electron microphotograph of thin film lines on 96-percent alumina. Beam leaded device mounted on them is 0.029 by 0.030 by 0.005 in with 0.5-mil thick beam leads.

material. The RF loss of these is not established and etching can be difficult. The thick-film bond to ceramic is partly mechanical, and a rough substrate yields better adherence.

Fig. 8(a) is a scanning electron micrograph of thick-film lines on 96-percent alumina. These screened lines (4 mils wide) are seen to have poor definition. The beam-leaded device bonded to them, shown for comparison, is 0.029 by 0.030 by 0.005 in and the beam leads are $\frac{1}{2}$ mil thick and 2 mils wide near the device. Accepted limits on screened thick-film lines as of this date are 3 mils wide, 3 mils separation. Etched thick-film circuits have line definitions that are far superior to those of Fig. 8(a) [18]. To obtain an acceptable definition the alumina must have a highly polished surface.

2) Thin Films: Fig. 8(b) is a scanning electron-micrograph of thin-film lines on 96-percent alumina. These lines show the roughness of the substrate and are less than 1 μm thick, but the edges are well defined. In order to obtain the definition (1 mil gap or better) that can be achieved in thin films, polished substrates and etched patterns are required. However, separations of 0.3 mil in microstrip lines are required for 3-dB directional couplers on 25-mil alumina [19]. These can only be achieved using thin-film materials.

C. Fabrication of Multilayered Circuits

Simple microstrip circuits can be fabricated in one layer of metal; hybrid capacitors and resistors can be attached later. On the other hand, if more sophisticated integration is to be employed, where all of the passive circuitry is deposited, several layers of material are required. This applies where resistors and capacitors are to be fabricated along with distributed circuitry, as well as with lumped-element circuits.

Fabrication techniques for lumped-element circuits have been described [13], [20] in previous papers. Basically, a three-layer sandwich of metal-dielectric-metal is used to form all the elements of the lumped element MIC [Fig. 9(a)]. A deposition of chrome-copper-chrome is made or sapphire [Fig. 10(a)]. Alternatively, titanium can be used instead of chrome, gold instead of copper, and/or various metal combinations, as will be discussed later. The bottom metal pattern is defined and etched [Fig. 10(b)]. An SiO_2 film on the order of 0.5 to 1.0 μm is applied using the low-temperature silane-decomposition deposition [21]. Unwanted oxide can be etched to expose bottom metal or substrate areas, but is not always necessary [Figs. 10(a), 11(c)]. The circuit oxide is then densified by heating to temperatures over 400°C [2], [22], [23]. This is necessary in order to obtain a low tan δ dielectric. A thin layer of top-metal is deposited, and the thick metal required for inductors and the rest of the circuit is selectively electroplated (Section IV-B). The thin unplated areas are etched clean [Fig. 10(d)]. The equivalent circuit of the layer shown in the sandwich of Fig. 9(a) is illustrated in Fig. 9(b). Note that the inductor is a "crossover" in that it has to be clear of metal directly underneath [2]. Resistive material can be incorporated as part of the adhesive layer instead of chrome or titanium.

The thick top metal shown in Fig. 10(d) is only required for inductors. The multilayered structure permits the fabrication of capacitors and crossovers. On the other hand, lumped capacitors

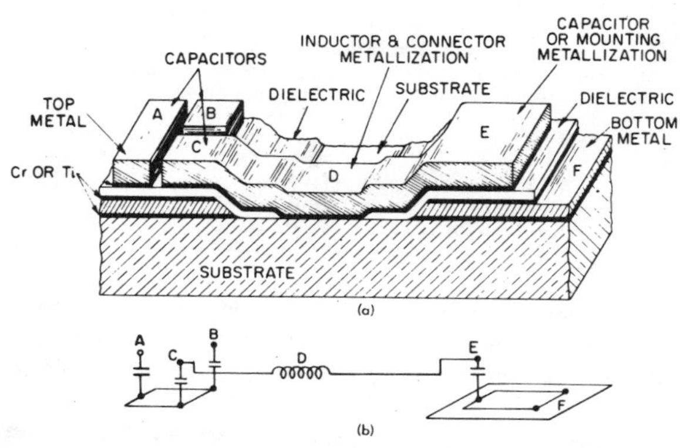

Fig. 9. Three-layer metal-dielectric-metal thin-films for MICs. (a) Cross section of integrated sandwich. (b) Equivalent circuit contacts.

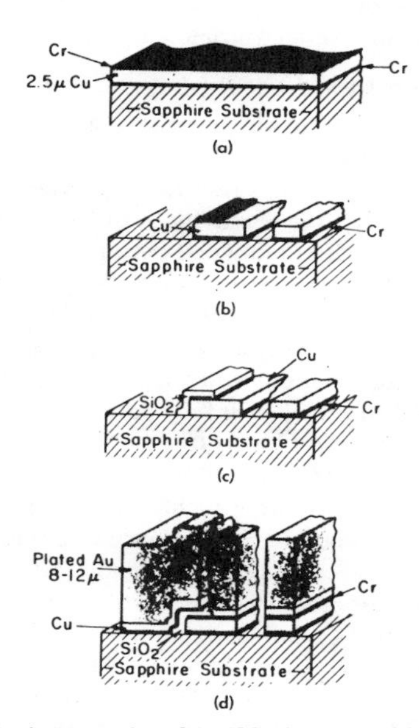

Fig. 10. Fabrication procedure for MICs demonstrating thin-film deposition techniques for transmission lines, capacitors, and inductors. (a) Sapphire with Cr–Cu–Cr. (b) Etched pattern prior to dielectric deposition. (c) SiO_2 deposited and etched. (d) Final layer of top metals defined.

good to 3 GHz can be fabricated with a single metal layer by using interdigitated capacitors of Fig. 3(c) [24].

Fig. 11 is a photograph of a lumped-element transistor power amplifier for operation at 2.25 GHz fabricated using the previous techniques. It can be tuned by adding capacitors or shorting inductors with bond wire. The circuit connections are identified. Fig. 12 is a photograph of a circuit tuned as described, with the transistor mounted and bonded in place. Fig. 13 shows the batch processing of 25 amplifiers on a single $\frac{3}{4}$ by 1 by 0.005 in sapphire substrate that is possible with these small circuits.

V. Choices in Film Technology

A. Thick versus Thin Films for MICs

In the previous section we described some of the difficulties in obtaining well-defined lines with both thick and thin films. In this section we will further develop the loss considerations for microstrip films and consider thick versus thin film performance for MICs.

Table V lists the results of computations of dielectric and con-

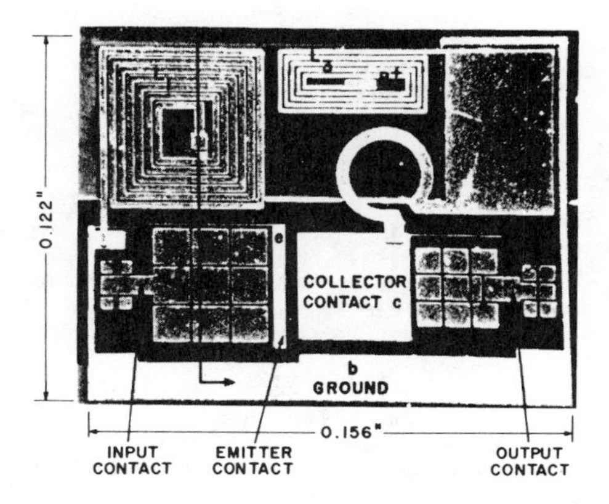

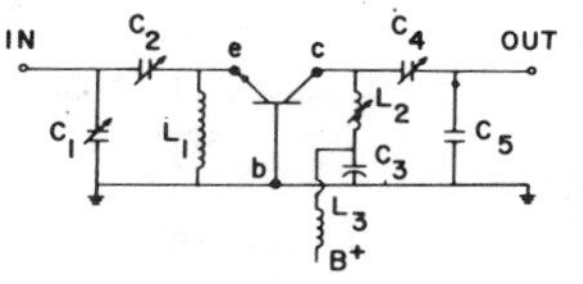

Fig. 11. Photograph and schematic of lumped-element microwave transistor circuit (1.8–2.5 GHz) including RF chokes (L_1, L_3) and by-pass capacitors C_3. Separation between adjacent capacitors of C_2, C_4, and C_5 is 1 mil. Circuit is on a 5–10-mil thick sapphire chip.

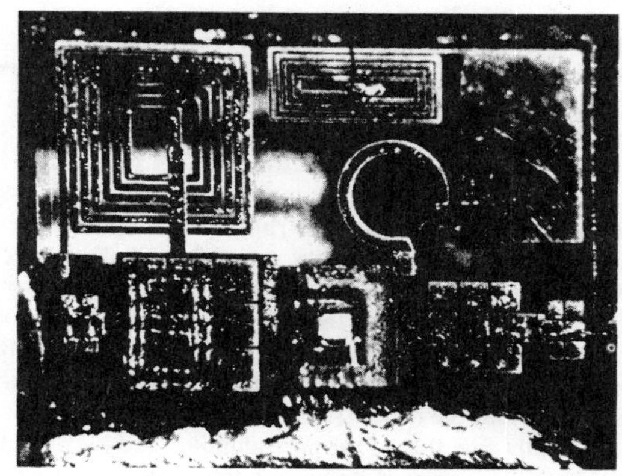

Fig. 12. The transistor amplifier circuit of Fig. 11 with a transistor mounted and the coaxial line input and output bonded at left and right. The removal of metallization from underneath the inductor area is evident. This transistor circuit gave performance close to the best achieved with the devices used.

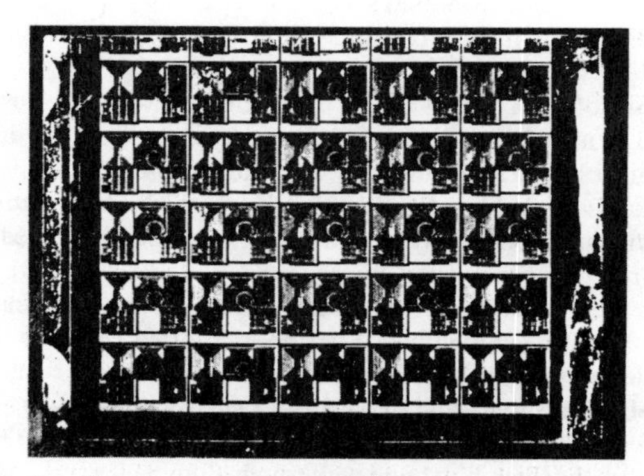

Fig. 13. Twenty-five transistor amplifier circuits of Fig. 12 batch-processed on a 0.75 by 1.0 by 0.010-in sapphire substrate.

TABLE V

CONDUCTOR AND DIELECTRIC LOSSES OF MICROSTRIP
(50Ω, 10–20-mil alumina – α' in dB/λ_g)

Substrate (Al_2O_3 Content)	Roughness (μin)	α_c' 10 GHz	α_c' 2 GHz	α_c' 0.2 GHz	α_d'
99.5%	<10	0.1	0.22	0.71	0.0025
96%	≈20	0.15	0.23	0.74	0.015
85%	≈50	0.20	0.34	0.85	0.038

TABLE VI

THICK AND THIN FILMS

Thick films on smooth alumina (99.5% and 96%)	measured loss 1.4 × greater than equivalent thin films does not stick under environmental hazards reasonable performance for etch defined lines—separations of 2 mils or better, 9 GHz receiver built
Thick films on rough alumina	thick film/thin film loss 3.5 × at 10.0 GHz 1.7 × at 2.0 GHz 1.25 × at 0.2 GHz line separation >3 mils, reasonable adherence

ductor losses of microstrip for several frequencies and for three different qualities of alumina. These computations were made using the loss relationships described in Section II-B. They are made for 50-Ω microstrip lines on 15-mil thick alumina. The conductor loss follows from (5). An experimental loss value of 0.1 dB at 10 GHz is considered for α_c' on pure smooth alumina. For other frequencies α_c' (dB/λ_g) varies as $f^{-1/2}$. A surface-roughness correction for the rougher alumina was taken from Fig. 5 and Table I. The dielectric loss was taken from (6).

For the less pure aluminas the conductor loss increases with surface roughness and the dielectric loss (tan δ) also increases due to the increased impurities. An important conclusion from these computations is that the loss at 10 GHz of the impure alumina increases drastically over that of the pure alumina, and the dielectric-loss contribution becomes a significant factor, $\alpha_d/\alpha_c = 19$ percent (10 GHz, 85-percent Al_2O_3). In order to obtain reasonable performance at 10 GHz and down to 2 GHz only very pure smooth substrates are permissible. At lower frequencies (200 MHz), the increase in total loss with poorer substrates is only of the order of 30 percent, and the dielectric contribution is only a few percent. Accordingly, at UHF frequencies the use of impure substrates will not lead to excessive losses.

The use of thick or thin films is also connected with the substrate choice. The use of thick films themselves will increase the conductor loss at microwave frequencies by a factor of 1.4 over the values quoted in Table V [25]. On the other hand, thick-film microwave circuits having good performance are feasible, as demonstrated by a 9-GHz receiver constructed by Microwave Associates [26]. The receiver was constructed using all thick-film metallization on smooth 99.5-percent alumina. It has been reported [18] that thick-film materials will not stick to highly polished material because the chemical bond is weak and in hazardous environments such as hot moist atmospheres the circuits will peel from the substrate. On the other hand, the thick-film bond with rough alumina is excellent, and thick films are suitable. Table VI summarizes the previous arguments, and compares the ratio of thick-to-thin-film loss as a function of frequency. There is little loss in performance using thick films at lower frequencies. At high frequencies, there is no choice, thin films on smooth substrates are required.

The relative cost of thin- or thick-film facilities as well as the cost of the processing has not been well established at this time. There are schools of thought that feel that for all integrated technology the purity of thin films, the ease of adherence and hybrid mounting, overweigh any cost differential which might exist.

TABLE VII

THIN-FILM METAL SYSTEMS

Chromium Based	Titanium Based
Cr–Cu	Ti–Au
Cr–Cu–Au	Ti–Pd–Au
Cr–Cu–Ni–Au	Ti–Pt–Au
Cr–Cu–Cr	Ti–Pd–Au–Pd–Ti
Cr–Au	Ti: W–Au

B. Monolithic versus Hybrid

It is now appropriate to examine the question of monolithic versus hybrid integration. Monolithic techniques usually involve a semiinsulating semiconducting substrate to provide reistive isolation. For microwave ICs the resistivity of the substrate should be much greater than 1000 Ω·cm for good circuit performance. Active devices are fabricated locally by growing them epitaxially in the insulating material. Silicon substrates have not been successful; it was not possible to maintain resistivity during processing. On the other hand, GaAs does have the required characteristics and should be successful once the technology is fully developed. Monolithic approaches may be required for higher frequency circuits (greater than 18 GHz) where hybrid parasitics limit performance.

High-quality MICs require a highly insulating substrate with good semiconductor material in appropriate places. The quasi-monolithic approach to combine these in simple processing, such as silicon-on-sapphire, or other techniques, still awaits improvements in the state of the art. Assuming monolithic MICs are feasible the question is: are they desireable? The total yield of MICs with devices on a single processing wafer will be far below that of any array of active devices produced in similar processing steps. It is uncertain whether economy will justify monolithic processing at frequencies where hybrid circuits are still feasible [16], [2].

Hybrid techniques use high-quality substrates with active devices, and sometimes chip capacitors, mounted and bonded in place. To date only hybrid techniques have yielded useful MICs.

C. Compatible Systems

We have listed individual materials in Tables II and III. As a final consideration it is important to consider the appropriate combinations that have been used for MIC circuits. In this vein we note that many of these considerations apply for all integrated circuit packaging, not only at microwave frequencies. However, for MICs, the desired thickness of the good conductor metals (~5 μm) or greater, requires special attention.

Thin-film systems can be categorized as 1) chromium, 2) titanium, or 3) tantalum based technologies. Chromium and titanium are used as a basis for thin-film metal systems. The chromium and titanium are used as a basis for thin-film metal systems. The chromium combined with nickel (Nichrome) can also form the basis to incorporate resistors in the integration. Table VII lists some metal systems that have been used for MICs. In all of these the thickness of the category I good conductors (Table II), such as Cu

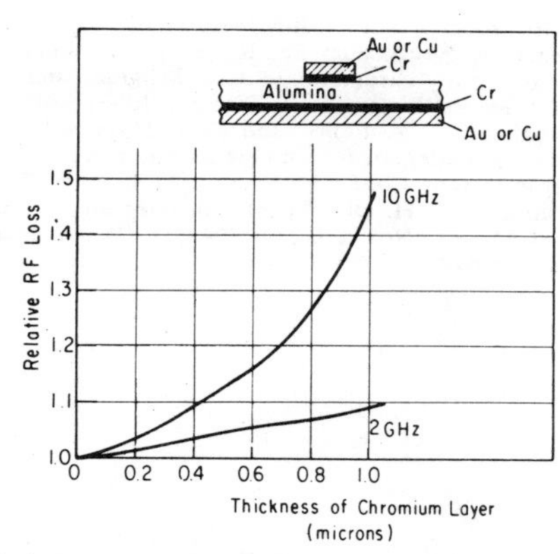

Fig. 14. Variation of relative RF loss (chrome-metal loss/pure metal loss) versus thickness of chrome at 2 and 10 GHz.

or Au, is at least 2 μm thick, while the category II adhesive metals Cr, Ti, or category IV barrier metals Pt and Pd, are only several hundred angstroms in depth. The use of thin layers of these adhesive films has very little influence on the RF loss. Fig. 14 shows the computed relative loss of a microstrip line formed by a thin layer of chrome and a category I conductor. The effect of even a thousand angstroms of chromium produces a negligible increase of RF loss, even at 10 GHz.

In the systems described in Table VII the more complicated layers, i.e., Cr–Cu–Cr, or Ti–Pd–Au–Pd–Ti, are used to 1) adhere to the substrate and 2) use the second layer of Cr or Pd–Ti as an adhesive for a dielectric deposition. This is typical for lumped-element circuits or where bypass capacitors are being integrated into the circuit.

The choice in metal systems is still being evaluated. One of the most commonly used systems for microstrip MICs is Cr–Au. This particular combination is also known to be poor in environmental extremes [27], [28], particularly as the diffusion of chrome into gold results in a material possessing resistivities greater than $\times$ 10 the bulk value of pure gold. However, when very thin layers of chromium are used (50 ~ 100 Å) in conjunction with thicker gold (> 2 μm), this phenomenon has not been observed [27]. The use of chromium (and/or Nichrome) and gold is generally suspect and the system awaits full evaluation. The Cr–Cu system can take diffusion without deleterious effects, and the other chrome systems without gold have been used. However, they all require a more complete evaluation.

The titanium systems have been devised to avoid chrome and still use gold. Here barrier metals are required. Ti–Pt–Au and Ti–Pd–Au have been used in MICs [22], Ti–W–Au [28] has been judged good for integrated circuits from the point of view of corrosion resistance, but has not yet been considered for MICs.

The tantalum system has been developed by Bell Laboratories [29]. Table VIII illustrates some combinations for conductors, dielectrics, and resistors. One of the best applications for tantalum is for resistors. The systems listed have been used and a titanium conductor system is compatible with tantalum-nitride resistors.

VI. Conclusions

We have shown how the film-technology requirements develop according to the amount of integration (ε_{eff}) at microwave frequencies. In particular, ε_{eff} describes the size reduction and much of the performance capabilities. The development of the material technology requirements pointed up the difficulties of achieving the size reduction, performance, reliability, and reproducibility using

TABLE VIII

Tantalum System

Conductors
Ta–Al–Au
Ta–Ti–Au (or Cu)
Ta–Cr–Au (or Cu)
Dielectrics
Tantulum pentoxide + SiO or SiO_2 or · · ·
Resistors
Tantalum nitride

thin and/or thick films with various metal systems. It is easier to achieve a satisfactory technology by using circuit media with lower ε_{eff}. The lines are wider, the dimensions less critical, and the losses are lower. Obviously the integration of microwave circuits places more stringent requirements on the materials used and thin-film processing is a necessity.

Microwave circuitry has been undergoing a revolution in the last few years, and it will be interesting to see what transpires during the 1970s.

References

[1] F. Assadourian and E. Rimai, "Simplified theory of microstrip transmission systems," *Proc. IRE*, vol. 40, Dec. 1952, pp. 1651–1657.
[2] M. Caulton, B. Hershenov, S. P. Knight, and R. E. DeBrecht, "Status of lumped elements in microwave integrated circuits—present and future," *IEEE Trans. Microwave Theory Tech.* (*Special Issue on Microwave Integrated Circuits*), vol. MTT-19, July 1971, pp. 588–599.
[3] R. E. DeBrecht, "Impedance measurements of microwave lumped elements from 1 to 12 GHz," to be published in *IEEE Trans. Microwave Theory Tech.* (*Special Issue on Microwave Measurements*), vol. MTT-20, Jan. 1972.
[4] M. V. Schneider, "Microstrip lines for microwave integrated circuits," *Bell Syst. Tech. J.*, vol. 48, May–June 1969, pp. 1421–1444.
[5] H. A. Wheeler, "Transmission-line properties of parallel strips separated by a dielectric sheet," *IEEE Trans. Microwave Theory Tech.*, vol. MTT-13, Mar. 1965, pp. 172–185.
[6] A. Presser, "RF properties of microstrip line," *Microwaves*, Mar. 1968, p. 53.
[7] R. S. Englebrecht and J. W. West, "Microwave integrated circuits," *Bell Lab. Rec.*, vol. 44, Oct./Nov. 1966, pp. 328–333.
[8] S. G. Cohn, "Slot-line—an alternative transmission medium for integrated circuits," *IEEE 1969 Int. Microwave Symp. Dig.*, May 1968, pp. 104–109.
[9] C. P. Wen, "Coplanar waveguide: A surface strip transmission line suitable for nonreciprocal gyromagnetic device applications," *IEEE Trans. Microwave Theory Tech.*, vol. MTT-17, Dec. 1969, pp. 1087–1090.
[10] M. Caulton, S. P. Knight, and D. A. Daly, "Hybrid integrated lumped-element microwave amplifiers," *IEEE Trans. Electron Devices*, vol. ED-15, July 1968, pp. 459–466.
[11] M. Caulton, J. J. Hughes, and H. Sobol, "Measurements on the properties of microstrip transmission lines for microwave integrated circuits," *RCA Rev.*, vol. 27, Sept. 1966, pp. 377–391.
[12] R. A. Pucel, D. J. Massé, and C. P. Hartwig, "Losses in microstrip," *IEEE Trans. Microwave Theory Tech.*, vol. MTT-16, June 1968, pp. 342–350.
[13] M. Caulton and H. Sobol, "Microwave integrated-circuit technology—a survey," *IEEE J. Solid-State Circuits*, vol. SC-5, Dec. 1970, pp. 292–303.
[14] S. P. Morgan, "Effect of surface roughness on eddy current losses at microwave frequencies," *J. Appl. Phys.*, vol. 20, Apr. 1949, pp. 352–362.
[15] R. D. Lending, "New criteria for microwave component surface," *Proc. Nat. Electron. Conf.*, vol. 11, 1955, p. 391.
[16] H. Sobol, "Applications of integrated circuit technology to microwave frequencies," *Proc. IEEE* (*Special Issue on Microwave Semiconductors*), vol. 59, Aug. 1971, pp. 1202–1213.
[17] W. W. Snell, Jr., "Low-loss microstrip filters developed by frequency scaling," *Bell Syst. Tech. J.*, vol. 50, July–Aug. 1971.
[18] J. Bunker, Microwave Associates, Inc., private communication.
[19] L. S. Napoli and J. J. Hughes, "Characteristics of coupled microstrip lines," *RCA Rev.*, vol. 31, Sept. 1970, pp. 479–498.
[20] M. Caulton, "The lumped element approach to microwave integrated circuits," *Microwave J.*, vol. 13, May 1970, pp. 51–58.
[21] N. Goldsmith and W. Kern, "The deposition of vitreous silicon-dioxide films from silane," *RCA Rev.*, vol. 28, Mar. 1967, pp. 153–165.

[22] M. Caulton *et al.*, "UHF film integrated circuits," Final Rep., under Contract DAAB07-68-C-0296, ECOM-0296-F.
[23] S. Krongelb, "Environmental effects on chemically vapor-plated SiO_2," *Electrochem. Technol.*, vol. 6, 1968, p. 251.
[24] G. D. Alley, "Interdigital capacitors and their application to lumped-element microwave integrated circuits," *IEEE Trans. Microwave Theory Tech.*, vol. MTT-18, Dec. 1970, pp. 1028–1033.
[25] R. N. Patel, "Microwave conductivity of thick-film conductors," *Electron. Lett.*, vol. 6, July 23, 1970, p. 455.
[26] A. Botka, J. Bunker, and M. Gilden, "Integrated *X*-band radar receiver front end," *Microwave J.*, vol. 11, July 1968, pp. 65–71.
[27] J. H. Rairden, C. A. Neugebauer, and R. A. Sigsbee, "Interdiffusion in thin conductor films—chromium/gold, nickel/gold, and chromium silicide/gold," General Electric Rep. 70-C-235, July 1970.
[28] J. A. Cunningham, C. R. Fuller, and C. T. Haywood, "Corrosion resistance of several integrated-circuit metallization system," presented at Int. Electron Devices Conf., Washington, D. C., Oct. 29, 1970.
[29] D. A. Mclean and W. H. Orr, "Tantalum integrated circuits," *Bell Lab. Rec.*, vol. 44, Oct.–Nov. 1966, pp. 304–311. (Whole issue devoted to integrated circuits.)

Manufacturing Technology for GaAs Monolithic Microwave Integrated Circuits

T. Andrade
Avantek, Inc., Santa Clara, California

Gallium arsenide monolithic microwave integrated circuit technology represents a natural extension of discrete GaAs metal-semiconductor field effect transistor (MESFET) technology. A GaAs manufacturing process architecture is described which provides the microwave circuit designer with a full component capability including MESFETs, resistors, capacitors, inductors, and integral backside grounding connections. The integration of these components is illustrated on a 2–12 GHz monolithic amplifier.

Over the past several years Monolithic Microwave Integrated Circuit (MMIC) technology has evolved into a high performance, cost effective technology suitable for high volume manufacturing applications [1]. At frequencies near or above 4 GHz, microwave circuit designers use discrete MESFETs (Metal Semiconductor Field Effect Transistors) and various assembly techniques to realize microwave circuitry. Below 4 GHz, silicon bipolar MMICs are finding uses in microwave systems as are discrete silicon bipolar transistors for higher frequency oscillator circuits [2, 3]. GaAs MMICs, however, are just emerging from production fabrication lines and whether they will find widespread use in microwave systems is yet to be determined [4]. Hybrid microwave technology represents a high performance, moderate cost benchmark against which to measure the overall GaAs MMIC performance. It is not the intent here to weigh the merits of monolithic and hybrid microwave circuits. This has been discussed elsewhere [5–7]. Naturally, the lowest cost and highest performance product will prevail. But as cost and performance are application dependent, it is safe to say that both technologies will remain viable as they are linked together by their use of the GaAs MESFET.

To understand the natural evolution from discrete MESFET to MMIC, consider the present state of commercial MESFETs. Four companies offer transistors with sub-half-micron gates! The processes for these high performance MESFETs establish a baseline for a high performance MMIC process. For an MMIC process, adapting a MESFET process has the inherent advantage that high performance MESFETs will be an MMIC process subset. This coupling allows the two to coexist in the same processing area and data accumulated on MESFET parameter variations can be applied to MMIC designs. As discrete MESFET technology advances, MMIC processes will keep paçe. Additionally, the discrete MESFET is very die area efficient. As cost is proportional to die area, MMIC area needs to be minimized.

Putting high performance MESFETs aside temporarily, GaAs processing in general differs greatly from Si processing [8] and microwave applications exaggerate some of the differences. These include mandatory use of submicron lithography for MESFET gates and the frequent use of low capacitance cross-over structures ("air bridges"). Other Si-GaAs process differences are solely material dependent such as the GaAs use of Au wire connections (and ohmic contacts) and the relative ease of device isolation. Microwave use of GaAs, however, has relieved some important material constraints. GaAs MESFET threshold voltage control which presently may not be adequate for digital applications, is totally adequate for microwave applications. Epitaxial layer growth, ion implantation, and crystal growth are subjects reviewed elsewhere [9, 10] and while these are important aspects of device fabrication, they are essentially the same as for discrete MESFETs. For MMICs, control of these processes has already been demonstrated in manufacturing environments. Therefore, an n-type GaAs layer formed on a semi-insulating ($\varrho > 10^7$ ohm-cm) GaAs wafer is assumed as the starting point for both discrete MESFET and MMIC processing.

n Type GaAs
Semi-Insulating GaAs
Mesa (M) Mask, Wet Etch GaAs, Isolation Check, Clean
Sloped Edge Mesa
Contact (C) Mask, Evaporate Metal, Lift Off, Alloy, Resistance Check
AuGe/Ni/Au
Gate (G) Mask, Current Check, Channel Etch, Deposit Metals, Clean
Au Conductor
Refractory Barrier
(a)

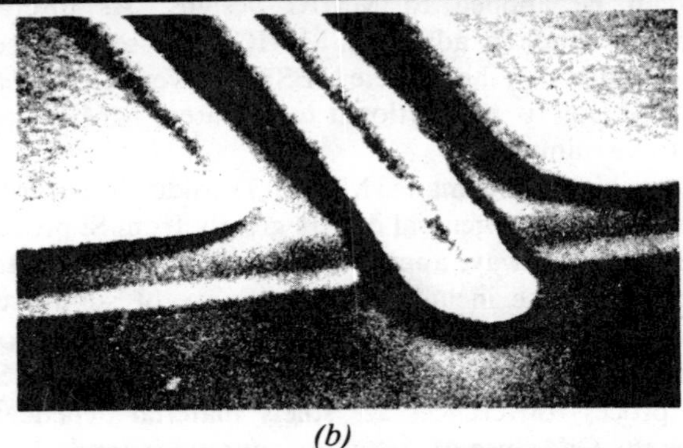
(b)

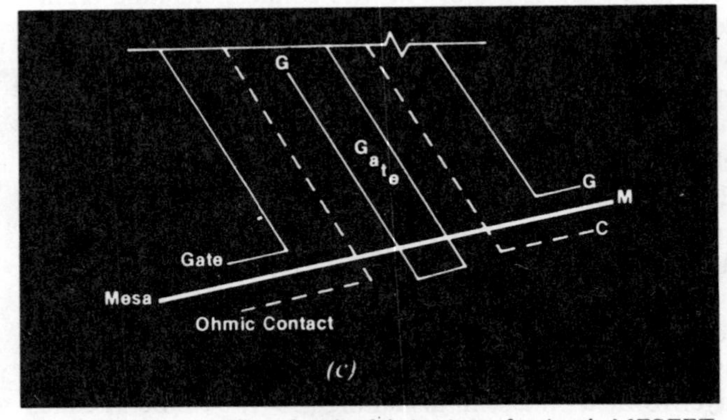

(c)

Fig. 1—(a) Process flow for the fabrication of a simple MESFET; (b) SEM photograph of a simple MESFET; (c) Mask level physical design of the MESFET in (b).

Simple MESFET

With this starting material at hand, consider the process flow for a simple GaAs MESFET shown in Fig. 1 and the MESFET produced by it. Only three mask levels are required to produce this MESFET which, by virtue of the semi-insulating GaAs substrate, is isolated from other structures. The n-type GaAs layer is about 1500 Å thick and has $3 \times 10^{17}/cm^3$ active donors. Its sheet resistance has been checked with a contactless resistivity probe and verified to be about 500 ohms/sq and varying by no more than ± 10% across the wafer. This thin n-type layer may be grown epitaxially or ion implanted, but in either case a 2500 Å mesa etch in an acid-peroxide solution provides a nearly planar structure of electrically isolated mesas. Ohmic contact to this layer is provided by alloying a thin layered metal system consisting of an Au-Ge eutectic alloy, followed in situ by a thin layer of Ni and Au [11]. A simple lift off technology is used to define this layer, as the total layer thickness is less than 2000 Å. The defined pattern is then alloyed at 400°C in an H_2 ambient and the resulting gateless transistor structure of Fig. 1 checked for ohmic metal-semiconductor contacts and sheet resistance.

Most of the MESFET process complexity surrounds the definition of the submicron gate [12–14]. While the gate needs to be narrow where it contacts the channel (minimized gate to channel capacitance and minimized carrier transport time under the gate), high reliability and low loss gate structures require large gate cross-sections. This explains the triangular shape of the gate cross-section or "mushroom gate" as it is frequently called. The thick gate metal (typically 0.7 microns) is also used to increase the current handling capacity of the ohmic contact regions. Gold is the preferred choice for the gate metal as it has low bulk resistance, high electromigration resistance, and as the ohmic contacts contain Au, the risk of intermetallic compound failures is greatly reduced. However, Au itself is a rapid diffuser in GaAs and quickly degrades GaAs channel conductivity. To prevent this, a metallurgical barrier consisting of either 1000 Å of a Ti:W composite or 1000 Å each of Ti and Pt must be deposited prior to deposition of the Au gate [10]. Just prior to any gate metal deposition, the dc current of the MESFET is adjusted. The part of the channel left exposed by the gate resist opening is slowly etched in an acid-peroxide solution until the saturated current flow drops to a specified amount. When the gate metals are deposited, the saturated channel current (gate connected to one of the ohmic terminals) will be somewhat lower than the premetallized channel current. The drop in current is due to the change in the GaAs surface potential where the gate metal was deposited. This etched-down-gate process minimizes the parasitic channel resistances between the gate and the ohmic contacts by leaving a thicker GaAs channel outside of the channel. The wet etching of the channel introduces a minimum amount of device dc non-uniformity.

If the MESFET of Fig. 1 were fabricated with a 0.5 micron length and 1 mm width gate, the typical device specifications for a 3 volt drain to source voltage and 0 volt source to gate voltage would be as follows: gate to source capacitance = 1.2 pf, drain to source current = 200 mA,

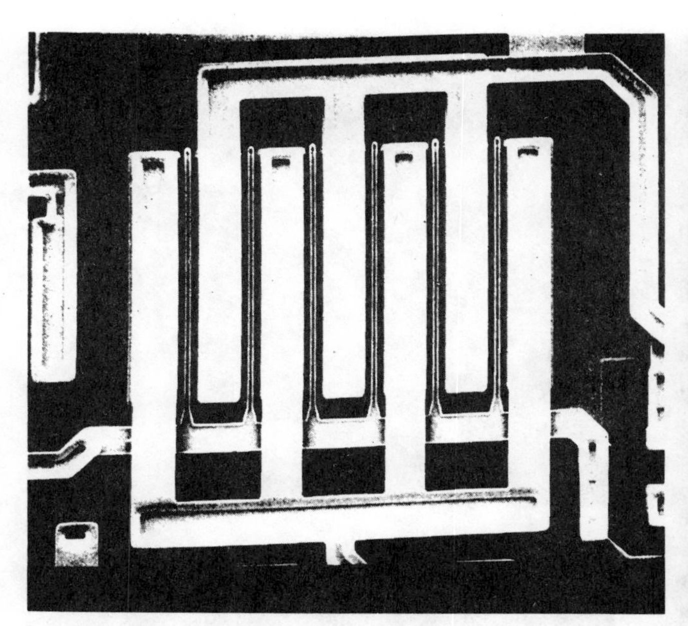

Fig. 2—Interdigitated gate finger MESFET with 500 μm total gate periphery.

and common source transconductance = 150 mS. Hence this MESFET would have a unity gain cut-off frequency of $f_T = G_m/2\pi C_{gs}$ of 20 GHz independent of device width. After dc testing of the MESFET, a nominal 2000 Å thick layer of Si_3N_4 is applied to all exposed GaAs surfaces to prevent degradation of the surface during the remaining processing steps and to improve the device reliability [15].

A simple linear 1 mm wide MESFET such as that in Fig. 1, is clearly difficult to integrate into a circuit layout. Furthermore, a 1 mm structure on GaAs is longer than ¼ of a wavelength at 10 GHz! For optimum performance, all the gate sections must be driven in phase and the channel currents summed in phase. Figure 2 shows a 0.5 mm wide MESFET with six gate fingers each 84 microns wide. This intentionally compact structure was adapted from a discrete MESFET design for use in MMICs, but such an interdigitated gate transistor requires more processing steps than the simple MESFET. The wide source connections cross over the common gate feed which at the least would require one additional layer of metal after the gate metal. The Si_3N_4 GaAs passivation could act as the cross-over dielectric for this extra layer except that the wide source cross-overs (low inductance lines) represent a very high and detrimental cross-over capacitance. To minimize this capacitance, a thick (greater than 1 micron) dielectric is used to separate the layers. The low dielectric constant material used is air.

Air Bridges

Figure 3a shows the process flow for an air dielectric cross-over or air bridge [9]. The process begins with a bottom layer metal already in place and suitable openings already etched in the Si_3N_4 passivation layer. The wafer is coated with a thick photoresist (e.g., AZ1375) and then the bridge supports and bridge contact openings are defined. The resist forms a scaffold structure for electroplating the bridge. After the support resist is developed and the open-

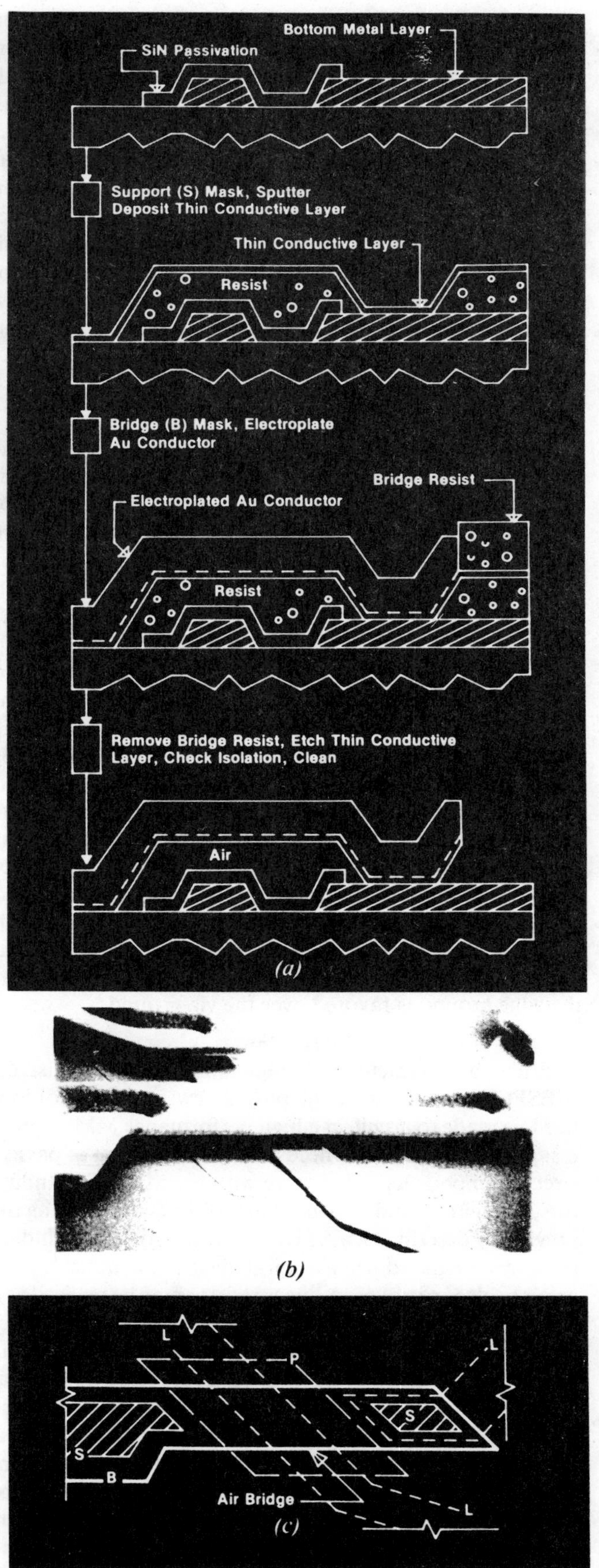

Fig. 3—(a) Process flow for an air bridge cross-over; (b) SEM photograph of an air bridge cross-over; (c) Mask level physical design of the air bridge in (b). L, P are link and passivation masks.

ings cleaned, a thin conductive metal layer is deposited on the entire wafer which is again coated with photoresist. This bridge resist is then patterned into areas to be electroplated. Electrical contact to the bridges is made through the thin conducting interlayer. The exposed interlayer is electroplated in an Au bath to a thickness of 1.5 microns. Next, the top layer resist is removed and the interlayer either ion milled or wet chemically etched. For this process, the electroplated bridge metal acts as an etch mask and the bottom layer resist (support) acts as an etch stop. Finally, the support resist is removed leaving an air bridge cross-over with a maximum current capability of 8 mA/micron of width and with a sheet resistance of less than 25 milliohms/sq.

Backside Connection

The last addition to the high performance MESFET is the element of integral chip grounding. The inductances associated with wire bond lengths have proved to be excessive for many microwave applications. Integral backside grounding is unique to microwave device processing and this subject is treated at length elsewhere [9, 16]. These grouding techniques fall into two broad classes both shown in Fig. 4. The edge ground metallizes the edge and backside of the chip and connects top side structures to the edge ground ring and then onto the backside. For small chips and moderate complexity circuits, having ground access only on the chip edge represents only a minor layout penalty. For thin GaAs chips (thickness less than 50 microns), the backside via ground process allows the chip designer to arbitrarily position circuit ground nodes. The chip area used with via grounding is usually less than 60 microns square per via. Still, the processing of 50 micron thick wafers is difficult. Grounded source discrete MESFETs have been fabricated with both grounding processes. At the low levels of integration used in discrete transistors and MMICs, the chip area efficiency of the edge ground is favored over the via ground.

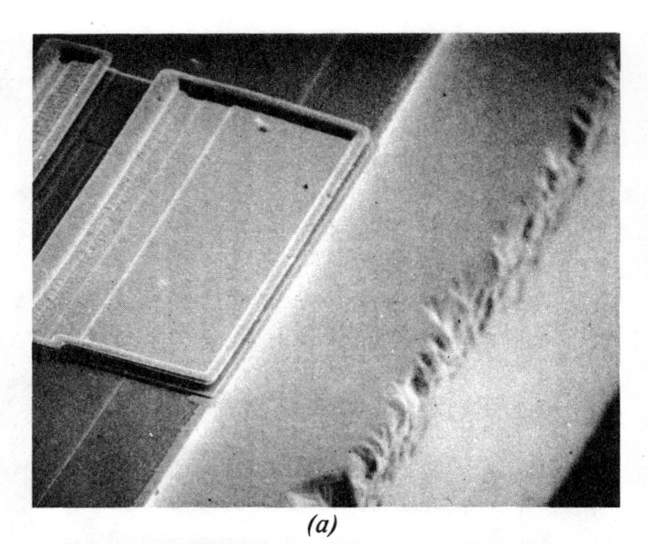

(a)

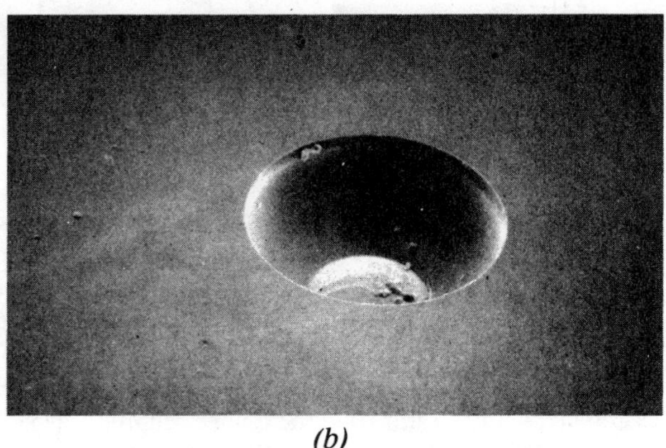

(b)

Fig. 4—(a) 75 μm wide edge ground connection; (b) 150 μm diameter, backside etch, via ground (prior to metallization).

MMIC Process

With a characterized high performance discrete MESFET process at hand, only a few process additions need be made to architect a high performance MMIC process. A microwave circuit needs a full complement of passive circuit components to integrate with the MESFET. Inductors, capacitors, and resistors can be fabricated by using the previously described MESFET process. A flat spiral inductor may be realized using a spiral length of conductor with an air bridge crossover. A linear resistor may be realized as a MESFET without a gate and a metal-insulator-metal capacitor realized between the gate metal and bridge metal. The latter is designed as a contact between gate and bridge metal with the Si_3N_4 not etched away (see Fig. 3). While the MESFET process may be used to implement passive components, MESFET performance must be protected from compromises made in the optimization of passive component processes. The submicron MESFET gate and the starting n-type material are the two key elements of the MESFET which require this process separation. With these design constraints, two extra masking levels must be added to the discrete MESFET process to adapt it for use in MMICs. The first addition is a gate-like layer to be used as an underpass metal as in Fig. 3. This extra layer, named the link layer, is not of submicron dimensions and frees the gate mask level to fabricate only MESFETs. The GaAs n-type material could be used as a resistor; however, the starting sheet resistance is optimized for use in the MESFET. To relieve this constraint, another mask layer, the resistor layer, is added to thin the n-type material of a resistor and thus provide an appropriate final sheet resistance nearly independent of the starting sheet resistance.

Table I shows the devices and structures that may be fabricated using the nine masks and process operations already described. The MESFET becomes a subset of the MMIC process architecture. This protects the MESFET performance, allows application of the MESFET data to MMIC designs, and minimizes the cost of fabricating the MMIC by sharing tooling costs with discrete MESFETs.

MMIC Amplifier

As an illustration of an MMIC implemented in this architecture, consider the two stage feedback amplifier shown in Fig. 5 and the components in the accompanying schematic. This 2–12 GHz amplifier was fabricated within a 0.5–1.0 mm^2 area or roughly one-hundredth the area of its hybrid equivalent [17]. A 2-inch diameter wafer contains over 3500

Table I—Realizable Components with the 9 Mask MMIC Process

Mask/ Process	Device/Structure MESFET	MMIC	Resistor	Capacitor Inductor
1. Mesa	X	X	X	
2. Contact	X	X	X	
3. Gate	X	X	X*	
4. Link		X		X
5. Resistor		X	X	
6. Passivation	X	X	X	X
7. Support	X	X		X
8. Bridge	X	X		X
9. Ground	X	X		

*For improved reliability

such chips, thus helping reduce the amplifier's cost. A feedback amplifier approach was chosen so as to increase the immunity of the amplifier performance to the expected process variations. For this two stage amplifier, direct interstage coupling was chosen to reduce the number of components. A single power supply design was chosen to make the circuit easier to use. Together, these design aspects have produced a high performance, highly uniform, low cost microwave amplifier.

For a closer inspection of the passive components used in Fig. 5, consider the MMIC resistor shown in Fig. 6. The resistor (200 ohms) is fabricated as a gateless MESFET using the mesa (M) and contact (C) masks. The resistance of this GaAs resistor is adjusted by etching the GaAs exposed by the resistor (R) mask. The area to be etched is bounded by the resistor mask opening and accounts for exactly 50% of the resistor surface area. Resistors formed in this way achieve tolerances better than ± 15% across the wafer with temperature coefficients of resistance less than 300 ppm. The power handling capability of all resistors on GaAs is limited by the thermal conductivity of the GaAs and not by the thermal characteristics of the resistor material itself.

Figure 7 shows the detail of an MIM (Metal Insulator Metal) capacitor shown in Fig. 5. The capacitor area is defined as the area in which the support mask (S) covers the link mask (L) and the link mask is left covered by Si_3N_4 (passivation mask, P). Contact to the top capacitor plate is made by means of an air bridge. This air bridge connection eliminates any potential capacitor shorting due to a thinner Si_3N_4 at the link metal edge. The link metal forms the bottom capacitor electrode and is optimized to be both low loss and smooth. This link metal is evaporated and subsequently lifted by means of a multilayer resist lift-off structure. An 0.8 μm thick refractory-metal Au refractory-metal sandwich provides high conductivity, high current handling capability, and a smooth surface on which to deposit plasma assisted CVD Si_3N_4. In this way, 1700 Å of Si_3N_4 provides a 400 pf/mm² MIM capacitor with a breakdown voltage over 30 V. Inductors and lines also use link metal; its use is identical to that with the crossover shown in Fig. 3.

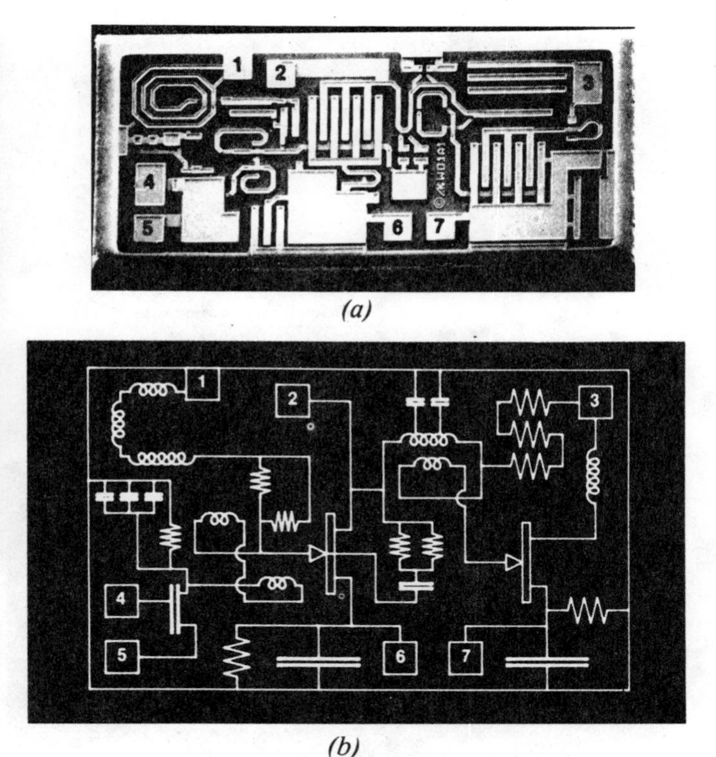

Fig. 5— (a) SEM photograph of a 2-12 GHz amplifier chip [17]; (b) Positionally correct circuit schematic for (a).

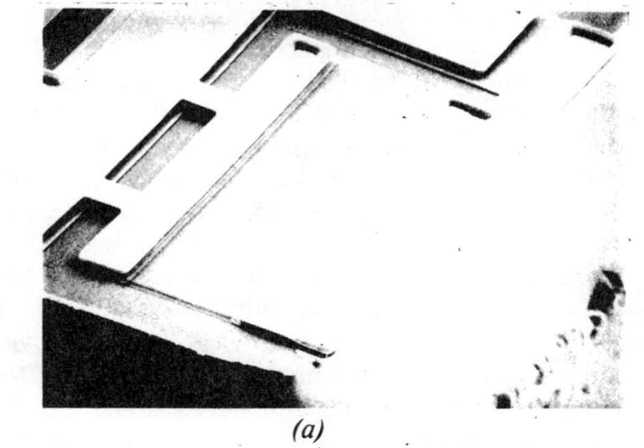

(a)

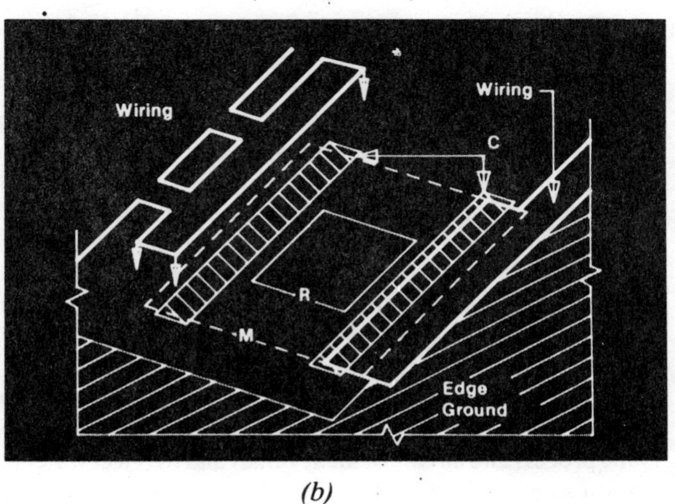

(b)

Fig. 6—(a) SEM photograph of a 200 ohm MMIC resistor; (b) Mask level physical design of the resistor in (a).

(a)

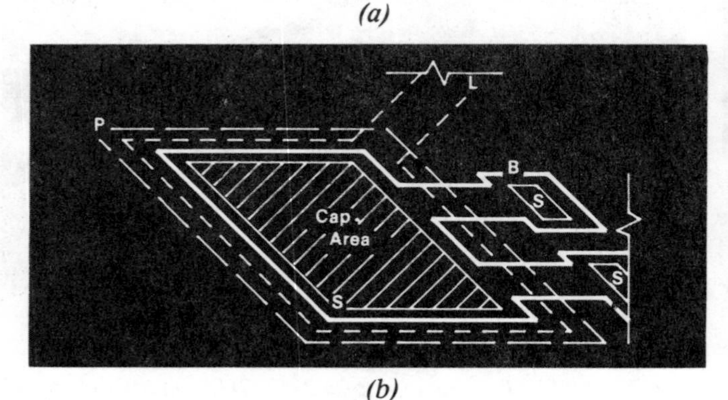

(b)

Fig. 7— (a) SEM photograph of a 1.0 pf MMIC capacitor; (b) Mask level physical design of the capacitor in (a).

Cost and Control

While the issue of fabrication cost is usually proprietary, some estimates are available. GaAs wafers are presently available from over twenty vendors at about $35/sq. in. The material cost is small when compared to wafer fabrication cost estimates which range from $500 to $3000 per wafer depending on the estimator [18, 19]. Choosing $2000 per wafer as a representative example of present cost, the cost per die for a 2 inch diameter wafer is only about $\$1/mm^2$ divided by the cumulative circuit yield. If the total yield is high, the example of a 0.5 mm^2 die is a very cost effective replacement for the several hundred dollar equivalent hybrid circuit.

The first main yield check for each circuit is an automatic dc wafer probe (e.g., correct dc bias voltages and currents, correct component values, shorts, and opens). This test is performed on each circuit. The highest possible fault coverage is sought at this rather inexpensive dc screen point. The microwave test yield, which may be measured automatically for some circuits [20], is usually measured on a sample basis. Samples of the circuits which pass the dc screen are bonded into microwave test fixtures and full-function tested. Areas of the wafer are then identified which contain MMICs with the specified performance.

During wafer fabrication, dc and low frequency capacitance tests are performed on process monitor cells such as the one shown in Fig. 8. The monitor is used to certify both the process and circuit element values and to reject wafers as soon as a problem is identified. The process monitor also contains a structure for testing the gate to source capacitance of the MESFET. By monitoring this capacitance variation, single mask level changes allow reactive circuit elements to be added or deleted as shown in Fig. 9. Both capacitance and inductance may be tuned with this scheme. This mask level tuning is inexpensive, and while it is preferable to avoid tuning, wafer level tuning increases the microwave test yield.

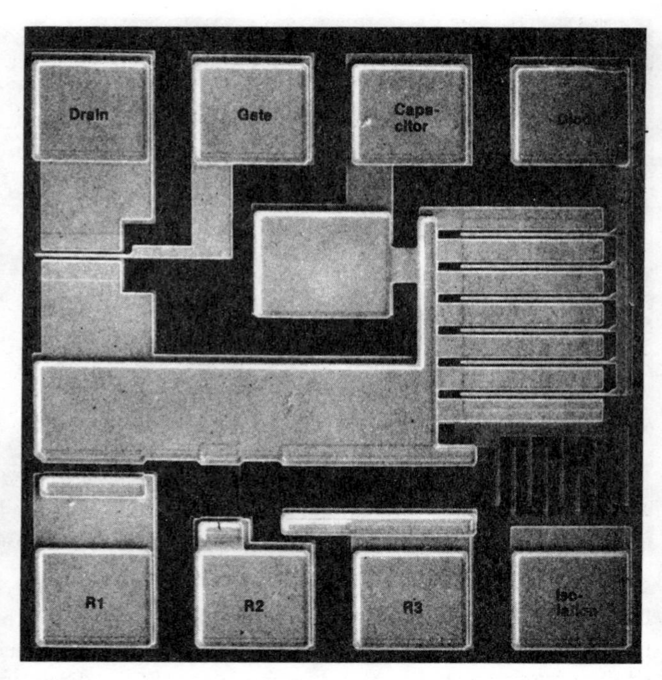

Fig. 8—Process control component array used during MMIC fabrication to verify component performance.

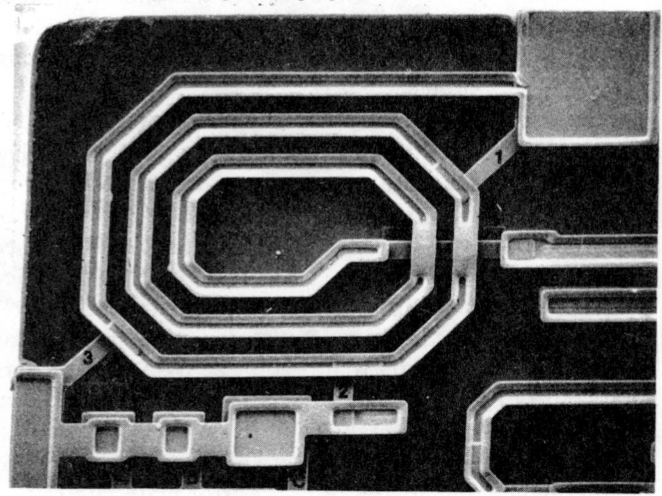

Fig. 9—Single mask wafer level circuit tuning as illustrated with deletable inductor (numbers) and capacitor (letters) connections.

Summary

An MMIC process architecture capable of total passive component realization has been described and illustrated by a 2–12 GHz microwave amplifier. By using a dense layout and adapting processes from a 20 GHz f_T MESFET, a microwave circuit designer is provided with a method for producing high performance, low cost MMICs.

Acknowledgments

The author would like to thank A. Mattos for the SEM photographs, and S. Moghe for the 2–12 GHz amplifier design. The many discussions on the subject of MMIC architecture with C. Snapp, the individuals of the Avantek GaAs Research and Development Group, and W. O. Camp, Jr., of IBM, are also gratefully acknowledged.

References

1. D. N. McQuiddy, Jr., et al., "Monolithic Microwave Integrated Circuits: A Historical Perspective," *IEEE Tr. Microwave Theory and Techniques.*, vol. MTT-33, pp. 997–1007 (1984).
2. C. P. Snapp, "Advanced Silicon Bipolar Technology Yields Usable Monolithic Microwave and High Speed Digital ICs," *Microwave Journal,* Aug. 1983.
3. C. P. Snapp, "Bipolars Quietly Dominate," *Microwave Systems News,* Nov. 1979.
4. K. J. Sleger, "Government Systems Incorporate GaAs Monolithics," *ibid.*, Sept. 1983.
5. H. Yamasaki, D. Maki, "Hybrid vs. Monolithic—Is More Monolithic Better?," *Microwave Journal,* Nov. 1982.
6. R. S. Pengelly, "Hybrid vs. Monolithic Microwave Circuits—A Matter of Cost," *Microwave Systems News,* Jan. 1983.
7. D. R. Decker, "Are MMICs a Fad or Fact?," *ibid.*, July 1983.
8. C. E. Weitzel, J. M. Frary, "A Comparison of GaAs and Si Processing Technology," *Semiconductor Int'l.*, June 1982.
9. R. E. Williams, "GaAs Processing Techniques," Artech House, Dedham, MA, 1984.
10. J. V. DiLorenzo, D. Khandelwal, ed., "GaAs FET Principles and Technology," Artech House, Dedham, MA, 1982.
11. N. Braslau, "Alloyed Ohmic Contacts to GaAs," *J. Vac. Sci. Technol.*, vol. 19, pp. 803–807 (1981).
12. P. W. Chye, C. Huang, "Quarter Micron Low Noise GaAs FETs," *IEEE Tr. Electron Device Lett.*, vol. ED6-3, pp. 401–403, Dec. 1982
13. H. Ishiuchi, et al., "0.3 μm Gate Length Super Low Noise GaAs MESFET," *IEDM Tech. Dig.*, pp. 590–593 (1982).
14. P. C. Chau, et al.,"0.2 Micron Length Mushroom Gate Fabrication Using a New Single-Level Photoresist Technique," *IEDM Tech. Dig.*, pp. 415–418 (1982).
15. S. H. Wemple, et al., "Long-Term and Instantaneous Burnout in GaAs Power FETs; Mechanisms and Solutions," *IEEE Tr. Electron Devices,* vol. ED-78, pp. 834–840 (1981).
16. A. D'asaro, et al., Conference on GaAs and Related Compounds, Vienna, 1980.
17. S. Moghe, T. Andrade, H. Sun, C. Huang, "A Manufacturable GaAs MMIC Amplifier with 10 GHz Bandwidth," *IEEE 1984 Microwave and Millimeter-Wave Monolithic Circuits Symposium Digest,* pp. 37–40.
18. D. Ch'en, "DBS High Volume Market for GaAs MMICs," *Microwave Journal,* Feb. 1983.
19. C. Bownes, "GaAs MMICs: A Matter of Cost vs. Yield Compromise," *Microwave Systems News,* Aug. 1984.
20. K. R. Gleason, T. M. Reader, E. Strid, "Precise MMIC Parameters Yielded by 18 GHz Wafer Probe," *ibid.*, May 1983.

CHAPTER V

MICROWAVE INTEGRATED CIRCUIT MEASUREMENT AND TESTING

Papers in this chapter describe techniques for measurements of important microwave IC parameters, such as characteristic impedance and substrate dielectric constant. A general review is given by Caulton, *et al.* Measurement techniques to obtain characteristic impedance and dispersion properties of microstrip lines are presented by Getsinger; Edwards, *et al.*; and by Seckelmann. Mueller describes a technique to obtain dispersion for unshielded coplanar waveguides, and Howell describes a simple method for measuring substrate dielectric constant. Carlton, *et al.*, discuss a useful wafer probing technique using the coplanar waveguide concept.

Measurement and Modeling of the Apparent Characteristic Impedance of Microstrip

WILLIAM J. GETSINGER, FELLOW, IEEE

Abstract —**Voltage and current cannot be defined uniquely for microstrip except at zero frequency, and therefore microstrip has not been rigorously incorporated into circuit theory. However, in engineering practice, microstrip exhibits an apparent characteristic impedance, denoted here by *ZA*, that can be measured.**

Three methods of measuring *ZA* were devised and used in measuring three impedance levels of microstrip. These methods are described and experimental results presented. The measurements of *ZA* were found to be consistent with the power-current characteristic impedance definition of the approximate longitudinal-section electric (LSE) model of microstrip. Simple approximate formulas for representing *ZA* are also discussed.

I. INTRODUCTION

IMPEDANCE IS a fundamental concept in microwave circuit design because the impedances of circuit elements and their interconnections determine the distribution of power within a circuit. The ability of a microwave engineer to predict circuit performance will partially depend on the accuracy of the knowledge of impedances for available circuit elements.

This paper examines the frequency variation of the apparent characteristic impedance of a microstrip transmission line. From a practical viewpoint, the term "characteristic impedance" used here is the impedance parameter of a circuit-theory based model of a transmission line which is used in a circuit description with other elements to predict the actual performance of a physical circuit. An example is the parameter $Z0$ used in a computer-aided design (CAD) program, such as SUPER-COMPACT™. Microstrip is not a TEM line, and so voltage and current, and thus characteristic impedance, cannot be defined uniquely. The term "apparent characteristic impedance" is used to denote a parameter that describes how microstrip exchanges power with a TEM line, just as characteristic impedance is the parameter that determines how one TEM line exchanges power with another. The purpose of this

Manuscript received September 7, 1982; revised March 15, 1983. This paper is based on work performed at COMSAT Laboratories under the shared sponsorship of the Communications Satellite Corporation and the COMPACT Engineering Division of COMSAT General Integrated Systems Corporation.

The author is with COMSAT Laboratories, Clarksburg, MD 20871.

usage is to accommodate microstrip to circuit theory and to interconnections with TEM elements, while recognizing that it is not a TEM structure itself.

This definition distinguishes the concept presented in this paper from definitions of convenience or intuition, such as those discussed by Bianco *et al.* [1] or from those based on wave impedance, as proposed previously [2]. There is wide disagreement in the microwave community about how microstrip characteristic impedance should be defined. As shown clearly by Bianco *et al.* [1], different reasonable definitions have widely different variations with frequency. The work described in this paper attempted to further resolve the question by making actual measurements of apparent characteristic impedance. Napoli and Hughes [3] made measurements intended to display microstrip characteristic impedance, but their results appear to be obscured by connector and transition reflection interactions.

Three measurement methods will be described, along with the results of measurements on microstrip lines of three nominal impedance levels. Then, mathematical models of different complexity will be discussed. First, however, some background theory will be given to explain the present confusion over the frequency variation of microstrip characteristic impedance, and illuminate the apparent impedance variations observed on measurements of microstrip lines.

II. Theoretical Background

A transmission line is completely characterized in circuit theory by characteristic impedance $Z0$, a propagation constant γ, and length l, using voltage V and current I as variables (Fig. 1). The problem to be discussed would not be avoided by employing wave formalism rather than voltage and current. If a microstrip transmission line (Fig. 2) is to be designed into circuits which also have lumped elements and TEM transmission lines, then V, I, and $Z0$ for the microstrip need to be defined to be unique and compatible with V, I, and Z of the other circuit elements.

Microwave circuit theory, which is employed in microwave frequency-domain CAD programs, such as SUPER-COMPACT™, requires that Kirchoff's voltage and current laws hold at junctions interconnecting all elements such as lumped elements, transmission lines, and other n-ports. A port can be represented by two wires carrying equal but opposite sinusoidal currents of maximum value I and having maximum sinusoidal voltage V between the wires. Then average power P entering the port is

$$P=\frac{1}{2}\,\mathrm{Re}\,VI^* \tag{1}$$

and the impedance Z presented by the port is

$$Z=V/I. \tag{2}$$

Now, P is an absolute physical quantity, but Z is relative to an arbitrary definition or reference level. That is, either V or I could be set arbitrarily and the other adjusted to give the required value of P. However, V and I of low-frequency circuit theory are related to electric and mag-

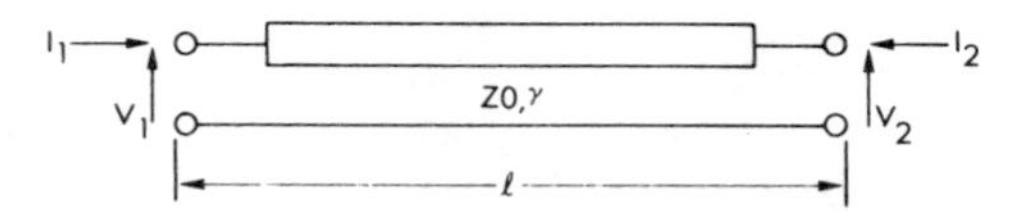

Fig. 1. Circuit theory representation of a transmission line.

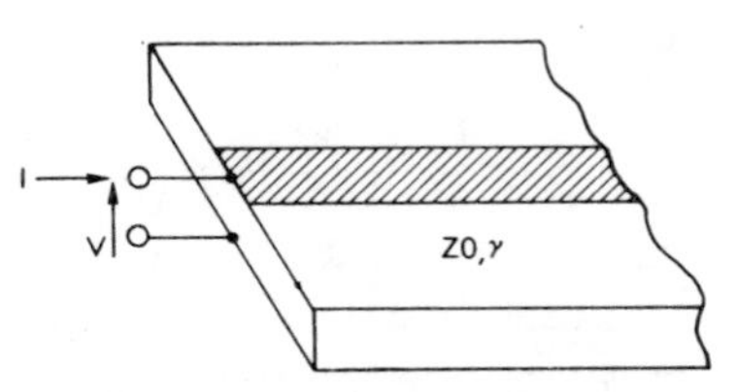

Fig. 2. Microstrip transmission line.

netic fields $\bar{E}$ and $\bar{H}$ at a port of a physical two-conductor circuit element by

$$V=-\int_{C1}^{C2}\bar{E}\cdot d\bar{l} \tag{3}$$

and

$$I=\oint_{C}\bar{H}\cdot d\bar{l} \tag{4}$$

where the first integral is taken from one conductor ($C1$) to the other ($C2$), and the second integral is taken around one of the conductors (C). The power entering the element in terms of the fields is given by

$$P=\frac{1}{2}\,\mathrm{Re}\int_{A}\bar{E}\times\bar{H}^*\cdot d\bar{A} \tag{5}$$

where A is a surface through which power flows and on which the paths of integration of (3) and (4) lie. Thus, A is a terminal surface for a physical two-port. Of course, (1) and (5) must be equal if the circuit element is to be represented in circuit theory terms.

Equations (3) and (4) for voltage and current are useful because they are unique, that is, independent of the path of integration on the terminal surface. This is the case for elements, junctions, and ports which have dimensions that are small in wavelengths. These equations are special cases of Maxwell's curl equations for charge and current-free regions

$$\oint\bar{E}\cdot d\bar{l}=-\frac{\partial}{\partial t}\int_{A}\bar{B}\cdot d\bar{A} \tag{6}$$

$$\oint\bar{H}\cdot d\bar{l}=\int_{A}\bar{i}\cdot d\bar{A}+\frac{\partial}{\partial t}\int_{A}\bar{D}\cdot d\bar{A}. \tag{7}$$

The path of integration for (6) can be considered to go from one conductor to the other and return via a different path, thus generating the surface A over which the integral on the right is taken.

For low frequencies, the time variation of the integrands on the right of (6) and (7) is nearly zero; these equations are independent of path and equivalent to the voltage and current equations (3) and (4).

At the terminal surface of a TEM transmission line, there are no longitudinal components of the fields to contribute to the surface integrals of (6) and (7); therefore, these equations again are equivalent to the voltage and current equations. Thus, unique values of voltage and

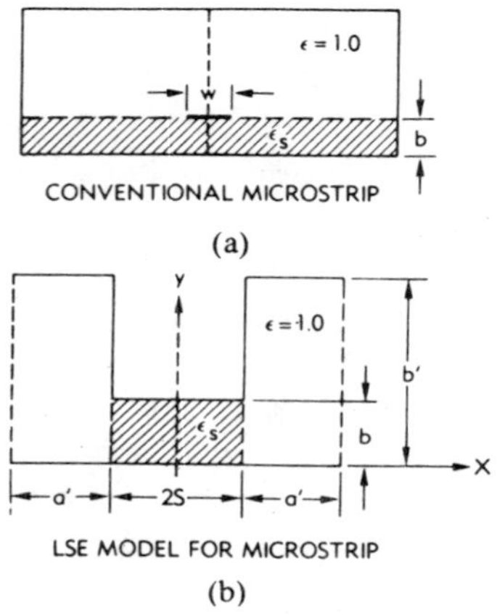

Fig. 3. (a) Conventional microstrip and (b) its LSE model.

current can be defined by (3) and (4) for the TEM line, and if it is terminated without reflection, (2) yields its characteristic impedance $Z0$.

A microstrip line, however, has longitudinal components of both electric and magnetic fields, except at zero frequency [4]; consequently, the integrals on the right of (6) and (7) cannot be neglected. Therefore, voltage and current cannot be defined independently of the path of integration by (3) and (4). Thus, (1) and (2) do not hold, and microstrip cannot be incorporated rigorously into circuit theory.

The differing variations of microstrip characteristic impedance with frequency illustrated by Bianco *et al.* [1] can be traced to the use of (3) and (4) with different paths of integration, and the fact that transverse field configurations in microstrip are not constant with frequency as they are for all homogenous transmission lines and waveguides. Nevertheless, a microstrip line is used in practical circuits with conventional lumped elements and TEM lines. Its propagation constant can be calculated by rigorous [4] or approximate [5] analytical methods or measured on the bench. Microstrip characteristic impedance at zero frequency is predictable; only its frequency variation cannot be defined uniquely. However, it appears to have a specific characteristic impedance at each frequency when measured against a transmission line of known $Z0$, as will be shown. This apparent characteristic impedance will be referred to as ZA to emphasize that it is not defined in terms of voltage and current, but in terms of its exchange of power with another circuit that can be described in terms of voltage and current.

An analytical approach to ZA is possible by sacrificing rigor and employing the longitudinal-section electric (LSE) model of microstrip [5]. This approximate model has been used to predict microstrip dispersion [5], the filling factor, and the frequency variations of different definitions of characteristic impedance [1].

Cross sections of both microstrip and the LSE model are shown in Fig. 3. The LSE model is characterized by an electric field which is entirely tangential to the air–dielectric interfaces. It is a hypothetical inhomogenous transmission line that carries a single LSE mode [6], and its zero-frequency parameters can be the same as those of the microstrip that it is to simulate. Its single-mode simplicity makes it useful for calculating the frequency behavior of microstrip parameters.

Expressions for the fields of the LSE model are given in the Appendix. It should be observed that the model has a longitudinal magnetic field but no longitudinal electric field. Therefore, (6) and hence (3) for voltage are path dependent; however, (7) and (4) defining longitudinal current are equivalent. Thus, a unique current, consistent with circuit theory, can be defined for the LSE model from its field configuration, but a unique voltage cannot. It follows that ZA for the LSE model can be defined in terms of power and current by

$$ZA = 2P/I^*I \tag{8}$$

and that voltage for the LSE model can be given by

$$V = 2P/I^*. \tag{9}$$

Equations (8) and (9) are consistent with both electromagnetic theory and circuit theory for the LSE model.

In the Appendix, an expression for ZA is derived from the fields of the LSE model in terms of commonly employed microstrip parameters. The measurements of ZA will now be discussed to investigate how well the LSE model characterizes actual microstrip transmission lines.

III. Measurement Methods and Measured Results

Three different methods were used to perform measurements on microstrip lines having nominal impedances of 32.5 Ω, 48 Ω, and 70 Ω. In each case, the microstrip line was abruptly joined to a coaxial line of known characteristic impedance, $Z1 = 50.0$ Ω. Even though the connection was abrupt, the physical discontinuity created a transition circuit between the two uniform lines as indicated in Fig. 4.

The transition circuit can be represented by a tee or pi LC network, as shown in Fig. 5. In most practical microstrip-to-coaxial-line transitions, the LC product is much less than $1/\omega^2$ at the highest frequency normally used. This constraint allows the transition circuit to be represented with reasonable accuracy by either a tee or a pi, or by an L-section of either orientation. Also, all of one element and some of the other can be made to simulate a short section of transmission line of specified impedance and can be appended to either the coaxial line or the microstrip, leaving only a single residual lumped reactance or susceptance. The lumped-element equivalences of Fig. 5 can be demonstrated comparing their $ABCD$ matrices with small terms suppressed according to $\omega^2 LC \ll 1$. The transmission-line equivalents can be demonstrated by conversion to their image-impedance lumped element representations.

The underlying philosophy of the measurement was to minimize errors and obtain maximum information about the microstrip line. To this end, the test pieces were based on a substrate 10 times thicker than the 0.025-in thick substrate widely used for microwave circuits. This increased wavelengths and reduced the effects of mechanical tolerances. It allowed the use of GR-900 connectors which have small reflections (VSWR less than $1.001 + 0.001 \times f$(GHz) per connector, used in pairs) at the reduced

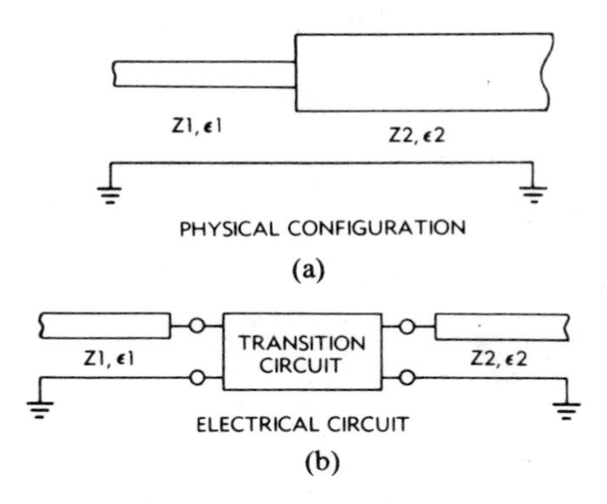

Fig. 4. Junction of dissimilar lines. (a) Physical configuration. (b) Electrical circuit.

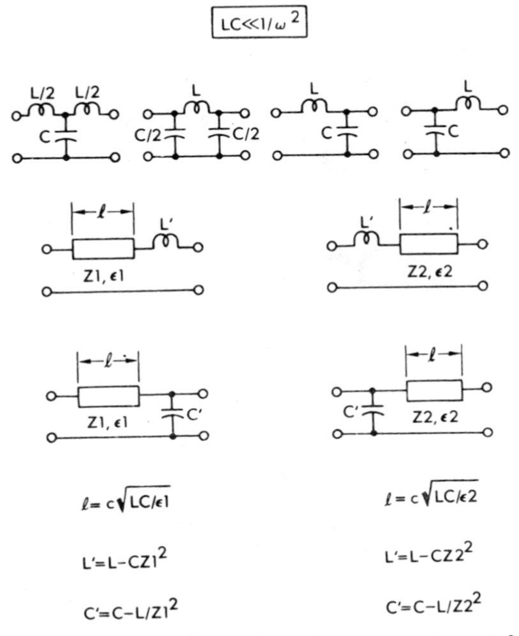

Fig. 5. Equivalent transition circuits for $LC \ll 1/\omega^2$.

frequency range so that their effect on the measurements could be neglected.

The microstrip lines used for the measurements were defined by photolithography using electroless copper-plated alumina substrates $2.0 \times 10.0 \times 0.25$-in size, and having a dielectric constant of 9.74 measured at low frequency. The final metallization thickness was about 1.3 mils. In most cases, the conductors were gold-flashed to ensure good contacts. The substrate enclosure was an aluminum bed with removable sides that held the substrate against the bed by means of small ridges. These sides extended about 1.5 in above the substrate. A metal top was available for the substrate enclosure, but was seldom used because it had negligible effect below about 3 GHz, and above that frequency accentuated the effects of higher mode resonances. The ends of the enclosure were tapped to accept either a GR-900 connector or a flat copper plug. With a copper plug in place, the microstrip was effectively terminated at that end by a flat plate short with no discontinuity effect.

With copper plugs at both ends, the microstrip could be

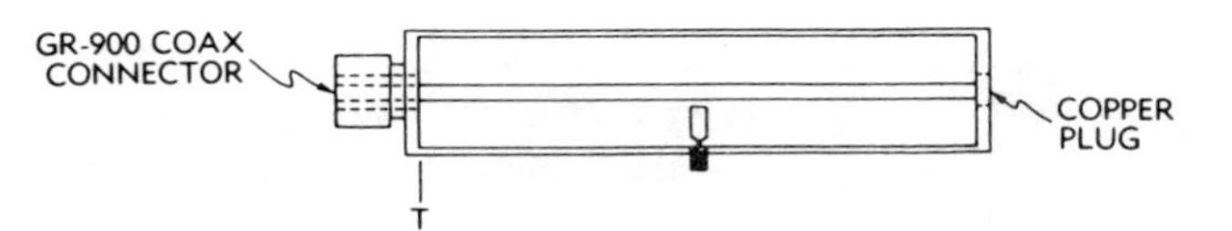

Fig. 6. Microstrip test piece.

MEASURE RESONANT FREQUENCIES OF LONG MICROSTRIP
SHORTED AT BOTH ENDS

ZA, ϵ_e

FIT DATA TO DISPERSION FUNCTION, $\epsilon_e(f)$

REPLACE ONE SHORT WITH TRANSITION TO COAXIAL LINE

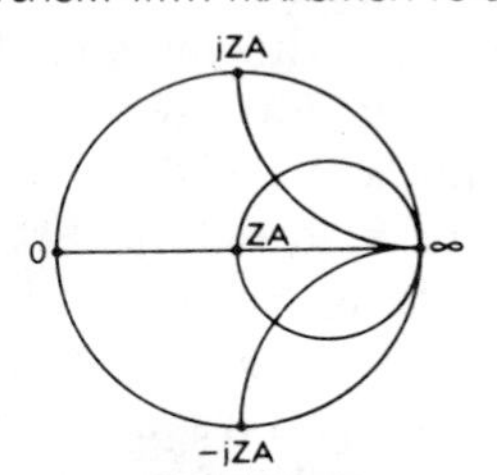

PREDICT CHARACTERISTIC FREQUENCIES PRESENTING
IMPEDANCES OF 0, ∞, ± jZA AT TRANSITION

(a)

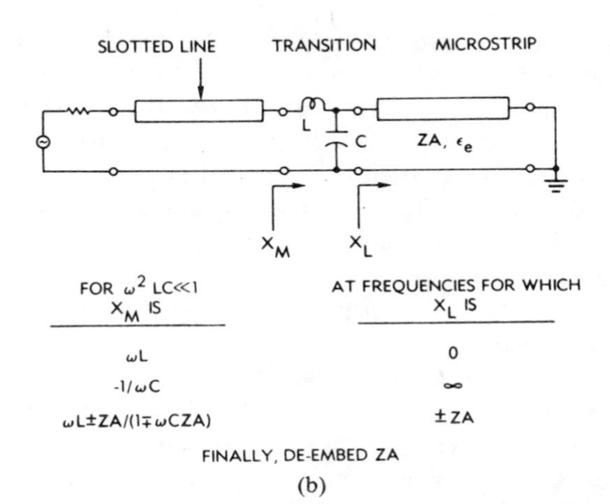

FOR $\omega^2 LC \ll 1$ X_M IS	AT FREQUENCIES FOR WHICH X_L IS
ωL	0
$-1/\omega C$	∞
$\omega L \pm ZA/(1 \mp \omega CZA)$	$\pm ZA$

FINALLY, DE-EMBED ZA

(b)

Fig. 7. (a) Slotted line method (dispersion measurement). (b) Slotted line method (transition and impedance measurement).

resonated with a temporary stub attached to an OSM connector in the side of the enclosure midway along the line, as shown in Fig. 6. By observing reflection coefficient dips, resonant frequencies were measured for two gap widths, and the results extrapolated for infinite gap width. Alternatively, at each resonance, the gap width was gradually increased and the frequency observed at which the resonant dip approached the swept frequency baseline. The microstrip line widths were 0.10, 0.25, and 0.50 in.

Three measurement methods were tested; they are denoted as the slotted line, the real-axis intercept, and the group-delay methods. The slotted line method is outlined in Fig. 7. First, the copper plugs are used to terminate the microstrip at both ends with flat plate shorts. Resonant frequencies are measured and, if necessary, corrected for probe capacitance. These frequencies are investigated graphically versus the order of the resonance for smoothness and used to compute the frequency dependent effective dielectric constant ϵ_e

$$\epsilon_e = \left(\frac{nc}{2fl}\right)^2 \tag{10}$$

where n is the number of half-wavelengths along the line, c is the speed of light in vacuum, f is the resonant frequency, and l is the length of the line.

The discrete values of ϵ_e are fitted to any appropriate mathematical function to allow prediction of ϵ_e with frequency. Then, when one copper plug is replaced by a GR-900 connector, frequencies can be predicted for which the shorted line presents (lossless assumption) shorts, opens, or $\pm jZA$ at the junction with the connector, as indicated on the Smith chart of Fig. 7(a). Reactance at each of these frequencies is measured with a GR-900 slotted line, using a shorted coaxial reference to define the terminal plane at the connector end of the microstrip.

A slotted line is used because it eliminates equipment calibration; only distance and frequency are measured. The stability of a synthesizer makes frequency errors negligible. Uncertainty in distance is about ± 0.1 mm, or less than 0.1 percent, in wavelengths at 2 GHz. The author believes that most of the scatter in this type of measurement arises not from the measuring equipment or technique, but from the test piece itself. Possible sources of error are inhomogeneity of the substrate, imperfect uniformity of the line width, and extraneous resonance effects resulting from contact problems, particularly with the ground plane.

As indicated in Fig. 7(b), the reactance measurements yield ωL, $-1/\omega C$, and $\omega L \pm ZA/(1 \mp \omega CZA)$ allowing ZA to be determined. The values of L and C found were small [7], justifying the use of a two-element transition circuit in accordance with Fig. 5. Although not illustrated in this paper, both L and C of the transition appeared to increase with frequency [7]. This is believed to be caused by the change with frequency of the field configuration of microstrip as the power becomes more concentrated in the dielectric-filled part of the line.

The results of measurements on a 0.25-in-wide line are shown in Fig. 8. Point-by-point values of L and C were used to de-embed ZA for one curve and best-fit constant values of L and C for the other curve.

If there is a consistent error in the value used for L or C, values found for ZA at consecutive measured frequencies will alternate above and below the correct value. When this saw-toothed effect is found in the reduced data, the best value for ZA lies halfway between alternating consecutive points.

Fig. 8 illustrates a characteristic that will be found for ZA measurements of all lines by all methods. First, there is a gradual decrease in ZA with frequency followed by an increase to beyond the zero-frequency value of ZA as frequency continues to rise.

The real-axis intercept method of measurement is illustrated in Fig. 9. A long, uniform, symmetrical microstrip

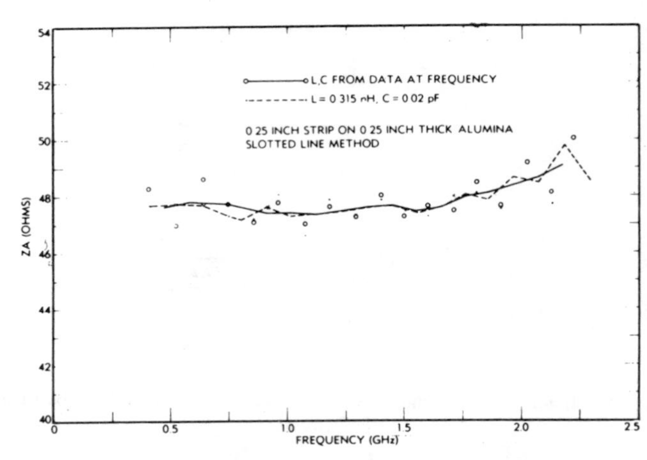

Fig. 8. Measured ZA of 0.250-in line by slotted line method.

LONG, SYMMETRICAL MICROSTRIP
LOW REFLECTION CONNECTORS

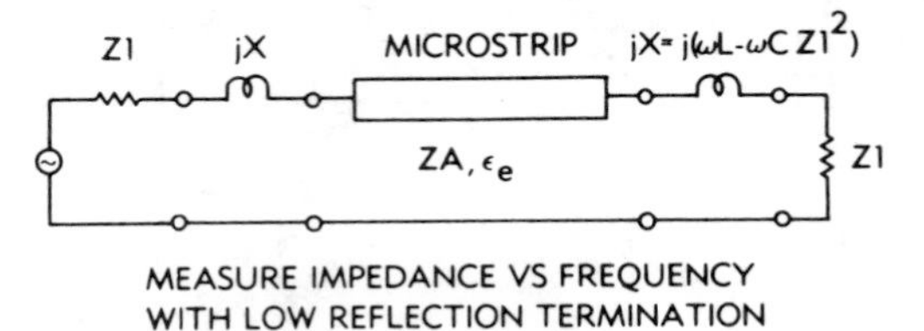

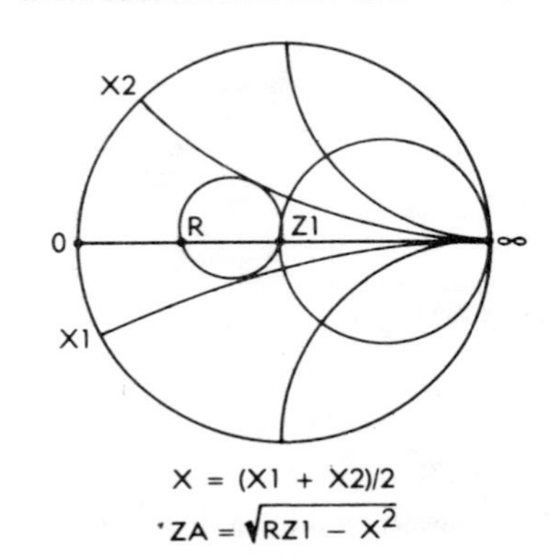

Fig. 9. Real-axis intercept method.

is placed in a measuring system having very low internal reflections, including connectors and a matched load. As pointed out in the discussion on transitions (Fig. 5), the transition circuit can be incorporated into the transmission line external to the microstrip, except for a single residual reactance or susceptance. This measurement arrangement can be represented by the circuit of Fig. 9.

Conventional circuit analysis indicates that as frequency is swept, the input impedance makes nearly circular spirals on the Smith chart. $X1$ and $X2$ are the extreme values of reactance whose algebraic average X is the residual reactance of the transition; that is, $X = (X1 + X2)/2$. On each rotation, the spiral passes through the center of the Smith chart and crosses the real impedance axis again at some value R. Solution of the expression for input impedance of the circuit of Fig. 9 for zero imaginary part yields the value R. Rearrangement of the result gives ZA as

$$ZA = \sqrt{R \cdot Z1 - X^2}. \tag{11}$$

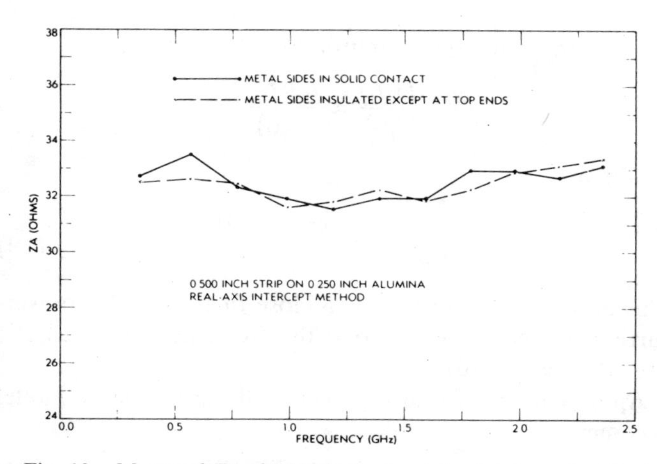

Fig. 10. Measured ZA of 0.500-in line by real-axis intercept method.

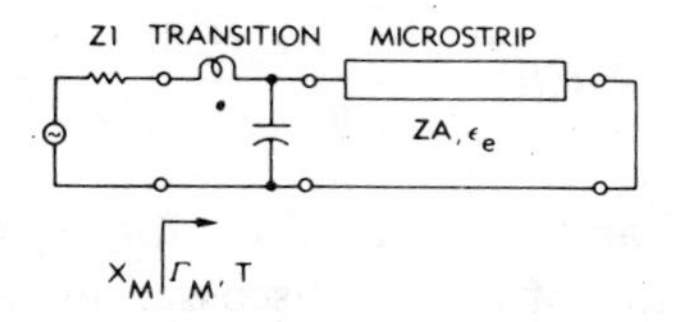

Fig. 11. Group-delay method.

Rigorously, X^2 should be referred to the frequency at which R was measured; however, in practice, it was found to be small enough to be neglected altogether. If R is near $Z1$, the impedance locus is nearly parallel to the real axis, and a small internal reflection in the measuring system can cause a significant error in the real-axis crossing. Thus, poor accuracy would be expected for $ZA \approx Z1$.

Fig. 10 shows the results of real-axis intercept measurements on a strip 0.5-in wide. The decline, then rise, of impedance with frequency is similar to that observed for the 0.25-in-wide line using the slotted line method. For one set of measurements, the contact of the enclosure sides was broken, except at the top ends, to perturb any surface wave or higher mode currents. No significant effect was observed up to 3 GHz.

The group-delay method of measuring ZA is important because it is almost independent of the transition, and it is relatively simple to perform. As is illustrated in Fig. 11, it requires a relatively long microstrip terminated with a flat plate short. The reflection delay [8] T is measured about frequencies for which the shorted microstrip presents zero reactance X at the transition.

$$T = -\frac{d\beta}{d\omega} = -\frac{1}{2\pi}\cdot\frac{d\angle\Gamma}{df} \approx \frac{2}{\pi Z1}\cdot\frac{dX}{df}. \tag{12}$$

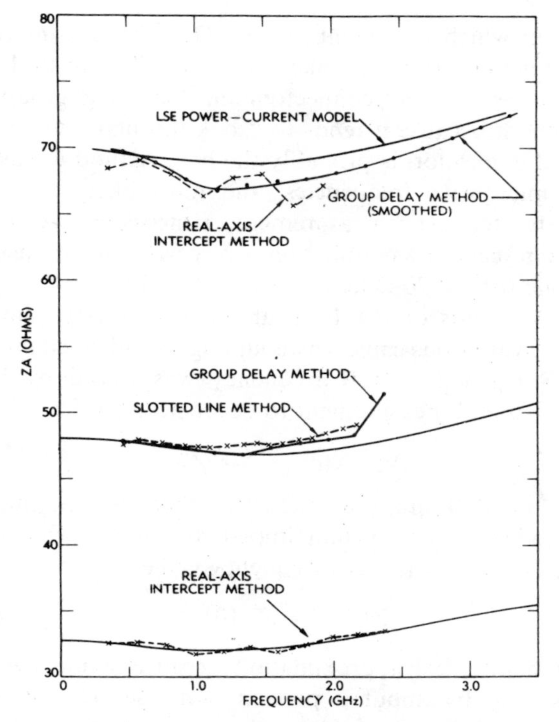

Fig. 12. Measured ZA of three line widths by three methods.

In (12), β represents the total phase shift of the reflected wave with respect to the incident wave (i.e., the angle of the reflection coefficient Γ), measured at the input port.

ZA is given by

$$ZA = Z1\frac{fT}{n(1+D)} \tag{13}$$

where n, an integer, is the length of the microstrip in half-wavelengths at f and

$$D = \frac{1}{2}\cdot\frac{f}{\epsilon_e}\cdot\frac{d\epsilon_e}{d_f} \approx \frac{(\epsilon_s-\epsilon_e)(\epsilon_e-\epsilon_e(0))}{\epsilon_e(\epsilon_s-\epsilon_e(0))} \tag{14}$$

where ϵ_s is the substrate relative dielectric constant, and $\epsilon_e(0)$ is the effective dielectric constant at zero frequency. The final term in (14) was derived from the approximate expression for ϵ_e developed in [5].

Equation (13) was derived by taking the derivative with respect to frequency of the input reflection coefficient or reactance of the shorted microstrip, including the rate of change of the effective dielectric constant, for those frequencies at which the input reactance is zero.

One measurement technique used by the author was to find the small frequency difference needed for a specified reflection phase difference observed on a network analyzer, and to approximate the terms of (12) with differentials.

Fig. 12 shows ZA measurements for lines 0.1-, 0.25-, and 0.5-in wide on the 0.250-in-thick alumina substrate. ZA for all lines has the decline and rise characteristic observed previously. The agreement of the different measurement methods is considered quite satisfactory.

In summary, it can be observed that the slotted line method gives the most information—dispersion, transition elements, and ZA—but is the most difficult to perform and from which to de-embed ZA. The real-axis intercept method is the easiest to make and from which to find ZA, but requires excellent connectors and load. The group-delay method, because it tends to "look through" the transition and connector, is probably the best method for use at actual microwave frequencies, and most likely could be automated for faster measurements, if necessary. Also, the delay data can be smoothed on a piecewise-linear basis as was done for the 70-Ω line shown in Fig. 12.

Measurements of ZA from about 3 to 5 GHz showed excessive variations caused by coupling to undesired modes. The LSM_{11}-mode cutoff frequency was found by both calculation and measurement to occur near 3 GHz.

IV. Models of ZA

The first and simplest microstrip characteristic impedance model is the constant impedance model which approximates ZA by its zero-frequency value

$$ZA(f) = ZA(0). \tag{15}$$

This is a practical approximation because actual ZA decreases only by about 2 percent and rises to the zero-frequency value again at about the maximum frequency at which the substrate would be used. For example, an alumina substrate 0.025-in thick would be used up to a maximum of 18 GHz, typically.

The next simplest model is the wave impedance model [2], so-called because it describes the characteristic impedance variation with frequency of any mode on a homogeneous transmission line. For microstrip, this would require ZA to be proportional to the reciprocal of the square root of the effective dielectric constant

$$ZA(f) = ZA(0)\sqrt{\epsilon_e(0)/\epsilon_e(f)}\,. \tag{16}$$

The wave impedance model for ZA follows the measurements in the lower frequency range more accurately than the constant impedance model, but continues to decline even when measured ZA reverses its slope.

The LSE model predicted that the power-current impedance definition could be expected to describe microstrip ZA approximately; however, "goodness of fit" could be determined only by measurement. As shown in Fig. 12, the power-current model has zero slope at zero frequency, declines to a broad minimum of about the same value at about the same frequency as the measurements, and increases thereafter at about the same slope.

A derivation of an algebraic expression for the LSE power-current model of ZA is given in the Appendix. The result, while easily programmed, is too complicated for evaluation by a hand calculator. A simpler expression, termed the group-delay model is found by replacing f/n in (13) by its equivalent determined from (10), and then forming the ratio $ZA(f)/ZA(0)$

$$\frac{ZA(f)}{ZA(0)} = \frac{T(f)}{T(0)} \cdot \frac{\sqrt{\epsilon_e(0)/\epsilon_e(f)}}{1+D(f)}\,. \tag{17}$$

Making the heuristic assumption that

$$\frac{T(f)}{T(0)} \simeq \frac{\epsilon_e(f)}{\epsilon_e(0)} \tag{18}$$

results in

$$ZA = ZA(0)\frac{\sqrt{\epsilon_e/\epsilon_e(0)}}{1+D}\,. \tag{19}$$

This approximate formula is a close fit to the LSE power-current model to well beyond the frequency at which ZA rises through $ZA(0)$.

Approaching infinite frequency, the group-delay model becomes

$$ZA(\infty) = ZA(0)\sqrt{\epsilon_s/\epsilon_e(0)} \tag{20}$$

while the LSE power-current model becomes

$$ZA(\infty) = ZA(0)\cdot\frac{\pi^2}{8}\cdot\sqrt{\frac{\epsilon_e(0)}{\epsilon_s}\cdot\frac{\epsilon_s-1}{\epsilon_e(0)-1}}\,. \tag{21}$$

These differ by about 30 percent for a 50-Ω line on alumina. Derivation of (21) is discussed in the Appendix.

V. Discussion

Repeatability of impedance measurements was within about 0.5 percent. Scatter varied from about 0.5 percent to 2 or 3 percent, and occasionally more. It was greater for the 70-Ω test pieces than for the others. Above 3 GHz, higher mode coupling was clearly a major source of error. Some ideas about measurement error were given in the section on measurements. In general, there appeared to be a number of causes of scatter, but they were not tracked down.

Differences between the actual measurements and the LSE power-current (or group-delay) model arise from three possible sources: the actual microstrip is not ideal (inhomogeneities of substrate and line width, and contact problems); measurements are not ideal (effect of small reflections and instrument calibrations); or the model only approximates microstrip (other coupled modes not included). No attempt has been made to separate the errors from these sources at this time (below 3 GHz).

The surprisingly large frequency variation of the measured impedance of the 70-Ω line and its deviation from the model are unexplained and indicate the need for corroborative investigation. However, of the ZA models described, the LSE power-current model is the most faithful over the widest frequency range to the characteristics measured on actual microstrip and has sufficient accuracy for microstrip circuit design.[1]

[1] One of the reviewers of this paper has proposed that other power-current models of microstrip might give better results than the LSE model, and suggests specifically computations based on the actual microstrip field [12], and the planar waveguide model with frequency dependent effective width [13]. The author believes that such a comparison of models (with relation to experimental results) would be a useful investigation, but is beyond the scope of this paper.

This conclusion is supported by the work of Jansen and Koster [9], who found that a hybrid-mode numerical analysis of junctions between microstrips of different widths agreed best with circuit representations when a power-current definition of ZA was assumed. Their work also tends to confirm that ZA is the same for a microstrip-to-microstrip junction as for a coaxial line-to-microstrip junction. Thus, Bianco's suggestion of a frequency-sensitive ideal transformer at the transition [10], while mathematically possible, need not be invoked.

The power-current LSE model probably holds only for thin strips which, with their ground planes, are in intimate contact with their substrates. It would not be likely to hold for suspended substrate lines or thick center conductors [11], because the LSE assumption (electric field tangential at the interface) would not hold as well, and so neither voltage nor current could be defined uniquely.

Appendix
Power-Current Impedance Analysis

The power-current definition of the characteristic impedance ZA of the LSE model for microstrip is derived below.

Following Collin [6], a Hertzian vector $\bar{\pi}$ in the x-direction with a wave function ψ is used to determine the fields of the fundamental LSE (or TE, in this case) mode in the structure of Fig. 3, assuming propagation in the z-direction. Let

$$\bar{\pi} = \hat{x}_0 \psi_i e^{-\gamma z} \tag{A1-a}$$

$$\psi_i = \frac{B_i}{\omega^2} \cosh \gamma_i x_i \tag{A1-b}$$

in which

$\hat{x}_0$	unit vector along the x-axis;	
$\gamma = j(\omega/c)\sqrt{\epsilon_e}$	propagation constant;	(A1-c)
ω	radian frequency;	
c	speed of light in vacuum;	
ϵ_e	frequency dependent effective dielectric constant;	
i	index denoting dielectric (1) or air (2) regions;	
ϵ_i	dielectric constant of the region i, $\epsilon_1 = \epsilon_s$ and $\epsilon_2 = 1$;	(A1-d)
$\gamma_i^2 = (\omega/c)^2 (\epsilon_e - \epsilon_i)$	transverse (x-directed) propagation constant in the region i; and a constant.	(A1-e)

Also

$$x_1 = x \qquad \text{for } 0 \leqslant x \leqslant s \tag{A1-f}$$

and

$$x_2 = s + a' - x \text{ for } s \leqslant x \leqslant s + a'. \tag{A1-g}$$

The term ω^2 introduced into the denominator of (A1-b) prevents the fields from disappearing at zero frequency.

It can be shown [6] that

$$\bar{E} = - j\omega\mu \nabla \times \bar{\pi} \tag{A2-a}$$

and

$$\bar{H} = \nabla \nabla \cdot \bar{\pi} + k_i^2 \bar{\pi} \tag{A2-b}$$

where μ is the permeability of free space, that

$$k_i^2 = \left(\frac{\omega}{c}\right)^2 \epsilon_i \tag{A2-c}$$

and that the propagation constants are related by

$$\gamma^2 + \gamma_i^2 + k_i^2 = 0. \tag{A2-d}$$

An approximate solution for γ was found in [5]. It follows that with z-variation suppressed, the fields are

$$E_x = E_z = 0 \tag{A2-e}$$

$$E_{y_i} = j \frac{\mu \gamma B_i}{\omega} \cosh \gamma_i x_i \tag{A2-f}$$

$$H_{x_i} = - \frac{B_i \gamma^2}{\omega^2} \cosh \gamma_i x_i \tag{A2-g}$$

$$H_y = 0 \tag{A2-h}$$

$$H_{z_i} = (-1)^i \frac{\gamma \gamma_i B_i}{\omega^2} \sinh \gamma_i x_i. \tag{A2-i}$$

Power in the z-direction, P of (5), can be written in terms of the fields as

$$P = -\frac{1}{2} \operatorname{Re} \int E_y H_x^* \, dx \, dy. \tag{A3}$$

The wave impedance Z_w is

$$Z_w = -\frac{E_y}{H_x} = \frac{j\omega\mu}{\gamma} \tag{A4}$$

which is independent of position or region on a transverse surface [2].

Now, substituting (A4) into (A3), and integrating over dielectric and air regions separately gives

$$P = \frac{j\omega\mu}{\gamma} \left[\int_0^b \int_0^s |H_{x_1}|^2 \, dx \, dy + \int_0^{b'} \int_s^{s+a'} |H_{x_2}|^2 \, dx \, dy \right]. \tag{A5}$$

Similarly, an expression for longitudinal current I on the conductors of both regions is

$$I = 2 \int_0^s H_{x_1} \, dx + 2 \int_s^{s+a'} H_{x_2} \, dx. \tag{A6}$$

Now, if the z-directed magnetic fields are matched at the air–dielectric interface, the electric potential will also be matched if γ is maintained in agreement with the transverse resonance condition in [5, (8)]. Matching the H_{zi} gives

$$B_1 \gamma_1 \sinh \gamma_1 s = - B_2 \gamma_2 \sinh \gamma_2 a'. \tag{A7}$$

Employing (A1-d) and (A1-e) and rearranging gives

$$\frac{B_2}{B_1} = \sqrt{\frac{\epsilon_s - \epsilon_e}{\epsilon_e - 1}} \cdot \frac{\sin(\omega/c)\sqrt{\epsilon_s - \epsilon_e}\, s}{\sinh(\omega/c)\sqrt{\epsilon_e - 1}\, a'}. \tag{A8}$$

The power-current definition of apparent characteristic impedance ZA was given in (8) of the text. Equations (A5) and (A6) are substituted into (8), using (A2-g) and (A8), and the resulting expression is simplified by employing equalities of the following form:

$$\operatorname{sinc}|\gamma_1|s = \frac{\sin(\omega/c)\sqrt{\epsilon_s - \epsilon_e s}}{(\omega/c)\sqrt{\epsilon_s - \epsilon_e s}} \tag{A9-a}$$

$$\operatorname{sinch}\gamma_2 a' = \frac{\sinh(\omega/c)\sqrt{\epsilon_e - 1}\, a'}{(\omega/c)\sqrt{\epsilon_e - 1}\, a'}. \tag{A9-b}$$

This leads to the final relationship for ZA, the power-current characteristic impedance of the LSE model

$$ZA = \frac{\eta_0 b/s}{4\sqrt{\epsilon_e}} \left\{ \frac{(1 + \operatorname{sinc} 2|\gamma_1|s) + \dfrac{a'b'}{bs}\dfrac{\epsilon_s - \epsilon_e}{\epsilon_e - 1} \cdot \left(\dfrac{\sin|\gamma_1|s}{\sinh\gamma_2 a'}\right)^2 (1 + \operatorname{sinch} 2\gamma_2 a')}{\left[\operatorname{sinc}|\gamma_1|s + \dfrac{a'}{s}\cdot\sqrt{\dfrac{\epsilon_s - \epsilon_e}{\epsilon_e - 1}} \cdot \left(\dfrac{\sin|\gamma_1|s}{\sinh\gamma_2 a'}\right)\operatorname{sinch}\gamma_2 a'\right]^2} \right\} \tag{A10}$$

where η_0 is the impedance of free space. The relations [5, (4a) and (4b)] are, in the notation of this paper

$$\frac{a'}{b'} = \frac{\eta_0}{2ZA(0)\sqrt{\epsilon_e(0)}} \cdot \frac{\epsilon_s - \epsilon_e(0)}{\epsilon_s - 1} \tag{A11-a}$$

$$\frac{s}{b} = \frac{\eta_0}{2ZA(0)\sqrt{\epsilon_e(0)}} \cdot \frac{\epsilon_e(0) - 1}{\epsilon_s - 1}. \tag{A11-b}$$

Use of (A11-a) and (A11-b) will leave the factor b'/b to be evaluated. This quantity must be found experimentally for microstrip, as observed in [5].

When (A11-a) and (A11-b) are substituted into (A10) and frequency allowed to approach zero, all sinc and sinch tend to unity, and $\sin|\gamma_1|s/\sinh\gamma_2 a'$ becomes

$$(s/a')\sqrt{(\epsilon_s - \epsilon_e(0))/(\epsilon_e(0) - 1)}\,.$$

The predicted zero-frequency impedance is

$$ZA(0) = \frac{\eta_0 b/s}{2\sqrt{\epsilon_e(0)}} \cdot \frac{\epsilon_e(0) - 1}{\epsilon_s - 1}. \tag{A12}$$

This can be seen to be equivalent to a rearrangement of (A11-b), which was derived in [5] by forcing agreement between microstrip and LSE parameters at zero frequency. Thus, $ZA(0)$ is the same as static determinations of microstrip characteristic impedance.

The apparent power-current characteristic impedance at infinite frequency $ZA(\infty)$ is found by observing that the second terms of both denominator and numerator of (A10) go to zero, and that γ_1 is indeterminate. The indeterminacy is resolved by appeal to the transverse resonance relation [5, (8)], which requires that $|\gamma_1|s \to \pi/2$ as $\omega \to \infty$. The result is given in (21).

Equations (A10), (A12), and (21) show that ZA is indeterminate for $\epsilon_s = \epsilon_e(0) = 1$. This occurs because dimensions are related to impedance by means of ratios of differences of dielectric constants for the LSE model. Resolution of the indeterminacies would require knowledge of the functional relation between $\epsilon_e(0)$ and ϵ_s as ϵ_s approaches unity.

ACKNOWLEDGMENT

The author is pleased to express his thanks to A. Berman of COMSAT Laboratories, and to S. March of COMPACT Engineering, CGIS, for their helpful technical discussions and continuing support during the course of the work.

REFERENCES

[1] B. Bianco *et al.*, "Some considerations about the frequency dependence of the characteristic impedance of uniform microstrips," *IEEE Trans. Microwave Theory Tech.*, vol. MTT-26, pp. 182–185, Mar. 1978.

[2] W. J. Getsinger, "Microstrip characteristic impedance," *IEEE Trans. Microwave Theory Tech.*, vol. MTT-27, p. 293, Apr. 1979.

[3] L. Napoli and J. Hughes, "High frequency behavior of microstrip transmission lines," *RCA Rev.*, vol. 30, pp. 268–276, June 1969.

[4] M. K. Krage and G. I. Haddad, "Frequency dependent characteristics of microstrip transmission lines," *IEEE Trans. Microwave Theory Tech.*, vol. MTT-20, pp. 678–688, Oct. 1972.

[5] W. J. Getsinger, "Microstrip dispersion model," *IEEE Trans. Microwave Theory Tech.*, vol. MTT-21, pp. 34–39, Jan. 1973.

[6] R. E. Collin, *Field Theory of Guided Waves.* New York: McGraw-Hill, 1960, pp. 225–228.

[7] W. J. Getsinger, "Measurement of the characteristic impedance of microstrip over a wide frequency range," in *IEEE MTT-S Int. Microwave Symp. Dig.*, June 1982, pp. 342–344.

[8] S. J. Mason and H. J. Zimmermann, *Electronic Circuits, Signals and Systems.* New York: Wiley, 1965, pp. 366–369.

[9] R. H. Jansen and N. H. Koster, "New aspects concerning the definition of microstrip characteristic impedance as a function of frequency," in *IEEE MTT-S Int. Microwave Symp. Dig.*, pp. 305–307, June 1982.

[10] B. Bianco *et al.*, "Launcher and microstrip characterization," *IEEE Trans. Instrum. Meas.*, vol. IM-5, pp. 320–323, Dec. 1976.

[11] F. Arndt and G. Paul, "The reflection definition of the characteristic impedance of microstrips," *IEEE Trans. Microwave Theory Tech.*, vol. MTT-27, pp. 724–731, Aug. 1979.

[12] T. Itoh and R. Mittra, "A technique for computing dispersion characteristics of shielded microstrip lines," *IEEE Trans. Microwave Theory Tech.*, vol. MTT-22, pp. 896–898, Oct. 1974.

[13] H. Pues and A. Van de Capelle, "Approximate formulas for frequency dependence of microstrip parameters," *Electron. Lett.*, vol. 16, no. 23, pp. 870–872, Nov. 6, 1980.

2–18-GHz Dispersion Measurements on 10–100-Ω Microstrip Lines on Sapphire

TERENCE C. EDWARDS AND ROGER P. OWENS

***Abstract*—Dispersion measurements on microstrip lines with characteristic impedances between 10 and 100 Ω are described, covering the frequency range 2–18 GHz. Single-crystal sapphire cut with a specified crystal orientation was used as the substrate material. Microstrip effective permittivities were calculated from the resonant frequencies of open-ended straight resonators using a technique which eliminated end-effect. The experimental results are compared with some recent dispersion theories. An empirical dispersion formula is independently developed, and is shown to provide well-fitting curves for all the measured dispersion results.**

I. Introduction

The accurate design of microstrip circuits requires comparably accurate and reliable information on the dispersive behavior of the microstrip lines to be used. Currently available information on this behavior is incomplete. Experimentally, dispersion at frequencies above about 12 GHz is rarely investigated, and the range of line impedances considered has also been rather restricted. Available theoretical predictions have therefore not been tested over sufficiently wide frequency and impedance ranges.

In this paper we present the results of an extensive experimental investigation into the dispersive nature of microstrip lines on 0.5-mm-thick 25-mm-square monocrystalline sapphire substrates. The frequency range is extended up to 18 GHz and a broad characteristic impedance (Z_0) range, 10–100 Ω, is considered. Certain available theoretical treatments are also compared with our results; including the spectral domain analysis of Itoh and Mittra [1] and the analytical formulation due to Getsinger [2]. Each shows slight departure from the measured results over certain parts of the frequency range. An empirical formula tailored to the measured points is independently developed, and incidentally shown to work effectively for a high-purity alumina substrate with thickness differing from that of the sapphire.

II. Measurement Method and Accuracy Considerations

We used resonance measurements to determine microstrip effective permittivities ε_{eff} for a set of resonant frequencies f. The procedure was repeated for several microstrip width-to-substrate-height ratios (W/h) between 0.1 and 10 to obtain a family of dispersion points covering the frequency range 2–18 GHz in each case. Measurements were originally made on ring resonators, but towards the two extremes of the linewidth range we encountered difficulties associated with 1) curvature effects, 2) frequency pulling due to coupling problems, and 3) the manufacture and physical measurement of high-tolerance thin rings.

As a result there were unacceptable variations between ε_{eff} results for nominally very similar rings, and they were abandoned in favor of end-fed open-ended straight resonators. These gave more repeatable results for all the microstrip lines studied. The manufacturing and measurement difficulties were greatly eased, and it was possible to obtain adequate coupling without pulling the resonant frequency. End-effect was eliminated by working with pairs of straight resonators, nominally of identical width W and with identical coupling gaps g, but with physical lengths chosen so that the nth-order resonant frequency of the shorter resonator f_1 corresponded very closely with the $2n$th-order resonance of the longer resonator f_2. The physical lengths were, respectively, l_1 and l_2. Suppose l_e represents the sum of the coupling-gap end-effect length l_g and the open-line end-effect length l_0 [3] and that l_e is the same for each resonator. The following equations can then be simply derived from the resonance conditions for each resonator [4]:

$$\varepsilon_{eff} = \left[\frac{nc(2f_1 - f_2)}{2f_1 f_2(l_2 - l_1)}\right]^2 \quad (1)$$

and

$$l_e = \frac{f_2 l_2 - 2f_1 l_1}{(2f_1 - f_2)} \quad (2)$$

where c is the velocity of light.

Equations (1) and (2) hold provided both ε_{eff} and l_e may be regarded as constant between f_1 and f_2. We make $l_2 \simeq (2l_1 + l_e)$ to ensure that f_1 and f_2 are close. Equal coupling gaps are essential because l_g, and hence l_e, is dependent upon g [3]. This approach assumes that l_e is independent of the resonator length. There is evidence that this may not necessarily be true [5], but for a substrate with relative permittivity comparable to sapphire, data are only available for $h = 1.27$ cm and $W = 2$ cm. A scaling exercise has been carried out on Itoh's results which shows that all the resonators used in this study lie in the region where l_e is essentially constant.

The special requirements arising from this method are that, for each set of results, a pair of resonators must be made with identical widths and coupling gaps. They may both lie on a single substrate, or each may occupy one of a pair of substrates with very closely matched thicknesses, in order to accommodate a long resonator across a diagonal or to avoid resonator interaction. These requirements were

Manuscript received January 17, 1975; revised January 26, 1976.
The authors are with the Department of Electrical and Electronic Engineering, Royal Military College of Science, Shrivenham, Swindon, Wilts., England.

Fig. 1. 103-Ω resonator pair, with inset showing gap region.

TABLE I

Line No.	1	2	3	4	5	6	7	8	9	10	11
W, mm	4.490	2.445	1.921	1.068	0.642	0.415	0.275	0.178	0.111	0.073	0.050
h, mm	0.491	0.492	0.512	0.496	0.510	0.507	0.502	0.480	0.507	0.502	0.496
ϵ_{req}	11.50	11.43	11.39	11.29	11.18	11.08	10.99	10.91	10.82	10.76	10.73
ϵ_{eo}	9.733	9.057	8.732	8.108	7.594	7.263	7.019	6.832	6.640	6.524	6.448
Z_o, ohms	10.03	16.53	20.46	30.05	41.29	51.24	60.98	70.64	83.86	94.26	103.58

achieved even for the narrowest resonators with $W = 50\ \mu m$, $g = 10\ \mu m$, and lengths $l_1 = 9.4$ mm and $l_2 = 19.2$ mm. Fig. 1 is a photograph of this particular resonator pair, with an inset enlargement of the gap region. Additional values of ε_{eff} were obtained from the odd-mode resonances of the longer resonators using

$$\varepsilon_{eff} = \left[\frac{nc}{2f_2(l_2 + l_e)}\right]^2 \tag{3}$$

where l_e may be interpolated between the values calculated from (2). In fact l_e was found to be substantially independent of frequency for most resonator pairs. Measurements were made using a network analyzer and a frequency counter with a repeatability of $< \pm 2$ MHz. It was essential to have accurate measurements of resonator lengths (to $\pm 5\ \mu m$) and widths (to $\pm 1\ \mu m$) and to be sure that the coupling gaps were equal to within $\pm 1\ \mu m$. The substrate thickness h not only governs the W/h ratio but also influences the dispersive behavior, particularly for wide lines, so it was also necessary to measure this parameter to $\pm 5\ \mu m$ in $500\ \mu m$.

III. Derivation of Quasi-Static Parameters of Experimental Microstrip Lines

Before comparing the experimental results with theoretical dispersion curves, it is necessary to establish the substrate relative permittivity ε_r and, for each microstrip line, the low-frequency (LF) limit of microstrip effective permittivity ε_{e0}. In practice, ε_r is normally obtained from a separate experiment, then knowing W/h for the line, both ε_{e0} and Z_0 may be computed from available quasi-static microstrip analysis theories [6]–[8]. The situation with monocrystalline sapphire substrates is complicated by the fact that the material is uniaxially anisotropic. All our substrates are cut with the crystal C axis perpendicular to the microstrip ground plane. The material permittivity is then constant everywhere in the plane of the substrate, and the microstrip line behavior is unaffected by its orientation in this plane. The quasi-static behavior of microstrip on sapphire cut with this particular C-axis orientation is dealt with theoretically in another paper [9]. It is shown there that the conventional quasi-static microstrip theories are applicable provided that ε_r is replaced by a parameter called the equivalent isotropic-substrate relative permittivity ε_{req}, which is a function of W/h. In Table I are listed the W and h measurements of the experimental microstrip lines and the corresponding values of ε_{req} computed from W/h as described in [9], using $\varepsilon_\perp = 9.40$ and $\varepsilon_\parallel = 11.60$ as the principal relative permittivities of sapphire. In addition, the parameters ε_{e0} and Z_0 computed from Bryant and Weiss theory [7], [8] are tabulated.

IV. Comparison of Experimental Results with Selected Dispersion Theories

The experimental results for all measured lines are shown in Fig. 2, each set being identified by its line number. The ε_{e0} values given in Table I are also plotted and they fit in quite well with the trend of the ε_{eff} results at low frequencies, allowing for the fact that error bounds of up to 0.5 percent should be placed on each value of ε_{req} [9]. This is a good indirect experimental check on the theoretical predictions of [9].

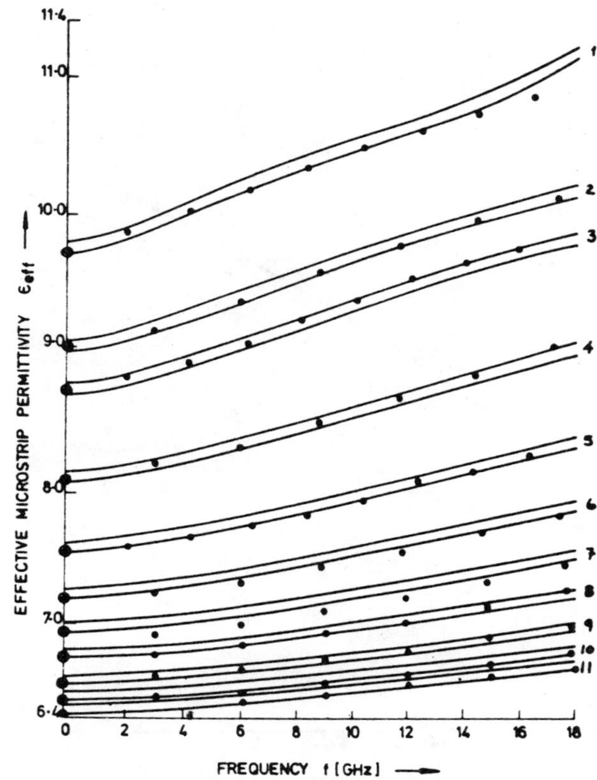

Fig. 2. Effective microstrip permittivity versus frequency. • Experimental results. ⊕ Predicted ε_{eo} results [8]. Continuous curves from Itoh theory [1]. Double lines represent ε_{req} ± 0.05.

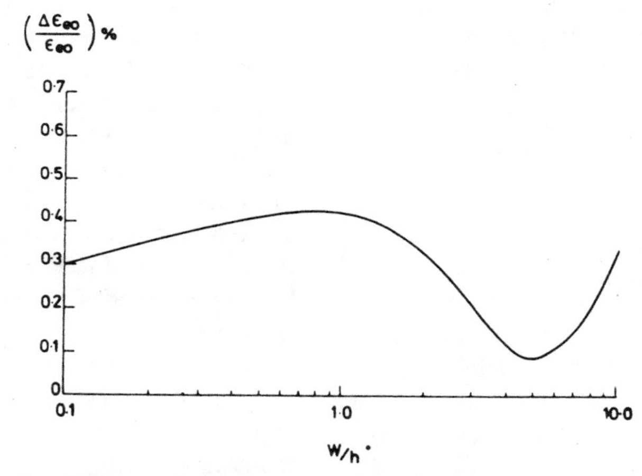

Fig. 3. Difference between Itoh predictions and Bryant and Weiss calculations of ε_{eo} plotted against W/h.

A rigorous theoretical analysis of microstrip dispersion using a spectral domain approach has recently been carried out for microstrip in a conducting box [1]. Apart from box size, the data required for calculation of ε_{eff} down to very low frequencies, are: W, h, and ε_{req}. These data, listed in Table I, have been applied to a computer program kindly supplied by Dr. T. Itoh, which implements the theory of [1]. For each line, the box size was increased until further increase had a negligible effect on the computed ε_{eff} values. Fig. 2 shows the continuous curves thus generated, which are drawn in pairs in this instance, representing ε_{req} (from Table I) ± 0.05 to account for the error bound previously mentioned. For many lines the curves are in very good agreement with the measurements, although for the narrower lines it is the lower bound curve which best fits the points, and for lines 6 and 7, for example, the points lie even below this curve. This displacement may be partly due to the slight discrepancy between the values of ε_{eo} calculated from quasi-static theory (given in Table I) and the values predicted by the Itoh and Mittra theory. This causes the curves of Fig. 2 to fall less sharply at their low-frequency ends than might be expected. The difference involved is less than 0.5 percent and it is plotted in Fig. 3 as a percentage deviation from the Bryant and Weiss [7], [8] quasi-static value versus W/h. If Wheeler theory is used [6], the discrepancy rises to almost 1 percent around $W/h = 0.6$.

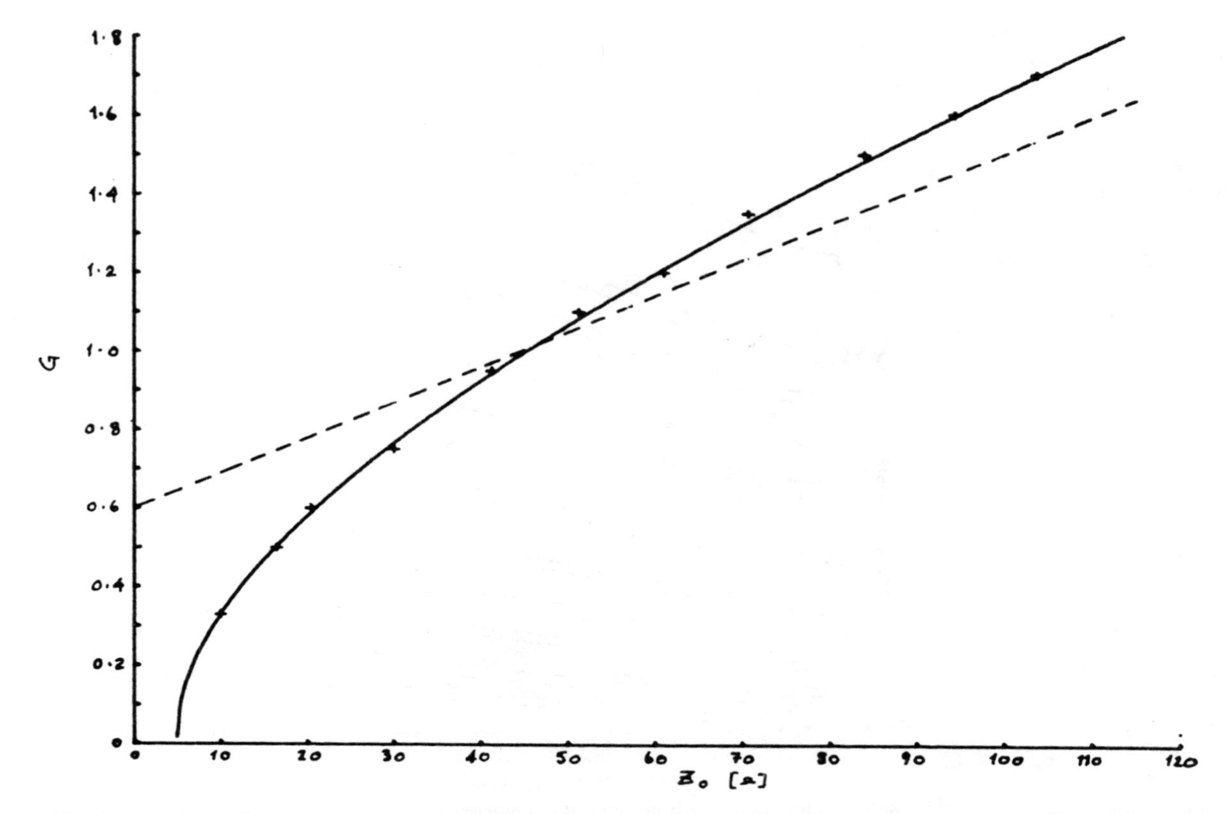

Fig. 4. Getsinger G parameter versus Z_0. + Optimized using measured dispersion curves. ———— Plotted from (7). — — — — Plotted from (6).

For computer-aided design purposes, analytical formulas such as those published by Getsinger [2] and Carlin [10], are of particular value. The Getsinger formula is

$$\varepsilon_{eff} = \varepsilon_{req} - \frac{(\varepsilon_{req} - \varepsilon_{e0})}{1 + G(f/f_p)^2} \tag{4}$$

where

$$f_p = \frac{Z_0}{2\mu_0 h} \tag{5}$$

and μ_0 is the free-space permeability. The parameter G is purely empirical, thereby giving some flexibility to the formula. G is dependent mainly on Z_0 but also on h, and Getsinger deduced from measurements of ring resonators on alumina that

$$G = 0.6 + 0.009Z_0 \tag{6}$$

when h is 0.635 mm.

The range of the present measurements, the method employed, and the different substrate thickness, required that a new value of the G-factor should be determined by curve fitting to each set of experimental results. Only the measured results were used in the curve fitting. For each line ε_{req} was allowed to deviate from the value given in Table I if necessary, so that ε_{e0} could also deviate according to the quasi-static relationship between the two permittivities. The resulting optimized values of G are plotted against Z_0 in Fig. 4. The equation

$$G = \left[\frac{Z_0 - 5}{60}\right]^{1/2} + 0.004Z_0 \tag{7}$$

is plotted as a continuous curve in the figure and is seen to fit the optimized points very well. The Getsinger expression (6) for G is also plotted for comparison. There is clearly a considerable difference between the two curves, particularly at the low-impedance end of the figure.

The continuous curves of Fig. 5 were drawn using the Getsinger formula with the new expression for G. The broken curves a drawn in Fig. 5 for several representative lines were produced using G calculated from (6). As the line impedance falls, these curves are seen to deviate progressively more at the higher frequencies as the difference between the G-factors increases.

Selected curves using the theory of Carlin [10] are also shown as curves b in Fig. 5. This theory calculates ε_{eff} from an equation of the form

$$\varepsilon_{eff} = \varepsilon_{e0} + \frac{(\varepsilon_{req} - \varepsilon_{e0})Af^2}{1 + \sqrt{A^2 f^4 + 1}} \tag{8}$$

where A is a function of Z_0 and h which can be derived from [10]. No attempt was made to optimize A for these curves, which also rise sharply at the high-frequency ends for the low-impedance lines, but it is anticipated that a similar improvement in the fit could be obtained.

V. Discussion of Results

The analytical equation of Getsinger provides a fairly accurate prediction of microwave dispersion over the wide range of frequencies and line impedances covered by the present measurements, provided that the proper expression for the parameter G is used. In order to obtain a good overall fit to the measured points, however, the curves of

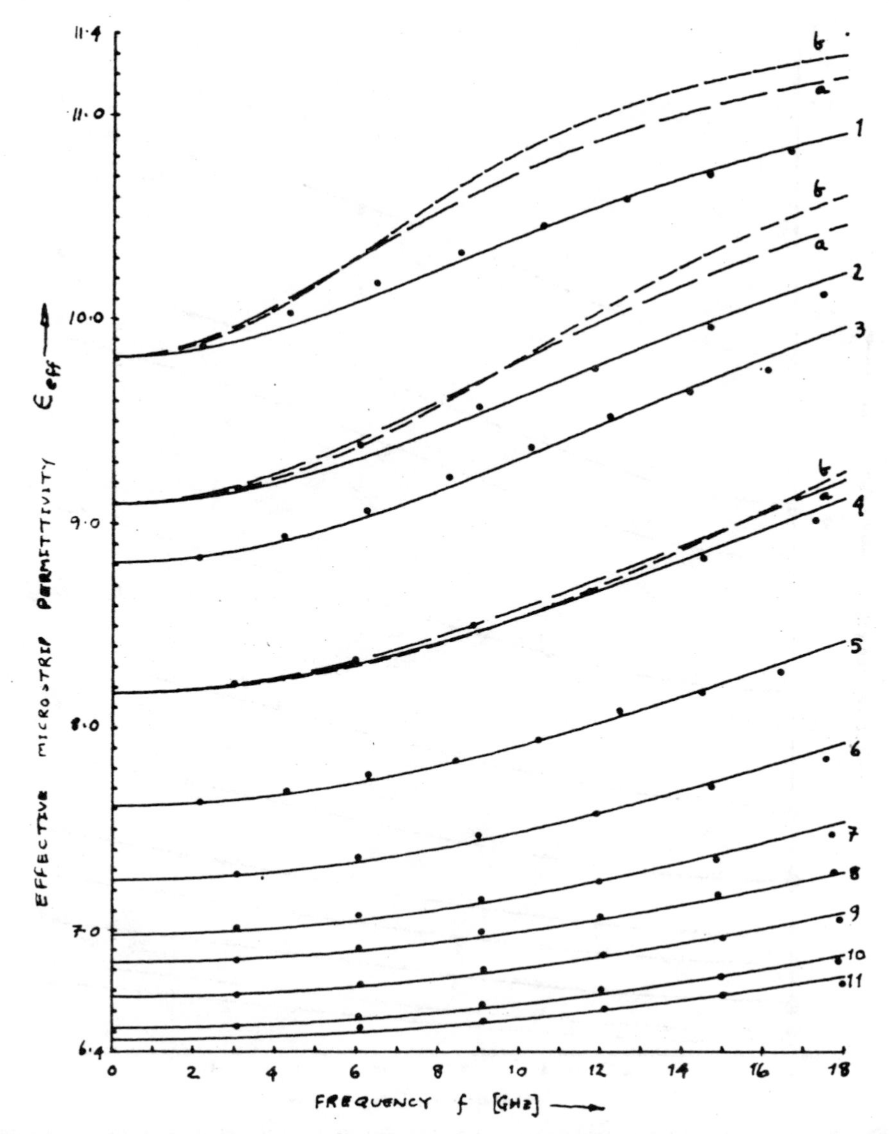

Fig. 5. Effective microstrip permittivity versus frequency. • Experimental results. ———— Getsinger curves using (7) for G. Curves a, Getsinger curves using (6) for G. Curves b, Carlin curves using (8) with A values from [10].

Fig. 5 in general fall slightly below the points at the lower end of the frequency range, but rise above them at the high-frequency end. There is, therefore, scope for an alternative analytical dispersion equation which can take this consistent discrepancy into account by including higher order powers of frequency in the expression for the dependent variable ε_{eff}.

In its most general form, such an equation will be as follows:

$$\varepsilon_{eff} = \varepsilon_{req} - \frac{(\varepsilon_{req} - \varepsilon_{e0})}{1 + P} \tag{9}$$

where P is a polynomial

$$P = a_2 f^2 + a_3 f^3 + \cdots + a_n f^n. \tag{10}$$

This equation obeys the three conditions 1) $\varepsilon_{eff} = \varepsilon_{e0}$ when $f = 0$; 2) $d(\varepsilon_{eff})/df = 0$ when $f = 0$; 3) $\varepsilon_{eff} \rightarrow \varepsilon_{req}$ as $f \rightarrow \infty$. The coefficients a_n must be functions of h and Z_0 to allow for the dependence of dispersion on these two microstrip parameters. It will be noted that if $a_2 = G/f_p^2$ and $a_n = 0$ $(n > 2)$, Getsinger's equation is recovered. Similarly, after rearrangement of (9) into the form of (8), it may be seen that if $A^2 f^4 \gg 1$, Carlin's formula is obtained by putting $a_2 = A$ and $a_n = 0$ $(n > 2)$. Thus (9) is a natural progression from (4) and (8) involving one or more extra empirical parameters in addition to G or A.

It is only necessary to include the extra term $a_3 f^3$ in the polynomial to obtain a good fit to the experimental results. A simple relationship between the optimized coefficients a_2 and a_3 and h/Z_0 for each line was observed, and the final form of the polynomial P to be used in (9) was found to be

$$P = (h/Z_0)^{1 \cdot 33}[0.43 f^2 - 0.009 f^3] \tag{11}$$

where h is in millimeters and f is in gigahertz.

Fig. 6 shows the curves generated using this polynomial, illustrating the very close agreement with the experimental results. The empirical equations clearly cover a wide range

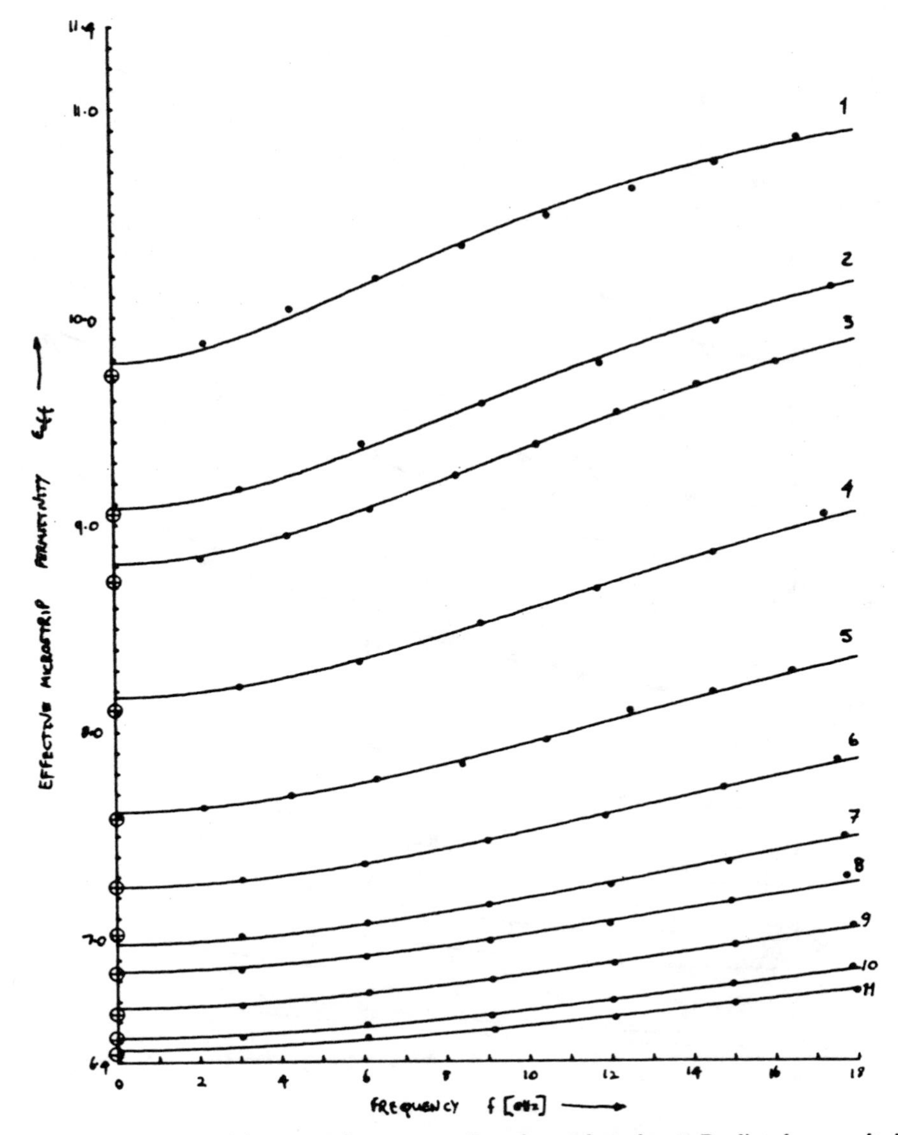

Fig. 6. Effective microstrip permittivity versus frequency. • Experimental results. ⊕ Predicted ε_{e0} results [7]. Continuous curves from combined (9) and (11).

TABLE II

Line Number	1	2	3	4	5	6	7	8	9	10	11
ε_{req} (theoretical)	11.50	11.43	11.39	11.29	11.18	11.08	10.99	10.91	10.82	10.76	10.73
ε_{req} (analytical formula)	11.56	11.46	11.50	11.38	11.21	11.06	10.92	10.93	10.87	10.75	10.75

of line impedances, but the validity of the h-dependence has not been checked with sapphire substrates of different thickness. As was also observed with the Getsinger curves, the ε_{e0} and ε_{req} values predicted by the curves of Fig. 6 are in general slightly higher than those obtained theoretically. Table II shows the relative values of ε_{req}. The differences involved are quite small and are mostly accounted for by the ± 0.05 error on the theoretical ε_{req} values. An alternative explanation is that, as predicted by the Itoh curves (Fig. 2), the slope $d(\varepsilon_{eff})/df$ may remain fairly constant down to very low frequencies, particularly for wider lines. In contrast the analytical formulas predict a square-law relationship below about 3 GHz and therefore a somewhat higher ε_{e0} on the fitted curve. The fact that the discrepancy increases for wider lines lends support to this explanation.

The polynomial formula clearly works up to 18 GHz, but at 31.85 GHz, dP/df, and hence $d(\varepsilon_{eff})/df$, are maximized, and above this frequency the formula is ill-behaved. This expression should therefore be used with caution at frequencies much above 18 GHz.

TABLE III

Line number	W mm	ε_{eo}	Z_o Ω	Getsinger G-factor
1	1.450	7.354	31	0.7
2	0.585	6.736	51	0.95
3	0.260	6.420	71	1.15

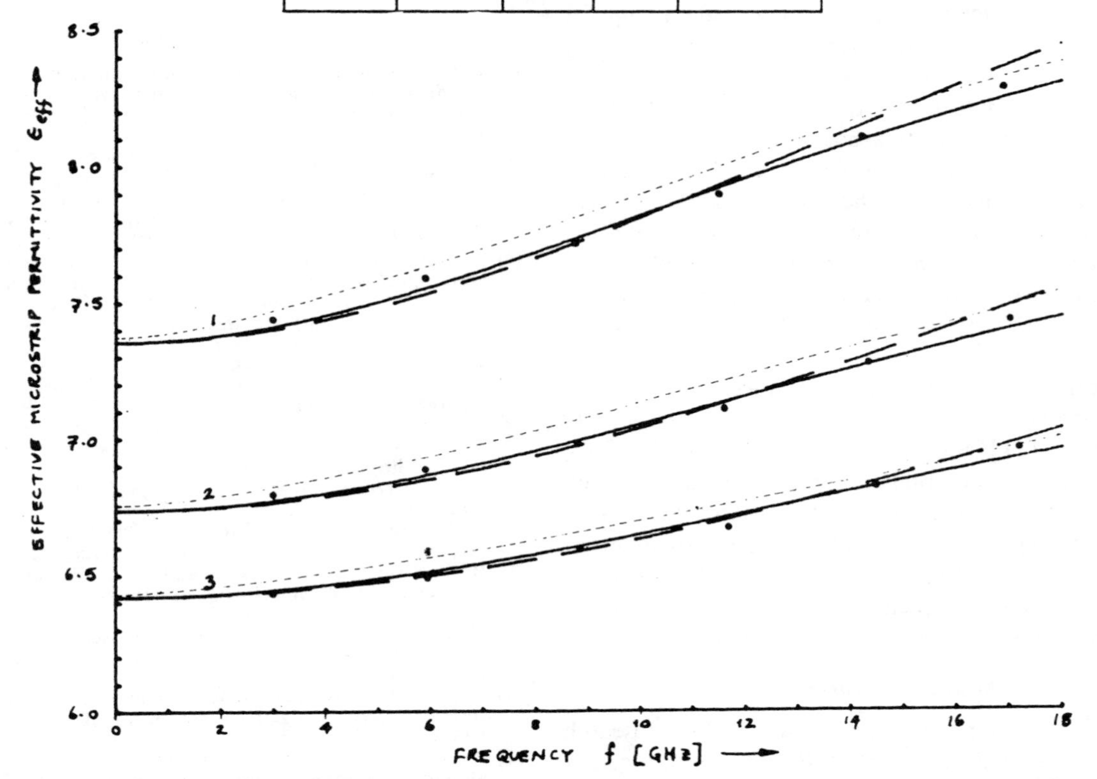

Fig. 7. Dispersion results for microstrip lines on alumina. • Experimental results. ———— Polynomial curves [(9) and (11)]. — — — — Getsinger curves (optimized G-factor). - - - - - - - Itoh curves. For line parameters see Table III.

The influence of the sapphire substrate anisotropy on dispersion has not been taken into account, although it might be argued that any discrepancy between our results and the theoretical predictions could be attributed at least partly to such an effect. Intuitively, one might expect that the normal increase in ε_{eff} with frequency would be opposed by some decrease due to a progressively larger component of electric field in the plane of the air–dielectric interface, where the sapphire permittivity has the lower value $\varepsilon_{\perp}$. The determination of the magnitude of this effect would be a subject for separate study, but the following discussion of measurements with microstrip resonators on alumina is relevant to this problem.

Preliminary experiments have been conducted using high-purity alumina substrates ("Alsimag" 805) with the quoted permittivity $\varepsilon_r = 10.1$ (at 1 MHz). Table III lists the parameters of each line. The substrate height was 0.65 mm. The value $\varepsilon_r = 10.15$ was obtained by curve fitting using the analytical formulas, and ε_{e0} and Z_0 follow from this. The G-factors required to obtain a good fit using the Getsinger formula are included in the table, and it is seen that these differ from values calculated using either (6) or (7).

Fig. 7 shows the measured results, together with curves using Itoh theory, the Getsinger equation with optimized G, and the polynomial expression. The latter results provide quite satisfactory confirmation that the dispersion formula using (9) and (11) is applicable to thicker alumina substrates without further change in the polynomial parameters. The behavior of the Itoh and Getsinger curves is similar to that observed earlier for microstrip on sapphire. In addition, the measured high-frequency dispersion behavior closely resembles that observed using sapphire substrates, strongly suggesting that the effect of sapphire anisotropy on dispersion is very small.

VI. Conclusions

By careful measurements we have obtained, repeatable and accurate dispersion data for open microstrip lines on sapphire substrates in the characteristic impedance range $10 < Z_0 < 100$ Ω, and for frequencies up to 18 GHz. Dispersion predictions using the theory of Itoh and Mittra have been shown to compare very well with experiment. There is, however, a slight discrepancy at frequencies approaching the LF limit when compared with previously accepted accurate quasi-static calculations [7]. The theory has the advantage that it does not involve any empirical factor and only the parameters W, h, and ε_r are required. Despite the necessity for lengthy computation it is therefore particularly suitable for predicting the dispersion of lines on a substrate with arbitrary height and permittivity.

The Getsinger analytical expression has been shown to be capable of fitting experimental results quite well, but only after suitable tailoring of the empirical parameter G. The limited results for microstrip on alumina suggest that for each new substrate the G parameter must be experimentally determined to account for different substrate height and permittivity. This limits the potential of the formula for predicting the dispersion of an arbitrary line on an arbitrary substrate. Similar limitations probably apply to the new dispersion equation involving the polynomial, which was developed to predict the fine detail of the experimental ε_{eff} versus frequency curves and includes two empirical parameters. The alumina results, however, seem to indicate that this formula is not too sensitive to changes in substrate parameters.

When working with alumina, the uncertain electrical properties, including possible variable bulk permittivity with frequency [11] and unpredictable anisotropy [12], add to the difficulties of precision measurement. It is felt that in these experiments, the use of sapphire as the substrate, with its repeatable and established electrical properties, has been a distinct advantage in ensuring that accurate measurements of microstrip characteristics were not unduly influenced by variable substrate material behavior.

Acknowledgment

This work was done as part of an M.I.C. research program directed by Prof. M. H. N. Potok whom, together with Dr. J. E. Aitken, we wish to thank for several valuable discussions. Mrs. C. Garrett and V. Hartley are also thanked for their consistently high-grade microcircuit fabrication, under the general supervision of E. H. England. We are particularly grateful to Dr. T. Itoh for a copy of his microstrip dispersion program.

References

[1] T. Itoh and R. Mittra, "Spectral-domain approach for calculating the dispersion characteristics of microstrip lines," *IEEE Trans. Microwave Theory and Tech.*, vol. MTT-21, pp. 496–499, July 1973.

[2] W. J. Getsinger, "Microstrip dispersion model," *IEEE Trans. Microwave Theory and Tech.*, vol. MTT-21, pp. 34–39, Jan. 1973.

[3] J. G. Richings, "An accurate experimental method for determining the important properties of microstrip transmission lines," *The Marconi Review*, pp. 209–216, Fourth Quarter, 1974.

[4] J. Deutsch and H. J. Jung, "Measurement of the effective dielectric constant of microstrip lines in the frequency range from 2 GHz to 12 GHz," *NTZ*, vol. 12, pp. 620–624, 1970.

[5] T. Itoh, "Analysis of microstrip resonators," *IEEE Trans. Microwave Theory and Tech.*, vol. MTT-22, pp. 946–952, Nov. 1974.

[6] H. A. Wheeler, "Transmission-line properties of parallel strips separated by a dielectric sheet," *IEEE Trans. Microwave Theory and Tech.*, vol. MTT-13, pp. 172–188, March 1965.

[7] T. G. Bryant and J. A. Weiss, "Parameters of microstrip transmission lines and of coupled pairs of microstrip lines," *IEEE Trans. Microwave Theory and Tech.*, vol. MTT-16, pp. 1021–1027, Dec. 1968.

[8] T. C. Cisco, "Design of microstrip components by computer," NASA Contractor Report CR-1982, March 1972, Program C267.

[9] R. P. Owens, J. E. Aitken, and T. C. Edwards, "Quasi-static characteristics of microstrip on an anisotropic sapphire substrate," this issue, pp. 499–505.

[10] H. J. Carlin, "A simplified circuit model for microstrip," *IEEE Trans. Microwave Theory and Tech.*, vol. MTT-21, pp. 589–591, Sept. 1973.

[11] S. Arnold, "Dispersive effects in microstrip and alumina substrates," *Electronics Letters*, vol. 5, no. 26, pp. 673–674, 27 Dec. 1969.

[12] J. W. C. van Heuven and T. H. A. M. Vlek, "Anisotropy in alumina substrates for microstrip circuits," *IEEE Trans. Microwave Theory and Tech.*, vol. MTT-20, pp. 775–777, Nov. 1972.

Technical Paper Section

ON MEASUREMENTS OF MICROSTRIP PROPERTIES

ROBERT SECKELMANN
American Electronic Laboratories, Inc.*
Colmar, Pennsylvania

INTRODUCTION

Microstrip lines on alumina substrates have become widely used for miniaturized microwave circuits. First experimentally determined propagation properties of such lines have been reported by T. M. Hyltin[1] and M. Caulton, J. J. Hughes and H. Sobol.[2] H. A. Wheeler[3] derived a general approximate solution for a similar problem theoretically. His basic approximation was to assume TEM-mode propagation and to use conformal mapping techniques. H. E. Green[4] and K. C. Wolters and P. L. Clar[5] derived numerical solutions for similar lines. They also assumed TEM-mode propagation but mapped the fields by using finite-difference approximations of Laplace's equations with a successive over-relaxation program on a digital computer.

It is the purpose of this paper to present further experimental data for impedances and effective dielectric constants for microstrip transmission lines for a wide range of parameters, and to discuss several methods used to measure these properties. In the course of these measurements, a method to determine characteristic impedances by nodal shift measurements only has been found. The results of this method will be cited, the method itself will be described in a separate paper.[6]

It turns out that the experimental data are in good agreement with Wheeler's theoretical results, that is, that the assumption of TEM-mode propagation is a very good approximation. Thus, one should be able to also use the theoretical results for materials and geometries not covered by the experiments reported here. To facilitate designs based on theoretical results, these data, constructed from Wheeler's graphs, are redrawn here in a convenient form for selected parameters. The experimental data are shown in these plots.

EXPERIMENTAL PROCEDURES

A problem in determining the microwave properties of microstrip transmission lines is to connect these lines to laboratory test equipment and to separate the effects measured into those due to the microstrip and those caused by the connecting element. This task requires a careful choice of both the test fixture and the measurement method.

Experimental Apparatus

Of several test fixtures used in the course of this investigation, the one sketched in Fig. 1 proved to be the most versatile one. The sample under test is an alumina substrate 0.010 to 0.030 inch thick. The bottom side is completely metallized, the top side is metallized with one or several strips parallel to each other and separated by unmetallized areas six or more times the widths of the strips. A semirigid 50 ohm cable (Uniform Tube UT85) with teflon between inner and outer conductor and with 0.020 inch diameter of the inner conductor, 0.065 inch inner diameter of the outer conductor and 0.085 inch overall diameter, ending in a miniature connector was used to connect the test line with the test equipment. The test sample was placed on an aluminum block as shown in Fig. 1, with the cable being held in a mechanical stage adjustable in three mutually perpendicular directions.

In the case of wide test lines (more than 0.030 inch wide), the contact is made as shown in the upper left corner of Fig. 1. A gap about 0.040 inch wide is left between sample and cable holder. The outer cable conductor ends in the plane of the cable holder, the inner conductor protrudes about 0.050 inch and is pressed onto the microstrip line. For narrow lines, the same contact was often made, in many cases, however, the inner and outer cable conductors ended in the plane of the cable holders, and the sample was placed against the cable and holder without a gap, as shown in the upper right corner of Fig. 1. Indium was used to connect the strip and the inner conductor. In first experiments, the aluminum block holding the sample was provided with proper holes and connected to a vacuum pump to hold the alumina substrate firmly on the holder. Later on, scotch tape was found to provide the same service. Finally, Phenyl-Salicylate was applied to the edges of the substrate to bond the sample to the sample holder. Phenyl-Salicylate melts at about 45°C, hardens within seconds when applied

* *This investigation was carried out while the author was with General Electric's Electronics Laboratory in Syracuse, New York.*

selectively. No difference was detected between the samples purchased with and without the metallization.

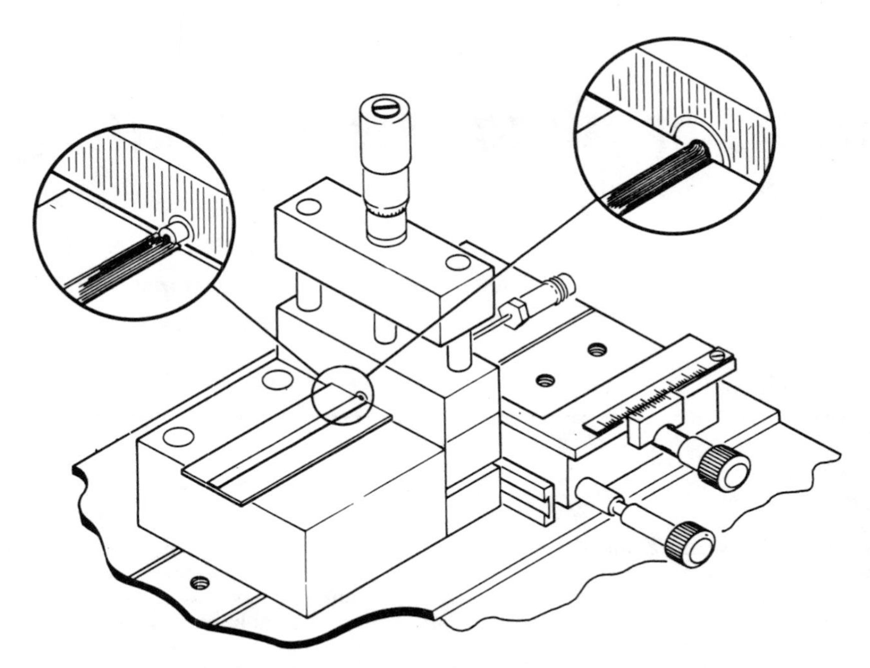

Fig. 1 — Fixture to test microstrip transmission lines.

to a material at room temperature and dissolves easily in acetone.

The test fixture shown in Fig. 1 was used for reflection type measurements with the microstrip ending in an open circuit. The standing wave ratio in this case for low loss microstrip lines, that is short and wide lines, was about 28 dB. This is approximately as high as the VSWR obtained with the coaxline ending as an open circuit (inner and outer conductor ending in one plane). This open circuit coax cable was used to determine reference nodes in slotted line measurements. The nodes and VSWR's obtained this way were compared with those obtained with a shorted coax line (a drop of solder put over the previously open line). The VSWR did not change (28 to 30 dB), the nodes moved by $\lambda/4$. The test was performed at six frequencies spaced equally between 4 and 18 GHz. Thus, the use of open circuits in these experiments was justified.

The test fixture was designed so that a second mechanical stage with cable could be added for transmission type experiments or to terminate the microstrip line in a coaxial load. Aluminum sample holders of different lengths were used to accommodate substrates of different length. To measure four-port devices (couplers) less versatile test fixtures were built. Whenever possible, miniature coaxial equipment was used (precision loads and slotted lines).

Preparation of Test Samples

A detailed description of the preparation of test samples is beyond the scope of this report. Suffice it to say that two approaches were used. One was to obtain alumina substrates (American Lava "Alsimag") with properties as shown in Table I, and to metallize these substrates in our laboratory. The second was to buy the metallized substrates. In any case, the metallization is only for conductive circuits a layer of nickel 50 micro-inches thick followed by 150 micro-inches gold. At 10 GHz the gold is about 5 skin depths thick. In the most recent tests the layer of nickel was made only about 2 micro-inches thick.

For circuits requiring resistances, the gold is deposited on top of a layer of nichrome and can be etched away

Table I

PROPERTIES OF AMERICAN LAVA's ALSIMAG 772*

Water Absorption	0	%
Specific Gravity	3.89	
Hardness	80	Rockwell 45N
Thermal Expansion	6.0×10^{-6}	at 25 - 300°C.
Linear Coefficient	7.5×10^{-6}	at 25 - 700°C.
Per °C	8.3×10^{-6}	at 25 - 1000°C.
Flexural Strength	50,000	lbs. per sq. in.
Dielectric Strength		
Specimen thickness .250″	220	Volts per mil
Specimen thickness .030″	500	
Dielectric Constant at 1 MHz	9.6	25°C.
Dissipation Factor at 1 MHz	0.0002	25°C.
Loss Factor at 1 MHz	0.0019	25°C.
Density	99.5	%
Surface finish, better than	10	micro inches

* According to American Lava's Bulletin 661

MEASUREMENT METHODS

Time Domain Reflectometry

The fastest and simplest way to determine impedances was to use time domain reflectometry (TDR). This method is amply described by vendors of this equipment (e.g. Tektronix, Hewlett-Packard). The Tektronix unit used has a source pulse rise time of 50 picoseconds, and a system rise time of 140 picoseconds, which means that in the spectrum making up the step function the amplitude at 3.9 GHz is 70% of the dc amplitude. Thus, the results measured are meaningful only up to about 4 GHz unless it can be shown that at all frequencies of interest the microstrip line propagates essentially a TEM mode with frequency-independent impedance and propagation-constant. This could be shown with slotted line measurements. The accuracy of the TDR measurements seems to be limited not by the frequency spectrum of the step function, but by the homogeneity of the reference line used and of the line under test. While the thickness of most substrates purchased varied by about 0.001 to 0.002 inches over a 1 inch by 1 inch substrate, some samples (which were rejected) varied by as much as 0.005 inch. The widths of the strips varied by less than 0.001 inch over the strip length. Since for most lines of interest this variation was less than 5% while the substrate thickness variation was also about 5%, no attempt was made to significantly reduce this width variation.

Transmission Type Measurements

To determine the microstrip line losses one could use several lines of different lengths but otherwise equal properties, and measure the variation in loss as a function of length differences. Since at the time the experiments were performed, no high directivity couplers with miniature connectors were available for the frequency range of interest, no such measurements were made. For the same reason, no bridge type measurements were made.

Reflection Type Measurements

The reflection coefficient was measured on a slotted line as a function of frequency. All samples were tested between 8 and 12.4 GHz. In many cases the test range was extended up to 18 GHz and down to 1 GHz. The frequency intervals were almost always 250 MHz. Several methods used were:

1) The microstrip line was terminated with a precision coaxial load and the VSWR was measured as a function of frequency. With Z_0 as the reference line impedance (50 ohms) the characteristic microstrip line impedance Z_ε is determined by

$$(Z_\varepsilon / Z_0)^{\pm 1} = \sqrt{\mathrm{VSWR}_{max} \cdot \mathrm{VSWR}_{min}} \qquad (1)$$

where the exponent +1 goes with high impedance lines, −1 with low impedance lines. Since the general behavior of Z_ε/Z_0 as a function of geometry was known from TDR measurements as well as from previous theoretical and experimental results, the question whether to use +1 or −1 never arose. The results confirmed the TDR measurements.

2) The complex reflection coefficient was measured for an open ended microstrip line as a function of frequency and plotted on a Smith chart. The resulting curves were somewhere between circles and spirals. In most cases the curves were not very well defined. Looking at the magnitude and the phase of the reflection coefficients separately, it appeared that the VSWR suffered most from parasitic reactive effects. The phase was what it should be if an ideal lossless line had been connected to the slotted line with only comparatively small phase shifts due to reactances in the plane of the junction. Consequently, this Smith-chart method gave only poor information on the line losses. A method was developed, however, to determine the characteristic line impedance as well as the propagation constant from the phase information — the nodal shift — only. This method is developed and its application demonstrated in a separate paper.[6] Suffice it to say here that the experimental results of this method were in good agreement with theory.

RESULTS

Impedances measured by different techniques are listed in Table II. It appears that the impedance values obtained with Time Domain Reflectometry are as accurate as any, and that propagation constants can most accurately be determined by nodal shift measurements. With $\beta_\varepsilon = \beta_0 \sqrt{\varepsilon'_{eff}}$ the propagation constant can be expressed in terms of an effective dielectric constant. Figs. 2 and 3 show the characteristic impedances and effective dielectric constants for alumina substrates as functions of the ratio linewidth/substrate height (w/h). Also shown in these figures are selected theoretical data obtained by Wheeler[3] and Green[4] with the bulk material dielectric constant as parameter. The theoretical effective dielectric constants in Fig. 3 have been obtained with Wheeler's expression

$$\varepsilon'_{eff} = 1 + q'' (\varepsilon' - 1)$$

The parameter ε' is the dielectric constant for the bulk material. The field form factor q'' is shown as a broken line in Fig. 3 as given by Wheeler. Thus one can calculate ε'_{eff} for ε'-values not shown in Fig. 3. Note the inverted scale for q''.

Whenever the effective dielectric constant in Fig. 3 is given as a point, it is frequency independent between 1 and 18 GHz. When given as a vertical line, it increases slowly with frequency. So far no pattern has been detected why in some cases the effective dielectric constant increases with frequency.

It seems that the accuracy of the measured data is limited by the tolerances with which the dimensions of the microstrip line (width, substrate height) can be measured and maintained constant (about ±3%), as well as by the accuracy with which the impedance of a reference line is known. Caulton et al.[2] give correction values for the line width yielding an "effective line width" slightly wider

Table II

IMPEDANCES MEASURED BY DIFFERENT METHODS

height in inch	width in inch	method / frequency in GHz	TDR	$\sqrt{S_{max} S_{min}}$	Smith chart	nodal-shift
0.025	0.025	8 - 11	52Ω		48Ω	
0.023	0.208	2 - 6	12.3Ω			12Ω
0.025	0.040	7 - 12	39Ω	38Ω		
0.025	0.015	7 - 12	65Ω	67Ω		

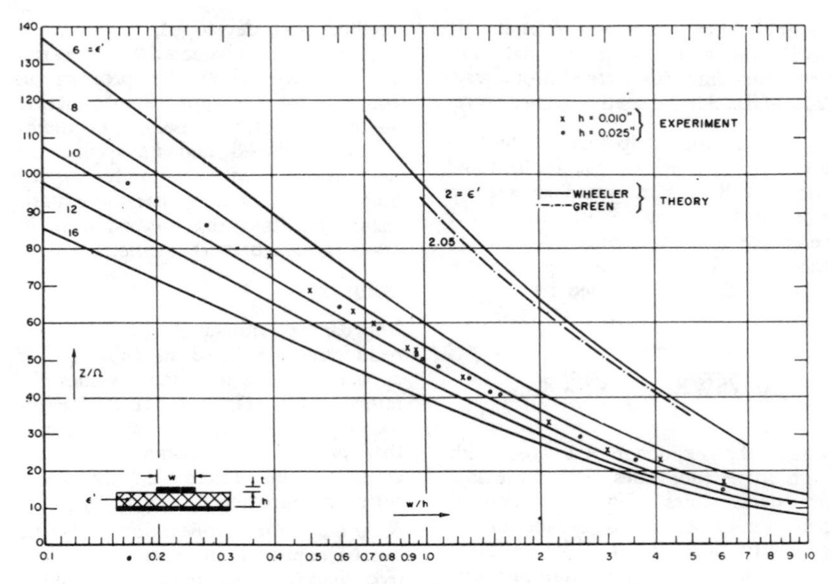

Fig. 2 — Impedances of microstrip transmission lines.

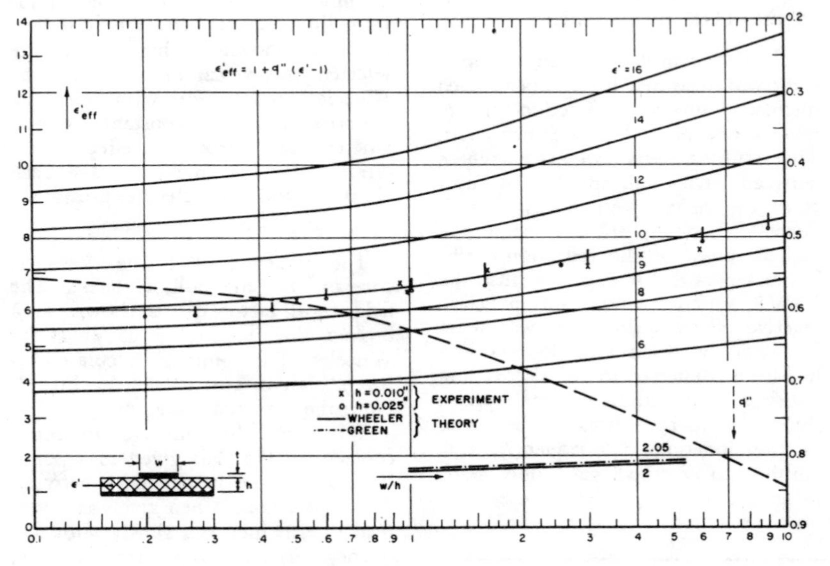

Fig. 3 — Effective dielectric constants for microstrip transmission lines.

than the actual one, the increase being the larger the thicker the metallized strip is. They discuss the applicability of these correction values. For the lines investigated these values were so small that they have been neglected.

CONCLUSIONS

Propagation characteristics for microstrip transmission lines have been measured for alumina substrates for a wide range of parameters. The experimental data agree fairly accurately with the theoretical results obtained with Wheeler's analysis.[3] It, therefore, appears that the theoretical results should be as accurate for other substrate materials.

The propagation characteristics of microstrip-transmission lines can be determined from nodal shift measurements only. The relation between characteristic impedances sought and nodal shifts measured is given in a separate publication.[6] The mode of propagation is very nearly TEM. Thus impedances can be determined by Time-Domain-Reflectometry.

ACKNOWLEDGMENT

All samples tested have been prepared by Messrs. J. Dietz and R. Hill. It is a pleasure to thank these colleagues for their cooperation.

REFERENCES

1. Hyltin, T. M., "Microstrip Transmission on Semiconductor Dielectrics", *IEEE Trans. on Microwave Theory and Techniques,* Vol. 13, November 1965, pp. 777-781.
2. Caulton, M., F. F. Hughes and H. Sobol, "Measurements on the Properties of Microstrip Transmission Lines for Microwave Integrated Circuits", *RCA Review,* Vol. 27, September 1966, pp. 377-391, and Vol. 27, December 1966, p. 645.
3. Wheeler, H. A., "Transmission Line Properties of Parallel Strips Separated by a Dielectric Sheet", *IEEE Trans. on Microwave Theory and Techniques,* Vol. 13, March 1965, pp. 172-185.
4. Green, H. E., "The Numerical Solution of Some Important Transmission-Line Problems", *IEEE Trans. on Microwave Theory and Techniques,* Vol. 13, September 1965, pp. 676-692.
5. Wolters, K. C. and P. L. Clar, "Microstrip Transmission Lines on High Dielectric Constant Substrates for Hybrid Microwave Integrated Circuits", IEEE International Microwave Symposium, Boston, Mass., May 1967, paper V-2.
6. Seckelmann, R., "Nodal Shift Measurements to Determine Transmission Line Properties", to be published.

MEASUREMENT OF THE EFFECTIVE RELATIVE PERMITTIVITY OF UNSHIELDED COPLANAR WAVEGUIDES

Indexing term: Microstrip

The dependence of the effective relative permittivity of coplanar waveguides is measured as a function of frequency in the frequency range from 3–12 GHz and is compared with the computed values.

The first publication by Wen[1] on the electrical characteristics of coplanar waveguides (c.p.w.) (Fig. 1) was followed by a series of further works, in which the computation of phase velocity and characteristic impedance was achieved from static, as well as dynamic, field formulations.[2-4] In the publication by Dupuis *et al.*,[5] the characteristic impedance was measured with time-domain reflectometry; however, as far as the author knows, there exist no published measured values on the phase velocity or effective relative permittivity of such lines. The qualification of static field formulations, however, is decisively dependent on the dispersion characteristics if such lines are used in the gigahertz range.

The dependence of the effective relative permittivity

$$\epsilon_{eff} = \left(\frac{\lambda_0}{\lambda}\right)^2 = \left(\frac{c_0}{f \cdot \lambda}\right)^2$$

on frequency f, where λ_0 is the free-space wavelength, λ is the wavelength on the c.p.w. and c_0 is the velocity of light, is shown in Figs. 2 and 3. It was measured with the help of straight open-circuit resonators on a 2 X 2 in alumina substrate ($\epsilon_r = 9{\cdot}8$). The end effects were compensated by halving the length of the resonator;[6] coupling capacitances were minimised by minimum coupling.

In Fig. 2, the conductor widths w and b (Fig. 1) of the curves 1–4 were kept constant and the slot width s was changed. The variations of the ratios w/h and b/h depend on different substrate thicknesses. For greater slot widths a gradual increase of ϵ_{eff} can be stated—similar to the behaviour of microstrip lines. The broken horizontal lines show the computed values of ϵ_{eff} found with static field formulations (subarea method) and which differ from the measured values at 4 GHz by less that 1·5%. The computer time was about 5 s (CDC 6600) with a maximum deviation of less than 1% from the exact static value.

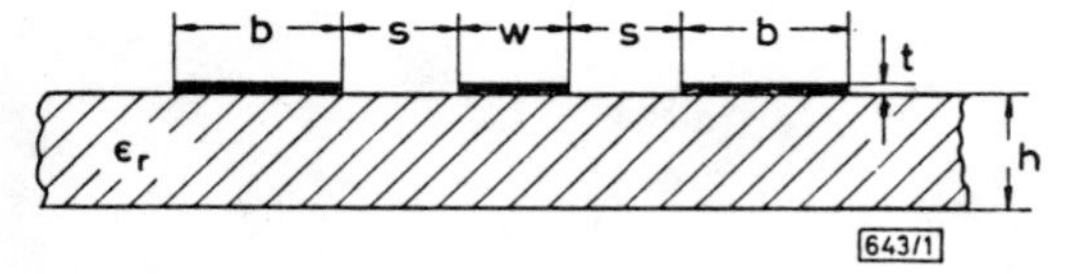

Fig. 1 *Coplanar waveguide*

As the broken curve 5 shows, the width of the outer conductor has no influence worth mentioning on the dispersion behaviour of the c.p.w., if the slot width and the inner conductor have appropriate dimensions. This curve is of further interest, however, because it allows a direct comparison with the theoretical dynamic solution of Knorr *et al.* (Reference 4, Fig. 8*a*). Contrary to the values given there, between 1 and 5 GHz ϵ_{eff} is nearly constaņt for $w/h = s/h = 1$.

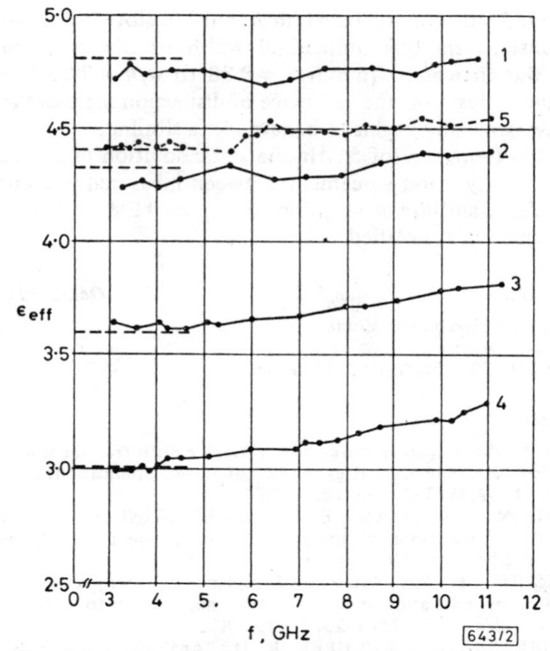

Fig. 2 *Effective relative permittivity ϵ_{eff} as function of frequency f*

(1) $w/h = 2{\cdot}04, b/h = 11{\cdot}64, s/h = 0{\cdot}15$
(2) $w/h = 1{\cdot}95, b/h = 11{\cdot}61, s/h = 0{\cdot}66$
(3) $w/h = 1{\cdot}85, b/h = 10{\cdot}93, s/h = 1{\cdot}80$
(4) $w/h = 1{\cdot}89, b/h = 11{\cdot}38, s/h = 3{\cdot}59$
(5) $w/h = 1{\cdot}00, b/h = 35{\cdot}00, s/h = 1{\cdot}09$
The thickness of the substrate ($\epsilon_r = 9{\cdot}8$) is about 0·65 mm

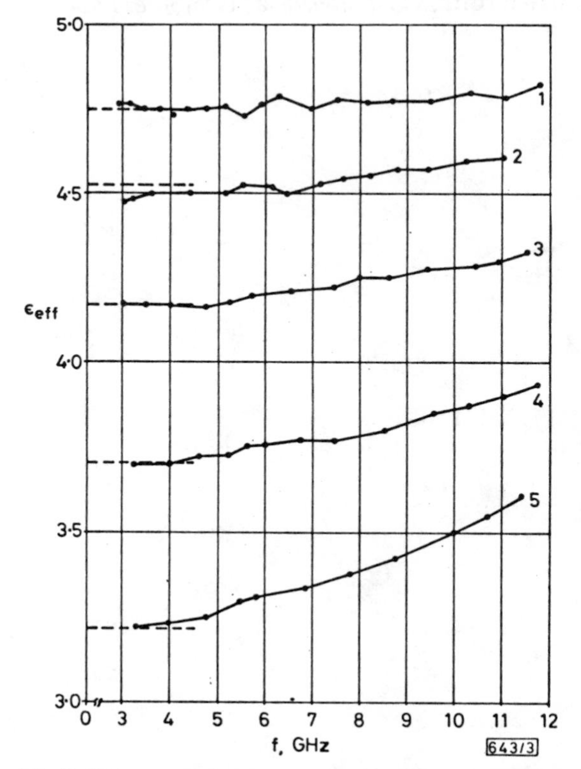

Fig. 3 *Effective relative permittivity ϵ_{eff} as function of frequency f*

(1) $w/h = 0{\cdot}37, b/h = 7{\cdot}75, s/h = 1{\cdot}03$
(2) $w/h = 0{\cdot}76, b/h = 7{\cdot}75, s/h = 1{\cdot}03$
(3) $w/h = 1{\cdot}55, b/h = 7{\cdot}80, s/h = 1{\cdot}03$
(4) $w/h = 3{\cdot}10, b/h = 7{\cdot}75, s/h = 1{\cdot}04$
(5) $w/h = 7{\cdot}70, b/h = 7.70, s/h = 1{\cdot}01$
The thickness of the substrate ($\epsilon_r = 9{\cdot}8$) is about 0·65 mm

In Fig. 3, the conductor width b and the slotwidth s were kept constant and the normalised width of the inner conductor was increased from $w/h = 0{\cdot}38$ to $w/h = 7{\cdot}70$. With increasing ratios w/h, the influence of dispersion increases and the c.p.w. gradually begins to behave like a slotline.

Up to a frequency of 5 GHz the static solution in any case leads to a very good agreement between measured and computed values, and the assumption of a quasi-TEM wave in this frequency range is justified.

E. MUELLER

Institut für Hochfrequenztechnik
Universität Stuttgart
Postfach 560, 7000 Stuttgart 1, W. Germany

25th October 1977

References

1 WEN, C. P.: 'Coplanar waveguide: a surface strip transmission line suitable for nonreciprocal gyromagnetic device applications', *IEEE Trans.*, 1969, **MTT-17**, pp. 1087–1090

2 DAVIS, M. E., WILLIAMS, E. W., and CELESTINI, A. C.: 'Finite-boundary corrections of the coplanar waveguide analysis', *ibid.*, 1973, **MTT-21**, pp. 594–596

3 HATSUDA, T.: 'Computation of coplanar-type strip-line characteristics by relaxation method and its application to microwave circuits', *ibid.*, 1975, **MTT-23**, pp. 795–802

4 KNORR, J. B., and KUCHLER, K. D.: 'Analysis of coupled slots and coplanar strips on dielectric substrate', *ibid.*, 1975, **MTT-23**, pp. 541–548

5 DUPUIS, P. A. J., and CAMPBELL, C. K.: 'Characteristic impedance of surface-strip coplanar waveguides', *Electron. Lett.*, 1973, **9**, pp. 354–355

6 DEUTSCH, J., and JUNG, H. J.: 'Measurement of the effective dielectric constant of microstrip lines in the frequency range from 2 GHz to 12 GHz', *Nachrichtentech. Z.*, 1970, pp. 620–624

A Quick Accurate Method to Measure the Dielectric Constant of Microwave Integrated-Circuit Substrates

JOHN Q. HOWELL

***Abstract*—A technique is described that makes possible the accurate measurement of the dielectric constant of microwave integrated-circuit substrates. The substrate is metallized on all sides, hence forming a tiny resonant cavity, and the resonant frequencies are determined either from transmission or reflection. The dielectric constant is then calculated to an accuracy of better than 1 percent.**

Manuscript received June 1, 1972; revised July 13, 1972.
The author is with the NASA Langley Research Center, Hampton, Va. 23365.

Introduction

Before microstrip circuits can be accurately designed, it is necessary to know the dielectric constant of the substrate material being used. This is particularly important when using alumina because of the wide variations encountered among different venders and even different orders from the same vender [1]. The technique described by Lenzing in [1] has the disadvantage that it requires specially prepared substrates and a specially constructed substrate holder. While this technique is very accurate, there is still need of a method that can be used in the laboratory to quickly measure the dielectric constant of a substrate upon which a microstrip circuit will be constructed. Napoli and Hughes [2] gave such a method, but its accuracy is questionable due to radiation losses. This short paper presents a variation of the Napoli–Hughes technique that is more accurate while still being easily and quickly implemented.

Technique

This technique, like Lenzing's, uses a substrate metallized on all sides so that a small microwave cavity is formed. Solving the cavity resonant-frequency equation for the dielectric constant one obtains

$$\epsilon = \frac{c^2}{4f_{pq}^2}\left\{\frac{p^2}{a^2} + \frac{q^2}{b^2}\right\} \tag{1}$$

where ϵ is the dielectric constant, c is the speed of light, a and b are the substrate dimensions, and f_{pq} is the cavity resonant frequency for the (p, q) mode. Napoli and Hughes suggested detecting the resonant frequencies by using either a network analyzer or a sweep generator and a crystal detector to measure the energy transmitted through the cavity as a function of frequency. Regardless of the equipment used the corners of the cavity should be cleared of the metallization and inserted in the ends of the APC-7 connectors as they suggested. It was also found that either male- or female-type N connectors could be similarly used. Peaks in the curve of transmission versus frequency as shown in Fig. 1 correspond to the resonant frequencies of the cavity, and from (1) the dielectric constant can be computed. Table I gives the measured and calculated data obtained for the two cases shown in Fig. 1. It is also possible to detect dips in the reflection from the cavity, but the transmission peaks are somewhat easier to observe.

Discussion

Referring to Fig. 1 and Table I a comparison can be made between the Napoli–Hughes technique and the method suggested in this short paper. Note that when using their technique the resulting Q's were much lower, indicating that the edges were radiating instead of being open circuits as they assumed. Hence the resonant frequencies are shifted and the calculated dielectric constants are lower and not as self-consistent as the results obtained using the method described here.

The substrate used to make the above comparison had open edges. The closed-edge measurements were made by painting the edges with silver conducting paint. It is very important to apply enough paint so that the conducting surface is several skin depths thick. Coupling holes were then provided by scraping the edges at opposite corners. It is also helpful to use tinfoil or small strips of metal to block alternate transmission paths on the outside surface of the cavity.

From (1) it is seen that the two sources of error are the frequency and length measurements. If the length is accurate to 0.1 percent, then it contributes 0.2-percent error to the dielectric constant. If a counter is used to measure frequency, the error in the resonant frequency will be mainly that caused by wall losses. If the Q is measured, the following correction can be made [3]:

$$f_0 = f_m \bigg/ \left(1 - \frac{1}{2Q}\right) \tag{2}$$

where f_m is the measured frequency and f_0 is the corrected frequency that should be used in (1) above. If the correction given by (2) is not made, the method described in this short paper results in error from this source of less than 0.4 percent. Hence, unless extremely accurate results are desired, it is not necessary to measure the Q of each resonance and apply (2) to correct the frequency.

In conclusion a simple technique is described that allows the microwave engineer to accurately and quickly measure the dielectric constant of a substrate that is later used for a microstrip circuit. This technique applies to any substrate material but is particularly useful when applied to alumina because of the wide variations of dielectric constants that are observed.

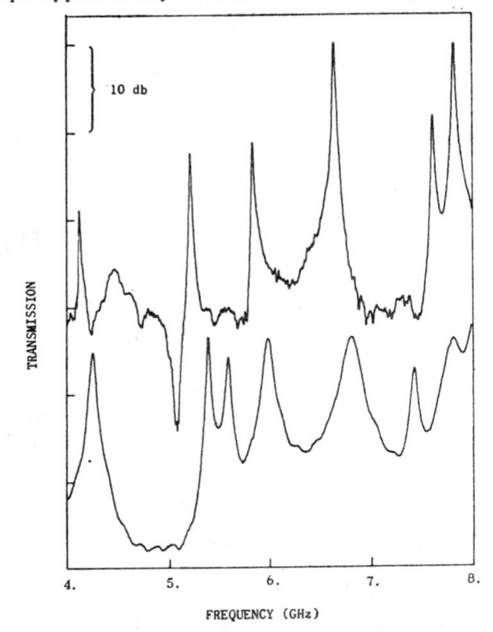

Fig. 1. Upper curve is the closed-edge cavity transmission using the technique suggested in the paper. Lower curve is the open-edge cavity transmission using the Napoli–Hughes technique. The same alumina substrate (0.994 in by 0.994 in by 0.025 in) was used for both curves.

TABLE I

Comparison of Q and Dielectric Constant for Open- and Closed-Edge Substrate Resonators

Mode Numbers (p,q)	Resonant Frequency GHz	Q	Dielectric Constant
Closed-Edge Substrate Resonator			
(2,1)	4.124	258	10.36
(2,2)	5.218	290	10.36
(3,1)	5.836	292	10.35
(2,3)	6.651	332	10.36
(1,4)	7.613	346	10.34
(3,3)	7.830	326	10.35
Open-Edged Substrate Resonator (Napoli–Hughes)			
(2,1)	4.230	88	9.85
(2,2)	5.392	154	9.70
(3,0)	5.576	133	10.20
(3,1)	5.972	73	9.88
(3,2)	6.803	63	9.90
(4,0)	7.438	114	10.19
(4,1)	7.768	55	9.93

References

[1] H. F. Lenzing, "Measurement of dielectric constant of ceramic substrates at microwave frequencies," presented at the Electronics Division, American Ceramic Society Meeting, Washington, D. C., May 10, 1972, Paper 41.
[2] L. S. Napoli and J. J. Hughes, "A simple technique for the accurate determination of the microwave dielectric constant for microwave integrated circuit substrates," *IEEE Trans. Microwave Theory Tech.* (Corresp.), vol. MTT-19, pp. 664–665, July 1971.
[3] R. E. Collin, *Foundations for Microwave Engineering.* New York: McGraw-Hill, 1966, pp. 354–355.

MEASUREMENTS ON THE PROPERTIES OF MICROSTRIP TRANSMISSION LINES FOR MICROWAVE INTEGRATED CIRCUITS

BY

M. CAULTON, J. J. HUGHES, AND H. SOBOL

RCA Laboratories
Princeton, N. J.

Summary—*The conformal mapping theories of Wheeler have been used to derive a set of design curves for microstrip transmission lines applicable over a wide range of geometries, frequencies, and substrate materials. Design data are presented for characteristic impedance, wave-length, attenuation, and circuit Q. A broadband in-line coaxial-to-microstrip transition has been developed. This transition is adaptable over a wide variety of substrate sizes and materials and is suitable for connection to microwave integrated circuits. The properties of microstrip lines at S-band were measured on alpha-alumina, sapphire, and polyolefin substrates. The agreement between the measured values and the design curves is good.*

INTRODUCTION

ADVANCES in microwave solid-state devices and materials technology have led to integrated microwave circuits. The transmission line, a basic element of microwave circuits, is required for matched interconnections, resonators, and filters, and as integral parts of phase shifters, isolators, and circulators. In general, fairly high unloaded Q (low-loss) lines are required for resonant circuits, while relatively high loss per unit length can be tolerated in interconnecting lines because of the very short distances between active elements in an integrated circuit.

In this paper we consider the microstrip transmission line shown in Figure 1. The insulating layer serves as the substrate for either monolithic or hybrid devices and can be a high-resistivity semiconductor or a low-loss ceramic dielectric. Microstrip lines on semiconducting substrates have been previously discussed[1] and the present paper is devoted primarily to a study of the line with a ceramic substrate.

The first extensive study of microstrip lines for propagation of

---

[1] T. M. Hyltin, "Microstrip Transmission on Semiconductor Dielectrics," *IEEE Trans. Microwave Theory and Techniques*, Vol. MTT-13, p. 777, Nov. 1965.

microwave energy was published nearly fifteen years ago.[2] Much of the earlier disagreement between theory and measurements appears to have been overcome by the recent work of Wheeler.[3,4] Since a significant part of the microwave energy is propagated in the fringe field, circuitry using the microstrip line suffers from cross-coupling difficulties and is also susceptible to detuning due to nearby metallic disturbances. The Triplate or Strip-line structure using two ground planes confines the fringe field, and has been used more extensively than the microstrip line for conventional microwave circuits. However, in integrated circuits, use of the microstrip line, which is nearly a planar structure, is

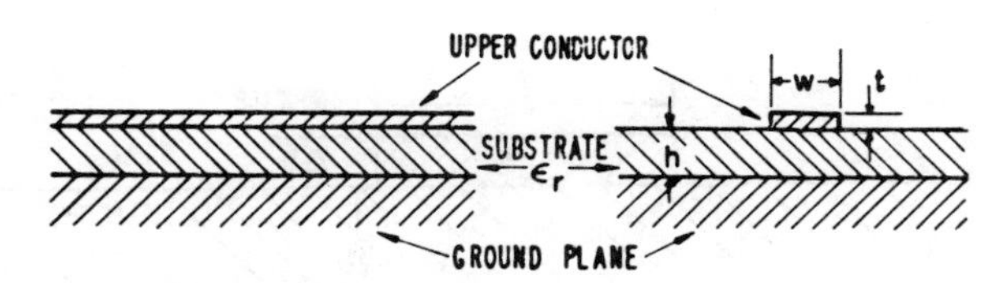

Fig. 1—Microstrip line.

more suitable. Most applications will require a metallic enclosure or packaging for hermetic sealing and strength, and this will confine the fringe field. If the distance from the conductor to the metallic enclosure is several (3 to 5) times the height of the insulating layer, the propagation characteristics are only slightly perturbed. The design data and experimental results presented below are for unshielded lines, and it may be necessary to make some slight corrections for the effects of the enclosure in an actual circuit.

Conventional microstrip lines are usually fabricated on standard Teflon impregnated fiberglass or polystyrene printed circuit boards 1/32 to 1/16 inch thick, and use copper lines of the order of 1/16 to 1/8 inch wide. For integrated circuits alumina, sapphire, beryllia, or high-resistivity semiconductors 10 to 30 mils thick are used as substrates for the lines. The conductors may be copper, aluminum, gold, or silver, and are of the order of 8 to 30 mils wide.

This paper presents a study of the properties of microstrip lines. Theoretical design data based on the work of Wheeler[3,4] are discussed first. A miniature coaxial-to-microstrip transition useful for a wide

---

[2] F. Assadourian and E. Rimai, "Simplified Theory of Microstrip Transmission Systems," Proc. IRE, Vol. 40, p. 1651, Dec. 1952.

[3] H. A. Wheeler, "Transmission-Line Properties of Parallel Wide Strips by a Conformal-Mapping Approximation," *IEEE Trans. Microwave Theory and Techniques*, Vol. MTT-12, p. 280, May 1964.

[4] H. A. Wheeler, "Transmission-Line Properties of Parallel Strips Separated by a Dielectric Sheet," IEEE Trans. *Microwave Theory and Techniques*, Vol. MTT-13, p. 172, March 1965.

range of substrate dimensions is then described, and, finally, measurements of lines for use in integrated circuits are presented and compared with the theory.

Theoretical Background

The microstrip line has not been amenable to an exact analysis, and until recently, reasonable predictions of characteristics over a wide range of impedances and dielectric characteristics were not available. Approximate analyses by Assadourian[2] and others[5] have provided useful design equations for impedances of less than 50 ohms

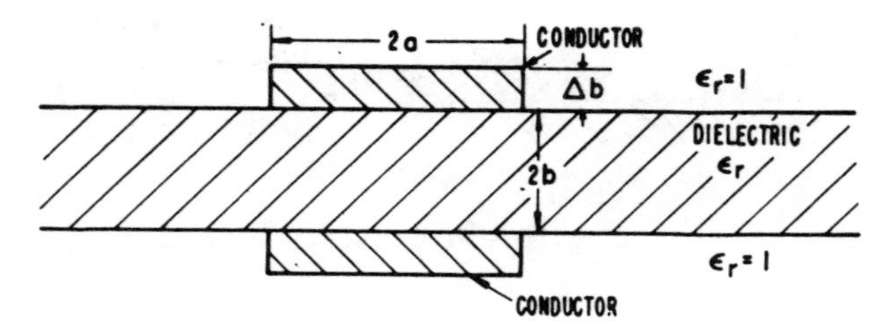

Fig. 2—Parallel plane geometry of Wheeler[3, 4] (equivalent to Figure 1 when $h \doteq b$, $2a = w$, $\Delta b = t$).

or for ratios of the width of the line w to height above the ground plane h (Figure 1) much greater than unity. Somewhat less accurate formulas have been found for impedance levels in excess of 50 ohms or $w/h \leq 1$. The main difficulty in obtaining a complete solution is that it is necessary to take into account the dielectric discontinuity at the insulator boundary, fringe fields, finite conductor sizes, and radiation losses. The approximate theories, which are based on TEM propagation, account for the fringing electrostatic fields, but neglect the dielectric discontinuity. In his more elaborate theory, Wu[6] purports to account for some of the above effects, but the theory has not been reduced to practical terms. The electrolytic tank studies of Dukes[5] are useful in obtaining some information on the phase velocity through a consideration of the "effective dielectric constant" of the line when both the fringe field propagating in air and the field propagating in the dielectric are accounted for. Recently Wheeler[3,4] has published a conformal mapping analysis of TEM propagation that does account for the dielectric discontinuity. Wheeler's calculations are for the parallel-plane waveguide shown in Figure 2, but, with a simple transformation,

---

[5] J. M. C. Dukes, "An Investigation Into Some Fundamental Properties of Strip Transmission Lines With the Aid of an Electrolytic Tank," *Proc. IEE* (London), Vol. 103B, p. 319, 1956.

[6] T. T. Wu, "Theory of the Microstrip," *Jour. Appl. Phys.*, Vol. 28, p. 299, 1957.

the results are applicable to the microstrip line. The dimensions of Wheeler's parallel-plane guide in Figure 2 apply to the microstrip line of Figure 1 with $2a = w$, $b = h$. The wavelength of the parallel-plane guide is equal to that of the microstrip, and the impedance of the microstrip is one-half the impedance of the parallel-plane guide. It will be shown that Wheeler's results show fairly good correlation with

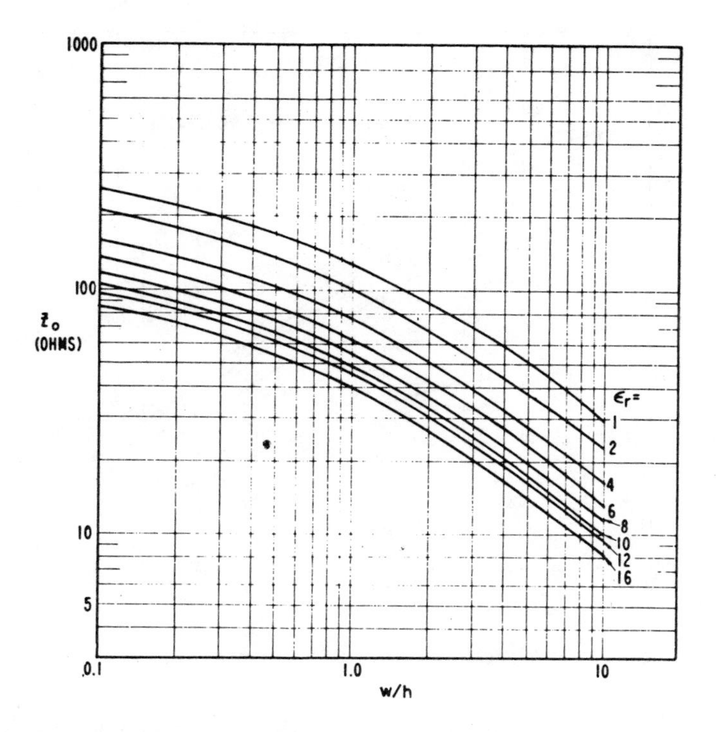

Fig. 3—Calculated characteristic impedance Z_0 of microstrip lines as a function of w/h and ϵ_r.

experiment for all lines, including those with w/h ratios less than unity and impedances in excess of 50 ohms. The above transformations were applied to Wheeler's results, and the characteristic impedance Z_0 and wavelength λ were calculated for a zero-thickness conductor and an infinitely wide ground plane. The characteristic impedance as a function of w/h is plotted in Figure 3. The wavelength λ normalized to that of a microstrip line completely imbedded in a dielectric (λ_{TEM}) is shown in Figure 4.

Since the first-order effect of a line of finite thickness t is to increase the capacitance, an approximate correction can be made by using an effective width,

$$w_{eff} = w + \Delta w \qquad (1)$$

where

$$\Delta w = \frac{t}{\pi}\left(\ln\frac{2h}{t} + 1\right) \tag{2}$$

for $w/2 > h/(4\pi) > t$. The correction factor Δw can be derived from the low-impedance closed-form approximations or from the theory of

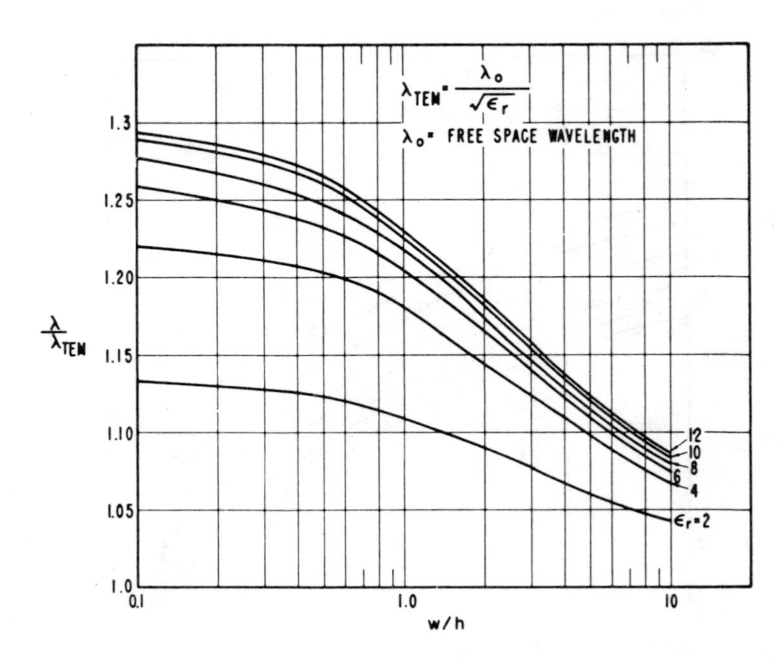

Fig. 4—Calculated normalized wavelength as a function of w/h and ϵ_r.

Wheeler. The value of the correction $\Delta w/t$ is plotted for various h/t ratios in Figure 5. The effective width should be used when applying the design curves. Wheeler cautions regarding the effectiveness of this edge correction for high-dielectric-constant media, since $\Delta w \rightarrow 0$ for $\epsilon >> \epsilon_0$. However, Equation (2) should be regarded as a limit correction for lines where the fringe fields make up an appreciable part of the total fields, a condition that applies for the lines studied in this paper.

The loss per unit length of a line may be expressed as

$$\alpha = \alpha_{c1} + \alpha_{c2} + \alpha_d = \frac{r_1 + r_2}{2Z_0} + \frac{gZ_0}{2}, \tag{3}$$

where

α_{c1} is the loss in the conductor in nepers/meter,

α_{c2} is the loss in the ground plane in nepers/meter,

α_d is the dielectric losses in nepers/meter.

r_1 and r_2 are the effective series resistance per meter of the conductor and ground plane, respectively, and

g is an effective conductance representing the total dielectric losses in mhos per meter.

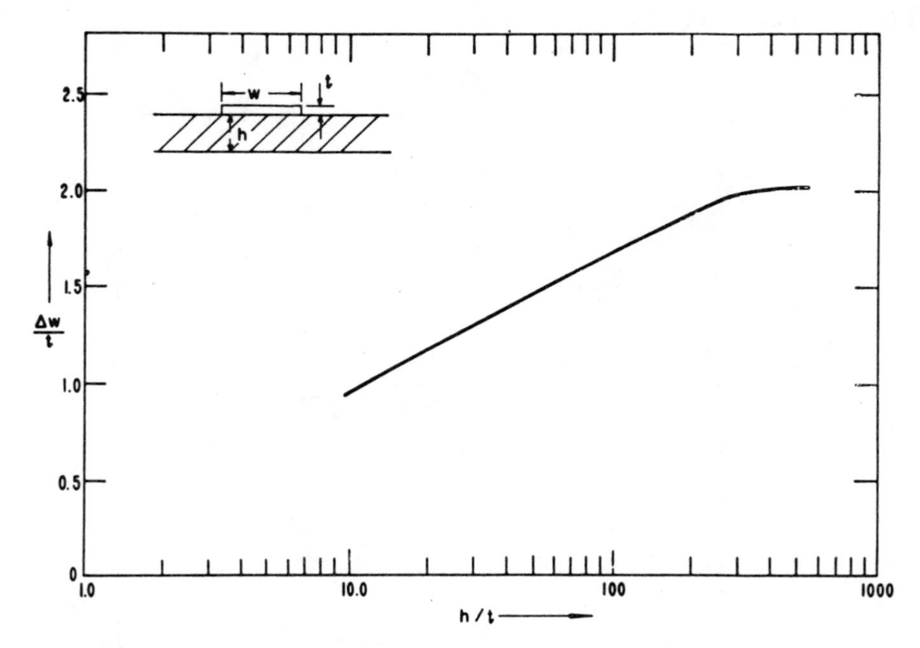

Fig. 5—Line-width correction for finite-thickness substrates.

The conductor losses $\alpha_c = \alpha_{c1} + \alpha_{c2}$ can be calculated approximately assuming a uniform current across the width of the conductor and also assuming that the ground-plane current is distributed uniformly under the conductor. Subject to these approximations, the conductor loss is

$$\alpha_c = \alpha_{c1} + \alpha_{c2} = \frac{\sqrt{\pi f \mu}}{2Z_o w}\left(\frac{1}{\sqrt{\sigma_{c1}}} + \frac{1}{\sqrt{\sigma_{c2}}}\right), \tag{4}$$

or

$$\alpha_c = \frac{R_{s1} + R_{s2}}{2Z_0 w}, \tag{5}$$

where σ_c is the conductivity in mhos per meter and R_s is the surface resistivity in ohms per square. A normalized conductor attenuation may be calculated using the impedance data presented in Figure 3.

Figure 6 shows curves of the conductor attenuation α_c in db per meter normalized as shown on the figure for a wide range of parameters. The dielectric loss α_d is independent of geometery and is given as

$$\alpha_d = \frac{gZ_0}{2} = \frac{\omega}{2}\left(\frac{\mu}{\epsilon'}\right)^{\frac{1}{2}} \frac{\epsilon''}{\epsilon'}\epsilon', \tag{6}$$

where ϵ' is the real part of the permittivity of the dielectric and ϵ'' is the imaginary part of the permittivity.

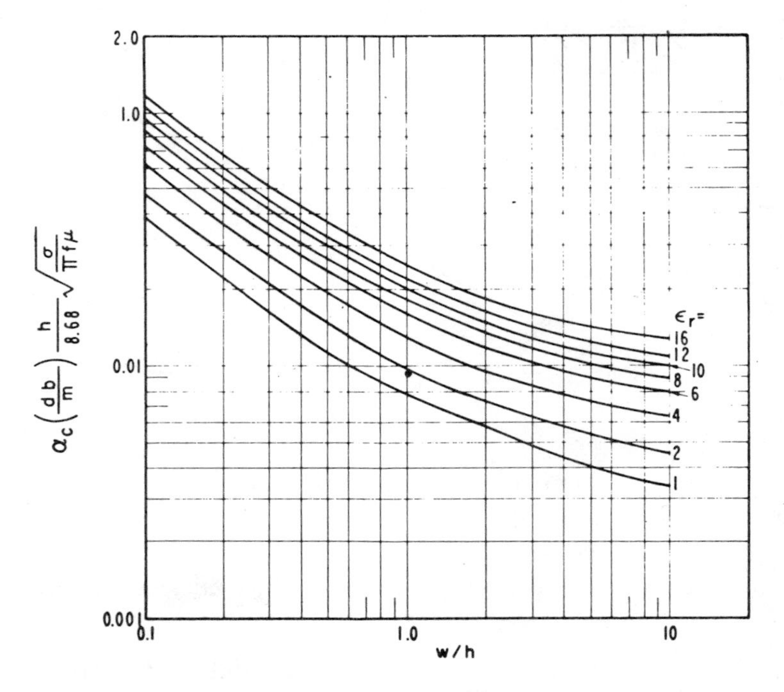

Fig. 6—Calculated normalized conductor loss as function of geometry · w/h and ϵ_r (MKS units).

As an estimate of the performance of the microstrip line in circuit applications, consider a $\lambda/4$ shorted resonator. The unloaded Q of the resonator can be expressed as

$$\frac{1}{Q} = \frac{1}{Q_c} + \frac{1}{Q_d}, \tag{7}$$

where Q_c is the quality factor of the conductors and Q_d is the quality factor of the dielectric.

Q_c for the case of the conductor and ground plane fabricated from the same material is

$$Q_c = \frac{\omega_0 Z_0^2 C}{r_s}, \tag{8}$$

where ω_0 is the resonant frequency, C is the capacitance per unit length, and r_s is the total series conductor loss per unit length. Q_c can be expressed in normalized form as

$$\frac{Q_c}{h\sqrt{f_{GHz}}} \frac{6}{\sqrt{\sigma_c}} = \frac{\lambda_{TEM}}{\lambda} \frac{w}{h} Z_o\sqrt{\epsilon_r}. \tag{9}$$

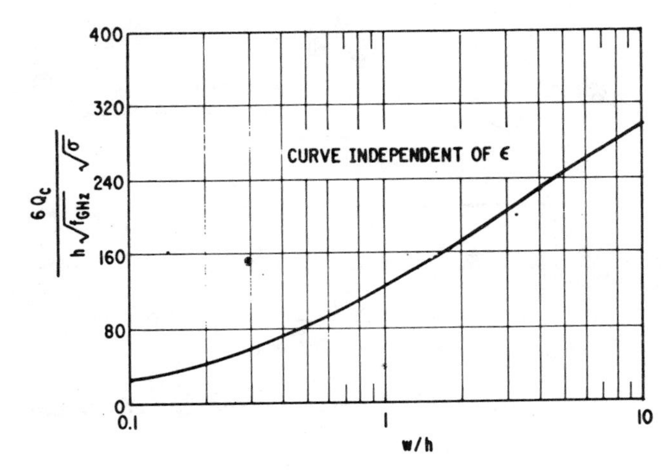

Fig. 7—Calculated normalized Q_c as function of w/h (MKS units).

The results of Figures 3 and 4 may be used to calculate the normalized conductor Q_c presented in Equation (9). This is plotted in Figure 7. The dielectric quality factor is the ordinary Q value of the material used.

The design data given above apply to microstrip lines in general. Application of the results applied to microstrip lines of the sizes used for typical integrated-circuit applications is discussed later.

Coaxial-to-Microstrip Transition

The standard input and output connector of most microwave equipment (X-band and lower) is coaxial. It is necessary, therefore, to use a transition from the substrate circuitry to the external coaxial equipment. For testing and application of integrated microwave circuits, it is desirable to have a small inexpensive broad-band transition that is easy to connect and can accommodate a wide range of substrates, line sizes, and materials.

The transition from a coaxial line to a microstrip line can be either the "in-line" type, where the coaxial axis is parallel to the plane of the microstrip line, or the "right-angle" type, where the axes are perpendicular. The right-angle type has been used in standard-size commercial equipment but requires the insertion of a pin through the ground

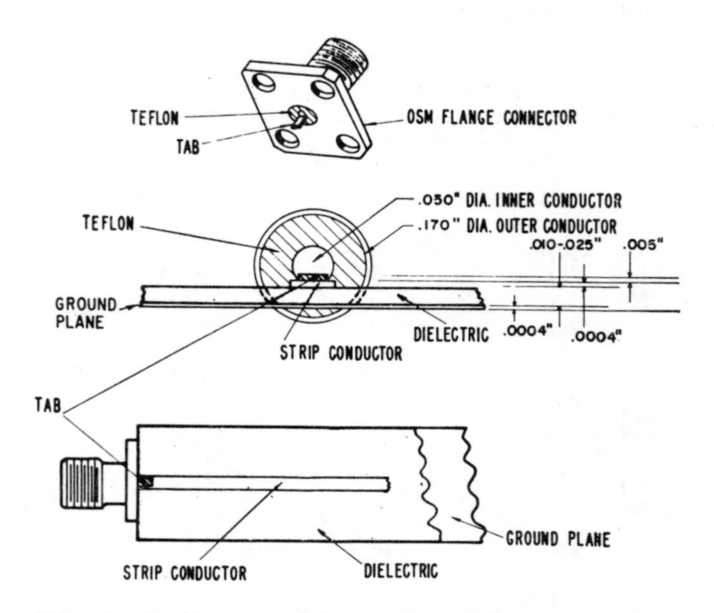

Fig. 8—In-line coaxial-to-microstrip transition.

plane and insulator and, in general, does not satisfy the requirements for a versatile and inexpensive transition. The in-line transition, on the other hand, can satisfy these requirements and was used in the work reported below. It is illustrated in Figure 8. The coaxial connector used is in the miniature 50-ohm OSM* series and is suitable for use with integrated circuits over a wide frequency band. This transition is simple to design when the coaxial center-pin diameter is of the order of the line width, as is the case for substrates with thicker dielectrics and lower ϵ_r. On the other hand, for thin substrates where the thickness is much less than the distance between the inner and outer coaxial conductor, a capacitive discontinuity can exist. If this discontinuity is large enough to warrant tuning, a limited bandwidth will result.

The thicker dielectric and lower ϵ_r is typified by a copper-clad circuit board of Polyguide† ($\epsilon_r = 2.32$). Here a line width of the order of the diameter of the OSM center conductor (0.050 inch) is required for a 50-ohm line ($w/h \cong 2.8$). A reasonable match with a minimum

* Trademark of Omni-Spectra.
† Tradename.

capacitive discontinuity is obtained simply by extending the center pin over the microstrip line on the substrate.

Microwave integrated circuits usually have thin high-dielectric-constant substrates. In the tests reported here alumina ($\epsilon_r = 9.0$), alpha-alumina (polycrystalline sapphire, $\epsilon_r = 9.9$), and sapphire with $\epsilon_r = 9.35$, 11.7 were used. For thicknesses of 0.010 to 0.015 inch the line width is of the order of the thickness; the 0.050-inch-diameter center pin of the OSM connector will form a capacitive discontinuity.

Hyltin[1] tapers the coaxial line until the center pin is of the order of the line width. It is possible to avoid this tapered section by shearing

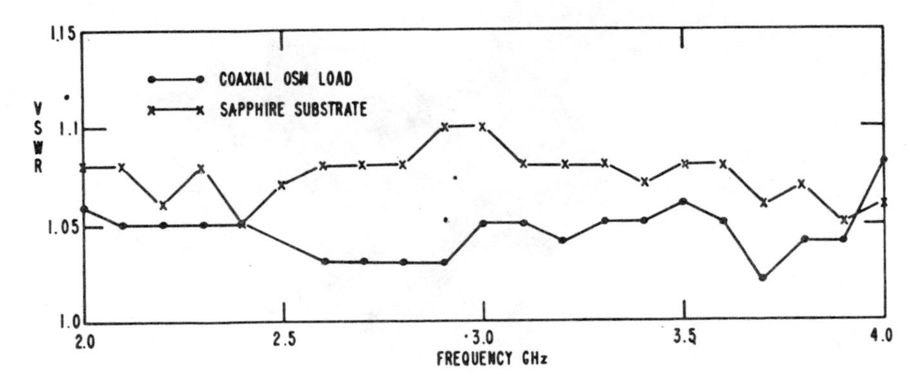

Fig. 9—VSWR as a function of frequency (GHz) for in-line transition.

the pin flush with the end of the coaxial connector and fastening on the end of the pin a thin metal strip that overlaps the microstrip line, as shown in Figure 8. The width of the strip or tab is equal to or less than the width of the strip conductor. This junction results in a capacitance discontinuity, but calculations show that this is less than 0.01 pf. Measured values of the VSWR over S-band are less than 1.1 for a w/h of 0.8 to 1.0 on a 10-mil substrate of alpha-alumina for this transition (Figure 9). Low VSWR's were measured from L-band to X-band. At 10 GHz the VSWR was as high as 1.2. However, the line did not extend to the end of the substrate, with the result that a tab smaller than the line presented a series inductive discontinuity. This could have been removed by more carefully adjusting the size of tab on the line or by extending the line to the edge of the substrate. A photograph of a transition jig that quickly attaches to various size substrates is shown in Figure 10.

The same transition was used successfully on the larger size lines ($\cong$ 0.050 inch) constructed on Polyguide of 0.022-inch thickness; the VSWR, while not quite as good, is under 1.15). The 0.050-inch center conductor extending over the microstrip line gave comparable matches to the tab. This would be expected, since the diameter of the center conductor and the Stripline width are now close in size.

It is concluded that this simple in-line coaxial-to-microstrip transition is suitable over a wide range of frequencies and for a wide variety of substrates.

Fig. 10—Photograph of coaxial-to-microstrip transition (microstrip transmission line on ceramic substrate attached).

Properties of Microstrip Lines on Substrates

With the establishment of a satisfactory transition, three properties of microstrip lines were measured: (1) characteristic impedance Z_0, (2) wavelength λ, and (3) the attenuation α.

Determination of Z_0

Three different substrate materials were used for measurements of Z_0. These were Polyguide ($\epsilon_r = 2.32$, $h = .022$ inch), alpha-alumina (GE Lucalox†, $\epsilon_r = 9.9$, $h = 0.10$ inch), and sapphire with two orientations of the C axis. The sapphire substrate with the C-axis at an angle of 33° from the plane of the substrate has an effective ϵ_r calculated to be 9.9 for TEM propagation, while for a C-axis in the plane of the substrate the ϵ_r is stated in the literature to be 9.35.

The measurements of Z_0 were made by determining the VSWR using a GR900 slotted line. This method gives only approximate re-

† Tradename.

Table I—Z_0 as a Function of Line Width w and Substrate Thickness h

Material	h (inches)	t (inches)	w (inches)	w/h	$\sqrt{VSWR_{MAX}}$	Z_0 (ohms)
Polyguide	.022	.0010	.0495	2.23	1.13	56.4
$\epsilon_r = 2.32$			.0540	2.44	1.09	54.6
			.0585	2.68	1.06	53.1
			.0640	2.90	1.11	45.4
			.0695	3.13	1.15	44.0
			.0735	3.36	1.19	42.4
Alpha-alumina	.010	.0002	.0067	.67	1.11	55.6
$\epsilon_r = 9.9$			.0077	.77	*	50.0
			.0087	.87	*	50.0
			.0097	.97	1.09	46.5
			.045	4.5	2.61	19.1
Sapphire	.0158	.0002	.0104	.66	1.16	58.1
$\epsilon_r = 9.9$			.0125	.74	*	50.0
			.0136	.86	*	50.0
			.0158	1.0	1.10	46.2
Sapphire	.0095	.0004	.0066	.695	1.17	58.6
$\epsilon_r = 9.35$			.0085	.895	1.06	53.0
			.0087	.915	†	50.0
			.0095	1.0	†	50.0
			.0110	1.155	1.11	45.0
			.0140	1.47	1.23	40.5
			.0155	1.63	1.30	38.0
			.0404	4.25	2.47	20.6

* VSWR < 1.09

† VSWR < 1.10

sults. Our accuracy in S-band for 50 ohms is of the order of ±2.5 ohms. The VSWR as a function of frequency showed long-line characteristics giving VSWR maxima and low minima at appropriate frequencies across the band. The Z_0 was then calculated as 50 ohms divided or multiplied by the geometric mean of these values, which was close to the square root of the maximum VSWR. The results for various substrates and line widths are shown in Table I.

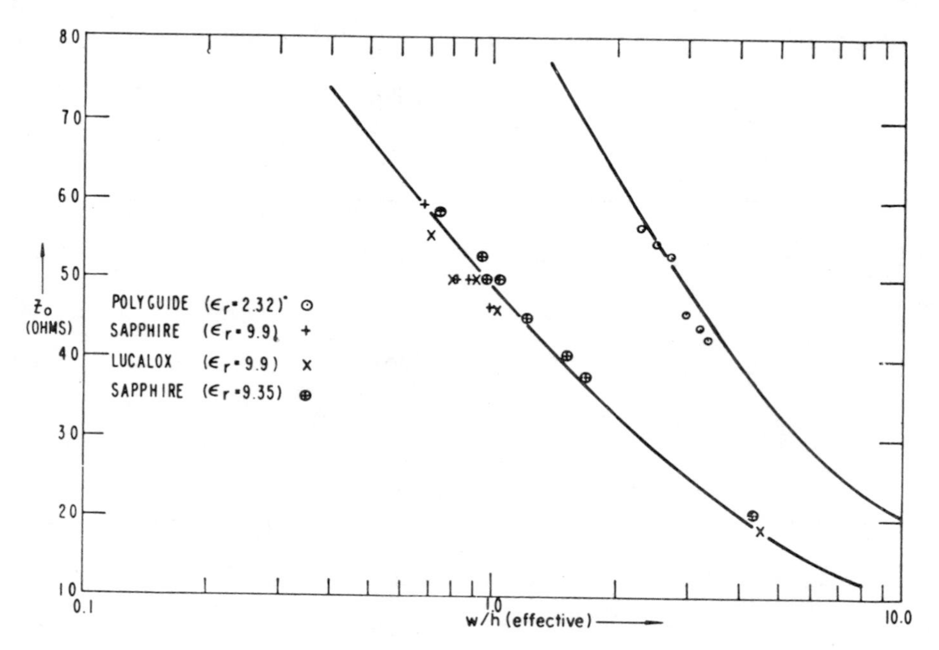

Fig. 11—Characteristic impedance Z_0 as a function of w/h of microstrip line.

Figure 11 shows curves (Z_0 versus w/h) extracted from Figure 3 for the values of ϵ_r used in our measurements. The appropriate w/h correction, as discussed earlier is made. Thus $w_{eff} = w_{measured} + \Delta w$, where Δw is computed from Figure 5. This correction may be a limit, but the fringe fields still make up an appreciable part of the total field, and it is expected that Figure 5 should give a valid correction.

The w/h of Table I are modified to w_{eff}/h and are plotted in Figure 11. It is apparent that the adjusted values agree reasonably well with the theory of Wheeler.

Determination of λ

The values of λ for typical values of w/h have been measured on samples of both the sapphire and Polyguide substrates. The wavelength was determined by measuring the change in position of minima as the distance to either an open or a short circuit was varied. In Figure 12 the values for some sample measurements of λ are compared with curves extracted from the data of Figure 4. The errors in these measurements overlay the solid curves, and it is again concluded that the theory predicts the measured wavelength reasonably well.

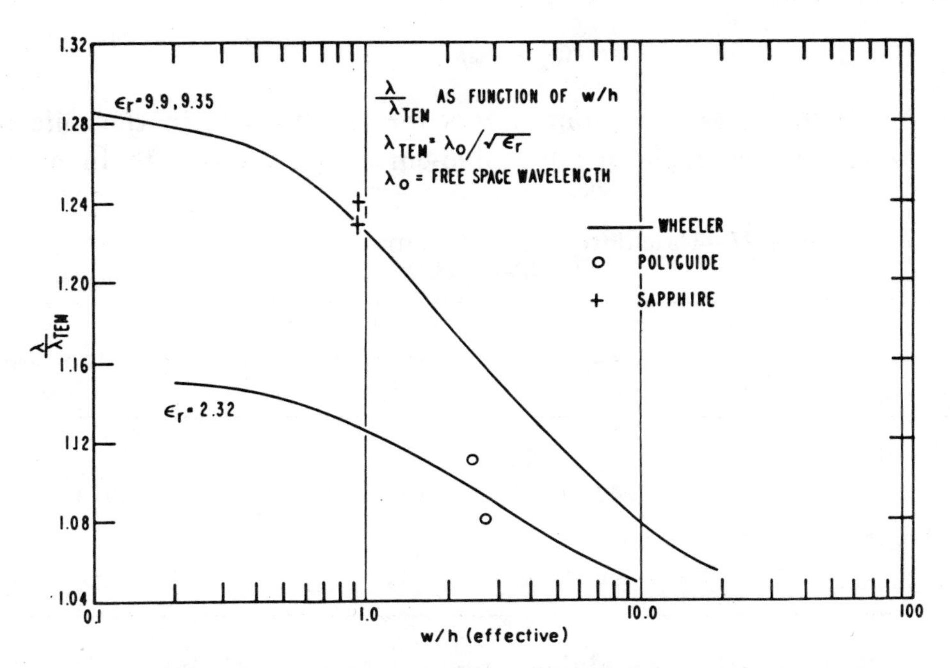

Fig. 12—Normalized wavelength as function of w/h of microstrip line.

Determination of α

The attenuation was determined by measuring the VSWR when the line was terminated by an open or short circuit. A good transition was assured by checking the VSWR for a well-matched line. Two methods of measuring the attenuation of the line were used. In one case the attenuation was measured for open- or short-circuited lines of varying lengths. The change in attenuation removes the effect of residual losses in the measuring system. A second method involved measuring the losses in the residual connectors and subtracting this from the total attentuation measured. The two methods gave reasonable agreement.

Table II gives the results of the loss measurements for sapphire and Polyguide substrates. The values of attenuation calculated from Figure 6 are also shown. The agreement between theory and measurement is considered well within the experimental error. The Q of quarter-wavelength resonators using these lines is calculated to be 58 and 87, respectively. The main loss mechanism here is the conductor loss; the dielectric loss is negligible. To obtain a higher Q, it is necessary to use thicker substrates. For example, an X-band resonator on a 25-mil-thick sapphire substrate has a theoretical Q of 285.

The dielectric loss plays a more important role in circuit Q when using high-resistivity silicon as a substrate. The substrate or "dielectric" Q is given as

$$Q_d = \omega\epsilon\rho \tag{10}$$

At low frequencies the primary loss for the lines is in the silicon substrate. As an example, a 2000 ohm-cm substrate results in a Q_d

Table II—Calculated and Measured Attenuation ($f = 2.25$ GHz)

Material	$\frac{w_{eff}}{h}$	Measured Loss (db/cm)	Calculated Loss (db/cm)
Polyguide			
$\epsilon_r = 2.32$	2.44	.015 ± .005	.013
Sapphire			
$\epsilon_r = 9.35$	.93	.08 ± .02	.074

of about 25 at 2 GHz. At higher frequencies the loss terms for the conductor and substrates are more nearly equal. With gallium arsenide of extremely high resistivity, on the other hand, a circuit Q comparable to that of ceramic substrates can be obtained.

Conclusions

A simple wide-band in-line microwave coaxial-to-microstrip transition proved very effective in studying microstrip transmission lines for integrated circuits.

Calculations based on Wheeler's theory were consistent with measurements of characteristic impedance, wavelength, and attenuation on sapphire, high-purity alumina, and Polyguide substrates. A set of design curves for use with microstrip transmission lines has been extracted from Wheeler's theory. It is expected that these can be used for the design of microstrip lines with reasonable accuracy.

Acknowledgment

The assistance of R. E. Chamberlain in the preparation of substrates is gratefully acknowledged.

Microwave Wafer Probing

Dale E. Carlton, K. Reed Gleason and **Eric W. Strid**
Cascade Microtech, Inc.
Beaverton, OR

Introduction

The advancement of all technology has its roots in the construction of tools to measure and quantify the world around us. Measuring distance, time and mass is the basis for change and improvement. Being able to directly measure the quantities of importance to us has a direct bearing on understanding and controlling those quantities. The microwave wafer probing described in this article is one of those advancements in measurement capability that will open new paths for the advancement of microwave semiconductor technology.

A major problem in the fast-paced microwave semiconductor industry today is achieving timely development of new microwave semiconductor processes and devices. The advancement of high-speed integrated circuit processes and devices is hampered by an inability to measure high frequency effects and model them. Without microwave wafer probing, devices first must be packaged and fixtured in order to measure their performance. Then bond wires, package, and fixture effects must be sifted out to determine the chip performance. Furthermore, dicing up the wafer destroys the positional relationship of device performance, and much valuable information is lost. This makes process evaluation difficult because process and device design effects, in most cases, cannot be separated from package and fixture effects.

Microwave wafer probing allows immediate middle- and post-processing measurement of actual device specifications and element parameters. There is also the added benefit in wafer mapping of those parameters to ferret out process and material related variations.

Wafer Probing for Microwave Circuit Design

Circuit element models, used to predict overall circuit performance, are only rough approximations because accurate microwave measurements cannot be made to verify and improve the design models. The measured performance of bonded dice is inaccurate due to bond wires, packaging and fixturing. Without microwave wafer probing the inability to get good data and process correlated data causes many costly process alterations and costly, time consuming device design turnarounds in order to achieve the desired results.

Production & Test

Once in production, spot checking of a few packaged devices has traditionally qualified entire batches of parts and provided monitoring of the process. Wide specification ranges are required to achieve acceptable yields, and lower quality levels sometimes result. Consequently, the investment in process design and equipment cannot realize its full value.

A significant barrier to the economical production of high speed digital and monolithic microwave integrated circuits is production testing. Complex device specifications and expensive packages require device testing "on wafer" at the specified device signal speeds. Until wafer probes were developed, high-speed device and integrated circuit performance improvements were slow to come and very costly. Process monitoring measurements indirectly indicated process "control" to consistently achieve the RF device performance of the end product. Microwave wafer probing can provide access to the measurements necessary to achieve production objectives.

Wafer Probe to get the Needed Measurements

Microwave wafer probing improves the development and production process by replacing the costly packaging and fixturing alternative and provides a means to acquire process information previously unavailable. The microwave wafer probing is a key ingredient to economical development and production of advanced high speed silicon and gallium arsenide integrated circuits and devices.

Either monolithic microwave circuits or ultra-high-speed digital circuits require precise knowledge of monolithic circuit element parameters and their variations and parasitics. The complex nature of some of these elements and their interactions has precluded accurate theoretical prediction or even scale modeling. Microwave wafer probes have been shown to be an accurate and convenient tool for the detailed network analysis of monolithic elements.[1,2] A wafer probe can be viewed as an adapter from coax to bonding pads, and as such will perturb microwave measurements in the same fashion that coaxial adapters affect measurements. Microwave wafer probes use the very same calibration procedures as coaxial interface calibrations.

Demonstrated microwave wafer probes allow uncorrected measurement accuracies similar to the accuracies achieved with SMA connectors. However, the combination of microwave probes with a corrected network analyzer and on-wafer impedance standards, which are much smaller than a wavelength, allows on-wafer S-parameter measurements with a new level of accuracy and unmatched repeatability and resolution.

Probe Requirements

There are three classes of signal degradations which an adapter such as a wafer probe can cause: losses, reflections, and crosstalk. When using a probe or adapter with a corrected network analyzer, the tolerable level of losses or reflections is relatively high: the only limit is maintaining sufficient signal level for good signal-to-noise ratio.

However, the losses and reflections must be as repeatable as the resolution desired. If significant signal power is radiated from the probe(s), the probe losses are normally not repeatable. This is because the wafer, wafer chuck, or other conductors are moved in relation to the probes, causing changes in the radiation impedance. Radiation from one line to another can also occur, creating crosstalk.

For two-port calibrations, the standard 12-element vector correction model[13] includes a leakage correction element for each direction, but the ability of this element to correct for crosstalk is very limited.[1] In practice, it has been found that limiting crosstalk between probe lines is simpler and more accurate than attempting to correct for it. Crosstalk can be caused by either coupling between transmission lines on the probe(s) or common-lead inductances. Since the crosstalk is uncorrected, even in a corrected measurement any crosstalk will appear in low-level transmission measurements. The allowable crosstalk level is approximately equal to the required transmission accuracy. Demonstrated pairs of single-line microwave probes achieve greater than 45-dB isolation through 18 GHz. Two-line probes with a signal-ground-signal contact configuration achieve a worst-case isolation of only about 20 dB through 18 GHz. This is due to the common-lead inductance of the ground contact (about 50 pH), the worst case being when all the contacts are shorted together.

On-Wafer Calibrations

A "two-tier" de-embedding approach[4] is possible, wherein the probe parameters are measured and stored for removal from parameters measured from a coax calibration. However, since the probe contact to the standards on the impedance standard substrate (ISS) is faster and more repeatable than making coax connections, two-tier de-embedding is a waste of time and accuracy. Therefore, the preferred approach in calibration is to use the on-wafer standards to calibrate directly at the probe tip(s) ("one-tier" de-embedding).

The wafer probe adapts from a coaxial transmission medium to essentially twinstrip or coplanar waveguide or other coplanar lines on the wafer surface. However, since the dimensions of many monolithic structures for ICs and for impedance standards are small with respect to a wavelength, these on-wafer structures are lumped in nature. The impedance standards for both one-port and two-port calibrations are analyzed for accuracy using theoretical predictions of parasitics, measurement at low frequency, comparison to other standards, and scale modeling. As with any standard, the verification of its accuracy is related to mathematical modeling of non-ideal characteristics such as simple physical structures and fundamental properties. Fortunately, the microwave wafer probe standards are very small in size and their non-idealness is correspondingly small.

Impedance standards have been built on GaAs, Si and alumina. The GaAs and alumina calibrations perform very similarly, while the Si calibrations show significantly more capacitance to the substrate, as expected.

The type of calibration standards used must correspond to the contact configuration of the probe(s). For simplicity, the standards for the probes shown in Figure 1[1,2] will be considered first. Generally, narrower contact spacings allow slightly more accurate calibration; bond pads as small as

50 μm wide on 100 μm centers are readily used.

One-Port Calibrations

Figure 2 shows the minimal set of two-port calibrations for the probes in Figure 1, and a GaAs FET with corresponding footprint. Note that this FET is laid out for microwave wafer probing. The source contact (common-ground) is available to the gate probe tip and the drain probe tip. In Figure 2, the short standard is simply an area of metalization which creates a low inductance between the contacts. The 50-ohm load is a 50 micron square resistor deposited on the GaAs. Its resistance can be measured at DC, its series inductance is calculated to be about 30 pH, and the parallel capacitance is calculated to be 4.9 fF on GaAs. The open-circuit standard is just the probe raised from the substrate. The stray capacitance can be empirically determined, as is done for coaxial calibrations. By ensuring that the corrected reflection coefficient magnitudes of high-Q coils and capacitors are less than one, the open capacitance can be determined to within about 3 fF.

Figure 3 shows one-port measurements of the calibration standards and other impedance standards after calibrating the system with a short, a 50-ohm termination, and an open circuit. The other standards are necessary to verify the accuracy of the calibration, since repetition of the calibration standards only proves that the system repeats its measurements. As can be seen in Figure 3, the resulting measurements are very tightly grouped and demonstrate the lumped nature of the elements.

The measurement of a 50 x 150 μm rectangle of metalization (just large enough to short the signal contact to the ground contact on the probe) is shown in Figure 4. About 30 pH of inductance is measured, comparing well with the expected inductance. Extra conductor under the end of the probe tip causes a small interaction between the conductor and the very end of the probe tip, resulting in an apparent negative inductance as large as -60 pH.

Two-Port Calibrations

Two-port corrected S-parameter measurements with the standard 12-element error model use the above calibration for each port, plus a through connection and isolation calibration standards. The through standard connects the two signal contacts together. For the isolation calibration, either the probes are open-circuited in air, minimizing any coupling between them, or the isolation error terms are simply set to zero.

Figure 5 shows the measurement of a 10-dB pad after the two-port calibration, verifying the basic accuracy of the standards. Figure 6 shows the measurement of a typical 1 x 300 μm GaAs FET, along with its lumped equivalent circuit.[5]

The above discussion illustrates the calibrations for a simple probe configuration. Calibrations for other types of probe footprints, including configurations for most commercially-available discrete FETs, are possible. Since most discrete devices have not been designed for RF probing, special

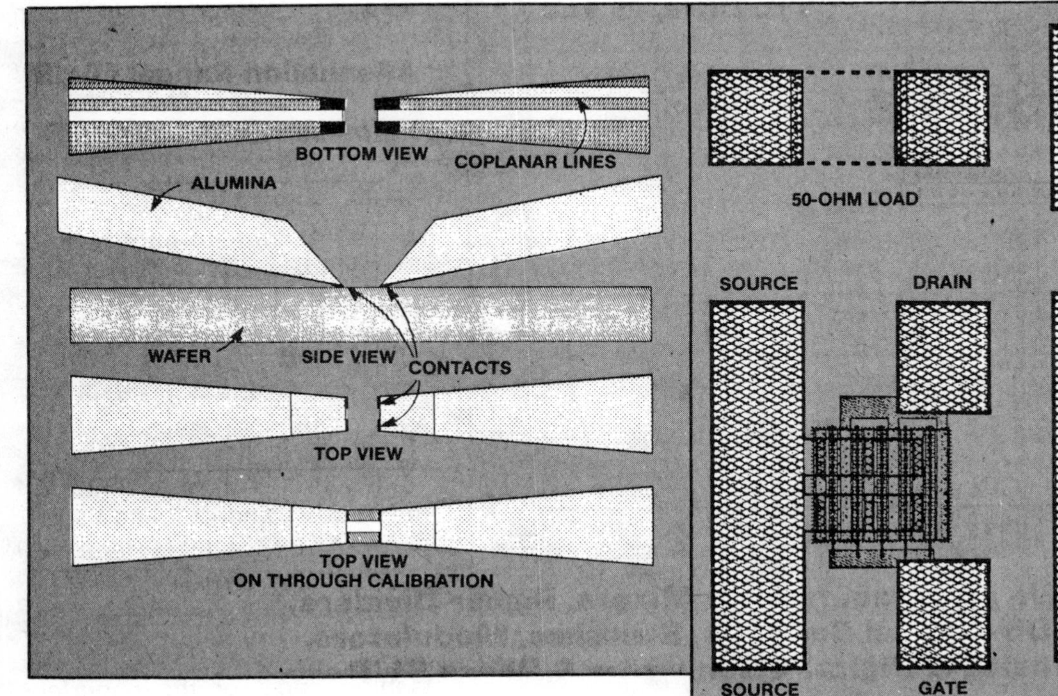

Fig. 1 Top, bottom, and cross-sectional views of two coplanar probe tips; a simple coplanar probe configuration which has achieved accurate microwave results. One probe head has a ground-signal contact configuration and the other probe head has a signal-ground contact configuration. Note that the probe contact areas are visible from the top, since they extend just beyond the end of the probe board.

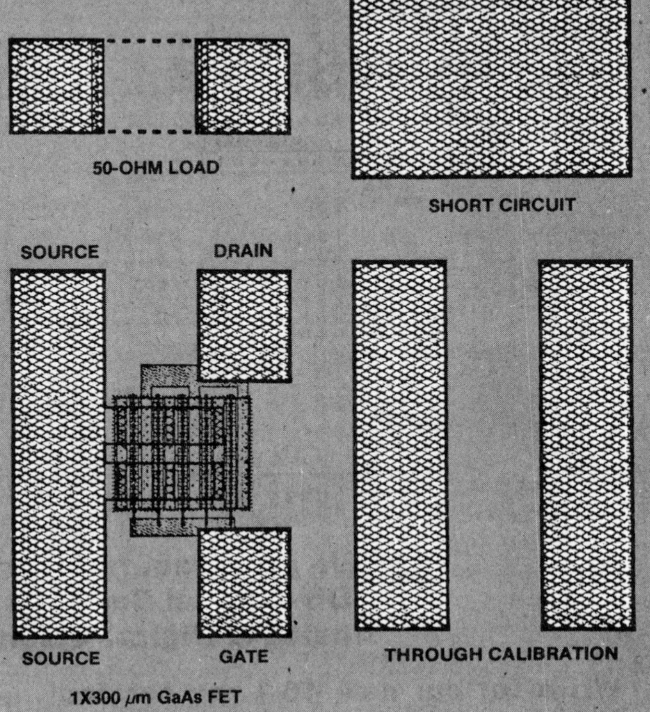

Fig. 2 Standard test FET with a corresponding minimal set of impedance standards. Minimum one-port and two-port standards for the probe footprint illustrated in Figure 1, and a GaAs FET with a corresponding footprint.

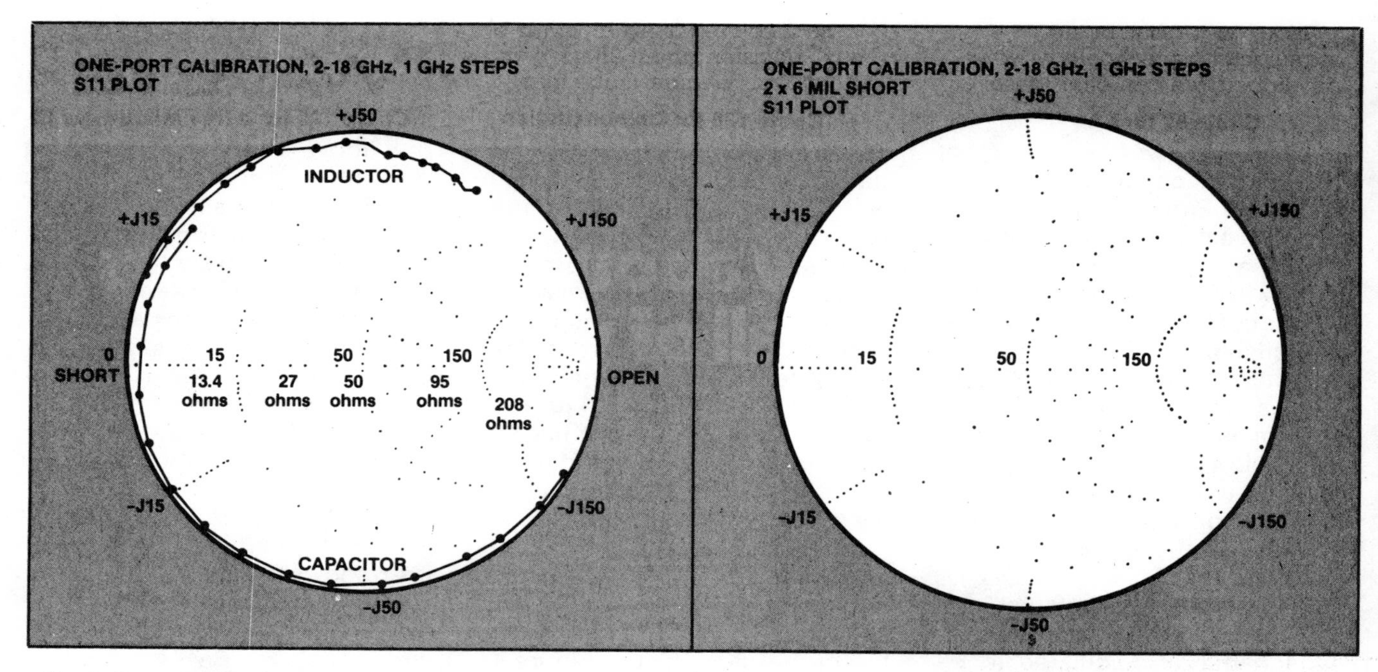

Fig. 3 Corrected one-port measurements of various on-wafer impedance standards. The short, the 50-ohm resistor, and the open were used as the three standards for calibration.

Fig. 4 Corrected one-port measurement of a 50 x 150 μm metalized rectangle, illustrating the ability to measure inductances below 50 ph.

ground connections between the gate probe tip and the drain probe tip are often necessary.

In the case of an MMIC, ground contacts should be provided next to the input and output pads to be probes, as well as next to any bias pads that require off-chip bypassing. Low-impedance bypass probes can be used for on-wafer testing, in place of the bypass capacitors to be used in the package. The through calibration standard for probing an MMIC with a fixed probe footprint is a 50-ohm transmission line with ends at positions corresponding to the input and output of the MMIC. However, greater accuracy can be achieved by using an adjustable probe footprint, as opposed to a fixed footprint probe card, since a minimum-length through calibration standard can be used.

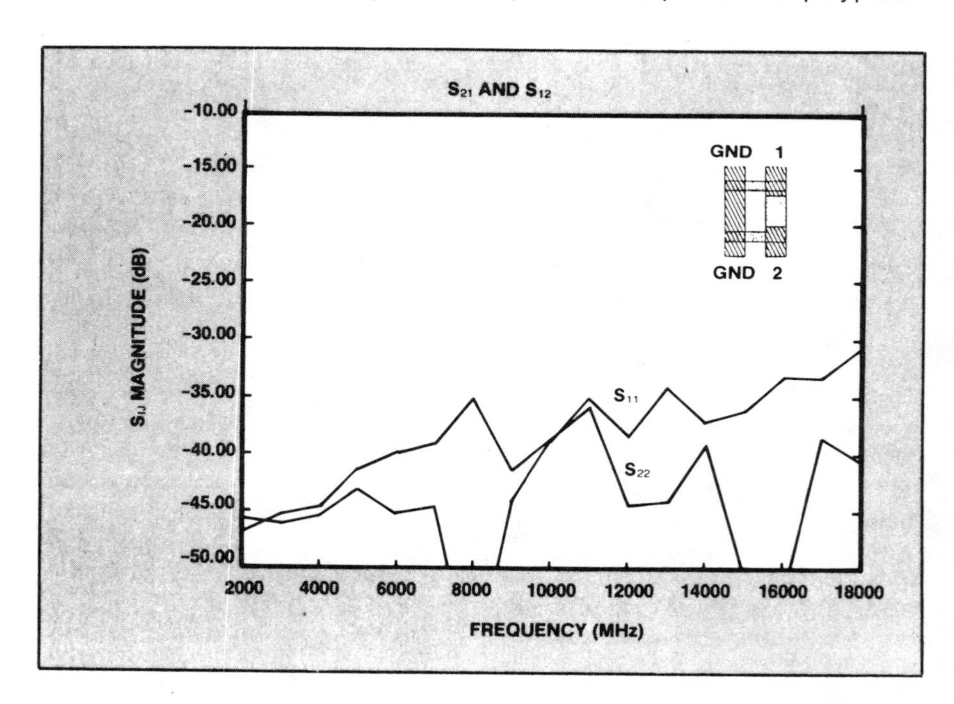

Fig. 5 Corrected two-port measurement of a small 10-dB pad. The measured S_{21} magnitude typically varies ±0.1 dB over 2 to 18 GHz.

Balanced Calibrations

One-port and two-port measurements with balanced probes have been performed. A 2-18 GHz 50-ohm balun (Cascade Microwave part number 010-019) is connected between each port of the network analyzer and its corresponding balanced probe, as in Figure 7. Neither probe head has a ground contact, but there is a virtual ground plane vertically through the center of each. In this fashion, most of the imperfections of the baluns are removed, as if they were just other adapters. The corrected one-port measurement results are very similar to those shown in Figure 3. A corrected two-port measurement of a 10-dB pad is shown in Figure 8.

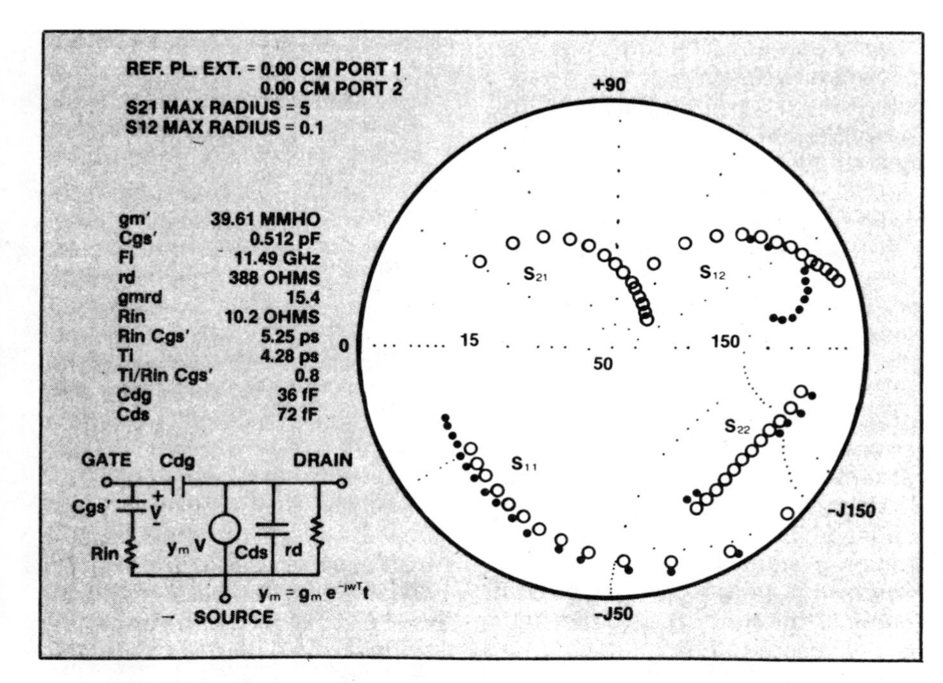

Fig. 6 Measured 2-18 GHz S-parameters of a typical 1.0 x 300 μm FET, using the microwave wafer probe. The circles are S-parameters of the simplified equivalent circuit calculated from the measured parameters.

Calibrations for Digital Measurements

The measurement of a nonlinear circuit will not in general be correctable using linear techniques, such as the error models for a corrected network analyzer. Correction of output signals for frequency response of the output lines (in software) can be useful, and precorrection of input pulses (in hardware) to counteract the response of the input lines may be practical in some cases. For the case of digital measurements, crosstalk and radiation again are not removable from the measurements.

The main problems with ultra-fast digital probing are the same problems with ultra-fast digital packaging: ground inductance and low-impedance power-supply requirements. Except for dice with balanced low-impedance outputs, wire probe tips are simply far too inductive. In addition to noise from common-lead inductance, crosstalk between transmission lines must also be minimized. For probe crosstalk measurements, a useful pattern is one which connects two signal line contacts and shoots them to a ground or power-supply contact. The transmission between two signal lines is a sensitive measure of the ground or power-supply impedance (usually a small inductance).

Typical Time-Domain Performance

In Figure 9 a 40-pS time-domain reflectometer (TDR) is used to measure the reflections of two probes (a Cascade Microwave WPH-001-04 and a WPH-002-04 probe head) contacting a through connection on the Impedance Standard Substrate.

The discontinuity at "A" is caused by a typical SMA connector on a semi-rigid cable. "B" is

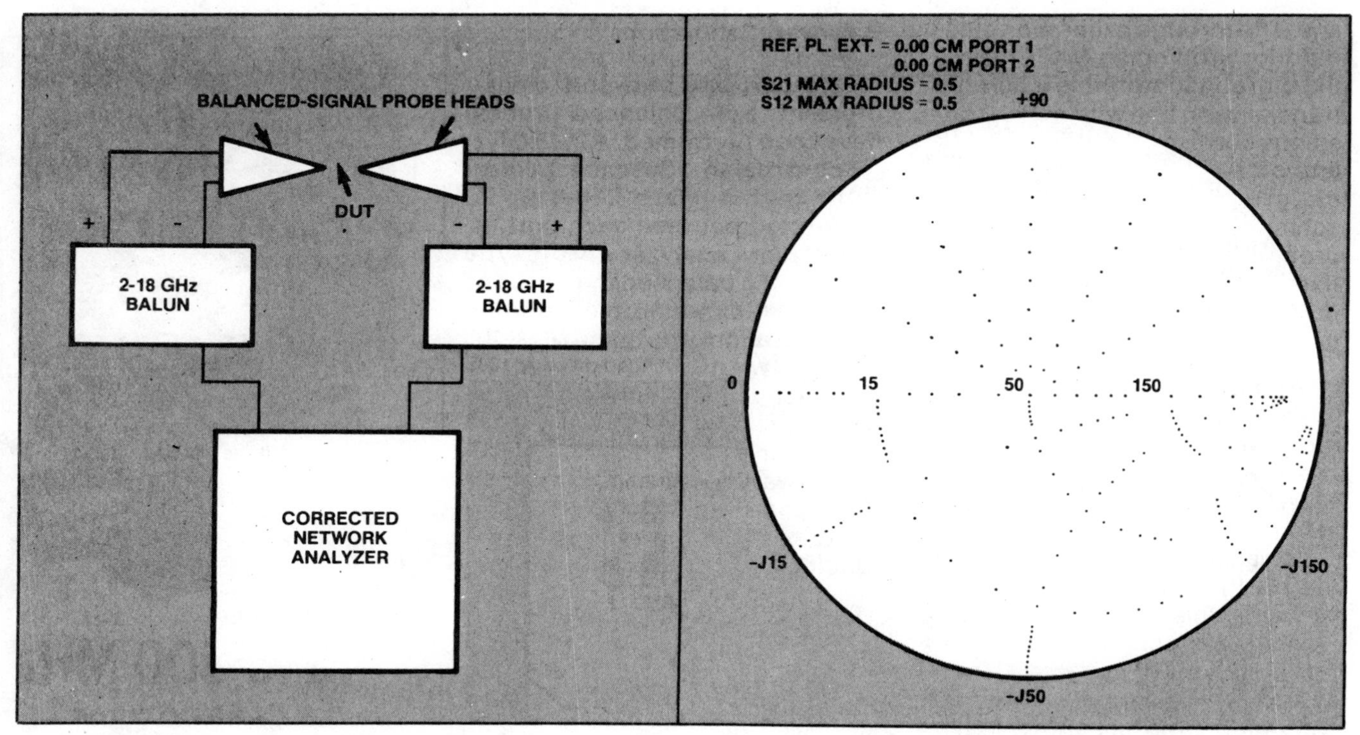

Fig. 7 Connection of balanced probe heads with wideband baluns and a corrected network analyzer to achieve balanced on-wafer measurements.

Fig. 8 Corrected two-port measurement of a balanced 10-dB pad, using the test setup shown in Figure 7.

where the semi-rigid cable connects to the first probe head. "C" is the discontinuity at the probe tips. "D" is the SMA connector on the second probe head, and "E" is an SMA termination.

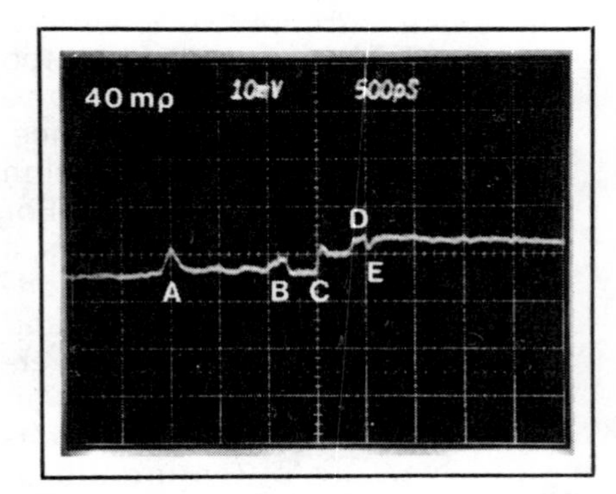

Fig. 9 TDR of two probe head cables and termination. Vertical scale is 40 mρ/div.

The same 40-pS step generator/sampler combination is used to measure the transmission characteristics of the pair of probe heads in Figure 10.

Curve "A" in Figure 10 shows the input from the step generator. Curve "B" shows the same step after passing through two typical 5-nS cable, 10-nS total. The normal dribble-up and degradation in risetime are apparent. Curve "C" shows the step after passing through a 5-nS cable, through the pair of probe heads and out the other 5-nS cable to the sampling oscilloscope. Thus, the main degradation is just the frequency response of the cables connecting to the probes. Taking the approximate rise-times of curves "B" and "C" as 80-pS and 85-pS respectively, the rise-time of the two probes together is:

$$t_r = \sqrt{85^2 - 80^2} = 28.7 \text{ pS}$$

About 14 pS for one probe.

In Figure 11, the worst-case crosstalk from a Cascade Microwave WPH-001-04 probe head to a WPH-002-04 probe head is shown. The worst case occurs when all probe tips (both grounds and both signals) are shorted together. In this example, both probe tips are contacting the same 8 x 4 mil pad.

Typical wire-tipped probes have very high crosstalk above 1 GHz, due to the inductance in the common leads. Figure 11 shows that the inductive spike "A" feeding through from the 40-pS 200-mV step "B" is only 1 mV in amplitude. The Cascade Microwave WPH-003-xx probe head has <10 mV feedthrough in this test, corresponding to a common-lead inductance of less than 60 pH.

Digital circuit risetimes do not yet approach the risetimes of available cables and printable transmission lines, so the need for waveshape correction is relatively minor. More important to the digital designer is the accurate measurement of propagation delays. Through connections for accurate delay calibrations with multi-line probes can be built in the same style as for two-port ANA standards, with lines at enough different angles and positions to make throughs between each pair of signal lines.

Conclusion

The accuracy available with state-of-the-art microwave wafer probes exceeds the best accuracies possible in bonded-chip test fixtures. Wafer-probe measurements are so repeatable that the user can resolve which side of a bond pad (about 50pH) is being contacted by the probe tip. In contrast, the bond wires in a chip test fixtures (at least 500 pH) often cannot be separated from the device under test. In addition to accuracy improvements, wafer-probe measurements can be performed nondestructively, and eliminate processing steps to dice and bond up prototype chips. Balanced-signal probes have been demonstrated through 18 GHz, allowing testing of MMIC designs which make use of virtual grounds. During the design stage, MMICs should be laid out with RF on-wafer testing in mind. Microwave wafer probing is a significant contribution to the productivity of the microwave semiconductor industry. ■

REFERENCES

1. Strid, E.W. and K.R. Gleason, "A DC-12 GHz Monolithic GaAsFET Distributed Amplifier," *IEEE Trans. Microwave Theory and Tech.*, Vol. MTT-30, No. 7, pp. 969-975, July 1982, and *IEEE Trans. on Electron Devices*, Vol. ED-29, No. 7, pp. 1065-1071, July 1982.
2. Gleason, K.R. et. al., "Precise MMIC Parameters Yielded by 18-GHz Wafer Probe," *Microwave System News*, pp. 55-65, May 1983.
3. Fitzpatrick, J., "Error Models for Systems Measurement," *Microwave Journal*, pp. 63-66, May 1978.
4. Swanson, D., "Ferret Out Fixture Errors with Careful Calibration," *Microwaves*, pp. 79-84, Jan. 1980.
5. Minasian, R.A., "Simplified GaAs MESFET Model to 10 GHz," *Elect. Lett.*, Vol. 13, No. 8, pp. 549-551, Sept. 1, 1977.

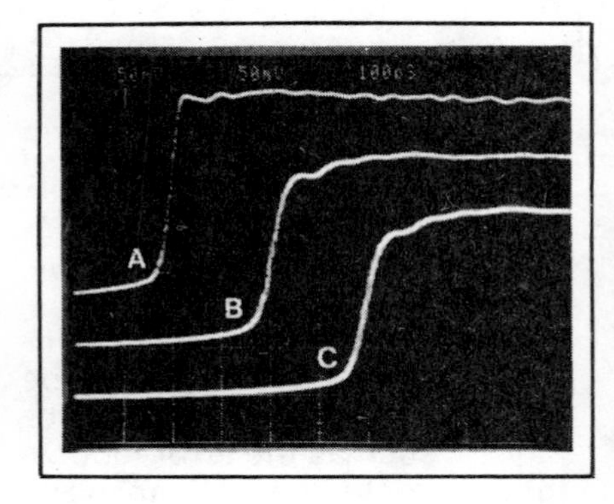

Fig. 10 Transmission response of two probe heads.

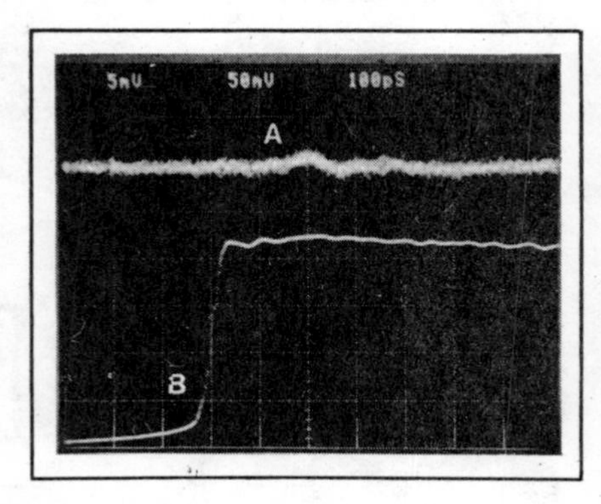

Fig. 11 Crosstalk between the two probes with all the tips shorted together.

CHAPTER VI

MONOLITHIC MICROWAVE INTEGRATED CIRCUITS

The article by Pucel and that by Pengelly and Eng present the essential elements of monolithic integration with several examples. Frey and Wada summarize the physics of GaAs MESFET operation, the key active element in MMICs. Monolithic components such as couplers are described by Kumar, and phase shifters by Sokolov. Several passive monolithic components at millimeter wave frequencies are discussed by Neidert and Binari. Bhasin, *et al.*, discuss packaging and interconnection considerations for MMICs, while Benet describes an ingenious testing technique for MMICs.

Design Considerations for Monolithic Microwave Circuits

ROBERT A. PUCEL, FELLOW, IEEE

MTT National Lecture Invited Paper

Abstract—Monolithic microwave integrated circuits based on silicon-on-sapphire (SOS) and gallium arsenide technologies are being considered seriously as viable candidates for satellite communication systems, airborne radar, and other applications. The low-loss properties of sapphire and semi-insulating GaAs substrates, combined with the excellent microwave performance of metal-semiconductor FET's (MESFET's), allows, for the first time, a truly monolithic approach to microwave integrated circuits. By monolithic we mean an approach wherein all passive and active circuit elements and interconnections are formed into the bulk, or onto the surface of the substrate by some deposition scheme, such as epitaxy, ion implantation, sputtering, evaporation, and other methods.

The importance of this development is that microwave applications such as airborne phased-array systems based on a large number of identical circuits and requiring small physical volume and/or light weight, may, finally, become cost effective.

The paper covers in some detail the design considerations that must be applied to monolithic microwave circuits in general, and to gallium arsenide circuits in particular. The important role being played by computer-aided design techniques is stressed. Numerous examples of monolithic circuits and components which illustrate the design principles are described. These provide a cross section of the world-wide effort in this field. A glimpse into the future prospects of monolithic microwave circuits is made.

I. Introduction

THE LAST two to three years have witnessed an intensive revival in the field of analog monolithic microwave integrated circuits (MMIC's), that is, microwave circuits deposited on a semiconductor substrate, or an insulating substrate with a semiconductor layer over it. In this paper, we shall address the design and technology considerations of monolithic microwave integrated circuits as well as the potential applications of these circuits to microwave systems, such as satellite communications and phased-array radar, as well as instrumentation.

It is important that the reader understand what we mean by the term "monolithic"circuit. By monolithic, we mean an approach wherein all active and passive circuit elements or components and interconnections are formed into the bulk, or onto the surface, of a semi-insulating substrate by some deposition scheme such as epitaxy, ion implantation, sputtering, evaporation, diffusion, or a combination of these processes and others.

It is essential that the full implication of this definition be understood, since it strikes at the very core of why one would want to design and fabricate a microwave monolithic circuit. The reasons are embedded in the following promising attributes of the monolithic approach:

1) low cost;
2) improved reliability and reproducibility;
3) small size and weight;
4) multioctave (broad-band) performance; and
5) circuit design flexibility and multifunction performance on a chip.

The importance of this development is that systems applications based on a large number of identical components, for instance, space-borne phase-array radars planned for the future which require lightweight and reliable, low-cost transmit–receive modules, may finally become cost effective. One might consider this type of application as the microwave system analog of the computer (which spurred the growth of the silicon digital monolithic circuit market), since both require a large number of identical circuits.

Maximum cost effectiveness, as well as improved reliability, derives in part from the fact that wire bonding is eliminated in MMIC's, at least within the chip itself, and is relegated to less critical and fewer locations at the periphery of the chip. Wire bonds have always been a serious factor in reliability and reproducibility. Furthermore, wire bonding, being labor intensive, is not an insignificant factor in the cost of a circuit.

Small size and volume, and their corollary, light weight, are intrinsic properties of the monolithic approach. Small size allows batch processing of hundreds of circuits per wafer of substrate. Since the essence of batch processing is that the cost of fabrication is determined by the cost of processing the entire wafer, it follows that the processing cost per chip is proportional to the area of the chip. Thus, the higher the circuit count per wafer, the lower the circuit cost.

The elimination of wire bonding and the embedding of active components within a printed circuit eliminate many of the undesired parasitics which limit the broad-band performance of circuits employing packaged discrete devices. The monolithic approach will certainly ease the difficulty of attaining multioctave performance. Furthermore, such broad-banding approaches as distributed

Manuscript received January 16, 1981. This work summarizes the lecture given by the National Lecturer throughout the United States, Canada, and Europe, during 1980–1981.

The author is with the Research Division, Raytheon Company, Waltham, MA 02254.

amplifier stages, heretofore shunned as too wasteful of active elements, will now become feasible, because a cost penalty will not accrue from the prolific use of low-gain stages, and because the unavoidable parasitics associated with the active devices will be incorporated in the propagating circuit and rendered less harmful.

The small circuit size intrinsic to the monolithic approach will enable circuit integration on a chip level, ranging from the lowest degree of complexity such as an oscillator, mixer, or amplifier, to a next higher "functional block" level, for example a receiver front end or a phase shifter. A still higher level of circuit complexity, for example, a transmit–receive module, will be integrated, most likely in multichip form.

So far we have discussed only the virtues of the monolithic approach. Now let us consider some of its disadvantages and problem areas. These are principally the following:

1) unfavorable device/chip area ratio;
2) circuit tuning (tweaking) impractical;
3) trouble-shooting (debugging) difficult;
4) suppression of undesired RF coupling (crosstalk), a possible problem; and
5) difficulty of integrating high power sources (IMPATT's)

The first item refers to the fact that only a small fraction of the chip area is occupied by devices, hence the high processing cost and lower yield associated with active device fabrication is unavoidably applied to the larger area occupied by the circuitry. A corollary of this is that the lower yield processes of device fabrication dominate the overall chip yield. Although these problems diminish as the chip size becomes smaller, that is, for higher frequencies, they are absent in the hybrid approach where the circuit and device technologies are separated.

The second and third items are related and can be considered together. The small chip sizes characteristic of the monolithic approach make it virtually impossible to tune ("tweak") and troubleshoot circuits. Indeed, to want to do so would violate one of the precepts of this approach, namely, to reduce costs by minimizing all labor-intensive steps. What then can be done about these very real problems?

First, it is necessary to minimize the need for tweaking. This can be done by adopting a design philosophy which leads to circuits that are insensitive to manufacturing tolerances in the active devices and physical dimensions of the circuit components. This will be a difficult compromise to accept on the part of the circuit designer, who expects the ultimate in performance from each active device by circuit tuning. However, here computer-aided design (CAD) techniques come to the rescue. Not only will CAD techniques play a major, if not mandatory, role in monolithic circuit design, they will also be used to assess the effect of tolerances on circuit performance during the design phase—and rather easily. CAD program for doing this

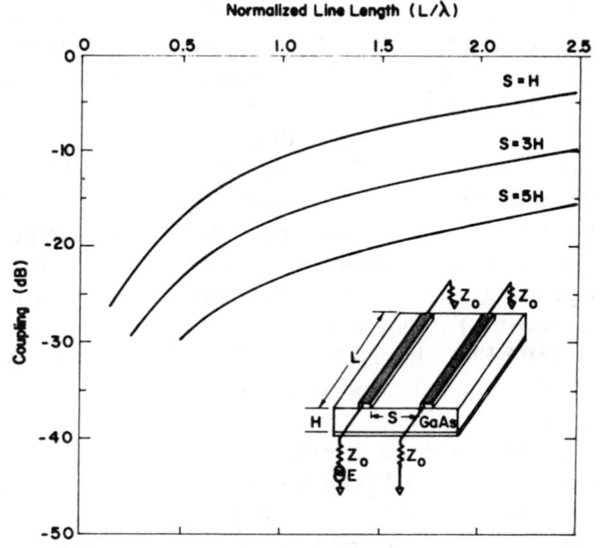

Fig. 1. Calculated coupling between adjacent parallel microstrip lines as a function of spacing and frequency.

reside on many internal computer systems and are also available commercially [4].

The use of CAD also helps alleviate the problem of troubleshooting a working circuit. Until microwave probes suitable for monolithic circuits become practical [19], troubleshooting must be based on terminal RF measurements of the circuit, usually the input and output ports. If a certain component is suspected of being faulty, it is a simple matter of building this defect into the CAD data file and comparing the resultant calculated circuit response with that measured. This can be done for a series of suspected faults, and convergence to the true fault can be achieved rather expeditiously.

The potential problem of undesirable RF coupling within the circuit is real because of the small chip sizes involved. To illustrate this point, Fig. 1 is a theoretical calculation of the coupling between two parallel microstrip lines on a GaAs substrate, one of which is excited by a generator. Both lines are matched at either end. Shown is the fraction of power coupled from the excited line to the adjacent line as a function of line length and line spacing. It is obvious that the coupling can become unacceptably high for long line lengths approaching a wavelength or more. Even for short lines, of the order of a quarter-wavelength or less, a feedback problem may exist if, say, a high-gain amplifier exists in one of the lines. In practice, line spacings of the order of three substrate thicknesses or more ($S > 3H$) have been found adequate in most cases. This proximity "rule" plays a major role in determining the chip area and, hence, the chip cost. This restriction on circuit packing density, somewhat unique to MMIC's, can be alleviated measurably if direct-coupled circuitry is used, that is, if no distributed or lumped componentry is involved. We shall see examples of this approach later.

Turning to the fifth item, though both low-noise and power FET circuitry can easily be integrated on the same chip, where very high powers, more precisely, power densities are involved, the monolithic approach may face some fundamental limitations. These limitations are associated with the need for special means of removing heat from the device. A case in point is the diamond heatsink used with millimeter-wave IMPATT diodes. Though it would be desirable to integrate avalanche diode sources in monolithic circuits for millimeter wave applications, the high-power densities involved cannot be handled by heat transfer through the chip. This is not a problem with power FET's, but of course, FET's cannot deliver the powers available from IMPATT's. Integration of high power sources in monolithic circuits is a problem that, as yet, has not been addressed.

TABLE I
SOME PROPERTIES OF SEMICONDUCTORS AND INSULATORS

Property	GaAs	Silicon	Semi-insulating GaAs	Semi-insulating Silicon	Sapphire	Alumina
Dielectric Constant	12.9	11.7	12.9	11.7	11.6 (C-axis)	9.7
Density (gm/cc)	5.32	2.33	5.32	2.33	3.98	3.89
Thermal Cond. (watts/cm-°K)	0.46	1.45	0.46	1.45	0.46	0.37
Resistivity (ohm-cm)	---	---	10^7 - 10^9	10^3 - 10^5	$>10^{14}$	10^{11} - 10^{14}
Elec. Mobility (cm^2/v-sec.)	4300*	700*	---	---	---	---
Sat. Elec. Vel. (cm/sec.)	1.3×10^7	9×10^6	---	---	---	---

* At $10^{17}/cm^3$ doping

Even for FET power amplifiers, tradeoffs must be made between good thermal performance and good RF design. For example, to minimize the thermal resistance through the substrate, it is desirable to use as thin a wafer as practical. However, a thin wafer increases the circuit skin effect losses, and hence the attenuation. Furthermore, since heat-sinking requires metallization of the chip bottomside, additional parasitic capacitance to ground is introduced and corrections must be made to planar inductors to account for "image" currents in the ground plane.

Despite these limitations on power, it is possible that with on-chip power combining techniques applied to FET's which are thermally isolated from each other [17], power outputs of the order of 10-W CW or so may be realizable from a single chip at the lower microwave frequencies, that is, at *X*-band.

II. MMIC's—A Brief History

The concept of MMIC's is not new. Its origin goes back to 1964 to a government-funded program based on silicon technology, which had as its objective a transmit–receive module for an aircraft phased-array antenna. Unfortunately, the results were disappointing because of the inability of semi-insulating silicon to maintain its semi-insulating properties through the high-temperature diffusion processes. Thus, very lossy substrates resulted, which were unacceptable for microwave circuitry [12]. Because of these and other difficulties the attempt to form a monolithic circuit based on a semiconductor substrate lay dormant till 1968 when Mehal and Wacker [15] revived the approach by using semi-insulating gallium arsenide (GaAs) as the base material and Schottky barrier diodes and Gunn devices to fabricate a 94-GHz receiver front end. However, it was not until Plessey applied this approach to an *X*-band amplifier, based on the Schottky-gate field-effect transistor, or MESFET (MEtal-Semiconductor Field-Effect Transistor), as the key active element that the present intense activity began [16].

What brought on this revival? First, the rapid development of GaAs material technology, namely, epitaxy and ion implantation, and the speedy evolution of the GaAs FET based on the metal Schottky gate during the last decade led to high-frequency semiconductor device performance previously unattained. A few examples are high-efficiency and high-power amplifier performance through *Ku*-band, low-noise amplifiers, variable-gain dual-gate amplifiers, and FET mixers with gain. The dual-gate FET will play a major role in MMIC's because of its versatility as a linear amplifier whose gain can be controlled either digitally or in analog fashion. With dual-gate FET's, multi-port electronically switchable RF gain channels are feasible. Second, resolution of many troublesome device reliability problems made FET's more attractive for systems applications. Third, recognition of the excellent microwave properties of semi-insulting GaAs (approaching that of alumina), removed the major objection of silicon. Fourth, hybrid circuits were becoming very complex and labor intensive because of the prolific use of wire bonds, and hence too costly. Fifth, the emergence of clearly defined and discernible systems applications for MMIC's became more apparent. Thus it was the confluence of all of these factors, and others, which stimulated the development of GaAs MMIC's within the last five years.

III. Silicon or Gallium Arsenide?

It is ironic that this revival based on GaAs technology has, in turn, restimulated the interest in silicon MMIC's—but now based on the silicon-on-sapphire (SOS) approach [13]. There are understandable reasons for this. First, the use of sapphire as a substrate eliminates the losses associated with semi-insulating silicon mentioned earlier. Second, silicon technology is an extremely well developed technology—much more so than GaAs. Third, the availability of the simpler MESFET technology, developed in GaAs, could now be used in place of the more complex bipolar technology, which, however, was still available should it be needed. Nevertheless, gallium arsenide has the "edge" for reasons to be discussed next.

Table I lists some of the pertinent physical and electrical properties of GaAs and silicon (n-type) in their insulating and semiconducting states, as well as that of sapphire and alumina. As is evident from this table, as a high-resistivity substrate, semi-insulating GaAs, sapphire, and alumina are, for all practical purposes, comparable. Also evident is that the carrier mobility of gallium arsenide is over six times that of silicon. For this reason and others, GaAs MESFET's are operable at higher frequencies and powers than silicon MESFET's of equivalent dimensions. For example, silicon MESFET's based on 1-μm gate technology will be limited in operation to upper S-band at best, whereas GaAs MESFET's operate well at X-band and higher. Therefore, it is highly likely that the performance of 1-μm gate silicon MESFET's will be matched, and perhaps exceeded by that of 2-μm gate GaAs MESFET's at S-band. The near-future availability of much larger GaAs wafers, approaching 3.5 in in diameter [20], obtained by the Czochralski method, will overcome the size limitations imposed by the present 1-in wafers grown by the Bridgman method. The early success of direct-coupled FET analog circuitry [11], [21], which leads to high component density at S-band, will also help overcome wafer size limitations in GaAs. Finally, the proven success of gigahertz high-speed GaAs logic circuitry will allow, for the first time, complete integration of logic and analog microwave circuitry. This opens up the feasibility of high-speed signal processing on a chip.

We do not wish to imply that MMIC work based on SOS technology should be diminished; however, we believe its major role will be found in the range below 2 GHz, for example, in IF circuitry and other applications. In light of this conclusion, we shall direct the following discussion to the GaAs approach. However, much of what we shall say, as will be obvious to the reader, will also apply, with minor changes, to the SOS approach or to other approaches which may emerge in the future. Nevertheless, we maintain that before this decade is over, it will be GaAs monolithic integrated circuits that will exert the greatest influence on the way solid-state device circuitry is used in microwave systems.

IV. The Gallium Arsenide Approach

A cornerstone of the monolithic approach will be the availability of a highly reproducible device technology. This in turn is related, in part, to the control of the starting material, especially the active (semiconducting) layer.

Two general techniques are available for forming this layer on GaAs substrates, namely, epitaxy and ion implantation. Of the two approaches, the former at present is more widely used and developed. In this approach a doped single crystal semiconducting layer is deposited on a semi-insulating GaAs substrate, usually with an intervening high-resistivity epitaxial "buffer" layer to screen out diffusion of impurities from the substrate during the active layer growth. With ion implantation, dopant atoms are implanted directly into the surface of a semi-insulating GaAs substrate. This procedure requires a higher state of purity of the substrate—a problem at present.

Expitaxy does not have the control or flexibility associated with implantation. With implantation, more uniform conducting layers are possible over a large area—more uniform in doping level as well as in thickness. Furthermore, with implantation, selective doping is easy, that is, formation of different doping profiles in different parts of the wafer is easy to achieve, whereas with epitaxy it is difficult. The potential device reproducibility achievable with implantation is a definite advantage for it.

It should be added that implantation can also be used in conjunction with epitaxy. One such application is the isolation implant, wherein oxygen is implanted in the unused portions of the epitaxial layer to produce a high-resistivity region within the epitaxial layer onto which microwave circuitry may be situated. Thus a truly planar surface is maintained, since no mesa etching is required to remove the undesired regions of epitaxial layer. This also eliminates yield problems associated with metallization patterns extending over mesa steps.

It is likely that, once substrate purity reaches the necessary level for ion implantation (as it is approaching with unintentionally doped Czochralski-pulled crystals), ion implantation will supplant epitaxy as the preferred method for monolithic circuits.

The processing technology used for FET fabrication is also applicable to the monolithic circuit elements. The high degree of dimensional definition associated with FET photolithography is more than adequate for the circuit elements.

V. General Design Considerations

We turn now to a discussion of the design considerations for MMIC's.

A. Constraints on Chip Size

Present substrate sizes corresponding to that of GaAs boules are approximately 1 in in diameter, though larger boules approaching 3 in in diameter are now being grown by the Czochralski method. Given the expected limits on substrate size, it is instructive to estimate the circuit count/wafer achievable as a function of frequency, since the processing cost per circuit is inversely proportional to this density.

We assume that the maximum linear dimension per circuit will fall between $\lambda_g/10$ and $\lambda_g/4$, where λ_g is the wavelength of the propagation mode (microstrip-coplanar, etc.) in GaAs. The lower limit takes into account the approximate maximum size of lumped elements; the upper limit, the typical maximum size of distributed elements. It seems reasonable to assume that in the vicinity of 10 to 20 GHz some distributed elements of the order of $\lambda_g/4$ (for example, hybrid and branch line couplers) will be used. Therefore, above this frequency range, linear circuit dimensions of the order of $\lambda_g/4$ will be the rule. Let us choose 16 GHz as the demarcation frequency. We then postulate a "linear" admixture of lumped- and distributed-element weighting so that we obtain $\lambda_g/10$ at 1 GHz and $\lambda_g/4$ at 16 GHz as the probable linear dimension of a circuit function "chip."

Fig. 2 is a plot of the approximate density of these circuits as a function of frequency for two sizes of wafer. (The 2-in square wafer corresponds to a 3-in diameter

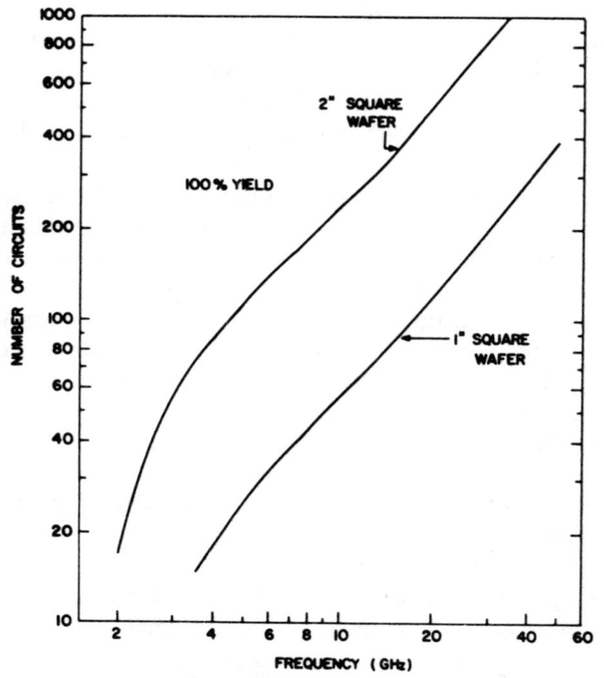

Fig. 2. Estimated number of circuits per wafer taking dicing and edge waste into account.

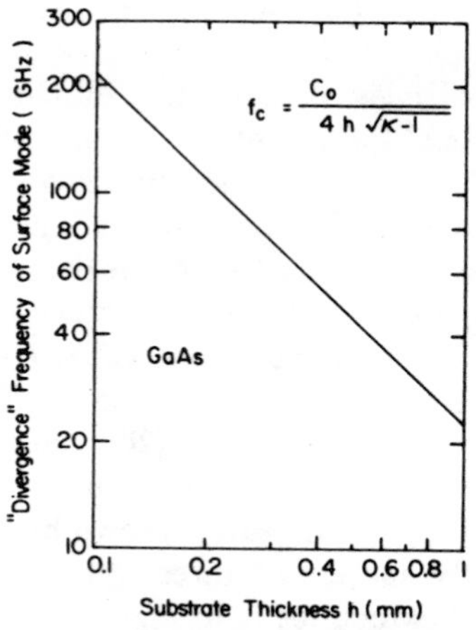

Fig. 3. Frequency of onset of lowest order TE surface wave on a GaAs substrate as a function of substrate thickness.

wafer.) The circuit density estimates take into account edge and cutting waste, but not "proximity effects," wafer yield, and other factors which will reduce these numbers.

A yield factor is associated with each fabrication step, the overall yield being the product of the individual yield factors. Thus, since active devices generally require the most processing steps (about 40 for an FET), the overall yield is determined by the device processing technology. The "proximity effect," that is, the RF coupling problem mentioned earlier, will put stringent limitations on how closely packed the signal lines may be, and hence how much circuitry can be compressed into the chip area, which is fixed by wavelength or lumped-element dimensions as just described.

The circuit count estimate must be modified for very low microwave frequencies (below *C*-band) if active components such as FET's are used to simulate resistors and capacitors and if inductors are dispensed with because tuning is not necessary. In this so-called direct-coupled design, packing densities approaching those normally associated with digital circuitry is possible [21], that is, much higher than that indicated in Fig. 2. However, it must be cautioned that this circuit approach is not suitable for all monolithic applications, for example, high-efficiency power amplifiers or low-noise circuits. The reason is that the use of active (FET) devices as resistive elements in the gate and drain circuits introduces high dc power dissipation and mismatch, as well as additional noise [11].

It is appropriate at this time to point out that the size advantages of GaAs MMIC's will be lost if proper packaging techniques are not used. Perhaps the efficient techniques adopted for low-frequency and digital circuitry can be suitably modified for microwave applications. Much thought must be devoted to this very important problem.

B. Constraints on Wafer Thickness

So far we have discussed requirements on the substrate area. There also are constraints imposed on the substrate thickness. Some of these are:

1) volume of material used;
2) fragility of wafer;
3) thermal resistance;
4) propagation losses;
5) higher order mode propagation;
6) impedance-linewidth considerations; and
7) thickness tolerance versus impedance tolerance.

Obviously, to keep material costs down one wishes to use as thin a substrate as can be handled without compromising the fragility. Thermal considerations also require the thinnest wafer possible. On the other hand, a thin wafer emphasizes the effect of the ground plane. For example, propagation losses increase inversely with substrate thickness in the case of microstrip. Furthermore, the *Q*-factor and inductance of thin-film inductors decrease with decreasing substrate thickness. In contrast, undesired higher-order surface mode excitation is inhibited for thinner substrates.

Fig. 3 is a graph of the frequency denoting the onset of the lowest order (TE) surface mode as a function of substrate thickness. For example, for a substrate thickness of 0.1 mm (4 mils) the "safe" operating frequency range is below 200 GHz. It appears that, for presently contemplated circuit applications, surface mode propagation is not a limiting factor in the choice of substrate thickness. The linewidth dimensions for a given impedance level of some propagation modes, such as microstrip, are proportional to substrate thickness. Therefore, thicker substrates alleviate the effect of thickness and linewidth tolerances.

The point being made here is that the choice of substrate thickness is a tradeoff of the factors listed above, being strongly dependent on the frequency of operation and the

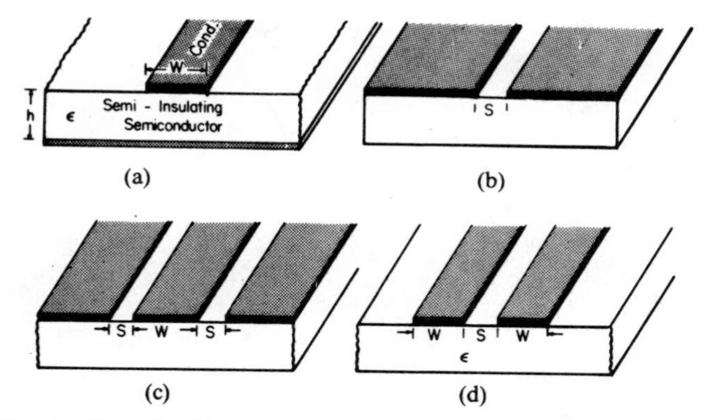

Fig. 4. Four candidate propagation modes for monolithic circuits. (a) Microstrip (MS). (b) Slot line (SL). (c) Coplanar waveguide. (d) Coplanar strips (CS).

power dissipation of the circuit. It is true that perhaps the most important of the factors is the thermal consideration. We believe that in the frequency range up to 30 GHz a substrate thickness of the order of 0.1 mm to 0.15 mm is appropriate for power amplifier circuits, with thicknesses up to 0.6 mm tolerable for low-noise amplifiers and similar circuits, provided a satisfactory means of dicing the thicker wafers can be found.

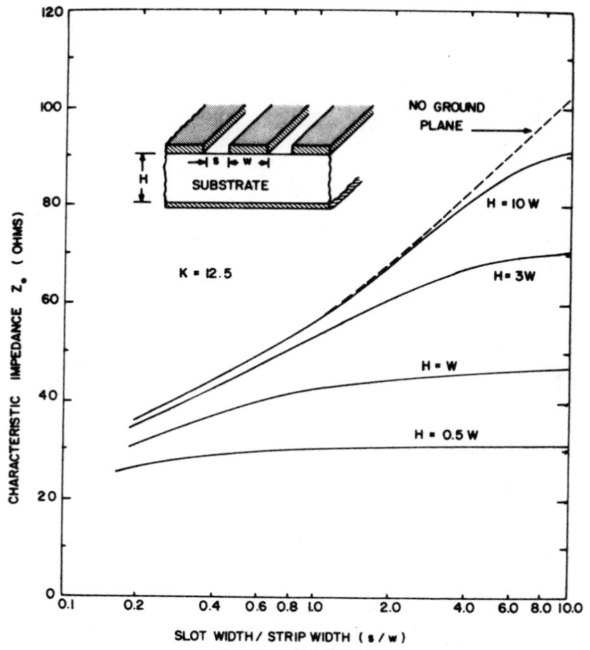

Fig. 5. Effect of ground plane on characteristic impedance of a coplanar waveguide.

C. Propagation Modes

At microwave frequencies, the interconnections between elements on a high dielectric constant substrate such as GaAs, where considerable wavelength reduction occurs, must be treated as waveguiding structures. On a planar substrate, four basic modes of propagation are available, as illustrated in Fig. 4. The first mode (Fig. 4(a)) is microstrip (MS), which requires a bottomside ground metallizaton. Its "inverse," slot line (SL), is shown in Fig. 4(b). The third mode is the coplanar waveguide (CPW) shown in Fig. 4(c); it consists of a central "hot" conductor separated by a slot from two adjacent ground planes. Its "inverse," the coplanar stripline (CS), is illustrated in Fig. 4(d); here, one of the two conductors is a ground plane. Both the coplanar waveguide and coplanar strips are generally considered to be on infinitely thick substrates. Of course, this condition cannot be met. We shall see the implication of this later.

Of the four modes, only the slot line is not TEM-like. For this reason, and because it uses valuable "topside" area, we do not expect slot line to be a viable candidate for monolithic circuits, except possibly in special cases.

The principal losses of microstrip and the coplanar modes consist of ohmic losses. Since the coplanar structures are, in essence, "edge-coupled" devices, with high concentration of charge and current near the strip edges, the losses tend to be somewhat higher than for microstrip, as verified by experiment [5].

The lack of a ground plane on the topside surface of the microstrip structure is a considerable disadvantage when shunt element connections to the hot conductor are required. However, as we shall see later, there are ways to overcome this disadvantage. Table II summarizes, in a qualitative way, the features of the four modes of propagation illustrated in Fig. 4.

TABLE II
QUALITATIVE COMPARISON OF PROPAGATION MODES

	MICROSTRIP	COPLANAR WAVEGUIDE	COPLANAR STRIPS	SLOT LINE
Attenuation Loss	low	medium	medium	high
Dispersion	low	medium	medium	high
Impedance Range (ohms)	10-100	25-125*	40-250*	high
Connect Shunt Elements	diff.	easy	easy	easy
Connect Series Elements	easy	easy	easy	diff.

*Infinitely thick substrate

The impedance range achievable with CPW and CS is somewhat greater than for MS, particularly at the higher end of the impedance scale, provided an infinitely thick substrate is assumed for CPW and CS. This range is reduced considerably when practical substrate thicknesses are used and the bottomside of the chip is metallized. Fig. 5 shows how the high impedance end of the scale is lowered when substrates of the order of 0.1–0.25 mm thick are mounted on a metal base (for heat-sinking purposes). The considerable reduction in Z_0 makes the design of monolithic circuitry with CPW nearly as dependent on substrate thickness as with MS, at least at the high end of the impedance scale.

Microstrip has its own unique restriction on the realizable impedance range. This is dictated by technology considerations. The limitation stems from the fact that for MS

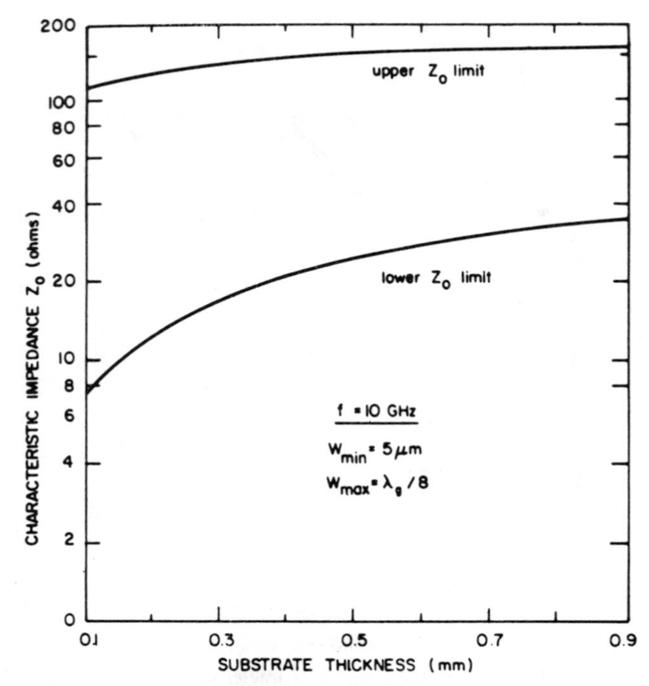

Fig. 6. Range of characteristic impedance of microstrip on GaAs substrate as a function of substrate thickness.

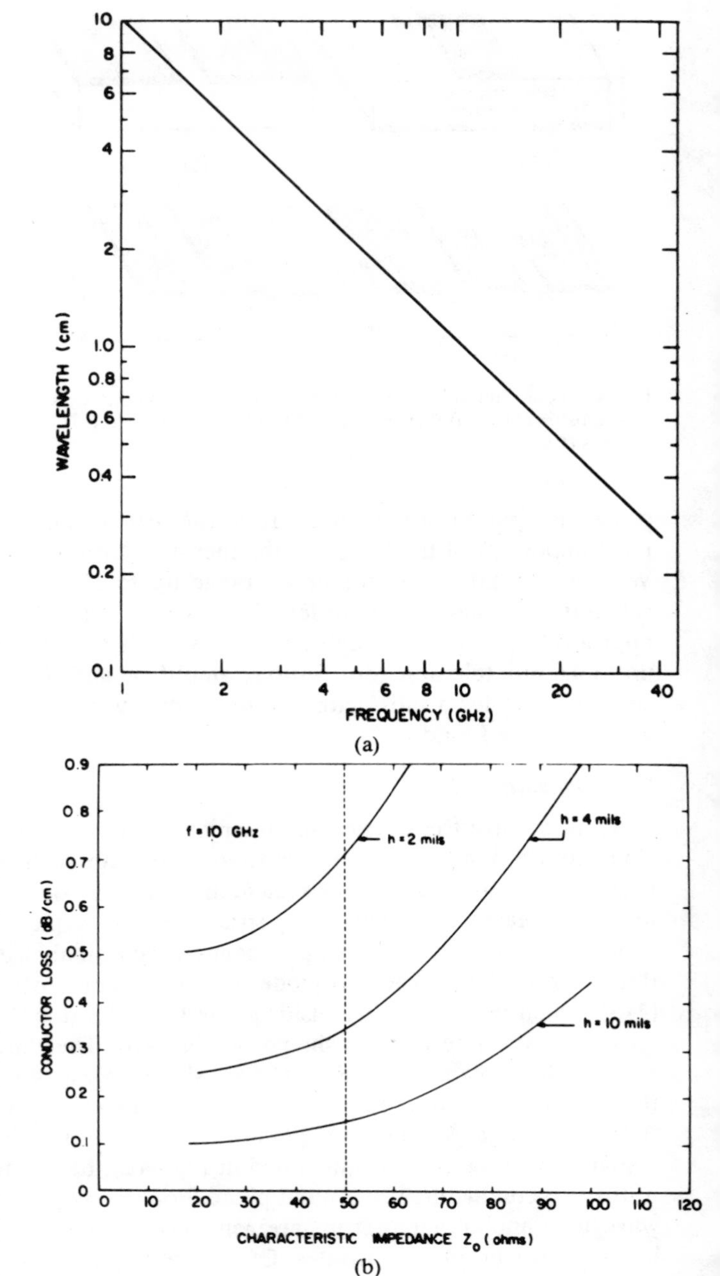

Fig. 7. (a) Wavelength as a function of frequency for microstrip on a GaAs substrate for $h=0.1$ mm. (b) Conductor loss of microstrip on a GaAs substrate as a function of substrate thickness and characteristic impedance for $f=10$ GHz.

the characteristic impedance Z_0 is a function of the ratio W/H (see Fig. 4). The highest achievable impedance is determined by the smallest linewidth W that can be realized with acceptable integrity over a long length, say, a quarter of a wavelength. Our experience is that a minimum linewidth of 5 μm is reasonable. With this restriction, and an additional limit imposed on the maximum linewidth to be well below a quarter-wavelength, say, one-eighth-wavelength, the realizable range of characteristic impedance as a function of substrate thickness and frequency is constrained within the range indicated by Fig. 6

It is evident that the usable impedance range for a 0.1-mm thick substrate is approximately 10–100 Ω, and somewhat less for thicker substrates and higher frequencies. For higher frequencies, the lower curve moves "up." This limited impedance range is a severe restriction in the design of matching networks, a problem not faced in the hybrid approach.

Weighing all of these factors, we believe that of the four candidate modes, MS and CPW are the most suitable for GaAs monolithic circuits, with preference toward MS. Indeed, there will be instances where both modes may be used on the same chip to achieve some special advantage. The transition from one mode to the other is trivial. Most of the examples of MMIC's to be described later are based on MS.

Fig. 6(a) is a graph of the wavelength of a 50-Ω MS line on GaAS as a function of frequency, with dispersion neglected. The wavelength of CPW is similar. Fig. 7(b) illustrates the attenuation of MS as a function of characteristic impedance and substrate thickness at 10 GHz. The loss in decibels per centimeter increases as the square root of frequency. The loss per wavelength, on the other hand, decreases as the square root of frequency. Note the inverse dependence of loss on substrate thickness.

D. Low Inductance Grounds and Crossovers

Microstrip and coplanar waveguide are adequate for interconnections that do not require conductor crossovers or that are not to contact the bottomside ground metallization. Often, however, such connections are needed. In particular, with MS, which does not have any topside ground planes, some means of achieving a low-inductance ground is essential.

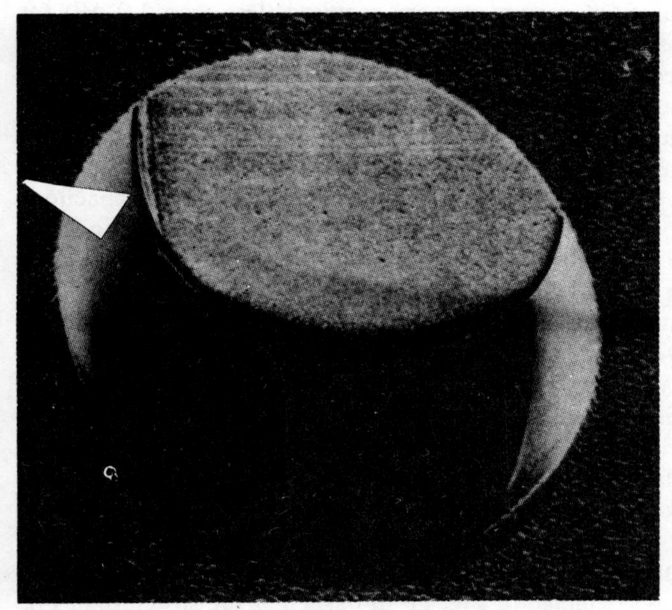

Fig. 8. 50-μm diameter "via" hole etched in a GaAs wafer.

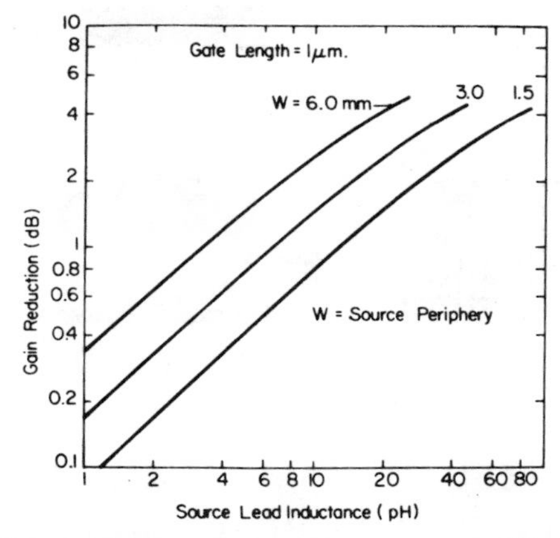

Fig. 9. Calculated gain reduction of a GaAs power FET as a function of source lead inductance.

Two general methods of grounding are available: 1) the "wrap-around" ground; and 2) the "via" hole ground. The former requires a topside metallization pattern near the periphery of the chip which can be connected to the chip ground. The "via" hole technique, on the other hand, allows placement of grounds through the substrate where desired. Holes are chemically milled through the substrate until the top metallization pattern is reached. These holes are subsequently metallized at the same time as the ground plane to provide continuity between this plane and the desired topside pad. A microphotograph of such a "via" hole etched through a test wafer of 50-μm thickness is shown in Fig. 8. The hole diameter, in this case, is only 50 μm, much smaller than those normally used in monolithic circuits. The estimated inductance of a via hole is approximately 40–60 pH/mm of substrate thickness. Examples of circuits using both grounding techniques will be described later.

Low inductance grounds are especially important in source leads of power FET's. An inductance in the source lead manifests itself as resistive loss in the gate circuit, and hence a reduction in power gain. To illustrate this, Fig. 9 is a graph of the calculated gain reduction as a function of source lead inductance for an unconditionally stable power FET, corresponding to a power output of 1, 2, and 4 W (W=1.5, 3.0, and 6.0 mm).

The second interconnect problem arises when it is necessary to connect the individual cells of a power FET without resorting to wire bonds. A requirement is that these interconnects also have a low inductance. Here the so-called "air-bridge" crossover is useful. This crossover consists of a deposited strap which crosses over one or more conductors with an air gap in between for low capacitive coupling.

Fig. 10(a) is a cross-sectional view of a source crossover which interconnects two adjacent source pads of a power FET. The air gap is approximately 4 μm. Clearly shown is the 1-μm gate and the larger drain pad underneath the crossover. Fig. 10(b) is a closeup, angular view of a power FET which employs an airbridge (overlay) interconnect bus.

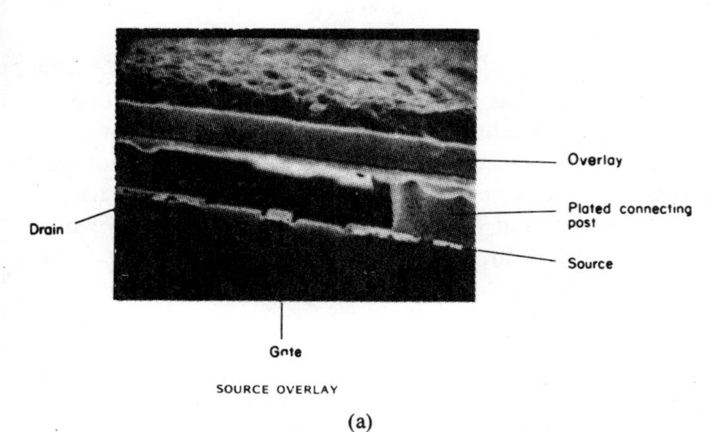

(a)

(b)

Fig. 10. (a) SEM microphotograph of a segment of source overlay (airbridge) of a power FET showing gate and drain contacts. (b) Top view of a GaAs power FET showing an air-bridge overlay connecting all source pads.

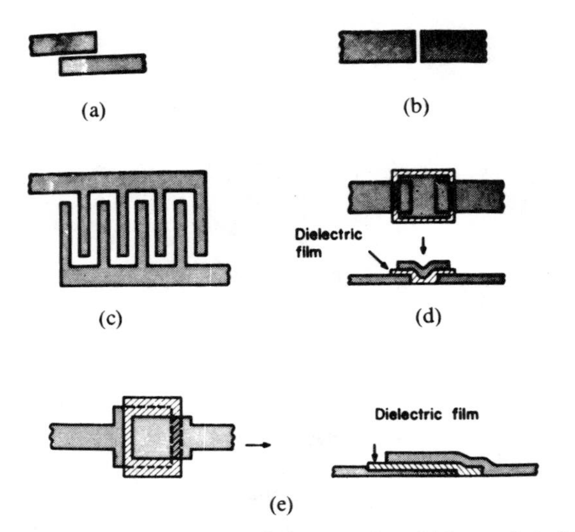

Fig. 11. Some planar capacitor designs. (a) Broadside coupled. (b) End coupled. (c) Interdigitated. (d) End-coupled overlay. (e) Overlay.

It is evident that the airbridge technology allows one to interconnect all cells without recourse to wire-bonding and therefore nicely satisfies the criterion for a monolithic circuit. Airbridge interconnects, of course, are also useful for microstrip and other crossovers. A good example is a planar spiral inductor, which requires a contact to the inner terminal.

E. Thin-Film Components

A flexible monolithic circuit design philosophy must include both lumped elements (dimensions <0.1 wavelength) and distributed elements, that is, elements composed of sections of transmission line. Lumped elements, R's, C's, and L's, are also useful for the RF circuitry, and in some cases mandatory, as for example, in thin-film resistive terminations for couplers. Lumped thin-film capacitors are absolutely essential for bias bypass applications, because of the large capacitance values required. Planar inductors can be extremely useful for matching purposes, especially at the lower end of the microwave band where stub inductors are very large, physically.

The choice of lumped or distributed elements depends on the frequency of operation. Lumped elements are suitable through X-band up to, perhaps, 20 GHz. It is likely, however, that beyond this frequency range, distributed elements will be preferred. It is difficult to realize a truly lumped element, even at the lower frequencies, because of the parasitics to ground associated with thin substrates. In this section we shall review the design principles of planar lumped elements.

1) Planar Capacitors: There are a variety of planar capacitors suitable for monolithic circuits—those achieved with a single metallization scheme, and those using a two-level metallization technology in conjunction with dielectric films. Some possible geometries for planar capacitors are shown in Fig. 11. The first three, which use no dielectric film and depend on electrostatic coupling via the substrate, generally are suitable for applications where low values of capacitance are required (less than 1.0 pF) for instance, high-impedance matching circuits. The last three geometries, the so-called overlay structures which use dielectric films, are suitable for low-impedance (power) circuitry and bypass and blocking applications. Capacitance values as high as 10 to 30 pF are achievable in small areas.

Two sources of loss are prevalent in planar capacitors, conductor losses in the metallization, and dielectric losses of the films, if used. Since the first three schemes illustrated in Fig. 11 are edge-coupled capacitors, high charge and current concentrations near the edges tend to limit the Q-factors. At X-band, typical Q-factors measured to date have been in the range of 50, despite the fact that no dielectric losses are present. The last three geometries distribute the current more uniformly throughout the metal plates because of the intervening film. However, even here, Q-factors only in the range of 50–100 are typical at X-band (10 GHz) because of dielectric film losses. Let us turn now to a more detailed analysis of the overlay structures depicted in Fig. 11, in particular the structure in Fig. 11(e).

First, we review briefly some general requirements of dielectric films for the overlay geometry. Some properties of dielectric films of importance are 1) dielectric constant, 2) capacitance/area, 3) microwave losses, 4) breakdown field, 5) temperature coefficient, 6) film integrity (pinhole density, stability over time), and 7) method and temperature of deposition. This last requirement is obviously important, because the technology used for film deposition must be compatible with the technology used for the active device (FET). Dielectric films which easily satisfy this criterion are SiO_x and Si_3N_4.

Some useful figures of merit for dielectric films are the capacitance-breakdown voltage product

$$F_{cV} = \left(\frac{C}{A}\right) V_b \tag{1a}$$

$$= \kappa \epsilon_0 E_b \tag{1b}$$

$$\cong (8-30) \times 10^3 \text{ pF} \cdot \text{V/mm}^2$$

and the capacitance-dielectric Q-factor product

$$F_{cq} = \left(\frac{C}{A}\right) Q_d \tag{1c}$$

$$= \frac{(C/A)}{\tan \delta_d} \tag{1d}$$

where C/A is the capacitance per unit area, V_b is the breakdown voltage, E_b is the corresponding breakdown field, κ is the dielectric constant, and $\tan \delta_d$ is the dielectric loss tangent. Breakdown fields of the order of 1–2 MV/cm are typical of good dielectric films. Dielectric constants are in the order of 4–20. Loss tangents can range from 10^{-1} to 10^{-3}. It is desirable to have as high figures of merit as possible. Table III is a list of candidate films and their properties.

We return, now, to the overlay structure of Fig. 11(e). A closeup perspective view is shown in Fig. 12. Taking into

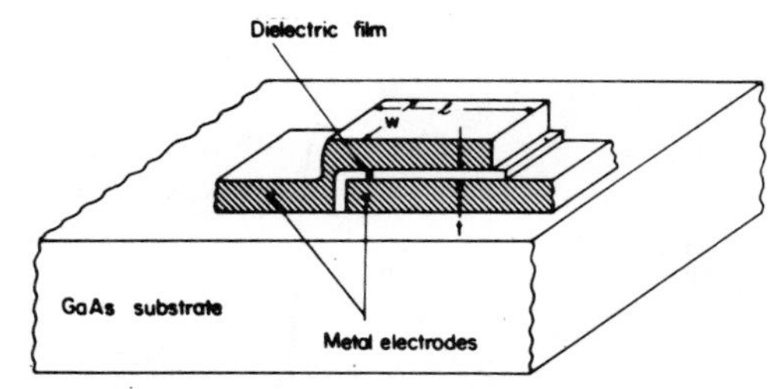

Fig. 12. Perspective of an overlay thin-film capacitor.

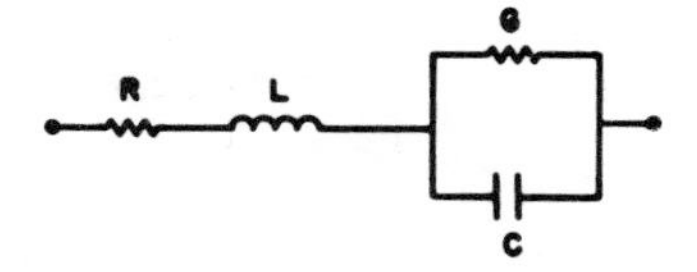

Fig. 14. Equivalent circuit of a thin-film capacitor. $R=2/3\ rl$. $C=cl$. $G=\omega c \tan\delta$. $L=\mathfrak{L}l$. $r=$ resistance/length (electrodes). $c=$ capacitance/length. $\mathfrak{L}=$inductance/length (electrodes). $\tan\delta=$loss tangent of dielectric film.

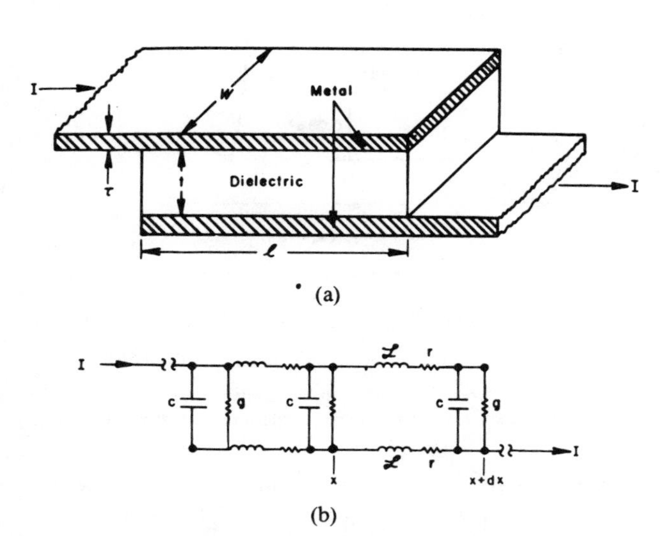

Fig. 13. Diagrams relevant to analysis of impedance of a thin-film capacitor. (a) Thin-film capacitor. (b) Circuit model.

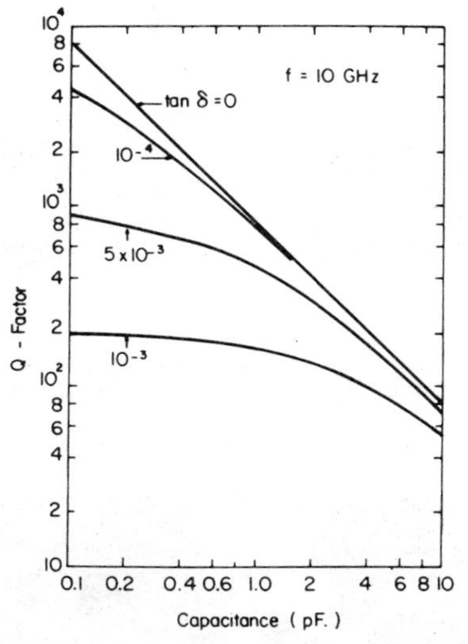

Fig. 15. Quality factor of a square thin-film capacitor as a function of capacitance and dielectric loss tangent for $f=10$ GHz.

TABLE III
PROPERTIES OF SOME CANDIDATE DIELECTRIC FILMS

DIELECTRIC	κ	TCC (ppm/°C)	C/A* (pF/mm²)	$(C/A)\cdot Q_d$	$(C/A)\cdot V_b$	COMMENTS
SiO	4.5-6.8	100-500	300	low	medium	Evaporated
SiO_2	4-5	50	200	medium	medium	Evaporated, CVD, or Sputtered
Si_3N_4	6-7	25-35	300	high	high	Sputtered or CVD
Ta_2O_5	20-25	0-200	1100	medium	high	Sputtered and Anodized
Al_2O_3	6-9	300-500	400	high	high	CVD, anodic oxidation, sputtering
Schottky-Barrier Junction	12.9	--	550	very low	high	Evaporated Metal on GaAs
Polyimide	3-4.5	-500	35	high	--	Spun and Cured Organic Film

*Film thickness assumed = 2000 Å, except for polyimide, 10,000 Å.

account the longitudinal current paths in the metal contacts, one may analyze this device as a lossy transmission line as indicated in Fig. 13. In Fig. 13(b), $\mathfrak{L}$ and r represent the inductance and resistance per unit length of the metal plates, and c and g denote the capacitance and conductance per unit length of the dielectric film. The relation between g and c is determined by the loss tangent, $g=\omega c \tan\delta_d$. The series resistance in the plates is determined by the skin resistance if the metal thickness exceeds the skin depth, or the bulk metal resistance if the reverse is true. Usually, the bottom metal layer is evaporated only, and hence is about 0.5 μm thick, which may be less than the skin depth. The top metal is normally built up to a thickness of several micrometers or more by plating.

For a well-designed capacitor, the longitudinal and transverse dimensions are small compared with a wavelength in the dielectric film. In this case, a good approximation to the capacitor is the equivalent circuit shown in Fig. 14. When the skin loss condition prevails, the Q-factor corresponding to these losses is given by the expression

$$Q_c=\frac{3}{2\omega R_s(C/A)l^2} \tag{2}$$

where R_s is the surface skin resistivity and l is the electrode length (see Fig. 12). Note the strong dependence on electrode length. This arises because of the longitudinal current path in each electrode. Note that if one electrode, say the bottom plate, is very thin, Q_c is decreased.

The dielectric Q-factor is $Q_d=1/\tan\delta$, and the total Q-factor is given by the relation $Q^{-1}=Q_d^{-1}+Q_c^{-1}$. Fig. 15 is a graph of the calculated Q-factor as a function of capacitance for various loss trangents. Note that for a 1-pF capacitor, and no dielectric losses, the predicted Q-factor is approximately 800! Yet, experimentally, values more like one-tenth of this are obtained, suggesting that dielectric films are extremely lossy—much more so than their bulk counterparts. No satisfactory explanation for this observation has yet been advanced.

2) Planar Inductors: Planar inductors for monolithic circuits can be realized in a number of configurations, all achieved with a single-layer metallization scheme. Fig. 16 illustrates various geometries that can be used for thin-film inductors. Aside from the high-impedance line section, all

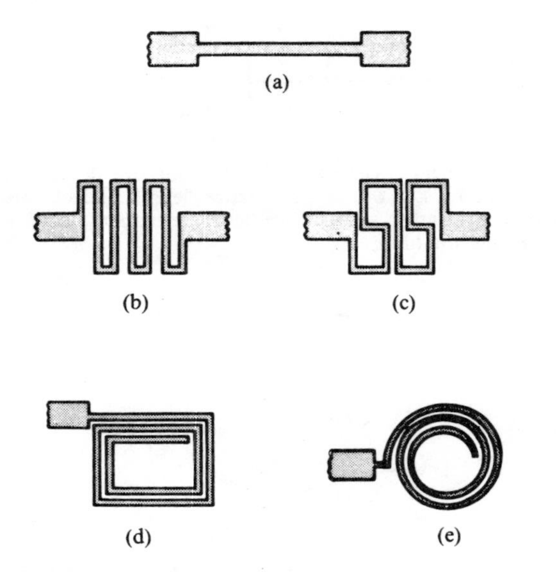

Fig. 16. Some planar inductor configurations. (a) High-impedance line section. (b) Meander line. (c) S-line. (d) Square spiral. (e) Circular spiral.

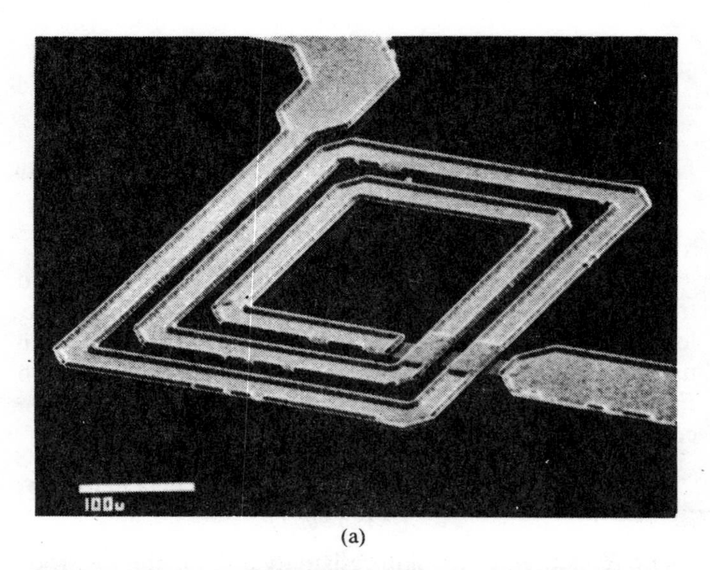

(a)

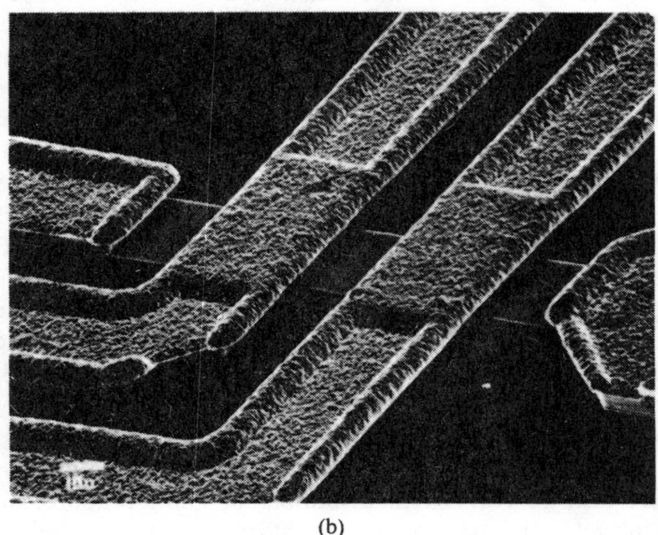

(b)

Fig. 17. SEM photographs of a thin-film square spiral inductor showing air-bridge crossovers.

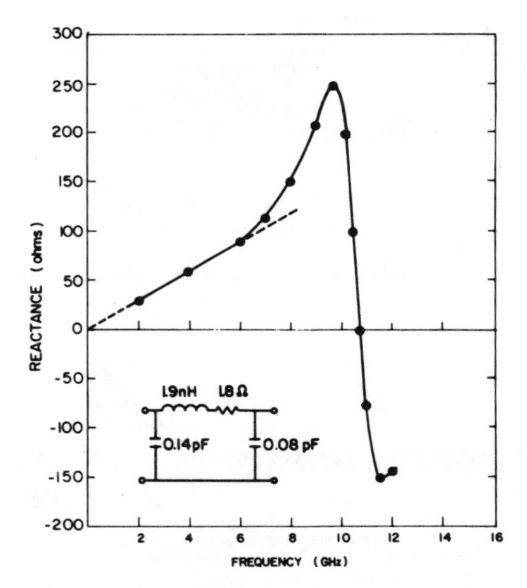

MEASURED REACTANCE OF A TEN-SEGMENT
SQUARE-SPIRAL GROUNDED INDUCTOR
ON A 0.1 MM THICK SI-GaAs SUBSTRATE

Fig. 18. Measured reactance of a ten-segment square spiral inductor on a 0.1-mm thick GaAs substrate (equivalent circuit shown in inset).

of the structures depend on mutual coupling between the various line segments to achieve a high inductance in a small area. In any multisegment design, one must insure that the total line length is a small fraction of a wavelength, otherwise the conductor cannot be treated as "lumped." Unfortunately, this latter condition is not often satisfied. Fig. 17 is a SEM photograph of a multisegment square–spiral inductor. Note the crossover connections.

When thin substrates are used, corrections must be made to the calculated inductance to account for the ground plane. These corrections are always in the direction to reduce the inductance, and are typically in the range of 15 percent, though for large-area inductors, the reduction can be as high as 30 percent.

Typical inductance values for monolithic circuits fall in the range from 0.5 to 10 nH. The higher values are difficult to achieve in strictly lumped form because of intersegment fringing capacitance. A more serious problem is that of shunt capacitance to ground, especially in the case of the microstrip format. This capacitance to ground can become important enough to require its inclusion in determining the performance of the inductor.

An illustration of the serious effect of capacitance to ground is demonstrated by the data of Fig. 18. This is a graph of the measured reactance of a ten-segment square spiral inductor as a function of frequency. The inductor is approximately 0.4 mm square, consisting of segments 1 mil wide, separated by 1 mil (see Fig. 17). The inductance, as designed, was nominally 1.9 nH. Note that above 10 GHz the reactance becomes capacitive! The equivalent circuit, as deduced from two-port S-parameters, is shown in the inset. The substrate thickness was 0.1 mm.

Of course, the inductor is usable, provided all of the parasitics indicated in Fig. 18 are taken into account.

Unfortunately, these parasitics are not known in advance. Thus, in a computer-aided approach, corrections to the circuit in which the inductor appears must be made in later iterations. This can become a costly procedure. It is often more sensible to use an inductive transmission line segment whose electrical behavior is known in advance.

Some of the skin losses in the inductor reside in the ground plane (assuming a metallized bottom side) and increase as the ground plane approaches the film inductor (not unlike shielding losses). However, the dependence on substrate thickness is mild, since most of the losses reside in the film turns, because of their small cross section.

In practice, inductor Q-factors of the order of 50 are observed at X-band, with higher values at higher frequencies. There appears to be no way to improve the Q-factor significantly, because of the highly unfavorable ratio of metal surface area to dielectric volume.

Somewhat higher Q-factors are achievable with microstrip resonant stub sections. These are more properly considered as distributed inductors, or more correctly, as distributed resonant elements. Three sources of loss are important here, skin losses, dielectric losses, and radiation losses. For microstrip stubs, the skin losses are those associated with microstrip, as are the dielectric losses. Skin losses vary inversely with the substrate thickness, and increase as the line impedance increases. Assuming negligible dielectric losses, one may show that the conductor Q-factor for a quarter-wave open circuit stub is given by

$$Q_c = \frac{27.3}{(\alpha\lambda g)} \tag{3}$$

where $(\alpha\lambda g)$ is the loss in the line section in decibels per wavelength. Since $(\alpha\lambda g)$ decreases as $f^{-1/2}$, Q_c increases as the square root of frequency, as for thin-film inductors. On the other hand, radiation losses from the open circuit end vary as [8]

$$Q_r = \frac{R}{(fh)^2} \tag{4}$$

where h is the substrate thickness and R is a function of w/h and the dielectric constant of the substrate. (The radiation factor R is considerably larger for a quarter-wave stub grounded at its far end.) Note that the radiation Q decreases as the square of the frequency and the substrate thickness h. Thus any attempt to increase the conductor Q-factor by increasing the frequency and substrate thickness is eventually overcompensated by the decrease in radiation Q. Fig. 19 illustrates this fact for practical substrate thicknesses. Thus, above X-band, open-circuit stub resonators are dominated by radiation losses, unless the substrate is less than 0.25 mm thick. This radiation also can cause coupling to adjacent circuits. A way to overcome both problems is to use a ring resonator.

The choice then as to whether reactive lumped elements or distributed elements should be used must be considered for each individual application. If high-Q narrow-band circuits are to be realized, distributed elements are recommended, provided space is available. On the other hand, broad-band circuits are probably easier to design with lumped elements, though even here synthesis techniques based on transmission line stubs are now available. Some circuits are more readily designed with distributed elements. Examples are four-port couplers and power combiners/dividers.

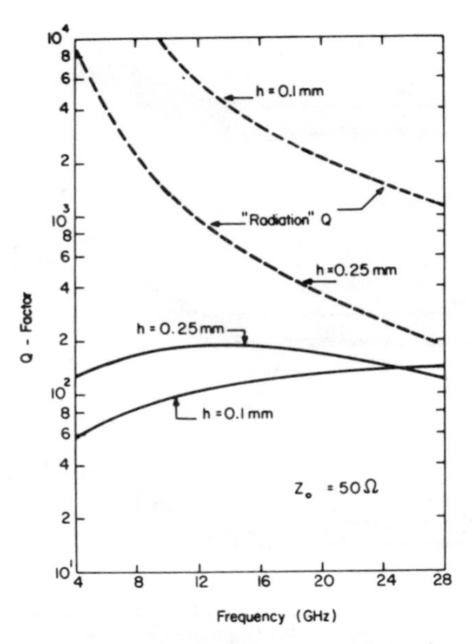

Fig. 19. Quality factor of a quarter-wave microstrip resonator on a GaAs substrate.

3) Planar Loads: Planar loads are essential for terminating such components as hybrid couplers, power combiners and splitters, and the like. Some factors to be considered in the design of such loads are: 1) the sheet resistivity available; 2) thermal stability or temperature coefficient of the resistive material; 3) the thermal resistance of the load; and 4) the frequency bandwidth. Other applications of planar resistors are bias voltage dividers and dropping resistors. However, such applications should be avoided in monolithic circuits, where power conservation is usually an objective.

Planar resistors can be realized in a variety of forms but fall into three categories: 1) semiconductor films; 2). deposited metal films; and 3) cermets. Resistors based on semiconductors can be fabricated by forming an isolated land of conducting epitaxial film on the substrate, for example, by mesa etching or by isolation implant of the surrounding conducting film. Another way is by implanting a high-resistivity region within the semi-insulating substrate. Metal film resistors are formed by evaporating a metal layer over the substrate and forming the desired pattern by photolithography. These techniques are illustrated in Fig. 20. Cermet resistors are formed from films consisting of a mixture of metal and a dielectric. However, because of the dielectric, they are expected to exhibit an RC frequency dependence similar to that of carbon resistors, which may be a problem in the microwave band.

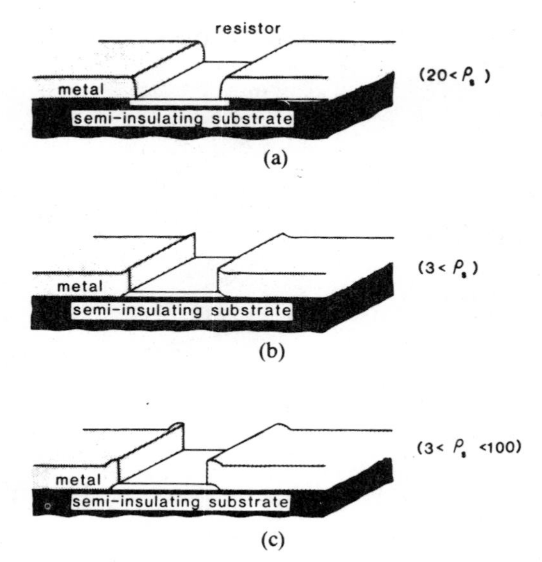

Fig. 20. Examples of planar resistor designs. (a) Implanted resistor. (b) Mesa resistor. (c) Deposited resistor.

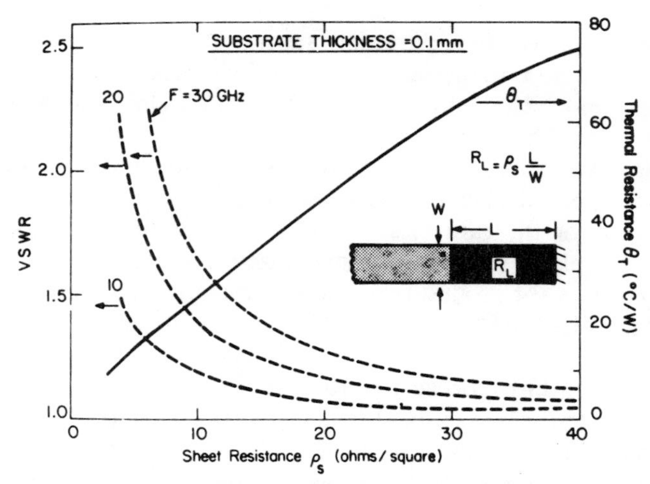

Fig. 21. Thermal resistance and VSWR of a planar resistor as a function of sheet resistance and frequency.

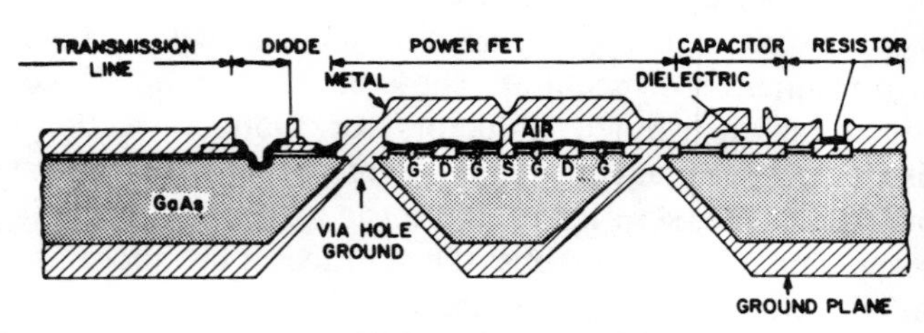

Fig. 22. Composite sketch illustrating technologies used in monolithic circuits.

TABLE IV
PROPERTIES OF SOME RESISTIVE FILMS

MATERIAL	RESISTIVITY (μΩ-cm)	TCR (ppm/°C)	METHOD OF DEPOSITION	STABILITY	COMMENTS
Cr	13 (BULK)	+3000 (BULK)	EVAPORATED SPUTTERED	G-E	EXCELLENT ADHERENCE TO GaAs
Ti	55-135	+2500	EVAPORATED SPUTTERED	G-E	EXCELLENT ADHERENCE TO GaAs
Ta	180-220	-100 TO +500	SPUTTERED	E	CAN BE ANODIZED
Ni Cr	60-600	200	EVAP. (300°C) SPUTTERED	G-E	STABILIZED BY SLOW ANNEAL AT 300°C
TaN	280	-180 TO -300	REACTIVELY SPUTTERED	G	CANNOT BE ANODIZED
Ta_2N	300	-50 TO -110	REACTIVELY SPUTTERED	E	CAN BE ANODIZED
BULK GaAs	3-100 ohms/sq.	+3000	EPITAXY OR IMPLANTATION	E	NONLINEAR AT HIGH CURRENT DENSITIES

Metal films are preferred over semiconducting films because the latter exhibit a nonlinear behavior at high dc current densities and a rather strong temperature dependence—as some metal films do. Not all metal films are suitable for monolithic circuits, since their technology must be compatible with that of GaAs. Table IV lists some candidate metal films along with GaAs.

A problem common to all planar resistors used as microwave loads is the parasitic capacitance attributable to the underlying dielectric region and the distributed inductance of the film, which makes such resistors exhibit a frequency dependence at high frequencies. If the substrate bottomside is metallized, one may determine the frequency dependence by treating the load as a very lossy microstrip line.

For low thermal resistance, one should keep the area of the film as large as possible. To minimize discontinuity effects in width, the width of the resistive film load should not differ markedly from the width of the line feeding it. This means that the resistive element should be as long as possible to minimize thermal resistance. This length is specified by the sheet resistivity of the film and is given by the formula

$$l = \frac{wR}{\rho_s} \tag{5}$$

where w is the width of the film, R the desired load resistance, and ρ_s the sheet resistance of the film.

If one increases the length of the load (by decreasing the sheet resistivity) to achieve a low thermal resistance, one may get into trouble because the load may begin to exhibit the behavior of a transmission line (albeit a very lossy one) rather than a lumped resistor. Fig. 21 shows how the VSWR increases dramatically at low values of ρ_s because the length of the load becomes too large. Also shown is the thermal resistance. Clearly, a tradeoff is necessary between VSWR and thermal resistance.

All of the technologies we have discussed above are conveniently summarized in the cross-sectional view of a hypothetical monolithic circuit shown in Fig. 22.

4) Transmission Line Junction Effects: The many junctions and bends required of transmission lines in monolithic circuits to achieve close packing introduce unwanted parasitic inductances and capacitances. Fig. 23 illustrates some of the circuit representations of these junctions. Since such discontinuities cannot be avoided, but only minimized, the frequency dependencies must be taken into account, especially when the frequency is above X-band. It is particularly important to include junction effects in any broad-band design, that is, octave bandwidths. Unfortunately, though much work has been done on this topic, the results are not generally in a form useful for the circuit

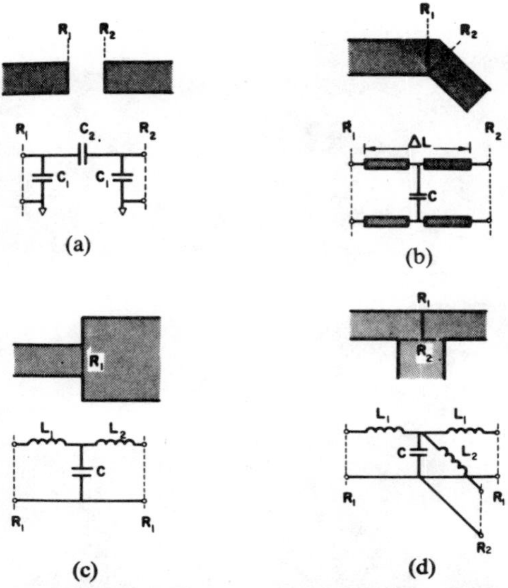

Fig. 23. Some microstrip discontinuities and their equivalent circuits. (a) Gap. (b) Bend. (c) Width discontinuity. (d) Tee junction.

designer. As a consequence, computer-aided design programs do not incorporate corrections for junctions at present.

VI. Examples of Monolithic Circuits

We shall present examples of some practical monolithic circuits which demonstrate the design principles discussed above. These circuits are representative of the research being conducted at laboratories around the world.

Fig. 24 is a photograph of a GaAs chip containing a single-stage four-FET power combiner designed at Raytheon (Research Division) [17]. This amplifier, an *X*-band microwave circuit, was the first to dispense with wire bonds on the chip by use of "via" holes for grounding the source pads. Built on a chip 4.8×6.3×0.1 mm in size, and using a microstrip format with on-chip matching to a 50-Ω system, the circuit exhibited a 5-dB small-signal gain at 9.5 GHz and a saturated CW power output of 2.1 W at 3.3-dB gain (see Fig. 25). Bias was supplied through bias tees via the RF terminals. Although large by present standards, the chip area could be reduced by 30 percent if the capacitive stubs were replaced by thin-film capacitors, which were not available at the time.

An extension of this technology to a two-stage *X*-band power amplifier also designed at this laboratory [22] is shown in Fig. 26. In this circuit, thin-film capacitors, based on SiO or Si_3N_4 technology, were incorporated on the chip for RF blocking and bias applications. Another innovation, clearly evident in the future, is the use of extended integral (grown) beam leads, an offshoot of the airbridge technology. The beam leads allow off-chip bonding of the RF and dc supply connections to the chip, thus avoiding damage to the chip. The amplifier, built on a 2.5×3.2 ×0.1-mm chip, exhibited a saturated CW power output of 550 mW and 8.5-dB gain at 9.5 GHz and a small-signal gain of 10 dB.

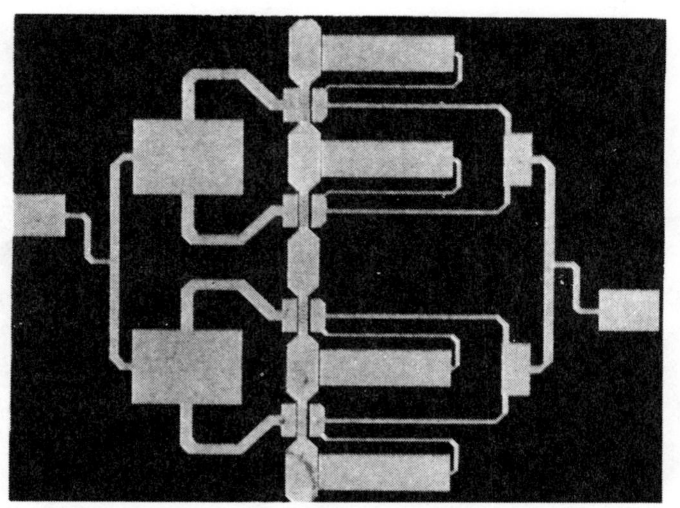
Fig. 24. Monolithic GaAs four-FET *X*-band power combiner. Chip size is 4.8×6.3×0.1 mm. (Raytheon Company.)

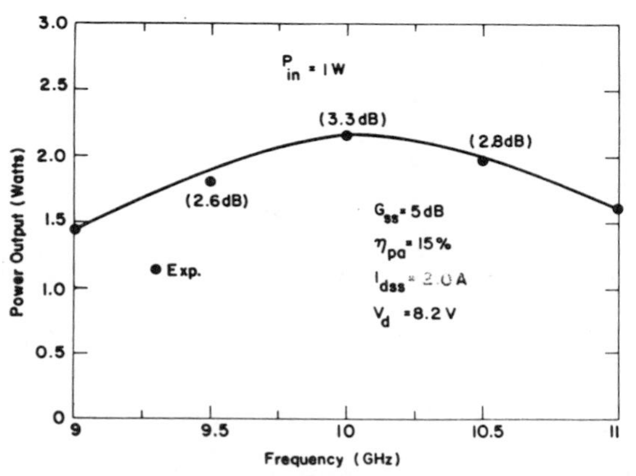

Fig. 25. Power output–frequency response for monolithic GaAs four-FET power combiner.

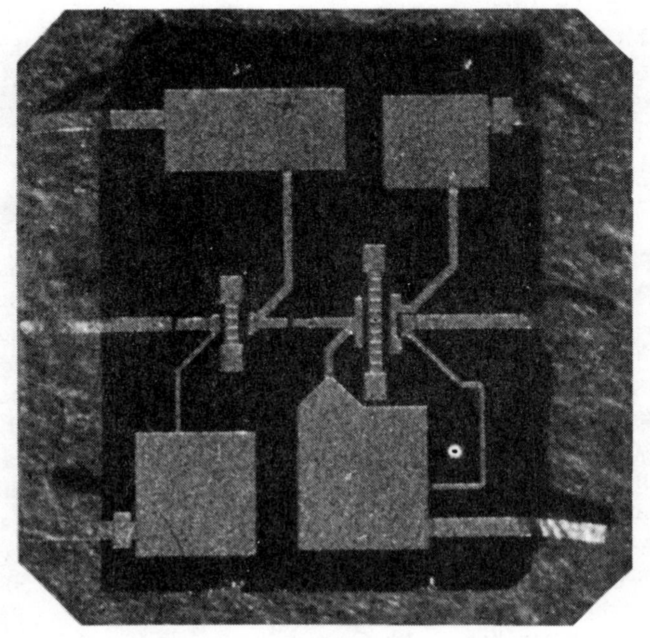
Fig. 26. Two-stage GaAs monolithic *X*-band amplifier. Chip size is 2.5×3.2×0.1 mm. (Raytheon Company.)

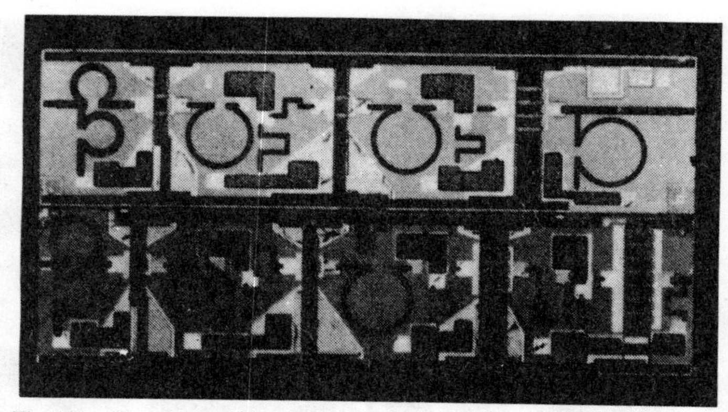

Fig. 27. Three- and four-stage GaAs monolithic X-band power amplifiers. Circuit sizes are 1.0×4.0×0.1 mm (Courtesy, W. Wisseman, Texas Instruments, Inc.)

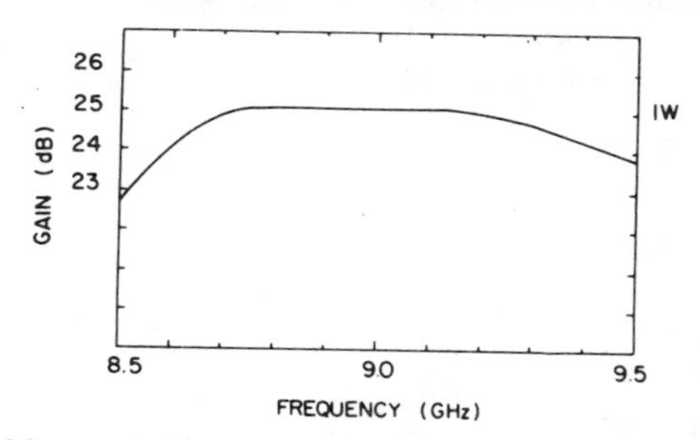

Fig. 28. Measured power gain–frequency response of four-stage amplifier of Fig. 27. (Courtesy, W. Wisseman, Texas Instruments, Inc.)

Turning to results obtained at other laboratories, Fig. 27 represents some of the research at Texas Instruments [18]. Shown is a chip containing side-by-side X-band amplifiers: the top, a three-stage FET amplifier; the bottom, a four-stage amplifier. Each chip is 1×4×0.1 mm in size. Both designs are based on a lumped-element approach which uses spiral inductors, clearly evident in the photographs, and thin-film capacitors of the end-coupled variety (Fig. 11(d)). Grounding is achieved by means of a metallized peripheral strip, and bias connections are made by wire-bonds to pads on the chip. The three-stage amplifier delivers 400 mW at 23-dB gain and the four-stage delivers 1 W at 27-dB gain and 15–17-percent power-added efficiency in the 8.8 to 9.2-GHz range (see Fig. 28).

Another circuit reported by this laboratory [18] is the push–pull amplifier shown in Fig. 29. Each channel is a two-stage power amplifier, again based on the lumped-element approach, situated on a 2.0×2.0×0.1-mm chip. Although not monolithic in the strict sense of the word because inductive wire bonds interconnect the two channels, the design is unique in that a "virtual" ground is achieved by connection of the corresponding source pads of the adjacent channels; thus the need for a low inductance ground for the sources is avoided. Over 12-dB gain was obtained at 9.0 GHz with a combined CW power output of 1.4 W. All three amplifiers interface with a 50-Ω system.

An octave bandwidth GaAs amplifier designed at Westinghouse (R. and D. Center) is shown in Fig. 30. This

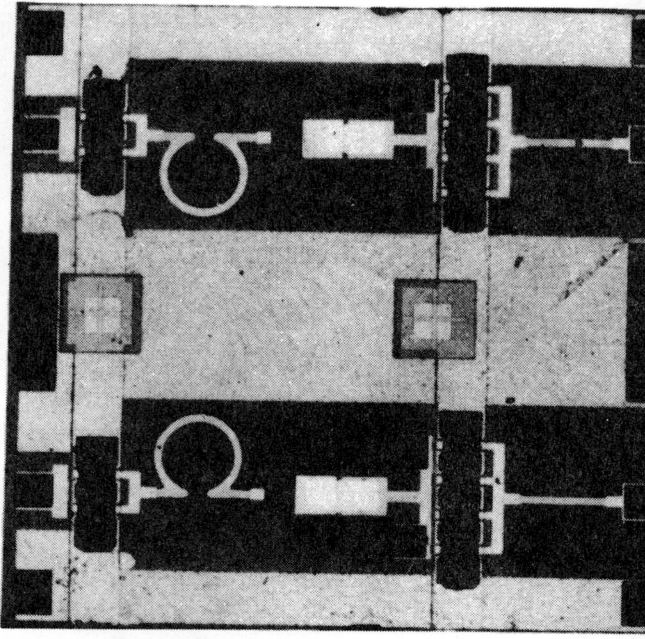

Fig. 29. Two-stage GaAs monolithic X-band push–pull amplifier. Ch size is 2.0×2.0×0.1 mm. (Courtesy, W. Wisseman, Texas Instrumen Inc.)

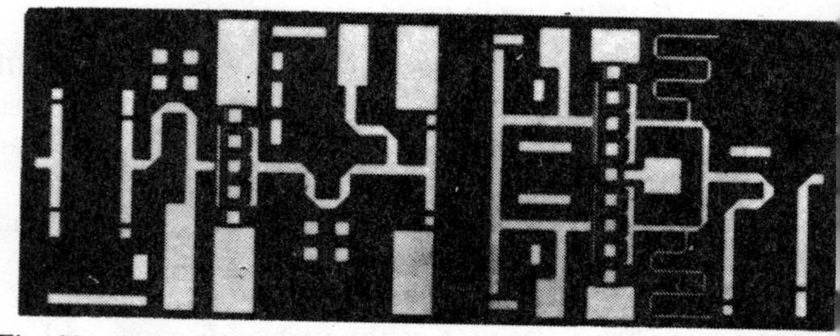

Fig. 30. Two-stage 5.7–11-GHz GaAs monolithic power amplifier. Ch size is 2.0×4.75×0.1 mm. (Courtesy, J. Oakes, Westinghouse.)

circuit, similar to the one reported by Degenford *et al.* [7 consists of 1200-μm and 2400-μm periphery power FET in cascade formed by selective ion implantation into semi-insulating substrate. Built on a 2.0×4.75×0.1-m chip, the circuit is based on a microstrip format with vi holes, and makes liberal use of interdigitated capacitor Source pads are grounded individually with vias. Th amplifier produces a power output of 28±0.7 dBm at gain of 6±0.7 dB across the 5.7 to 11-GHz band.

Another monolithic wideband amplifier is the 4–8-GH eight-stage GaAs circuit reported by TRW [3] shown i Fig. 31. The design, based on the lumped-element ap proach (spiral inductors and SiO_2 thin-film capacitors) use a coplanar feed at the input and output 50-Ω ports, wit coplanar ground planes extending the full length of th 2.5×5.0-mm chip.

A departure from the GaAs approach is the SOS three stage L-band amplifier built at Raytheon (Equipment Divi sion) [13] (Fig. 32). This circuit, occupying a chip 7.5×7. ×0.46 mm in size, delivers 200-mW CW output at 20-d gain at 1.3 GHz. The circuit uses spiral inductors. Dielec

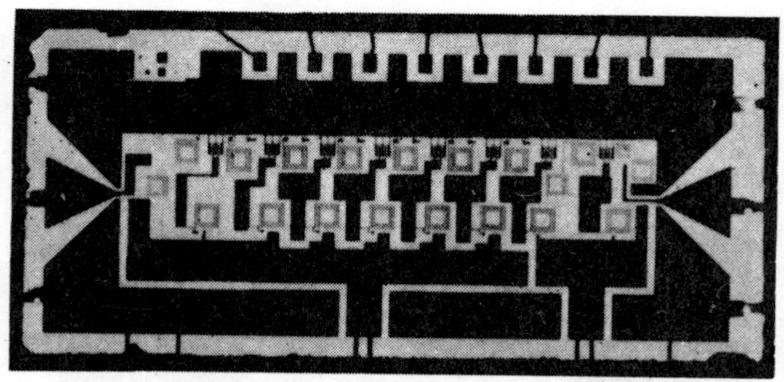

Fig. 31. Eight-stage 4–8-GHz GaAs monolithic amplifier. Chip size is 2.5×5.0 mm. (Courtesy, A. Benavides, T.R.W., Inc.)

Fig. 32. Three-stage *L*-band silicon-on-sapphire amplifier. Chip size is 7.5×7.5×0.46 mm. (Courtesy, D. Laighton, Raytheon Company.)

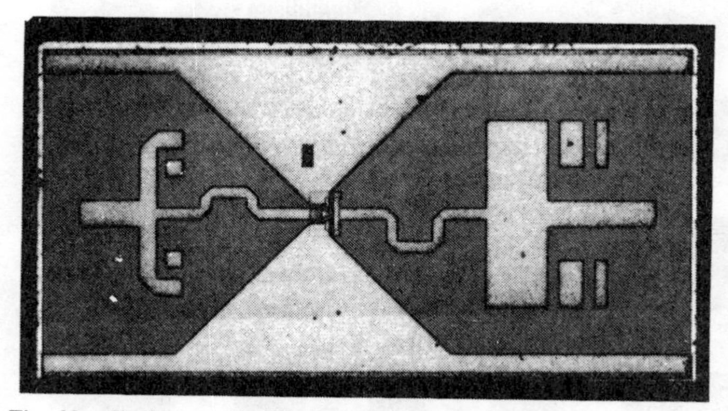

Fig. 33. Single-stage 20-GHz GaAs monolithic low-noise amplifier. Chip size is 2.75×1.95×0.15 mm. (Courtesy, A. Higashisaka, Nippon Electric Company.)

tric (SiO_2) films are used for capacitors and conductor crossovers.

So far we have described power amplifiers only. The first monolithic low-noise amplifier was reported by NEC (Central Research Laboratories) [10] (Fig. 33). This is a one-stage circuit on a 2.75×1.95×0.15-mm GaAs chip. The matching circuits use microstrip lines and stubs to interface with a 50-Ω system through bias tees. Large topside pads are used for the source RF grounds. The circuit, using a 0.5-μm gate, exhibited a noise figure of 6.2 dB and an associated gain of 7.5 dB in the 20.5–22.2-GHz band.

Most of the circuits we have described so far are based on the lumped-element or the microstrip approach or on a

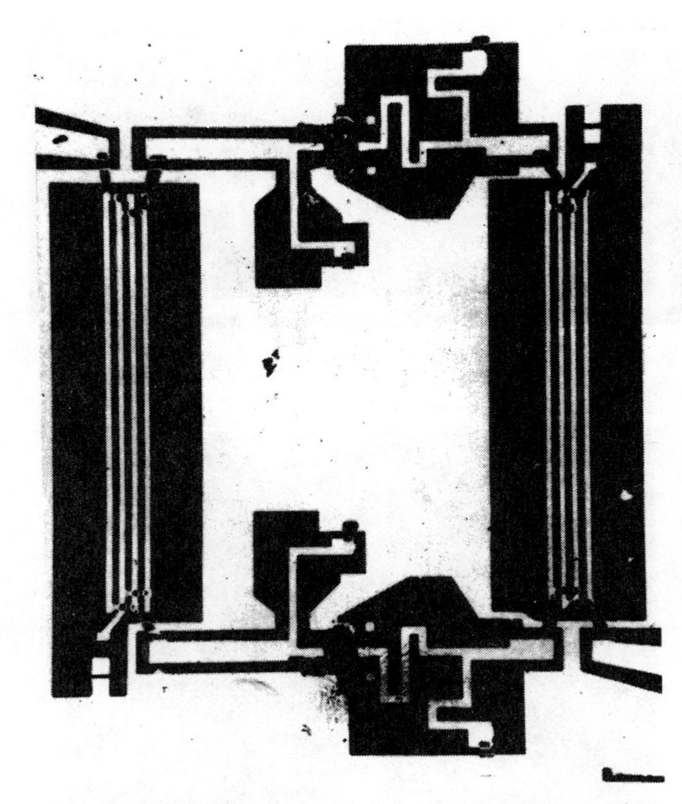

Fig. 34. *X*-band GaAs monolithic balanced amplifier using coplanar coupler. Chip size is 4.0×4.0 mm. (Courtesy, E. M. Bastida, CISE SpA.)

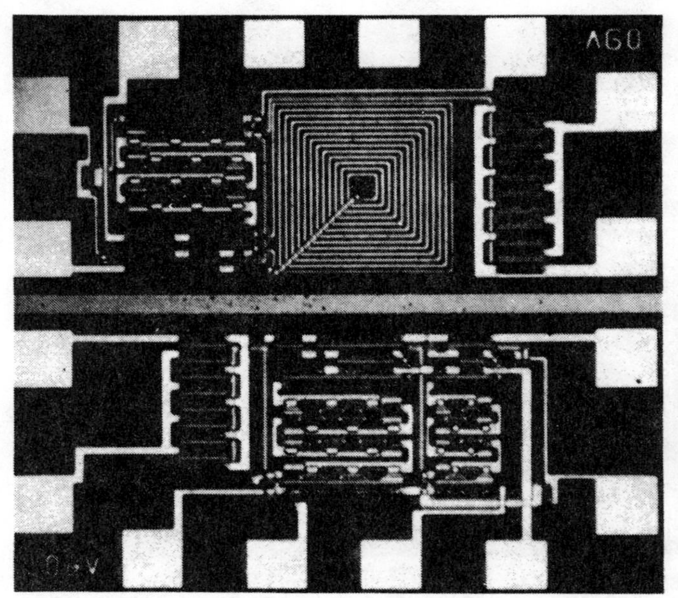

Fig. 35. Multistage direct-coupled GaAs monolithic amplifiers. Circuit sizes are 300×650 μm. (Courtesy, D. Hornbuckle, Hewlett Packard.)

combination of the two. Fig. 34 is a photograph of an *X*-band circuit using coplanar waveguides. This is a balanced amplifier reported by CISE SpA [2] built on a 4.0×4.0-mm GaAs chip, which uses two 90°, 3-dB broadband couplers. The couplers employ CPW rather than MS to obviate the need for micron-line spacings which are necessary with MS couplers. Lumped inductors and thin film (SiO_2) capacitors are used for RF matching and bypass. The circuit utilizes 0.8-μm gate MESFET's and has demonstrated a gain slightly below 10 dB between 8.5 and 11 GHz.

The next circuits, Fig. 35 represent a complete departure from the design philosophy considered so far. Shown is a photograph of two wide-band (0–4.5 GHz) amplifiers de-

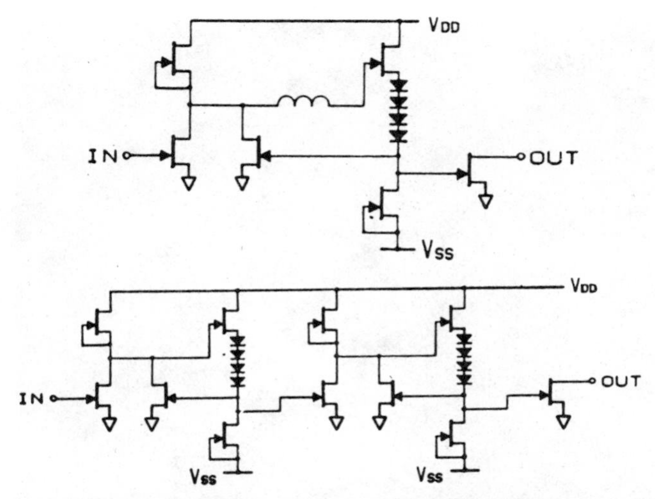

Fig. 36. Circuit schematics for direct-coupled amplifiers shown in Fig. 35. (Courtesy, D. Hornbuckle, Hewlett Packard.)

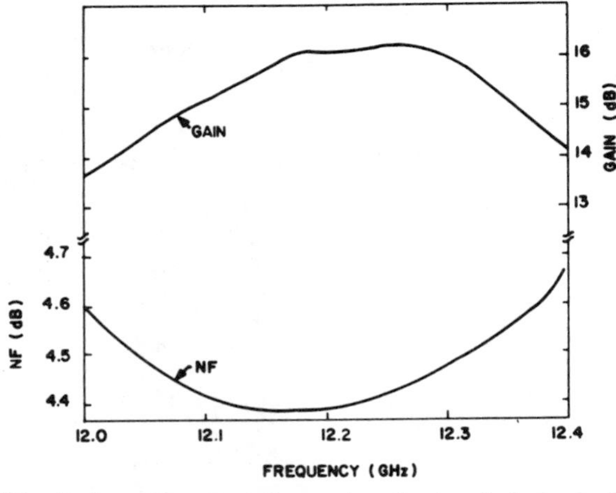

Fig. 38. Performance curves for receiver front end shown in Fig. 37. (Courtesy, P. Harrop, LEP.)

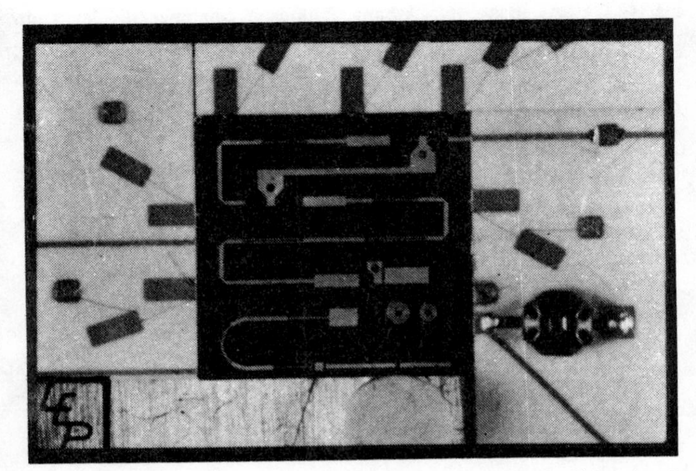

Fig. 37. 12-GHz GaAs monolithic receiver front end. Chip size is 1.0×1.0 cm. (Courtesy, P. Harrop, LEP.)

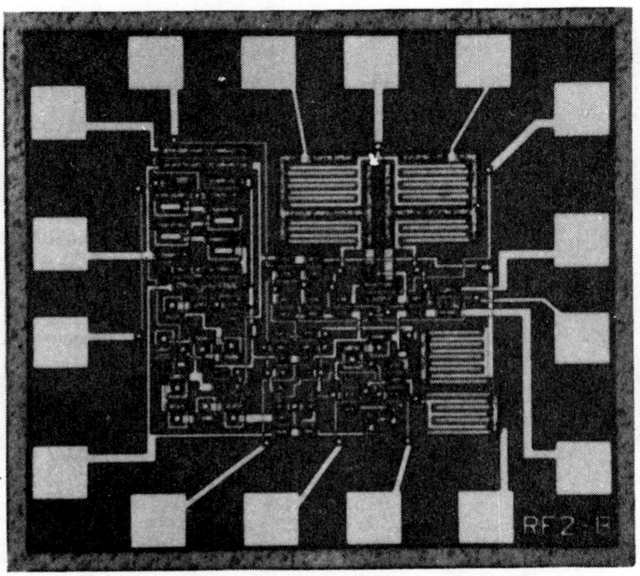

Fig. 39. Direct-coupled GaAs monolithic FET RF signal generation chip. Chip size is 600×650 μm. (Courtesy, R. Van Tuyl, Hewlett Packard.)

signed at Hewlett Packard [11]. What is unique about these circuits is the fact that, except for the spiral inductor, MESFET's are used throughout as active devices and as replacements for resistors and capacitors. The elimination of lumped elements, in conjunction with a direct-coupled circuit approach, allows a very high circuit packing density. Fig. 36 illustrates the circuit complexity achieved in each 0.3×0.65-mm area. Both amplifiers exhibited a gain in excess of 10 dB over the band.

Up until now we have described circuits which earlier we referred to as the lowest level of complexity. The next series of circuits represent integration on a functional block level. The first circuit (Fig. 37) is an integrated receiver front end on a GaAs chip intended for 12-GHz operation. This was reported by LEP [9]. The circuit, deposited on a large 1-cm square chip of GaAs, consists of a two-stage low-noise 12-GHz MESFET amplifier, an 11-GHz FET oscillator, and a dual-gate FET mixer. The matching circuits use microstrip lines and quarter-wave dc blocks. The oscillator is stabilized by an off-chip dielectric resonator. Bias circuits are included on the surrounding alumina substrate. Preliminary results are summarized in Fig. 38. The circuit is intended for a potential consumer market for domestic satellite-to-home TV reception planned for Europe.

Another example of the functional block approach is the monolithic GaAs FET RF signal generation chip (Fig. 39) designed at Hewlett Packard [21]. An extremely high degree of integration was achieved by use of the direct-coupled approach described earlier. Contained within the 0.65×0.65-mm chip is the circuit shown in the schematic of Fig. 40. The local oscillator is resonated by an off-chip inductor which is tuned over the 2.1–2.5-GHz range by an on-chip Schottky barrier junction capacitor. The circuit is intended for an instrument application.

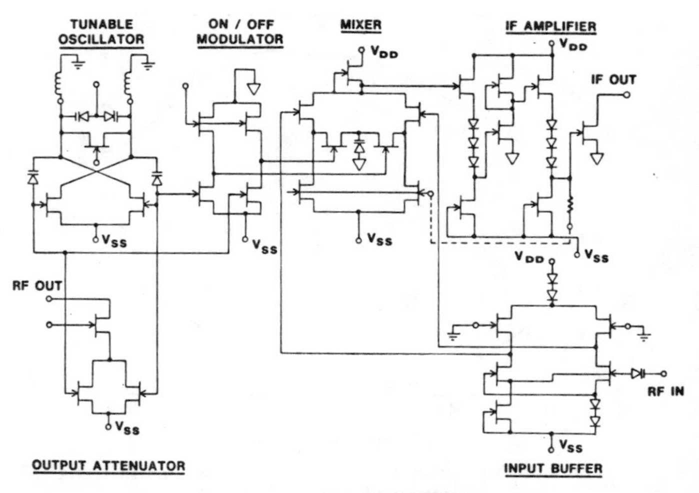

Fig. 40. Schematic for direct-coupled signal generation chip shown in Fig. 39. (Courtesy, R. Van Tuyl, Hewlett Packard.)

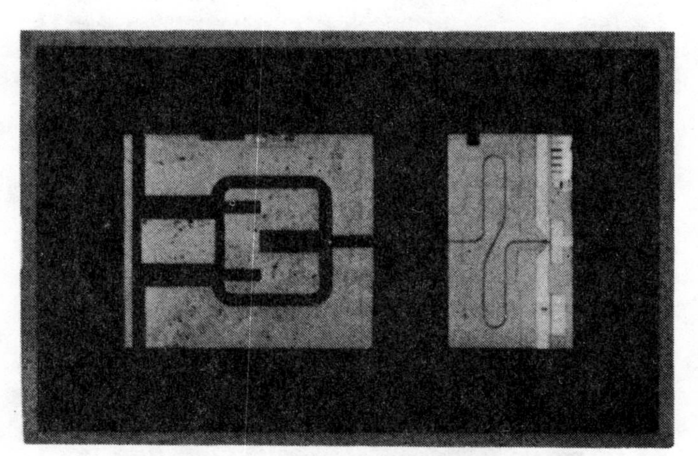

Fig. 41. GaAs monolithic mixer/IF circuit for millimeter-wave receiver applications. Chip size is 2.7×5.3×0.18 mm. (Courtesy, R. Sudbury, Lincoln Laboratories.)

Our final functional block circuit is the monolithic balanced Schottky-barrier diode mixer/IF FET preamplifier chip illustrated in Fig. 41. This MS circuit, reported by Lincoln Laboratories [6], is built on a 2.7×5.3×0.18-mm GaAs chip in MS format. The circuit operates between a 31-GHz signal source and a 2-GHz IF output. An external oscillator signal is injected through one of the coupler ports. The circuit exhibits an overall gain of 4 dB and a single-sideband noise figure of 11.5 dB.

We now turn to some special passive components fabricated in monolithic form. The first is a Wilkinson combiner/divider reported by Raytheon [23] shown in Fig. 42. Built on a 1.5×2.5×0.1-mm chip, the circuit uses a thin-film titanium balancing resistor and was designed to operate at a center frequency of 9.5 GHz. Note the extended beam leads. As an illustration of the extremely good electrical balance that one can achieve with the high-resolution photolithography intrinsic to the monolithic approach, we show in Fig. 43 a graph of the power division and phase balance measured for the two 3-dB ports.

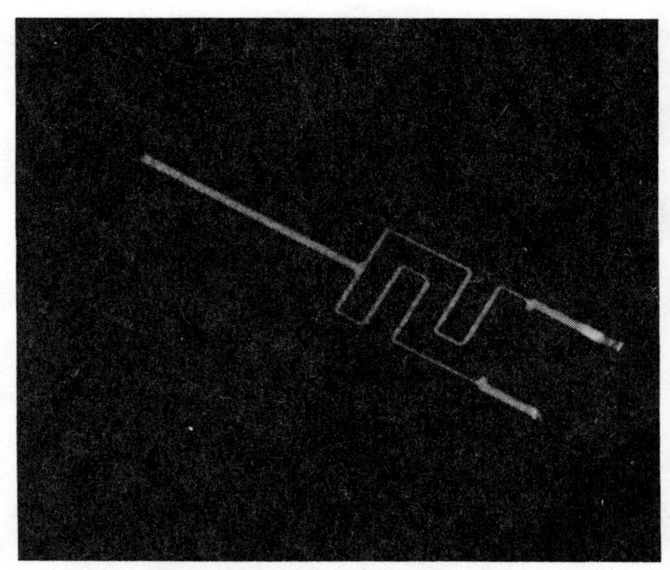

Fig. 42. GaAs monolithic *X*-band Wilkinson combiner/divider. Chip size is 1.5×2.5×0.1 mm. (Raytheon Company.)

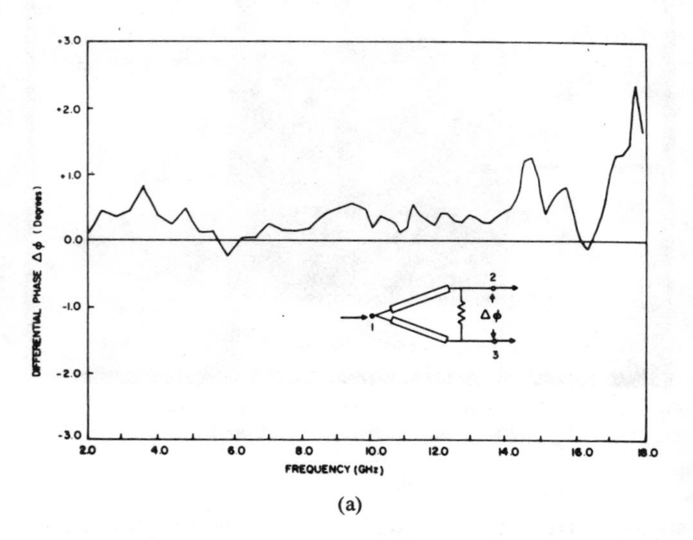

(a)

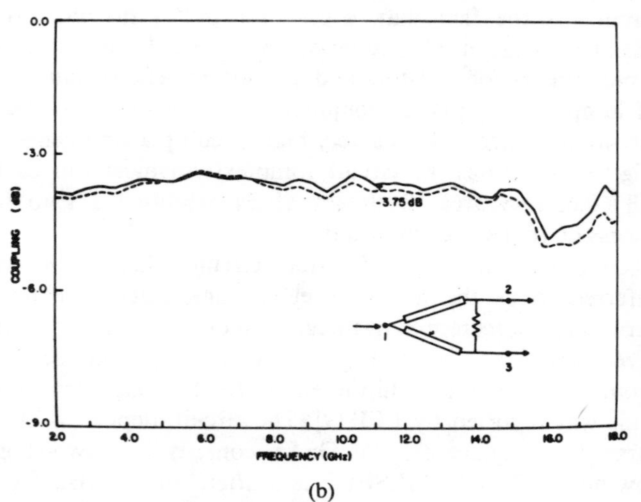

(b)

Fig. 43. Measured phase and power balance of Wilkinson divider shown in Fig. 42.

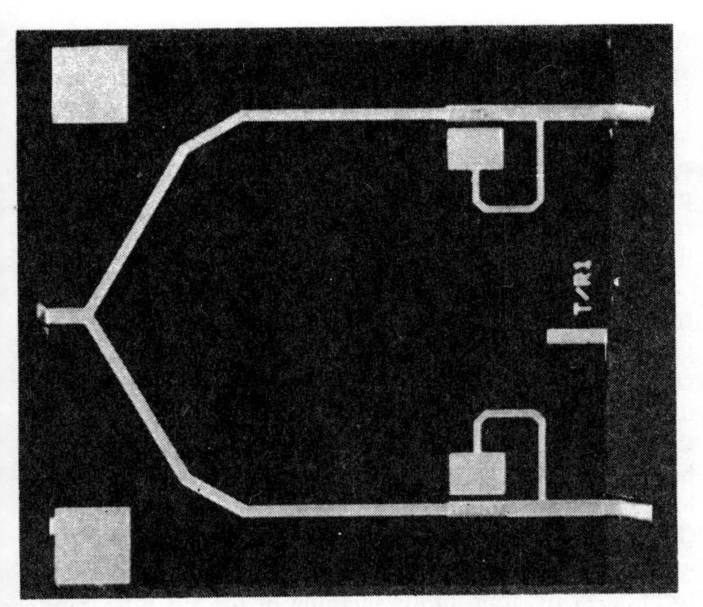

Fig. 44. GaAs monolithic *X*-band transmit/receive switch. Chip size is $3.0 \times 3.0 \times 0.1$ mm. (Raytheon Company.)

Another component designed at this laboratory is the all-FET T/R switch shown in Fig. 44 [1]. This switch, intended for phased-array applications at *X*-band, requires no dc hold power in either state. Built on a $3.0 \times 3.0 \times 0.1$-mm chip, the switch exhibits an isolation in excess of 33 dB between the transmitter and receiver ports in the 7–13-GHz range, and an insertion loss as low as 0.5 dB within this band. An alternative approach, also using FET's, was reported by McLevige *et al.* [14]. Both approaches utilize the change in source–drain resistance with gate bias.

The examples we have shown, though not exhaustive, are representative of the work reported so far (December 1980) and are intended to give the reader a good perspective of the advances made in the field during the last two years. Needless to say, the next several years will see the emergence of a still higher level of circuit integration in this rapidly developing field.

VII. Future Developments

We have so far concerned ourselves primarily with the technical aspects of monolithic circuits—their technology, design considerations, and microwave performance. Problems have been described and their solutions demonstrated. This is as it should be in the early stage of development of a new technical venture. No major unsolvable technical problems are evident; therefore, on the basis of technical considerations alone, there is no reason why the steady rate of progress already established cannot be maintained, indeed, accelerated.

What then will determine the future course of progress? The answer is simple—cost! Because the development of MMIC's requires a large capital investment and involves time-consuming and expensive processing technology plus a sophisticated testing procedure, the future development of this field will rest squarely on the as yet unproven expectations of reductions in cost and, to a lesser extent, improvements in reliability and reproducibility accruing from the monolithic approach.

The matter of cost reductions, in turn, rests on the answers to two questions.

1) Will the many complex technology steps required of MMIC's lend themselves to a high-yield production process?

2) Will a mass market develop in the microwave system area—a mass market necessary to capitalize on the high-volume low-cost attributes of batch processing?

Both of these requirements were eventually satisfied for silicon technology. Will this happen for gallium arsenide microwave technology? Time will tell. Since the silicon development was helped along by a vast domestic market (radios, TV's, etc., and more important, the commercial computer) and military markets, what are the expected large-volume markets for MMIC's?

Two potentially large markets appear to be developing, one military, the other consumer. In the military area, one such market includes electronically scanned radar systems, especially airborne and space-borne systems being planned for the future. For it is in the phased-array antenna, which may require modules as high as 10^5 in number, that we find a microwave system analog of the computer, which gave impetus to the growth of the silicon IC market. The antenna module requirements have already spurred developments of such module subsystems as transmitters, low-noise receivers, phase shifters, and transmit–receive (T/R) switches, some examples of which were described earlier. Here, along with cost, important design performance criteria will be reliability and small weight and size.

Another military application is in ECM systems, which require low-cost high-gain broad-band amplifiers. The difficult technical problems and projected high manufacturing cost associated with the hybrid integrated approach to this task have in essence mandated the use of monolithic circuits. Finally, the possibility of merging high-speed GaAs digital and microwave circuitry on the same chip may encourage use of such circuitry in signal processing at the RF level.

Turning to the nonmilitary markets, one potentially large outlet may be receiver front ends for the direct satellite-to-home-TV consumer market. Numerous such systems are being planned, for example, in Europe. We have described earlier one circuit intended for this market.

A third potential market, though much smaller in size, is instrumentation. Here cost and possibly circuit packing density are most important. Several examples of circuits earmarked for this application have been described.

We have not said much of the millimeter-wave spectrum. It is perhaps premature to do so, as this field itself is in its early stage of development. Here monolithic applications might develop, more for technical reasons than for economic reasons, because of the important role played by undesired packaging parasitics associated with discrete devices at these high frequencies. It is not unlikely that here too, as at lower frequencies, military applications may spur initial development. Now we turn to the question of costs.

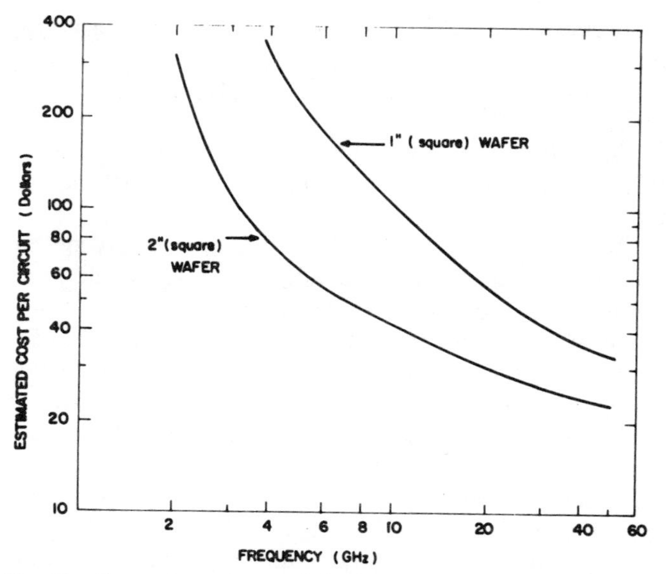

Fig. 45. Zero-order estimate of circuit cost as a function of frequency and wafer size.

Cost being the crucial item that it is, what are the factors contributing to it? They are the following:

1) materials;
2) materials processing;
3) circuit/device technology;
4) circuit assembly and packaging; and
5) testing (dc and RF).

These items, as is evident, do not include the important but nonrecurring costs such as capital investment, engineering, and mask design. In the materials category we include cost of substrate qualification, epitaxial growth and/or ion implantation, and profile evaluation, among others. Testing includes both dc and RF testing at the wafer probe level as well as circuit performance evaluation at the jig or package level.

Can a dollar figure be attached to these costs? At this stage, no! It is hazardous, at best, to attempt an accurate cost analysis based on laboratory experience, for large volume production, because ultimate module costs will be directly dependent on circuit yield in a manufacturing environment.

It is helpful, nevertheless, to attempt at least a "zeroth" order estimate of potential circuit costs, not so much to obtain an absolute level of cost, but to pinpoint the high cost items in the list above. To do this we have estimated the number of available circuits per wafer as a function of circuit operating frequency. This estimate was shown in Fig. 2. In the context of our present discussion, a circuit is equivalent to one submodule, for example, a transmitter stage or two, a phase shifter, etc. Using this estimate, we have determined the cost per circuit as a function of operating frequency. This data is shown in Fig. 45.

The cost estimates were derived by assumption of a 50-percent processing yield, independent of frequency. The base cost includes material cost, fully loaded labor cost, and circuit qualification at the dc and RF level. We feel that the cost estimates shown are useful guidelines but they should not be considered accurate in any absolute sense. For instance, depending on circuit complexity, current laboratory yields at *X*-band range from near zero to 20 percent. The development of a 50-percent yield fabrication process technology, deemed necessary, requires much additional experience and substantial simplification of monolithic circuit fabrication techniques.

Adjustments may be necessary at either end of the frequency scale. For example, in the range below 3–4 GHz, a drastic cost reduction may ensue, at least for some circuit applications, if the direct-coupled approach can be used. At the other end of the scale, above, say, 10–12 GHz, the cost figures should be elevated. The reason is that, because of the necessity of submicron gate technology, the lower throughput of the ultrahigh resolution electron beam (EB) lithography will increase costs substantially. Here what will be needed is optimization of the processing technology by appropriate merging of the EB lithography for the active devices and the higher throughput photolithography which is more than adequate for the circuit elements. This problem has not yet been addressed.

On the basis of our cost analysis, certain definite conclusions can be reached about the expected relative cost of the several items listed above. First, the two materials factors, under large production lots (>100 K parts) will contribute a negligible amount to the total cost—of the order of 5 percent or less. Second, next to wafer processing, the cost of packaging and microwave testing will be the largest cost factor. Indeed, because these latter costs will be fairly independent of the frequency band, and because of the decreasing processing cost per circuit with increasing frequency and wafer size, it is expected that packaging and testing will be the dominant cost factor at the higher frequencies (perhaps above 10 GHz).

It seems evident that, in light of this conclusion, the reduction of assembly and testing costs will be of paramount importance and must be addressed rather soon. Not only must as many functions as possible be integrated on one chip, consistent with high yield, but RF testing of chips and monolithic circuits and modules must be automated, just as dc tests have been. This will be very difficult because RF probes small enough for chip use are still in the laboratory stage, and their extension to performance tests on an entire circuit are nonexistent.

VIII. Conclusions and Summary

Monolithic microwave circuits based on gallium-arsenide technology have finally become a practical reality. Owing its origin to early experiments based on silicon bipolar technology, the gallium-arsenide approach, except for some scattered results in the sixties, emerged as a serious development only within the last three years.

The factors most responsible for this rapid growth can be traced to: 1) the development of the Schottky-barrier field-effect transistor; 2) the excellent microwave properties of semi-insulating GaAs as a low-loss substrate; 3) the perfection of GaAs epitaxy and ion implantation; 4) the establishment of GaAs crystal pulling facilities capable of large-diameter crystal growth; and 5) the emergence of potential systems applications for monolithic microwave circuits.

We have attempted to demonstrate in this paper some of the many design considerations and tradeoffs that must be made to optimize the performance of GaAs monolithic microwave circuits. Attention has been focussed, primarily, on the nondevice aspects of monolithic circuit design.

Despite the small physical size of the circuitry, interconnections between components often must be treated as wave-propagating structures because of the high dielectric constant of GaAs, which reduces the wavelength within the substrate. Both coplanar waveguide and microstrip lines, as well as combinations of both, are appropriate for monolithic circuits.

A typical circuit design may use both distributed and lumped-element components. Lumped elements, it was shown, are not truly lumped, because of built-in parasitics arising from the dielectric substrate. These must be taken into account at X-band and higher frequencies. A major drawback of thin-film inductors and capacitors is the limited Q-factor achieved to date. Much has yet to be learned about loss reduction in thin dielectric films.

We have shown that MMIC's are realized rather easily. Via hole grounding and source airbridge interconnections are eminently suited for them. Computer-aided design techniques are a "must" to reduce the number of iterations necessary.

Many examples of monolithic circuits have been shown which demonstrate the design principles described. These circuits, representing a world-wide cross section of the efforts in this field, have emerged within the last two to three years, and demonstrate the variety of circuit applications amenable to the monolithic approach. The promising attributes of the monolithic technology to cut fabrication costs, improve reliability and reproducibility, and reduce size and weight will overcome many of the shortcomings of the hybrid approach.

We have argued that, based on the cost considerations, the potential markets for MMIC's will be for the most part systems requiring large quantities of circuits of the same type. Because of this, and because of the large capital expenditures required of an organization to become a viable contender for these markets, it is most likely that the major efforts in MMIC's will eventually reside in the systems houses themselves.

Acknowledgment

The progress reported in this paper represents the cumulative effort of many people, too numerous to mention individually. However, the author wishes to express his deep appreciation to his associates at Raytheon, whose work is described here, and to his colleagues at many other laboratories who so graciously gave him permission to use their photographs and latest results to help describe their research.

References

[1] Y. Ayasli, R. A. Pucel, J. L. Vorhaus, and W. Fabian, "A monolithic X-band single-pole, double-throw bidirectional GaAs FET Switch," in *GaAs IC Symp. Res. Abstracts*, 1980, paper no. 21.

[2] E. M. Bastida, G. P. Donzelli, and N. Fanelli, "An X-band monolithic GaAs balanced amplifier," in *GaAs IC Symp. Res. Abstracts*, 1980, paper no. 25.

[3] A. Benavides, D. E. Romeo, T. S. Lin, and K. P. Waller, "GaAs monolithic microwave multistage preamplifier," in *GaAs IC Symp. Res. Abstracts*, 1980, paper no. 26.

[4] L. Besser, "Synthesize amplifiers exactly," *Microwave Syst. News*, pp. 28–40, Oct. 1979.

[5] D. Ch'en and D. R. Decker, "MMIC's the next generation of microwave components," *Microwave J.*, pp. 67–78, May 1980.

[6] A. Chu, W. E. Courtney, L. J. Mahoney, G. A. Lincoln, W. Macropoulos, R. W. Sudbury, and W. T. Lindley, "GaAs monolithic circuit for millimeter-wave receiver application," in *ISSCC Dig. Tech. Pap.*, pp.144–145, 1980.

[7] J. E. Degenford, R. G. Freitas, D. C. Boire, and M. Cohn, "Design considerations for wideband monolithic power amplifiers," in *GaAs IC Symp. Res. Abstracts*, 1980, paper no. 22.

[8] E. Denlinger, "Losses of microstrip lines," *IEEE Trans. Microwave Theory Tech.*, vol. MTT-28, pp. 513–522, June 1980.

[9] P. Harrop, P. Lesarte, and A. Collet, "GaAs integrated all-front-end at 12 GHz," in *GaAs IC Symp. Res. Abstracts*, 1980, paper no. 28.

[10] A. Higashisaka, in *1980 IEEE MTT-S Workshop Monolithic Microwave Analog IC's.*

[11] D. Hornbuckle, "GaAs IC direct-coupled amplifiers," in *1980 IEEE MTT-S Int. Microwave Symp. Dig.*, pp. 387–388.

[12] T. M. Hyltin, "Microstrip transmission on semiconductor substrates," *IEEE Trans. Microwave Theory Tech.*, vol. MTT-13, pp. 777–781, Nov. 1965.

[13] D. Laighton, J. Sasonoff, and J. Selin, "Silicon-on-sapphire (SOS) monolithic transceiver module components for L- and S-band," in *Government Microcircuit Applications Conf. Dig. Pap.*, vol. 8, 1980, pp. 299–302.

[14] W. V. McLevige and V. Sokolov, "A monolithic microwave switch using parallel-resonated GaAs FET's," in *GaAs IC Symp. Res. Abstracts*, 1980, paper no. 20.

[15] E. Mehal and R. W. Wacker, "GaAs integrated microwave circuits," *IEEE Trans. Microwave Theory Tech.* vol. MTT-16, pp. 451–454, July 1968.

[16] R. S. Pengelly and J. A. Turner, "Monolithic broadband GaAs FET amplifiers," *Electron. Lett.* vol. 12, pp. 251–252, May 13, 1976.

[17] R. A. Pucel, J. L. Vorhaus, P. Ng, and W. Fabian, "A monolithic GaAs X-band power amplifier," in *IEDM Tech. Dig.* 1979, pp. 266–268.

[18] V. Sokolov and R. E. Williams, "Development of GaAs monolithic power amplifiers," *IEEE Trans. Electron Devices*, vol. ED-27, pp. 1164–1171, June 1980.

[19] E. Strid and K. Reed, "A microstrip probe for microwave measurements on GaAs FET and IC wafers," in *GaAs IC Symp. Res. Abstracts*, 1980, paper no. 31.

[20] R. N. Thomas, "Advances in bulk silicon and gallium arsenide materials technology," in *IEDM Tech. Dig.*, 1980, pp. 13–17.

[21] R. Van Tuyl, "A monolithic GaAs FET RF signal generation chip," in *ISSCC Dig. Tech. Pap.* 1980, pp. 118–119.

[22] J. L. Vorhaus, R. A. Pucel, Y. Tajima, and W. Fabian, "A two-stage all-monolithic X-band power amplifier," in *ISSCC Dig. Tech. Pap.*, pp.74–75, 1980.

[23] R. C. Waterman, W. Fabian, R. A. Pucel, Y. Tajima, and J. L. Vorhaus, "GaAs monolithic Lange and Wilkinson couplers," *GaAs IC Symp. Res. Abstracts*, 1980, paper no. 30.

GaAs monolithic microwave circuits for phased-array applications

R.S. Pengelly, M.Sc., C.Eng., M.I.E.E.

Indexing terms: *Semiconductor materials, Microwave circuits, Semiconductor devices, Radar, Amplifiers, Switches, Transmitters, Schottky-barrier devices, Field-effect transistors*

Abstract: The use of gallium arsenide as a material for monolithic microwave circuits where active devices, such as f.e.t.s, diodes etc., are integrated onto the same piece of material as passive components is now receiving considerable attention in Europe and the USA. The paper concentrates on the specific role of monolithic circuits in phased-array-radar applications with descriptions of the use of f.e.t.s in switches, phase shifters, attenuators, receivers and transmitters. A summary of GaAs f.e.t. device performance is included allowing some insight into the noise figures, output powers and efficiencies obtained from low-noise and power amplifiers, respectively, at frequencies in S- and X-band. Some examples of GaAs monolithic circuit designs are given and methods of using active as against passive matching to achieve higher packing densities are described. The yield and cost of monolithic techniques is reviewed in the light of present and predicted circuit design and technology improvements. The impact of such costs on the realisation of phased-array systems with large numbers of elements is reviewed.

1 Introduction

The use of gallium arsenide as a material for monolithic microwave circuits (m.m.c.s) where active devices, such as f.e.t.s, diodes etc, are integrated onto the same piece of material as passive components is now receiving considerable attention in Europe and the USA. This paper will concentrate on the specific role of monolithic circuits in phased-array-radar applications with descriptions of the use of f.e.t.s in switches, phase shifters, attenuators, receivers and transmitters.

A summary of GaAs f.e.t. device performance is included allowing some insight into the noise figures, output powers and efficiencies obtained from low-noise and power amplifiers, respectively, at frequencies in S- and X-band.

Many phased-array-radar systems for the future, presently being conceived, will require large numbers of receive and transmit elements. The ability to be able to include integrated circuits within the antenna elements themselves is also receiving considerable attention. Such systems will require low-cost components which also have the attributes of reproducible performance, a high mean time to failure, small size and the efficient use of d.c. power. For these reasons gallium-arsenide monolithic circuit technology may well have advantages over other, more conventional, methods. As with Si i.c.s, relatively complicated r.f. and i.f. functions can be included on one chip. Only where very high powers are envisaged, will the GaAs monolithic approach have fundamental limitations. However, for many applications output powers per element up to 30 W peak power is quite sufficient.

Monolithic circuits using GaAs are in their infancy. This paper is intended as a review of some of the current work aimed at introducing hardware to the phased-array-radar-systems engineer in the next few years.

2 GaAs f.e.t. device performance

The GaAs f.e.t. is now well established as a low-noise device up to 20 GHz. Currently device noise figures of 1·7 dB at 12 GHz with 10 dB associated gain have been achieved whilst noise figures of 3 dB with 8 dB associated gain are possible at 18 GHz with 0·5 μm gate length f.e.t.s.[1] At frequencies below 4 GHz device noise figures of less than 1 dB can be achieved with 15 dB associated gain. Low noise 2·7 to 3·2 GHz amplifiers, for S-band radar applications, have been built with overall noise figures of 2·5 dB (including limiter loss). At X-band, radar front-end amplifiers having noise figures of 3·3 dB are currently being produced.

Thus it may be appreciated that the GaAs f.e.t. is capable of being included in phased-array type systems requiring low-noise figure receiver preamplifiers.

The GaAs Schottky barrier f.e.t. (also known as the m.e.s.f.e.t.) has been widely reported as a power amplifier. Currently, development work concentrates on producing higher powers with compact device and circuit structures. For example power outputs in S-band of 15 W c.w. have been reported with power-added efficiencies of 28%.[2] In order to produce such output power, f.e.t. chip and individual cell combining techniques are used and recent results[3] suggest that bandwidths of up to one octave are realisable with output powers of the order of 1 W in X-band. The GaAs f.e.t. offers the best overall performance when power output, bandwidth and efficiency are considered simultaneously. Recently it has become apparent that under pulsed conditions the f.e.t. device can achieve useful increases in output power.[4]

At S-band the advantages of the GaAs f.e.t. over the Si bipolar transistor are somewhat more unclear although it would appear that, under c.w. operation, the GaAs m.e.s.f.e.t. can be more successfully matched over broader bandwidths than the Si bipolar device. Performance improvements with Si bipolar-junction-transistor power devices are being attained with ion-implanted base and emitter profiles; the device geometries having a higher emitter periphery to base area ratio.

However, the lack of the ability to fully integrate silicon power devices with other passive and active components on the same substrate material is a serious disadvantage of conventional silicon i.c.s at high frequencies caused by the substrate material having poor characteristics. Silicon-on-

Paper 849F, first received 15th April and in revised form 5th June 1980

The author is with Plessey Research (Caswell) Limited, Allen Clark Research Centre, Caswell, Towcester, Northants, England

sapphire technology now under development in the USA may produce fully integrated circuits capable of operation up to S-band.

Gallium arsenide, however, has the unique ability at the present time of allowing the integration of both low-noise and power f.e.t. devices over a wide frequency range. The depletion mode f.e.t. is also capable of being used in a variety of other circuits.

2.1 Low-noise monolithic amplifiers

As has already been outlined, the noise performance of conventional hybrid amplifiers using GaAs f.e.t.s has reached a level, particularly at frequencies below X-band, where further improvements will be difficult to implement. On the other hand, the noise figure of monolithic amplifiers still depends to a large extent on the circuti design concept. Results to date, using conventional lumped-element matching techniques indicate that a noise figure penalty of approximately 0·7 dB is paid at S-band for a 1·5 dB to 2 dB low-noise amplifier. This penalty is because of the loss of the matching components, particularly inductors. At X-band broadband amplifiers[5] have shown noise figures approximately 0·4 dB higher than their direct equivalents using microstrip techniques. Where techniques more closely akin to Si i.c. design are used, such as common-gate/common-source/source-follower feedback amplifiers, noise figures can be somewhat higher than the optimum for the f.e.t. device type used – by as much as 3 dB in S-band.

In order to achieve a good yield of working circuits, and achieve a low cost, certain performance figures such as the noise figure may well have to be compromised in a GaAs i.c. solution.

2.2 Mixers – f.e.t.s

Dual-gate field-effect transistors are now gaining popularity as low noise mixers where the device can give attractive conversion gains. Cripps *et al.*[6] have reported an rejection mixer having a conversion gain of up to with an image rejection of at least 20 dB at X-bai with a noise figure of approximately 8 dB. The basic arrangement is shown in Fig. 1. An attractive alterna the dual-gate mixer which can achieve much lowe figures is to use a double-gate f.e.t. with a single-gate f.e.t. as shown in Fig. 2.

The r.f. and l.o. frequencies are combined in the first f.e.t. where the r.f. port is tuned for minimum noise figure. Isolation between the l.o. and r.f. ports is very similar to the reverse isolation of the device and is typically – 20 dB. The second single gate f.e.t. is biased to optimise the conversion gain and output compression point. For example a mixer circuit using such a technique at 4 GHz with a 200 MHz i.f. has a single-sideband noise figure of 3 dB with a conversion gain of 15 dB (using 0·5 μm f.e.t.s). Thus, for low-noise-receiver front ends, the use of a GaAs f.e.t. preamplifier and dual-gate f.e.t. mixer is capable of producing a low overall receiver noise figure with low-cost relatively-high-noise-figure i.f. amplifiers.

Lower-frequency f.e.t. mixers essentially employ a variable-gain amplifier stage where the gain modulating function is provided by f.e.t. variable resistors. Recently Van Tuyl[7] has reported a double-balanced mixer which operates up to approximately 3 GHz using such a technique (Fig. 3). Such a circuit can be extended to higher frequencies on GaAs than it can using similar approaches with Si bipolar transistors or m.e.s.f.e.t.s.

Monolithic balanced mixers at higher frequencies (where the f.e.t.s are operating closer to their cut-off frequency) can be realised using circuit techniques such as that shown in Fig. 4. Here use is made of active power splitters and

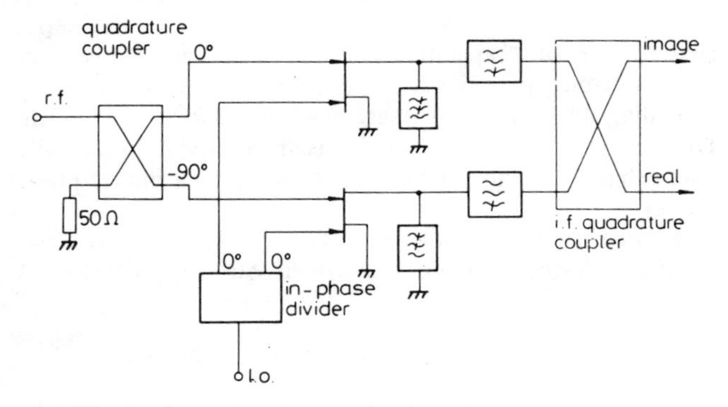

Fig. 1 *Dual-gate f.e.t. image rejection mixer*

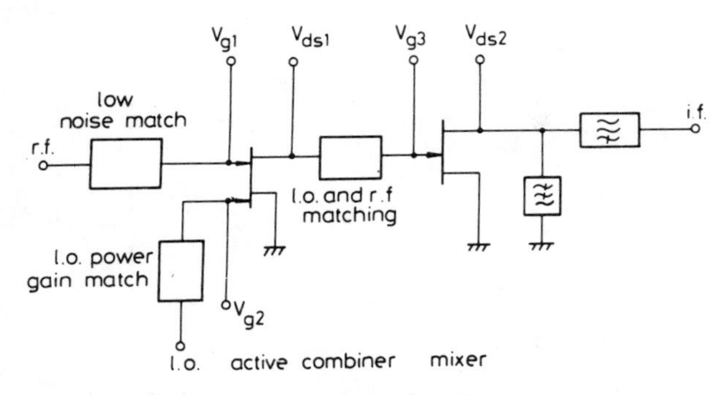

Fig. 2 *Double-gate/single-drain f.e.t. mixer*

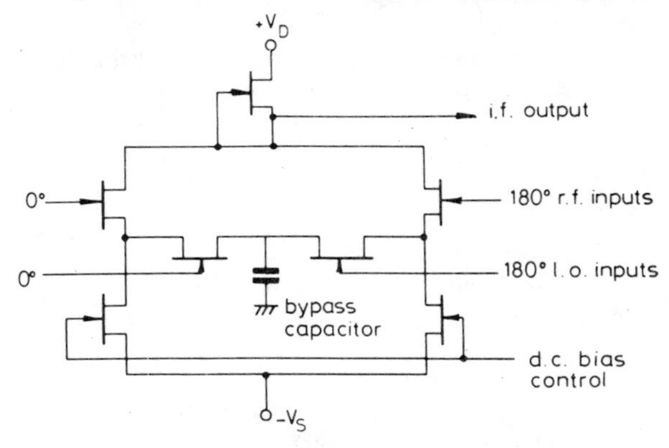

Fig. 3 *Double balanced monolithic mixer circuit*

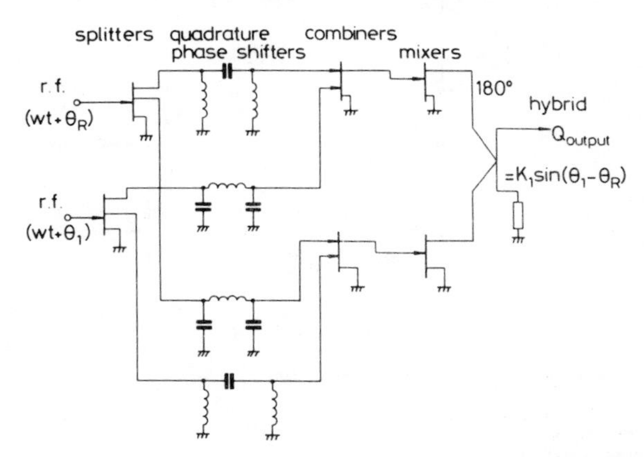

Fig. 4 *Balanced monolithic mixer circuit for 4 GHz and above*

combiners to produce either quadrature or antiphase r.f. and l.o. signals which are then applied to two single-gate mixers. The resulting two i.f. components can be combined in a conventional 180° i.f. hybrid coupler or by the use of an active circuit employing f.e.t.s, the latter being particularly convenient for monolithic circuits.

2.3 *Diodes*

Ristow *et al.*[8] have shown that planar GaAs Schottky-barrier diodes can be monolithically integrated to produce a mixer with an s.s.b. noise figure of 10 dB (including a 1·5 dB i.f. noise contribution) at 15 GHz (i.f. being 70 MHz). Further work by Courtney *et al.*[9] has produced mixers with noise figures of 11 to 12 dB at 30 GHz which have been monolithically integrated with a GaAs f.e.t. i.f. amplifier at 2 GHz.

2.4 *Switches*

The use of both single and dual-gate GaAs f.e.t.s has received considerable attention in the design of fast switches. Several configurations are possible to implement the f.e.t. as a switch (shown in Fig. 5). The series configuration makes use of the saturation and pinch-off conditions of the f.e.t. and provides an inherently broadband (untuned) response with zero d.c. bias power since the gate-source Schottky diode is always reverse biased and no external voltage is applied to the drain of the f.e.t. Gaspari and Yee[10] have reported an 8-way switch utilising a tuned series connected f.e.t. switch. The single or dual-gate f.e.t. can be used in a conventional amplifier configuration with tuning and/or attenuator pads on gate and drain to maintain low input and output v.s.w.r.s under on and off conditions (Fig. 5*c*).

An alternative configuration giving high broadband isolation is the π network of f.e.t.s as shown in Fig. 5*d*. This circuit may also be used as a matched attenuator and only relies on having known voltage-to-attenuation laws for the series and shunt f.e.t.s much as with *pin* diodes.

Vorhaus has reported a multithrow dual-gate f.e.t. switch[11] having isolations in excess of 25 dB in X-band using a novel 4-sided structure with a common-source connection to ground. This ground is supplied by introducing a via through the GaAs substrate. Most of the f.e.t. structures used to date as switching elements are small signal devices. Extensions to the dual-gate switch using power f.e.t.-type structures, i.e. long gate width devices, are currently under investigation. Garver[12] has also proposed a 'control f.e.t.' which, by controlling the doping density of the 'channel' region and employing an overlay dielectric, should enable the switching of, at least, several watts of r.f. power. Work to date using conventional 600 μm wide power f.e.t.s has shown that powers in excess of 200 mW can be switched at X-band with 20 dB of isolation using this method.

2.5 *Phase-shifting circuits*

Phase-shifting circuits associated with the receivers of phased arrays are usually *pin* diode controlled circuits while circuits for very high peak power applications depend on the use of ferrite materials.

Four types of phase-shifter configurations are generally employed: the switched line, reflection, loaded line and high-pass/low-pass. Of these the most promising for monolithic realisation using either planar Schottky diodes or m.e.s.f.e.t.s as the switching elements is the high-pass/low-pass. Of these the most promising for monolithic realisation using either planar Schottky diodes or m.e.s.f.e.t.s as the switching elements is the high-pass/low-pass structure.[12] The circuit is capable of being made small on GaAs by the use of lumped elements as shown in Fig. 6. The circuit uses f.e.t.s as switches so the insertion loss of the circuit is determined mainly by the 'on' resistance of the series switch. The 'off' capacitance of the f.e.t. is also important. Such a circuit provides a matched transmission behaviour providing up to 180° of phase shift over a 20% bandwidth. The dual-gate f.e.t. can itself be used to provide phase shift particularly for the smaller phase angles of a digital phase shifter.

From Fig. 7*a* it may be seen that, provided the designer sacrifices device maximum available gain, a multitude of

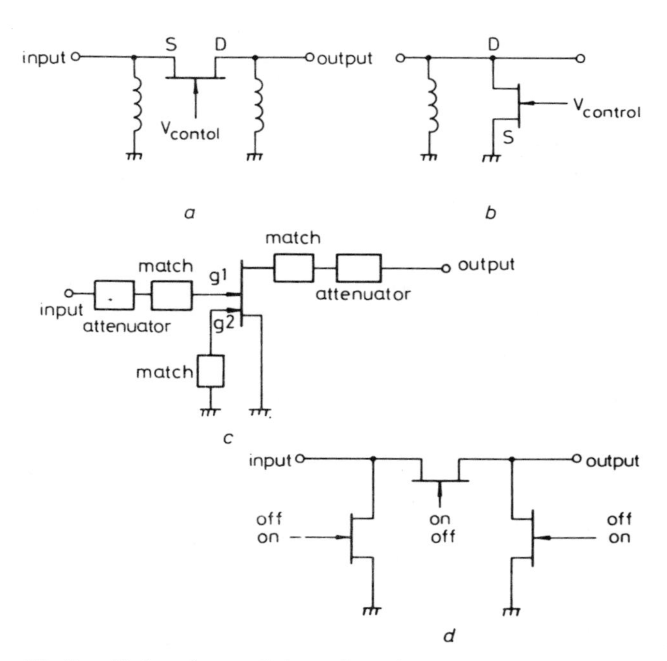

Fig. 5 *Various f.e.t. switch configurations*

a Series configuration
b Shunt configuration
c Dual-gate switch
d Matched attenuator

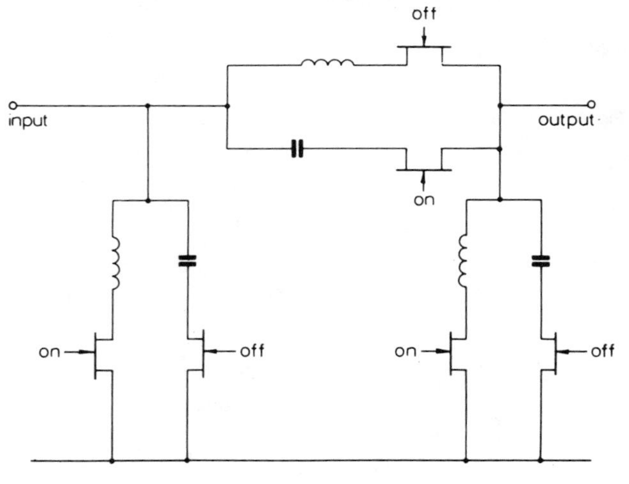

Fig. 6 *High-pass/low-pass phase shifter using m.e.s.f.e.t. switches*

voltage settings on the first and second gate are available for a specific gain G. By matching the device over a specified bandwidth somewhat greater than that required it is possible to produce a variable transmission phase shift with two different voltages on gate 1 and 2 as shown in Fig. 7*b*.

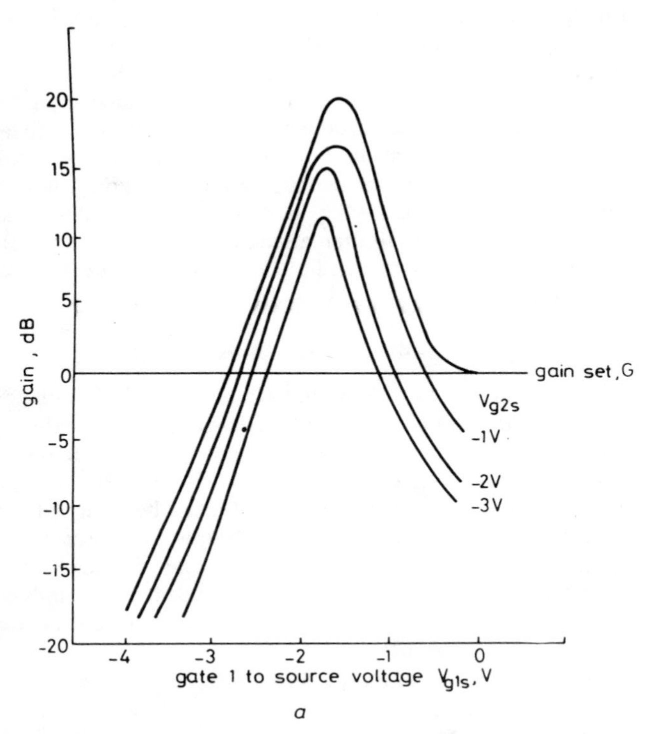

Fig. 7A *Dual-gate GaAs f.e.t. gain variation with first and second gate voltages*

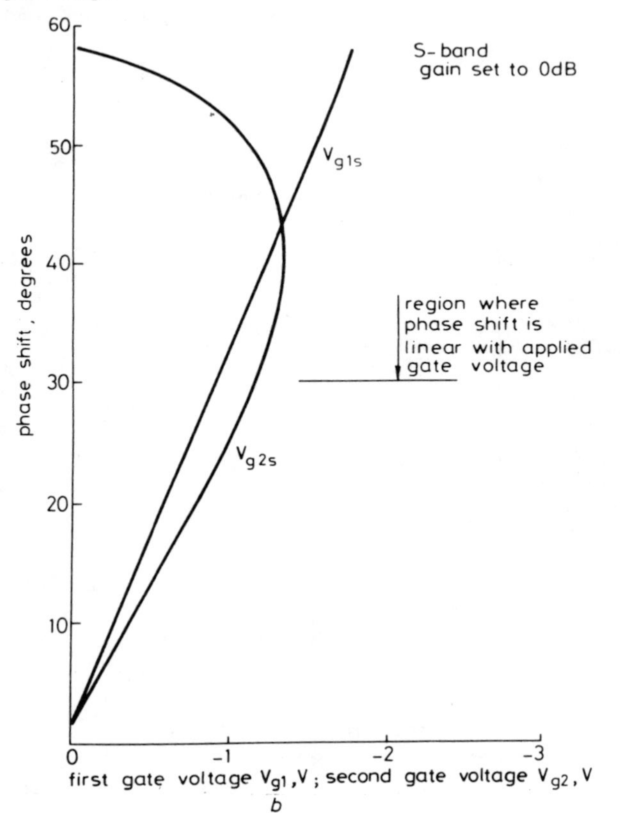

Fig. 7B *Voltages needed on gates 1 and 2 of dual-gate f.e.t. to achieve the phase shift on S 21 shown*

In X-band, phase shifts of over 50° have been obtained (Fig. 8). As the S_{11} of the dual-gate f.e.t. changes with the first gate voltage, amplitude changes are incurred at the band edges as shown in Fig. 9, and these are somewhat larger than deemed acceptable particularly for the higher

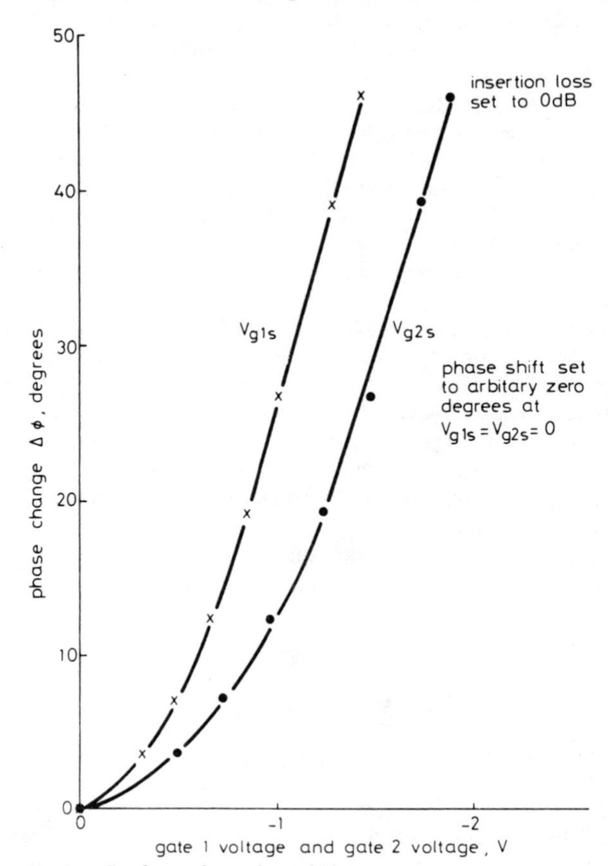

Fig. 8 *Dual-gate f.e.t. phase shifter*

X-band; 9·75–10·25 GHz

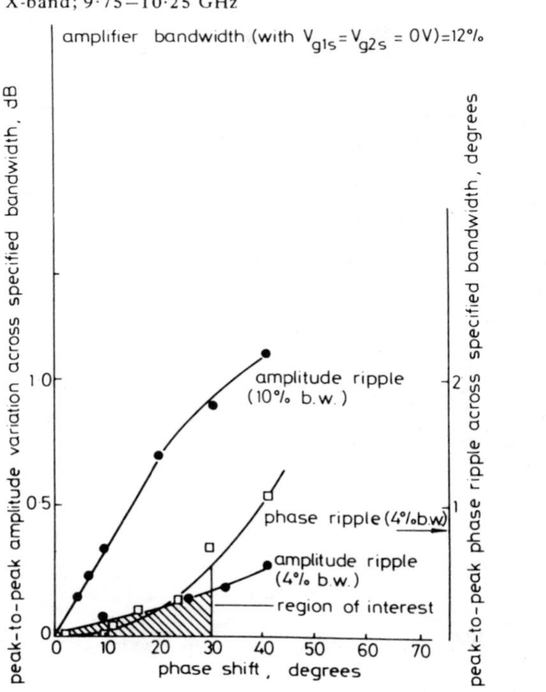

Fig. 9 *Amplitude and phase variations with bandwidth for dual-gate f.e.t. phase shifter*

phase shifts. However, by matching over a bandwidth typically 100% greater than is needed phase and amplitude ripples can be reduced substantially. For example (Fig. 9), if a phase shifter element giving 22·5 degrees needs to operate to an amplitude ripple of ± 0·1 dB over the 2·7 to 3·2 GHz bandwidth then the matching circuits into the gates and drain of the device need to produce flat gain over the 2·2 to 3·7 GHz band.

A major advantage of this scheme is that the circuit is truly analogue allowing phase adjustments which are not quantised as in a digital phase shifter. Variations in transmission phase caused by temperature can be compensated by varying the gate bias. Phase variations between modules in a phased-array system can be adjusted by the use of such a technique thus improving sidelobe levels.

Amplitude adjustment (under constant phase conditions) can also be produced using the circuit arrangement as shown in Fig. 10A, where gate 1 and gate 2 bias are set to minimise transmission phase variations over the wanted level of attenuation. Fig. 10B compares the transmission phase variations over the attenuator settings with the second gate voltage variations and both the first and second gate voltage variations.

A circuit somewhat like that schematically shown in Fig. 11 can be adopted to produce a 5 bit phase-shifter

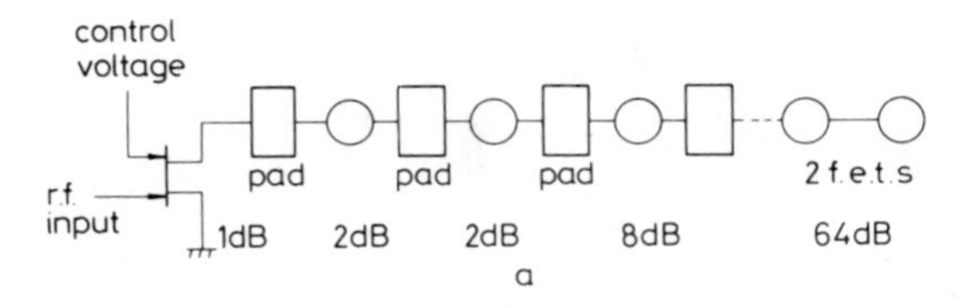

Fig. 10A *Single ended 6-bit attenuator chain using dual-gate f.e.t.s*

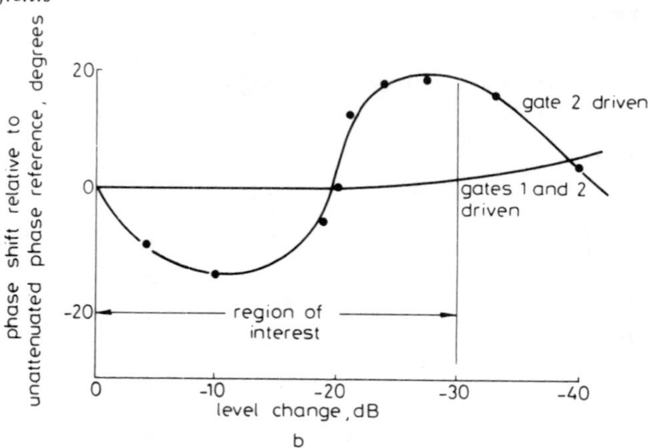

Fig. 10B *Phase shift of S_{21} with attenuation level for dual-gate GaAs f.e.t. switch over 20% b.w. centred at 5·68 GHz*

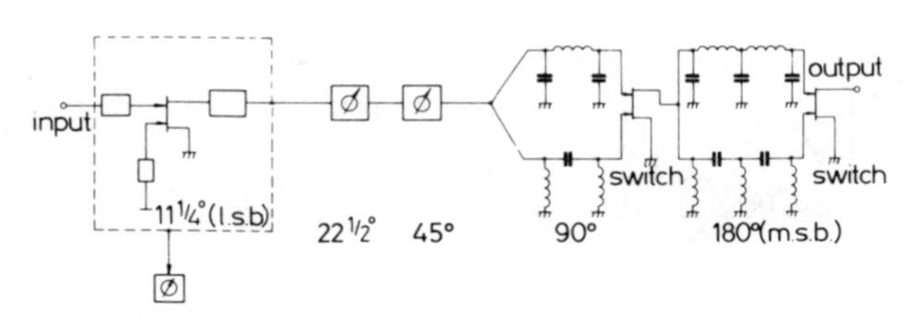

Fig. 11 *Dual gate f.e.t. active-phase shifter*
Matching circuits not shown

where the $\pi/2$ and π phase shifts can be produced using active combiners, the overall unit having insertion gain. Both the $\pi/2$ and π phase shift circuits can use lead/lag phase networks where each f.e.t. cell of the combiner is turned on or off in turn such that, in any one switch state, the impedance presented to the matching circuits is the same as in the other state. Alternatively, control f.e.t.s can be introduced into $\pi/2$ and π phase bits as switches.

GaAs f.e.t. active splitters or active combiners can be realised having good amplitude and phase equality as well as high port-to-port isolation. Such techniques are very useful in monolithic circuits for producing f.e.t. 'versions' of well known passive circuits such as 3 dB quadrature couplers. Such techniques lead to dramatic reductions in GaAs usage. For example, at S-band a reduction of at least 60% in GaAs is possible.

2.6 Monolithic GaAs f.e.t. oscillators

It is now well established that GaAs f.e.t. oscillators are efficient and have less stringent power-supply and heat-sink requirements than other solid-state oscillators. Being a planar device the f.e.t. is also ideally suited for monolithic microwave-oscillator functions and can be married to varactor-diode tuning capacitors if required. For a three terminal device, like the f.e.t., suitable feedback and impedance matching elements are needed to induce negative resistance and consequently provide useful power at microwave frequencies.

Monolithic GaAs f.e.t. oscillator circuits using grounded-gate arrangements have been realised. In these circuits the feedback element is a lumped inductor on the gate terminal. Overall oscillator size is less than 2 x 2 mm at X-band. Circuits providing 10 mW output power at 8·4 and

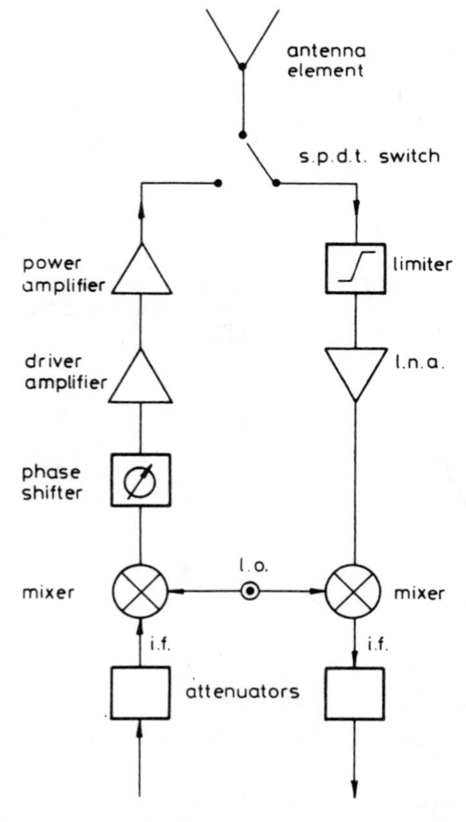

Fig. 12 *Active phased-array schematic diagram*

12·8 GHz have been realised at 6% and 4% d.c. to r.f. conversion efficiency, respectively.[14] Further work on frequency stabilisation and electronic tuning is in progress.

3 Active-array modules

Considering the circuit of Fig. 12 it may be appreciated that all the individual 'building blocks' to which reference has already been made may be fabricated using GaAs f.e.t. technology. Fig. 13 shows a low-noise receiver front-end realisation for an image rejection mixer. The r.f. signal is equally divided into two channels where a phase lead/lag network is employed to produce the 0 and $\pi/2$ signals for a 'single-ended' mixer. The l.o. buffer amplifier/splitter uses a common-gate/common-source combination to produce 18 to 20 dB gain at S-band whilst providing + 10 dBm l.o. power to the dual-gate mixers. A lumped-element hybrid version of this latter circuit is shown in Fig. 14 together with its response.

The dual-gate mixer for this particular low-noise receiver module was designed using the large-signal S-parameters on gate 2 of the f.e.t. which differ markedly from the small-signal parameters as shown in Fig. 15. The r.f. is terminated in a short circuit at the drain of the device whilst the 50 Ω shunt resistor provides stabilisation at r.f. The i.f. is extracted via a low-pass filter at a 200 Ω impedance level. The image-rejection feature is introduced by combining the two i.f. outputs (Fig. 13) in a quadrature coupler which is a conventional lumped-component circuit.

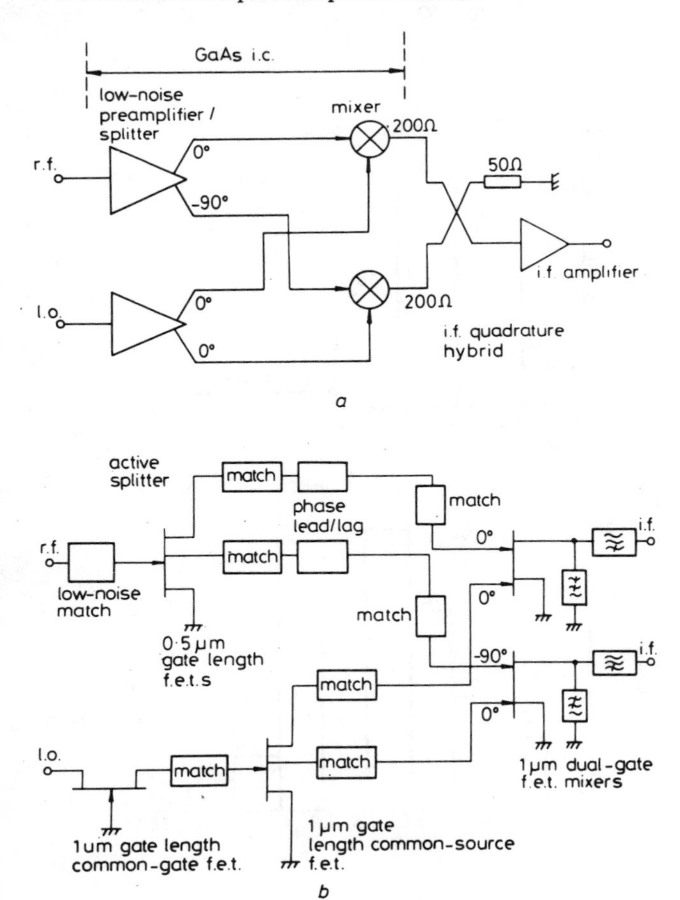

Fig. 13 *GaAs i.c. S-band receiver*

a Schematic diagram
b Detail of front-end

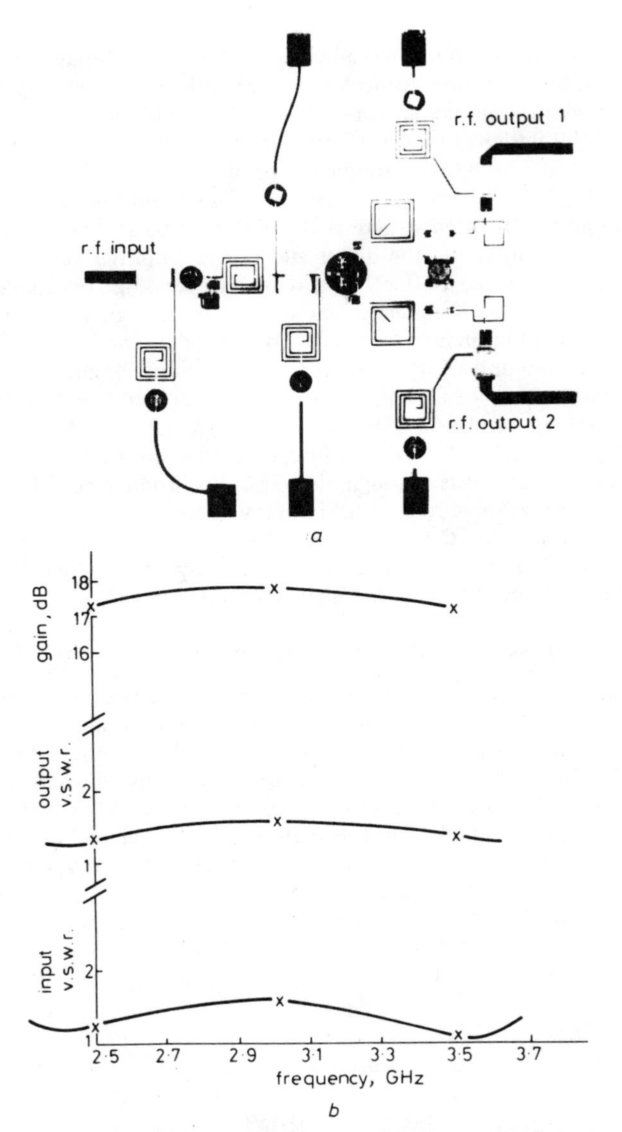

Fig. 14 *Common-gate/common-source f.e.t. amplifier/splitter*

a Photograph
b Response curves

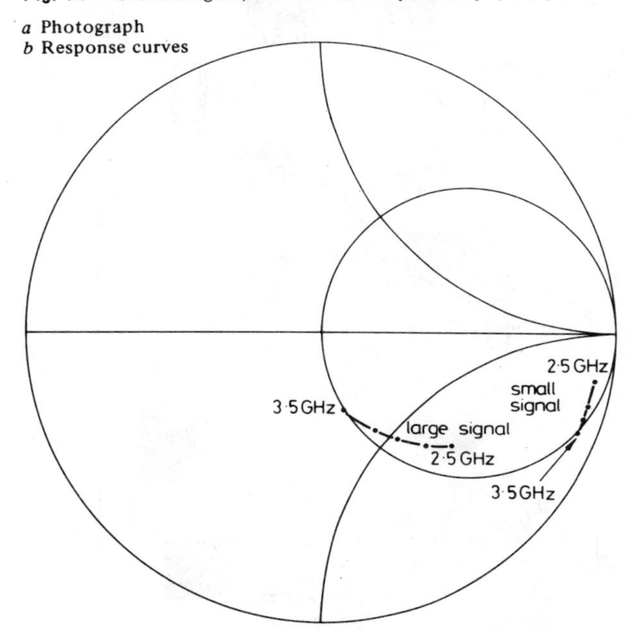

Fig. 15 *Small and large signal reflection coefficients of second gate of dual-gate f.e.t. mixer*

The r.f. preamplifier/splitter, l.o. buffer and mixers can be fabricated monolithically on GaAs. Fig. 16, for example, shows the chip layout for an S-band low-noise preamplifier/splitter designed to give 10 dB gain and a 2·0 dB noise figure in the 2·7 to 3·4 GHz frequency band.

Fig. 12 also shows an example of a transmit module for an array. Of interest here is the ability to be able to monolithically integrate the driver and power amplifier stages to produce a cost-effective circuit. Depending on radar function and frequency, circuits being designed at the present time include stages capable of delivering 0·5 to 1 W at X-band and up to 15 W at S-band.[15] Such circuits use a combination of microstrip and lumped-component matching on GaAs with substrate thicknesses of 100 μm. Use is made of both air-bridge connected f.e.t. source contacts and vias through the GaAs to produce very low-source reactance to ground. In many cases the use of pulsed d.c. drive to the f.e.t.s can be considered producing substantial increases in output power especially when the f.e.t.s are produced with a high power/area ratio.

4 GaAs monolithic-circuit technology

The potential performance advantages of GaAs over silicon as a high-frequency i.c. material have been recognised since the early 1960s, but early results with linear microwave circuits were disappointing. Silicon technology advanced at a tremendous pace because of the well-controlled diffusion processes available for the material. Diffusion techniques for GaAs, however, are virtually useless and early GaAs material varied in quality. The development of the GaAs Schottky-barrier gate f.e.t., using thin epitaxial *n*-type active layers on buffered semi-insulating material, was the first major breakthrough in producing monolithic microwave circuits.

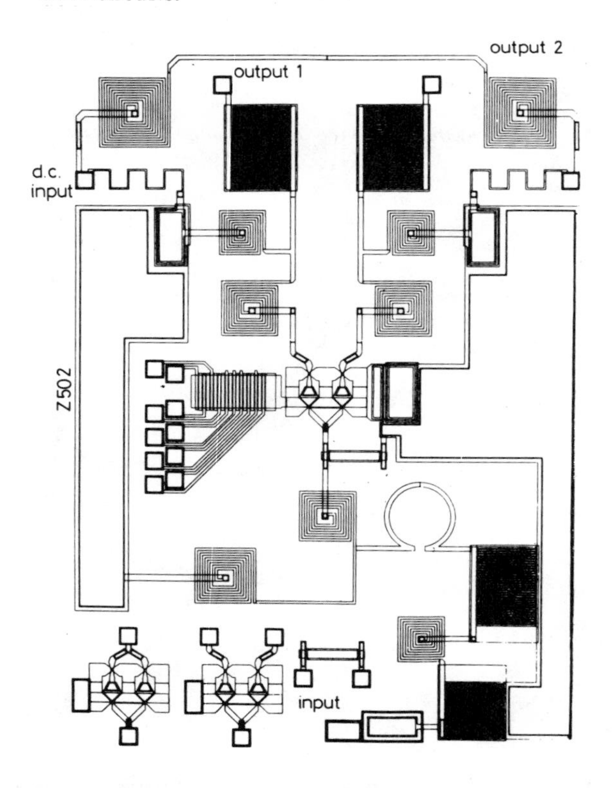

Fig. 16 *Chip layout for GaAs i.c. (S-band low-noise preamplifier/splitter)*

Circuits produced on GaAs contain both active and passive components where the active components are fabricated on either an *n*-type epitaxial layer or an *n*-type implanted layer. Passive components are produced on the semi-insulating GaAs material which has a low microwave loss and a dielectric constant of 13. There are basically two techniques that can be used to produce microwave passive components on the material – either lumped elements or distributed transmission lines. For frequencies below X-band, and where power dissipation is not a problem, lumped-element matching is to be preferred since it enables the the optimum usage of GaAs area. For frequencies in J-band and above and where thermal dissipation is important (such as in power f.e.t. amplifiers) microstrip techniques are preferred.[16]

Lumped-element characterisation has received considerable attention over the years[17, 18] but is still subject to

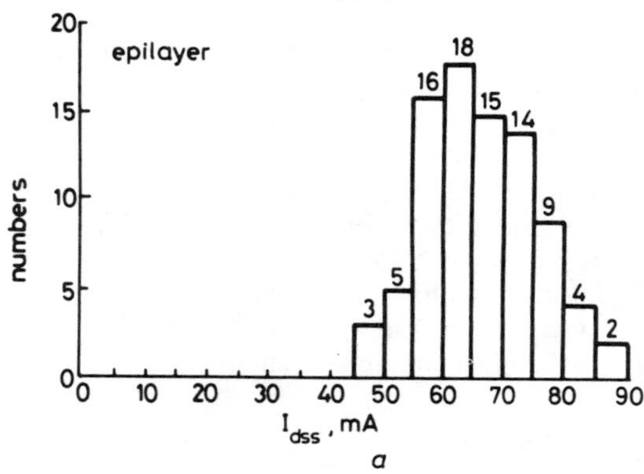

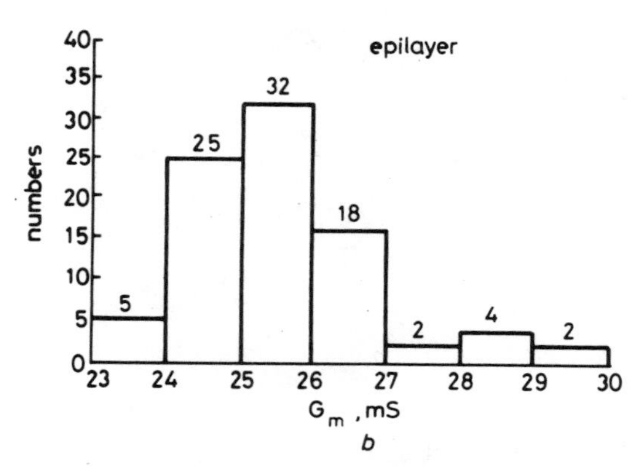

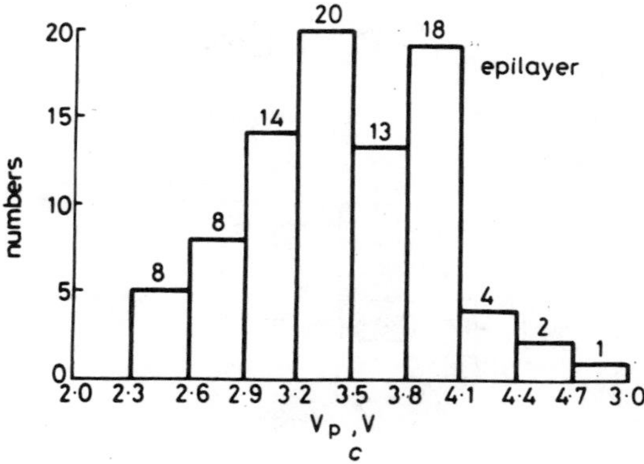

Fig. 17 *GaAs f.e.t. over wafer with v.p.e. grown layer*

a Saturated drain current
b Transconductance variation
c Pinch-off voltage
Number of samples = 86

investigation as new frequency bands and components are included. Results are now available for a considerable number of inductor, capacitor and resistor structures indicating the applicability of both classical and more modern analytical methods to their design. Obviously the i.c. design is as accurate as the determination of passive component values and the accuracy of both models and S-parameter characterisation of active devices. Thus, in many cases at the moment, it is necessary to either introduce some form of adjustment into the monolithic circuit or prepare initial mask sets covering a limited number of possible alternative solutions to a particular problem.

Qualification of GaAs material is also essential in enabling the circuit designer to guarantee a confidence limit on active-device performance variations. The uniformity of d.c. characteristics of f.e.t.s over a typical epitaxially grown layer is shown in Fig. 17 in terms of saturated drain current I_{dss}, transconductance g_m and pinch-off voltage V_p. Such parameters control the bias current of the f.e.t.s in a self-biased approach such as that adopted in Fig. 16 for example. It may be seen that the standard-deviation values are of the order of 10%.

Depletion-mode GaAs i.c.s at present use n^+ on n vapour phase epitaxy material. The n^+ region is 0·4 μm thick and the doping level is 10^{18} carriers/cm^3; the n region is similarly 0·4 μm thick with $1{\cdot}5 \times 10^{17}$ carriers/cm.^{3} The n^+ region is used to lower the ohmic contact resistance of source and drain contacts for f.e.t.s and for low-resistance diodes. The epitaxial layer is grown on a high-resistivity buffer layer (10^{13} carriers/cm^3) to isolate it from the GaAs substrate. This ensures long-term stability of the material parameters and, together with the uniformity of thickness and doping concentration in the n region, is an important factor in yield control.[19]

Where Schottky mixer diodes are fabricated on the same chip as f.e.t.s, an n on n^+ on n structure is used. This enables the diode to be placed between the upper n region and the n^+, and the f.e.t.s between the n^+ and the lower n region.

GaAs material technology has been progressing steadily since the early sixties. Vapour phase epitaxial processes have centred around the AsCl-Ga-H_2 process, developed by Knight *et al.*,[20] and the alkyl process.[21] The former process produces very high purity GaAs and together with the development of the buffer layer has lead to the introduction of state-of-the-art f.e.t.s. The technology has been extended to cope with 5 cm circular wafers upon which is grown a multilayer structure suitable for high-frequency monolithnic circuits. Present uniformity is ± 3% in doping density and ± 2% in thickness leading to a variation of 8% in pinch-off voltage of the completed devices.

GaAs i.c.s are being fabricated from layers produced by ion implanting donor species directly into semi-insulating substrate material and into epitaxial high-resistivity buffer layers. These devices have demonstrated similar performance to those produced from epitaxial wafers. The ion implanter is capable of implanting 90 5 cm diameter wafers in one processing sequence with a high degree of uniformity.

By combining large area wafers with selective ion implantation the feasibility of producing low-cost GaAs circuits becomes available. By selectively implanting n and n^+ regions a planar processing technique can be used to produce m.m.c.s. The conventional mesa isolation structure is no longer required since the intrinsic isolation afforded by the substrate is directly used. Thus overall process yield is improved since metalisation no longer has to go over mesa edges and some increase in packing density is also possible.

5 Circuit design of analogue monolithic circuits

5.1 Lumped elements

In order to design low-noise amplifiers, for example, with lumped-component matching it is necessary to accurately measure the scattering parameters of a large number of lumped inductors, capacitors and resistors. Fig. 18 shows the physical appearance of single-loop and multiturn spiral inductors and capacitors used at present. The single-loop inductors and interdigitated capacitors are used for small-value components and the multitrun square-spiral inductors and overlay capacitors for larger-value requirements. The equivalent circuits of each element including parasitic capacitances and resistive losses are used in the c.a.d. of monolithic circuits.

The Q values achieved for lumped inductors are shown to be around 50 with the correct geometry, and the inter-digital capacitor Q can be optimised by the correct use of dimensions, metal thickness and aspect ratio.

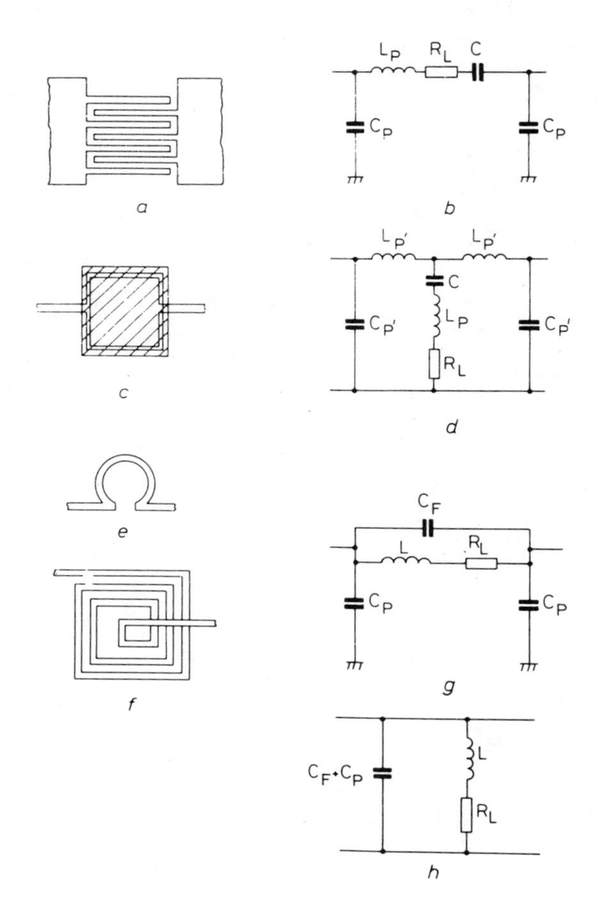

Fig. 18 *Lumped elements for GaAs i.c.s*

a Interdigital capacitor
b Series-capacitor equivalent circuit
c Overlay capacitor
d Shunt-capacitor equivalent circuit
e Single-loop inductor
f Multiturn square spiral inductor
g Series inductor equivalent circuit
h Shunt-inductor equivalent circuit

5.2 Circuit design

Figs. 19*a*, *b* and *c* show three realisations of broadband-matching circuits for the Plessey GAT 5 device, the first being a semidistributed/semilumped design suitable for a monolithic circuit, the second being a purely lumped design and the third being a purely distributed circuit.

Fig. 19*d* shows the same circuit as 19*c* but includes discontinuity parasitics caused by the transmission line T junctions, changes in line width etc., following Easter *et al.*[22] Fig. 20 shows the effects of these discontinuities on the gain of the circuit of Fig. 19*c* and also shows a reoptimised design including parasitics following c.a.d. It may be appreciated that the effect is dramatic and indeed this is usually the case throughout the frequency range S- to J-band where at the lower frequencies the impedances presented by GaAs f.e.t.s for example tend to be sensitive to loss and certain parasitic components. Fig. 21 is a similar graph resulting from the design of Fig. 19*b* with and without consideration of lumped-element loss and parasitics.

6 Yield and cost of GaAs monolithic circuits

Just as with the well established Si i.c. technologies of the 1970s and lower-frequency circuits it is envisaged that the GaAs i.c. will be able to make significant inroads into the reduction in the cost of microwave circuits particularly where high-volume requirements are concerned. This is because batch processing of the total microwave circuit becomes a small part of the cost of the units. In the case of phased-array radars where the number of elements can vary from a few hundred to many thousands, GaAs monolithic circuits become attractive in making such systems feasible.

In order to estimate the cost of a typical monolithic circuit it is necessary to assess accurately the overall yield of individual chips throughout the various production stages. In order to do this consider three examples of typical chips using different technological approaches:

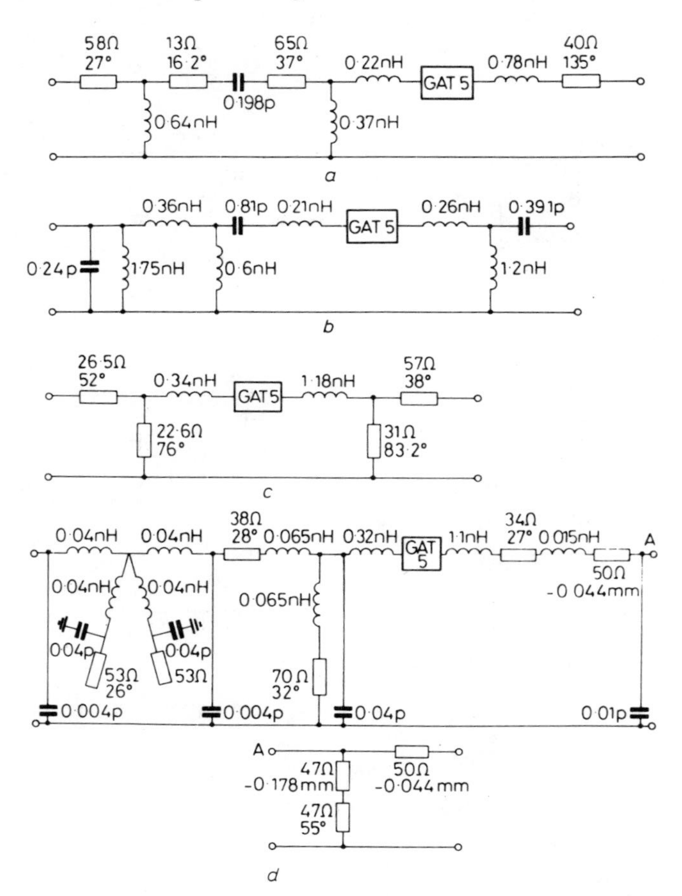

Fig. 19 *Broadband matching circuits for Plessey GATS device*

a Semidistributed/semilumped circuit
b Lumped circuit
c Distributed circuit
d Distributed circuit including discontinuities

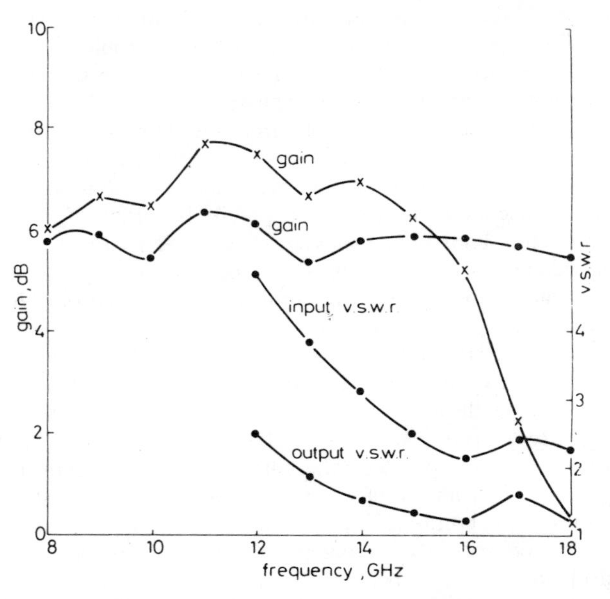

Fig. 20 *Theoretical gain and v.s.w.r. of microstrip distributed amplifier*

x Unoptimised for discontinuity parasitics
• Optimised to include discontinuity parasitics
Only optimised values of v.s.w.r. shown

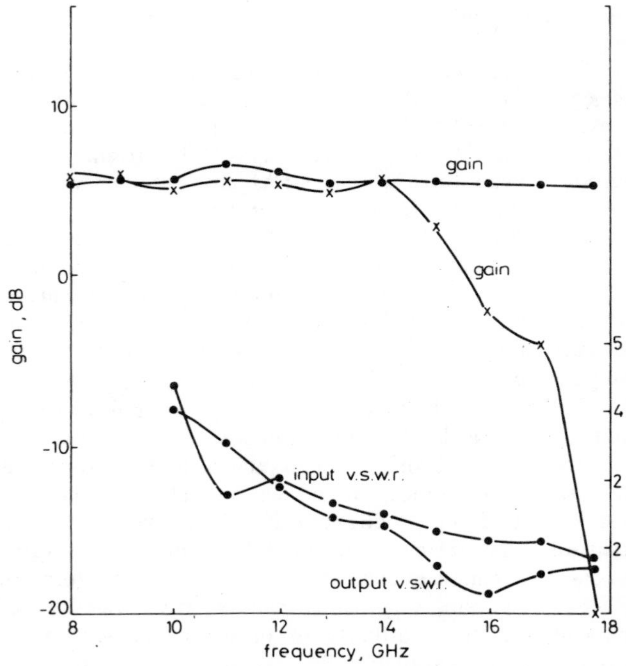

Fig. 21 *Theoretical gain and v.s.w.r. of monolithic amplifiers*

x Unoptimised for L.e. parasitics and loss
• Optimised to include parasitics and loss
Only optimised values for u.s.w.r. shown

Table 1: Yields of GaAs i.c.s on vapour phase epitaxial and ion implanted material

Circuit description	Present small area v.p.e.	5 cm v.p.e.	7·5 cm v.p.e.	5 cm ion implanted	7·5 cm ion implanted
0·3 μm e.b. preamplifier	15%	38%	42%	63%	70%
0·5 μm photolithography mixer	15%	38%	42%	63%	70%
1 μm photolithography i.f. amplifier	30%	46%	50%	65%	73%

(*a*) The realisation of a low-noise J-band amplifier using electron-beam exposed f.e.t.s with 0·3 μm gate lengths.

(*b*) The realisation of a low-noise single-ended mixer using dual-gate f.e.t.s with 0·5 μm gate lengths.

(*c*) The realisation of an i.f. amplifier with an a.g.c. facility using 1 μm gate length f.e.t.s.

Table 1 gives a comparison of the expected yields of the three circuits based on the use of present-day processing techniques. Many of the relatively simple monolithic circuits already realised in the USA and Europe have used small area v.p.e. material. Present yields are dominated by three factors:

(i) edge of wafer defects which account for 35% loss on typical v.p.e. wafer areas

(ii) gate metallisation faults

(iii) variations in d.c. parameters over the slice caused by active-layer thickness variations and material defects; surface defects usually account for a small percentage of failures

As indicated in Table 1 the use of 5 cm diameter GaAs wafers greatly increases the yield while going to ion-implanted material gives an overall yield of around 60%. On 5 cm material edge defects account for 12% of failures.

On this basis, assuming the chip sizes to be approximately 4 mm^2, 400 0·3 μm gate-length f.e.t. working circuits would be produced per 5 cm ion-implanted wafer while between 500 and 600 working chips for the mixer and i.f. circuits would be produced.

This review of the use of GaAs i.c.s in phased arrays has so far not considered the impact of cost – obviously most important.

In order to accurately assess the cost of a particular monolithically based module, consider the example of combining the three previously mentioned circuits into an overall receiver front end. For circuits presently being considered this involves the chips being put into a microwave package much as shown in Fig. 22 together with d.c. regulation circuits, temperature sensing circuits etc. Thus the overall cost of a module can be subdivided into:

(i) cost of basic materials including GaAs

(ii) cost of packaging – microwave chip package and – overall module

(iii) cost of processing GaAs m.m.c.s

(iv) cost of d.c. regulators etc (using the lowest cost techniques available e.g. thick film or i.c.)

(v) assembly cost

(vi) testing cost (including individual chip testing)

As may be appreciated from Table 2, for 5 or 7·5 cm ion-implanted GaAs wafers, the ultimate cost of each module is dictated by the assembly and testing stages. Thus it becomes apparent that, in order to realise the lowest cost, assembly must be reduced by eventually integrating as many functions as possible onto chip and must be made as simple as possible to the point where automatic procedures can be adopted. This is also equally applicable to testing where both d.c. and r.f. testing must be achieved on an automatic basis. Presently automatic d.c. probe testing is achieved and some work on automatic r.f. testing at the wafer stage has also been demonstrated. However, this is an area where much concentration will be needed in the future to enable the lowest production costs to be achieved for the higher volume applications.

The cost of a circuit consists of more than the cost of the component parts – to consider i.c. costs in isolation from the systems they go into may be wrong. However, it has already been indicated that the cost of phased-array components based on GaAs i.c.s is made up of the cost of making the chip, packaging it and testing it, taking account of the yield at each stage. The cost of design and product engineering has to be recovered as well.

The cost of producing the chips depends on the cost of the process in man hours, materials, capital depreciation and the yield. The cost of packaging is related to the number of chips in that package so that the more circuits to be put onto the same chip by increasing packing density the lower the package cost per function.

The cost of testing depends on the test time, the cost and depreciation of the test equipment, man hours and yield. This applies to both wafer probing and final testing. One major advantage of GaAs i.c.s is that they will require the minimum of adjustment and select on test procedures. The cost of assembly depends on package type, cost, labour, yield etc.

A yield loss at any stage is significant but it is desirable to achieve the best possible yield towards the end of the process. Testing cost does not depend heavily on the process technology used. Slice costs are expected to increase substantially as a result of going from 1 μm to sub-0·5 μm geometries because the processes used are

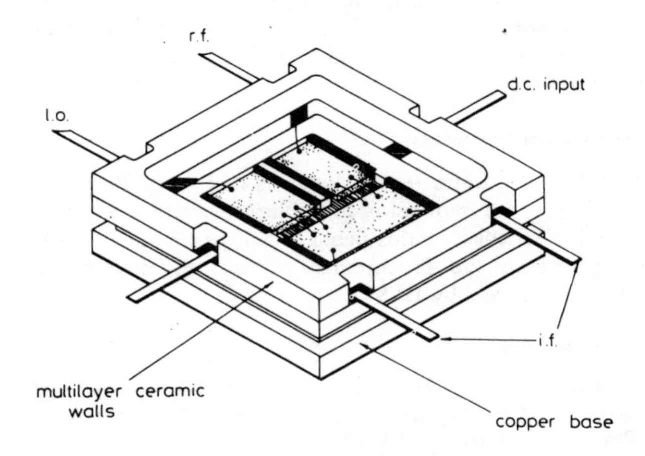

Fig. 22 *S-band GaAs receiver front-end package*

Table 2: Number of working Chips per slice for 5 cm ion implanted wafers

Cost breakdown for complete monolithic receiver front end for 500 off Process	Small area v.p.e. slice	5 cm ion implanted	5 cm ion implanted (2000 off)
preamplifier manufacture	31%	2%	3·5%
mixer manufacture	20%	1%	1·5%
i.f. manufacture	11%	1%	1·5%
packages	4%	10%	9·5%
assembly	25%	63%	56%
testing quality assurance	9%	23%	28%

Assumptions: (i) final number of working slices to 'start' slices is 1 in 3
(ii) assembly of chips into packages gives a 50% yield with 80% tested yield

Results: r.f. preamplifier chip 80
mixer/l.o. buffer amplifier chip 100
i.f. amplifier chip 175

Figures given are percentage costs of each stage towards total cost

different in terms of mask making, yield and higher capital costs involved. The use of electronbeam technology also produces a relatively lower throughput. Taking into account slice sizes (7·5 cm ion-implanted wafers) and packing density going from 1 μm to 0·25 μm f.e.t. devices will probably increase the chip cost on 'typical' chip complexities by a factor of at least two or three times. Photolithography costs are reflected in the cost of equipment – a factor of 5:1 between conventional u.v. and electron beam. The advantages to be gained in going to sub-0·5 μm geometries on GaAs i.c.s are very uncertain both for analogue and digital circuits because of the high capital cost of electron-beam equipment and the slow rate of throughput. This situation could be transformed by technical advances in electron-beam (e.b.) machines and/or high speed resists which could increase work rate and reduce capital cost per slice. Thus it is seen that the use of 0·5 μm or greater f.e.t. geometries combined with large area GaAs slices, simple packaging techniques and multifunction chips will significantly reduce the overall cost to a point where the use of GaAs i.c.s in phased-arrays systems can become a realistic concept.

7 Conclusions

This paper has attempted to give a general overview of the use of GaAs monolithic circuits as related to phased-array radars. Some of the circuits specifically related to such applications have been described including low-noise receiver preamplifiers, mixers, switches and phase shifters as well as power amplifiers all using the GaAs f.e.t. A summary of yield and cost targets for r.f. monolithic circuits has also been given since this is the area in which system feasibility is often defined.

8 Acknowledgments

The author is grateful to the directors of Plessey Research (Caswell) Ltd. for permission to publish this paper. Some of the work described in this paper is being carried out with the support of the Procurement Executive, Ministry of Defence, sponsored by DCVD.

9 References

1 SUZUKI, T., KADAWAKI, Y., ITO, M., NAKATANI, M., and ISHII, T.: 'Super low noise packaged GaAs FETs for Ku band'. Proceedings of the 1980 IEEE/MTT-S International Microwave Symposium Washington DC, May 1980, Paper S3
2 FUKATA, M., MINURA, T., SUZUKI, H., and SUYAMA, K.: '4 GHz 15 W power GaAs MESFET', *IEEE Trans.*, 1978, **ED-25**, pp. 559–563
3 TSERNG, H.Q., and MACKSEY, H.M.: 'Ultra wideband medium power GaAs MESFET amplifiers'. Digest of technical papers, ISSCC, San Francisco, Feb. 1980, pp. 166–167
4 WADE, P.C., and DRUKIER, I.: 'A low X-band pulsed GaAs FET'. Digest of Technical Papers, ISSCC, San Francisco, Feb. 1980, pp. 158–159
5 PENGELLY, R.S., and TURNER, J.A.: 'Monolithic broadband GaAs f.e.t. amplifiers', Electron. Lett., 1976, **12**, pp. 251–252
6 CRIPPS, S.C., NIELSEN, O., and COCKRILL, J.: 'An X-band dual gate MESFET image rejection mixer'. 1978 IEEE MTT-S International Microwave Symposium Digest, Ottawa, Canada (78CH1355–7 MTT), pp. 300–302
7 VAN TUYL, R.: 'A monolithic GaAs FET signal generation chip'. Digest of Technical Papers, ISSCC, San Francisco, Feb. 1980, pp. 118–119
8 RISTOW, D., ENDERS, N., and KNIEPKAMP, H.: 'A monolithic GaAs Schottky barrier diode mixer for 15 GHz'. European Microwave Conference Digest, Paris, 1978, pp. 707–711
9 COURTENAY, W.: Memorandum, Lincoln Laboratories, MIT, Lexington, Mass. USA
10 GASPARI, R.A., and YEE, H.H.: 'Microwave GaAs FET switching'. IEEE MTT-S International Microwave Symposium Digest, Ottawa, Canada (78CH1355–7 MTT), 1978, pp. 58–60
11 FABIAN, W., VORHAUS, J.L., CURTIS, J.E., and NG, P.: 'Dual-gate GaAs FET switches'. GaAs IC Symposium, Research Abstracts, Lake Tahoe, Sept. 1979, Paper 28
12 GARVER, R.V.: 'Microwave semiconductor control devices', *IEEE Trans.*, 1979, **MTT-27**, pp. 523–529
13 GARVER, R.V.: 'Broadband diode phase shifters', *ibid.*, 1972, **MTT-20**, pp. 314-323
14 JOSHI, J., COCKRILL, J., and TURNER, J.A.: 'Monolithic microwave GaAs FET oscillator'. Digest of GaAs IC Symposium, Lake Tahoe, USA, Sept. 1979
15 TSERNG, H.Q., and MACKSEY, H.M.: 'Microwave GaAs power FET amplifiers with lumped element impedance matching networks'. IEEE MTT-S International Microwave Symposium Digest, (79CH-1355–7 MTT), June 1978, pp. 282–284
16 PUCEL, R.A.: 'Some design considerations for gallium arsenide monolithic circuits'. Active microwave semiconductor devices and circuits, Cornell University, 14th–17th Aug., 1979
17 PENGELLY, R.S., and RICKARD, D.C.: 'Design, measurement and application of lumped elements up to J band'. 7th European Microwave Conference Proceedings, Copenhagen, Sept. 1977, pp. 460–464
18 HOBDELL, J.L.: 'Optimization of interdigital capacitors', *IEEE Trans.*, 1979, **MTT-27**, pp. 788–791
19 SLAYMAKER, N.A., and TURNER, J.A.: 'Microwave FET amplifiers with centre frequencies between 1 and 11 GHz'. Proceedings of the European Microwave Conference, Brussels, 1973, Paper A.5.1
20 KNIGHT, J.R., EFFER, D., and EVANS, P.R.: 'The preparation of high purity Gallium Arsenide by vapour phase epitaxial growth', *Solid-State Electron.*, 1965, **8**, pp. 178–180
21 MANESEVIT, H.M., and SIMPSON, W.I.: 'The use of metal-organics in the preparation of semiconductor materials', *J. Electrochem. Soc.* 1973, **120**, pp. 135–137

Monolithic GaAs Interdigitated Couplers

MAHESH KUMAR, MEMBER, IEEE, S. N. SUBBARAO, RAYMOND J. MENNA, MEMBER, IEEE, AND HO-CHUNG HUANG, SENIOR MEMBER, IEEE

***Abstract* — This paper describes the design, fabrication, and performance of two monolithic GaAs *C*-band 90° interdigitated couplers with 50- and 25-Ω impedances, respectively. A comparison of the performance of these two couplers shows that the 25-Ω coupler has the advantages of lower loss and higher fabrication yield. The balanced amplifier configuration using 25-Ω couplers will require a fewer number of elements in the input–output matching circuit of the FET amplifier. The fewer number of matching elements results in great savings in the GaAs real estate for microwave monolithic intergrated circuits (MMIC's). Both the couplers have been fabricated on a 0.1-mm-thick GaAs SI substrate. The measured results agree quite well with calculated results. The losses of the 50- and 25-Ω couplers are 0.5 and 0.3 dB, respectively, over the 4–8-GHz frequency band.**

I. Introduction

A monolithic interdigitated 90° coupler is an important passive component for microwave monolithic integrated circuit (MMIC) applications such as balanced amplifiers, mixers, discriminators, and phase shifters [1]. The monolithic interdigitated 90° hybrids reported in the literature [2], [3] thus far are confined to the conventional input and output impedances of 50 Ω. We report here the first realization of a monolithic 25-Ω impedance coupler on GaAs substrate that has some distinct advantages of low loss and small amplifier size over the conventional 50-Ω design.

The thickness of GaAs substrate used for most medium-power MMIC applications is 0.1 mm because of considerations in device thermal resistance and circuit loss [4]. The input and output impedances of a GaAs power FET are, in general, only a few ohms, which is much less than 50 Ω. In a conventional approach, the input and output impedances of the FET are matched to 50 Ω. To overcome such a large mismatch from a few to 50 Ω, multi-element matching networks have to be used. This leads to a high loss in the matching network and a relatively large matching network which consumes a large area of GaAs real estate. This problem becomes more severe when high power (e.g., a few watts) and wide bandwidth are required. By selecting a lower than 50-Ω system, such as 25 Ω, the matching circuits will result in fewer numbers of matching elements, leading to savings in the GaAs substrate area and reduction in the losses in the

Manuscript received June 7, 1982. This work was supported by the Office of Naval Research under Contract N00014-79-C-0568.

The authors are with RCA Laboratories, David Sarnoff Research Center, Princeton, NJ 08540.

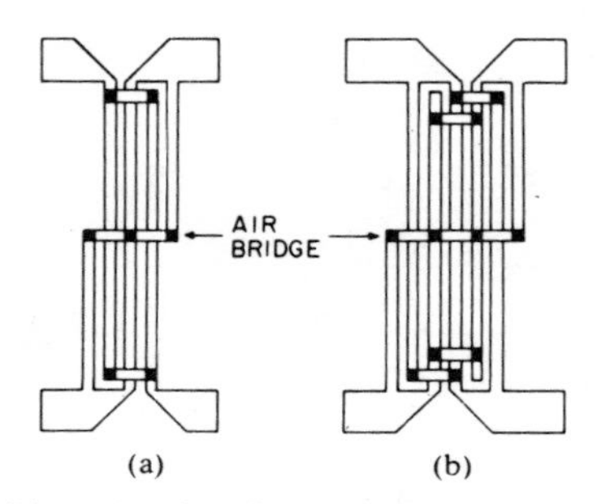

Fig. 1. Schematics of (a) four-line and (b) six-line couplers.

TABLE I
DIMENSIONS OF VARIOUS COUPLERS ON A 0.1-mm-THICK GaAs SI SUBSTRATE
(The length of coupling region is 4.39 mm for 4–8 GHz band.)

Coupler	50-ohm, 4-line	25-ohm, 4-line	25-ohm, 6-line
Conductor width (μm)	6.5	47.3	19.0
Spacing (μm)	7.0	4.3	11.0

matching circuits. Thus the 25-Ω coupler is useful in a multistage, balanced amplifier aiming for high-frequency and high-power applications.

The conductor loss in a coupler is inversely proportional to the metallization line width for a given metallization thickness. The line width of the coupler is in turn determined by the coupler impedance and the GaAs substrate thickness. Brehm and Lehmann [3] have used a 0.2-mm-thick GaAs semi-insulating (SI) substrate for obtaining wider conductor width to reduce the conductor losses. The conductor losses can be reduced by a factor of two if the width and spacing of the interdigitated lines are doubled by increasing the substrate thickness from 0.1 to 0.2 mm. For the case of the power FET, however, the thermal consideration dictates that the GaAs substrate thickness be about 0.1 mm or less [4]. Therefore, the choice of a 25-Ω six-line coupler for power combination at high frequencies is preferred.

The 25-Ω coupler has the width and spacing of 19.0 μm and 11.0 μm, respectively, as compared to 6.5 μ and 7.0 μm for a four-line 50-Ω coupler on a 0.1-mm-thick GaAs SI substrate. Thus the 25-Ω coupler has two advantages over the 50-Ω four-line coupler, namely, better matching to FET impedances and larger interdigitated conductor width resulting in lower loss and higher fabrication yield.

In the following sections, the design, fabrication, and performance of the couplers are presented. The method of measurement and the correction for fixture loss are discussed. The measured results agree quite well with the theoretical calculations. The losses for the 25- and the 50-Ω couplers are 0.3 and 0.5 dB, respectively, over the 4–8-GHz frequency band, with an isolation better than 18 dB for both couplers.

II. DESIGN OF THE COUPLERS

The four-line and six-line interdigitated 90° couplers are schematically shown in Fig. 1. The 50-Ω four-line and 25-Ω six-line interdigitated couplers were designed for operation over the 4–8-GHz frequency band. The length of both couplers is 4.39 mm. The design was done using CAD techniques based on the published theory [5], [6]. The dimensions of the two couplers are summarized in Table I.

For a 25-Ω coupler, the six-line interdigitated coupler was selected instead of the four-line interdigitated coupler for the following reason: the width and spacing of a 25-Ω four-line coupler are 47.3 and 4.3 μm, respectively, as compared to 19.0 and 11.0 μm for a six-line coupler on a 0.1-mm-thick SI GaAs substrate. The small spacing of 4.3 μm between interdigitated conductors of a four-line 25-Ω coupler will present some difficulties in the fabrication of this coupler. At 4 GHz, the skin depth is about 1 μm and, therefore, the conductor thickness has to be at least 3–4 μm to reduce the conductor loss. The spacing-to-conductor-thickness ratio of almost 1 to 1 is, in general, difficult to achieve with high yield. The dimensions of the six-line coupler, on the other hand, are easily realized. Because of this fabrication constraint, a six-line coupler was chosen for a 25-Ω coupler.

III. COUPLER FABRICATION

The fabrication process described here for interdigitated couplers is compatible with monolithic microwave integrated circuits fabrication technology. These couplers can be integrated with other active elements and passive components to form a monolithic GaAs integrated circuit.

The initial SI GaAs substrate thickness is 0.3 mm (12 mils). A 3000-Å-thick layer of Ti and 200-Å-thick layer of Au were evaporated on to the GaAs substrate to facilitate the plating of the interdigitated conductors. The interdigitated conductors were defined using thick photoresist (4–5 μm) and the gold was plated to a thickness of 4 μm (more than three times the skin depth). The interconnections between the interdigitated conductors were provided by thick (3 μm) gold-plated air-bridges. After removing the photoresist, the Ti–Au layer outside the gold-plated area was etched off. The substrate was then lapped to 0.1-mm thickness and a thick layer of Ti–Au (5–6 μm) was evaporated on the back side to form the ground plane.

IV. PERFORMANCE

A. 50-Ω Four-Line Coupler

The photograph of the 50-Ω four-line interdigitated coupler is shown in Fig. 2(a). The SEM micrograph of the air-bridge connection is shown in Fig. 2(b). The coupler was tested in a test fixture which has 50-Ω lines on a 0.0254-cm-thick alumina substrate on input and output side of the GaAs chip to connect the coupler parts to the 50-Ω SMA connectors. The losses in the test fixture were calibrated and later subtracted from the measured results to determine the true coupler performance. Fig. 3 shows the coupling at the coupled and the direct port as a function of frequency for the 50-Ω coupler. The theoretical results are also presented in the same figure. The measured performance is in close agreement with the theoretical prediction. The insertion loss and phase differences between the coupled and the direct port of the 50-Ω coupler as a function of frequency are presented in Fig. 4. The average insertion loss is 0.5 dB and the phase difference is $90 \pm 2°$ over the 4–8-GHz frequency band. The variation of isolation between coupled and direct ports is shown in Fig. 5. The isolation is better than 18 dB across the 4–8-GHz band. The variation of the return loss with frequency at one of the ports of the coupler is shown in Fig. 6. The typical return loss is better than 16 dB.

B. 25-Ω Six-Line Coupler

Fig. 7 shows the photograph of the coupler and the SEM micrograph of the air-bridge connection. Since the coupler has input and output impedances of 25-Ω, for testing in a 50-Ω system, a four-section $\lambda/16$, 25–50-Ω step transformer [7] on a 0.0254-cm-thick alumina substrate was used. The photograph of the coupler in the test fixture is shown in Fig. 8. The losses in the test fixture were calibrated and subtracted from the measured

(a)

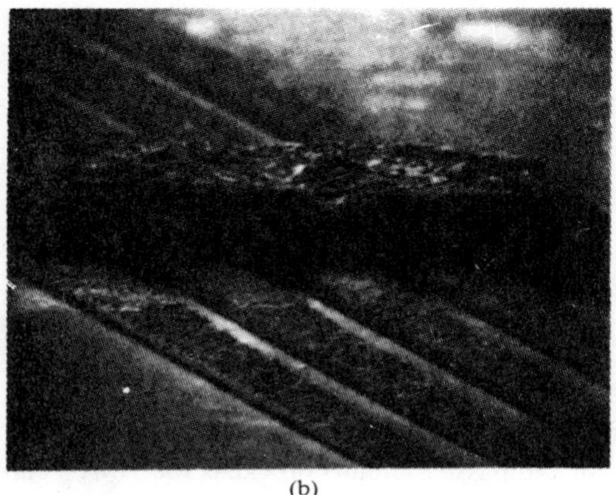

(b)

Fig. 2. (a) Photograph of the four-line coupler. (b) SEM micrograph of the air-bridge connection.

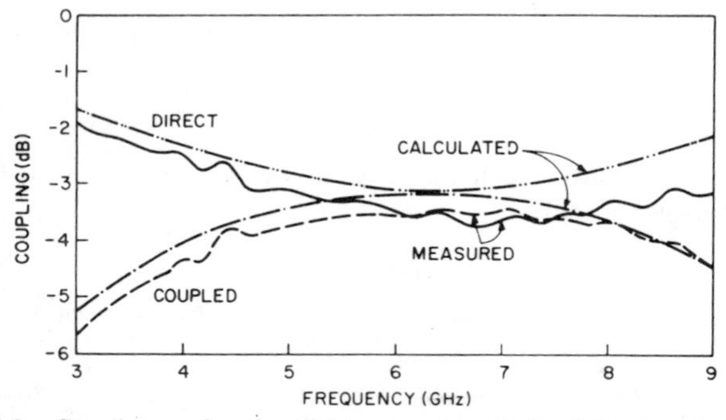

Fig. 3. Coupling as a function of frequency at coupled and direct ports of the four-line 50-Ω coupler.

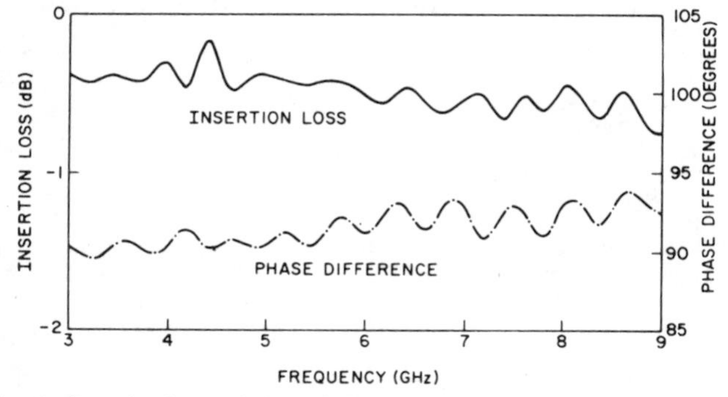

Fig. 4. Insertion loss and phase difference between coupled and direct ports of the four-line 50-Ω coupler.

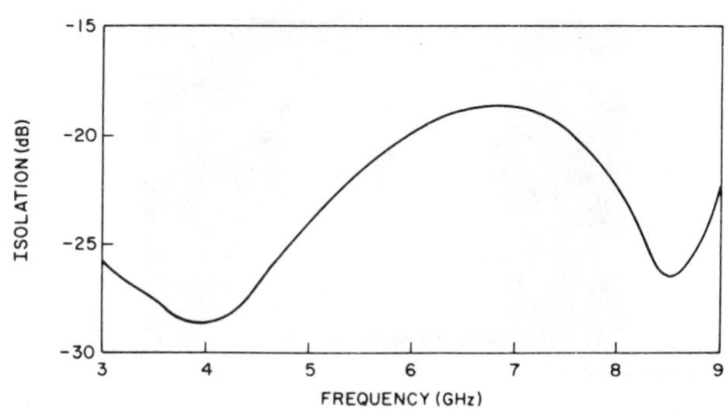

Fig. 5. Isolation between coupled and direct ports of the four-line 50 – Ω coupler.

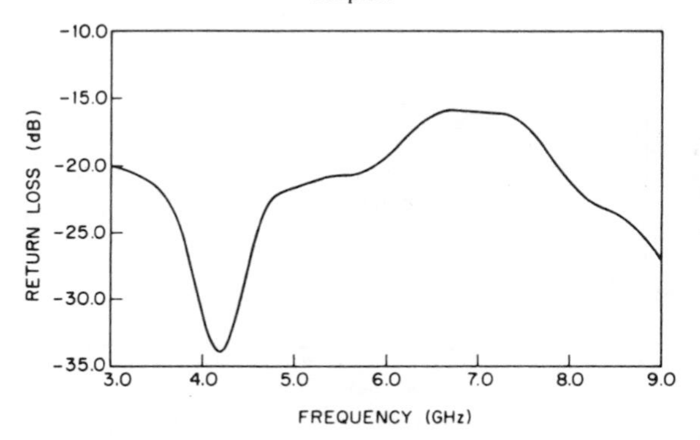

Fig. 6. Typical return loss at one of the ports of the six-line 25-Ω coupler.

(a)

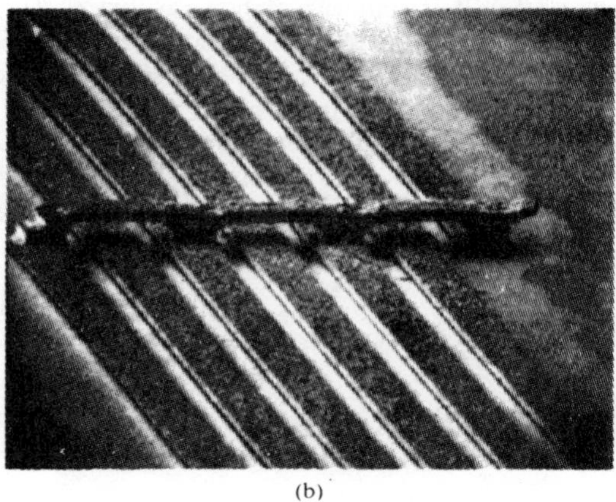

(b)

Fig. 7. (a) Photograph of the six-line 25-Ω coupler. (b) SEM micrograph of the air-bridge connection.

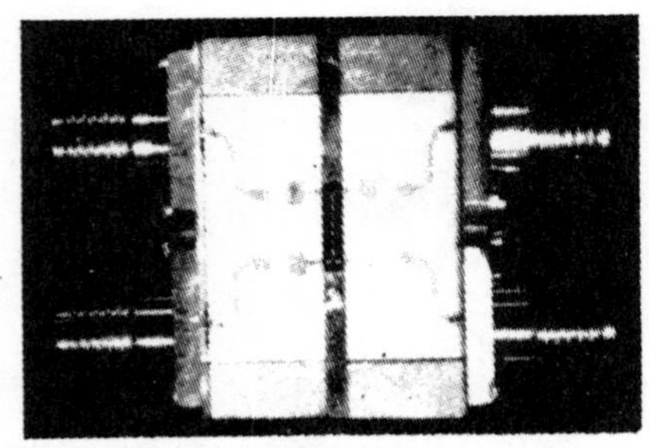

Fig. 8. Photograph of the test fixture (including coupler) used for measurement of the six-line 25-Ω coupler.

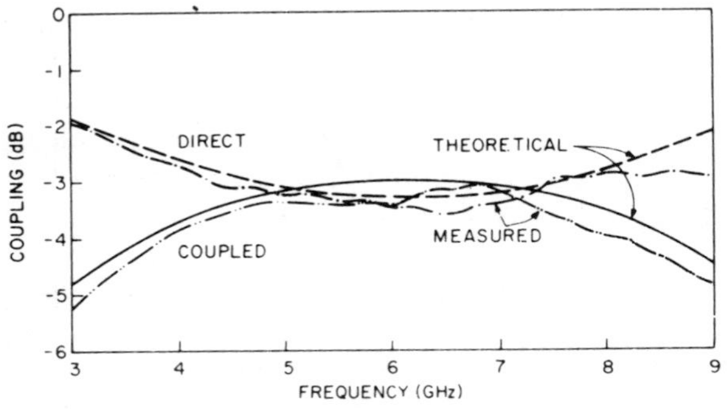

Fig. 9. Coupling as a function of frequency at coupled and direct ports of the six-line 25-Ω coupler.

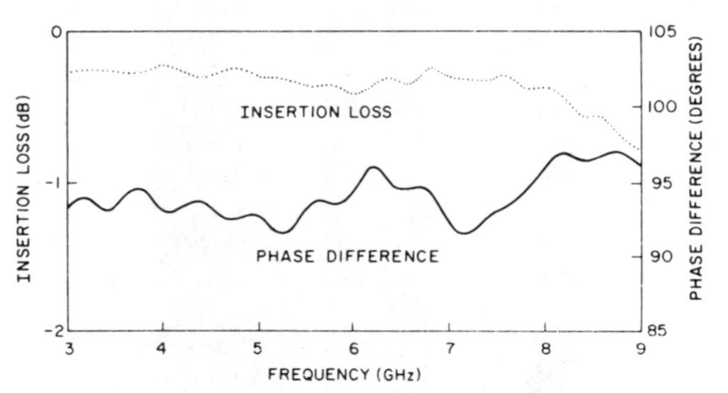

Fig. 10. Insertion loss and phase difference between coupled and direct ports of the six-line 25-Ω coupler.

results to extract the true performance of the coupler. The theoretical and experimental results of coupling at coupled and direct ports of this 25-Ω coupler are shown in Fig. 9. There is a close agreement between the theoretical and experimental results. The variation of insertion loss and phase difference between coupled and direct ports with frequency is presented in Fig. 10. The average insertion loss of the coupler over the 4–8 GHz-band is 0.3 dB, which is a significant improvement over the insertion loss of the four-line coupler. Fig. 11 shows the isolation between the coupled and direct ports of the coupler. The isolation is better than 17 dB over the band. The variation of the return loss with frequency at one of the ports of the coupler is shown in Fig. 12. The typical return loss is better than 17.4 dB over the 4–8-GHz band.

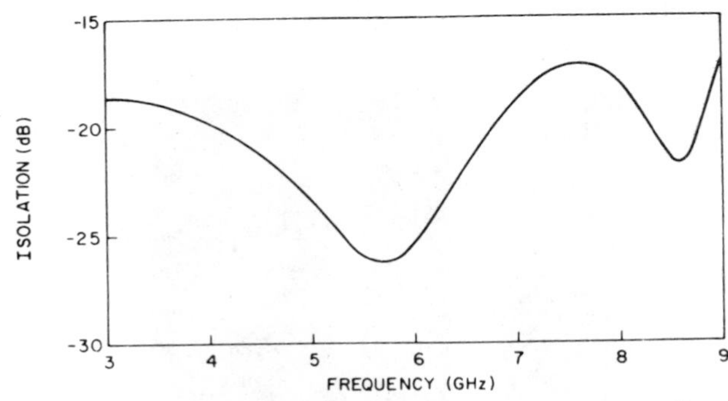

Fig. 11. Isolation between coupled and direct ports of the six-line 25-Ω coupler.

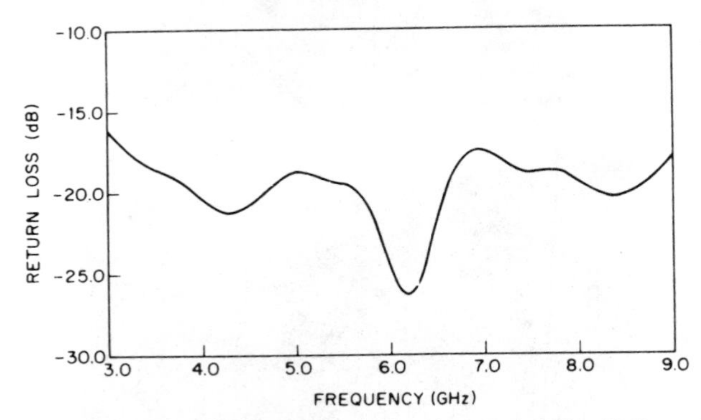

Fig. 12. Typical return loss at one of the ports of the four-line 50-Ω coupler.

V. Conclusions

Interdigitated 90° couplers for monolithic integration with other active and passive circuits on GaAs for MMIC applications have been presented. The 25-Ω coupler has the two-fold advantage over a 50-Ω coupler, namely, reduced loss and better matching to the impedance of the active devices. The loss of the 25-Ω coupler is 0.3 dB over the 4–8-GHz band. The experimental results agreed well with the theoretical results.

Acknowledgment

The authors wish to thank G. C. Taylor and R. Smith for their helpful suggestions.

References

[1] M. Kumar, R. J. Menna, and H. Huang, "Broad-band dual-gate continuously variable phase shifter," *IEEE Trans. Microwave Theory Tech.*, vol. MTT-29, pp. 1098–1102, Oct. 1981.

[2] R. C. Waterman, Jr., *et al.*, "GaAs monolithic Lange and Wilkinson couplers," *IEEE Trans. Electron Devices*, vol. ED-28, pp. 212–216, Feb. 1981.

[3] G. E. Brehm and R. E. Lehmann, "Monolithic GaAs Lange coupler at X-band," *IEEE Trans. Electron Devices*, vol. ED-28, pp. 217–218, Feb. 1981.

[4] Robert A. Pucel, "Design considerations for monolithic microwave circuits," *IEEE Trans. Microwave Theory Tech.*, vol. MTT-29, pp. 513–534, June 1981.

[5] D. D. Paolino, "Design more accurate interdigitated couplers," *Microwaves*, vol. 19, pp. 34–38, May 1976.

[6] W. P. Ou, "Design equations for an interdigitated directional coupler," *IEEE Trans. Microwave Theory Tech.*, vol. MTT-22, pp. 253–256, Feb. 1975.

[7] G. L. Matthaei, "Short-step Chebyshev impedance transformers," *IEEE Trans. Microwave Theory Tech.*, vol. MTT-14, pp. 372–383, Aug. 1966.

Physical Basis of Short-Channel MESFET Operation

TOSHIMI WADA AND JEFFREY FREY, MEMBER, IEEE

***Abstract*—Metal-semiconductor field-effect transistors (MESFET's) made of Si, GaAs, and InP have been numerically analyzed in two dimensions using the Cornell University Program for Integrated Devices (CUPID), in order to give physical insight into MESFET operation. Equilibrated electron drift velocity-versus-electric field characteristics and field-dependent anisotropic diffusivities are used in the analysis. Predicted figures of merit, such as cutoff frequency and gate-source capacitance, are compared with experimental results obtained by other authors. Electron transit time, and hence f_T, in 0.5- and 1.0-μm-gate Si, GaAs, and InP FET's is shown to be largely unrelated to the value of low-field mobility in these materials at drain voltages in excess of 1 V. The results relate to the choice of materials for devices in both VLSI digital circuits and microwave linear circuits.**

I. Introduction

TO ATTACK particularly the questions relating to the influence of high-field transport properties on the high-frequency performance of MESFET's and of MESFET's used in logic circuits, we have determined the steady states of operation of Si, GaAs, and InP devices by two-dimensional numerical analysis. This analysis, yielding an understanding of the physical basis of short-channel MESFET operation, should indicate directions for further development in device design and materials technology.

II. Previous MESFET Analyses

Earlier analyses of MESFET's (and related JFET's) range from highly simplified closed-form analytical approaches to complicated and expensive computer simulations. Some workers are now reverting to highly simplified analytical approaches in order to facilitate device design.

A. Analytical Approaches

The earliest theoretical treatment for the characteristics of FET's was presented by Shockley [1], who took the longitudinal electric field in the channel to be much smaller than the transverse field and assumed that the thickness of the "working channel" changed very gradually along its length. Shockley himself pointed out that his approximate treatment was not valid beyond current saturation, when gate-to-drain voltage is equal to the pinch-off voltage V_p

$$V_p = \frac{a^2 q}{2\epsilon_s \epsilon_0} N_D. \tag{1}$$

Manuscript received October 20, 1978; revised December 16, 1978. This work was supported in part by the Air Force Office of Scientific Research, Bolling AFB, DC 20332.

T. Wada was with the School of Electrical Engineering, Cornell University, Ithaca, NY 14853. He is now with the Institute of Industrial Science, University of Tokyo, Roppongi, Tokyo, Japan.

J. Frey is with the School of Electrical Engineering, Cornell University, Ithaca, NY 14853.

Shockley's model has been modified by many authors in order to explain more completely the conditions that apply both before and after pinch-off. Dacey and Ross [2] added the effects of drift velocity saturation at high electric fields, and Hauser [3] incorporated the effects of the shape of the junction depletion region near the ends of the gate by means of an approximation using the potential distribution characteristic of a semicylindrical electrode. Turner and Wilson [4] attempted to include velocity saturation in the characterization of the GaAs FET. Grebene and Ghandhi [5] obtained the potential in the fully depleted region by approximately solving a two-dimensional Poisson's equation. They did not take velocity saturation as occurring at the drain end of the gate, as did others. Lehovec and Zuleeg [6] replaced the constant mobility in the Turner-Wilson model with an approximate analytical field-dependent expression [7], and mated this model to that of Grebene and Ghandhi for the fully depleted region. In the model of Pucel *et al.* [8], a boundary plane between the gradual channel and the region of velocity saturation was established (as it was by Grebene and Ghandhi) where the electric field reached the critical value for saturation of the linearized velocity versus electric-field curve. In addition, the continuity of the channel current at this plane was explicitly included as one of the boundary conditions, in order to obtain the lengths of each region.

Although many of these analytical treatments could be made to agree with experimental results for devices with gate lengths down to 2 μm, none provided a continuous analytical solution valid both before and after saturation. Diffusion current is not generally taken into account in these treatments, although a recent 3-region solution by Dawson and Frey [9] has treated this subject approximately.

B. Two-Dimensional Numerical FET Analyses

Numerical analysis was first used by Kennedy and O'Brien [10] to determine the characteristics of the nonplanar Si JFET. Using a field-dependent mobility for electrons and holes in Si, as given by Ryder [11], these workers showed that the FET does not in fact have a sharply defined "depletion region" under the gate. As a result of using a realistic field-dependent carrier mobility, they noted the existence of regions of carrier accumulation and depletion. Reiser [12] analyzed the operation of 1-μm gate planar Si JFET's with conducting (but high-resistivity) substrates, showing that a considerable substrate current can flow in saturation, contributing to a large drain conductance. Reiser and Wolf [13] extended this investigation, showing that with aspect ratios smaller than about 4 the drain field has considerable influence on the carrier distribution in the entire channel and, therefore, on g_D.

Himsworth [14], [15] analyzed the characteristics of both GaAs and InP JFET's with nonplanar structures and low doping ($2.6 \times 10^{15}/\text{cm}^3$) in the channel. The velocity-field curves used in the analysis had velocity dropback. Yamaguchi *et al.* [16] first used a field-dependent diffusivity in FET analysis, applying a modified Einstein relation which included the effect of electron temperature. These workers also proposed certain simplifications, such as use of a sinusoidal approximation to the depletion-region carrier profile [17]-[19] to facilitate two-dimensional analyses.

The expense of two-dimensional computer simulations has precluded widespread use of this technique in device design. Such simulations are useful, however, in indicating what physical features must be included in more approximate analyses and possibly how they might be included. The simulations described here were performed in order to determine the effects of materials parameters on parasitic elements and other factors affecting device performance; these results should also be useful in the subsequent formulation of approximate device models.

III. Two-Dimensional Numerical Analysis: CUPID

The Cornell University Program for IC Devices (CUPID) solves Poisson's equation and that of current continuity. The materials properties and analytical methods we have used in solving these equations are discussed in this section.

A. Materials Properties

1) Si: We use the velocity-field curve for electrons in Si for a doping level of $10^{17}/\text{cm}^3$, as given by Jacoboni *et al.* [20]. The field-dependent diffusivity for Si was obtained by extrapolating diffusivity for high-purity Si, parallel to the electric field, to low fields and matching this value to that appropriate for the selected doping level at the selected matching field. This extrapolation is justified since the high-field transport properties in semiconductors with an impurity density of less than $10^{17}/\text{cm}^3$ at very high electric fields are almost the same as those in the pure materials [21]. The experimental results of Canali *et al.* [22] were used for fields above 10 kV/cm, and the extrapolation was performed by matching the relation [16]

$$D(E) = \frac{kT}{q} \frac{v(E)}{E} + \frac{2}{3} \tau \{v(E)\}^2 \qquad (2)$$

where τ is the energy relaxation time, to Canali's result at 10 kV/cm. Persky and Bartelink [23] showed that the diffusivities parallel and perpendicular to the electric field are almost equal, allowing us to take the high-field diffusivity to be isotropic and equal to the value for the parallel component only. Velocity- and diffusivity-field relationships used for all materials are shown in Figs. 1 and 2.

2) GaAs: Experimental velocity-field data at electric fields greater than 25 kV/cm [24], [25] and Monte Carlo calculations for fields below this value [26], [27] were used for GaAs with $N_D = 10^{17}/\text{cm}^3$. Anisotropic diffusivities as obtained by Fawcett and Rees [28] and by Bauhahn *et al.* [29] were used, again with a modified Einstein relation to extrapolate the high-field diffusivities to the low-field region. There is some

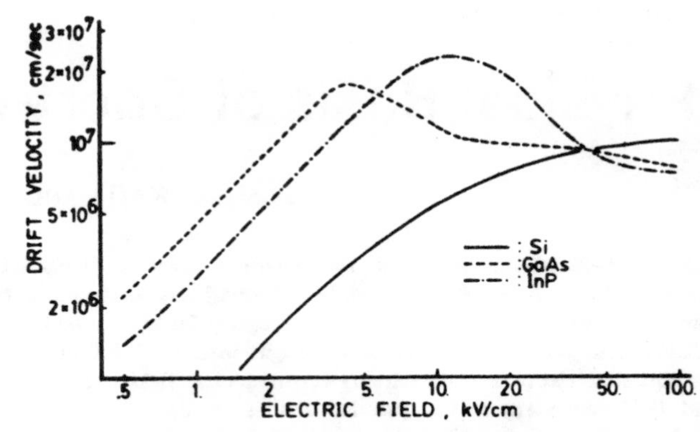

Fig. 1. Velocity-field curves for Si, GaAs, and InP: $N_D = 10^{17}\ \text{cm}^{-3}$.

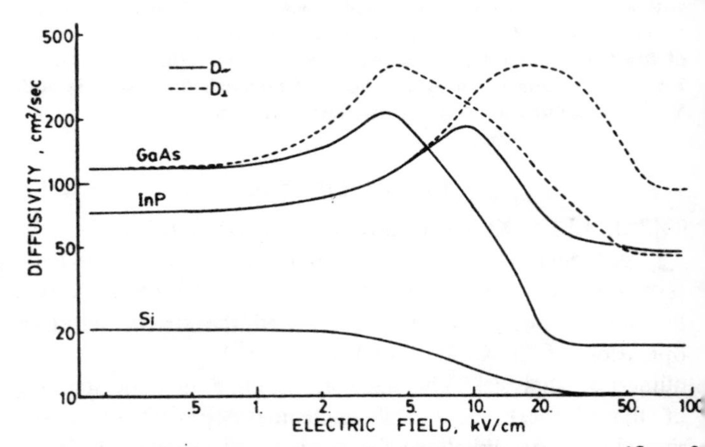

Fig. 2. Diffusivity-field curves for Si, GaAs, and InP: $N_D = 10^{17}\ \text{cm}^{-3}$

disagreement over the correct values of high-field diffusivities in both GaAs and InP, but all proposed values do not differ much from those used here.

3) InP: Experimental [30] and calculated [26], [27] velocity-field data for electrons in indium phosphide were used in conjunction with calculated anisotropic diffusivities [29].

Nonequilibrium electron transport properties (velocity overshoot [26], [27], [31], [32]) may well affect the characteristics of MESFET's with very short gates. These phenomena were not taken into account explicitly in the analysis but are discussed in Section V.

B. Method of Calculation

The transistor model used is shown in Fig. 3. The partial differential equations describing the model [10], [17] are converted to finite-difference forms using a 5-point difference approximation. The fast Fourier transform (FFT) program used for solution of Poisson's equation traces its lineage through Maloney's KETL [26] from Hockney's POT4 [33].

Successive underrelaxation (SUR) [34] was used to solve the current-continuity equations. The scheme of Scharfetter and Gummel [35] and Roache [36], first utilized in two dimensions by Slotboom [37], was used to circumvent nonphysical numerical instabilities in these solutions.

1) Boundary Conditions: On the boundaries of the model the normal derivatives of both potential and mobile carrier density are set to zero, since no current flows across the free surfaces of the MESFET. Surface potentials and surface

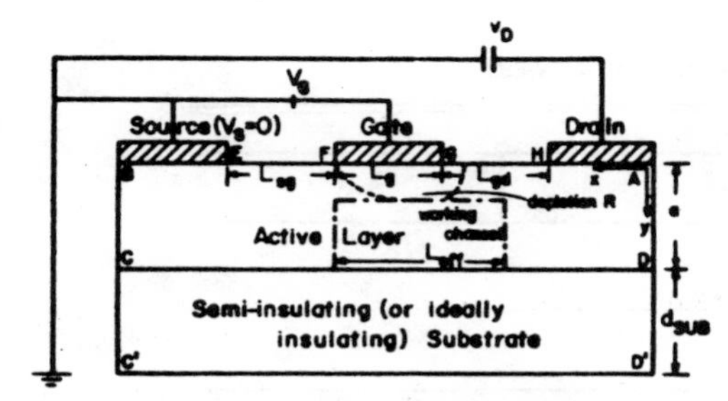

Fig. 3. Two-dimensional MESFET model.

recombination are taken as zero. At ohmic contacts potentials were fixed at applied values, and the mobile carrier densities just under these electrodes were set at the doping concentration of the active layer, i.e.,

$$\phi = V_s \text{ or } V_D$$

and

$$n = N_D$$

at the source or drain electrodes. For the Schottky-barrier gate, the potential at the electrode was fixed at

$$\phi = V_G - V_\phi$$

and the mobile carrier density just under the gate was fixed at

$$n = N_D \exp(q(V_G - V_\phi)/kT).$$

2) Mesh Spacing: The mesh spacing must be fine enough to properly resolve the variation of physical quantities in a cloud of charged particles. The Debye length

$$L_D = \sqrt{\frac{\epsilon_s \epsilon_0 kT}{q^2 N_D}} \tag{3}$$

is a measure of the maximum spacing allowed for the grid points. A mesh spacing of less than about 0.014 μm is thus required for the numerical analysis of a GaAs MESFET with a doping level of $10^{17}/\text{cm}^3$.

3) Convergence Criteria: Convergence of the Poisson's equation solution for potential can be taken to occur when the maximum difference between values calculated in successive iterations is kT/q. As an equivalent measure for current convergence, we took [38]

$$I_D \simeq I_S \simeq I_{\text{channel}}$$

where I_S is the current out of the source, I_D the current into the drain, and I_{channel} is the current flow along the channel

$$I_{\text{channel}} = \left(\sum_{i=ND}^{NS} I_i \right) \Big/ (NS - ND + 1) \tag{4}$$

where I_i is the current which crosses the ith cross-sectional area of the channel, and NS and ND correspond to the grid numbers in the x direction of the points E and H in Fig. 3.

4) Quantities of Interest: The following quantities of interest are calculated.

a) The total charge within the MESFET Q:

$$Q = \iint_{\text{FET}} q(N_D - n(x,y))\, dx\, dy. \tag{5}$$

b) The gate capacitance C_g:

$$C_g = \left. \frac{\Delta Q}{\Delta V_G} \right|_{V_D = \text{const.}} \tag{6}$$

c) The drain conductance g_D:

$$g_D = \left. \frac{\Delta I_D}{\Delta V_D} \right|_{V_G = \text{const.}} \tag{7}$$

d) The transconductance g_m:

$$g_m = \left. \frac{\Delta I_D}{\Delta V_G} \right|_{V_D = \text{const.}} \tag{8}$$

e) The average transit time τ:

$$\tau = \int_{L_{eff}} \frac{dx}{\langle v_x \rangle_y} \tag{9}$$

where $\langle v_x \rangle_y$ is obtained by averaging the v_x's in the working channel. The working channel is here defined as the region in the vicinity of the gate in which the mobile carrier density exceeds 30 percent of N_D. L_{eff} is defined by the length of the region of the working channel where longitudinal current density J_x exceeds 50 percent of the maximum current density which can be found in the channel. This definition of L_{eff} was chosen partly because current level plays an important role in the small signal parameters such as transconductance.

f) The current gain cutoff frequency f_T:

$$f_T = g_m / 2\pi\, C_g \tag{10}$$

or, in terms of transit time using (9)

$$f_T = 1/2\pi\, \tau. \tag{11}$$

IV. Results of Analysis

Simulations of 1- and 0.5-μm-gate length Si, GaAs, and InP MESFET's were performed using the geometry, materials parameters, and calculation methods listed in Table I. The results of these calculations are presented in this section, and the meaning of the results in terms of physical operation of MESFET's will be discussed in Section V.

A. Basic Results

1) Drain Characteristics: Calculated drain characteristics for the 0.5- and 1.0-μm FET's are plotted in Fig. 4 and there compared with experimental results and with the results of various one-dimensional analytical models. The model of Pucel *et al.* [8] was the analytical model used for the compound semiconductor FET's, with source-to-drain parasitic resistances taken as R_{ds} = 0.2 and 0.1 Ω/cm, respectively [40]. The Lehovec and Zuleeg model [6] was used for the Si FET's, with R_{ds} = 0.68 Ω/cm. Experimental points at V_D = 5 V obtained by Engelmann and Liechti [40] for GaAs and InP FET's and by Baechtold and Wolf [41] for Si FET's are also shown. For the Si device, the calculated and experimental values agree fairly well, and the drain characteristic before saturation calculated using the Lehovec and Zuleeg model lies close to the computed points at V_D = 0.5 and 1.0 V.

TABLE I
PARAMETERS FOR CALCULATION, 0.5- or 1-μm-GATE DEVICES

	Si	GaAs	InP
ϵ_s	11.7	13.1	12.4
N_D	$1 \times 10^{17}/cm^3$		
a	0.2 μm		
v-E curve	Equilibrium curves for $N_D = 10^{17}/cm^3$ @ 300K Ref.(20)	Refs. (26),(24),(25)	Ref. (26)
D-E curve	For $N_D = 10^{17}/cm^3$ @ 300K isotropic Ref.(20)	anisotropic Refs. (28), (29)	anisotropic Ref. (29)
V_ϕ	0.8V	0.8V	0.5V
$V_{p,}$ theory	3.09V	2.76V	2.92V

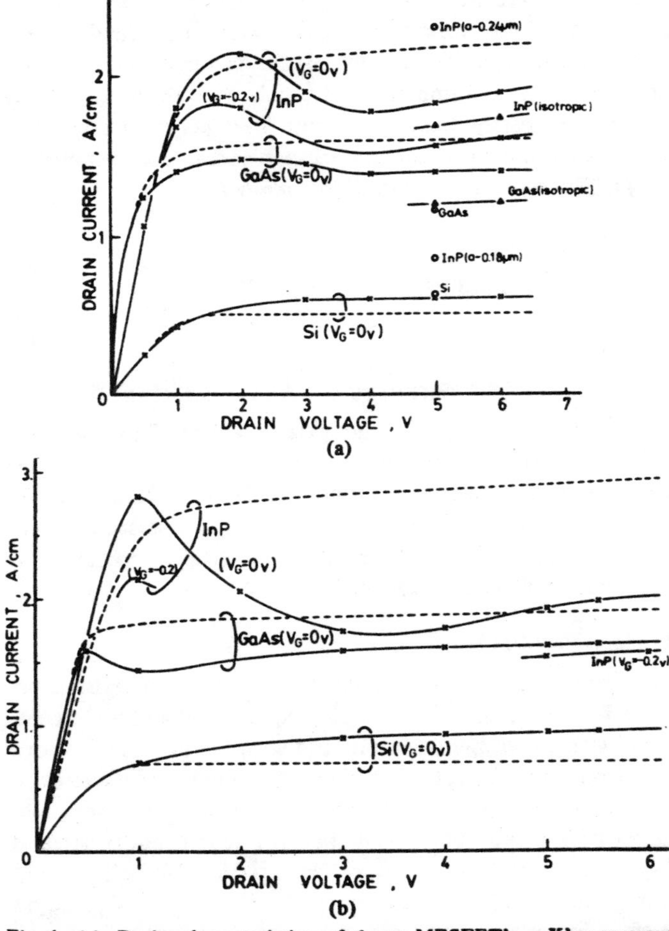

Fig. 4. (a) Drain characteristics of 1-μm MESFET's. X's represent computed points with anisotropic diffusivity for GaAs and InP. O's are experimental points by Baechtold and Wolf [41] for Si, and by Engelman and Liechti [40] for GaAs and InP. Analytical characteristics (broken lines) are from Lehovec and Zuleeg [6] for Si and by Pucel *et al.* [8] for GaAs and InP. ($N_D = 10^{17}$ cm^{-3}.) (b) Calculated drain characteristics for 0.5-μm-gate GaAs and InP MESFET's: $N_D = 10^{17}$ cm^{-3}, $a = 0.2$ μm. Broken lines are analytical solutions.

The discrepancy that exists between the results of our computation for the 1-μm GaAs MESFET and the experimental result may be due to an uncertainty in the active layer thickness of the experimental device, which might have been smaller than the stated 0.2 μm that was determined from the transconductance pinch-off behavior at $V_D = 4$ V. The calculated drain conductance g_D of the 1-μm InP device at $V_D = 5$ V is considerably larger than those of the GaAs and Si devices; this point will be discussed later.

Experimental devices either do not show the dropback of I_D discernible for GaAs and InP in Fig. 4 or oscillate when tested on a curve tracer. If the substrate allows even a moderate amount of conduction, the drain characteristics may not show the negative differential resistance region which was found here for the idealized FET without substrate, and the total drain current will increase. On the other hand, if the substrate is good enough, the dynamic negative resistance could lead to "bias-circuit" oscillations.

2) Charge Distribution: Charge distributions are presented as plots of equal-density contours for the 1-0.5-μm-gate devices for drain voltages of 5 and 1 V in Figs. 5–8. Kennedy and O'Brien [10] observed in their calculations a region of carrier accumulation in the channel of the Si FET; we found none. This discrepancy may be explained by their use of a velocity-field curve in which electrons reach a saturation velocity of 0.9×10^7 cm/s at the electric field $E_{c2} = 16.2$ kV/cm. In the velocity versus electric-field curve used here, the electron drift velocity has the value of only 0.68×10^7 cm/s at E_{c2} (see Fig. 1) and reaches 90 percent of its saturation value $v_s = 1.0 \times 10^7$ cm/s only above 40 kV/cm. We shall show later that the longitudinal electric field near the substrate for $V_D = 5$ V exceeds E_{c2} over three-quarters of the gate length in the 1-μm-device. Therefore, had we used the velocity versus electric-field curve used by Kennedy and O'Brien, we would have seen some accumulation near the drain end of the gate in order to satisfy the condition of continuity of channel current.

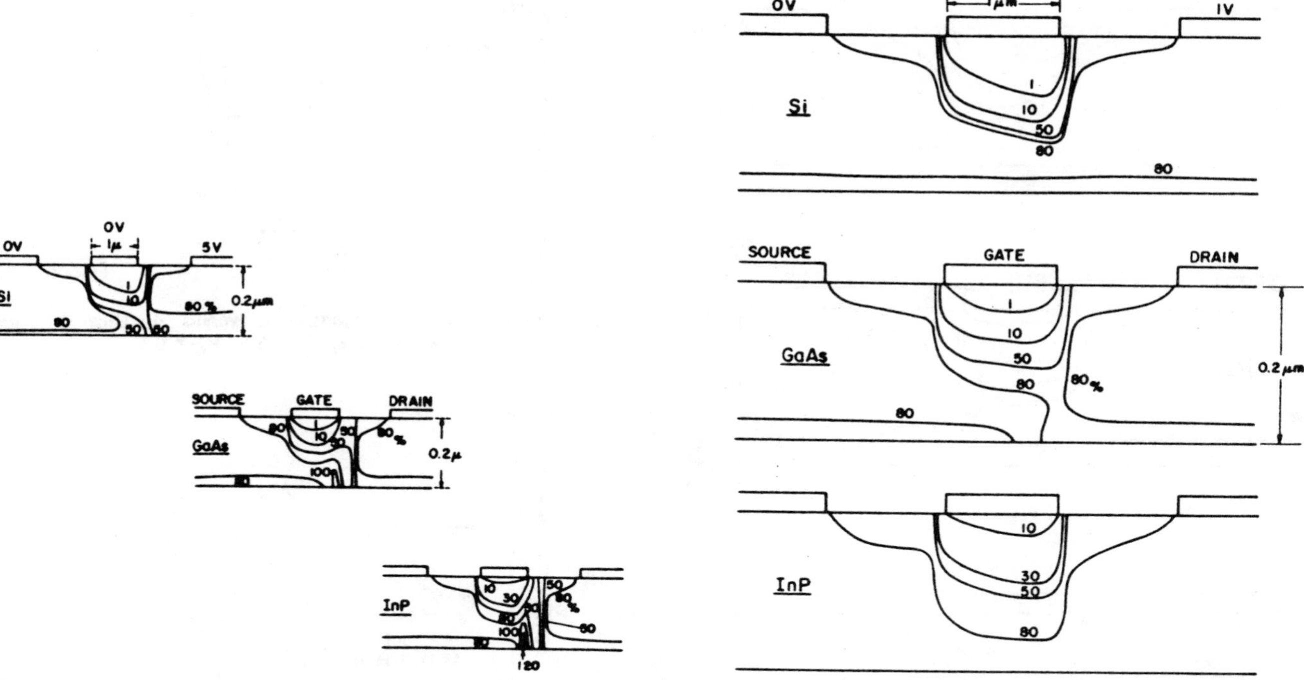

Fig. 5. Mobile carrier distributions in 1-μm-gate MESFET's: $V_D = 5$ V, $V_G = 0$ V, and $N_D = 10^{17}$ cm^{-3}. Contours are in percentages of background dopant density.

Fig. 6. Mobile carrier distributions in 1-μm-gate MESFET's: $V_D = 1$ V, $V_G = 0$ V, and $N_D = 10^{17}$ cm^{-3}.

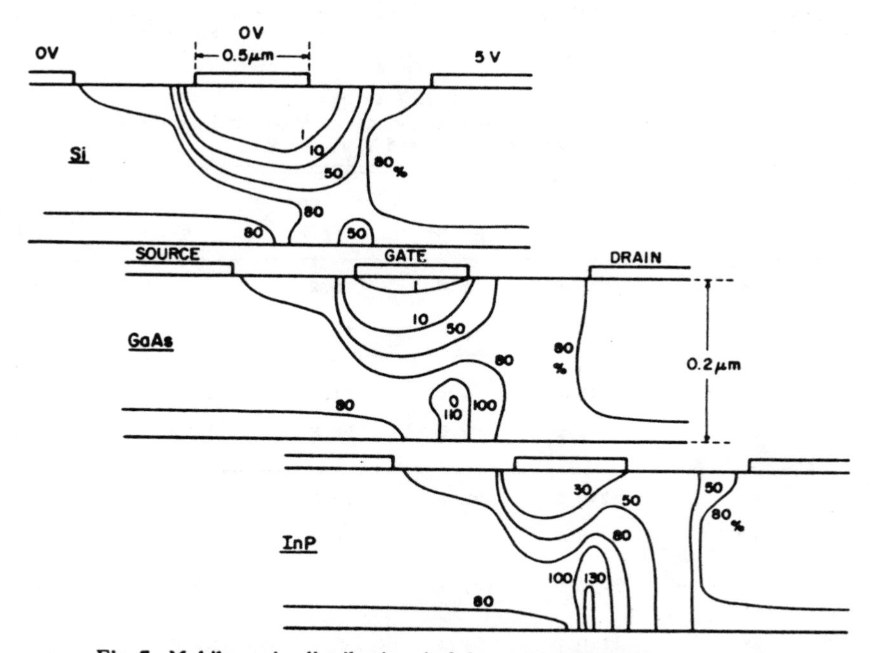

Fig. 7. Mobile carrier distributions in 0.5-μm-gate MESFET's: $V_D = 5$ V, $V_G = 0$ V, and $N_D = 10^{17}$ cm^{-3}.

Our GaAs and InP FET's, however, do exhibit carrier accumulation in the channel. Figs. 9 and 10 illustrate the magnitude of this accumulation in the 1- and 0.5-μm-gate devices at a depth of 0.173 μm.

3) Figures of Merit: The calculated figures of merit of the 1-μm-gate FET's at $V_D = 5$ V and $V_G = 0$ V are tabulated in Table II and are there compared with experimental results. Computed and experimental values of f_T, mutual transconductance g_m, and gate-to-source capacitance C_{gs} agree well. The predicted cutoff frequency f_T for the InP FET is about 50 percent larger than that for the GaAs FET.

Table II also shows that the predicted values of drain conductance for the Si and GaAs FET's are considerably lower than experimental values, and the predicted value for the InP FET is somewhat higher than the experimental value. In Fig. 4(a) it will be seen that the InP FET has a larger drain

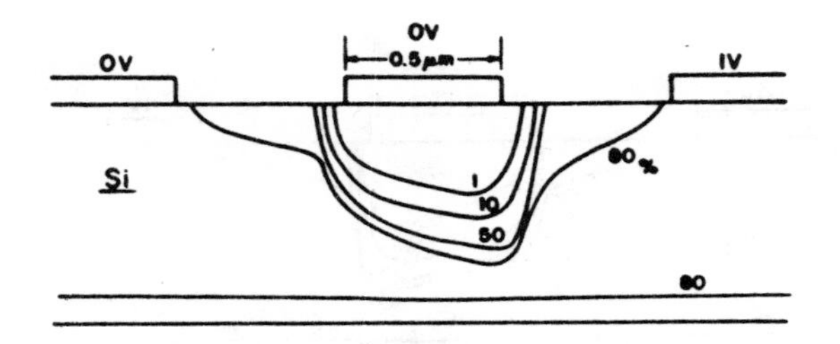

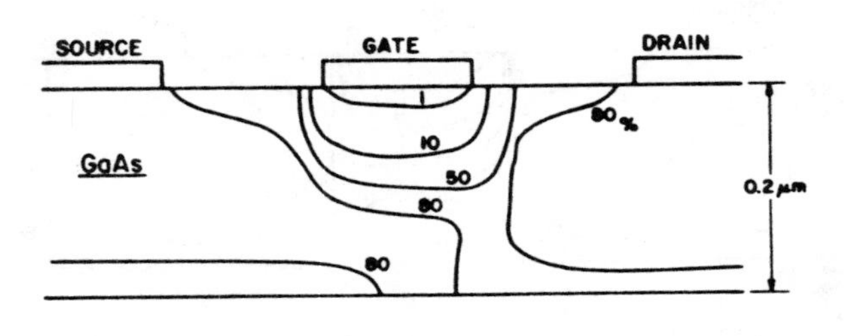

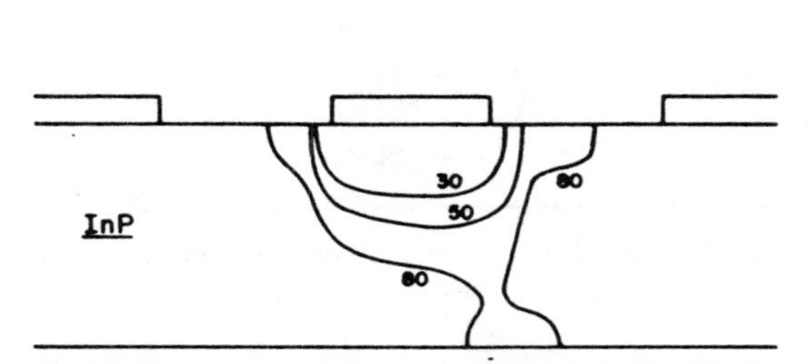

Fig. 8. Mobile carrier distributions in 0.5-μm-gate MESFET's: $V_D = 1$ V, $V_G = 0$ V, and $N_D = 10^{17}$ cm^{-3}.

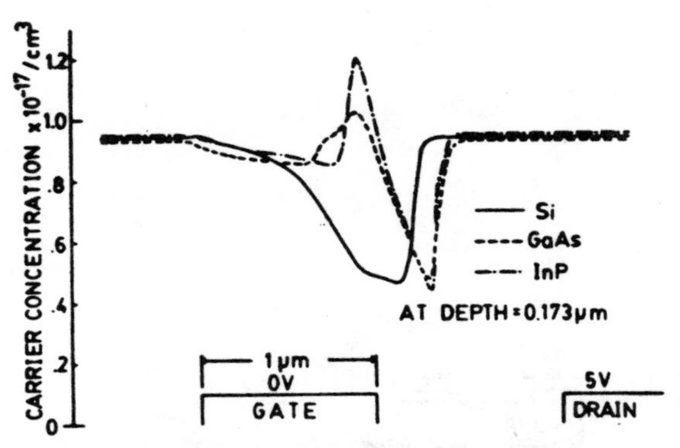

Fig. 9. Mobile carrier concentration versus distance in 1-μm-gate MESFET's: $V_D = 5$ V, $V_G = 0$ V.

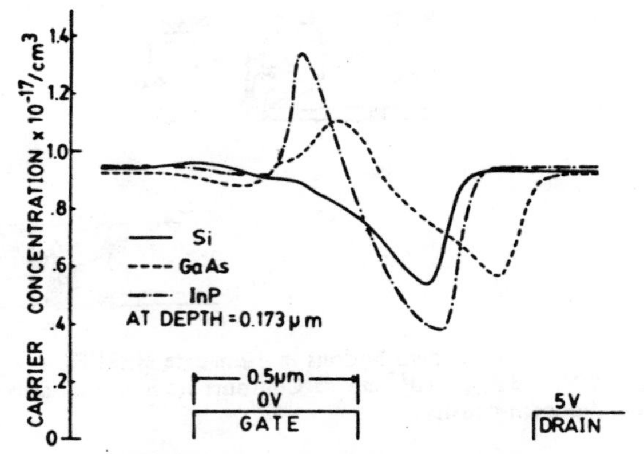

Fig. 10. Mobile carrier concentration versus distance in 0.5-μm-gate MESFET's: $V_D = 5$ V, $V_G = 0$ V.

TABLE II
CALCULATED AND EXPERIMENTAL FIGURES OF MERIT OF 1-μm-GATE MESFET's: $V_D = 5$ V, $V_G = 0$ V

		g_m mS/cm	g_D mS/cm	C_{gs} pF/cm	f_T GHz	f_{max} GHz
Si	(T)	314.9	5.6	8.2	6.2	23.0
	(E)[41]	325.0	37.3	10.8	6.4	15.0
GaAs	(T)	976.6	12.0	11.9	13.1	59.1
	(E)[40]	892.0	62.5	12.2	12.5	34.0
InP	(T)	1272.3	72.3	10.1	20.1	40.1
	(E)[40] a=0.18 μm	1018.0	59.7	9.8	16.5	18.0
	a=0.24 μm	1094.0	111.1	10.4	15.7	21.0
	(T)					
V_ϕ= 0.7V assumed		1110.0	56.3	9.0	19.6	43.5

conductance at a drain bias of 5 V than the GaAs device, larger even than that of the GaAs device just beyond the drain current dropback.

The calculated figures of merit for the 0.5-μm-gate devices are tabulated in Table III for $V_D = 5$ V and $V_G = 0$. The f_T value for the InP device is almost 60 percent greater than that for the GaAs device.

V. DISCUSSION: PHYSICAL BASIS OF MESFET OPERATION

In this section we shall discuss the results presented above in terms of materials properties. The values of the MESFET figures of merit will be seen to depend on a complex interaction among the shape of the velocity-field characteristics, values of

TABLE III
CALCULATED AND EXPERIMENTAL FIGURES OF MERIT OF 0.5-μm-GATE MESFETs: $V_D = 5$ V, $V_G = 0$ V

		g_m mS/cm	g_D mS/cm	C_{gs} pF/cm	f_T (GHz) by (Eq.10)
Si	(T)	413.8	16.2	6.3	10.4
	(E)[43]	465.0	74.6	7.5	9.9
GaAs	(T)	1029.0	15.6	10.2	16.0
	(E)[43]	700.0	30.0	5.0	22.3
InP	(T)	1949.0	65.1	12.2	25.4

diffusivity, amount of substrate conduction, and Schottky-barrier height.

A. Shapes of I–V Curves: Drain Conductance

Calculated drain conductance values at $V_D = 5$ V were lowest for Si and highest for InP for the 1-μm devices; for the 0.5-μm devices, the values for Si and GaAs were about the same, and that for InP was much higher than the Si/GaAs value. In every case where comparison was possible, experimental values were higher than theoretical values. Both the relative theoretical values and the differences between theoretical and experimental results can be explained partially in terms of the concept of rotation of the velocity vector [17], which is affected by the nature of the depletion region and carrier accumulation in the devices. Substrate conduction is also important in the experimental devices.

In the 1-μm-gate InP FET, as drain bias is increased from 2 to 4 V, current drops due to velocity saturation and dropback, accompanied by carrier accumulation (dipole formation) between gate and drain. At voltages between 2 and 4 V the dipole layer is just forming and most of the drain voltage is dropped across this layer, causing a reduction of the longitudinal component of electric field in the gradual part of the channel. At drain voltages larger than about 4 V, the dipole layer widens, and the longitudinal component of electric field in the gradual channel increases, causing a rotation of the drift velocity vector toward the drain end of the channel. Therefore, the channel current increases beyond about $V_D = 4$ V. At considerably higher voltages the velocity vector can be only slightly affected by increases in drain voltage since it is then virtually parallel to the bottom plane, resulting in little increase of the longitudinal component of the velocity vector and, therefore, in little increase of the channel current. The same phenomenon occurs in GaAs at lower voltages because the threshold field for GaAs is lower. Furthermore, in GaAs the effect is smaller, possibly because the smaller peak-to-valley ratio in GaAs results in less charge accumulation and hence in a smaller rate of change of longitudinal field, and hence, a longitudinal component of drift velocity with drain voltage.

The drain current dropback-and-recovery process that was found for the 1-μm InP FET is manifested in the drain char-

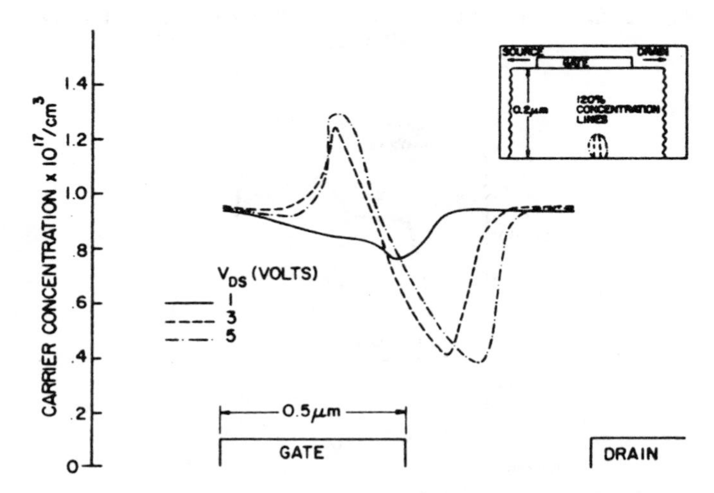

Fig. 11. Mobile carrier concentration for 0.5-μm-gate InP MESFET: $V_D = 1, 3$, and 5 V, $V_G = 0$ V.

acteristics of the 0.5-μm InP FET in the 1–5-V range. The formation and widening of the dipole layer, which plays a major role in this current dropback-and-recovery process, is indicated in Fig. 11.

Differences in drain conductance can also be related to the nature of the charge distribution under the gate, which depends on diffusion constants and Schottky-barrier heights. In Fig. 12, the mobile carrier concentration under the gate is illustrated at the vertical plane in each device at which the mobile carrier distribution is changed by the greatest amount in the channel with a change in applied gate voltage. Si, with the smallest diffusivity, has the deepest depleted region among these three devices; InP, with the largest diffusivity (as well as the lowest Schottky-barrier height), produces the softest depletion region. This result is qualitatively in agreement with an approximate expression, derived in Appendix I, which characterizes the abruptness of the depletion region as a function of diffusivity:

$$n(x,y) = n_0 \exp(CD_0 y/v_s) \cos(C^{1/2} x) \tag{12}$$

where $n(x,y)$ is the mobile carrier concentration, v_s = saturated electron velocity, D_0 is the diffusivity, and C and n_0 are constants. According to (12), when D_0 is small, $n(x,y)$ in-

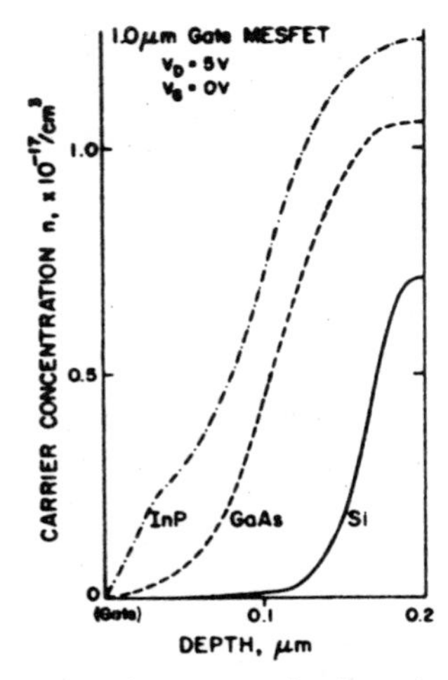

Fig. 12. Carrier concentration versus depth under gate in 1-μm-gate MESFET's.

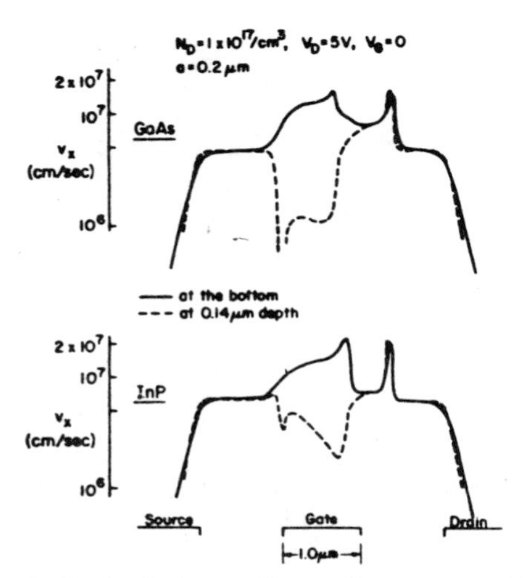

Fig. 13. Longitudinal velocity profiles at the bottom and at 0.14-μm depth in 1-μm-gate GaAs and InP MESFET's.

creases slowly in the vertical direction, resulting in a deeper region from which the mobile charge is excluded.

The influence of gate barrier height on the velocity vector is shown in Fig. 13. Although the drift velocity profiles for InP and GaAs devices do not differ much at the bottom of the channel, where the longitudinal fields are very large, considerable differences do occur nearer the device surface. These differences arise partly because a built-in voltage of only 0.5 V was used for the InP FET, thus allowing the drain field to affect the channel region near the depletion region edge more than in the GaAs device, and partly because the drift velocity-field curve of InP is flatter in the region of critical field than that of GaAs. In this GaAs FET, current is mostly confined close to the bottom of the channel; in this InP FET, current is much more evenly distributed in the channel and results in a greatly increased drain current.

The rotation of the drift velocity vector is quantifiable in terms of the angle θ of the drift velocity vector, defined by

$$\tan\theta = \frac{v_y}{v_x}$$

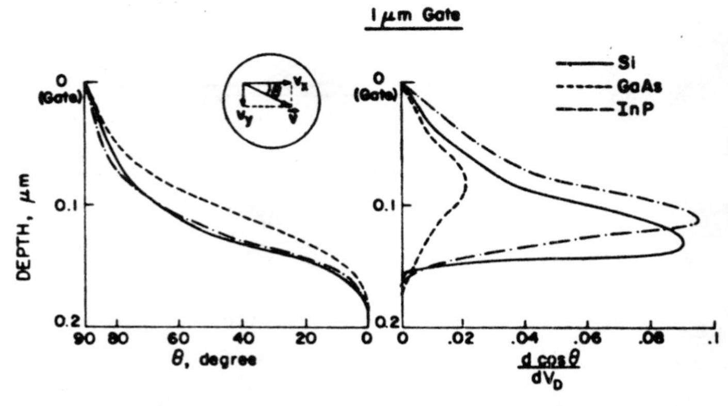

Fig. 14. Angle of velocity vector versus depth (left) and R versus depth (right) in 1-μm-gate MESFET's: $V_D = 5$ V, $V_G = 0$ V.

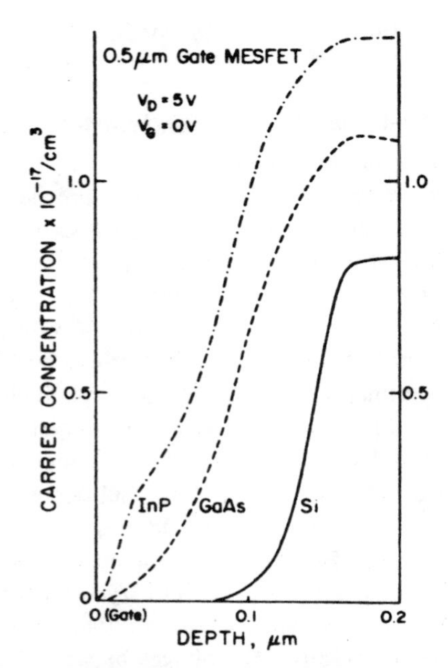

Fig. 15. Carrier concentration versus depth under gate in 0.5-μm-gate MESFET's.

and the quantity

$$R \equiv \frac{d(\cos\theta)}{dV_D}$$

which qualitatively represents the effect of the rotation of the drift velocity vector on the drain conductance, and is illustrated as a function of depth below the gate electrode in Fig. 14. This figure is plotted for a value of x at which the density of mobile carriers changed the greatest amount for a small (0.2-V) change in the gate voltage. The quantity R is much larger in the InP device than in the GaAs device for much of the channel depth. As a result of this large value of R plus the softness of the depletion, the InP FET has a larger drain conductance than the GaAs FET. The relatively large R in the Si device has much less influence on drain conductance because of the smaller diffusivity of this material and the resulting deep depletion in the Si FET.

When the substrate allows some conduction, the current dropback-and-recovery process apparent in the drain charac-

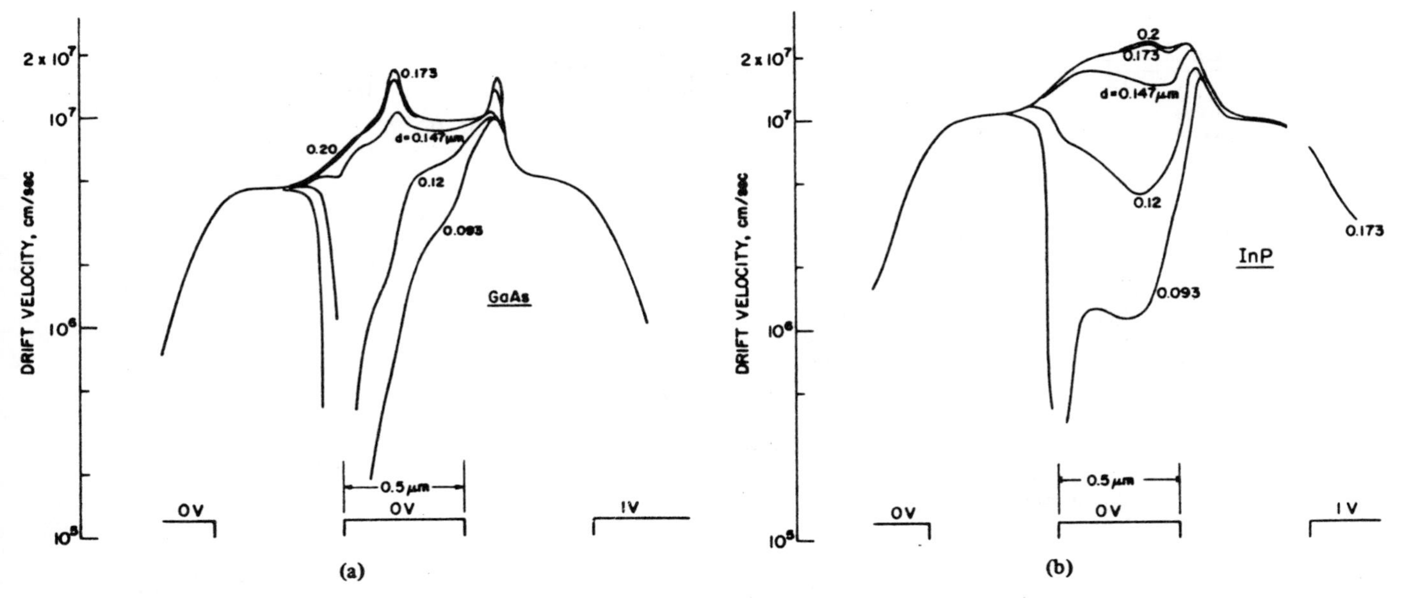

Fig. 16. Longitudinal velocity profiles at several depths for 0.5-μm-gate GaAs and InP MESFET's.

teristics for GaAs and InP hardly occurs, since the electric fields that must be developed across the dipole layer are effectively shorted-out by the substrate conductance [12], [17], [42]. In addition, because of this conduction—which can be considerable even in substrates with resistivity of the order of $10^8\ \Omega \cdot$ cm [12], [17]—any rotation of the velocity vector of electrons in the active layer contributes a smaller fraction to the total channel current than it would in the device without substrate, resulting in a smaller g_D in the experimental device (60 ms/cm at 5 V for the 1-μm-gate device) than was calculated for a perfect substrate (72 ms/cm).

The influence of the diffusivities and Schottky-barrier voltage on the mobile carrier concentration as a function of depth below the gate electrode in the 0.5-μm devices is shown in Fig. 15. In Fig. 16, drift velocity profiles at several depths are shown for InP and GaAs FET's.

B. Transconductance g_m

Transconductance depends on the amount of charge under the gate. The greater this charge, the larger the change in current at the drain that can be produced by a given change in gate voltage. In a long-channel device (i.e., one which approximates the conditions applicable for the gradual channel analysis), the amount of charge in the channel is directly related to the channel current through the low-field mobility; hence g_m in such devices is proportional to mobility. In the short-channel devices discussed here, on the other hand, the amount of charge under the gate depends on the nature of the depletion in that region, i.e., on the diffusivities and Schottky-barrier voltages. Thus, for example, while mobility in InP is only about half as large as that of GaAs, the predicted g_m of the 1-μm InP device is about 30 percent greater than that of the GaAs device. The decoupling of measurable parameters from mobility is evident from the computed results shown in Table IV for the 0.5-μm devices.

The volume of the depleted region when $V_D = 5$ V is largest in the Si FET, as shown in Figs. 5 and 7. Thus fewer mobile carriers are available to contribute to the modulation of the conductance in the working channel in the Si device than in the others, and the Si device has a much smaller transconductance than the others. For the GaAs and InP FET's the difference in g_m at $V_D = 5$ V is in the same ratio as the difference in the drain current levels. As noted above, a higher drain current level implies that more electrons are under the gate and are available to be modulated by small changes in gate voltage.

In the 0.5-μm-gate FET's studied here, channel thickness was not scaled with gate length. Thus more gradual depletion regions were produced than in the 1-μm-gate devices, because of the reach-through influence of the drain field on the field in the channel. The gradual depletion results in a softer pinch-off of the drain characteristics than for the 1-μm-gate devices. Because of the gradual depletion, more carriers can remain in the channel under the gate in any vertical plane than in the 1-μm-gate FET's, resulting in higher transconductance. The increase in carriers under the gate leads also to an increase in carrier accumulation in the 0.5-μm-gate FET's, as is shown in Fig. 10.

C. Gate Capacitance C_g

C_g is an important parameter for MESFET's used in logic gates. The nature of the depletion region edge affects C_g in a fashion similar to that in which it affects g_m. The more charge available for current modulation, the more the change in charge with a change in gate voltage, and the larger the value of C_g. Therefore, on the basis of Figs. 5–8, one would expect silicon devices to have the lowest value of C_g and InP the largest value for the parameters chosen. Fig. 17 shows the mobile carrier distributions as functions of depth from the gate electrode at the vertical plane in each device at which

TABLE IV
RELATIVE QUANTITIES AT $V_{DS} = 5$ V, $V_{GS} = 0$ V

Gate Length		Mobility	g_m (T)	g_m (E)	$I_D(T)$ (T)	f_T (T)	f_T (E)	Avg. velocity in channel at .173 micron
	Si*	1.0	1.0	1.0	1.0	1.0	1.0	1.0
1 μ	GaAs*	5.0	3.15	2.74	2.36	1.62	1.95	1.33
	InP**	2.4	4.04	3.13	3.18	2.13	2.56	1.69
	Si*	1.0	1.0	1.0	1.0	1.0	1.0	1.0
$\frac{1}{2}$μ	GaAs*	5.0	2.49	1.51	1.88	1.22	2.25	1.13
	InP**	2.4	4.71	----	2.25	1.78	----	1.19

*Built-in gate voltage = 0.8 V.
**Built-in gate voltage = 0.5 V.

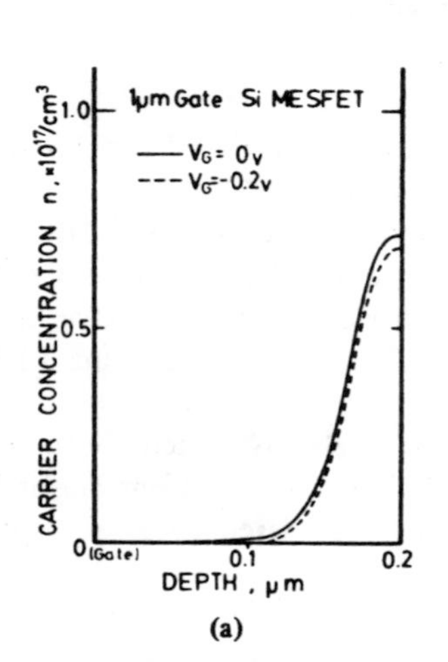

(a)

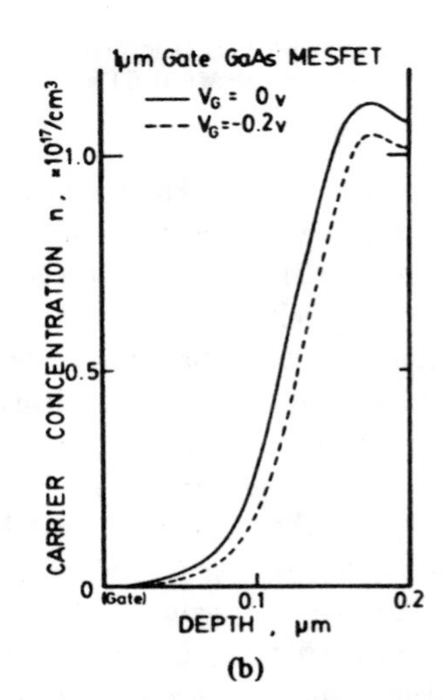

(b)

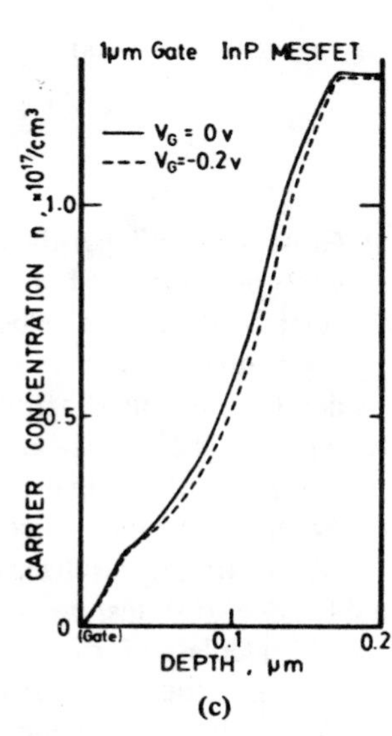

(c)

Fig. 17. Depletion depth modulation in 1-μm-gate MESFET's: $V_D = 5$ V.

carriers are modulated by the greatest amount in the channel. Changes in V_G modulate the depletion region in the Si FET in every direction, above all toward its bottom. However, because its depletion region is deepest, the total change in the amount of mobile carriers within that region is small, resulting in the smallest value of gate capacitance C_g in this device. On the other hand, in the GaAs FET, it is mostly the bottom of the depletion region that is modulated, and the change in total mobile carriers in the region is bigger than in the other devices, resulting in the largest value of C_g. In the InP FET, C_g is somewhat lower than in the GaAs device, because the depleted region is soft and because the influence of the drain field is large resulting in the small influence of the gate voltage.

D. Current-Gain Cutoff Frequency f_T

As was the case for the g_m results, in the light of both experimental and theoretical results, a revisionist point of view must be taken with respect to what physical properties determine f_T. Table IV shows that f_T, which is a measure of transit time through the "working channel," does not depend on low-field mobility or, in any simple way, on maximum achievable electron velocity. To clarify the situation we have plotted electric-field and equilibrated velocity profiles along planes typical of those in which the greatest part of current is carried from source to drain. Such plots are shown for the 1-μm device for $V_D = 5$ and 1 V, respectively, in Figs. 18 and 19.

Beyond the source–gate edge region, due to the high fields and velocity dropback the velocity profiles in the GaAs and InP FET's show a velocity drop between narrow velocity peaks ("ears"). Due to the time necessary for the velocity to equilibrate at high fields in GaAs and InP [31], the electron velocity cannot follow the field in such a short distance as the width of the ears. Therefore, the narrow peaks may not exist in the real device. Yet this "velocity overshoot" does not seem to affect the performance of the 1-μm devices, as shown in Table V where the average transit time τ defined by (9), the cut-off frequency f_T obtained from τ, the effective channel length L_{eff}, and the effective velocity v_{eff} defined by

$$v_{eff} = L_{eff}/\tau \tag{13}$$

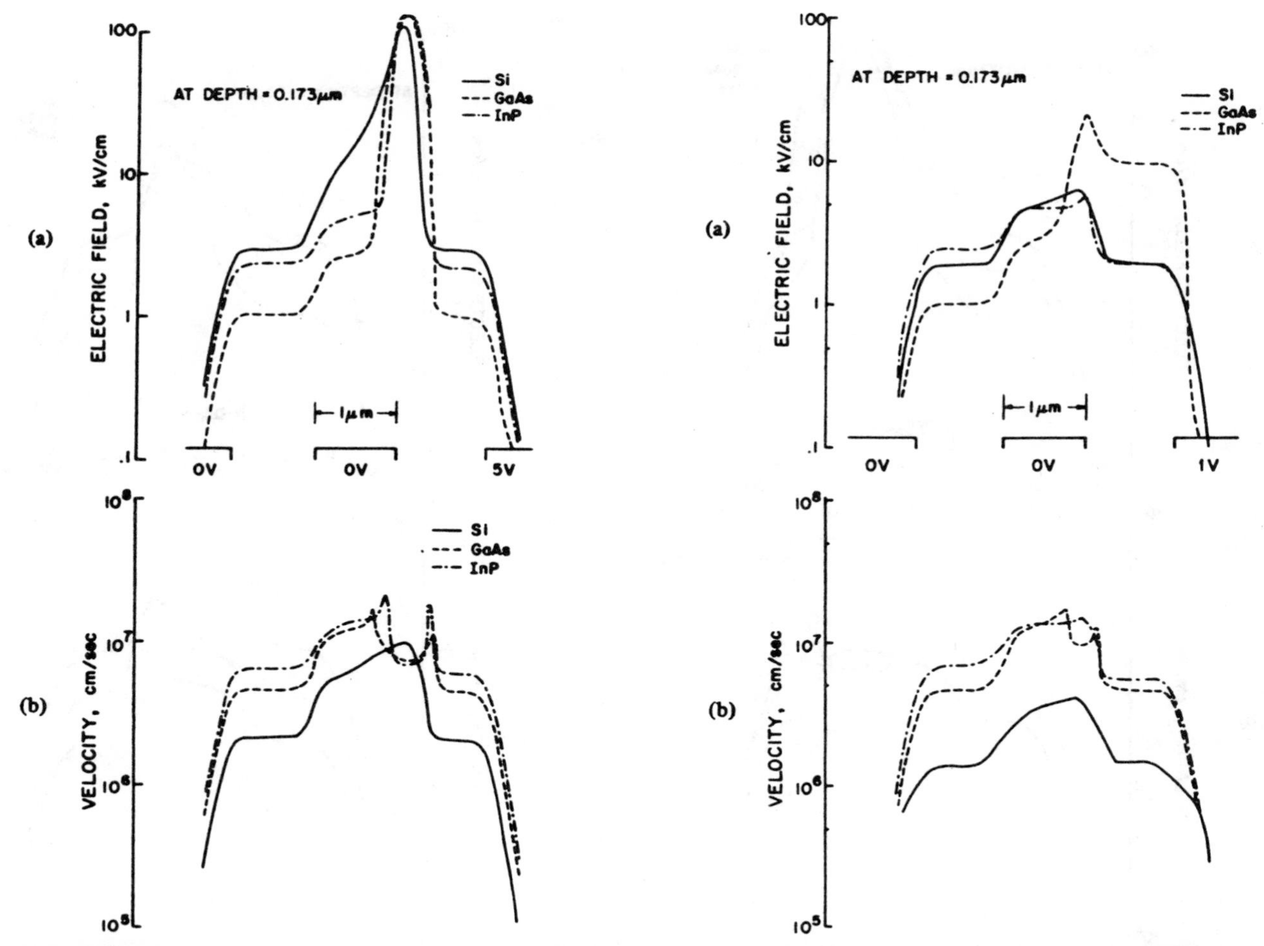

Fig. 18. Longitudinal field profile (a) and velocity profile (b) at 0.173-μm depth in 1-μm-gate MESFET's: $V_D = 5$ V, $V_G = 0$ V.

Fig. 19. Longitudinal field profile (a) and velocity profile (b) at 0.173-μm depth in 1-μm-gate MESFET's: $V_D = 1$ V, $V_G = 0$ V.

TABLE V
EFFECTIVE CHANNEL LENGTHS AND VELOCITIES FOR 1-μm-GATE DEVICES. TOTAL SOURCE/DRAIN DISTANCE = 3 μm

	τ (p sec)	f_T (GHz)		L_{eff} μm	v_{eff} cm/sec
		exp	Theo.		
Si	20.2	6.4[41]	7.9	1.34	$.67\times10^7$
GaAs	12.4	12.5[40]	12.8	1.10	$.89\times10^7$
InP	9.5	16.5[40]	16.8	1.07	1.13×10^7

are tabulated for the 1-μm devices. The calculated and experimental values of f_T show good agreement. Since f_T depends greatly on effective velocity, either the velocity overshoot in these devices does not lead to a significant change in effective velocity over the length of the gradual channel, or overshoot may cause the velocity to be higher but the gradual channel region (L_{eff}) to be longer as well.

Fig. 19 illustrates the electric field and drift velocity at a depth of 0.173 μm at the drain voltage of 1 V, about the saturation voltage. At this low drain voltage there are significant differences in the electric field distributions in the three devices, because while the low critical field of GaAs is exceeded, the higher critical field of InP is not. As a result, the GaAs FET has a saturated velocity region at the drain end of the gate even when $V_D = 1$ V; on the other hand, the Si device has a very low drift velocity throughout the channel. With $V_D = 1$ V the longitudinal electric field is so small that the magnitude of drift velocity in InP is almost the same as that in the GaAs FET.

Fig. 20 illustrates longitudinal electric-field and drift velocity in the 0.5-μm devices at a depth of 0.173 μm from the top surface when $V_D = 5$ V and $V_G = 0$ V. The situation is not qualitatively different from that in the 1-μm gate devices. Fig. 21 illustrates longitudinal electric-field and drift velocity at the same depth, $V_D = 1$ V. In this case in the InP FET the electric field is large enough for electrons to maintain a very high

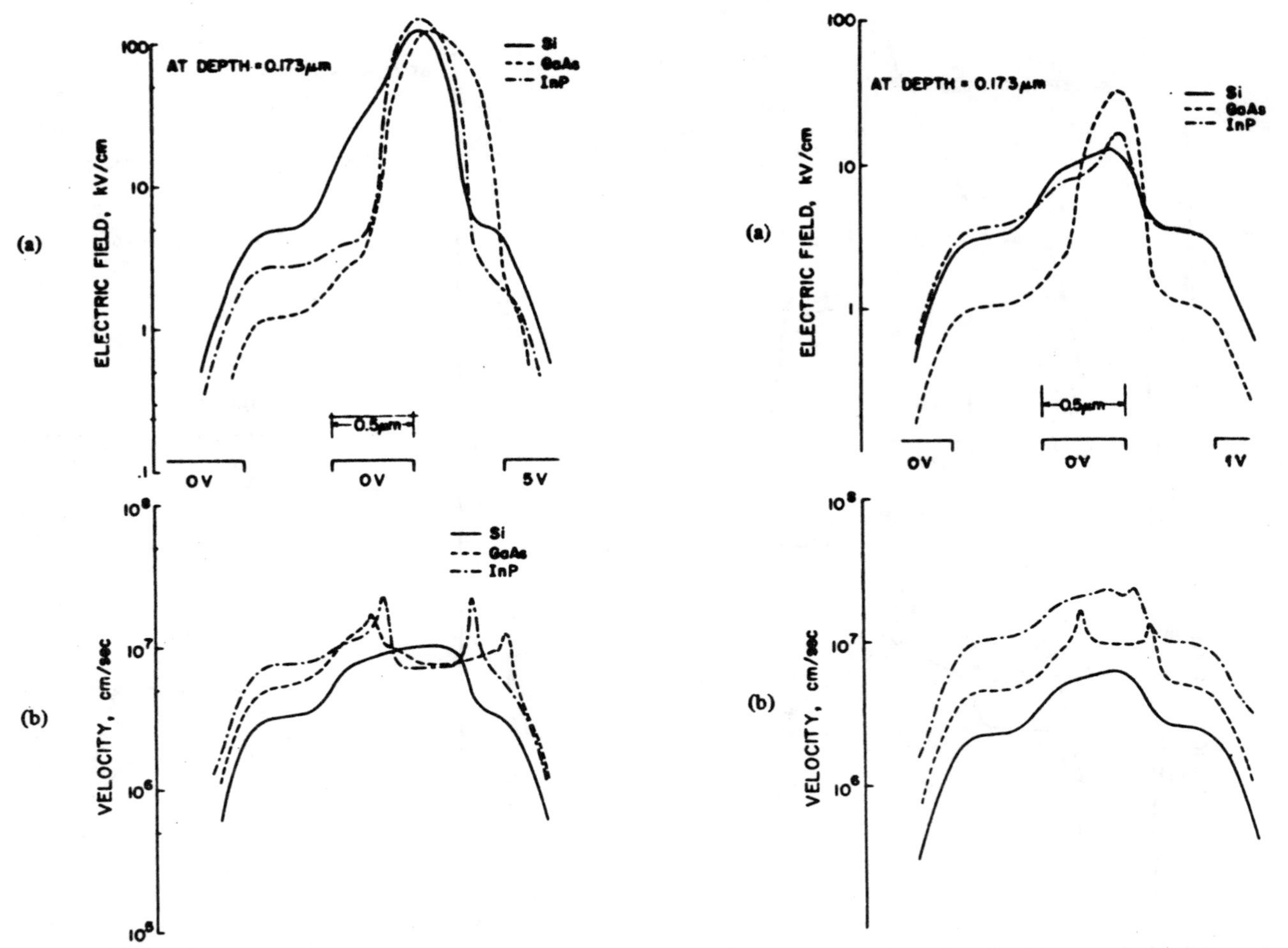

Fig. 20. Longitudinal field profile (a) and velocity profile (b) at 0.173-μm depth in 0.5-μm-gate MESFET's: $V_D = 5$ V, $V_G = 0$ V.

Fig. 21. Longitudinal field profile (a) and velocity profile (b) at 0.173-μm depth in 0.5-μm-gate MESFET's: $V_D = 1$ V, $V_G = 0$ V.

TABLE VI
EFFECTIVE CHANNEL LENGTHS AND VELOCITIES FOR 0.5-μm-GATE DEVICES.
TOTAL SOURCE/DRAIN DISTANCE = 1.5 μm

		τ (p sec)	f_T (GHz)		L_{eff} (μm)	v_{eff} (cm/sec)
			exp.	2-D		
V_D = 5V	Si	10.8	9.9[43]	14.7	.85	$.78\times10^7$
	GaAs	8.8	22.3[43]	18.0	.78	$.88\times10^7$
	InP	6.1		26.1	.57	$.93\times10^7$
V_D = 1V	Si	18.4		8.7	.79	$.43\times10^7$
	GaAs	6.0		26.5	.55	$.92\times10^7$
	InP	4.1		38.7	.71	1.72×10^7

velocity through most of the active channel. The sustained high electron velocity results in a very high level of drain current at $V_D = 1$ V, as is shown in Fig. 4(b). In Table VI the average transit time τ, cutoff frequency f_T, effective channel length L_{eff}, and effective velocity v_{eff} are tabulated for these 0.5-μm devices. Due to the low peak field values, overshoot should not occur in InP to modify the predicted f_T value of 38.7 GHz.

VI. SUMMARY

The fields and charge density and velocity profiles in Si, GaAs, and InP MESFET's were obtained in two dimensions using CUPID.

The nature of the depleted region under the gate affects conductance modulation and depends on diffusivity as well as built-in gate voltage. An anisotropic diffusivity, therefore, must be used in a numerical multidimensional device analysis

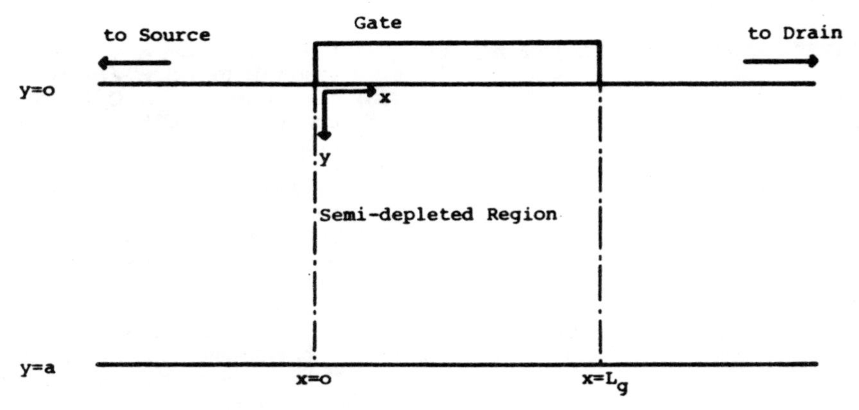

Fig. 22. A simple model for the "semidepleted region."

for GaAs and InP, in which diffusivities parallel and perpendicular to the electric field differ appreciably from each other.

The velocity dropback in the GaAs and InP velocity versus electric-field curves plays an important role in device performance. Carrier accumulation in the channel occurs in GaAs and InP FET's at moderate drain bias levels due mainly to this dropback. The formation and development of a carrier accumulation region and the rotation of the drift velocity vector in the channel cause a drain current dropback-and-recovery process which is pronounced in the drain characteristic of the compound semiconductor devices.

A large drain conductance in InP FET's results from a combination of such unavoidable material properties as a large peak-to-valley ratio, a large high-field diffusion constant, and low Schottky-barrier height.

In very short-channel compound semiconductor devices, velocity overshoot may lead to a higher effective velocity and, hence, to somewhat better performance than was predicted here for the 0.5-μm devices. However, since the tendency to form charge domains is reduced due to the velocity overshoot, a higher feedback capacitance C_{dg} can also be expected.

The effects of materials properties on the performance of MESFET's can be summarized as follows.

1) C_{gs} is related to the extent of carrier depletion under the gate: a) the larger the diffusivity, the smaller C_{gs}; b) the shorter the gate length, the smaller C_{gs}.

2) f_T is related to the transit time of carriers through the modulating portion of the channel: a) low-field mobility affects source resistance rather than f_T; b) f_T depends on materials properties, drain bias, and gate bias in a complicated fashion.

3) Pinch-off becomes softer in short-gate devices due to: a) punch-through of drain field to source region; b) substrate conduction, which reduces the build-up of charge domains and, therefore, increases punch-through.

Appendix I

The relationship of depletion to the diffusion constant can be understood using a simple model for the "semidepletion region" under the gate illustrated in Fig. 22. In the semidepleted region ($0 < x < L$ and $0 < y < a$) the following approximations are made:

1) E_x is much smaller than E_y, as in Shockley's gradual-channel approximation,

2) $v_{nx} \approx 0$, because E_x in the depletion region is very small,

3) $v_{ny} \approx v_s$, because E_y in the depletion region is generally greater than 10 kV/cm,

4) $D_{xx} \approx D_0$, because of 1) and 2),

5) D_{xy} and $D_{yx} \approx 0$, because of 1),

6) $D_{yy} \approx 0$, because of 1) and 3),

where D_0 is the diffusion constant at low field. Applying the approximations 1)–6) to the equation for current continuity we obtain:

$$J/q \approx \begin{pmatrix} D_0 \dfrac{\partial n}{\partial x} \\ v_s \cdot n \end{pmatrix}. \tag{I.1}$$

Consequently, the continuity equation becomes

$$D_0 \frac{\partial^2 n}{\partial x^2} + v_s \frac{\partial n}{\partial y} = 0. \tag{I.2}$$

Assuming that $n(x,y)$ has the form

$$n(x,y) = A(x)B(y) \tag{I.3}$$

(I.2) becomes

$$B(y)\frac{d^2A(x)}{dx^2} + \alpha A(x)\frac{dB(y)}{dy} = 0 \tag{I.4}$$

where

$$\alpha = v_s/D_0. \tag{I.5}$$

The exact analysis shows that even in the depletion region $n(x,y) \neq 0$. Thus (I.4) can be separated as

$$\frac{d^2A(x)}{dx^2} = -CA(x) \tag{I.6}$$

and

$$\frac{dB(y)}{dy} = \frac{C}{\alpha}B(y) \tag{I.7}$$

where C is a constant. The solution of (I.6) is

$$A(x) = A_0 \exp(j\sqrt{C}x) \tag{I.8}$$

and that of (I.7) is

$$B(y) = B_0 \exp\left(\frac{C}{\alpha}y\right) \tag{I.9}$$

where A_0 and B_0 are constants and $j^2 = -1$. Therefore, $n(x, y)$ can be written as

$$n(x,y) = n_0 \exp(CD_0 y/v_s) \cos(\sqrt{C}\, x) \quad (I.10)$$

where

$$n_0 = A_0 B_0. \quad (I.11)$$

Equation (I.10) satisfies (I.2), where C must be a positive number. Thus the dependence of $n(y)$ on the diffusion constant is exponential.

References

[1] W. Shockley, "A unipolar 'field-effect' transistor," *Proc. IRE*, vol. 40, p. 1365, 1952.
[2] G. C. Dacey and I. M. Ross, "The field effect transistor," *Bell Syst. Tech. J.*, vol. 34, p. 1149, 1955.
[3] J. R. Hauser, "Characteristics of junction field effect devices with small channel length-to-width ratios," *Solid-State Electron.*, vol. 10, p. 577, 1967.
[4] J. A. Turner and B. L. H. Wilson, "Implications of carrier velocity saturation in a gallium arsenide field-effect transistors," in *Proc. 1968 Symp. on GaAs, Inst. of Phys. and Physical Soc. Conf. Series*, vol. 7, p. 195, 1968.
[5] A. B. Grebene and S. K. Ghandhi, "General theory for pinched operation of the junction-gate FET," *Solid-State Electron.*, vol. 12, p. 573, 1969.
[6] K. Lehovec and R. Zuleeg, "Voltage-current characteristics of GaAs J-FET's in the hot electron range," *Solid-State Electron.*, vol. 13, p. 1415, 1970.
[7] F. N. Trofimenkoff, "Field-dependent mobility analysis of the field-effect transistor," *Proc. IEEE*, vol. 53, p. 1765, 1965.
[8] R. A. Pucel, H. A. Haus, and H. Statz, "Signal and noise properties of gallium arsenide microwave field-effect transistors," *Advances in Electron. Electron Phys.*, vol. 38, p. 195, 1975.
[9] R. Dawson and J. Frey, "A simple model to determine the effect of negative differential mobility and magnitude of saturated velocity on the performance of GaAs and Si field effect transistors," *Solid-State Electron.*, to be published.
[10] D. P. Kennedy and R. R. O'Brien, "Computer aided two dimensional analysis of the junction field-effect transistor," *IBM J. Res. Dev.*, vol. 14, p. 95, 1970.
[11] E. J. Ryder, "Mobility of holes and electrons in high electric fields," *Phys. Rev.*, vol. 90, p. 766, 1953.
[12] M. Reiser, "Two-dimensional analysis of substrate effects in junction F.E.T.s," *Electron. Lett.*, vol. 6, p. 493, 1970.
[13] M. Reiser and P. Wolf, "Computer study of submicrometer F.E.T.s," *Electron. Lett.*, vol. 8, p. 254, 1972.
[14] B. Himsworth, "A two-dimensional analysis of gallium arsenide junction field effect transistors with long and short channels," *Solid-State Electron.*, vol. 15, p. 1353, 1972.
[15] —, "A two-dimensional analysis of indium phosphide junction field effect transistors with long and short channels," *Solid-State Electron.*, vol. 16, p. 931, 1973.
[16] K. Yamaguchi, T. Toyabe, and H. Kodera, "Effect of field-dependent carrier diffusion on the two-dimensional analysis of a junction gate FET," *Japan J. Appl. Phys.*, vol. 14, p. 1069, 1975.
[17] K. Yamaguchi and H. Kodera, "Drain conductance of junction gate FET's in the hot electron range," *IEEE Trans. Electron Devices*, vol. ED-23, p. 545, 1976.
[18] K. Yamaguchi, S. Asai, and H. Kodera, "Two-dimensional numerical analysis of stability criteria of GaAs FET's," *IEEE Trans. Electron Devices*, vol. ED-23, p. 1283, 1976.
[19] K. Yamaguchi and H. Kodera, "Optimum design of triode-like JFET's by two-dimensional computer simulation," *IEEE Trans. Electron Devices*, vol. ED-24, p. 1061, 1977.
[20] C. Jacoboni *et al.*, "A review of some charge transport properties of silicon," *Solid-State Electron.*, vol. 20, p. 77, 1977.
[21] S. G. Kratzer, private communication.
[22] C. Canali *et al.*, "High-field diffusion of electrons in silicon," *Appl. Phys. Lett.*, vol. 27, p. 278, 1975.
[23] G. Persky and D. J. Bartelink, "High-field diffusivity of electrons in silicon," *J. Appl. Phys.*, vol. 42, p. 4414, 1971.
[24] P. A. Houston and A. G. R. Evans, "Electron velocity in n-GaAs at high electric fields," *Electron Lett.*, vol. 10, p. 332, 1974.
[25] P. A. Houston and A. G. R. Evans, "Saturation velocity of electrons in GaAs," *IEEE Trans. Electron Devices*, vol. ED-24, p. 584, 1976.
[26] T. J. Maloney, "Nonequilibrium electron transport in compound semiconductors," Ph.D. dissertation, Cornell University, Ithaca, NY, May 1976.
[27] G. Hill *et al.*, "Effect of ionized impurity scattering on the electron transit time in GaAs and InP F.E.T.s," *Electron. Lett.*, vol. 13, p. 235, 1977.
[28] W. Fawcett and H. D. Rees, "Calculation of the hot electron diffusion rate for GaAs," *Phys. Lett.*, vol. 29A, p. 578, 1969.
[29] P. E. Bauhahn, G. L. Haddad, and N. A. Masnari, "Comparison of the hot electron-diffusion rates for GaAs and InP," *Electron. Lett.*, vol. 9, p. 460, 1973.
[30] P. M. Boers, "Measurements on the velocity/field characteristics of indium phosphide," *Electron. Lett.*, vol. 7, p. 625, 1971.
[31] T. J. Maloney and J. Frey, "Frequency limits of GaAs and InP field-effect transistors," *IEEE Trans. Electron Devices*, vol. ED-23, p. 357, 1976.
[32] S. G. Kratzer, "Computer simulations of electron transport in gallium arsenide," M.S. thesis, Cornell University, Ithaca, NY, 1978.
[33] R. W. Hockney, "The potential calculation and some applications," *Meth. in Comp. Phys.*, vol. 9, p. 135, 1970.
[34] J. Todd, *Survey of Numerical Analysis*. NY: McGraw-Hill, 1962.
[35] D. L. Scharfetter and H. K. Gummel, "Large-signal analysis of a silicon read diode oscillator," *IEEE Trans. Electron Devices*, vol. ED-16, p. 64, 1969.
[36] P. J. Roache, *Computational Fluid Dynamics*. Albuquerque, NM: Hermosa Publishers, 1972.
[37] J. W. Slotboom, "Computer-aided two-dimensional analysis of Bipolar Transistors," *IEEE Trans. Electron Devices*, vol. ED-20, p. 669, 1973.
[38] H. K. Gummel, "A self-consistent iterative scheme for one-dimensional steady state transistor calculations," *IEEE Trans. Electron Devices*, vol. ED-11, p. 455, 1964.
[39] M. B. Das and P. Schmidt, "High-frequency limitations of abrupt-junction FET's," *IEEE Trans. Electron Devices*, vol. ED-20, p. 779, 1973.
[40] R. W. Engelmann and C. A. Liechti, "Bias dependence of GaAs and InP MESFET parameters," *IEEE Trans. Electron Devices*, vol. ED-24, p. 1288, 1977.
[41] W. Baechtold and P. Wolf, "An improved microwave silicon MESFET," *Solid-State Electron.*, vol. 14, p. 783, 1971.
[42] J. Frey, T. Wada, and T. Ikoma, "Charge accumulation, parasitic capacitance, and substrate effects in GaAs and InP FET's," presented at All-Japanese Conf. of Japan. Inst. Electric. Commun. Eng., Tokyo, Japan, Mar. 29, 1977.
[43] W. Baechtold *et al.*, "Si and GaAs 0.5-μm-gate Schottky-barrier field-effect transistors," *Electron. Lett.*, vol. 9, p. 232, 1973.

A *Ka*-Band GaAs Monolithic Phase Shifter

VLADIMIR SOKOLOV, MEMBER, IEEE, JOHN J. GEDDES, SENIOR MEMBER, IEEE, A. CONTOLATIS, PAUL E. BAUHAHN, MEMBER, IEEE, AND CHENTE CHAO, MEMBER, IEEE

***Abstract*—The design and performance of a GaAs monolithic 180° one-bit switched line phase shifter test circuit for *Ka*-band operation is presented. A self-aligned gate (SAG) fabrication technique is also described that reduces resistive parasitics in the switching FET's. Over the 27.5–30 GHz band, typical measured differential insertion phase is within 10–20° of the ideal time delay characteristic. Over the same band, the insertion loss for the SAG phase shifter is about 2.5–3 dB per bit. The SAG fabrication technique holds promise in reducing phase shifter insertion loss to about 1.5 dB/bit for 30-GHz operation.**

I. Introduction

As GAAS MONOLITHIC technology progresses to higher frequencies, it becomes natural to consider the development of specific integrated-circuit functions which are required by potential millimeter-wave system applications. The applications that take greatest advantage of monolithic circuit implementation include phased array systems for communications and radar, where a large number of small low-cost circuits are needed. For such systems, an essential circuit function is phase shifting at the carrier frequency. This paper presents design considerations and experimental results for a one-bit 180° phase shifter test circuit in *Ka*-band. Specifically, the work is aimed at potential application in a phased array satellite receiver operating in the 27.5–30-GHz band. Because of the receiver application, consideration is made for small-signal operation only. The monolithic GaAs chip incorporates passive switching FET's and microstrip transmission lines. The use of passive FET's is vital for low dc power consumption.

The FET's are fabricated by direct ion implantation into undoped LEC material, while the microstrip transmission lines are formed on the semi-insulating substrate. Two fabrication approaches are discussed: a conventional power FET approach and a self-aligned gate technique which reduces resistive parasitics in the switching FET's. The latter is especially important for millimeter-wave circuits.

II. Design Considerations

A. Chip Description

The design of the 180°-bit test circuit is based on a switched transmission-line type of configuration using switching FET's to RF switch between two microstrip lines. The differential electrical length of these lines is equal to 180° at center band, i.e., phase shifting is accomplished by true time delay. The FET's are passive in the sense that no dc bias is applied to the drain and only a switching voltage (0, −6 V) is used at the gate [1]–[3]. For broad bandwidth and low sensitivity to variations in device parameters, the circuit utilizes a pair of SPDT switches realized by four, 300-μm gate-width FET's in shunt across the 50-Ω transmission lines with each FET located at a distance of $\lambda g/4$ (0.8 mm at 30 GHz on GaAs) from either the input or output T-junction.

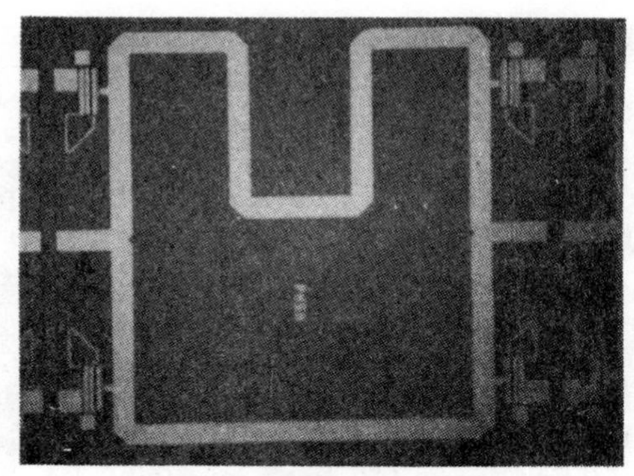

Fig. 1. Switched line phase shifter chip.

The circuit layout, shown in Fig. 1, is conservative in that the area required (chip dimensions are $3 \times 2.67 \times 0.2$ mm^3) has not been minimized. This was done to ensure that the coupling between adjacent sections of transmission lines would be negligible thereby facilitating evaluation of initial RF performance results. The 0.2-mm substrate thickness was chosen as a compromise between increased microstrip transmission-line loss and extraneous capacitive parasitics (thinner substrate), and increased circuit layout dimensions (thicker substrate). Since the circuit is passive, heat sinking of active elements is not an issue, and a relatively thick substrate can be used. As shown in Fig. 1, pads are provided at the edge of the chip for grounding. For these tests, ground connection is accomplished by a series resonant circuit consisting of an external 0.1-pF capacitor (bottom plate soldered to ground) and a mesh wire inductor connecting from the capacitor top plate to the grounding pad on the chip. To increase the high-impedance state ($V_g \cong -6$ V), a short section of line printed on the chip is used to resonate the pinchoff capacitance between drain and source ($C \cong 0.07$ pF) for each FET. High impedance to the gate terminal is provided by bonding wire inductance.

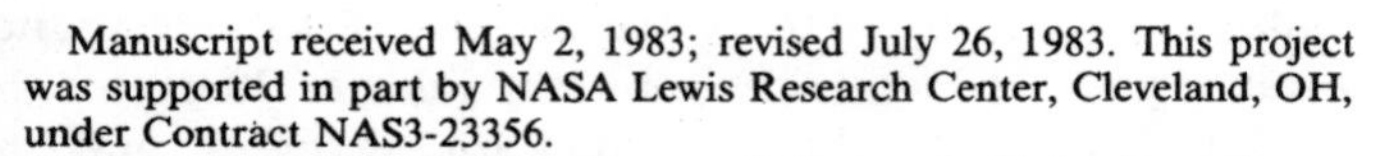

Manuscript received May 2, 1983; revised July 26, 1983. This project was supported in part by NASA Lewis Research Center, Cleveland, OH, under Contract NAS3-23356.

The authors are with the Honeywell Corporate Technology Center, Bloomington, MN.

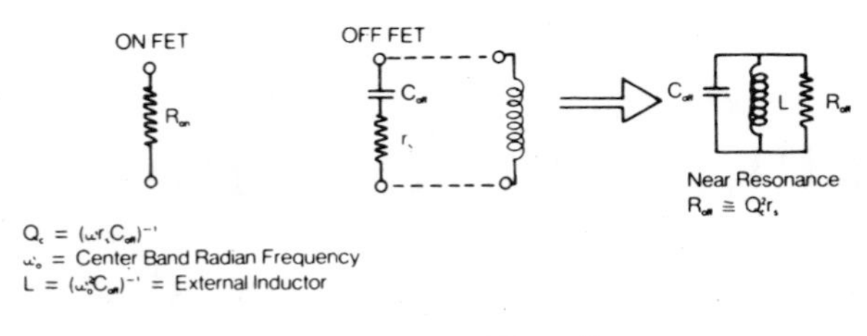

Switch Figure of Merit, $\hat{Q}$;

$$\hat{Q}^2 \cong [(\omega C_{OFF})^2 r_s R_{ON}]^{-1} = \frac{R_{OFF}}{R_{ON}}$$

Example: $\hat{Q}^2|_{10GHz} = 738$

$\hat{Q}^2|_{30GHz} = 82$

Fig. 2. Ideal equivalent circuits for ON and OFF FET's.

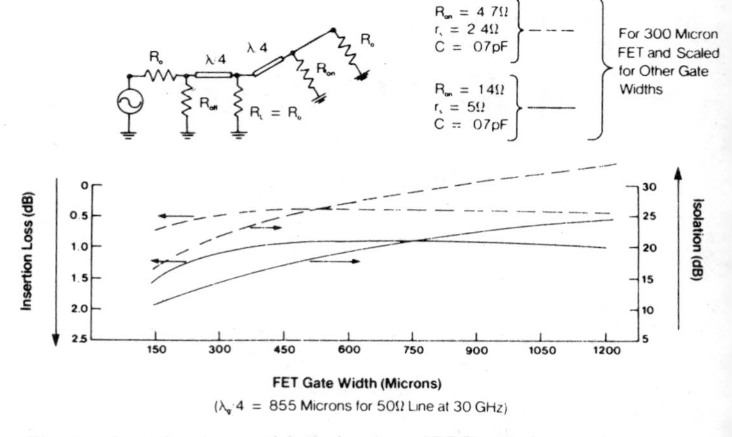

Fig. 3. Insertion loss and isolation in a SPDT switch as a function of FET gate width.

B. RF Losses

An important design consideration is the dissipative loss associated with the switches and the microstrip lines. As shown in the following, the dominant losses occur in the passive FET's.

Microstrip-line loss is calculated to be about 0.15 dB per wavelength at 30 GHz based on metal losses only and a gold thickness of 1.5 μm for a 50-Ω line on 0.2-mm-thick semi-insulating GaAs [4]. Experimentally, RF line losses measured at 30 GHz on GaAs ($\epsilon_r = 13$) and on sapphire ($\epsilon_r \approx 11$) substrates of the same thickness indicate comparable performance.

For the switching FET's, however, RF losses are much greater and are primarily associated with the parasitic resistances of the device. Fig. 2 shows simplified equivalent circuits for an ON and OFF FET, namely a single resistor for the ON (low-impedance) state and a series resistor capacitor combination for the OFF (high-impedance) state [2], [5]. The capacitor C_{off} is the total pinchoff capacitance between source and drain, and the resistor r_s is the total series residual resistance at pinchoff (undepleted channel resistance plus source and drain contact resistance). To increase the RF impedance of the OFF state, an inductor L parallel-resonates the RC combination. For this case, the effective RF OFF resistance at resonance R_{off} is closely approximated by $R_{\text{off}} = Q_c^2 r_s = (\omega r_s C)^{-2} r_s = (\omega C)^{-2} r_s^{-1}$. Note that the ratio $R_{\text{off}}/R_{\text{on}}$ is to first order, just the figure of merit as defined by Kurokawa and Schlosser for a switching device switching between two impedance states Z_1 and Z_2 [6]. For this case, $Z_1 = R_{\text{on}}$ and $Z_2 = r_s - j(\omega C)^{-1}$. Their figure of merit, denoted by $\hat{Q}$, is given by

$$\hat{Q}^2 = \frac{|Z_1 - Z_2|^2}{r_1 r_2} = \frac{(R_{\text{on}} - r_s)^2 + (\omega C)^{-2}}{R_{\text{on}} r_s}.$$

$\hat{Q}$ is a property of the device only and is invariant to any lossless impedance transforming imbedding circuit. If $(R_{\text{on}} - r_s) \ll (\omega C)^{-1}$ (which is a good approximation for switching FET's), then $\hat{Q}$ becomes

$$\hat{Q}^2 \cong (R_{\text{on}} r_s)^{-1} (\omega C)^{-2} = R_{\text{off}}/R_{\text{on}}.$$

From either point of view, i.e., $\hat{Q}$ or R_{off}, it is clear that for the same switching device both quantities degrade as the square of the frequency and have smaller values at millimeter-wave frequencies than they do at lower microwave bands. To maintain the figure of merit high it is essential to reduce R_{on} and r_s (and C if possible).

A specific example of an ideal RF switch incorporating conventional power FET's for the switching devices can illustrate the losses incurred at 30 GHz. For a typical 300-μm power FET, $R_{\text{on}} = 11-14\ \Omega$ and with $C = 0.07$ pF and $r_s = 5\ \Omega$, R_{off} is about 1000 Ω at 30 GHz. By choosing these ON and OFF resistance values and using them in an ideal SPDT switch configuration as shown in the inset of Fig. 3, we can calculate the ideal insertion loss and isolation of a single switch at center frequency. Furthermore, by scaling R_{on}, r_s, and C for other gate widths, an estimate can be made of the best compromise between isolation and insertion loss. The scaling is straightforward, i.e., if the gate width is doubled, then R_{on} and r_s are halved, and C is doubled. Note that this leaves the figure of merit $\hat{Q}$ invariant. These considerations are summarized in Fig. 3, where the insertion loss and isolation at 30 GHz are calculated as a function of gate width for two different $\hat{Q}$ values. The curves are similar to those presented by Atwater and Sudbury [5], except that the constant $\hat{Q}$ curves are given specifically as functions of gate width. The impedance relation between the device impedance (gate width) and the normalizing impedance R_0 (the 50-Ω transmission lines) is analogous to the lossless imbedding network discussed by Kurokawa and Schlosser, i.e., for the same device $\hat{Q}$ different gate widths yield different values for insertion loss and isolation. Note that for the dashed curves which represent a reduction in R_{on} and r_s (14 Ω to 4.7 Ω and 5 Ω to 2.4 Ω, respectively), the loss is reduced by 0.6 dB at a gate width of 300 μm, for a single SPDT switch. For a four-bit switched line phase shifter this amounts to nearly 5 dB less insertion loss. As shown in the next section, such reductions in the parasitic resistance are possible using the self-aligned fabrication process.

To see the effects of reducing these losses at other frequencies, Table I gives the insertion loss comparison for 40, 30, 20, and 10 GHz for the two sets of FET resistance values given in Fig. 3. The arbitrary value of 20 dB for the isolation characteristic is chosen for all cases, and the resulting smallest gate width and insertion loss calculated.

TABLE I

IDEAL LOSSES IN A SINGLE SPDT SWITCH WITH 20 dB ISOLATION USING MINIMUM GATE WIDTH FET'S

f (GHz)	300 micron FET Parameters* R_{on} (Ω)	r_s (Ω)	$\hat{Q}^2$	Ins. Loss** (dB)	Gate Width (microns)
40	14*	5*	46.2	1.22	650
	4.7**	2.4**	286	0.59	235
30	14	5	82.1	0.9	680
	4.7	2.4	509	0.52	240
20	14	5	185	0.66	700
	4.7	2.4	1146	0.48	240
10	14	5	738	0.5	710
	4.7	2.4	4583	0.45	240

$\hat{Q}^2 = [(\omega C)^2 r_s R_{on}]^{-1} \equiv R_{off}/R_{on}$

$\cdot C_{off} = .07$ pF, $\cdot\cdot$Isolation = 20 dB } All cases

* Typical parameters obtained from conventionally fabricated FETs.

** Projected parameters expected from FETs fabricated with an optimized SAG technique.

It is seen that the reduction in parasitic FET resistances has the most significance at millimeter-wave frequencies. Not only does the insertion loss go down, but the required gate width also decreases. This is very important for reducing reactive parasitics at high frequencies since it implies smaller layout dimensions, hence, less capacitance to ground from layout metallization. It also means that the FET layout can be made much smaller than a wavelength. At microwave frequencies, the advantage of such small gate widths is not as important. Nevertheless, the lower resistances permit even lower insertion loss than shown in Table I if larger gate widths are allowed.

One approach to reduce the FET resistances is to use a self-aligned gate fabrication technique as discussed next.

III. DEVICE FABRICATION

Two processes have been used for fabricating switches: one process uses a standard power FET implant; the second uses a self-aligned gate process. The power FET approach uses standard GaAs FET processing including silicon ion implantation for the channel region, mesa etching for device isolation, a Au/Ge/Ni ohmic contact, and a recess etch for the gate. A Ti/Au overlay is used for the microstrip circuit and pad metal. FET's fabricated by this approach have a dc ON resistance of 11–14 Ω. FET's fabricated using the self-aligned gate process can give dc ON resistance as low as 4–6 Ω.

The self-aligned gate process is an approach that has been primarily used for digital IC's [7]. This process offers the advantage of lower ON resistance than the power FET switch. The self-aligned gate allows a low sheet resistance n^+ implant to be brought up very close to the gate, thereby minimizing the resistance of material in the gate–source and gate–drain regions. The refractory metal gate is made of Ti/W silicide which can withstand the subsequent high-temperature implant anneal. The first implant anneal is done at 850 °C after the channel implant for good activation, the second anneal is done at 800 °C after the n^+ implant. The lower temperature for the second anneal

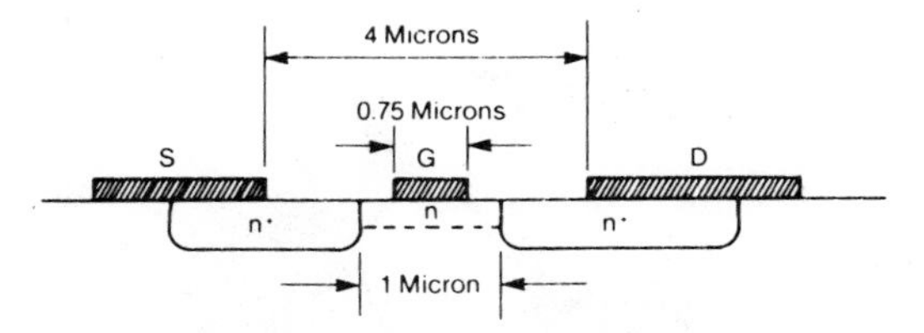

Fig. 4. Diagram of self-aligned gate switch FET showing parameters for resistance calculation.

allows reasonable n^+ activation while minimizing degradation of the Schottky contact. Ohmic level metal is applied and sintered after the second implant anneal.

The gate level metal is defined by an etch technique. Undercutting during the gate metal etch leaves a resist overhang which serves as an implant mask and separates the n^+ region from the gate. This technique gives self-aligned gate switches with reasonable gate breakdown voltages.

The ON resistance of the FET's is determined by three factors: the ohmic contact resistance, the sheet resistance of the n^+ implant, and the sheet resistance of the n or channel implant. For purposes of calculation, the dimensions shown in Fig. 4 are used. The source–drain ohmic contacts are separated by 4 μm and the n^+ implants are separated by 1 μm. The gate length is less than the separation between n^+ implants because a resist overhang is left beyond the gate edge after the gate is formed by reactive ion etching.

A typical measured value for the line resistance of the ohmic contacts is 0.063 Ω·mm, so a 300-μm gate width FET has a total contact resistance R_c of 0.42 Ω for the source and drain contacts. Typical values for the sheet resistance of the n and n^+ material are 660 Ω per square and 200 Ω per square, respectively. The total series resistance is 4.6 Ω for the self-aligned structure. By way of comparison, a conventional power FET would have the n material beneath the Schottky continued over the full 4-μm source–drain spacing so the total series resistance of the power FET switch would be 9.2 Ω, or twice the series resistance of the self-aligned gate FET.

Ultimately, the ON resistance of the self-aligned FET is limited by three factors. The first factor is the sheet resistance of the n^+ material. The resistance is limited by implant activation at high doses and by lateral diffusion of the implant species. The n^+ implant level will also affect the gate–source breakdown voltage of the switch. The second factor is the gate breakdown voltage. The resistance of the n layer beneath and immediately adjacent to the gate can be reduced by increasing the doping density thickness product of the channel. On the other hand, the doping density thickness product of the channel must be low enough so the device can be pinched off before gate breakdown occurs. The third factor is the contact resistance. A contact resistance corresponding to a line resistance of 0.05 to 0.1 Ω·mm is presently the best that is achieved. For most applications, the contribution of contact resistance to total resistance is small so there is little incentive to reduce contact resistance further.

Fig. 5. Test fixture.

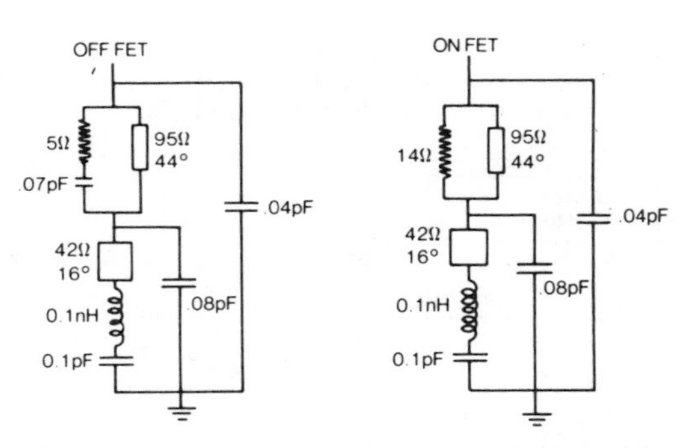

Fig. 6. FET switch circuit models including parasitics.

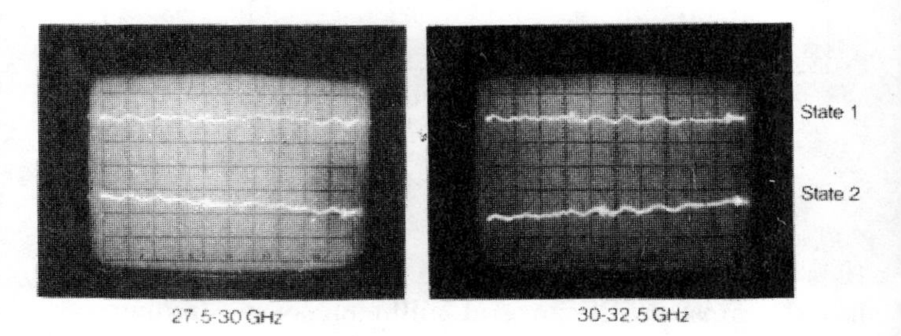

Fig. 7. Differential phase shift versus frequency for 180°-bit. Horizontal: 250 MHz/div, Vertical: 45°/div.

The TiW silicide gate metallization has a higher resistivity than the metals normally used for low-noise and power FET's. However, the gate resistance is not as critical for the present application since no RF signal is applied to the gate. The sheet resistance of the metal silicide is 6 Ω per square for a 4000-Å thickness. The metal resistivity is over an order of magnitude higher than gold or aluminum so it would not be suitable for low-noise FET's unless the unit gate width were made extremely small.

IV. Experimental Results and Comparison with Computer Calculations

A. Test Fixture

To interface the phase shifter chip with standard *Ka*-band circuitry, a test fixture having WR-28 waveguide input and output ports is used. Antipodal finline transitions fabricated on 0.25 mm thick RT/duroid are employed to transition from waveguide to microstrip [8], [9]. For a pair of back-to-back transitions including a 2.5-cm length of 50-Ω interconnecting transmission line etched on the same duroid card, the insertion loss is 0.6–0.8 dB from 26.5–37 GHz. For the phase shifter test circuit, the duroid card is cut in two, and each half soldered (at the ground plane side of the microstrip portion) to gold-plated brass blocks on the input and output side of the chip carrier block (see Fig. 5). To measure the insertion loss of this test fixture configuration, a 50-Ω microstrip line fabricated on a 0.13-mm-thick sapphire substrate is substituted for the phase shifter chip. In this way, transition losses from waveguide to microstrip on RT/duroid, as well as losses associated with the gold ribbon bond connection from the microstrip on duroid to the chip (mainly mismatch losses), can be taken into account. From 27 to 33 GHz, the measured test fixture loss is 1.4 dB. The test fixture with the phase shifter chip in place and the cover removed is shown in Fig. 5.

RF measurements of differential phase and insertion loss were performed on a network analyzer using the Hewlett-Packard 26–40-GHz waveguide reflection–transmission test set. A scalar reflectometer test set was also used to measure insertion loss and return loss.

B. Results with Conventionally Fabricated Phase Shifters

To compare the experimental results with the results of a computer analysis, a more elaborate circuit model that includes the ideal FET model discussed earlier, as well as additional circuit elements that represent our best estimate of the reactive and resistive circuit losses, is used. Fig. 6 shows the networks that are connected in shunt (four places) across the pair of 50-Ω transmission lines that constitute the switched lines of the 180°-bit phase shifter. In both networks, the section of 90-Ω line represents the printed loop that resonates the pinchoff capacitance during the OFF state. The 0.04 and 0.08-pF capacitors are part of the reactive parasitics associated with the layout metallization (assumed $Q_c = 100$), and the 0.1-pF capacitor is the external porcelain chip capacitor (assumed $Q_c = 50$) that series resonates the mesh wire inductance and provides an RF ground in close proximity to the "source" pad of each FET. Losses in the microstrip lines are also included in all the calculations.

Fig. 7 shows the measured differential phase shift for a conventionally fabricated phase shifter from 27.5 to 32.5 GHz. Over the frequency range of 27.5–31 GHz, the measured phase shift is within approximately 10–15° of the ideal time delay characteristic, i.e., a straight line through the origin with a slope of 6°/GHz corresponding to 180° at 30 GHz. (It should be noted that the 180° phase shifter test chip was originally designed for a center frequency of 30 GHz.) Beyond about 30 GHz, the measured differential phase changes slope and begins to decrease. Computer calculations of the phase shifter circuit using the FET models that include circuit parasitics have shown that such a decrease can result because of parasitic shunt capacitance loading the transmission line. Specifically, it was found that the metallization pattern of each FET contributes about 0.1–0.15 pF of shunt capacitance to ground, and when included in the calculations, a change of slope for the differential phase characteristic does indeed occur beyond 30 GHz. These results bring out the importance of minimizing the FET layout (by using smaller gate widths consistent with adequate isolation and insertion loss performance) and incorporating the FET into the transmission line as much as possible (via holes, if practical in a 0.2-mm-thick substrate, would help). Increasing the substrate thickness results in a larger layout and is therefore less desirable. Extraneous shunt capacitance also contributes to mismatch loss.

Calculated values of the phase shifter insertion loss (when transmission-line losses and the parasitic capacitances of the FET layout metallization are included) lie between 2.5 and 4.5 dB across the 27–32-GHz band using values of $R_{on} = 14\ \Omega$, $r_s = 5\ \Omega$, and $C = 0.07$ pF. Taking into account the 1.4-dB fixture loss, typical measured results lie between 3.2 and 5.5 dB across the same band. The 0.5–1-dB discrepancy may be due in part to not having all four of the FET's have exactly the same characteristics as is assumed in the computer calculations. The 14-Ω ON resistance was measured on the curve tracer for single FET's in the test pattern areas. The 5-Ω series residual resistance was based on dc measurements of source and drain contact resistances and an estimate of the resistance of the undepleted channel at pinchoff. The channel and parasitic resistances of individual FET's of the phase shifter may have different values. In addition, some substrate surface conduction was observed on some of the wafers on which phase shifter circuits were fabricated. Although mesa etching was used for isolation, increased loss due to surface conduction could still occur in the switching FET's. Such losses would be especially significant in the ON branch of the phase shifter when the shunt FET's are in their high-impedance state.

C. Results with Phase Shifters Fabricated by the Self-Aligned Gate (SAG) Technique

As discussed above, the self-aligned gate technology is one approach to reducing the resistive losses in switching FET's, especially at millimeter-wave frequencies. The experimental results reported in this section were obtained using the same 180° one-bit phase shifter test circuit of Fig. 1, but the chips were fabricated by means of the SAG technique.

The reduced parasitic resistances in SAG devices is clearly indicated by the dc FET characteristic of 300-μm gate width FET's taken from test pattern areas of the SAG phase shifter wafer. Instead of the usual 11–14-Ω ON resistance (slope of $V_g = 0$ drain characteristic) observed with conventional power FET's, a resistance of 7.8 Ω is obtained. Furthermore, I_{dss} is measured to be 225 mA instead of the usual 110–120 mA for 300-μm conventional power FET's. The improvement in RF results is shown in Fig. 8(a), where the phase shifter insertion loss, including test fixture losses, is measured from 27.5 to 32.5 GHz. Fig. 9 shows the comparison between the calculated and measured results including the 1.4-dB test fixture correction. As shown in the figure, the calculated values are based on

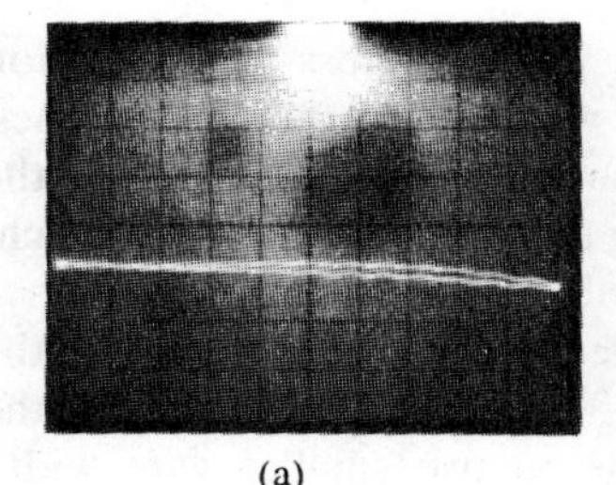

(a)

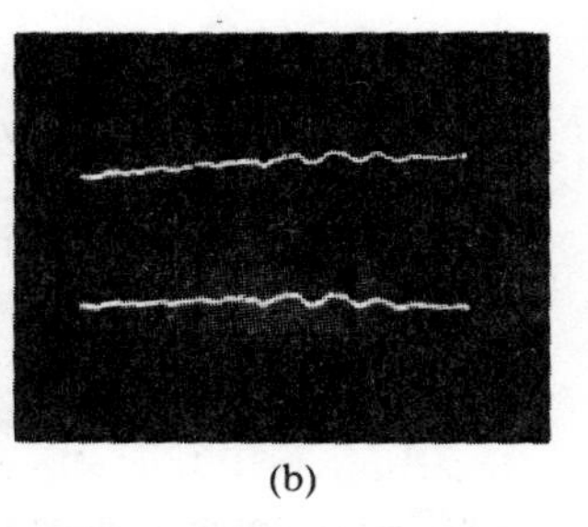

(b)

Fig. 8. Insertion loss and phase shift characteristics for SAG fabricated phase shifter. (a) Insertion loss. Vertical: 5 dB/div, Reference: Center line, Horizontal: 500 MHz/div; 27.5–32.5 GHz. (b) Differential insertion phase. Vertical: 45°/div, Horizontal: 250 MHz/div; 27.5–30 GHz.

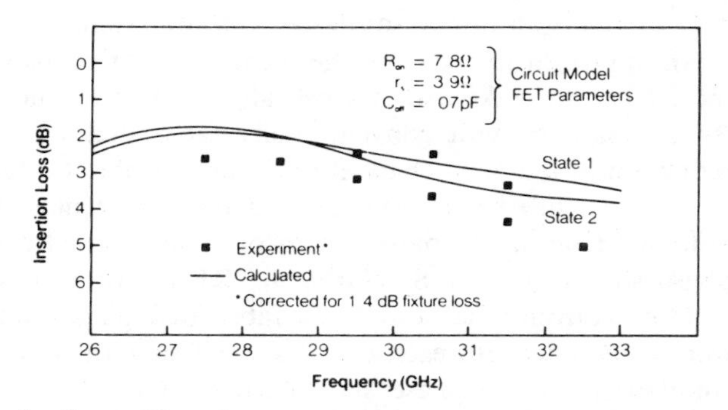

Fig. 9. Comparison of measured insertion loss results with computer calculations.

the values of the FET parameters measured off test FET's on the SAG wafer.

By comparison with the previous results, a reduction in insertion loss of about 1–1.5 dB across the entire band is achieved. The reasonable agreement between measured and calculated values justifies the use of our simple equivalent circuit model for the ON and OFF FET's.

Fig. 8(b) shows the measured differential insertion loss for the SAG phase shifter, from 27.5 to 30 GHz. Over this band, the phase is within 20° of the calculated curve. This discrepancy is greater than seen on previous runs. Although the exact cause of this discrepancy is not yet known, it is believed that it is not related to the intrinsic SAG process itself, but rather is indicative of the preliminary nature of these first results. With a better refined SAG process, it is expected that the insertion phase will track more accurately the theoretical values.

Finally, to estimate the insertion loss of a 1-bit phase shifter having FET's with characteristics comparable to the best expected SAG results, the computer calculations were repeated for $R_{on} = 4.7\ \Omega$, $r_s = 2.4\ \Omega$, and $C = 0.07$ pF, leaving all other elements (including capacitive parasitics) unchanged. The calculated results predict an insertion loss of 1.4–2.2 dB from 27–30 GHz. With a reduction in capacitive parasitics, an insertion loss of about 1.5 dB per bit across the same band should be possible.

V. CONCLUSIONS

By using a simple equivalent circuit for the ON and OFF FET's in a 180° switched-line phase shifter, an analysis is made to show how the FET parasitic resistances and gate width are related to switch insertion loss and isolation performance at 30 GHz, as well as at other frequencies. The analysis shows that the loss is dominated by the resistive dissipation occurring in the channels of the switching FET's, which is especially high at millimeter-wave frequencies. At the higher frequencies, a reduction in the FET parasitic resistances R_{on} and r_s not only reduces the insertion loss but allows one to use smaller gate width FET's to achieve acceptable insertion loss and isolation performance. Since extraneous parasitic shunt capacitance associated with the details of the FET layout contribute significantly to the total insertion loss (primarily as mismatch loss), the possibility of employing FET's with smaller gate widths is an important design consideration.

An approach to reducing the intrinsic resistive losses in the FET is to make use of a self-aligned gate technology. By comparison with conventionally fabricated FET's, a reduction in the open channel resistance by about a factor of 1.5 to 2 has been demonstrated for a switching FET obtained from a test pattern area of a self-aligned run of phase shifter circuits. Similarly, the RF insertion loss results of conventional and SAG fabricated phase shifters were compared with each other, as well as with computer simulations of the phase shifter circuit. Generally, more than 1-dB improvement was observed for the SAG devices. The reasonable correlation with calculated values justifies the use of the circuit models. Using this model to predict the performance of phase shifters having optimized SAG parameters, it is expected that 30-GHz phase shifters could be fabricated to have insertion loss of about 1.5 dB/bit. Results obtained on the SAG phase shifters to date have achieved about 2.5 dB/bit over the 27.5–30-GHz band. Over this frequency range, the differential phase shift is within 10–20° of the ideal time delay characteristic for both types of phase shifters.

For system applications requiring high efficiency such as in satellite-borne communications receivers, the self-aligned gate fabrication technique is a promising technology for implementation in switching circuits at millimeter-wave frequencies.

Acknowledgment

The authors thank S. Hanka for helpful discussions concerning the self-aligned technique and D. Hickman and S. Dice for technical assistance.

References

[1] R. A. Gaspari and H. H. Yee, "Microwave GaAs FET switching," in *1978 IEEE Int. Microwave Symp. Dig.*, pp. 58–60.
[2] W. V. McLevige and V. Sokolov, "Resonated GaAs FET devices for microwave switching," *IEEE Trans. Electron Devices*, vol. ED-28, pp. 198–204, Feb. 1981.
[3] Y. Ayasli, A. Platzker, J. Vorhaus, and L. D. Reynolds, Jr., "A monolithic single-chip *X*-band four-bit phase shifter," *IEEE Trans. Microwave Theory Tech.*, vol. MTT-30, pp. 2201–2206, Dec. 1982.
[4] M. W. Schneider, "Microstrip lines for microwave integrated circuits," *Bell Syst. Tech. J.*, vol. 48, no. 5, pp. 1421–1444, May–June 1969.
[5] H. A. Atwater and R. W. Sudbury, "Use of switching *Q* in the design of FET microwave switches," in *MTT-S Int. Microwave Symp. Dig.*, June 1981, pp. 370–372.
[6] K. Kurokawa and W. O. Schlosser, "Quality factor of switching diodes for digital modulation," *Proc. IEEE*, vol. 38, pp. 180–181, Jan. 1970.
[7] N. Yokoyama *et al.*, "Ti/W Silicide gate technology for self-aligned GaAs MESFET VLSIS," in *1981 IEDM Tech. Dig.*, Dec. 1981.
[8] J. H. C. van Heuven, "A new integrated waveguide-microstrip transition," *IEEE Trans. Microwave Theory Tech.*, vol. MTT-24, pp. 144–146, Mar. 1976.
[9] L. J. Lavedan, "Design of waveguide-to-microstrip transitions specially suited to millimeter-wave applications," *Electron. Lett.*, vol. 13, no. 20, pp. 604–605, Sept. 1977.
[10] V. Sokolov, P. Saunier, R. C. Bennett, and R. E. Lehmann, "20-GHz multistage FET power amplifiers," in *1981 Int. Telemetering Conf. Proc.*, Oct. 1981, pp. 845–853.

mm-Wave Passive Components for Monolithic Circuits

Robert E. Neidert and **Steven C. Binari**
Naval Research Laboratory,
Washington, DC

Introduction

One of the general problems with mm-wave components is that they are too small to be made by the same techniques used at low frequencies. A learning cycle is in progress in the microwave community to zero in on new component design and fabrication approaches which will lead to a more effective use of the 30 to 300 GHz portion of the spectrum. This paper describes some early results on a research program at the Naval Research Laboratory (NRL) attempting to see whether quasi-TEM, microstrip components are feasible for this frequency range. The components are being fabricated on indium phosphide (InP) substrates, but the technology is readily transferrable to gallium arsenide (GaAs) or silicon. Additional information on this and other areas of InP research at NRL are included in a paper entitled "InP Monolithic Integrated Circuits for Millimeter Wave Applications," which will appear in an upcoming issue of the *Microwave Journal*.

A few years ago, two important technologies were merged to produce monolithic circuits for low frequencies of 1 to 30 GHz: microstrip circuits from the microwave community and GaAs field effect transistors from the electron device community. The advantage of microstrip circuitry, applicable at mm-waves as well as at lower frequencies, is that it uses single sided circuitry, with a continuous, well-defined ground plane very nearby. The resultant RF field containment permits the use of complex, multi-component circuits in a small space without radiative interaction. The advantage of field effect transistors, to provide a three terminal amplifying device, is not available yet above 60 GHz or so.[1] However, some of the fabrication techniques for FETs and other semiconductor devices are directly applicable — techniques which are able to produce metal lines as narrow as one micrometer (μm) or less. For example, a 4-line, 3-dB Lange coupler on a 50 μm (2 mil) thick gallium arsenide, indium phosphide, or silicon substrate needs line widths and spaces in the 1 to 3 μm size range.

Therefore, the possibility exists that microstrip technology can merge with semiconductor fabrication technology to produce mm-wave, monolithic, quasi-TEM circuitry.

General Conditions

The circuits described here were designed for octave bandwidth operation from 75 to 150 GHz. This range was selected for many reasons, including the following:

- The frequency is too high to use low-frequency fabrication techniques, but low enough that test equipment is available;
- It includes the 94 GHz atmospheric attenuation window shown in Figure 1;[2]
- By designing all the circuits to have octave bandwidth, the 140 GHz window is also included;
- Circuits having wide bandwidth are useful in electronic warfare applications;
- The circuits can be tested over their full range with two standard waveguide setups: WR10 for 75 to 110 GHz and WR8 for 90 to 140 GHz.

The substrate thickness selected was 50 μm, to assure quasi-TEM operation through 420 GHz, the third harmonic of the 140 GHz atmospheric window. Concern for control of the propagation and termination of harmonics is important in all large-signal, nonlinear applications, such as oscillators and mixers. The lowest cutoff frequency of the possible surface-wave modes is.[3]

$$f_1 = \frac{c}{4\,t\,\sqrt{\varepsilon_r - 1}}$$

where

- c = the free space velocity of light,
- t = thickness of the substrate, and
- ε_r = its relative dielectric constant.

The substrate thickness also affects the value of the lowest impedance microstrip line which can be used. If the microstrip line width reaches approximately a half wavelength in the dielectric medium, a non-TEM mode can exist which has zero electric field at the center.[4] This corresponds, on 50 μm thick InP, to minimum usable impedance levels of about 13 ohms, 21 ohms, and 27 ohms for maximum quasi-TEM frequency limits of 140 GHz, 280 GHz, and 420 GHz, respectively. No single minimum impedance level can be specified since the harmonic content, or mixing product content, may be different at different points in a circuit.

Using the above guidelines, a set of building block passive components and semiconductor devices was established, from which a wide range of broadband circuits can be developed. Methods for testing the building block components were simultaneously devised and have been described elsewhere.[5]

Passive Components

The following passive components have been designed, fabricated, and tested over the 75 to 110 GHz range: waveguide to microstrip transitions, transmission lines, RF resistors including a 50-ohm load, resonators, a Lange coupler and a Wilkinson splitter. A Schiffman phase-shifter, and a sum/difference hybrid have been designed and fabricated, but not yet tested.

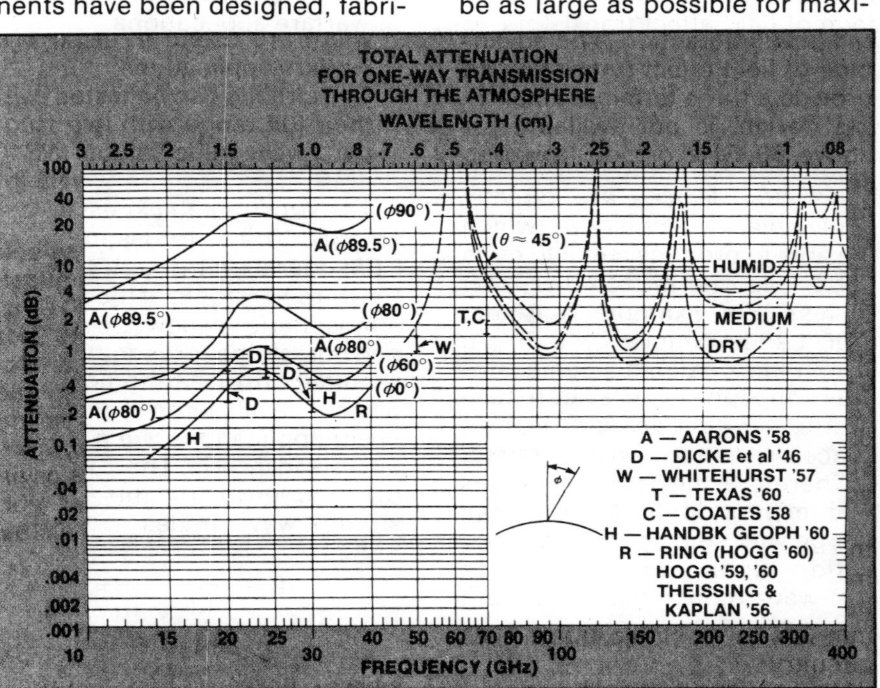

Fig. 1 Atmospheric attenuation versus frequency, showing loss windows at 94 and 140 GHz.

Transitions and Transmission Lines

The waveguide-to-microstrip transitions and the measured electrical characteristics of 50 ohm lines have been earlier reported.[5] All transmission lines were made 8000 angstroms (Å) or 0.8 μm thick, which is about three skin depths in gold at 100 GHz. The lines were formed by evaporation and lift-off of chrome-gold (Cr/Au-50Å/8000Å). The ground plane was 1.5 μm thick evaporated aluminum.

RF Resistors

The size of lumped resistors in mm-wave circuits, such as 50 ohm loads, must be minimized for maximum bandwidth. They should not behave as lengths of lossy transmission line, and dimensional discontinuities between the transmission lines and the resistors should be minimized. On the other hand, their area should be as large as possible for maximum power dissipation. Among many possible methods of resistor fabrication, selective ion implementation and resistive film deposition appear attractive. If selective area ion implantation evolves as the method of choice for semiconductor fabrication, then ion implantation might be used for low-power resistor fabrication. For initial fabrication simplicity, the resistors used in the components discussed here were made by resistive film deposition.[6] The following gives some details of the methods of deposition and contacting which were employed.

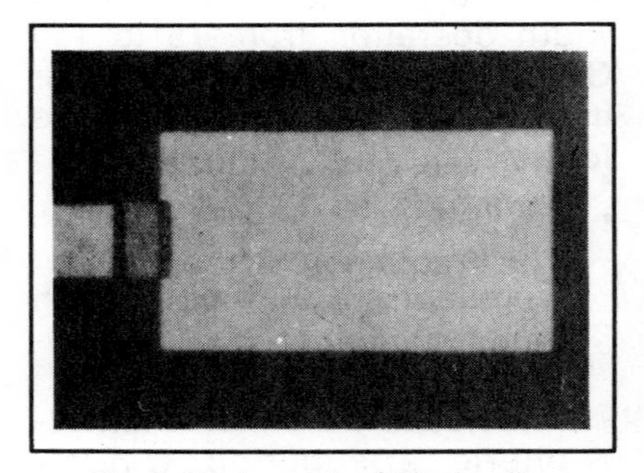

Fig. 2 Photograph of 50-ohm line termination, with 30-ohm open-circuited stub 187 μm long. Resistor is 36 μm (1.4 mils) wide by 18 μm (0.7 mils) long.

The resistive material used in the fabrication of the thin-film resistors was evaporated nichrome (NiCr-80 percent/20 percent by weight). The NiCr was evaporated directly onto polished, semi-insulating InP and was delineated by photoresist lift-off. After the NiCr lift-off, the Cr/Au (50Å/8000Å) transmission lines were evaporated and lifted. After the NiCr and Cr/Au patterns were in place, the NiCr was chemically etched to achieve a sheet resistance of 100 ohms/square.

The principles of resistor design are summarized here. If contact is made to the two ends of a slab of resistive material, whose end area is the product of its width, w, and its thickness, a, and

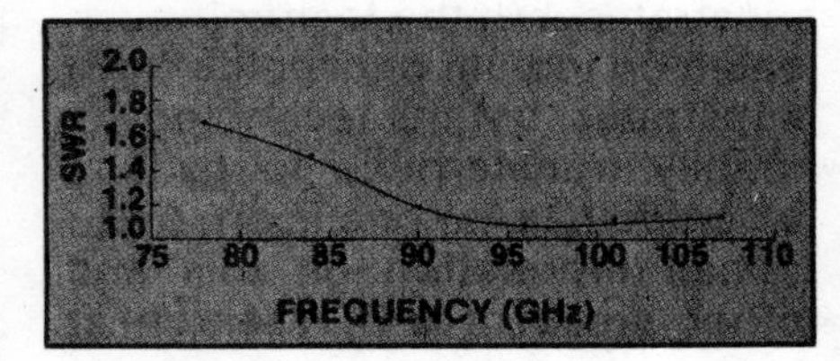

Fig. 3 Measured SWR of 50-ohm load, with nominal design center frequency of 112 GHz.

whose length between contacts is l, the resistance between the contacts is:

$$R = \rho \, l/(wa) \qquad (1)$$

where ρ is the resistivity of the material. For metals and metal compounds, such as nichrome, the resistivity is relatively fixed, although there is considerable variability among film deposition methods and conditions.[7] For doped semiconductors, the value of the resistivity is related to the doping level and the mobility.

With low field strength in the material, the resistivity of an n-type semiconductor is

$$\rho = 1/(q\,\mu_o\,n), \qquad (2)$$

where

- q = electron charge = 1.6×10^{-19} amp · sec,
- μ_o = low field electron mobility, in $cm^2/(V \cdot sec)$, and
- n = carrier concentration (cm^{-3})

For instance, the room temperature low field mobility of InP is approximately 2000 $cm^2/(V \cdot sec)$ at a doping level of $10^{18}/cm^3$, giving ρ = .003 Ω · cm. In ion implanted regions, a depth of 0.3 μm may be achievable, so that from equation (1)

$$R = 100\,\frac{l}{w}$$

giving a sheet resistivity of 100 ohms per square. The corresponding approximate parameters for certain other materials to produce a sheet resistivity of 100 ohms per square are: for GaAs, μ_o = 3400 $cm^2/(V \cdot sec)$ at a doping level of $6 \times 10^{17}/cm^3$, with a depth of 0.3 μm; and, for nichrome, which has a bulk resistivity of about .0001 Ω · cm, a thickness of about 100 angstroms. However, thin-film resistivities are generally higher than the bulk value. For this work, a film thickness between 300 and 500 Å was used. The above combination of material parameters and dimensions are all achievable and can produce circuit-compatible resistors. Therefore, resistors using a sheet resistivity of 100 ohms per square were designed into the mm-wave components to provide 50-ohm resistors for transmission line terminations and 100-ohm resistors for the isolation arm of the single-selection Wilkinson splitter.

The 50-ohm transmission line termination is shown in Figure 2. The width of the resistor is the same as the 50-ohm transmission line, about 36 μm (1.4 mils), to avoid any dimensional discontinuity between the two; its length is about half its width. The resistor is followed by an open-circuited section o[...] mission line, a quart[...] long at 112 GHz, to g[...] lated SWR of less than 1.4[...] to 150 GHz. The measure[...] from 75 to 110 GHz is show[...] Figure 3, corrected as well a[...] possible for the effects of the transitions and the line losses preceeding the resistor.

The power-handling capability of the resistors is estimated by treating the resistor as a head source capable of rising to about 120°C from a maximum sink temperature of 50°C, across the substrate of 50 μm thick GaAs or InP. The thermal conductivity of InP at 300°K is about 0.7 W/(°K · cm). The values for silicon and GaAs are about 1.5 and 0.5 W/(°K · cm), respectively. The general equation of static thermal conduction is:

$$P = k\,A\,\Delta t/\Delta x, \qquad (3)$$

where

- P = power being dissipated,
- k = thermal conductivity,
- A = the area of the thermal path, and
- Δt = the temperature drop across a path which is Δx long.

From Equation (3) and the parameters already given, the 50 Ω load resistor on InP can dissipate, conservatively, about 65 milliwatts (mW), in spite of its small size. They have been tested to 25 mW with no ill effects.

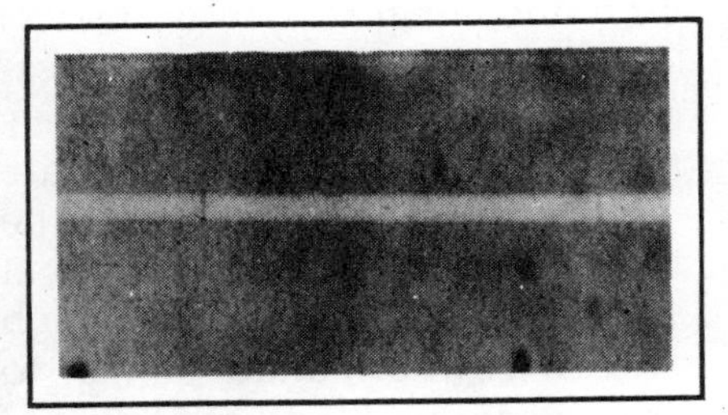

Fig. 4 Photograph of linear resonator with 2-μm coupling gaps.

Resonators

Two types of resonators were fabricated and tested — a linear resonator and a ring resonator. The linear resonator is shown in Figure 4. It consists of a 541 μm (21.3 mil) length of 50-ohm microstrip transmission line; it is coupled at each end by the series capacitance of a 2 μm-wide gap to 50 ohm input and output lines (36 μm wide). Figure 5 shows the measured transmission loss of the linear resonator, its equivalent circuit, and two transmission curves of analytical best-fit models. The modeled curve based on 12.38 for the substrate dielectric constant appears to fit the data slightly better than the curve based on 12.55, the measured low frequency value.[8] It is not felt, however, that the measurement accuracy of the work here is good

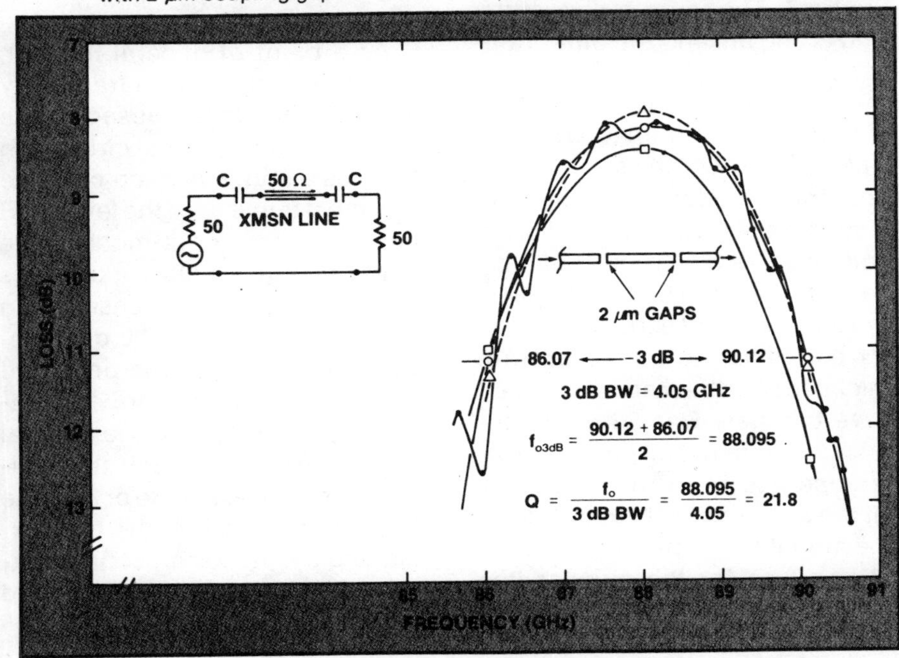

Fig. 5 Measured and modeled transmission loss through linear resonator. = Raw measured data; ⊖ = Smoothed measured data; ⊟ Model: ϵ_r (subst.) =12.55, C = .0047 PF, Line loss = 12.53 dB/inch; △ Model: ϵ_r (subst.) =12.38, C = .0049 PF, Line loss = 12.53 dB/inch.

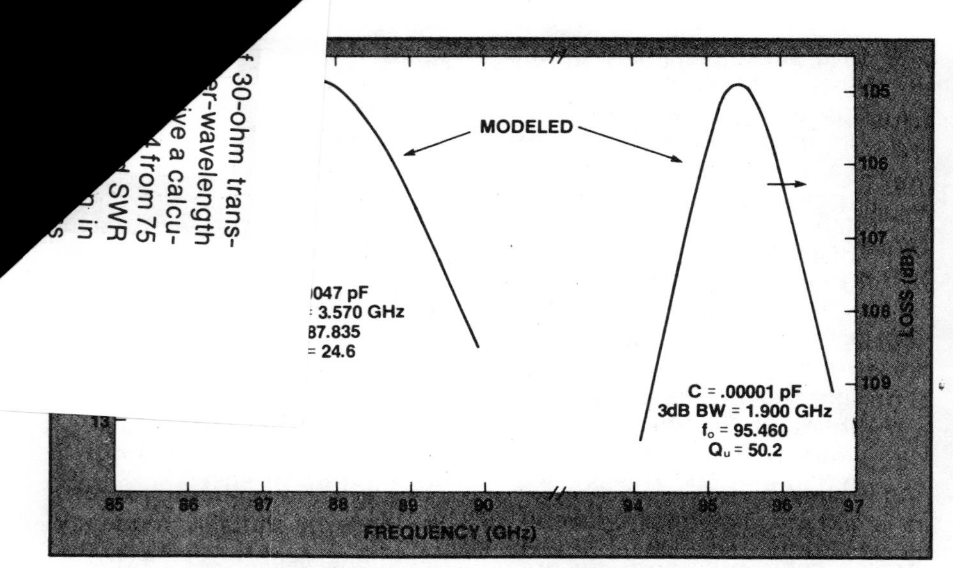

Fig. 6 Modeled transmission loss through linear resonator: left, coupled as fabricated; right loosely coupled.

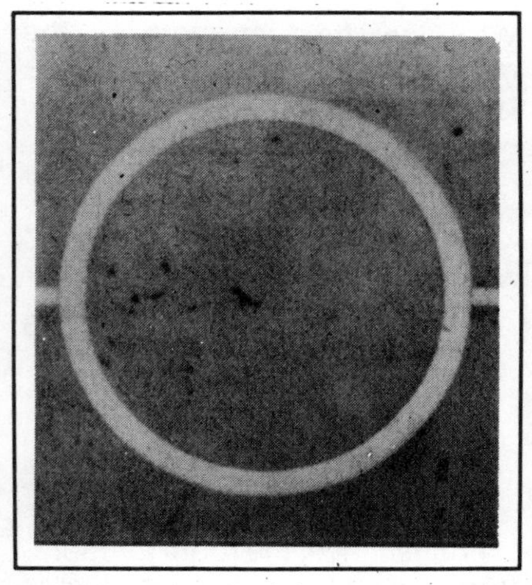

Fig. 7 Photograph of ring resonator with 2-μm coupling gaps.

enough to conclude that the dielectric constant is different from the low frequency value. Therefore, the model using 12.55 was used to arrive at the unloaded Q of the resonator by the method shown in Figure 6. The broader curve is the best-fit-modeled curve curve taken from Figure 5. Then, by allowing the coupling capacitors in the model to decrease in value until the Q of the curve reaches its asymptote, the unloaded Q of the resonator is established; it is equal to that asymptotic value. The loaded and unloaded resonant frequencies are also different, as shown. The narrower curve of Figure 6 is the "unloaded" (C = .0001 pF) transmission curve of the linear resonator, giving 50.2 for the unloaded Q, defined as the ratio of the center frequency to the 3-dB bandwidth. Also, the qualiy factor of transmission lines with predominant conductor loss, as is the case here, is given by:[9]

$$Q_c = \frac{27.3}{\alpha_c} \qquad (4)$$

where α_c is the conductor loss in dB per wavelength. At the unloaded resonant frequency of 95.46 GHz, using 8.434 for the effective dielectric constant and 12.53 dB/inch from the modeling optimization results, a value of 51.2 is given by Equation (4), which agrees suitably with the value of 50.2 obtained from Figure 6. It is also interesting to note that the computer optimized value of the coupling gap capacitance (.0047 pF) is in reasonable agreement with a theoretical value of .0053 pF, extrapolated from approximate closed-form expressions[10] describing the results of numerical calculations.

The ring resonator is shown in Figure 7. The inner radius of the ring is 350 μm and the outer radius is 400 μm. The gaps between the 36 μm wide, 50-ohm input and output microstrip lines are 2 μm wide. Figure 8 shows the measured transmission loss of the ring resonator, its equivalent circuit, and two curves from analytical best-fit models. The circular lines were modeled as isolated microstrip.[11] The actual substrate thickness for the resonator which gave this data was 56 μm rather than the nominal 50 μm. This difference was taken into account in all the analyses of the data and in the model calculations. The best-fit line loss for the circular line was 9.0 dB/inch. Similar to the case for the linear resonator, a modeled transmission curve, using a substrate dielectric constant value (12.61) slightly different from the measured low frequency value (12.55) appears somewhat better. The discrepancies from 12.55 in the deduced dielectric constant values are −1.4 percent from the linear resonator results, and +0.5 percent from the ring resonator results. It is more likely that the measurements here are that much in error, and that the low frequency value is correct and is maintained at least through 110 GHz. In a manner similar to that described earlier, the unloaded Q was determined as shown in Figure 9.

As a point of general interest, note the large shifts in frequency and midband loss, caused by the loading to the external circuits, in Figures 6 and 9. In each case the left-most curve uses the left LOSS axis and the right-most curve uses the right LOSS axis. This suggests that a total transmission loss in the order to 100 dB is required to measure the unloaded Q and unloaded resonant frequency directly. In the typical mm-wave lab this much sensitivity is often not available or leakage through alternate paths may exist, and the values must be determined indirectly as described here.

Lange Coupler

As was implied in the Introduc-

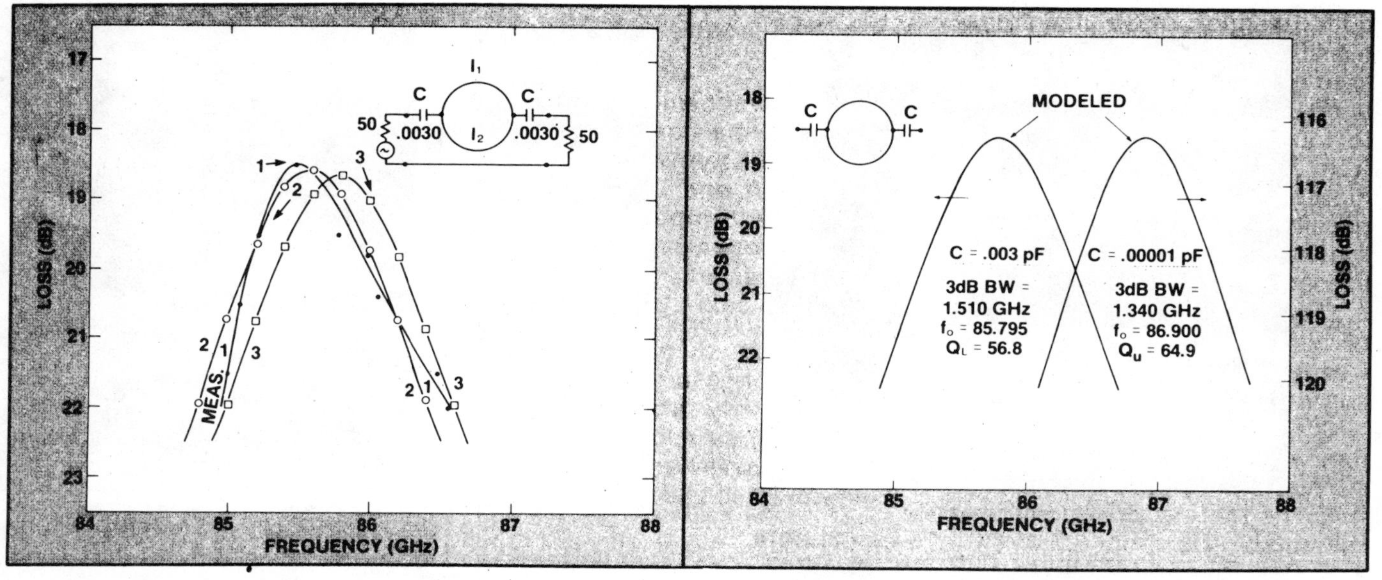

Fig. 8 Measured and modeled transmission loss through ring resonator.

Curve no. 1: Measured, smoothed; 2: Modeled: ε_r (subst.) = 12.61; 3: Modeled: ε_r (subst.) = 12.55.

Fig. 9 Modeled transmission loss through ring resonator: left, coupled as fabricated; right, loosely coupled.

tion, the Lange coupler, for use as a quadrature-phase power divider or combiner, was difficult to fabricate. As shown in Figure 10, Figure 11a, and Figure 11b, it uses four coupled lines which are nominally 1.6 μm wide and 0.8 μm thick, with air-bridge crossover connections. The coupling spaces are nominally 3 μm wide and the coupling length is approximately 250 μm. The coupler was designed by using an in-house synthesis program.[12] Line thickness correction in the coupling region was necessary.[13] The final design was confirmed on the COMPACT computer program. The computed and measured coupling results are given in Figure 12. This measured data is preliminary, in that the cause for the unexpected coupling behavior has not yet been investigated and resolved. The SWR of all ports was less than 1.7 and the isolation better than 13 dB.

The Lange coupler fabrication uses a combination of lift-off and plating technologies. The first-level metalization, which includes the coupled lines and the 50-ohm input and output lines, was formed using a 5000Å silicon nitride-assisted lift-off of Cr/Au (50Å /8000Å). After lift-off, a thin Au film is evaporated in the field to serve as a current path for electroplating. The air bridge "post" pattern is printed in photoresist and Au is plated in the "post" area. Plating is allowed to continue until the Au "posts" spread over the photoresist and join. After plating, the photoresist, the thin Au, and the silicon nitride are removed.

The microstrip bend chamfers, apparent in Figure 10, are stepped approximations of the commonly seen straight-line chamfer; they were stepped to simplify the mask-making procedure in the fabrication process. An analytical solution for the straight-line chamfer shown in Figure 13 was developed from available information[14,15,16] using one criterion often used but not formally proven: that the chamfer length should be 1.8 times the average of the

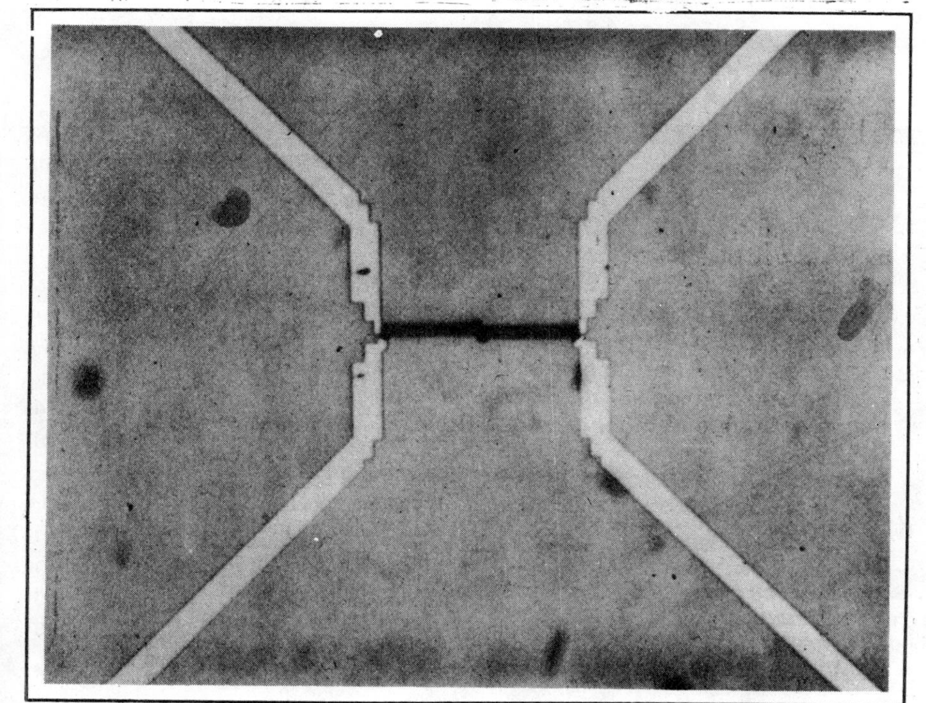

Fig. 10 Photograph of Lange coupler showing 36-μm wide input and output 50-ohm lines.

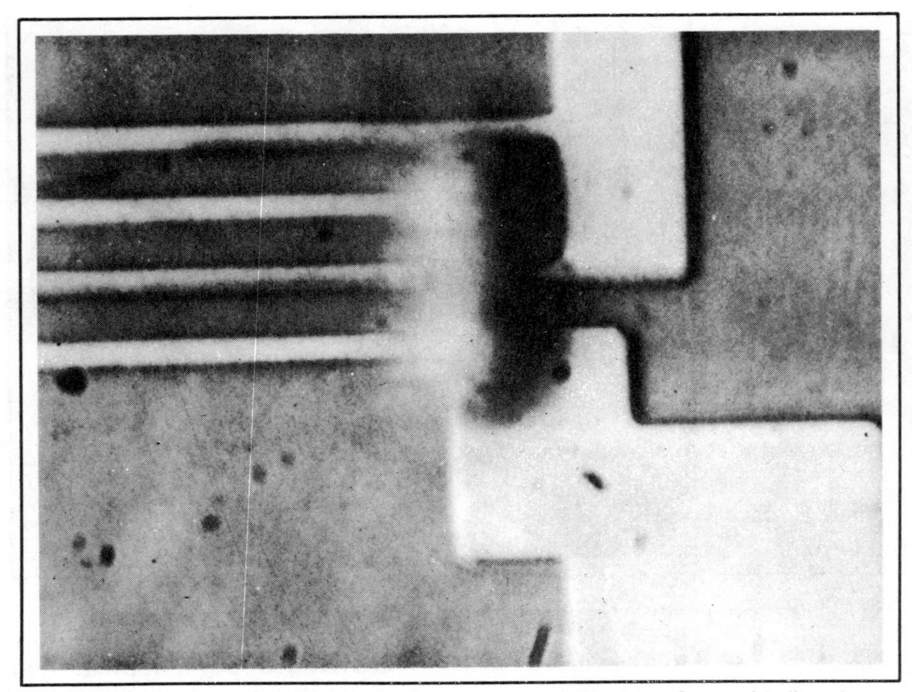

Fig. 11a Photograph of one end of Lange coupler, showing 1.6-μm-wide lines in coupling region.

Fig. 11b Scanning electron micrograph of Lange coupler air bridge.

two intersecting line widths. A second criterion, needed to obtain an unambiguous solution, was that the chamfer be located to remove maximum metal area, by requiring that, in Figure 13, the line segments BD and DC be of equal length. The following equations result for w_1 larger than w_2 and appear to be usable for bend angle, θ, between about 35 and 145 degrees:

$$\mathrm{OFFL} = \frac{.45\,(w_1 + w_2)}{\mathrm{COS}\,\frac{\theta}{2}} + \frac{w_1 - w_2}{\mathrm{SIN}\,\theta} - w_1\,\mathrm{TAN}\,\frac{\theta}{2} \qquad (5)$$

$$\mathrm{OFFR} = \frac{.45\,(w_1 + w_2)\,\mathrm{COS}\theta}{\mathrm{COS}\,\frac{\theta}{2}} - \frac{w_1 - w_2}{\mathrm{SIN}\,\theta} + w_1\,\mathrm{TAN}\,\frac{\theta}{2} \qquad (6)$$

$$\mathrm{HR} = \frac{.45\,(w_1 + w_2)\,\mathrm{SIN}\theta}{\mathrm{COS}\,\frac{\theta}{2}} \qquad (7)$$

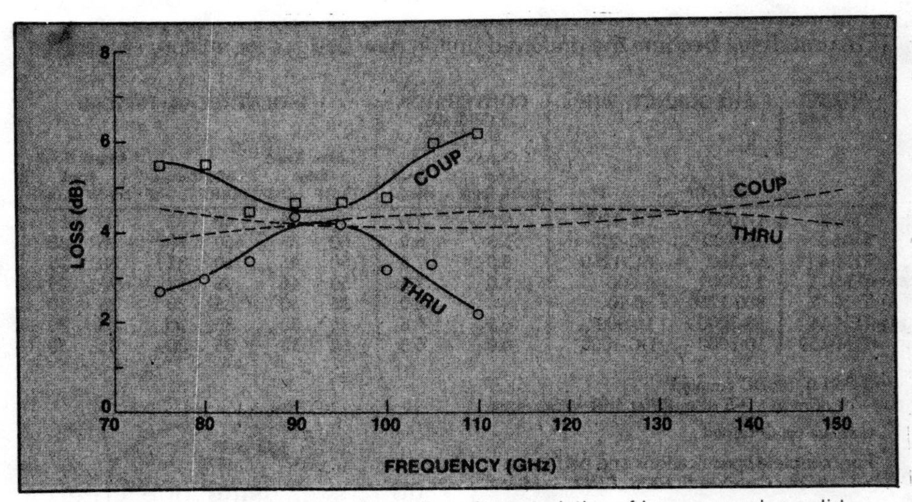

Fig. 12 Measured and modeled coupling characteristics of Lange coupler: solid = measured, dashed = modeled.

This systematic method of determining chamfer size and location was adopted for use on these mm-wave components.

Wilkinson Splitter

For in-phase power-dividing or combining, a single-section Wilkinson[17,18] divider was designed, fabricated and tested. Figure 14 shows this splitter, consisting of 50-ohm input and output microstrip lines (36 μm wide), two uncoupled 71-ohm lines (14 μm wide), and a 100-ohm isolation resistor (36 μm square, deposited thin-film nichrome). As nearly as the measurement could be read, the power split to the two output arms was equal, as is expected from the physical symmetry. The amplitude at each output arm was down from the input arm by the measured amount shown in Figure 15. The SWR of all three ports was less than 1.5 and the isolation between the two output ports was greater than 12 dB over the full 75 to 110 GHz band.

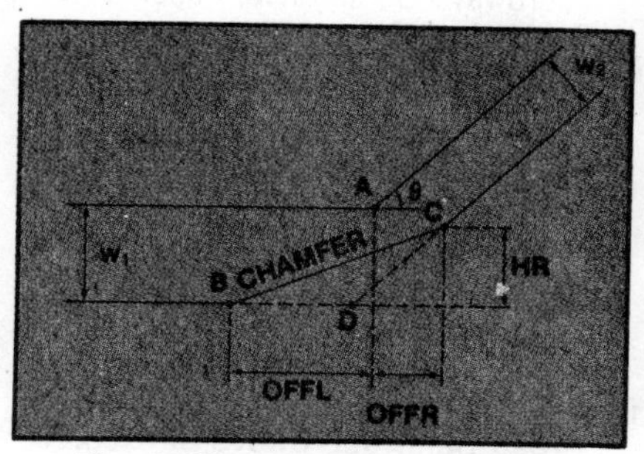

Fig. 13 Microstrip bend chamfer.

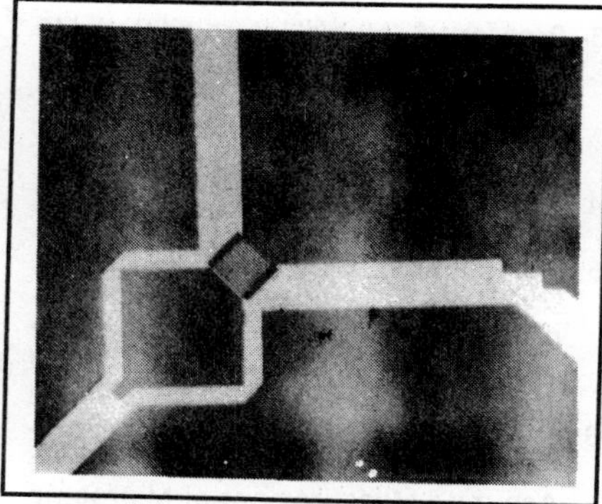

Fig. 14 Photograph of Wilkinson splitter showing 36-μm square isolation resistor.

Conclusion

The sum/difference hybrid, which is to serve as an antiphase power divider or combiner, has been designed and fabricated but not yet tested. It is pictured in Figure 16, consisting of a Lange coupler and a 90 degree Schiffman[19] phase-shifter with its reference line.

Certain semiconductor components are being developed for later monolithic integration with the passive elements described here. The building blocks for a full range of sophisticated, wideband mm-wave monolithic circuit functions are being investigated. The following characteristics are expected to distinguish circuits in the 30 to 300 GHz frequency range from those below 30 GHz: The substrates will be much thinner, there will be more distributed circuitry because lumped circuits will be too small, and initially there will be amplifiers and oscillators not employing three-terminal devices.

There is a need for monolithically compatible amplifier and oscillator techniques above 60 GHz. Indeed, a giant step to a surface-oriented, three-terminal gain device useful to 300 GHz would help open the door to that region. Meanwhile, this research program will pursue wideband balanced diode approaches for reflection amplifiers, along with new concepts for three-terminal devices.

The advantages of monolithic circuitry are well known. The research work described here is only to answer whether such circuitry is feasible up to a few hunderd gigahertz. These results clearly demonstrate that feasibility. ■

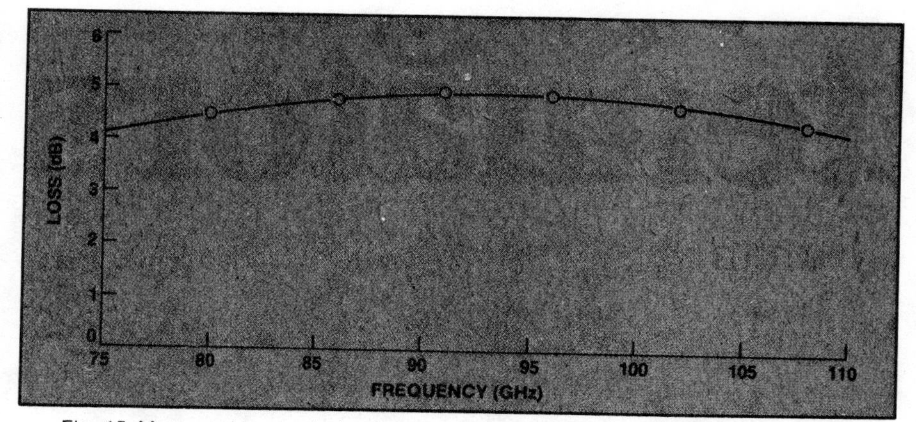

Fig. 15 Measured transmission loss to each output arm of the Wilkinson splitter.

Acknowledgments

The authors acknowledge G. Kelner, H.E. Heddings, J.B. Boos, B.R. Wilkins, R.L. Henry, and S. Sillmon for their contributions to this work.

This program was supported by the Office of Naval Research.

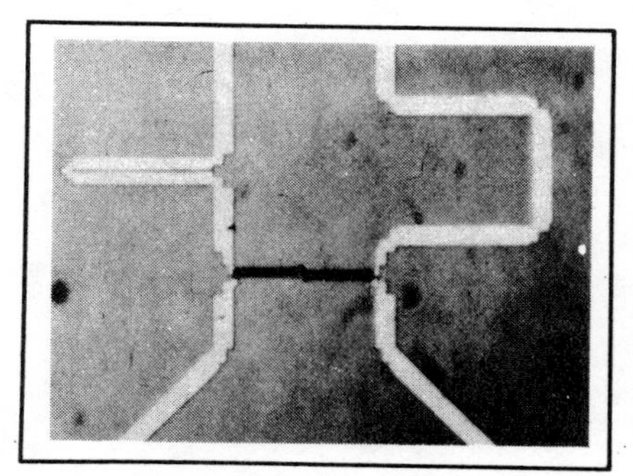

Fig. 16 Photograph of sum/difference hybrid. Schiffman phase-shifter coupling gap is 4.8 μm wide.

REFERENCES

1. Watkins, E.T., J.M. Schellenberg, L.H. Hackett, H. Yamasaki, and M. Feng, "A 60 GHz GaAs FET Amplifier," 1983 IEEE MTT-S International Microwave Symposium Digest, pp. 145-147.
2. Saad, T.S., Editor, "Microwave Engineers' Handbook — Volume 2," Artech House, Inc., Dedham, Mass., 1971, p. 77.
3. Collin, R.E., "Field Theory of Guided Waves," New York: McGraw-Hill, 1960, pp. 470-474.
4. Dukes, J.M.C., "The Application of Printed-Circuit Techniques to the Design of Microwave Components," Proceedings of the IEE, 1958, pp. 155-172.
5. Neidert, R.E., Waveguide-to-Coax-to-Microstrip Transitions for Millimeter-Wave Monolithic Circuits," *Microwave Journal,* June 1983, pp. 93-101.
6. Ho, Chen Y., "VSWR, Power Dissipation: Keys to Film Resistors," *Microwaves,* December 1981, pp. 69-78.
7. Rolke, Joachim, "Nichrome Thin Film Technology and its Application," Electrocomponent Science and Technology, vol. 9, no. 1, 1981, pp. 51-57.
8. Neidert, R.E., S.C. Binari, and T. Weng, "Dielectric Constant of Semi-Insulating Indium Phosphide," Electronics Letters, vol. 18, no. 23, November 11, 1982, pp. 987-988.
9. Liao, Samuel Y., "Microwave Devices and Circuits," Prentice-Hall, Inc., New Jersey, 1980, p. 429.
10. Gupta, K.C., Ramesh Garg, and I.J. Bahl, "Microstrip Lines and Slotlines," Artech, Dedham, Mass., 1979, pp. 132-136.
11. Wu, Y.S., and F.J. Rosenbaum, "Mode Chart for Microstrip Ring Resonators," IEEE Trans. on Microwave Theory and Techniques, vol. MTT-21, no. 7, July 1973, pp. 487-489.
12. Osmani, R.M., "Synthesis of Lange Couplers," IEEE Trans. on Microwave Theory and Techniques, vol. MTT-29, no. 2, February 1981, pp. 168-170.

13. Presser, Adolph, "Interdigitated Microstrip Coupler Design," IEEE Trans. on Microwave Theory and Techniques, vol. MTT-26, no. 10, October 1978, pp. 801-805.
14. Gupta, Garg, and Bahl, op. cit. (10), pp. 140-142.
15. Hammerstad, E.O., and F. Bekkadal, "Microstrip Handbook," SINTEF Report No. STF 44 A74169, University of Trondheim, Norwegian Institute of Technology, February 1975, pp. 94-98.
16. Easter, B., J.G. Richings, I.M. Stephenson, "Resonant Techniques for the Accurate Measurement of Microstrip Properties and Equivalent Circuits," Proceedings of the 1973 European Microwave Conference, Paper B.7.5, September 1973.
17. Wilkinson, Ernest, J., "An N-Way Hybrid Power Divider," IRE Transactions on Microwave Theory and Techniques, vol. MTT-8, no. 1, January 1960, pp. 116-118.
18. Cohn, Seymour B., "A Class of Broadband Three-Port TEM-Mode Hybrids," IEEE Trans. on Microwave Theory and Techniques, vol. MTT-16, no. 2, February 1968, pp. 110-116.
19. Schiffman, B.M., "A New Class of Broad-Band Microwave 90-Degree Phase Shifters," IRE Transactions on Microwave Theory and Techniques, April 1958, pp. 232-237.

THE DESIGN AND CALIBRATION OF A UNIVERSAL MMIC TEST FIXTURE

James A. Benet

Rockwell International
Collins Communication Systems Division
Anaheim, California

ABSTRACT

A universal test fixture suitable for performing repeatable, nondestructive microwave tests for characterizing various sized monolithic microwave integrated circuit (MMIC) chips has been developed at Rockwell International. The fixture, which encloses the MMIC chip, is designed to accommodate multiple RF inputs and outputs as well as up to 36 independent isolated bias connections. A method for calibrating the fixture on an automatic network analyzer (ANA) without the use of known precision calibration standards was also developed. A description of the fixture and the calibration method is presented in this paper.

INTRODUCTION

Advances in microwave gallium arsenide (GaAs) technology has lead to the emergence of monolithic microwave integrated circuits (MMIC) to solve the problem of mass producing low cost, high reliable microwave circuits. The MMIC combines many active (GaAs) devices with appropriate passive circuit elements to produce a single chip under one square centimeter in size which performs the electrical tasks equivalent to several microstrip circuits occupying ten to twenty times the area.

A problem arises with regard to testing and characterizing these devices. A method or technique needed to be developed to accurately measure the microwave performance without destroying the chip (for reuse). To solve this problem a project was initiated to develop an appropriate MMIC test fixture.

DESIGN AND FABRICATION

Design Objectives

The fundamental design goal was to develop a fixture system to perform accurate, nondestructive RF tests on a wide variety of chips which differ both functionally and physically. The fixture must allow for quick connections and disconnections of the MMIC. The fixture also must accommodate a large number of bias inputs without necessitating bonding during the testing process. Multiple RF input/output connections, as well as the multiple bias connections, must also be provided. Provisions for monitoring bias voltages is another desirable feature. Metal walls completely enclosing the input/output circuits and the MMIC chip must be provided to maintain RF shielding and reduce external noise inputs to the device under test. Since a subcarrier would be required, it must be designed such that it could be produced inexpensively. Finally, since the overall objective is to obtain accurate RF measurements, the fixture must provide a means by which it can be calibrated on an automatic network analyzer (ANA). Hence, the development of calibration pieces and appropriate measurement software must be included in the design objectives.

MMIC Subcarrier

To achieve nondestructive testing of the fragile MMIC chips and to avoid the necessity of making bonding connections during tests, the MMIC chip is bonded to a .062 inch thick, copper subcarrier which is made from a copper-backed dielectric (or PC) board. The subcarrier is shown in Figure 1. The dielectric material, which is .010 inch thick, is machined away in the center section of the subcarrier where the MMIC device is mounted. Bias lines are etched on the PC board sections which extend out on each side of the center section. These microstrip lines fan out to a pattern of 18 metallized pads which are .040 inch square. Small tabs extend outward in the center section along the measurement axis to interface with the fixture. The entire subcarrier is gold-plated to prevent copper oxidation.

The subcarrier is designed to accommodate MMIC chips of various sizes from .5 x .5 x .125 mm up to 10 x 8 x .625 mm with up to 36 independent isolated bias input. Leader microstrip substrates can be placed in front and in back of the MMIC device to accommodate very small chips or to convert the MMIC to a beam lead device. Small SiO chip capacitors are bonded to the subcarrier between the MMIC chip and the PC board to provide RF isolation on the bias lines.

The overall size of the subcarrier is 1.8 x .84 inches; however, this size can be reduced considerably after the testing is completed by merely shearing off the leader tabs and most of the PC board sections. The final dimensions could be as small as 2 mm long by 5 mm wide depending on the size of the chip and the bias capacitors. In the testing configuration the length of subcarrier with respect to the RF path is .4 inch or less. Although the size of the PC board sections with the bias pads is always fixed, the center section length is "customized" to fit the length of the particular MMIC chip which is being tested.

To produce the subcarrier inexpensively, the bias line pattern is repeated sixty times on a 16 by 10 inch panel. The entire panel is then etched and the individual PC boards are cut from the panel using an automatic (computerized) routing machine. The tabs and grooves are machined in for each size by stacking and machining the boards in lots of ten or more. Produced in this manner, the subcarriers can be built inexpensively.

The design of the subcarrier does not severely restrict the configuration in which the MMIC chip is packaged. For example, the chip can be built on a thin metal base and bonded or epoxied to the subcarrier. Alternatively, the subcarrier could be made part of a ceramic package to house the MMIC chip. The chip could also be built on a post or pill package and inserted into the subcarrier through a hole drilled in the center of the subcarrier. Furthermore, the subcarrier itself could be modified to use a thicker metal base or to change the width of the center groove in the dielectric, if necessary.

Test Fixture

An assembly drawing depicting the various components of the test fixture is shown in Figure 2. The fixture is built on a dove-tail assembly with a fixed center block and two end blocks which move in and out in unison by rotating a right- and left-hand threaded drive rod. Microstrip housings, which are open on the inside end, are spring-mounted on the end blocks and overhang them enough to come together midway at the center block. At this end, the bottom floor of the microstrip housing is thin (.031 inch) and a notch in the floor is cut away to expose the bottom surface of a .015 inch thick alumina microstrip substrate. When the MMIC subcarrier is set in place, the tabs on the subcarrier slip into the notches in the microstrip housing and the tops of the tabs make pressure contact with the bottom surface of the microstrip substrates to achieve the ground continuity. Four springs, located in the spring-mounted block, are used in mounting each microstrip housing to the movable end blocks so as to exert a sufficient amount of downward pressure on the substrate to assure an adequate ground contact to the subcarrier tabs. The two inside springs exert a downward force while the two outside springs exert an upward force. This forces the ground contact on the tabs to be made at the very end of the microstrip substrate. A tapered wedge, which is located between the end block and the spring mount block, is used to tilt the microstrip housing up at the inside end to allow the subcarrier to be inserted easily. The foam spring cushion in the beam lead pressure lid is used to exert pressure to hold the MMIC beam lead down on the microstrip center conductor.

The microwave path through the test fixture is completely enclosed with the use of three kinds of lid covers. The microstrip housing lid covers most of the microstrip housing near the connector end. The beam lead pressure lid covers the remaining microstrip at the open (inside) end of the housing. A top lid cover fits over the MMIC chip and rests on top of the other two lids. This cover is built with side walls in the center to provide extra shielding around the test device. The side walls come down to .025 inch above the dielectric material on the subcarrier. Four spring-loaded lid clamp assemblies, which are attached to the microstrip housing assemblies, exert sufficient pressure on the covers to maintain proper shielding.

The fixture is designed for considerable flexibility to handle a variety of potential testing requirements. For example, circuits requiring multiple RF inputs and outputs can be readily tested by using the two auxiliary connectors on each microstrip housing. The microstrip substrate inside the housing can easily be changed to a three-conductor pattern for this application. In addition, microstrip couplers can be incorporated in the substrate to monitor power or to inject additional signals into the MMIC circuit. Special filters, diplexers, bias chokes, by-pass capacitors, or attenuators could also be made on the microstrip circuits. The response of these circuits would be removed during the calibration procedure. If desired, the entire microstrip housings could easily be replaced with a microstrip-to-waveguide transition for making measurements above 18 GHz.

Bias Interface

To provide bias to the MMIC chip, wire bonds are made from the MMIC chip to the SiO chip capacitors and then to the PC board on the subcarrier. The bias lines fan out to the .040 inch square bias pads on the sides of the subcarrier. A set of 18 spring-loaded pins, closely spaced in a phenolic block, produce a positive pressure contact to the bias pads on the subcarrier. Two dowel pins on each side of the center section of the fixture position the bias block assembly directly over the bias pads on the subcarrier and two clamps swing over to hold the bias block down. Each pin is soldered on the top of the bias block assembly to a wire in a nineteen lead, wire harness that has a connector on the other end. The extra wire goes to the fixture base to establish the ground reference. The connector attaches to a bias interface box which consists of 36 pairs of banana jacks and 36 SPDT switches. These switches provide a convenient way to change the voltage between two states on any bias pad, which is particularly useful in testing multibit phase shifters or devices requiring bias on/off switches. The bias voltages can be monitored at the bias interface box or directly on the sub-carrier PC board by using a small probe.

FIXTURE CALIBRATION

Calibration Approach

Since the overall objective is to characterize MMIC chips (in particular with accurate S-parameter measurements), the calibration approach was derived for measurements on an automatic network analyzer (ANA). The software was written for measurements on a Hewlett Packard 8542B ANA, but it is applicable for any ANA model or system. The basic approach taken was to calibrate the fixture as part of the overall ANA system calibration, instead of characterizing the fixture separately from the ANA. The procedure used for calibration is described in the following paragraphs.

The twelve-term error model, outlined in Hewlett Packard Application Note 221A, forms the basis of the calibration. Since the equations for the forward and reverse parameters are identical in form, the notation used here will be given only for the forward direction. The equations for the reverse direction can be obtained by replacing S_{11} and S_{21} with S_{22} and S_{12}, respectively. The forward error terms become reverse terms. The equations for the measured reflection and transmission (Γ_m and T_m, respectively) are as follows:

$$\Gamma_m = E_D + \frac{E_R S_{11} - E_R E_L (S_{11}S_{22} - S_{12}S_{21})}{(1 - E_s S_{11})(1 - E_L S_{22}) - E_s E_L S_{12} S_{21}} \quad (1)$$

$$T_m = E_x + \frac{E_T S_{21}}{(1 - E_s S_{11})(1 - E_L S_{22}) - E_s E_L S_{12} S_{21}} \quad (2)$$

To determine the six error coefficients, reflection measurements are taken on a short and on an open, and both transmission and reflection measurements are taken on five offset transmission lines. Although five offsets are used, only three offsets are actually required to determine the error terms; however, the additional measurements are used to improve the accuracy by making use of a least error square fit of the data points. For the reflection measurements of the short and the open, S_{12} and S_{21} are assumed to be zero. For the short $S_{11} = -1$ and for the open $S_{11} = 1$. The measured reflection equation, (1), is reduced for the short and the open to:

$$\Gamma_{ms} = E_D - E_R/(1 + E_s) \quad (3)$$

$$\Gamma_{mo} = E_D + E_R/(1 - E_s) \quad (4)$$

For the reflection of the offset through transmission lines, $S_{11} = S_{22} = 0$ and $S_{12} = S_{21} = e^{\gamma}$, where γ is $\alpha l + J\beta l$. The reflection equations for the offsets reduce to:

$$\Gamma_{mT} = E_D + E_R E_L e^{2\gamma}/(1 - E_s E_L e^{2\gamma}) \quad . \quad (5)$$

The same assumptions are made for the transmission equation for offsets. Under these conditions equation (2) reduces to:

$$T_m = E_x + E_T e^{\gamma}/(1 - E_s E_L e^{2\gamma}) \quad . \quad (6)$$

Except for the open, the remaining calibration pieces are shown in Figure 4. These pieces are mounted on a gold-plated, .062 inch thick, copper subcarrier with interfacing tabs similar to the MMIC subcarriers. The short is a rectangular bar, .1 inch long with a cross-section of .015 by .015 inch. Beam leads are bonded to the top of the bar to interface with the microstrip center conductors in the microstrip housing. The offsets are made similarly, except that microstrip transmission lines on .015 inch alumina substrates replace the shorting bar. The offsets are made in incremental step sizes from .1 to .5 inch in length. No calibration piece is used to obtain the open. The housings are positioned slightly over the center section of the fixture with the wedge pushed back to raise the open end of the microstrip housing above the center section. Since both the center conductor and the ground plane of the microstrip are opened, the fringing capacitance is negligible.

The procedure used in the calibration is to make all the measurements first, store them, and then solve the equations to obtain the error coefficients. The effort term, E_D, is first determined from equation (5). The product of $E_s E_L$ is assumed to be very small compared to unity since these are source and load reflection error terms. If these terms are neglected initially, equation (5) will trace out a circle as a function of increasing offset lengths. The center of the circle is the E_D error term. The $E_s E_L$ product puts a small amount of distortion in the trace of the circle; but since the center of the circle is determined from a least-error equare fit of all five points, the resulting error in determining E_D is negligible. Since E_D is now known, E_R and E_s can be determined from Eqs. (3) and (4) for the reflections of the short and open, respectively.

To determine the remaining error terms, it is necessary to first determine the complex propagation constant, γ, for the incremental offsets. This is accomplished by averaging the ratio of the transmission equations, Eq. (6), of offset number n + 1 to offset number n. This technique assumes E_X and $E_S E_L$ are mathematically negligible, which turns out to be a valid assumption. In any case, the averaging technique will diminish the error caused by this assumption. The E_L error term can now be determined from the reflection equations of the offset transmission lines using equation (5). Since this equation is repeated for each of the five offsets, the unknown error term, E_L, is determined using a least-error square fit of all the data points. The remaining two terms, E_X and E_T, are determined in a similar fashion by evaluating the transmission equations, Eq. (6), using the least-error square fit for the set of all five offsets.

The mathematics in the calibration approach may appear to be somewhat cumbersome; however, the technique is significant because it allows the error coefficients to be determined accurately from a few simple, insertable calibration pieces.

Measurement Software

The calibration and measurement software allow for the measurement of up to 101 frequency points. These points do not have to be spaced at equal intervals apart because a frequency file is stored in the software. Based on a single measurement run of the four S-parameters, up to twelve pages of corrected data can be printed or displayed at the discretion of the user. (The corrected S-parameters are obtained directly from the measured data using the equations given in Application Note 221A.) The first two pages of output data provide listings of the S-parameters in a magnitude and phase format for page one and in dB magnitude format in page two. Data pages three through six present the data in a Smith Chart or polar graphics form for each of the four parameters. The Smith Chart for the reflection measurements can be presented either as an impedance chart or can admittance chart. Pages seven through ten present a frequency plot of the magnitude in dB of each S-parameter. Automatic horizontal and vertical scaling is used in the plots. Plots of the forward group delay and maximum available gain are presented on the last two pages.

One convenient feature of the measurement software is that the input/output reference plane can be rotated by specifying the rotation length in inches of microstrip. Since the propagation constants of the microstrip lines were determined in the calibration software, this data is used for obtaining accurate line rotations independent of line loss or dispersion as these effects have already been included in the measured data.

TEST RESULTS

To obtain a proper evaluation of the fixture and the system calibration approach each must be evaluated separately. The fixture was first evaluated on the automatic network analyzer for reflections in the frequency domain and the results were convoluted into the time (or distance) domain to determine the source of the reflections. The system was then evaluated using the developed calibration software to determine if calibration routine was successful in removing the fixture reflection errors.

Fixture Results

The overall fixture VSWR is shown in Figure 5. A .4 inch microstrip transmission was measured. These reflections were convoluted into the time domain to determine their origins and the results are displayed in Figure 6. The results indicated that there was a problem associated with the output SMA connector interface. The interface was later repaired to correct the problem. The reflections around subcarrier were converted back into the frequency domain to produce the plot shown in Figure 7. This plot represents the interactions between the VSWR of the subcarrier interfaces between the two housings. The maximum VSWR is 1.6 to 1 which is equivalent to a maximum reflection coefficient of .117 at each interface.

The biggest contribution to this reflection was caused by misalignment of the center conductors of the microstrip transmission lines. Before these conductors were realigned, the fixture was calibrated using the correction software to determine if these errors could be removed by the software.

System Software

After calibrating the fixture with the ANA using the developed software, .4 inch offset was remeasured with the reference planes rotated in by .2 inch. The return loss data is shown in Figure 8. It can be seen that the reflections have been significantly reduced to demonstrate the validity of the calibration approach. Also, the transmission phase angle is near zero degrees which validates the rotation technique.

Further testing on actual MMIC chips is now in progress; however, insufficient data has been obtained at the time of this writing for inclusion in this paper.

CONCLUSIONS

A universal MMIC test fixture has been developed which has several unique features. It can accommodate various chip sizes, it can be calibrated on an automatic network analyzer using just microstrip type calibration pieces, it has provisions for multiple RF inputs and outputs, and it has provisions for use of up to

36 independent bias lines. Furthermore, no bonding is required during tests and the device under test can be enclosed on all sides. The fixture has the flexibility that it can be easily modified for special or unusual chip devices or testing requirements.

In addition to the hardware, software for calibrating and measuring MMIC chips in the fixture in an automatic network analyzer has also been developed. The software removes the measurement errors contributed by the fixture.

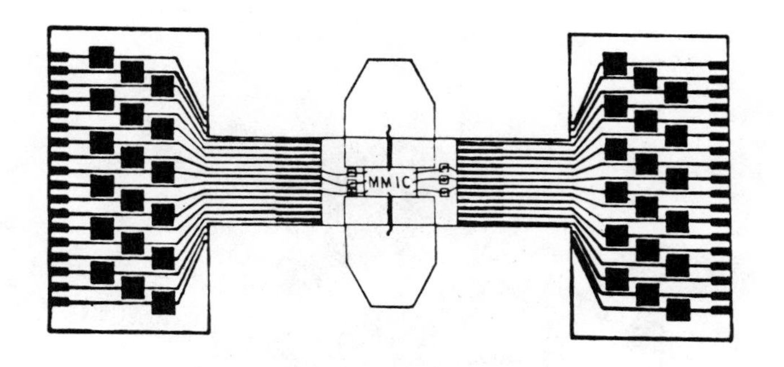

Figure 1. MMIC Subcarrier

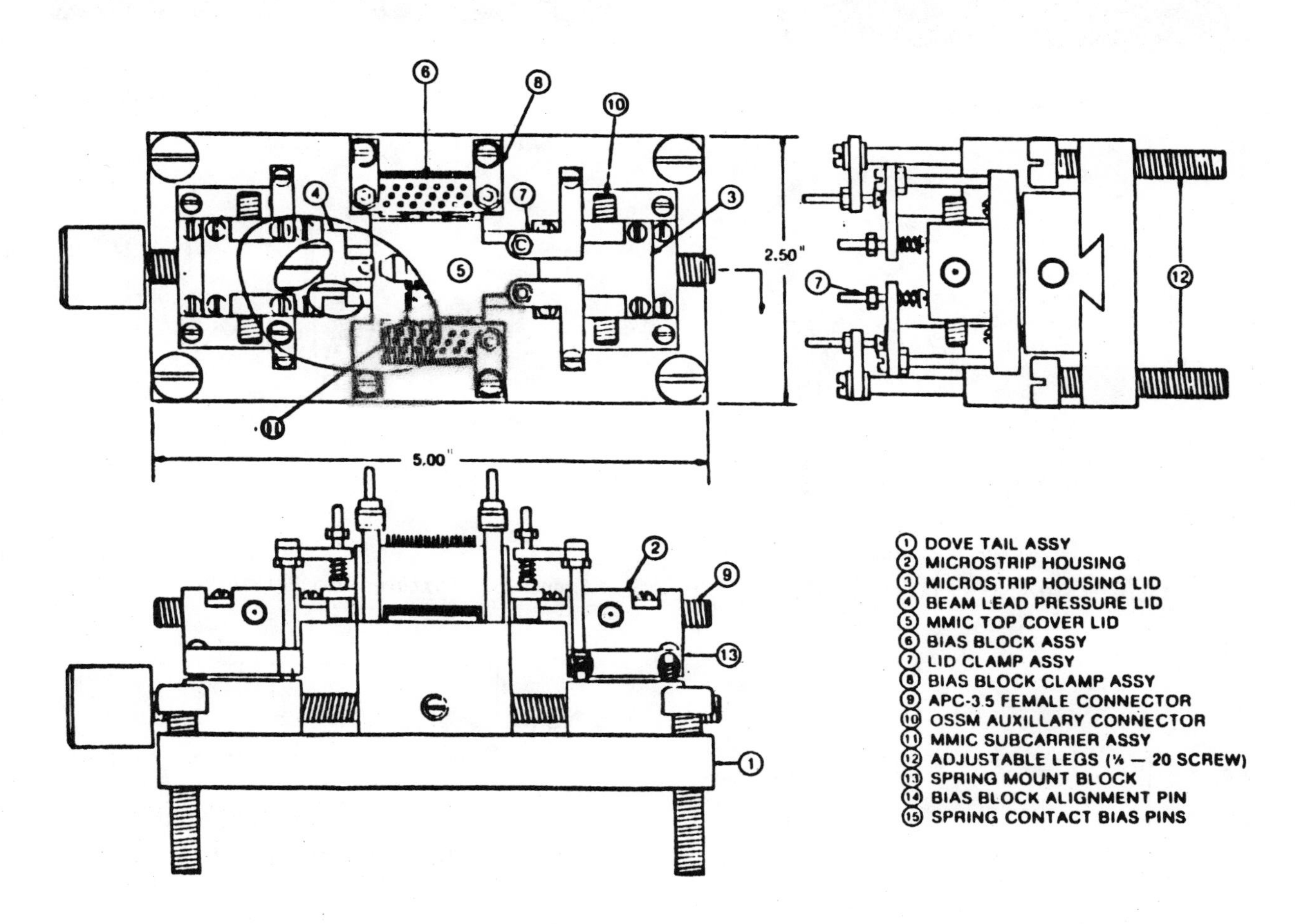

Figure 2. Test Fixture Assembly Drawing

Figure 3. MMIC Test Fixture

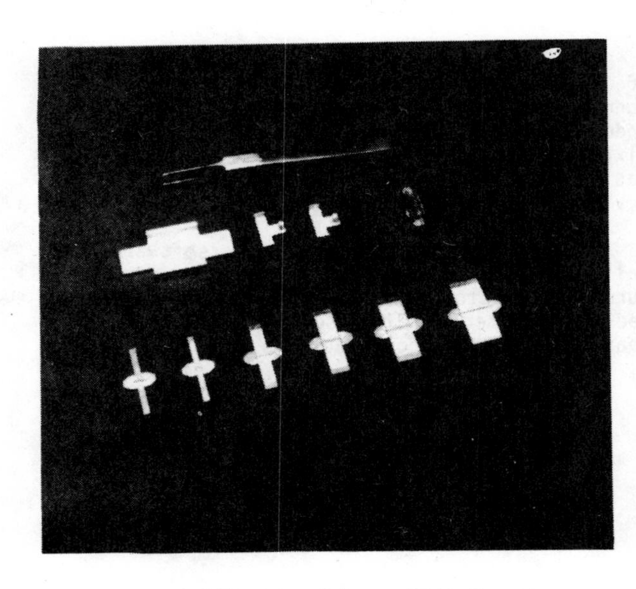

Figure 4. Calibration Pieces With Top Cover, BL Pressure Lid, and Subcarrier

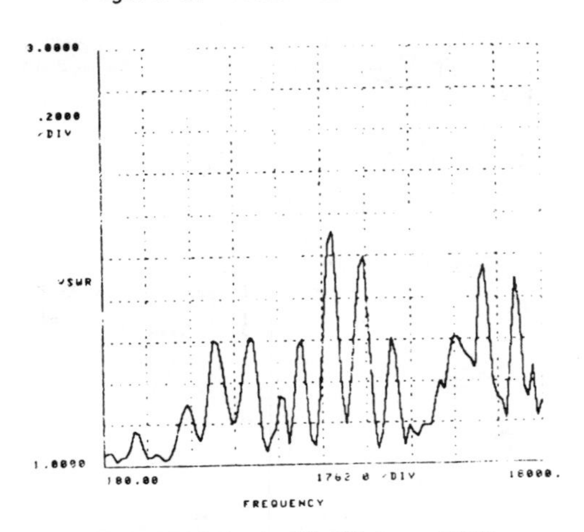

Figure 5. Overall Fixture VSWR

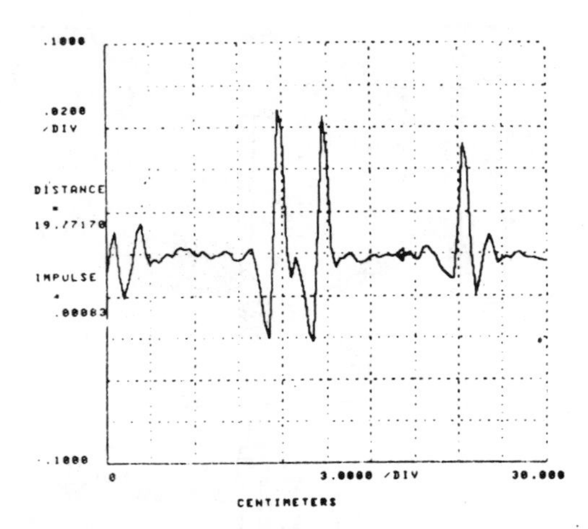

Figure 6. Fixture Time Domain Reflections

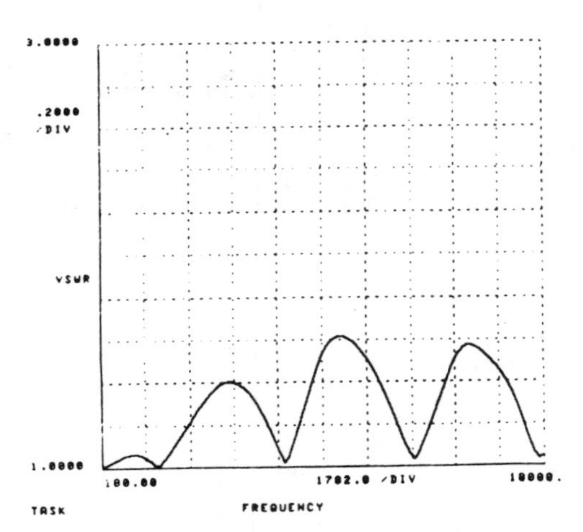

Figure 7. VSWR Without Connectors

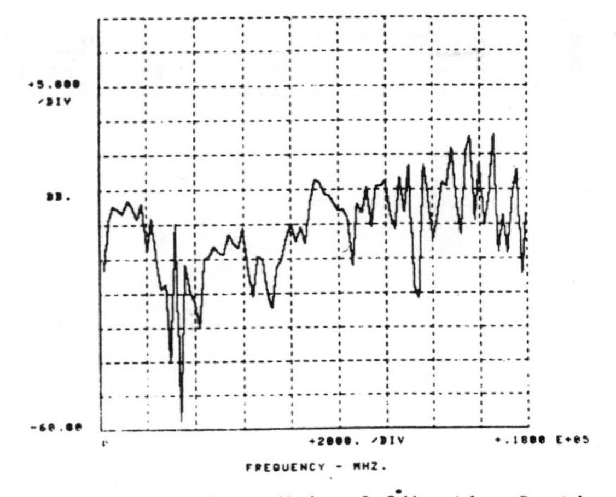

Figure 8. Return Loss Using Calibration Routine

MONOLITHIC MICROWAVE INTEGRATED CIRCUITS – INTERCONNECTIONS AND PACKAGING CONSIDERATIONS

by

K. B. Bhasin, A. N. Downey, G. E. Ponchak, R. R. Romanofsky, G. Anzic, and D. J. Connolly
National Aeronautics and Space Administration
Lewis Research Center
Cleveland, Ohio 44135

ABSTRACT

Monolithic Microwave Integrated Circuits (MMIC's) above 18 GHz are being developed because of important potential system benefits in the areas of cost, reliability, reproducibility, and control of circuit parameters. It is important to develop interconnection and packaging techniques that do not compromise these MMIC virtues. In this paper, currently available microwave transmission media are evaluated to determine their suitability for MMIC interconnections. An antipodal finline type of microstrip to waveguide transition's performance is presented. Packaging requirements for MMIC's are discussed in terms of thermal, mechanical, and electrical parameters for optimum desired performance.

INTRODUCTION

Advances in GaAs high frequency devices and materials technology[1] are making monolithic integration of microwave circuitry a possibility. GaAs monolithic microwave integrated circuits[2] (MMIC's) operating at high frequencies (Ku band and above) are showing promise for future space communications applications.[3] The lightweight, small size, and high reliability of MMIC's[4] make them candidates to enable superior space communications systems. The application of MMIC's in space communications systems requires the development of transmit and receive modules for phased array antenna systems.[5] In order to take full advantage of MMIC characteristics, the packaging and interconnection of MMIC's for integration at these frequencies requires numerous considerations. Low RF signal loss, wide bandwidth performance, manufacturability, and reliability are a few of them.

Characteristics of MMIC's which influence interconnections and packaging design, materials and fabrication requirements are described by presenting examples of MMIC's under development. For the RF input/output connections of MMIC's, a Van-Heuven type microstrip to waveguide transition which provides ease of MMIC integration for testing and packaging was chosen for detailed analysis. Improvements which have been obtained in the performance of this transition by modification in design and materials are discussed. Expected difficulties in obtaining maximum performance due to the high frequency of MMIC's are outlined. Based on available technology, packaging concepts are presented.

MONOLITHIC MICROWAVE INTEGRATED CIRCUITS

A prototype MMIC is illustrated in Fig. 1. Monolithic microwave integrated circuits (MMIC's) are mainly being fabricated on GaAs semi-insulating substrates. The monolithic approach allows the elimination of wire bonds (except for dc bias) used in hybrid microwave integrated circuits. The high dielectric constant (~13.0) of GaAs allows the fabrication of microstrip transmission line structures with small dimensions, facilitating the integration of various active and passive components on the same substrate. The high resistivity of a GaAs substrate allows the fabrication of active devices by epitaxial deposition of a doped layer or by an ion implantation process. The GaAs MESFET is the most used active device. Capacitors are formed using either interdigital or Metal-Insulator-Metal (MIM) structures, while resistors are formed using thin films of metals such as Cr, Ti, Ta, or cermets such as TaN.[4] The various active and passive elements which form monolithic integrated circuits can be seen in Fig. 2. The circuit is designed to operate at frequencies of 27.5 to 30 GHz and is an amplifier circuit for a receiver module. The circuit was designed and developed by Hughes Aircraft Company under contract from NASA-Lewis Research Center.[3]

The circuit shown in Fig. 1 is a transmit module which is being developed by Rockwell International for NASA-Lewis Research Center.[3] The microwave input and output connections are 50 ohm microstrip transmission line structures rather than simple pads. Also, dc connections are noticeable as pads on the top of the MMIC chip. The chip size is 4.8 mm by 6.4 mm. This is the initial design layout and includes diagnostic test circuitry. The final layout could produce a smaller chip size. The module consists of five cascaded single bit phase shifters, digital control circuitry, a two-stage buffer amplifier and a three-stage power amplifier. The typical RF power output is expected to be above 200 mW in the 17.7 to 20.2 GHz frequency range with gain of 16 db.

This chip will require both RF input/output and dc connections to the circuit as is shown in Fig. 1. This combination of RF/dc connections to the same chip is what makes packaging designs of MMIC's more difficult than for conventional IC's. In addition to the direct connections to the chip, a means of coupling the RF input (output) from the waveguide efficiently over the proper bandwidth to the microstrip must also be considered in any packaging scheme if the advantages of MMIC's are to be preserved.

MMIC INTERCONNECTIONS

The dc biasing lines of MMIC's are routinely brought out to a pad on the side of a chip where a wire bond can be made to the pad, or a commonly available bus termination with pins for connections to the pads can be used for dc biasing. The RF input/output lines of microwave devices require much more complicated structures. Fifty ohm matched microstrip transmission lines are the widely adopted structure for MMIC RF input/outputs. The integration of the MMIC into the rest of the system requires an interconnection between the microstrip of the MMIC and the external transmission media, which is relatively transparent to the microwave signal. Characteristics of the interconnection used must include the following requirements:

1. Low insertion loss
2. Wide bandwidth
3. Reproducibility
4. Ease of bondability
5. RF match
6. Small size

Transmission media which have been proposed for use at the frequency ranges being considered are shown in Fig. 3. The characteristics of these transmission media are summarized in Table I. From the table it can be seen that microstrip and coplanar transmission lines have several characteristics which are desirable for MMIC interconnections. Coplanar structures have the ground plane on the same side of the substrate as the transmission line, but have higher losses than microstrip structures.

Based on currently available technology, the microstrip transmission line is the structure most widely used[6] for the microwave frequencies since it possesses a wide bandwidth, small geometric sizes, and relative ease of interconnection to module components. In addition, microstrip structures are easily made by printed circuit board techniques on a wide variety of substrates. The disadvantages of a microstrip is its high loss relative to some of the other structures. For that reason, a waveguide is commonly used as a transmission structure for interconnection of devices separated by more than short distances. In addition waveguide is almost always used for interconnection to test equipment above 18 GHz. Therefore, a means of coupling the microstrip energy to waveguide energy must be included in the module design.

Several microstrip to waveguide transitions have been investigated. Basically there are three types of transitions: The first is a probe type[7] in which the microstrip is outside the waveguide and an antenna like probe couples energy to the microstrip. Another type is the Van-Heuven type transition[8] in which the microstrip is placed in the center (E-plane) of the waveguide on a printed circuit and a complex finline type structure couples the waveguide energy to microstrip energy. The third type of structure incorporates microstrip on one of the waveguide walls in the H-plane and an E-plane structure couples the energy to it. Examples of such structures are cosine tapers[9] and stepped ridged transitions.[10] Figure 4 shows the four transitions.

Van-Heuven Microstrip to Waveguide Transition

The transition proposed by Van-Heuven, and later modified by many others[9,12] as shown in Fig. 5, offers many advantages over the other types. Most important for packaging of MMIC chips in large numbers for use in complete systems, these transitions are in line with the waveguide making it highly suitable for system integration, are easily fabricated using low cost printed circuit board techniques, and are tunable in these characteristics by changing geometric parameters. Therefore, the Van-Heuven type transitions have been chosen for a detailed analysis since they seem to offer the best choice for packaging and testing of MMIC chips.

The effects of design and material parameters for this transition were studied in detail. For testing, transitions were fabricated on copper-clad Teflon type substrate material. Transitions were then tested in the test fixture shown in Fig. 6 by reflection and transmission measurements. It was shown that the shape of the curved position and the geometric lengths of the transition controlled the characteristics of the transition. Therefore, by changing the geometric parameters of the transition, the bandwidth and degree of flatness over the bandwidth could be controlled.

The loss of the transition was determined to depend on both the shape of the transition and on inherent microstrip properties. Figure 7 shows the effects of varying design parameters on the characteristics of the transition. By tuning for the lowest insertion loss, a transition was designed which had 0.9 db of loss for two back-to-back transitions connected by 2 in of microstrip. By tuning for the widest bandwidth, for two back-to-back transitions connected by 2 in of microstrip an insertion loss of 1.25 db with a ripple of ±0.1 db over the frequency band of 26.5 to 40 GHz was obtained. (This circuit was not made on the optimal substrate material for lowest loss).

A theoretical analysis was carried out to determine the source of the losses observed. These losses were attributed to the microstrip structure itself and mismatching. Microstrip losses were due to conductor loss (α_c), dielectric loss (α_d) and radiation loss (α_r). The total microstrip loss (α_T) is then given by:

$$\alpha_T = \alpha_c + \alpha_d + \alpha_r$$

As the frequency increases above K-band, conductor losses tend to dominate. Dielectric loss is proportional to the dielectric dissipation factor (tan δ) of the material (see Table II). It is typically small compared to α_c for ceramic substrates, but it is quite significant for polymeric substrates. The calculated losses[13] for Teflon type substrates with no interfacial roughness were:

$$\alpha_c = 0.32 \text{ dB at } 30 \text{ GHz}$$

$$\alpha_d = 0.27 \text{ dB at } 30 \text{ GHz}$$

The radiation losses were ignored as the microstrip is in a shielded environment. Thus, a 0.53 dB loss is associated with the microstrip section of the transition.

Further experimental investigation of microstrips were carried out to determine the effect of the material properties on the insertion loss. Series symmetrical gap resonator pairs[6] were constructed using unshielded microstrips on several Teflon-type substrates. Using an automatic vector network analyzer, data on loss and dispersion (variation of phase velocity with frequency) was taken to 20 GHz. The microstrip loss was obtained from the Q-factor measurements as determined by the resonant line center frequency and 3 dB bandwidth. Table II provides a summary of experimental results as well as published data on various substrate materials[14,15] commonly used at these frequencies. The microstrip loss is slightly higher for Teflon substrates than for ceramics. This is due in part to the higher dissipation factor (tan δ) of Teflon substrates and also because of their higher surface roughness.[16] It is also apparent that the ceramic type substrates tend to be more dispersive than Teflon types (due to higher dielectric constants).

The preliminary analysis of the Van-Heuven microstrip to waveguide transition has shown that improvements in design and materials can reduce losses to create a low loss transition.

MMIC PACKAGING

As presented earlier, the conventional packages used for IC's will not be suitable for MMIC packaging. Self-resonances,[17] RF insertion loss, and mismatching are some of the problems encountered with the conventional packages. Additionally, there are problems associated with high frequency operation. The following considerations must be taken into account to develop MMIC packages.

1. Environment
2. Thermal management
3. Mechanical
4. Insertion loss
5. Impedance matching
6. Ease of bondability

The ceramic chip carrier[18] will be a likely candidate to provide hermetic sealing and bondability to the microstrip. The chip carrier and its packaging into complete transmit/receive module is described below.

MMIC Chip Carrier

An ideal MMIC chip carrier must minimize parasitics to obtain maximum performance of the MMIC. A schematic diagram of a MMIC chip is shown in Fig. 8. The ceramic substrate on which GaAs is placed should be as close as possible to GaAs in dielectric constant to obtain matching between the width of the microstrip lines; sapphire and alumina are two good choices for use as a chip carrier. The interior of the ceramic chip carrier must be metallized to minimize self-resonances. The ground planes of the GaAs chip can be connected through via holes to the ceramic substrate. The microstrip input/output interconnection lines through the ceramic walls are also very critical. The seal ring between the microstrip and the metallized package wall increases parasitics if it is not properly designed. MMIC's will generate significant amounts of power. The thermal considerations will require that the ceramic chip carrier be mounted on a substrate such as copper-clad Invar, which has the same coefficient of thermal expansion as certain ceramic substrates. Copper provides the media for thermal dissipation and also can act as a ground plane. The substrate must also allow attachment to the transition.

Chip Carrier/Module Interface

The microstrip/waveguide transition can provide the interconnections desired for packaging. Several packaging concepts based on this are discussed in Fig. 9. The design concept is based on the Van-Heuven microstrip to waveguide transition.

The MMIC chip carrier mounted on a suitable substrate is attached to the bottom piece of the T/R module shown in Fig. 9. The input/output of the finline are attached to the microstrip of the chip carrier via the ribbon bonding process.

Another type of packaging design is based on the probe type of coupling which Hughes Aircraft Co. has demonstrated in testing. The MMIC chip carrier is attached to the microstrip and energy is coupled via probe to waveguides. The chip carrier can be integrated in the middle of the input/output waveguide connections. Developments in microstrip-waveguide transitions are providing a base for various MMIC packaging schemes. High frequency aspects will put considerable demands on several packaging schemes.

CONCLUSIONS

GaAs monolithic microwave integrated circuits, operating from 20 to 40 GHz, are approaching the level where they can be considered for system integration. Low cost interconnections and packaging techniques are required which will preserve the advantages and characteristics of MMIC's.

The requirements for MMIC interconnections and packaging are significantly different than conventional IC's. Microstrip to waveguide transitions can provide a convenient means to interconnect MMIC's for testing and packaging.

Van-Heuven type microstrip to waveguide transitions were designed and evaluated. Design modifications and improvements in materials provided further increases in performance. Packaging concepts based on this transition that allow MMIC's to be integrated in the same plane were presented.

The need for design knowledge at high frequencies for an MMIC package which can meet various testability and integrability criteria offer the most challenges. Novel approaches in interconnection and packaging techniques may be essential to take full advantage of MMIC's.

REFERENCES

1. J. V. Dilorenzo and D. D. Khandelwal, GaAs FET principles and technology, Artech House, 1982.

2. L. C. Upadhyayula, M. Kumar and H. C. Huang, "GaAs MMICS Could Carry the Waves of the High-Volume Future," Microwave Systems News, July 1983, pp. 58-82, vol. 13, no. 7.

3. G. Anzic, T. J. Kascak, A. N. Downey, D. C. Liu, and D. J. Connolly, "Microwave Monolithic Integrated Circuit Development for Future Spaceborne Phased Array Antennas," Communication Satellite Systems Conference, 10th, Orlando, Florida, March, 1984. (AIAA Paper 84-0656).

4. R. A. Pucel, "Design Considerations for Monolithic Microwave Circuits," IEEE Transactions on Microwave Theory and Techniques, June 1981, pp, 513-534, vol. MTT-29, no. 6.

5. B. J. Edward, "Integration of Monolithic Microwave Integrated Circuits into Phased Array Antenna Systems," Proceedings of the 1983 Antenna Applications Symposium, Electromagnetic Lab. University of Illinois, Urbanna, Illinois.

6. T. C. Edwards, Foundations for Microstrip Circuit Design, John Wiley and Sons, 1981.

7. E. T. Watkins, "GaAs FET Amp Uses One-Quarter Micron Gate, Heralding MIC Opportunities at up to 60 GHz," Microwave Systems News, Dec. 1983, pp. 52 to 62, vol. 13, no. 13.

8. J. H. C. Van Heuven, "A New Integrated Waveguide-Microstrip Transition," IEEE Transactions on Microwave Theory and Techniques, Mar. 1976, pp. 144-146, vol. MTT-24, no. 3.

9. D. Rubin and D. Sanl, "mm Wave MICs use low value dielectric substrates," Microwave Journal, Nov. 1976, pp. 35-39, vol. 19.

10. S. S. Moochalla and C. An, "Ridge Waveguide used in microstrip transition," Microwaves and RF, Mar. 1984, pp. 149-152, vol. 23.

11. D. Rubin and D. L. Sahl, "The Microstrip Diplexer - A new tool for Millimeter Waves," June 1980, pp. 55-57, vol. 23.

12. M. Dydyk and B. D. Moore, "Shielded Microstrip Aids V-Band Receiver Designs," Microwaves, Mar. 1982, pp. 77-82, vol. 21.

13. K. C. Gupta, R. Garg and R. Chadhar, Computer-Aided Design of Microwave Circuits, Artech House, 1981.

14. A. Gopinath, R. Horton, and B. Easter, "Microstrip Loss Calculations," Electronics Letters, Jan. 22, 1970, pp. 40-41, vol. 6, no. 2.

15. J. H. C. Van Heuven, "Conduction and Radiation Losses in Microstrip," IEEE Transactions on Microwave Theory and Techniques, Sept. 1974, pp. 841-844, vol. 22, no. 9.

16. K. B. Bhasin, D. C. Liu and R. R. Romanofsky, "Effect of Interfacial characteristics of Metal clad-polymeric Substrates on High Frequency Interconnection Performance," to be presented at the Materials Research Society Meeting, Boston, Mass., Nov. 1984.

17. Y. Hirachi, Y. Takeuchi, M. Igarashi, K. Kosemura, and S. Yamamoto, "A Packaged 20 GHz 1-W MESFET with a Novel Via-Hole Plated Heat Sink Structure," IEEE Transactions on Microwave Theory and Techniques, Mar. 1984, pp. 309-316, vol. MTT-32, no. 3.

18. F. J. Dance, "Interconnecting Chip Carriers: A Review," Circuits Manufacturing, 1983, pp. 60-70, vol. 23.

19. J. L. Zemany and W. J. SooHoo, "Packaging of a GaAs FET Solid State Amplifier for a communication Satellite," Proceedings of the Technical Conference, 3rd Annual International Electronic Packaging Conference, Itasca, IL, Oct. 24-26, 1983, pp. S1-S6.

TABLE I. - CHARACTERISTICS OF MICROWAVE/mm WAVE TRANSMISSION MEDIA

Type of transmission media/characteristics	Relative size	Integration to solid state devices	Q-factor	Power handling capability
Waveguide	Large	Difficult	1000 and above	Large
Microstrip line	Small	Easy	Several hundreds	Low
Coplanar transmission line	Small	Easy	Several hundreds	Low
Finline	Moderate	Easy	Several hundreds	Low
Suspended stripline	Moderate	Easy	Several hundreds	Low
Dielectric waveguide (image line)	Moderate	Difficult	1000 and above	Moderate

TABLE II. - REPORTED ELECTRICAL AND MECHANICAL CHARACTERISTICS

Substrate	Relative dielectric constant	RF loss at dB/λ	Dispersion		Surface roughness, μm	Tan δ	Thermal conductivity, W/cm °C
			Er at 10 GHz	Er at 20 GHz			
31 mil Cu Flon	2.1	0.09	1.83	1.88	0.8 to 1.0	0.00045	~0.003
31 mil Cu Clad 217	2.17	.12	1.92	2.00	.8 to 1.2	.0009	~ .003
31 mil RT/Duroid 5880	2.2	.10	1.92	1.95	.8 to 1.2	.0009	~ .003
25 mil Fused Silica	3.78	.07[a]	3.10	3.16	.03	.0001	.013
20 mil Alumina (99.5 percent)	9.35	.09	7.05	7.5	<.4	.00025	.25
20 mil Sapphire	11.6	------	7.4	8.0	.03	<.0001	.38

[a]Ra = 0.4 μm.

4.8 mm X 6.4 mm X 0.127 mm

D/A CONVERTER

INPUT

TEST CIRCUITS

PHASE SHIFTERS

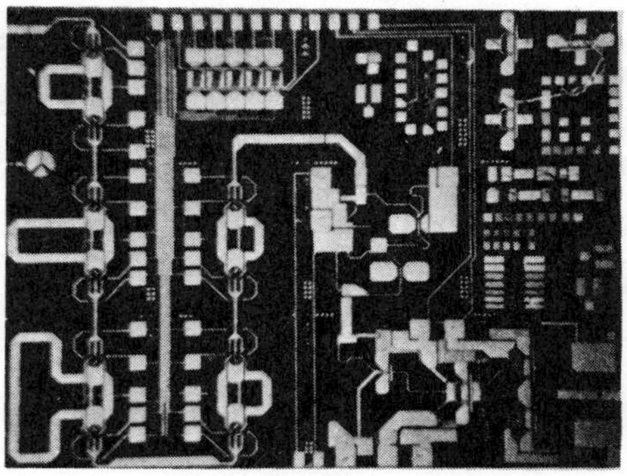

OUTPUT

2 STAGE BUFFER AND
3 STAGE FINAL AMPLIFIER

C-84-1139

Figure 1. - 20 GHz monolithic transmit module.

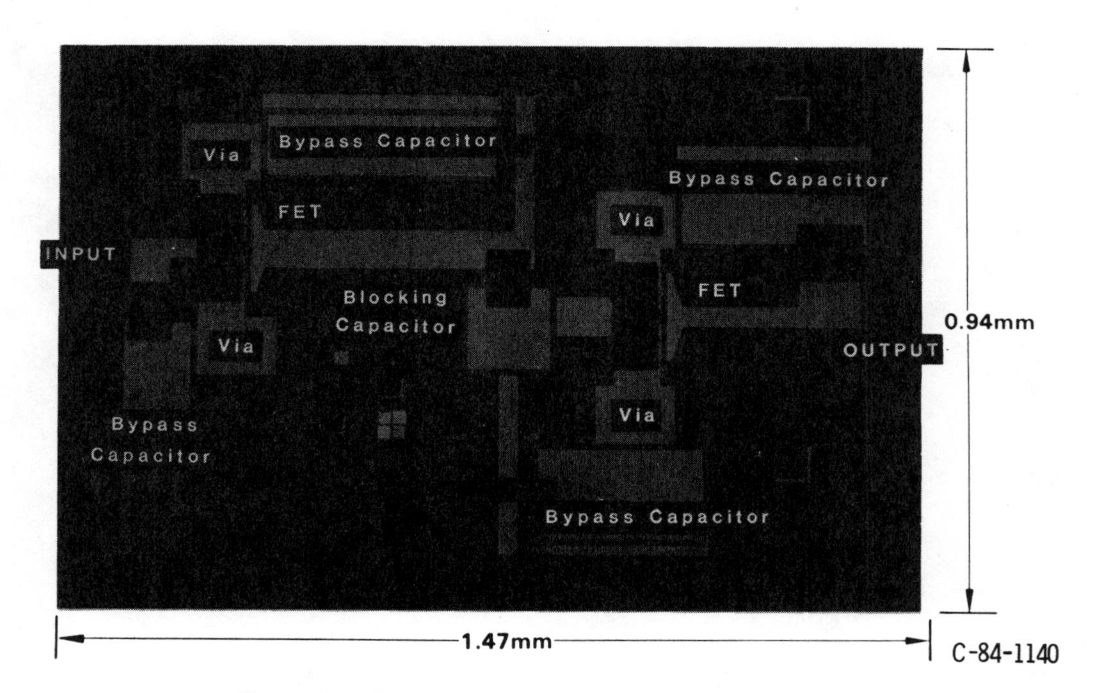

C-84-1140

Figure 2. - 27.5 - 30 GHz monolithic low noise amplifier.

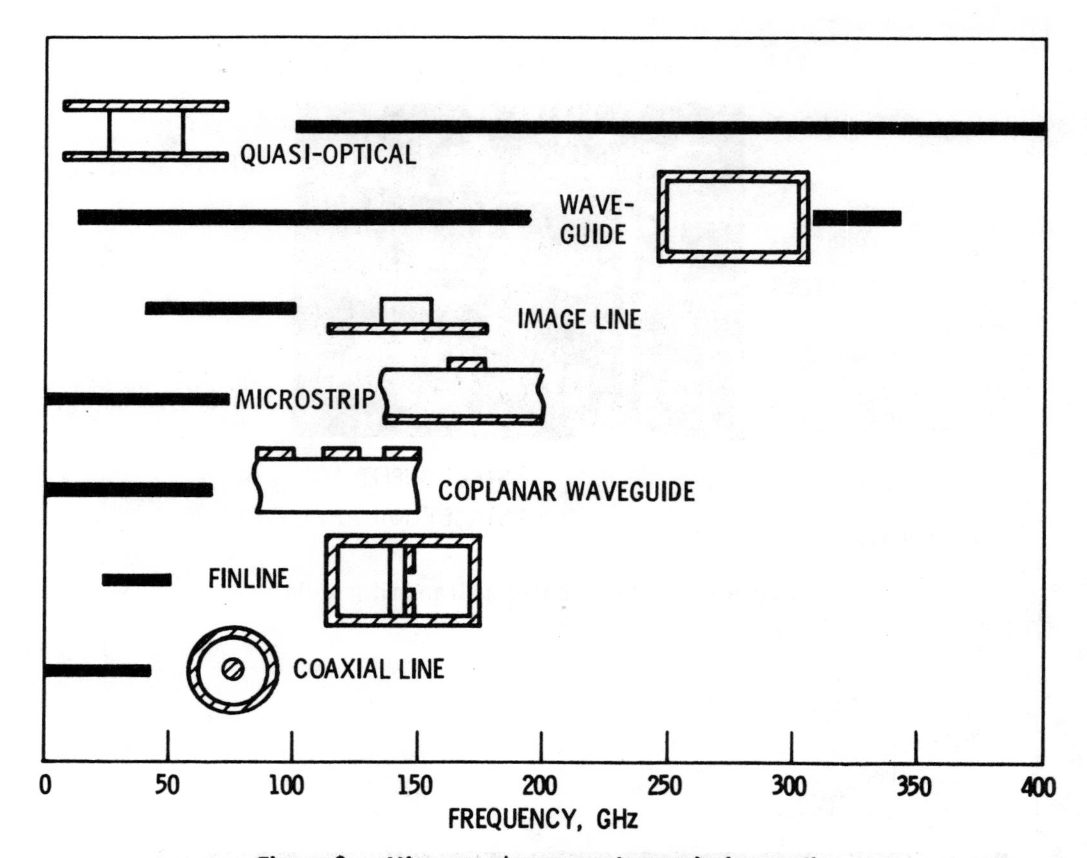

Figure 3. - Microwave/mm wave transmission media.

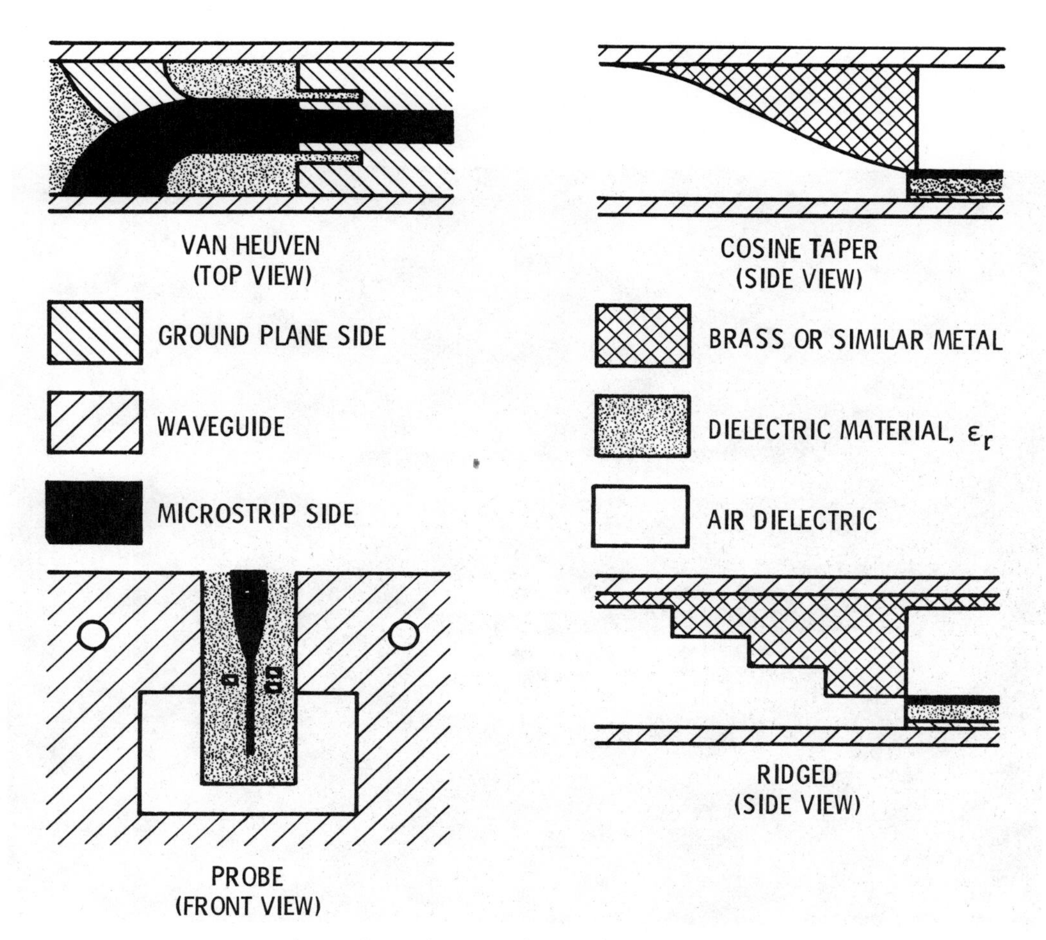

Figure 4. - Microstrip/waveguide transitions.

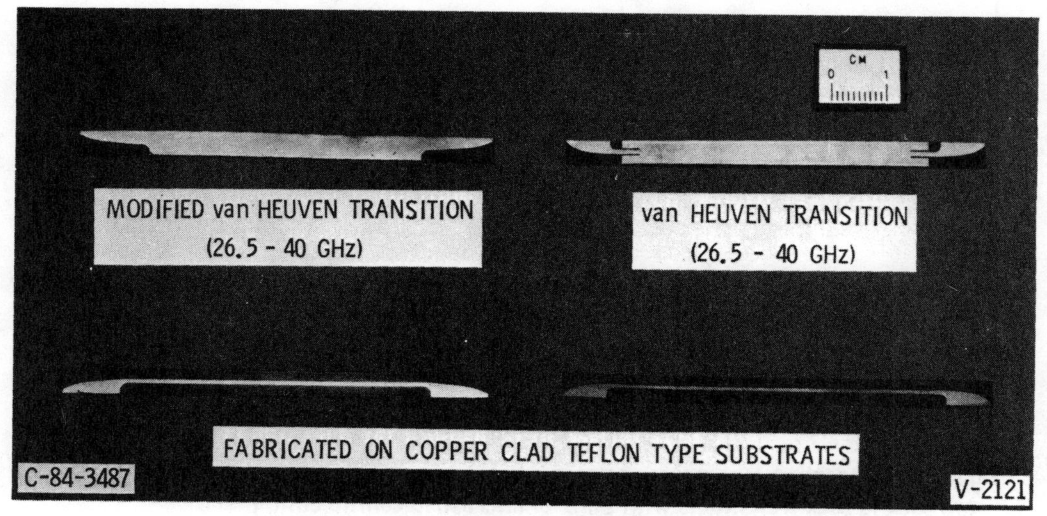

Figure 5. - Waveguide to microstrip transitions.

Figure 6. - 26.5 - 40 GHz waveguide to microstrip transition in test fixture.

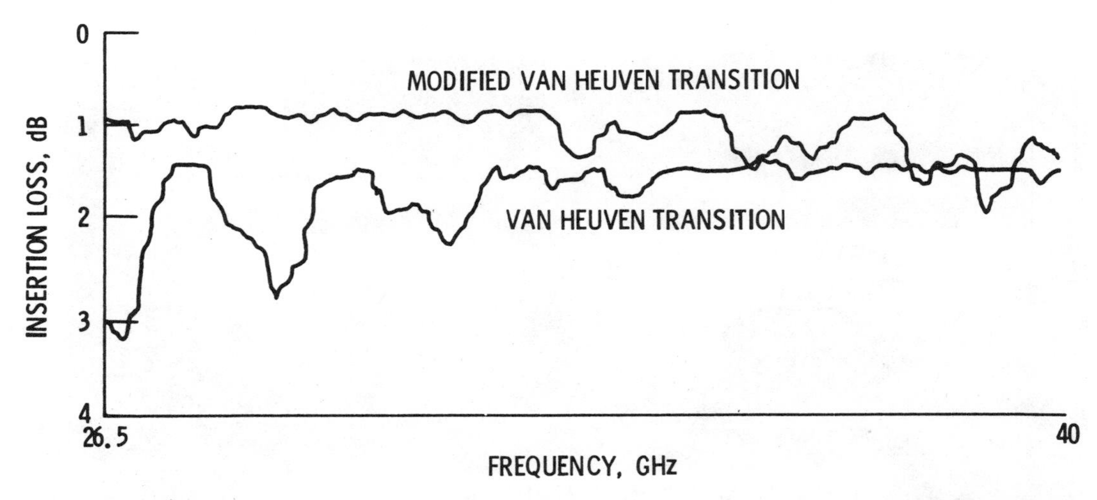

Figure 7. - Insertion loss measurements. Note: above two insertion loss plots are for two back to back transitions with 2 in. of microstrip connnecting them.

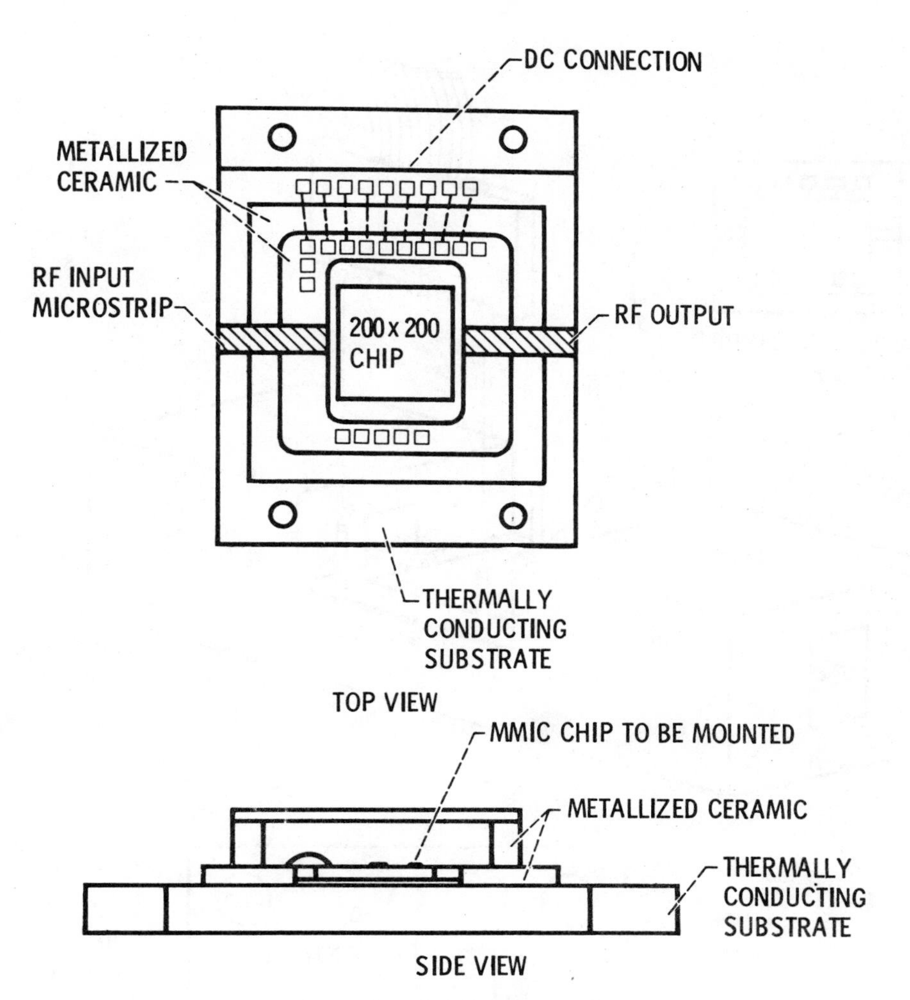

Figure 8. - MMIC chip carrier.

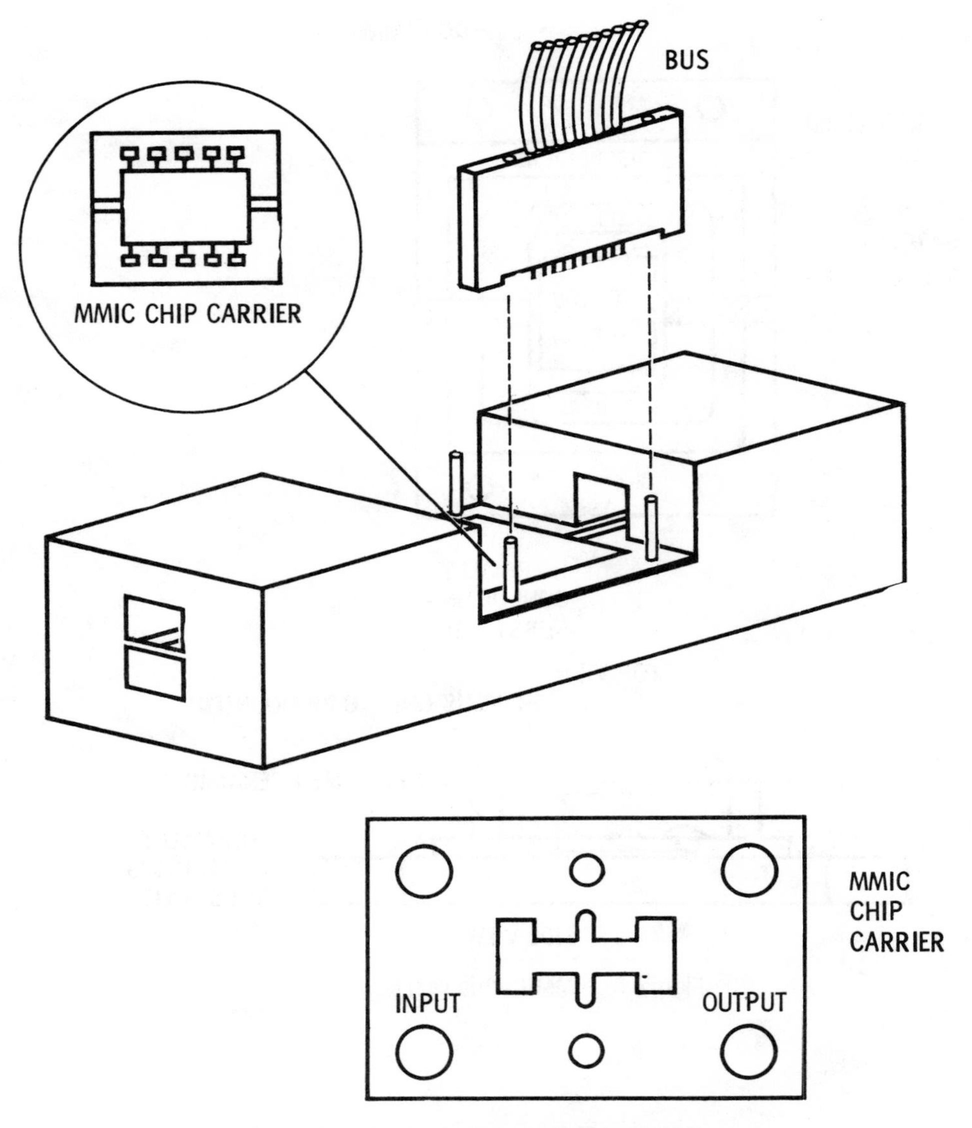

Figure 9. - Packaging concepts for MMIC's.

CHAPTER VII

APPLICATIONS

Several types of circuits intended for various applications in microwave systems, designed and constructed using the techniques described in this volume, are illustrated here. The examples given indicate possibilities for MIC system design and the directions that are most generally taken by designers. Power amplifiers that use hybrid MICs are described by Sechi, *et al.* Distributed GaAs monolithic amplifiers are discussed by Kennan, *et al.*, and traveling types, by Ayaski, *et al.* Microstrip circuits for a GaAs FET oscillator by Slaymaker and Turner, and an IMPATT oscillator by Morgan and Obe, are presented. Transmitters and receivers in hybrid form are discussed by Ogawa, *et al.* Finally, the development of GaAs MMICs for 20/30 GHz phased array antenna applications are presented by Anzic, *et al.*

Miniature Beryllia Circuits—A New Technology for Microwave Power Amplifiers

F. N. Sechi, R. Brown, H. Johnson, E. Belohoubek, E. Mykietyn, and M. Oz*
RCA Laboratories, Princeton, NJ 08540

ABSTRACT—A new technology for fabricating miniature circuits on glazed beryllium oxide has been developed that is particualrly well suited for miniature, light weight, high performance GaAs power amplifiers.

1. Introduction

Over the last few years a large number of efforts,[1] both government and company sponsored, have been aimed at applying monolithic process technologies to microwave circuits. Whereas in certain applications[2–4] monolithic integrated circuits offer distinct advantages, they are not well suited for high power applications, especially if optimum performance with high design flexibility is required and only moderate quantities are involved.

A new miniature hybrid technology is described here that combines the advantages of very small size, light weight, and the batch fabrication process of the monolithic approach with the flexibility of using separately attached active devices of the hybrid approach. The new process uses a combination of distributed and lumped circuit elements defined on beryllium oxide (BeO) to provide circuit substrates that combine high Q with excellent heat dissipation properties. The BeO substrates, which are rough even when polished, are selectively glazed to provide smooth surfaces for the definition of high-quality-factor

* On sabbatical leave from A.D.A., Israel.

lumped-element components, including inductors, thin-film capacitors and bridged interconnections. The active devices, GaAs power FETs in pellet form, are flip-chip mounted on unglazed sections of the BeO surface. A low parasitic ground connection for the FET source contacts is provided by a metal septum that is fabricated as an integral part of the BeO substrate. The fabrication process for the septum follows procedures developed originally for BeO carriers[5] for high power bipolar transistors.

The major advantages of the new technology are the small-size, light-weight properties of the circuits combined with excellent heat dissipation, and low loss. Since batch fabrication processes are used for the circuits, many of the advantages of monolithic circuits are preserved, while flexibility is maintained and the use of expensive GaAs substrates for the passive circuits (which often are one to two orders of magnitude larger than the active devices) is avoided. Since both circuits and devices are fabricated on separate substrates they can be better optimized for their intended functions. This is especially important for power applications where properties such as ease of mounting, good heat dissipation and low circuit losses are of paramount importance.

Circuit Description

Beryllium oxide, also called beryllia, has been the preferred mounting substrate for bipolar power transistors for many years. Since bipolar transistors are customarily fabricated with the back of the silicon chip as the collector, the mounting surface to which the transistor is attached must be dc isolated and becomes part of the rf matching circuit. BeO is ideally suited for this purpose.

With the advent of power GaAs FETs fabricated on semi-insulated substrates and featuring all three contacts—source, gate and drain—accessible on the top surface, the need for an electrically isolated mounting medium seemed to have disappeared. In effect, monolithic designs rely on the insulating substrate and on the availability of all three contacts at the top surface to easily integrate the active device with the rf circuit based on processing steps all performed on one side of the GaAs substrate.

This technology is well suited for low- and medium-power-level applications but leads to difficulties at higher power levels. The major reason is the incompatibility between requirements for good heat conduction and low rf losses. Specifically, for high power applications it is very important to fabricate the FETs on a very thin GaAs substrate—typically 2 to 4 mil thick—in order to dissipate the heat effectively. However, the very thin substrates cannot maintain a high Q for matching components of very small size. In addition, thin substrates cause severe mechanical interface problems due to the inherent fragility of GaAs.

High Q for the circuit components is particularly important for power amplifiers, since the active devices require very high impedance transformation ratios. Some recent work by Schellenberg[6] using hybrid technology shows that very good device efficiencies can be obtained for high power FETs even at Ku-band. This approach is based on combining many FET cells with very low impedance $\lambda/4$ transformers on thin substrates. In principle, this technique could also be applied to a fully monolithic design. However, large $\lambda/4$ matching lines are required, which results in an unfavorable ratio of circuit to device area, particularly at frequencies below 20 GHz.

In view of the above considerations and noting that, for most GaAs power amplifier applications of today, the fabrication volume is not large enough to justify a fully monolithic implementation, the need for a different approach is apparent. A new technology called MBC, short for miniature beryllia circuits, has been developed. It uses a common BeO substrate as the basic carrier for the devices and for all circuit components realized in either distributed or lumped form. Ground septums are provided wherever the circuit topology requires low inductance ground returns. The devices are flip-chip mounted on the BeO substrate which simultaneously provides very good heat conduction and low parasitic interconnections with the rf circuit. Since the thermal expansion coefficient of BeO and GaAs are nearly equal, the mounting of the devices can be achieved with very low thermal stresses.

Fig. 1 shows the principal implementation of the MBC technology for a two-stage power amplifier. Each stage has a ground septum that is the mounting base for the source contacts of the FET. In comparison with a hybrid technique, the elimination of wire bonds for interconnecting the devices with the circuit results in greatly improved reproducibility and a much lower assembly labor content. Mixed lumped and distributed circuits are used for input, interstage, and output matching. The substrate, containing two septums, is fabricated from three sandwiched BeO wafers, the center one having a thickness equal to the desired spacing of the ground septums. The BeO wafers are metallized with Cr-Cu and then thermocompression bonded at high temperature and pressure. After slicing and polishing, individual substrates, with thicknesses ranging typically from 10 to 50 mil, are available for circuit processing.

Since the surface quality of polished BeO is not suitable for the fabrication of thin-film capacitors, the BeO substrate is selectively

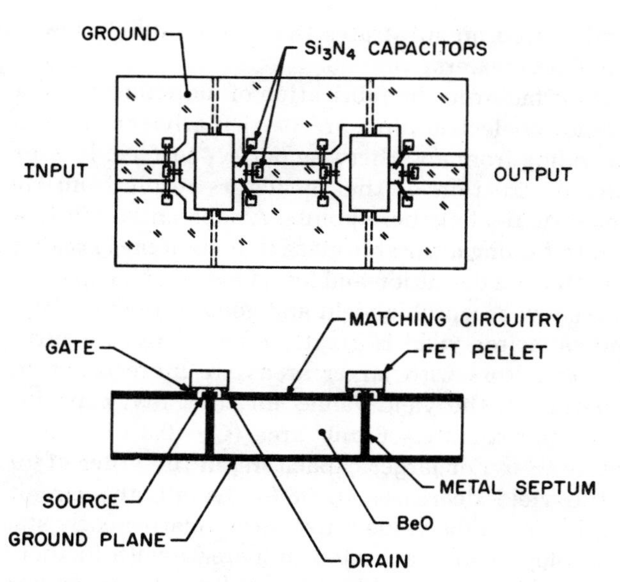

Fig. 1—Schematic drawing of two-stage MBC amplifier.

glazed to provide the necessary smooth, high-quality surface finish. Fig. 2 shows the individual layers of the MBC structure that is being used for high power amplifier applications. The thin-film base conductor forms the ground contacts, the bottom electrodes of the capacitors, and the first level of interconnections. A thin film of sputtered silicon nitride is the dielectric for the capacitors. Another metal layer forms the second layer of interconnections and the top electrodes of the capacitors. As a last step, air bridges are formed on top of the capacitors to provide a third level of interconnections. Air bridges are more reliable and reproducible than wirebonds and are thus expected to contribute to a low cost, reproducible circuit fabrication. The circuits

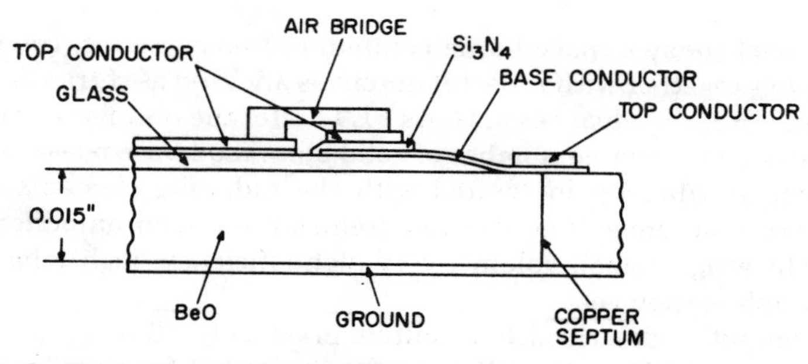

Fig. 2—Cross section of layered MBC structure.

are batch fabricated on substrates that are relatively low-cost when compared to GaAs wafers.

An important factor in the fabrication of matching circuits is a high capacitor yield. Dielectric films are particularly sensitive to isolated defects protruding from an otherwise perfect surface. Low breakdown voltages and destruction of the capacitors result from the greatly increased electric field at these points. A substantial effort was therefore devoted to finding a suitable glaze that combines excellent surface properties with good definition and low rf loss. Si_3N_4 capacitors formed on this glaze show acceptable yield and good reproducibility.

Since the capacitor yield is greatly affected by the surface defect population, capacitors with larger areas are more prone to failures. This is apparent in the yield values for the Si_3N_4 capacitors. Small capacitors of approximately 6 mil^2 area (C = 0.3 pF) show yields of approximately 98%. For larger capacitors, in the order of 100 mil^2 (C = 5 pF), the yield decreases to 96%. Overall, the circuit yield is approximately 85%. This value reflects the relative early stage of this process technology and is expected to increase with further improvements in the glaze's surface quality and in the Si_3N_4 deposition process.

Experimental Results

The new miniature BeO circuit technology was applied to the fabrication of two types of microwave power amplifiers, a medium power, very high efficiency amplifier at X-band for satellite applications and a high-power Ku-band amplifier module for light-weight radar applications. That the examples given here were designed to operate at the high end of the microwave frequency range is a result only of momentary program needs. The technology is suited for a wide range of frequencies and actually becomes more advantageous at S- and L-band where size and volume savings would be even more pronounced.

X-band High Efficiency Amplifier

For most of today's space borne communications systems, travelling wave tubes together with reflector antennas are used as rf transmitters to ground. Recent advances in GaAs FETs offer the promise to replace this system with a large number of solid-state moderate power amplifiers that are directly integrated with the radiating elements of an active array antenna. The key requirements for such amplifiers are very light weight/small volume, very high efficiency, high reliability, and low fabrication cost.

The amplifier described here fulfills practically all of these objectives; it is a 12-GHz, 150-mW amplifier optimized for very high efficiency operation and using the MBC technology, which results in very small size, good reproducibility, and the potential for large-volume batch fabrication. Fig. 3 shows a closeup of a single amplifier stage. The FET pellet, a 0.5 W MSC 88202 device, is mounted at the center of the H-shaped metal pattern grounded through the septum. The input and output tuning circuits are formed by short inductive lines, arranged in pairs, and by silicon nitride capacitors, connected to ground. These capacitors are connected to the circuit by means of short bond wires that eventually will be replaced by airbridge interconnections. By the selection of different capacitors, the center of the operating band can be tuned over approximately 1 GHz.

The amplifier was initially tuned for maximum gain based on small signal S-parameter measurements. A gain of 8.5 dB was obtained in this way at 12.4 GHz. To increase the available power output, both input and output matching networks had to be readjusted. Use of different size thin-film capacitors together with different bond wire lengths were used to change the transformation ratio between device and feedlines. The efficiency was optimized under the retuned condi-

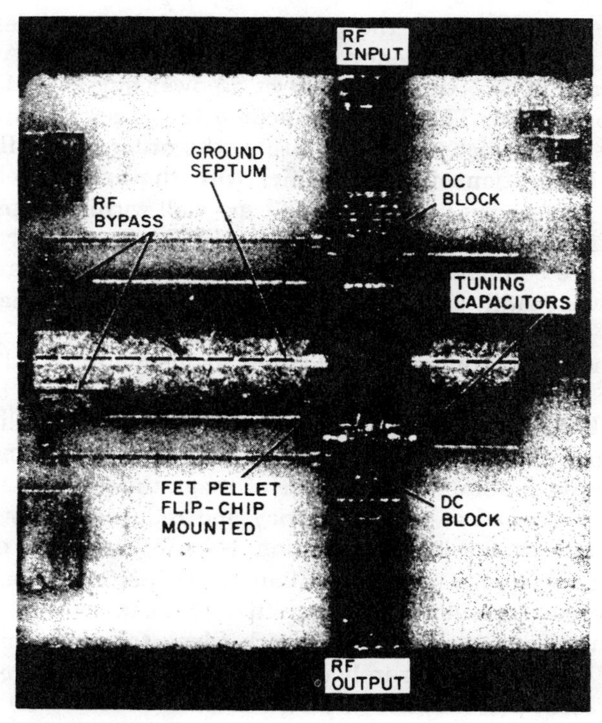

Fig. 3—12-GHz amplifier.

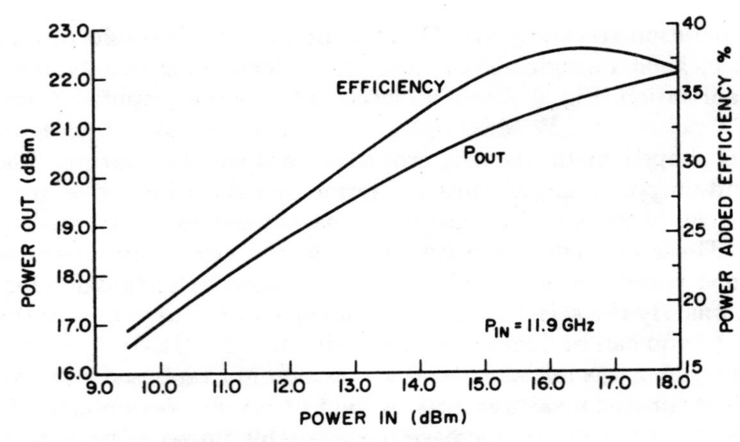

Fig. 4—Power performance of 12-GHz amplifier.

tions by varying the device bias voltages at various rf drive levels. To simplify the optimization procedure, extensive use was made of a computer aided efficiency optimization setup together with load-pull measurements. Fig. 4 shows the performance of the amplifier when adjusted for maximum efficiency at moderate power level. A power added efficiency of 38% was measured at a power output of 135 mW and a gain of 5.0 dB. These values include the losses of input and output connectors which at 12 GHz are in the order of 0.2 dB each. With direct integration of the amplifier with the antenna element, power added efficiencies in excess of 40% are well within the practical range using commercially available GaAs FETs in chip form. The MSC pellets are equipped with bumps on all three contacts and thus lend themselves readily to direct thermocompression mounting on the BeO carrier.

Because the FET is operated well below its maximum rated output and the heat sinking of the device is excellent, the operating temperature is very low and very long life expectancy is obtained. Preliminary data based on previous test results by MSC and temperature measurements on the device indicate an order of magnitude increase of the MTBF when operated at high efficiency and reduced power output compared to normal full-power operation. No effort has been devoted so far to optimizing the amplifier's bandwidth performance. Fig. 5 shows the measured results for the amplifier with a four-element input and two-element output matching network. Since, for communications applications, the bandwidth rarely exceeds 500 MHz in this frequency range, the present performance (1 dB bandwidth of 600 MHz) is close to being satisfactory.

Ku-band Power Amplifier

Another amplifier presently under development that uses the new beryllia based circuit technology is aimed at providing 1 W of power output over the frequency range from 16.0 to 16.5 GHz. This circuit, still in an early experimental stage, is more difficult to implement because the required device performance is at the limit of the state-of-the-art, and circuit losses and parasitics become more dominant at higher frequencies. Special efforts have thus been devoted to analyzing circuit losses and determining ways to achieve proper power sharing between multiple cells of the high power FET. Two types of devices are being considered for this amplifier: one is an RCA 16-gate, 4-cell FET with a nominal gate length of 1 μm, the other is the MSC 88204. Both devices have gate widths of approximately 2400 μm, have similar impedance levels, and are equipped with bumps for flip-chip mounting.

A photograph of a batch-processed strip of four circuits is shown in Fig. 6. The substrates are selectively glazed in the areas dedicated to thin-film matching circuits. The two center circuits have GaAs FET pellets mounted on the BeO in the unglazed section above the ground septum. The present size of a single amplifier circuit is 0.200 × 0.200 inches. Even though the circuit includes bias lines and dc bypass capacitors, it could be reduced further in size to approximately 1/8 × 1/8 inches without difficulty.

Fig. 7 shows a closeup of the Ku-band amplifier. Since the FET pellet is relatively large in transverse direction, proper sharing between individual cells presents a major problem. For instance, the lines of current circulating through the outer cells of the FET pellet enclose a

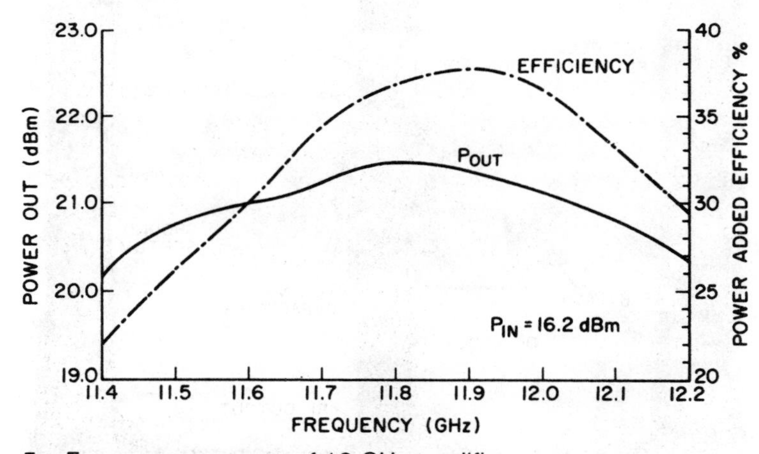

Fig. 5—Frequency response of 12-GHz amplifier.

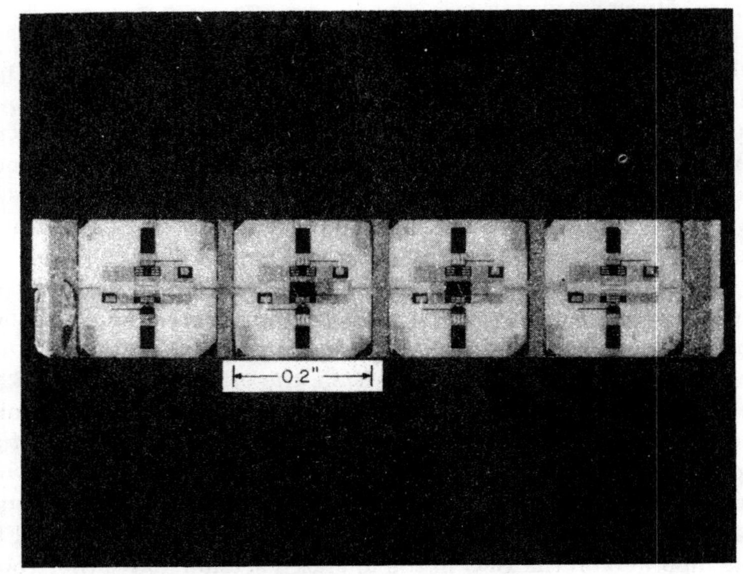

Fig. 6—Batch-fabricated strip of amplifiers.

smaller area than the lines circulating through the center cells. Therefore, the former have a lower associated inductance which results in detuning and an uneven impedance transformation. This effect has been counteracted by "necking down" the feedlines to the gate and

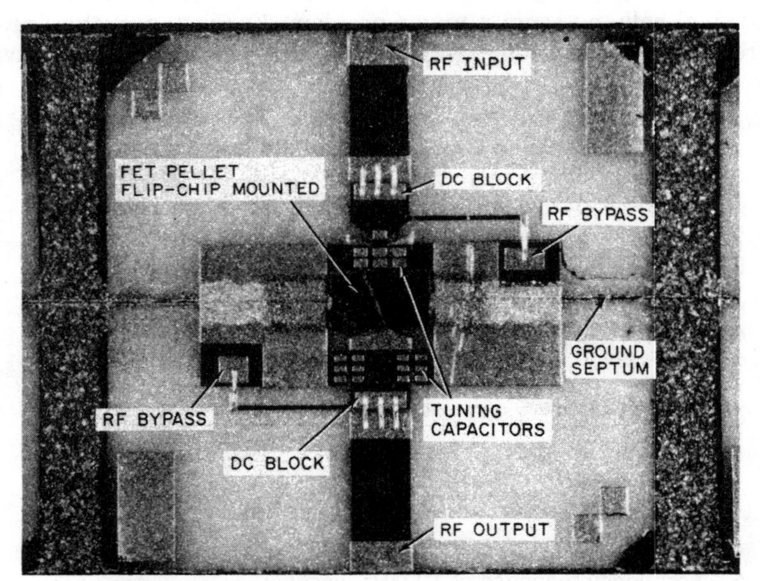

Fig. 7—16-GHz power amplifier.

collector contact pads in the area where the shunt capacitors are attached to ground. The tuning patterns for both the input and output matching are arranged in planar fashion on top of the BeO. The high reactive currents associated with the necessary large transformation ratios for power FETs thus remain on top and do not circulate through the ground septum. This reduces the normally existing negative feedback through the inductance of the septum and improves the gain. Also the tuning patterns are made symmetrical by using a shunt tuning capacitor on either side of the input and output lines.

The losses of the tuning circuits were determined using both a reflection and a transmission measurement technique. First, the reflection coefficient of a shorted tuning circuit was measured with the FET replaced by 5 short bond wires connected in parallel. A circuit computer model, which includes lossy elements, was then optimized to match the measured reflection coefficient under shorted-load conditions. Thus, the overall loss computed with this method under nominal loading conditions includes the ohmic losses in the inductors, in the capacitors, and in the septum. It also includes radiation losses that are present because of the large standing waves set up by the shorted load. Since radiation losses will be lower under normal operating conditions, this method indicates a total loss that exceeds the true value.

The other technique consisted of measuring the insertion loss of two identical circuits connected back to back. The loss of each circuit is simply one-half of the insertion loss of the combined structure. An attractive feature of this technique is that the circuits operate under nominal load conditions; thus radiation losses are representative of normal operation. Ohmic losses in the septum, however, are not included in this configuration since the septum is bypassed by the connection between the two circuits. Therefore the transmission method will indicate a loss lower than the true value.

A summary of the test results obtained at 16 GHz is shown in Table 1. The transmission and the reflection losses are listed for the input circuit, the output circuit, and for a low-loss control circuit designed for the same impedance transformation as the input circuit and built with a high-Q rutile capacitor and with inductive bond wires. The estimated true loss of the circuits is the average of the losses measured with transmission and the reflection methods.

Table 1—Comparison of Losses in Different Matching Circuits

	Loss (dB)		
Circuit	Trans.	Refl.	Estimated
Input	0.62	0.88	0.75
Output	0.40	0.45	0.42
Rutile Input	0.46	0.53	0.50

The input circuit, which is designed for a 50-to-1 impedance transformation ratio, shows a loss of 0.75 dB, a value 0.25 dB higher than the control. The estimated loss of the output circuit, designed for a 20-to-1 impedance transformation ratio, is 0.42 dB. These values of loss seem acceptable for the high transformation ratios, although an improvement of 0.2–0.3 dB should still be achievable with process improvements.

Conclusions

The new miniature BeO circuits technology offers excellent electrical and thermal properties for power amplifier applications, the possibility for batch processing of circuits separate from devices, and a very small circuit size that approaches that of the monolithic counterparts. The process is highly flexible which makes it suitable for small-to-moderate quantities at frequencies ranging from UHF to Ku-band. The fabrication and assembly processes involved are in principle well reproducible and hold great promise to become a low-cost production technology.

Initial experimental results illustrate the basic viability of this approach. A 12-GHz amplifier using commercially available FET pellets has shown a power output of 135 mW with a power-added efficiency of 38% and 5.0 dB of gain. The circuit portion for a 1-W, 16-GHz amplifier was developed and the high transformation ratio matching circuits showed reasonably low loss. Good yields have been demonstrated for lumped-element capacitances on glazed BeO.

Further work will be required in the flip-chip attachment of GaAs power FETs, which includes reshaping of the contact pads for best thermal conduction, ease of assembly, and high mounting strength.

Acknowledgment

The authors wish to acknowledge the contributions of G. Rolland, P. Jozwiak, and K. Lev in the fabrication and processing of the circuits, of P. Czajkowski, J. Brown, R. Marx, and J. Goldweber in the assembly and the rf measurement of the amplifiers, and of G. Filipsson (on leave from the National Research Insititute, Linköping, Sweden) for computer simulations of the microwave circuits.

References:

[1] J. Fawcette, "Competition Intensifies in Monolithic Gallium Arsenide," *Microwave System News*, p. 35, April 1979.

[2] R. Van Tuyl, "A Monolithic GaAs IC for Heterodyne Generation of RF Signals," *IEEE Trans.*, **ED 28**, p. 166, Feb. 1981.

[3] R. S. Pengelly, "GaAs Monolithic Microwave Circuits for Phased-Array Applications," *IEE Proc.*, **127**, pt.F, p. 301, Aug. 1980.

[4] P. Harrop, P. Lesartre, and A. Collet, "GaAs Integrated all FET Front-End at 12 GHz," *GaAs IC Symposium*, paper #28, Nov. 1980.

[5] E. Belohoubek, A. Presser, and H. Veloric, "Improved Circuit-Device Interface for Microwave Bipolar Power Transistors," *IEEE Trans.*, **SC-11**, p. 256, April 1976.

[6] J. M. Schellenberg and H. Yamasaki, "A New Approach to FET Power Amplifiers," *Microwave* J, p. 51, March 1982.

A 2–18-GHz Monolithic Distributed Amplifier Using Dual-Gate GaAs FET's

WAYNE KENNAN, THOMAS ANDRADE, MEMBER, IEEE, AND CHARLES C. HUANG, MEMBER, IEEE

Abstract—**This paper describes a 2–18-GHz monolithic distributed amplifier with over 6-dB gain, ±0.5-dB gain flatness, and less than 2.0:1 VSWR. Measured noise figure is below 7.5 dB, and power output capability is greater than 17 dBm. The amplifier is designed with dual-gate GaAs FET's instead of single-gate FET's for maximum gain over the design bandwidth. Cascaded amplifier performance will also be presented.**

I. Introduction

In the past several years, distributed amplification [1] has enjoyed a renaissance due to the GaAs FET [2]–[4]. Applied originally to electron tubes, this amplification technique has the unique capability of adding device transconductance without adding device parasitic capacitance. This is accomplished by linking the parasitic shunt capacitance of the devices with series inductors to form an artificial low-pass transmission line. By terminating these links with resistive loads, the unwanted signals are dissipated while the desired signals are added in-phase at the output of the amplifier. The result is unprecedented gain-bandwidth product with flat gain and low VSWR. The structure is shown in Fig. 1.

II. Circuit Design

The topology of the 2–18-GHz distributed amplifier is shown in Fig. 2, and a SEM photograph appears in Fig. 3. In this design, there are essentially three features which distinguish it from previous distributed amplifiers. First and most important, the design uses dual-gate GaAs FET's in place of the more traditional single-gate devices. The contribution of dual-gate FET's to distributed amplification is equivalent to that of cascode-connected single-gate devices [5]. The dual-gate FET, which is in fact modeled as a cascode connection of single-gate FET's, has an input impedance comparable to single-gate devices but much higher isolation and output impedance. This is evident from the equivalent circuit models shown in Fig. 4, which were derived from measured S-parameters. (Note that the models include a common inductance of 0.04 nH to account for ground path inductance in the monolithic chip.) High reverse isolation in the device is necessary for high amplifier isolation and often extends the amplifier's bandwidth. High device output impedance, on the other hand, improves gain flatness and output VSWR, and increases gain. This is because the single-gate FET's output resistance is relatively low (250 Ω for a 250-μm device) and a significant load on the drain transmission line.

At low frequencies where the output resistances of the devices are virtually in parallel, a four-section design would result in a 62.5-Ω resistive load on the 50-Ω impedance transmission line. This problem is completely eliminated with the dual-gate (or cascode-connected) device.

The second feature of this design is the distribution of total gate width among the individual devices. In order to achieve a minimum gain of 7 dB with devices scaled from the model of Fig. 4 and 8-μm cm-wide transmission lines,

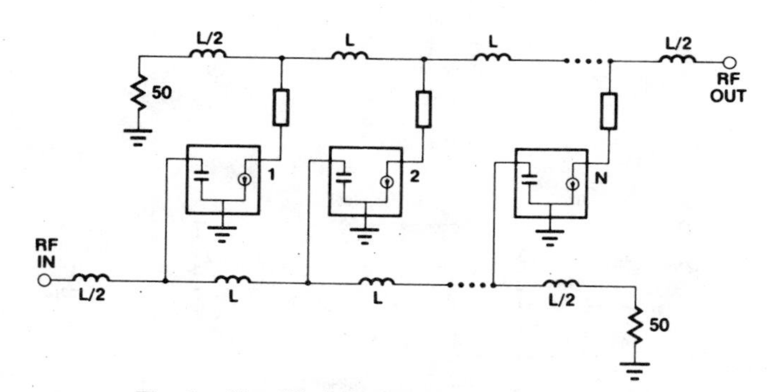

Fig. 1. Simplified distributed amplifier structure.

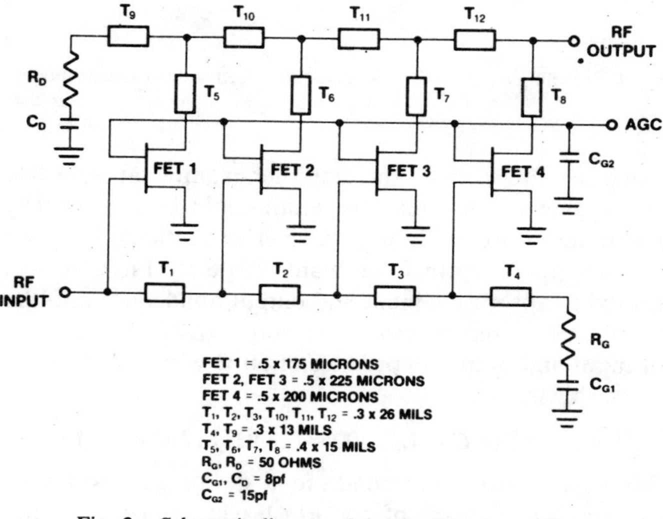

Fig. 2. Schematic diagram of the distributed amplifier.

Manuscript received May 3, 1984. This work was supported in part by the Office of Naval Research under Contract N00014-81-C-0101.

The authors are with Avantek, Inc., Santa Clara, CA 95951.

Fig. 3. SEM micrograph of the distributed amplifier.

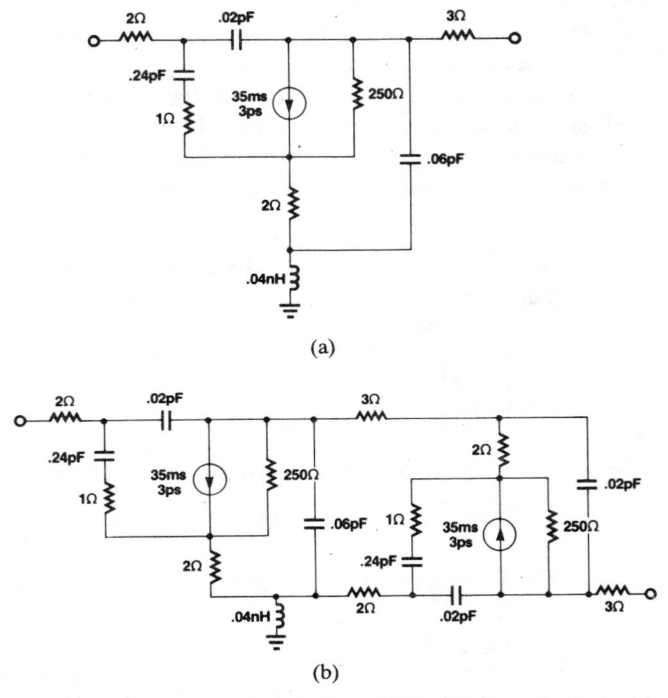

Fig. 4. (a) Single-gate and (b) dual-gate FET equivalent circuit models (250 μm).

which are fairly lossy, the amplifier requires at least 800 μm of gate width. This gate width could be theoretically partitioned into nearly any number of sections, but four sections prove optimal in many respects. First, it was desired to absorb the input and output bond wires into the distributed amplifiers input and output $L/2$ sections. For an input and output impedance of 50 Ω with 0.3-nH bond wires, this means

$$\sqrt{L/C} = 50 \text{ or } C = L/2500 = 0.3 \text{ nH}/1250 = 0.24 \text{ pF}.$$

This capacitance corresponds to a device gate width of 250 μm, but a choice of 200 μm leaves margin for error and the shunt capacitance of the high impedance transmis-

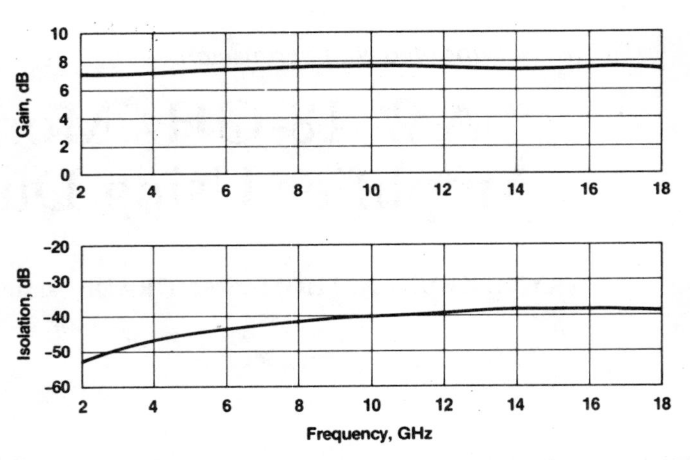

Fig. 5. Predicted gain and isolation of the dual-gate FET distributed amplifier.

sion lines. Secondly, the four-section design offers a good compromise in gain flatness, VSWR, and noise figure over other 800-μm designs. This was determined by simulating the alternatives with a microwave analysis program. The four-section design is also more area efficient than its alternatives and results in a nearly square chip for ease of handling. As a final touch, the four individual device gate widths were optimized for VSWR and gain flatness. As shown in Fig. 2, the first and last sections are smaller than the two internal devices. This is primarily to absorb the parasitic capacitance of the input and output bonding pads.

The third feature of the design is its small area. At 0.75 mm × 0.85 mm the chip area is 0.64 mm², which yields a potential of over 2500 amplifiers per 2-in-diam wafer. This is chiefly a result of the single-turn inductors and wraparound ground. The single-turn inductor is modeled with lengths of coupled transmission line to account for coupling between the two major lengths and coupling to the FET sources (ground). If these inductors were laid out in a straight line rather than coiled one turn, the chip height would be unchanged at 0.75 mm but its length would be increased by 1.5 mm to 2.35 mm. The resulting layout would occupy nearly three times the area of the present one. The wraparound ground is also helpful in reducing chip area since the perimeter of the chip is normally not used. Via-hole grounds, on the other hand, require prime chip area and may be significant in size.

The amplifier contains three capacitors which are used for RF bypass to ground. CG1 and CD are used to bypass the input and output terminating resistors, respectively, so that dc power is not dissipated in these elements. The third capacitor, CG2, is used to bypass the second gates of the dual-gate FET's. This provides isolation from external dc circuitry and insures that the dual-gate FET operates as a cascode circuit. The FET sources are all grounded, thus requiring two bias voltages—one positive for the drain and one negative for the gate.

The simulated gain and isolation of the dual-gate distributed amplifier are shown in Fig. 5. From 2–18-GHz, the predicted gain is 7.25 ± 0.22 dB with greater than 35-dB isolation. Predicted return loss is shown in Fig. 6 and is

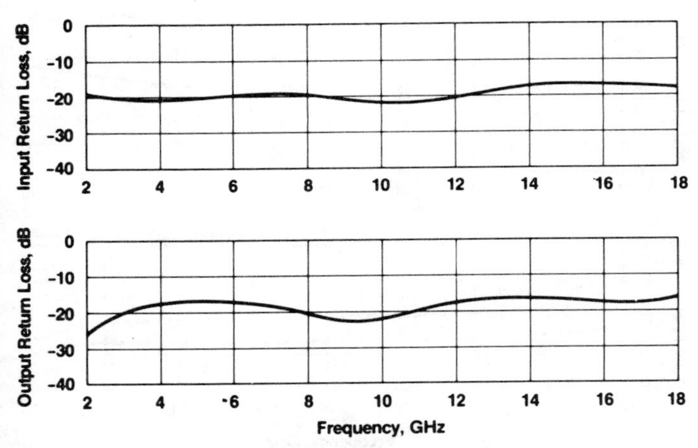

Fig. 6. Predicted input and output return loss of the dual-gate FET distributed amplifier.

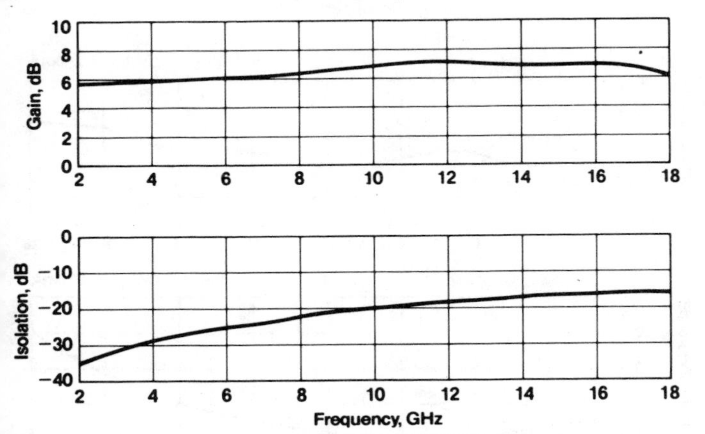

Fig. 7. Predicted gain and isolation of the single-gate FET distributed amplifier.

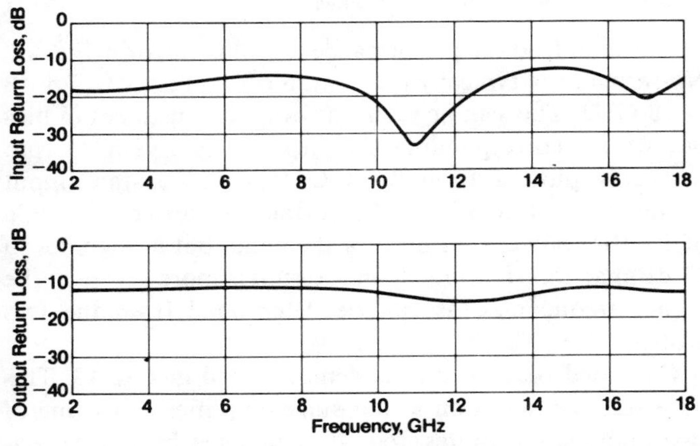

Fig. 8. Predicted input and output return loss of the single-gate FET distributed amplifier.

greater than 14 dB (1.5:1 VSWR) at both the input and output. Figs. 7 and 8 show the predicted performance of the same amplifier when the dual-gate FET models are replaced with the single-gate FET model from Fig. 4. It is clear that gain, gain flatness, isolation, output VSWR, and bandwidth are all degraded as expected. Noise figure, however, is lower in the single-gate design as shown in Fig. 9.

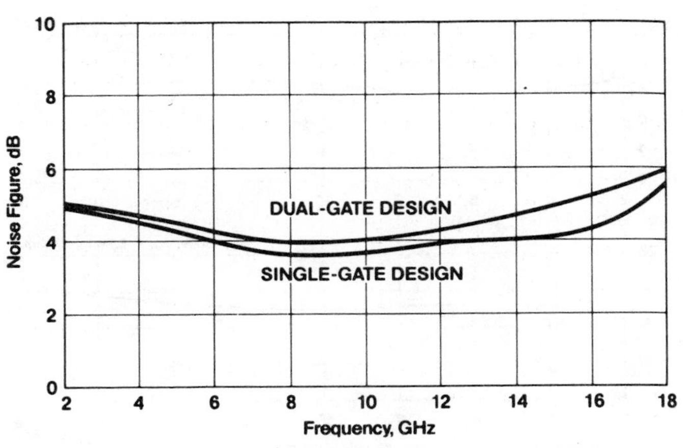

Fig. 9. Predicted noise figure of single-gate FET and dual-gate FET distributed amplifiers.

III. Circuit Fabrication

Ion-implanted GaAs is used as the starting material for the IC's due to its excellent uniformity and controllability. After implantation, the wafers are annealed at 800 °C until the active layer sheet resistance drops to approximately 500 Ω/square. This layer is then selectively etched to form mesas for the FET's and resistors. Later, the resistor mesas are trimmed to 800 Ω/square with a process that is controllable to a standard deviation of 15 percent.

The FET's in the IC are fabricated with the same process used for discrete FET's. The gates are formed on a nominally 0.5-μm-long base of TiW/Au, which is gold-plated to 0.7 μm. The resulting structure achieves very short gate length with large gate cross-sectional area for high device transconductance with low parasitic capacitance and resistance [6]. Source and drain ohmic contacts are formed with a AuGe/Ni/Au alloy.

Parallel-plate dielectric capacitors and surface passivation are provided by a thin layer of plasma-enhanced CVD silicon nitride. This process achieves a capacitance density of 390 pF/mm^2 with a standard deviation of less than 40 pF/mm^2.

Metallic interconnections are achieved with a two-level wiring process which provides surface connections, crossovers, and air bridges. The top level is situated 3 μm above the GaAs surface and is gold-plated to 1.5 μm. The bottom level rests directly on the semi-insulating substrate and is 0.8 μm thick. For additional thickness, the top level is deposited directly on the bottom level to achieve a thickness of 2.3 μm. These lines are designed for a dc current density not to exceed 5×10^5 amps/cm^2.

Wraparound ground technology is chosen over via-hole ground technology for low parasitic inductance and improved area efficiency. To form the wraparound ground, metal is first deposited and gold-plated to 2 μm on the frontside of the chips. The wafer is then lapped to 115 μm and backside metallized to complete the wraparound ground connection.

IV. Circuit Performance

Before backside-lapping and die-separation, the GaAs wafer is stepped and dc-probed for saturated current,

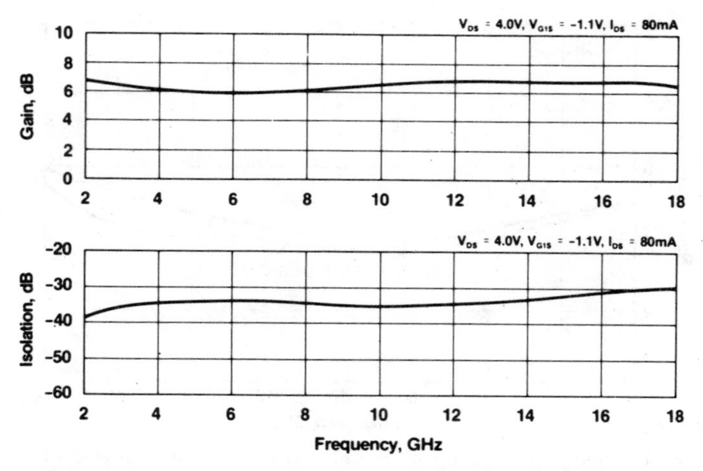

Fig. 10. Measured gain and isolation of the distributed amplifier.

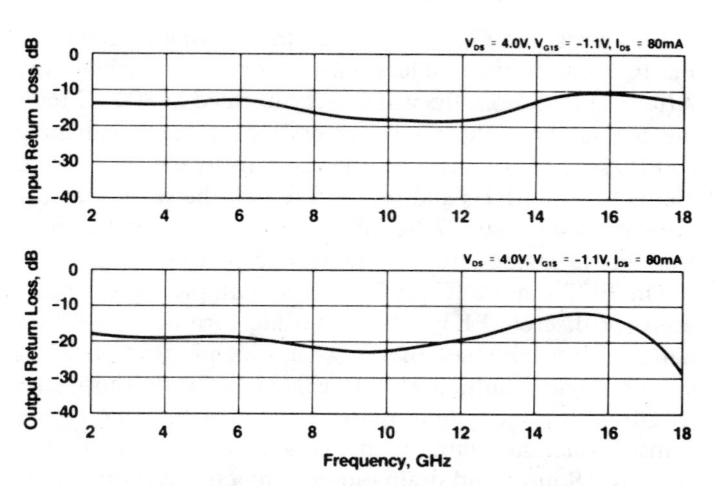

Fig. 11. Measured input and output return loss of the distributed amplifier.

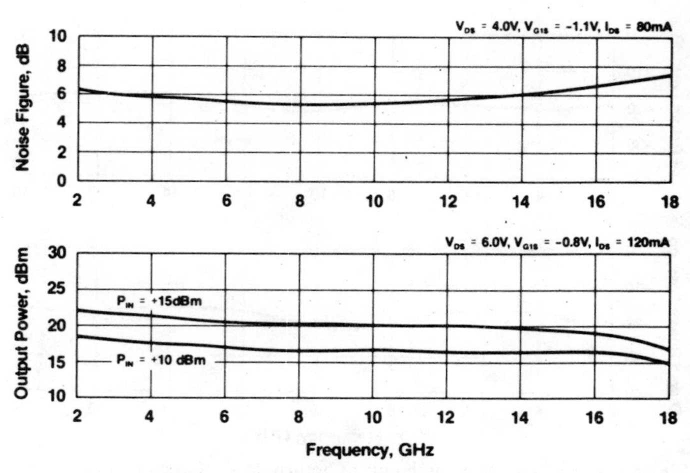

Fig. 12. Measured noise figure and output power of the distributed amplifier.

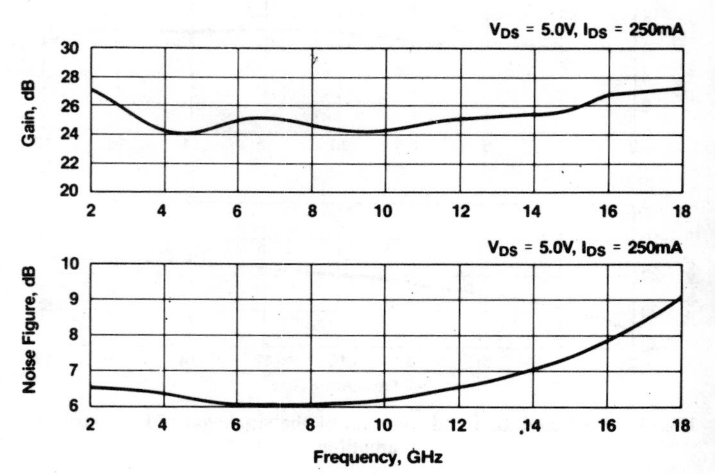

Fig. 13. Measured gain and noise figure of a four-stage distributed amplifier.

pinchoff voltage, and transconductance. Devices which are open-circuited, short-circuited, or otherwise fail the dc test are identified with an ink spot and later discarded. Data on passed devices is presented in summary form and may also be formatted into histograms for statistical analysis. The chips are then separated, visually inspected, and prepared for assembly into packages and thin-film hybrid circuits.

For RF evaluation, the amplifiers are mounted on 15-mil-thick alumina substrates. The substrate includes 50-Ω transmission lines, bias resistors, and plated through slots for ground. The data reported in this paper was measured on IC's mounted on the substrate with input and output bonding wires and no tuning. Bias was injected through external bias tee's.

Fig. 10 shows gain and isolation measured on a typical amplifier fabricated within process specifications. The gain is 6.3 dB ± 0.5 dB with greater than 25-dB isolation. Fig. 11 shows input and output return loss for the same chip. The worst case VSWR is 2.0 : 1 although it is less than 1.5 over most of the band. The device is biased at 4.0-V VDS, 80-mA IDS, which is half the saturated current level. Higher gain may be achieved with increased drain current, but gain flatness degrades slightly.

Noise and power performance are illustrated in Fig. 12. Noise figure is typically less than 6 dB and rises to 7.5 dB at 18 GHz. This can be reduced with an adjustment in bias but with a corresponding loss in associated gain. Output power is plotted from 2–18 GHz with constant input power levels of 10 dBm and 15 dBm. The device is capable of 20-dBm power over most of the band, but it degrades to 17 dBm at 18 GHz. Gain compression is more severe at the higher frequencies, as can be determined from the two plots.

Cascaded performance is demonstrated in Fig. 13. This data was measured on a four-stage amplifier consisting of two alumina substrates, four IC's, and ten bypass capacitors. The amplifier includes bias circuitry and measures only 5.1 mm × 12.7 mm × 0.38 mm (Fig. 14). This assembly shows that, even without integrating the blocking capacitors and bias circuitry on chip, a linear gain density of 50 dB per inch is easily achieved over the full 2–18-GHz band. With more compact hybrid layouts, this number could easily double.

The last figure (Fig. 15) illustrates a number of possible applications for the IC. As an AGC amplifier, gain variation is very flat over the full 2–18-GHz range when gate 2

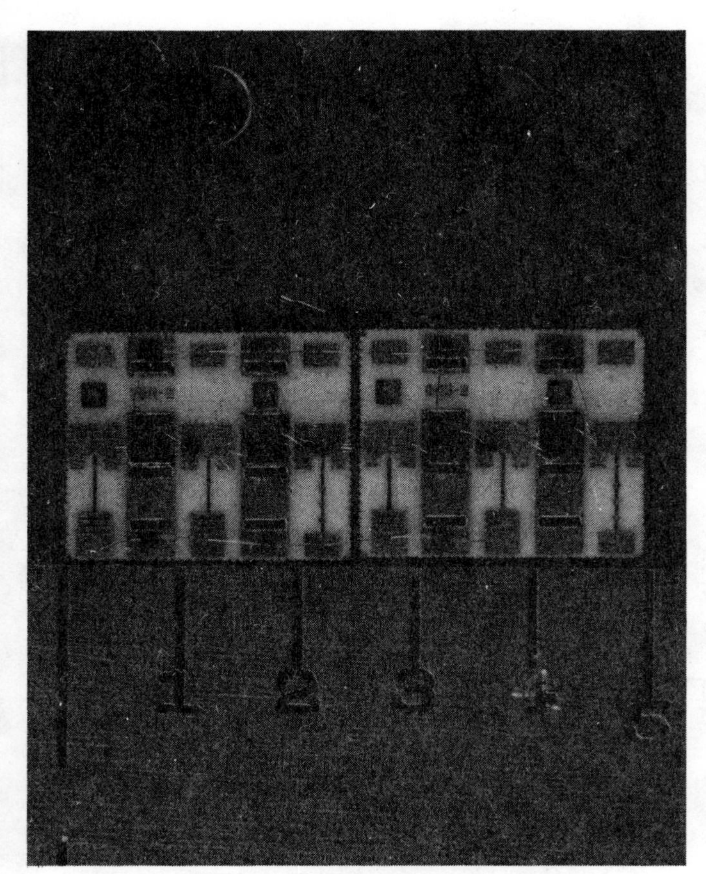

Fig. 14. Photograph of four-stage distributed amplifier.

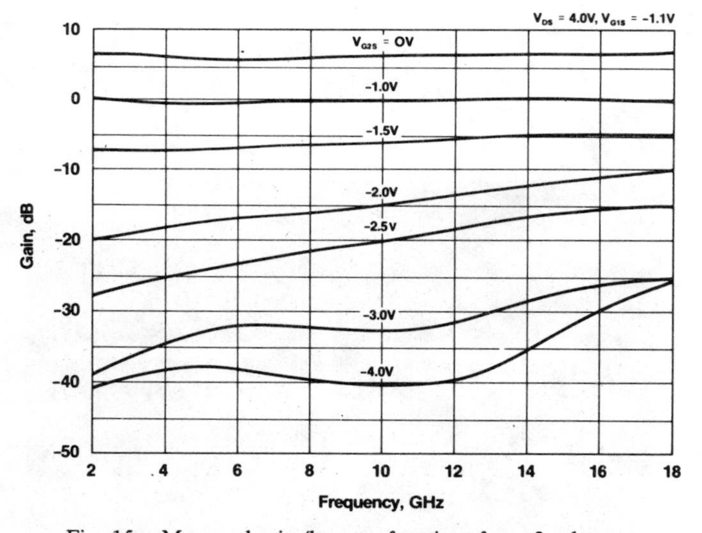

Fig. 15. Measured gain/loss as a function of gate 2 voltage.

voltage is varied between 0 V and −1 V. When the gate 2 voltage is made more negative, the amplifier becomes lossy and may be used as a limiter. Finally, when the voltage is increased to −4 V, the drain current drops to nearly zero and the amplifier provides over 25-dB isolation. This property could be used in switching applications since VSWR and reverse isolation remain less than 2:1 and greater than 25 dB, respectively, under all bias conditions.

V. Conclusion

A 2–18-GHz monolithic GaAs distributed amplifier with over 6-dB gain has been described. Dual-gate FET distributed amplifiers were compared to single-gate FET distributed amplifiers and were shown to provide more gain with better flatness, VSWR, and bandwidth. This is demonstrated in a four-stage amplifier which achieved 25.5-dB ± 1.5 dB gain from 2–18 GHz. The dual-gate FET distributed amplifier may also be used for many control functions by adjusting the gate 2 voltage.

References

[1] E. L. Ginzton, W. R. Hewlett, J. H. Jasburg, and J. D. Noe, "Distributed amplification," *Proc. IRE*, vol. 36, pp. 956–969, 1948.

[2] E. W. Strid and K. R. Gleason, "A dc-12 GHz monolithic GaAs FET distributed amplifier," *IEEE Trans. Microwave Theory Tech.*, vol. MTT-30, pp. 969–975, July 1982.

[3] Y. A. Ayasli, L. D. Reynolds, J. L. Vorhaus, and L. Hanes, "Monolithic 2–20 GHz GaAs traveling-wave amplifier," *Electron. Lett*, vol. 18, pp. 596–598, July 1982.

[4] K. B. Niclas, W. T. Wilser, T. R. Kritzer, and R. R. Pereira, "On theory and performance of solid-state microwave distributed amplifiers," *IEEE Trans. Microwave Theory Tech.*, vol. MTT-31, pp. 447–456, June 1983.

[5] D. E. Dawson, M. J. Salib, and L. E. Dickens, "Distributed cascode amplifier and noise figure modeling of an arbitrary amplifier configuration," in *1984 IEEE Int. Solid-State Circuits Conf. Dig.*, pp. 78–79.

[6] C. Huang, A. Herbig, and R. Anderson, "Sub-half micron GaAs FETs for applications through *K*-band," *IEEE 1981 Microwave Symp. Dig.*, pp. 25–27.

MONOLITHIC 2–20 GHz GaAs TRAVELLING-WAVE AMPLIFIER

Indexing terms: Semiconductor devices and materials, Amplifiers, Circuit design

A two-stage monolithic GaAs travelling-wave amplifier operating in the 2–20 GHz frequency range with 12 dB flat gain is reported.

Introduction and circuit description: A new approach to travelling-wave or distributed amplification which is more suitable for obtaining wideband gain at microwave frequencies has been reported previously.[1–3] In this approach GaAs FETs are used as the active elements. The amplifier is truly distributed, with the gate and drain lines being two microstrip transmission lines loaded periodically by GaAs FET cells.

In this letter we describe a two-stage travelling-wave amplifier which operates in the 2–20 GHz frequency range. The schematic circuit diagram for the amplifier and the description of the circuit components are shown in Fig. 1.

Experimental results: The circuit shown in Fig. 1 is realised on a single 2·2 × 5·5 × 0·1 mm chip. A finished chip is shown in Fig. 2. Total gate periphery is 4 × 150 μm per stage, with gate lengths varying in the 0·8 to 0·9 μm range. The design calls for 12 dB gain in the 2–20 GHz frequency range.

The experimental performance of the two-stage travelling-wave amplifier is shown in Figs. 3 and 4 for two different gate bias conditions.

The data shows small-signal gains in the 11 to 13 dB range. Input and output ports are matched with a return loss no worse than 7 dB and in general better than 10 dB across the band. Isolation of the input from the output is better than −50 dB at the low end and better than −30 dB at the high end of the frequency band.

Conclusion: The extreme wideband travelling-wave amplification possible with GaAs monolithic technology is demonstrated. A complete 2–20 GHz two-stage GaAs travelling-wave amplifier with 12 dB flat gain is realised on a single 2·2 × 5·5 × 0·1 mm chip. The initial experimental results are in excellent agreement with the theoretical predictions.

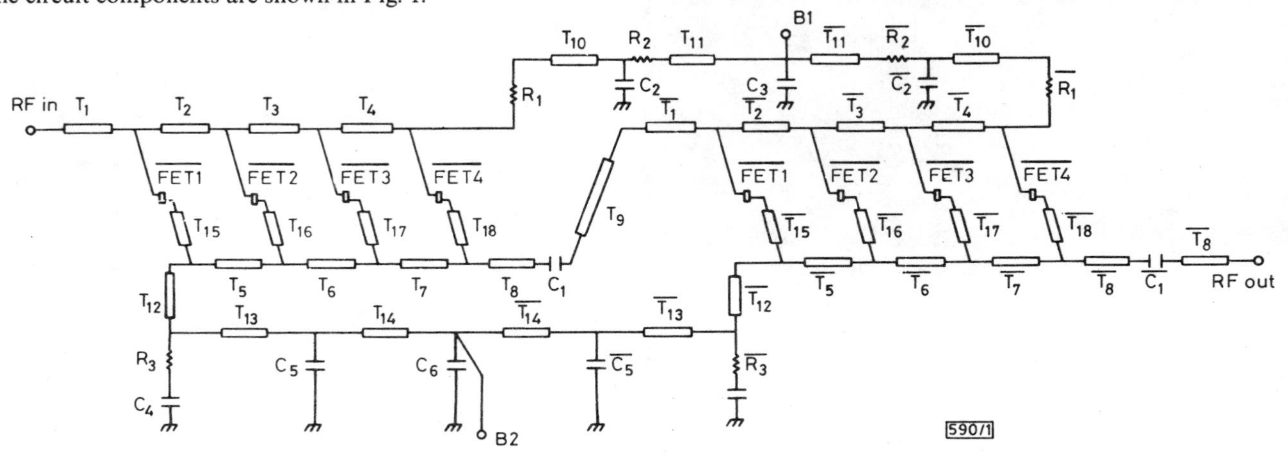

Fig. 1 *Schematic circuit design for a two-stage small-signal amplifier*

Components with a bar on top refer to the second stage

Description of circuit components:

T_1, T_8, T_9 = input and output matching transmission-line sections
T_2, T_3, T_4 = gate-line transmission-line sections
T_5, T_6, T_7 = drain-line transmission-line sections
T_{10}, T_{11} = transmission-line sections for gate-bias circuitry
T_{12}, T_{13}, T_{14} = transmission-line sections for drain-bias circuitry
T_{15}, T_{16}, T_{17}, T_{18} = RF matching transmission-line sections
C_1 = DC blocking capacitor
C_2, C_3 = gate-bias circuitry RF bypass capacitors
C_4, C_5, C_6 = drain-bias circuitry RF bypass capacitors
R_1, R_2 = gate-bias circuitry resistors
R_3 = drain-bias circuitry resistor
FET 1 to FET 4 = 150 μm gate periphery MESFETs
$B1$ = gate DC bias terminal
$B2$ = drain DC bias terminal

Each stage employs four 150 μm FETs. Because each section is well matched for the 50 Ω system, no complicated interstage matching circuitry is required. Full DC gate and drain bias circuitry is included in the design. Gate and drain bias circuits serve a second function of providing the optimum gate and drain line complex load impedances over the complete design band. Both stages are biased from the same gate and drain bias ports. DC blocking capacitors are included in series with the drain output RF lines to allow direct cascading of individual chips.

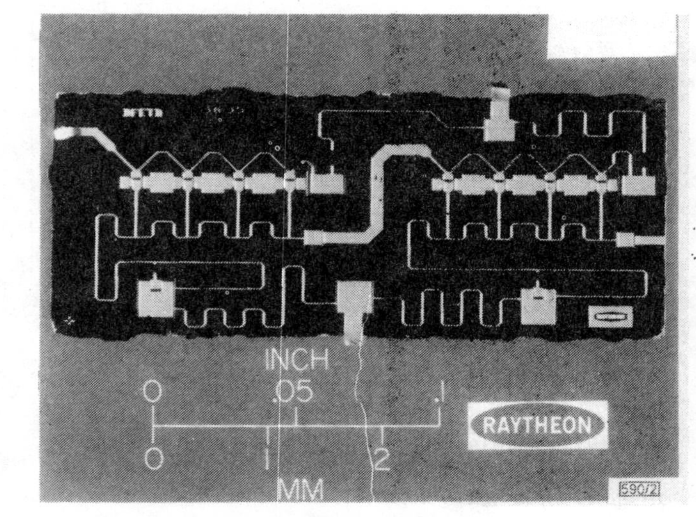

Fig. 2 *Two-stage travelling-wave amplifier chip*

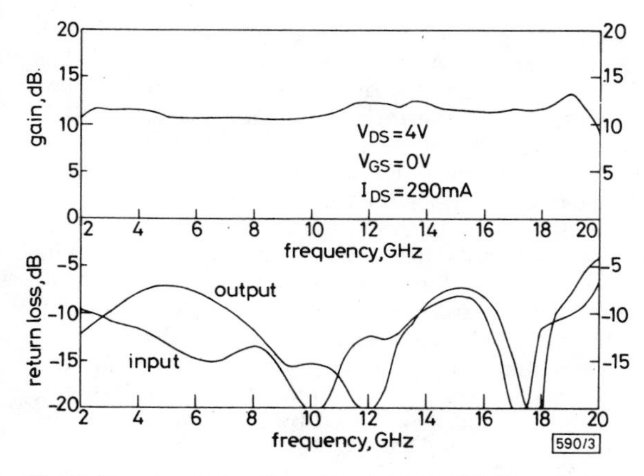

Fig. 3 *Experimental performance of a 2–20 GHz travelling-wave amplifier*

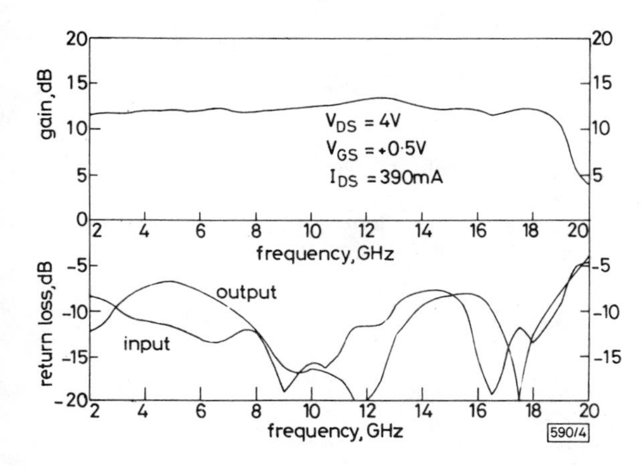

Fig. 4 *Experimental performance of a 2–20 GHz travelling-wave amplifier*

Acknowledgment: This work is sponsored by Air Force Wright Aeronautical Laboratories, Avionics Laboratory, Air Force Systems Command, United States Air Force, Wright-Patterson Air Force Base, Ohio 45433.

Y. AYASLI
L. D. REYNOLDS
J. L. VORHAUS
L. HANES

Raytheon Research Division
131 Spring Street
Lexington, MA 02173, USA

2nd June 1982

References

1 AYASLI, Y., VORHAUS, J. L., MOZZI, R. L., and REYNOLDS, L. D.: 'Monolithic GaAs travelling-wave amplifier', *Electron. Lett.*, 1981, **17**, pp. 413–414

2 AYASLI, Y.: 'Monolithic GaAs travelling-wave amplification at microwave frequencies'. Invited talk at 8th Biennial Conference on active microwave semiconductor devices and circuits, Cornell University, Ithaca, New York, 1981

3 AYASLI, Y., MOZZI, R. L., VORHAUS, J. L., REYNOLDS, L. D., and PUCEL, R. A.: 'A monolithic GaAs 1 to 13 GHz travelling-wave amplifier', *IEEE Trans.*, **MTT** and **ED** special issue, July 1982

ALUMINA MICROSTRIP GaAs F.E.T. 11 GHz OSCILLATOR

Indexing terms: Field-effect transistors, Microwave oscillators, Solid-state microwave circuits, Stripline components

A small, lightweight 11 GHz f.e.t. oscillator has been developed. An output power of 10 mW with an efficiency of 10% was easily produced using a GaAs f.e.t. designed for small-signal amplifier applications. Its low power consumption makes it a suitable low-noise source for integrated-receiver applications.

The high-gain low-noise properties of GaAs f.e.t.s at X band frequencies are well known. Less investigated[1, 2] are the device's oscillation characteristics. The initial results presented here confirm the promising features of the f.e.t. for oscillator applications. Fig. 1 shows the GaAs f.e.t. used.

The GAT 3 device has gate dimensions of $1 \times 120\ \mu m$ and is made by an electron-beam technique. In single-stage amplifiers, it realises over 7 dB of gain at frequencies around 11 GHz.[3] It has also been used in a multistage, tuned, microstrip amplifier to produce 42 dB of gain from 11·0 to 11·5 GHz.[4]

Fig. 2 shows the microstrip oscillator circuit, built on 0·6350 mm-thick alumina. In this circuit, the transistor is operated in

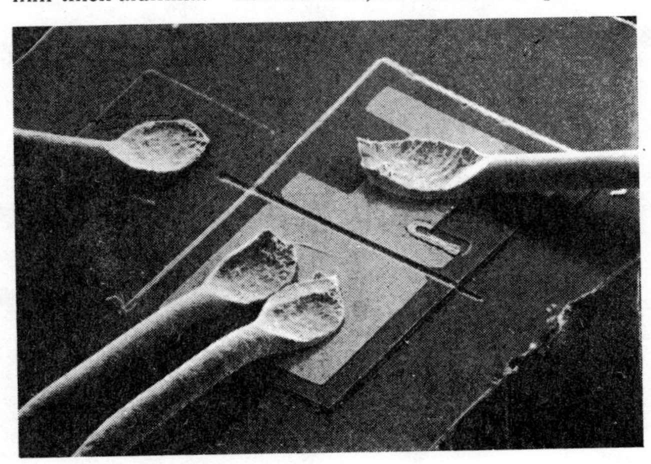

Fig. 1 *Bonded type GAT 3 f.e.t.*

the common-source configuration, with the source connected to the microstrip ground plane via a 11·43 mm length of 2·032 mm-wide 'wrap-around' metallisation. This structure resonates at 11·75 GHz, and, at the oscillation frequency of 11·125 GHz, presents an impedance of about $6-j26\ \Omega$ to the source. This reduces the Rollett stability factor K of

Fig. 2 *Microstrip 11 GHz-oscillator circuit*

the transistor to −0·2. When the gate is terminated by a short circuit, a stable oscillation is readily obtained. The high/low-impedance sections of the microstrip output line in Fig. 2 match the transistor's output impedance to 50 Ω. It is the wrap-around structure that gives this oscillator the high stability and low-noise performance that is more characteristic of coaxial than microstrip circuits.

With a drain voltage of 7·6 V, the drain current is 13 mA and the output power is 10 mW at 11·125 GHz, representing an efficiency of 10%. Since no attempt has been made to heatsink the device, this was the highest power produced, but the power and efficiency were still increasing with drain voltage at this point. Varying the drain voltage produced a remarkably smooth variation in output power. For instance, the output power could be adjusted by 23 dB by varying the drain voltage from 2·5 to 7·6 V.

These results were obtained with the gate terminated by a microstrip short circuit. With a coaxial short circuit, the spectral width of the oscillation was 30 kHz at a power level 20 dB down on the carrier. These results indicate that this small, light microstrip oscillator, with a power consumption of only 100 mW, could challenge Gunn and IMPATT sources as low-noise local oscillators at X band frequencies.

Acknowledgments: This work was part of a programme carried out in 1973 with the support of the Procurement Executive, UK Ministry of Defence, and the European Space Research Organisation. This letter is published by permission of the directors of the Plessey Company Ltd.

N. A. SLAYMAKER
J. A. TURNER

29th May 1975

Allen Clark Research Centre
The Plessey Company Ltd.
Caswell, Towcester, Northants., England

References

1 MAEDA, M., TAKAHASHI, S., and KODERA, H.: 'C.W. oscillation characteristics of GaAs Schottky-barrier gate field-effect transistors', *Proc. Inst. Elec. Electron. Eng.*, 1975, **62**, pp. 320–321

2 PUCEL, R. A., BERA, R., and MASSE, D.: 'An evaluation of GaAs FET oscillators and mixers for integrated front-end applications'. IEEE ISSCC, 1975, Paper WPM 7.1

3 SLAYMAKER, N. A., and TURNER, J. A.: 'Microwave FET amplifiers with centre frequencies between 1 and 11 GHz'. European Microwave Conference, 1973, Paper A.5.1

4 LUXTON, H. E. G.: 'GaAs FETs—their performance and applications up to X-band frequencies'. European Microwave Conference, 1974, Paper B.2.2

MIC IMPATT DIODE OSCILLATOR STABILISED BY TEMPERATURE COMPENSATED DIELECTRIC RESONATOR

Indexing terms: Impatt diodes, Microwave oscillators, Integrated circuits

Barium nonatitanate resonators offer simple microwave circuit designs for stabilised oscillators. An integrated circuit X-band impatt diode oscillator was designed and results are presented for both the stabilised and unstabilised oscillator. There was a considerable improvement in the stabilised oscillator spectrum and temperature sensitivity, e.g. the unstabilised oscillator had a line width of 0·5 MHz at 38 dB below the peak whereas the stabilised oscillator had a 0·5 MHz linewidth at 52 dB below the peak. The temperature sensitivity of the stabilised oscillator was ~40 kHz/°C over the range 0 to 60°C, which was about a third of that of the unstabilised oscillator.

Low loss barium nonatitanate resonators have been used at C, X and J bands to stabilise transistor and Gunn oscillators,[1–3] but no work has been reported on the stabilisation of impatt diode oscillators. This letter reports preliminary studies of the use of barium nonatitanate resonators to stabilise an X-band impatt diode oscillator fabricated as a microwave integrated circuit. Spectra and temperature characteristics are presented for both free running and stabilised oscillator. It is also pointed out that barium nonatitanate has a low loss at Q-band (R. Whatmore (Plessey), private communication, 1980) where present techniques of stabilisation include subharmonic injection locking—a technique that requires fairly complicated circuitry[4] to achieve improvements which are essentially similar to those obtained with simple resonator oscillators.

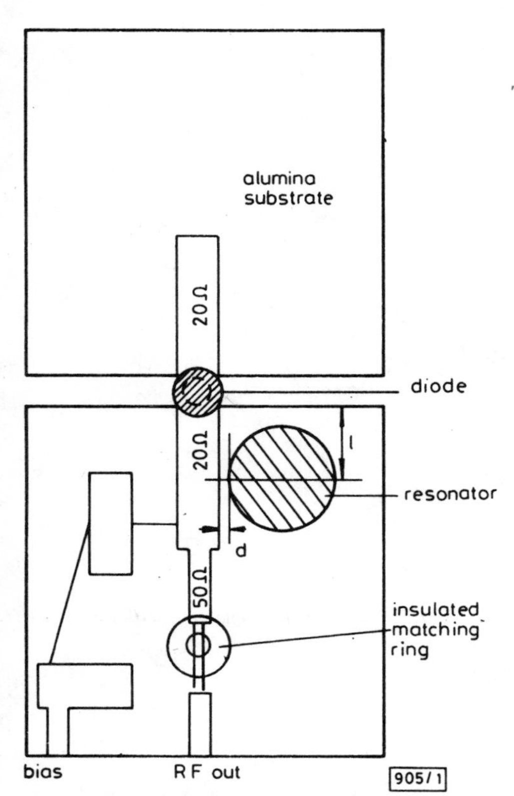

Fig. 1 *Layout of MIC impatt diode oscillator (showing resonator in position)*

The techniques for designing i
well known (e.g. Hewlett Packard ap
whilst the theory of stabilised negative re
has been given by Makino and Hashima,[3] wh
Gunn diodes. In view of this only the diode characteris
circuit will be presented. The procedure was to firstly design
impatt diode oscillator using microstrip and determine its characteristics, and then couple that oscillator to the resonator and determine the characteristics of the stabilised oscillator.

Unstabilised impatt diode oscillator: The impatt diode was a silicon p^+-n diode (Microwave Associates type ML 4705 in an ODS 91 package) mounted by means of a copper collet onto an aluminium heat sink and situated immediately adjacent to a microstrip circuit on an alumina substrate. The breakdown voltage of the diode was 70 V and the slope resistance of the diode's static current voltage curve was 4 mS. When terminating a microstrip 50 Ω line the diode was resonant at a frequency of 9·3 GHz and had an AC small signal negative resistance of −9 Ω. The room temperature AC impedance of the diode is given below as a function of frequency. It had been previously determined that the resonator worked at ~8·90 GHz.

f, GHz	8·6	8·8	9·0	9·2	9·4
Z, Ω	$8 - j16$	$9{\cdot}5 - j12$	$9{\cdot}5 - j5$	$9{\cdot}5 - j1{\cdot}5$	$8 + j2$

A schematic diagram of the circuit of the oscillator is shown in Fig. 1, together with the position of the dielectric resonator used in the design of the stabilised oscillator. The diode is placed between two 25·4 mm square alumina substrated 0·625 mm thick (Omni Spectra) and was thus between the 20 Ω open circuit resonant line and the output line. The RF choke on the DC bias line was implemented by the conventional technique of high (70 Ω) and low (20 Ω) quarter wave lines, whilst the DC block was realised using a pair of quarter wave interdigital lines of width 160 μm and separation 25 μm. The impedance of the output line was arbitrarily taken to be 20 Ω. When the diode was biased to 90 V the DC current was 90 mA and the frequency of oscillation was 9·0 GHz. However, the output power was low, so that a matching insulated ring of ID 3·3 mm and OD 5·9 mm was positioned at the DC block and moved so as to maximise the output power at a value of ~60 mW. The spectrum of this oscillation may be seen in Fig. 2a where at 38 dB below the peak the bandwidth is 0·5 MHz.

The impedance of an impatt diode is temperature sensitive[5] so that the effect of temperature on the frequency of the oscillator was measured over the range 0°C to 60°C. The variation of the centre frequency with temperature is given by the dashed line of Fig. 3, showing that the centre frequency changed by about 8·0 MHz over the 60°C temperature range.

Stabilised impatt diode oscillator: The barium nonatitanate ceramic resonator used to stabilise the above oscillator was a right cylinder of diameter 8·9 mm and thickness 2·96 mm and was developed at the Plessey Research, Caswell. The dielectric properties at 5·75 GHz were: permittivity $\varepsilon_r = 39$; tan $\delta < 2 \times 10^{-4}$; temperature coefficient of resonant frequency = 6 ppm/°C. When magnetically coupled to an open 50 Ω microstrip line it was found that the lowest resonant frequency was ~8·94 GHz, the exact value depending on the position of the resonator with respect to the line.

e resonator was placed on the alumina substrate close to output 20 Ω line at a distance of about half a wavelength om the diode. With the resonator just touching the line the esonator was moved parallel to the 20 Ω microstrip and the output power observed on a Hewlett Packard spectrum analyser (type 8555) for various positions. The resonator was then placed a distance d away from the 20 Ω line, and again moved parallel to the line and again the spectral output was noted. It was found that the maximum output power was obtained at $d \simeq 0{\cdot}8$ mm with l about 4 mm (where l is the distance between the outside of the diode package and the centre of the resonator disc). The spectrum of this oscillation is given in Fig. 2*b*. It had a centre frequency of 8·91 GHz and at 52 dB below the peak, the line width was 0·5 MHz wide. The corresponding power was 25 mW. The effect of temperature on this oscillator was to change the frequency by about 50 kHz/°C for temperatures ranging between 0 and 60°C (see solid line of Fig. 3). This frequency dependence is about the same as for waveguide oscillators stabilised with invar cavities and similar to values obtained for dielectric resonator stabilised Gunn diode oscillators. However, it is four times as large as the corresponding figure for FET oscillators.

The variation of the frequency of the stabilised oscillator with bias voltage was also determined and around 90 V the pushing figure was 1·2 MHz/V.

Acknowledgment: We wish to thank the Plessey Company (Caswell) for giving us the dielectric resonators.

G. B. MORGAN
G. O. OBE

Department of Physics, Electronics & Electrical Engineering
University of Wales Institute of Science & Technology
Cardiff CF1 3NU, Wales

18th December 1980

References

1 PLOURDE, J. K., LINN, D. F., TASSUGUCHI, I., and SWAN, C. B.: 'A dielectric resonator oscillator with 5 ppm long term frequency stability at 4 GHz', *IEEE MTT-S Dig.*, 1977, pp. 237–276

2 ISHIHARA, O., MORI, T., SAWANO, H., and NAKATANI, M.: 'A highly stabilised GaAs FET oscillator using a dielectric resonator feedback circuit in 9–14 GHz', *IEEE Trans.*, 1980, **MTT-28**, pp. 817–824

3 MAKINO, T., and HASHIMA, A.: 'A highly stabilised MIC Gunn oscillator using a dielectric resonator', *ibid.*, 1979, **MTT-27**, pp. 639–643

4 HAYASHI, R., and ASANO, Y.: 'Highly effective subharmonic injection locking of a mm wave impatt oscillator', *ibid.*, 1979, **MTT-27**, pp. 500–504

5 SCHROEDER, W. E., and HADDAD, G. I.: 'The effect of temperature on the operation of an IMPATT diode', *Proc. IEEE*, 1979, **59**, pp. 1242–1244

0013-5194/81/020072-03$1.50/0

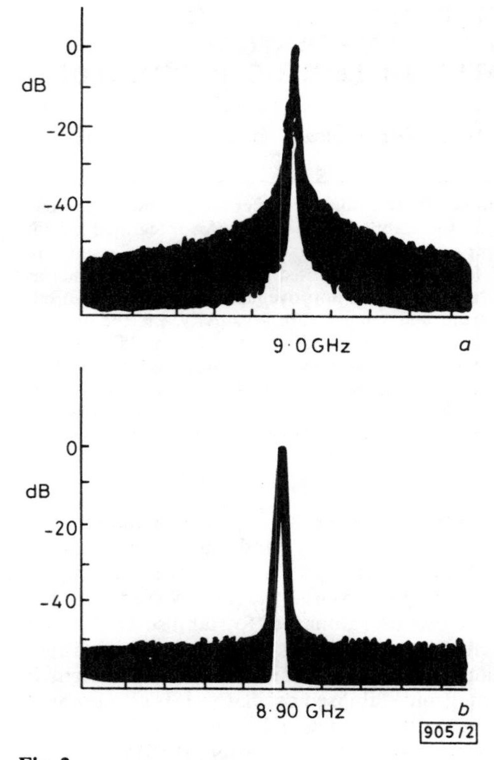

Fig. 2
a Spectrum of unstabilised oscillator. Centre frequency = 9·0 GHz
b Spectrum of stabilised oscillator. Centre frequency = 8·90 GHz
In both cases vertical scale is 10 dB/div, horizontal scale is 0·5 MHz/div and bias voltage was 90 V

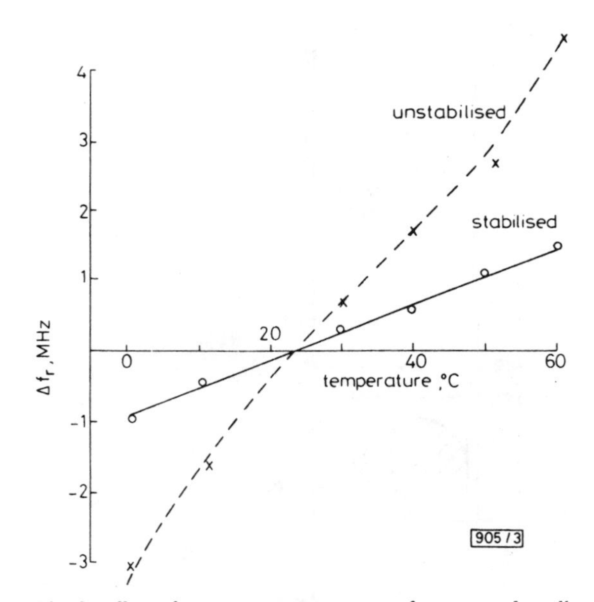

Fig. 3 *Effect of temperature on resonant frequency of oscillator*
--- Unstabilised
—— Stabilised

A 26-GHz High-Performance MIC Transmitter/Receiver for Digital Radio Subscriber Systems

HIROYO OGAWA, MEMBER, IEEE, KAZUYUKI YAMAMOTO, MEMBER, IEEE, AND NOBUAKI IMAI

Abstract —A high-performance 26-GHz microwave integrated circuit (MIC) transmitter/receiver using frequency-shift-keying (FSK) modulation has been developed. All RF components are fabricated using MIC technology and integrated into a single compact module. Newly developed MIC components include an FSK modulator, a time division multiple access (TDMA) switch, and a single-balanced mixer. The FSK modulator is composed of an IMPATT diode, a varactor diode, and a dielectric resonator. A high-frequency stability of 50 ppm is obtained in the temperature range of −10–45°C. The configuration and performance of the TDMA switch with a high ON/OFF ratio and a low insertion loss are described. A transmitting power of 21 dBm and a receiving noise figure of 8.7 dB are obtained. The bit error rate is measured to evaluate the overall transmitter/receiver performance. The required carrier-to-noise ratio (CNR) has been considerably improved by adopting FSK modulation and by using the MIC transmitter/receiver described in this paper.

I. Introduction

In recent years, there have been increasing demands for high-speed digital communication services, including computer data, facsimile, and video transmission. In order to meet these demands, the Dendenkosha Subscriber Radio (DSR) system has been developed at the Yokosuka Electrical Communication Laboratory [1], [2]. This system is a point-to-multipoint communication system using time division multiple access technology (TDMA) in the 26-GHz band [1]. It was necessary to build a compact and inexpensive transmitter/receiver, in order to realize this system. The application of microwave integrated circuits (MIC's) was considered to be the best method for meeting these space and cost requirements. A 26-GHz MIC transmitter/receiver using amplitude-shift-keying (ASK) modulation was previously reported [3]. The purpose of this paper is to present the improved design and performance characteristics of the 26-GHz MIC components and transmitter/receiver module which have been achieved using frequency-shift-keying (FSK) modulation. The main features of the present work follows:

1) An FSK modulation method has been adopted to reduce the required carrier-to-noise ratio (CNR). The modulator, TDMA switch, and single-balanced mixer have been designed and developed using MIC technology.

Manuscript received April 26, 1984.
The authors are with the Yokosuka Electrical Communication Laboratory, Nippon Telegraph and Telephone Public Corporation, Yokosuka, 238-03 Japan.

2) Transmitting power and receiving noise figures have been improved by minimizing circuit losses which are usually fairly large in high-frequency MIC's.

3) A highly reliable and high-performance transmitter/receiver module has been constructed by integrating the MIC components. Measurement of bit error rate confirm excellent overall performance.

II. Transmitter/Receiver Configuration

The configuration of the MIC transmitter/receiver is shown in Fig. 1(a). It is composed of an MIC transmitter/receiver, an antenna and transmit/receive branching filters, and an IF/baseband (BB) section. The MIC transmitter/receiver consists of an FSK modulator, TDMA switch for TDMA control, transmitting power monitor, receiving mixer, receiving local oscillator, and circulators. These components are integrated using MIC technology. The FSK modulator is driven by a 16.384-MHz pulse driver in the IF/BB section. The modulated signal is switched by the TDMA switch and then converted into the burst mode for the TDMA system. The data stream in the transmitter/receiver is shown in Fig 1(b).

The transmit-receive branching filters are constructed using waveguide circuits. These filters are connected to the MIC transmitter/receiver by means of antenna-type waveguide-to-microstrip transitions [4].

III. MIC Components

A. FSK Modulator

The FSK modulator is composed of an IMPATT diode, a dielectric resonator, and a varactor diode. Its circuit configuration is shown in Fig. 2. A band-reflection-type oscillator has been adopted because stable oscillation can be easily obtained with low stabilization loss [5]. The IMPATT diode used here is an encapsulated Si DDR type with a diamond heatsink. The diode is embedded into a dielectric substrate and connected to microstrip lines by Au ribbons. The dielectric resonator is made of $Ba(Zn_{1/3}Nb_{2/3})O_3-Ba(Zn_{1/3}Ta_{2/3})O_3$ and has an unloaded Q of 3000 [6]. A quartz spacer is inserted in order to avoid degradation of the unloaded Q.

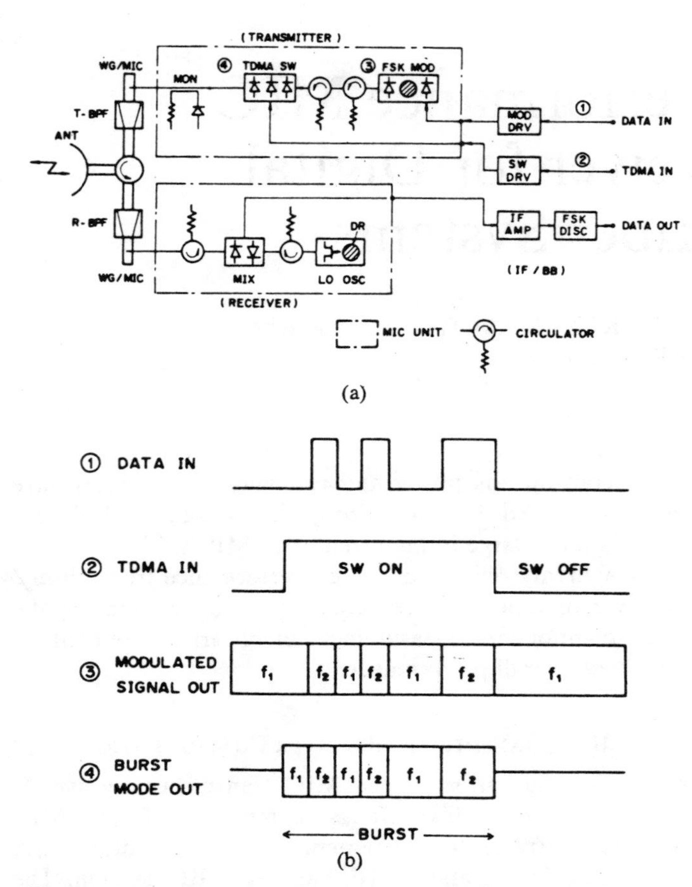

Fig. 1. MIC transmitter/receiver. (a) Block diagrams. (b) Data stream.

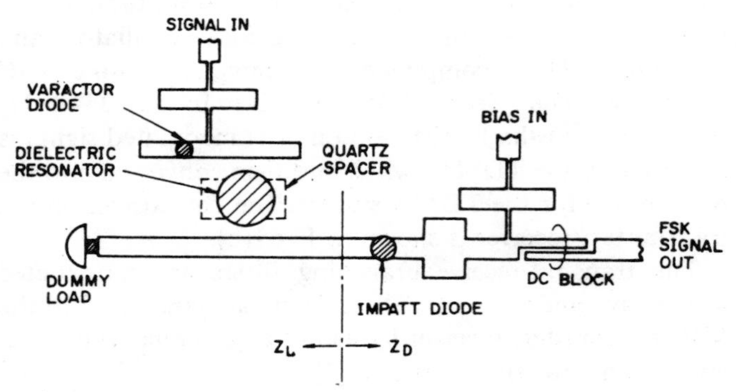

Fig. 2. MIC FSK modulator. The circuit is fabricated by conventional photolithographic techniques on an alumina substrate with a relative permittivity of 9.6.

In order to achieve stable oscillation, the device line ($-Z_D$) and load line (Z_L) were measured and plotted on a Smith chart, as shown in Fig. 3. The intersection of the lines corresponds to the load impedance at the point where an oscillation occurs.

FSK modulation is achieved using a resonance circuit consisting of a varactor diode and a microstrip line. Linearization of differential modulation characteristics has been achieved by optimizing the coupling between the varactor diode and the dielectric resonator [7]. Fig. 4 shows output power and oscillation frequency deviation versus varactor bias voltage. A modulation sensitivity of 3.7 MHz/V and an output power variation of less than 0.6 dB

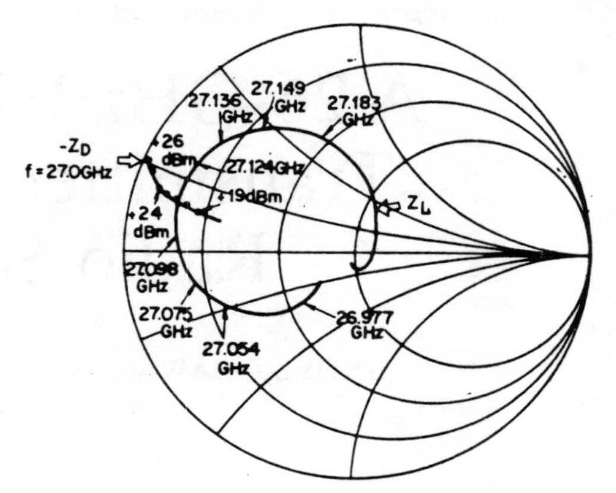

Fig. 3. Relation between device line ($-Z_D$) and load line (Z_L).

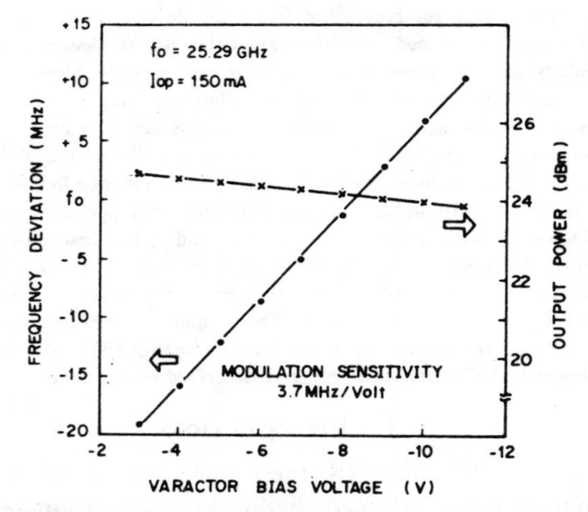

Fig. 4. IMPATT FSK modulator modulation characteristics. The IMPATT diode current (I_{op}) is 150 mA and the center oscillation frequency is 25.29 GHz.

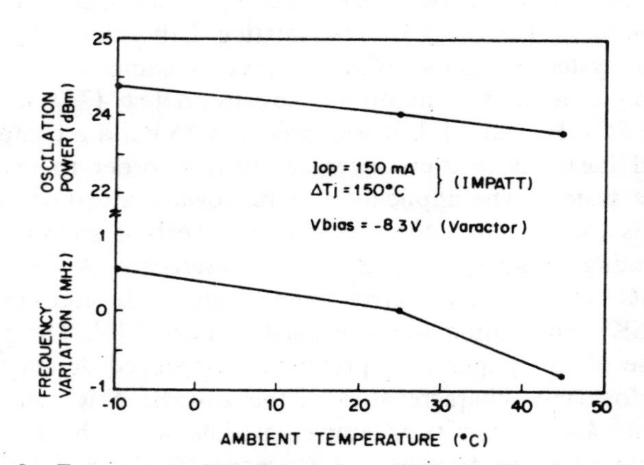

Fig. 5. Temperature dependence of an FSK modulator power and frequency. The junction temperature (ΔT_j) of the IMPATT diode is estimated to be 150°C and the varactor bias voltage (V_{bias}) is -8.3 V.

are obtained. Modulation linearity is better than 1 percent in the frequency deviation range of ± 8 MHz.

Oscillation characteristics as a function of temperature are shown in Fig. 5. An output power of 24 dBm, a power deviation of 1.5 dB, and a frequency variation of 50 ppm are obtained in the temperature range of -10–45°C. The operating diode junction temperature is less than 150°C

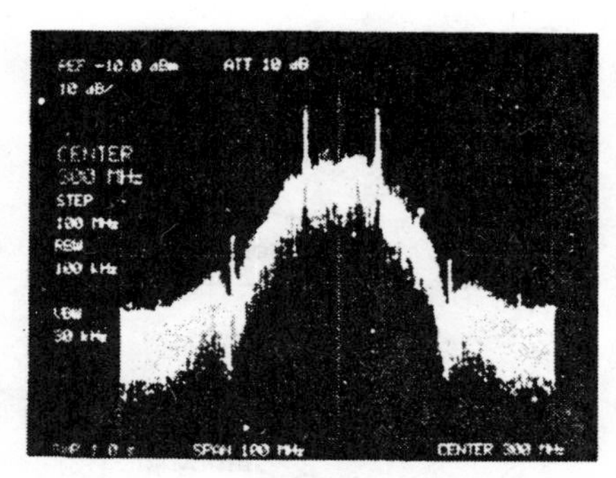

Fig. 6. Output spectrum of an FSK modulator (modulation index = 1.0). Horizontal scale: 10 MHz/div. Vertical scale: 10 dB/div.

above ambient (ΔT_j), which ensures high reliability. The RF spectrum of the FSK modulator is shown in Fig. 6 (modulation index of 1.0).

B. TDMA Switch

An ON/OFF switch, referred to as a TDMA switch, is used to transmit signals in the burst mode. This switch must attain a high ON/OFF ratio and a low insertion loss in order to prevent burst-signal interference, as well as to effectively utilize the FSK modulator output. The switch consists of three p-i-n diodes and Au wires, as shown in Fig. 7. It operates as a low-pass filter when the diodes are in the OFF state and as a short circuit when they are in the ON state [8].

Fig. 8 shows the equivalent circuit in the three-stage TDMA switch, where Z_0 indicates the characteristic impedance of the input/output microstrip lines. Wire inductance is represented by L. The parallel elements R_s, C_j, and R_j correspond to the equivalent circuit of a p-i-n diode. The notations R_s, C_j, and R_j represent series resistance, junction capacitance, and junction resistance, respectively.

The theoretical characteristics of the switch are shown in Fig. 9. Theoretical investigations indicate that the performance of the switch in the millimeter-wave band is greatly dependent on the wire inductance and diode parameters (C_j, R_s). In order to achieve an ON/OFF ratio greater than 60 dB and an insertion loss less than 1 dB, a high-quality diode ($C_j = 0.1$ pF, $R_s = 1.5\ \Omega$) and low inductance wire ($L = 0.15$ nH) are necessary.

The experimental results are also shown in Fig. 9. An ON/OFF ratio greater than 60 dB, an insertion loss of less than 1.5 dB, and a VSWR of less than 2 are attained for the frequency range of 24–28 GHz. The increase in insertion loss is attributed to wire inductance and the increase in R_s. The switch circuit, including diodes, wires, and microstrip line portions, has been packaged and high reliability has been verified.

C. Receiving Mixer

A single-balanced mixer is used as the receiving mixer, in order to reduce the size of the circuit pattern and the number of diodes. Fig. 10 shows the configuration of the mixer which consists of microstrip lines, slotlines, an Au wire, and two beam-lead Schottky barrier diodes. In this

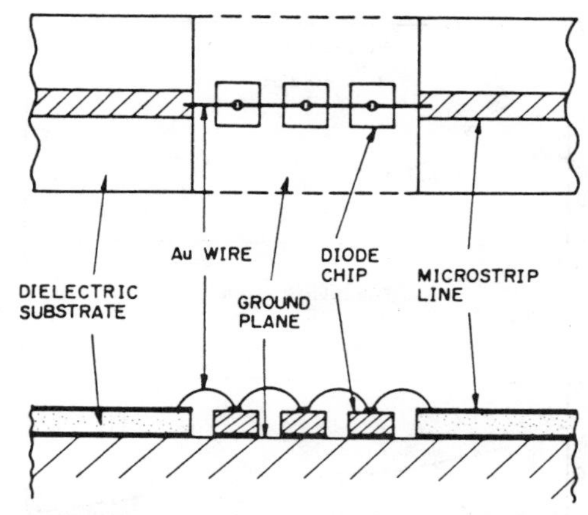

Fig. 7. A TDMA switch. Three p-i-n diodes are bonded on the ground plane with solder and are connected to microstrip lines with Au wires.

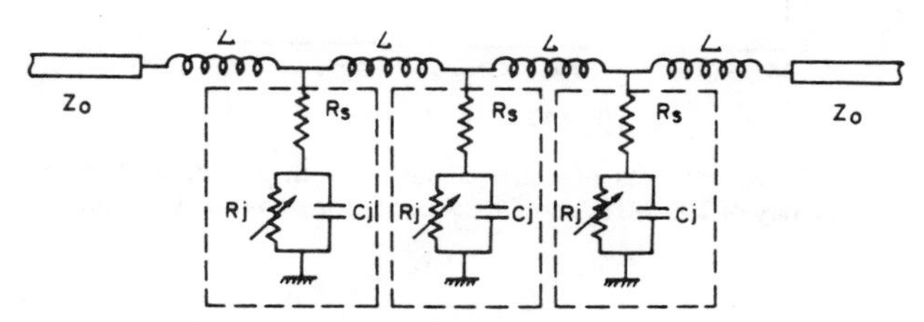

Fig. 8. Equivalent circuit of a TDMA switch. Z_0: characteristic impedance of microstrip lines; L: inductance of wire; and R_s, C_j, R_j: series resistance, junction capacitance, and junction resistance of a p-i-n diode, respectively.

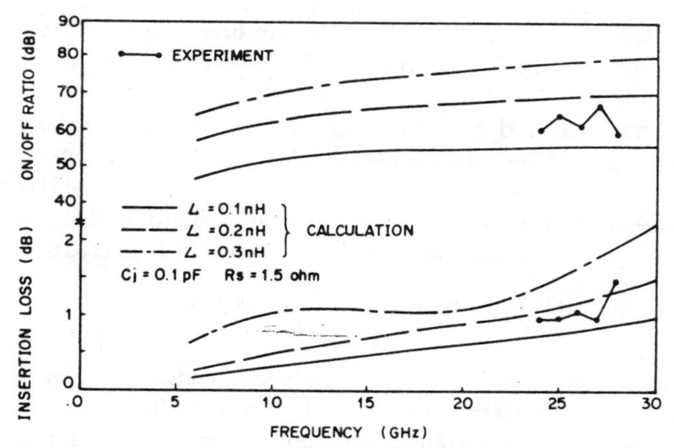

Fig. 9. Performance characteristics of a TDMA switch. Fine lines represent calculated values on condition that the p-i-n diode has a junction capacitance of 0.1 pF and a series resistance of 1.5 Ω, and that the wire inductance is varied from 0.1 to 0.3 nH. The heavy lines containing dots represent experimental results.

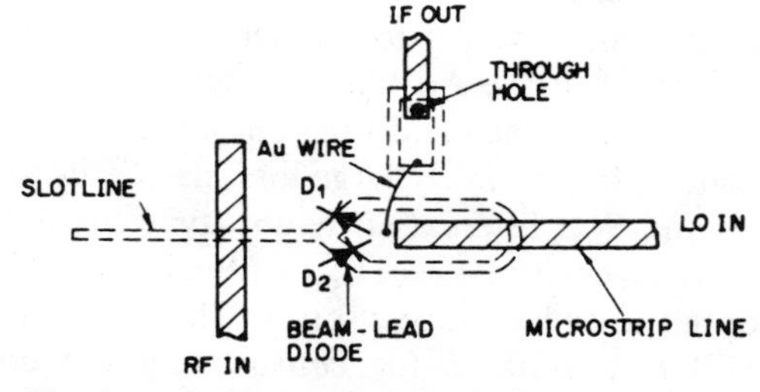

Fig. 10. Circuit configuration of single-balanced mixer. Solid lines show microstrip lines on the substrate, dotted lines show slotlines on the reverse side of the substrate. Two beam-lead diodes are bonded on the slotline.

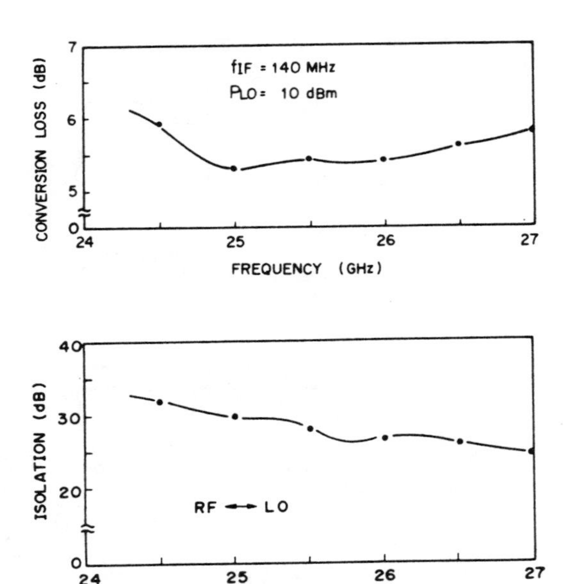

Fig. 11. Conversion loss of balanced mixer, with a fixed intermediate frequency of 140 MHz and a local oscillator power of 10 dBm.

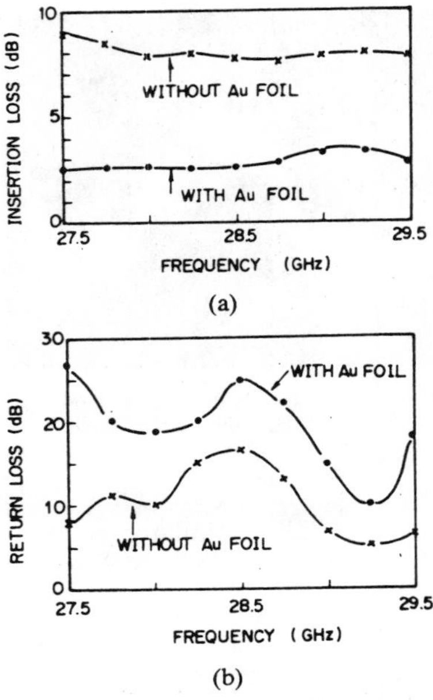

Fig. 12. Transmission characteristics of eight cascaded microstrip lines. With Au foil and without Au foil correspond to the cases, where an Au foil is or is not inserted under the substrates, respectively. (a) Insertion loss. (b) Return loss.

figure, solid lines indicate microstrip lines on the substrate surface, while dotted lines indicate slotlines on the reverse side. Since the Au wire behaves as a low-pass filter due to its series inductance, and the RF electromagnetic field is concentrated in the slotline, the IF circuit composed of an Au wire, coplanar line, and microstrip line is isolated from the RF circuit. Two beam-lead diodes are bonded on the slotline.

The measured conversion loss for a fixed intermediate frequency of 140 MHz is presented in Fig. 11(a). A conversion loss of less than 5.5 dB is obtained over a 1-GHz bandwidth. Isolation between the local oscillator and signal input ports is greater than 20 dB, as shown in Fig. 11(b).

IV. MIC Transmitter/Receiver Performance

MIC components are assembled and integrated in the transmitter/receiver module. Connection losses are fairly large in millimeter-wave bands due to imperfect electrical contact at the substrate ground conductor [3]. In order to evaluate the connection loss between the substrate, eight sections of microstrip lines are cascaded and measured with and without Au foils. Fig. 12 shows the transmission characteristics of microstrip lines having seven connection points. The insertion loss between the substrates is improved by inserting the Au foil under the substrates. The measured loss when the Au foil is under the substrates is evaluated to be less than 0.1 dB per one connection point.

Other causes for the fairly large loss may lie in the MIC circulators and WG filters. Ferrite-disk-type circulators [9] and cylindrical cavity-type (TE_{011}^{0}) filters [10], [11] have been adopted to reduce excess losses. The cylindrical cavity-type filter is suitable for constructing the compact subscriber radio equipment, because the input/output port location of the filter can be optionally chosen due to its configuration.

Careful consideration has been given to ensure the reliability of the transmitter/receiver. Encapsulated IMPATT and varactor diodes are used. p-i-n diodes are packaged together with the surrounding circuits, and the beam-lead diodes are sealed using Si coating materials. Narrow gaps in microstrip line circuits, e.g., the dc block, are also sealed. Photographs of the subscriber radio equipment are shown in Fig. 13. The sizes of the MIC transmitter and receiver themselves are 2.7 and 3.2 cm^2, respectively. This compact MIC transmitter/receiver is located at the rear of the antenna.

The major characteristics of the transmitter/receiver are summarized in Table I. The transmitting power is 21 dBm and the frequency stability of the transmitter is within 50 ppm for the temperature range between -5–45°C. The ON/OFF ratio of the transmitting power is greater than 60 dB. The receiving noise figure is 8.7 dB.

Fig. 14 shows the measured bit error rate of the newly developed FSK equipment compared with that for previously reported ASK equipment. The required CNR for FSK at an error rate of 10^{-4} is about 7 dB smaller than that for ASK. The FSK modulation method is excellent for constructing subscriber radio equipment.

V. Conclusion

A new 26-GHz band MIC transmitter/receiver employing FSK modulation has been developed for the DSR system. MIC technology has been adopted in all RF active and passive circuits, thereby realizing very compact and inexpensive subscriber radio equipment with excellent performance and high reliability. The new equipment has been successfully tested in a year-long field trial. MIC technology can be further extended to develop a transmitter/receiver which can operate in even higher frequency bands.

(a)

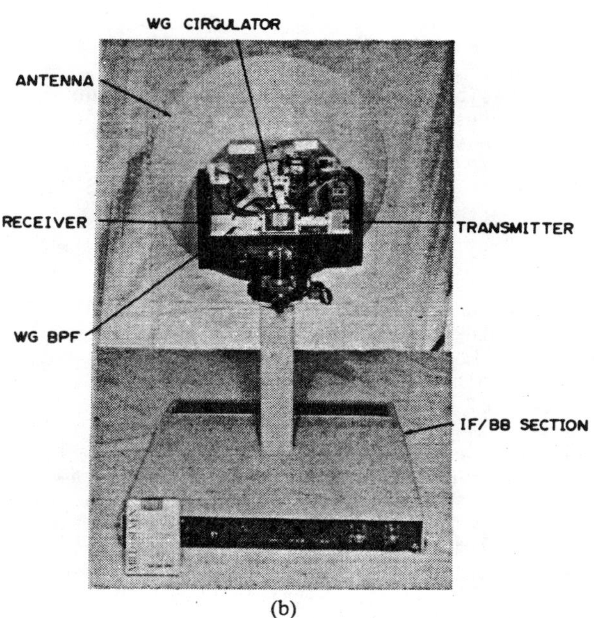

(b)

Fig. 13. Photographs of subscriber radio equipment. (a) Internal view of MIC transmitter/receiver. (b) External view of radio equipment.

TABLE I
MIC Transmitter/Receiver Characteristics.

Item	Characteristics
RF frequency	26-GHz band
Modulation method	FSK
Modulation index	1.0
Clock rate	16.384 MHz
Transmitting power	21 dBm
ON/OFF ratio	60 dB
Frequency stability	50 ppm (-10°C ~ 45°C)
Power variation	1.5 dB (-10°C ~ 45°C)
Receiving noise figure	8.7 dB
Local oscillator leakage	-50 dBm
IF frequency	300MHz
Power consumption	30 W
Dimensions	6.5 cm x 3.9 cm x 1.5 cm

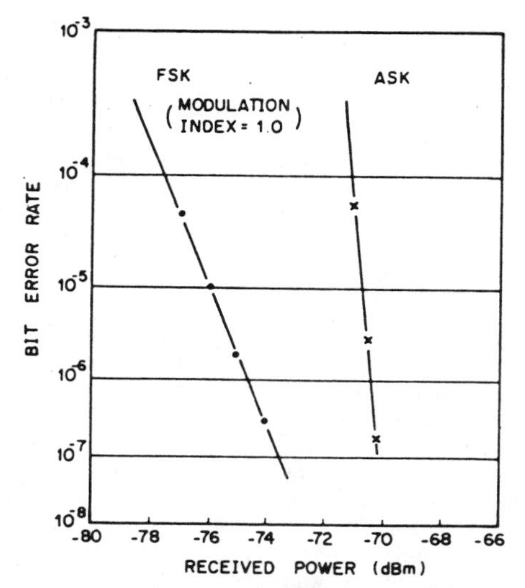

Fig. 14. Measured bit error rate for FSK and ASK. Modulation index for FSK is set to 1.0.

Acknowledgment

The authors would like to thank D. K. Kohiyama, Dr. O. Kurita, and Dr. S. Shindo for their valuable suggestions and guidance.

References

[1] S. Shindo, O. Kurita, and M. Akaike, "Radio subscriber loop system for high-speed digital communications," in *Proc. ICC'81*, 66.1.

[2] S. Shindo, Y. Nakamura, H. Ogawa, and M. Shinji, "TDMA for radio local distribution system," in *Proc. ICC'83*, b.2.3.

[3] E. Hagihara, H. Ogawa, and M. Akaike, "A 26-GHz miniaturized MIC transmitter/receiver," *IEEE Trans. Microwave Theory Tech.*, vol. MTT-30, pp. 235–242, Mar. 1982.

[4] R. H. Knerr, "A new type of waveguide-to-stripline transition," *IEEE Trans. Microwave Theory Tech.*, vol. MTT-16, pp. 192–194, Mar. 1968.

[5] K. Kohiyama and K. Monma, "A new type of frequency-stabilized Gunn oscillator," *Proc. IEEE*, vol. 59, pp. 1532–1533, Oct. 1971.

[6] K. Kawashima *et al.*, "Dielectric properties of $Ba(Zn_{1/3}-Nb_{2/3})O_3-Ba(Zn_{1/3}Ta_{2/3})O_3$ ceramics at microwave frequency," in *Proc. 1st Meet. Ferroelectric Mater. their Applic.*, Nov. 1977, pp. 293–296.

[7] K. Kohiyama and K. Monma, "Frequency modulation of Gunn oscillator using varactor," *Trans. IECE Japan*, vol. J56-B, no. 10, Oct. 1973.

[8] F. G. Ananasso, "Optimizing wide-band MIC switch performance," *IEEE Trans. Microwave Theory Tech.*, vol. MTT-30, pp. 294–296, Mar. 1982.

[9] H. Ogawa, M. Akaike, M. Aikawa, T. Karaki, and J. Watanabe, "A 26-GHz band integrated circuits of a double-balanced mixer and circulators," *IEEE Trans. Microwave Theory Tech.*, vol. MTT-30, pp. 34–41, Jan. 1982.

[10] H. A. Bethe, "Theory of diffraction by small holes," *Phys. Rev.*, vol. 66, pp. 163–182, Oct. 1944.

[11] G. L. Matthaei, L. Young, and E. M. T. Jones, *Microwave Filters, Impedance-Mathing Networks, and Coupling Structures.* New York: McGraw-Hill, 1964.

MICROWAVE MONOLITHIC INTEGRATED CIRCUIT DEVELOPMENT FOR FUTURE SPACEBORNE PHASED ARRAY ANTENNAS

G. Anzic, T. J. Kascak, A. N. Downey, D. C. Liu, and D. J. Connolly
National Aeronautics and Space Administration
Lewis Research Center
Cleveland, Ohio 44135

Abstract

The development of fully monolithic gallium arsenide (GaAs) receive and transmit modules suitable for phased array antenna applications in the 30/20 gigahertz bands is presented. Specifications and various design approaches to achieve the design goals are described. Initial design and performance of submodules and associated active and passive components are presented. A tradeoff study summary is presented highlighting the advantages of distributed amplifier approach compared to the conventional single power source designs.

Introduction

Studies have identified the use of multiple scanning beam antenna systems as a major factor in achieving minimum cost and efficient use of the frequency and orbital resources for the future generation of the communications satellite systems. The Advanced Communications Technology Satellite (ACTS), scheduled for launch in the late 1980's will employ the scanning beam antenna technology in the 20/30 gigahertz bands to maximize the operating efficiency. Future communications satellite systems may use monolithic receive and transmit module technology which is expected to further increase the system operating efficiency. In support of the development of advanced antenna concepts, a key area therefore, is the development of compatible monolithic receive and transmit modules at the above stated frequencies.

Gallium arsenide (GaAs) monlithic microwave integrated circuits (MMIC) offer substantial performance advantages in the proposed frequencies of interest. Since entire microwave circuits can be fabricated on a single chip, utilizing deposition, epitaxy and ion implantation techniques, the resulting circuit is free of parasitics, losses and component value uncertainties normally associated with wire bonds and other external interconnects. Monolithic circuits can therefore be designed, developed and produced for optimum performance with no circuit adjustments after assembly.

In addition to monolithic circuit performance advantages mentioned, additional, very attractive advantages are offered by microwave monolithic integrated circuits in areas of cost, weight per function and reliability. As technology matures and substantial volumes of production are achieved, all advantages will be more fully realized.

NASA Lewis Research Center is pursuing the following MMIC developments which promise maximum impact for the future communications systems in the 30/20 GHz frequency range.

30 GHz Monolithic Receive Module

Two parallel efforts to develop a 30 GHz monolithic receive module are in progress at Hughes-Torrance Research Center (HAC-TRC) and Honeywell Corporate Technology Center (H-CTC). The receive module's performance goals are listed in Table 1. The module's final configuration, consisting of four functional submodules integrated on a single chip is shown in Fig. 1. Basic technologies employed in the fabrication include sub-micron gate length field effect transistor (FET) fabrication using refractory metalization systems, ion implantation for low noise amplification and microstrip circuitry fabricated on semi-insulating gallium arsenide (GaAs) substrate.

Since the receive module's intended application is for steerable phased array antennas where a large number of receive - transmit elements is employed, a possible element might be a waveguide radiator. Figures 2 and 3 show a proposed module layout and its possible incorporation in a waveguide radiator (fixture) employing suitable waveguide to microstrip transitions[1] with control and power connections.

Low Noise Amplifier Submodule (LNA)

The design and fabrication approaches chosen by both contractors in the development of the low noise amplifier modules are similar. Sub half-micron gate length FET's have been designed and are in process of fabrication for use in the low noise amplifiers. Both conventional photolithography supplemented by the E-beam lithography are used for circuit and active component fabrication. Since LNA submodules are still in the final design and early fabrication stages, only preliminary test results are available. Figure 4 shows the Hughes LNA design, its calculated characteristics and component layout. Significantly better results are expected in the FET gain and noise performance areas in the future. Typical low noise FET performance in the band of interest is expected to improve by approximately 1 dB during the duration of this development effort. Consequently, the module noise figure goal of 5 dB or less is expected to be achieved without difficulty. Figure 5 shows the initial amplifier design employed by Honeywell. A single gate FET version of the amplifier is expected to be used in the LNA. Noise performance is similar to the Hughes version described above.

Phase Shifter Submodule

Possibly the most challenging part of the proposed effort to develop a monolithic receive module is the development of the phase shifter submodule. The performance goals of the submodule require its operation at five different phase states between zero and 180 degrees controlled by a digital input signal. The phase shifter is to use a true time delay phase shift scheme, where in any state of the phase shifter the total module phase shift is proportional to frequency within the 27.5 to 30 gigahertz passband.

AIAA-84-0656

A large variety of monolithic phase shifters has been developed for various applications. Most of these phase shifters were designed and built at X-band frequencies or lower where area per phase shift bit requirements were relatively large. At 30 gigahertz, the area requirements will be reduced by about a factor of four, making the approach more practical, although more challenging problems are expected in the areas of insertion loss, phase error and circuit yield.

Both contractors are investigating the designs of digital phase shifters based on switched transmission line configuration using large periphery unbiased FET's as RF switches. Phase shifting is accomplished by true time delay between the differential electrical length of microstrip lines in the circuit. Two of the most common rf switch circuits in use employ FET's either in shunt or series-mounted configuration. Figure 6 shows a single bit phase shifter in a shunt mounted FET switch configuration. Honeywell's initial approach was to build a single bit (180°) switched line phase shifter employing 300 micron gate periphery power FET's as switches in a shunt mounted configuration. The FET dc on resistance exhibited was 11 to 14 ohms.[2] The insertion loss per bit was approximately 4 dB over the 27.5 to 30 gigahertz band.

A subsequent improvement in dc on resistance by a factor of 1.5 to 2 has been achieved by fabricating the switch FET's by the use of the self-aligned gate (SAG) technology.[3] Generally, the SAG phase shifters to date have achieved about 2.5 dB/bit insertion loss over the band mentioned above. It is expected that future 30 gigahertz phase shifters could be fabricated with an insertion loss of 1.5/dB bit. A comparison of measured and calculated insertion loss for a SAG phase shifter is shown in Fig. 7. Honeywell's design for an improved phase shifter employing four series FET switches fabricated by SAG technique is shown in Fig. 8. The design features a more compact layout with no rf grounding requirements which promises lower insertion loss and better phase performance.

Hughes' initial approach was to investigate an analog phase shifter as shown in Fig. 9. The phase shifter is based on a branch line coupler approach which is very simple and occupies a relatively small area. Although not a true time delay phase shifter, it's simplicity and projected high circuit yield makes it a good candidate for further investigation. A 30 gigahertz Lange coupler has been fabricated and the investigation of its characteristics continues. Identical Shottky-barrier diodes are connected in series with the inductors to ground. By proper biasing of the diodes their capacitance can be varied which subsequently changes the phase of the transmitted signal. Loaded line circuit designs are being considered for the two minor bits of 11.25 and 22.5 degrees. While they do not provide true time delay, these designs are considerably smaller and are projected to introduce negligible phase errors.

Gain Control Submodule

As shown in Table 1, the receive module RF/IF gain performance goal stipulates that maximum gain be equal or greater than 30 dB with six intermediate steps as shown. The intermediate gain steps are commanded using a digital signal. Two different approaches in controlling the receive module gain are presented in Fig. 1. Honeywell's proposed approach is to control the gain at rf while the Hughes' proposed approach is to vary the module gain at IF. Both approaches utilize dual gate FET's where variation of second gate bias controls the gain of the amplifier. Figures 10 and 11 show the proposed circuit and submodule layout designs. Both designs are preliminary and changes are expected before final designs are approved.

Since both submodules depend on gain variation due to FET bias voltage changes a digital to analog converter will be required for each approach. Designs and proven fabrication techniques exist for digital to analog converters and no difficulties are expected in this area. It is expected that the submodule sizes for both approaches, including the D/A converter circuitry, will be approximately 1 mm x 2 mm.

RF-IF Submodule

The RF-IF submodule's two main functions are to convert the 27.5 to 30 gigahertz input rf signal to the specified IF frequency in a mixer and to amplify the external reference signal which serves as a local escillator input to the mixer. Both contractors chose to amplify the given 15 microwatt reference signal to serve as the local oscillator. A multistage, low noise, high gain monolithic amplifier will be developed for this purpose.

Although no final design choices have been made, Hughes' choice for the mixer design was a dual gate FET while Honeywell's baseline approach was a balanced Shottky diode mixer with a rat race hybrid. The IF amplifier, required in Honeywell's approach (see Fig. 1) is expected to be a simple, low gain, low noise figure monolithic type, operating in the suggested IF frequency band between 4 and 8 gigahertz. No experimental results are available for this submodule at present.

20 GHz Transmit Module

A monolithic transmit module is under development at Rockwell International, Thousand Oaks, California. The technology goals for the 30-month contract are given in Table 2. The MMIC module uses a microstrip approach in which all active and passive devices are fabricated on a GaAs substrate. Figure 12, shows a block diagram for an initial layout of the fully monolithic transmit module chip. The module consists of five cascaded single bit phase shifters each employing a switched line approach using FET devices for switches. The digital control circuitry portion accepts a TTL input signal and provides the signals to switch in or out each of the five phase shifters. A two-stage buffer amplifier follows the phase shifters to compensate for the phase shifter losses. Finally, a three-stage power amplifier completes the module. The chip size is 4.8 mm by 6.4 mm, however this initial design layout includes diagnostic test circuitry and the final layout could produce a smaller chip size. It was determined that a staged development for the fully monolithic transmit module was the most feasible approach to follow. This consisted of a design for the fully monolithic module and then a division of the total circuit into submodule designs which were of a suitable scale for fabrication, characterization and evaluation.

The first phase of the work consisted of developing submodules demonstrating the phase shifter, digital control and power amplifier functions. The initial mask set consisted of the following nine submodule chips: digital control circuitry; one-stage buffer amplifier and discrete FET, two-stage buffer amplifier; wafer test circuitry; and five phase shifter submodules of 11.25°, 22.5°, 45°, 90°, and 180° bits. Total reticle size is is 4.8 mm x 4.8 mm and contains the nine 1.5 mm x 1.5 mm size chips and separation channels. A photo of a typical chip (two-stage buffer amplifier submodule) is shown in Fig. 13. A second mask set consisted of submodule chips of the full three-stage power amplifier and various one and two stage combinations of this full three-stage amplifier.

The design approach for these submodule developments was accomplished by the extensive use of computer aided design (CAD). The CAD included equivalent circuits for the FET's, accurate modeling of passive elements and careful characterization of parasitics and inter-element coupling. The objectives of the design were minimal chip size with high yield processing and low potential cost to provide reliable modules meeting the goals of Table 2.

With approximately two-thirds of the program completed, submodules have been fabricated and tested demonstrating all of the necessary circuit functions, however design refinements are still required. More detailed information on the design, fabrication and test of the two-stage buffer amplifier and three-stage power amplifier submodule developments have been reported by Petersen and Gupta[4,5] of Rockwell. The 20 GHz two-stage buffer amplifier development is probably the most advanced as seen in Fig. 14 which shows the predicted and measured gain results. The three-stage power amplifier submodule operated but at a reduced gain level. A saturated output power of approximately +21 dBm was measured across the 2.5 GHz band, with the goal being +23 dBm. The phase shifter submodules also operated but with an approximate 3.5 dB insertion loss (goal of 2.5 dB) per phase shifter bit.

Although the submodules still require further development, sufficient information has been obtained and design iterations developed that the mask set for the fully monolithic transmit module has been designed and fabricated. The remaining time of this contractual effort will continue with the fabrication, test and evaluation of the fully monolithic transmit module.

20 GHz Variable Power Amplifier (VPA) Module

Texas Instruments is presently developing a 20 GHz monolithic variable power amplifier module. The performance goals of this monolithic amplifier module are shown in Table 3. The objective is to develop a 17.7 to 20.2 GHz monolithic GaAs variable power amplifier exhibiting high efficiency at various output power levels. The amplitude control provides for five output power states at nominal levels 500, 125, 50, and 12.5 mW and zero. The amplitude control is to operate on a digital basis and be TTL compatible.

Development Approach

This development program uses a four-stage dual-gate FET amplifier design approach. A block diagram of the VPA module is shown in Fig. 15. The second gates of all the FET's are connected with interstage matching networks as shown. Digital control inputs for gain control are converted to analog voltage using a digital to analog (D/A) converter. The nominal gains as a function of the control voltage V_{g2} are also shown.

The VPA module is divided into two submodules, the amplifier module and the amplitude control module. The two modules will be monolithically integrated later onto a single 4.5 mm x 1.5 mm GaAs chip. Dual-gate power FET devices suitable for 20 GHz operation were first developed. These devices are to be incorporated into the four-stage amplifier module. Concurrently, a four-stage single-gate FET monolithic amplifier module for 20 GHz operation and the D/A converter module for amplitude control were also developed.

Four-Stage, Single-Gate Amplifier

For the four-stage, single-gate amplifier, GaAs FET's with gate widths of 300 um were used in the first and second stages while FET's with gate widths of 600 um and 1500 um were used in the third and fourth stage, respectively. FET equivalent circuit models were used for the amplifier design. High impedance transmission lines with a characteristic impedance of 70 ohms were used for impedance matching. The required capacitors were implemented with the metal-insulator-metal (MIM) silicon nitride overlay types. The chip size is 4.4 mm x 1.4 mm.

At midpoint of the program, the four-stage, single-gate amplifier showed good gain control with either changing gate bias or changing drain bias. The amplifier has a gain of at least 18 dB across the 18 to 20 GHz frequency band. It was anticipated that with a minor design iteration (increased interstage drain matching inductances), an output power of at least 500 mW with 20 dB gain can be achieved.

Dual-Gate FET

Dual-gate FET models with cascade connected common-sources, common-gate stages were obtained by comparing measured devices S parameters with models generated from SUPER-COMPACT. The element values of the models were obtained by optimization.

Hybrid single-stage dual-gate FET amplifiers with gate width up to 1200 um have achieved gains in excess of 10 dB over the 18 to 20 GHz band with a range of gain control greater than 30 dB.

Using the measured S parameters, complete dual-gate equivalent circuit models have been obtained for amplifier design. A four-stage, dual-gate amplifier based on complete device models for the different stages has been designed. A gain in excess of 25 dB was predicted. Figure 16 shows the computed gain-frequency response and input/output VSWR performance.